MODERN AIRMANSHIP

VNR VAN NOSTRAND REINHOLD COMPANY
NEW YORK CINCINNATI TORONTO LONDON MELBOURNE

Van Nostrand Reinhold Company Regional Offices:
New York Cincinnati Chicago Millbrae Dallas

Van Nostrand Reinhold Company International Offices:
London Toronto Melbourne

Library of Congress Catalog Card Number: 71–143545

Manufactured in the United States of America

Published by Van Nostrand Reinhold Company
450 West 33rd Street, New York, N.Y. 10001

Published simultaneously in Canada by Van Nostrand Reinhold Ltd.

15 14 13 12 11 10 9 8 7 6 5 4 3 2 1

To those who would fly.

Foreword

Man has now stretched his wings beyond his own world and is moving toward the planets. Our progress in the era of flight staggers the imagination. We are now flying airplanes so large that the Wright brothers' first flight could have been conducted within the lengths of their fuselages.

To keep abreast of such changes in this dynamic field is a monumental task. This edition of "Modern Airmanship," edited by Major General Neil D. Van Sickle, USAF (Retired), admirably accomplishes this task. It is a basic, comprehensive text for the student and the professional flyer, the civilian and the military pilot. More, it is a book for any lay person who is interested in airmanship.

Wide in scope, yet detailed and fully authoritative, the technical material is readable and understandable. General Van Sickle and his contributors have produced a significant addition to the technical literature of aviation.

JOHN D. RYAN
General, USAF
Chief of Staff
United States Air Force

Preface

A professional outlook marks the modern airman. Whether he flies for profit or pleasure, his own view of flying determines whether he can use the refined aircraft capabilities now available. At the same time that refinements in aircraft and avionics have simplified the multiple tasks of flying, either in the wilderness or in aerial traffic jams, the cost of useful flight is so high that economy and efficiency are parallel with safety.

Yet flying remains an enthralling, inspiring magic. Aerial acrobatics and powerless flight, at the pinnacle of flying for pleasure, have increased their following. The world is tuned to air transportation, and thousands routinely fly together faster, safer, and more casually than ever before.

Airmanship is the key. In this book the Editor has tried to illuminate the facets of flight which contribute most to the highest quality of modern airmanship.

The names of contributing authors to this edition appear with each chapter. As for each previous edition, every expert in civil and military aviation and in industry who was asked responded enthusiastically. Many readers contributed helpful suggestions to improve both clarity and content.

The Editor is again indebted to the United States Air Force Air Training Command for the excellence of its training publications and the willing help of many of its staff and instructors, including Lt. Gen. Sam Maddux, USAF (Ret.), then Commander.

Particular thanks go to Mr. David V. Stockman, Chief of Instrument Development, USAF Aeronautical Systems Division; Brig. Gen. LeRoy J. Manor, Commander, Air Force Special Operations Force (TAC); Mr. Dan W. McGrogan, TWA Training Center; Lt. Col. G. M. Holland of the Air Force Office of Information; Professor

Charles F. Holleman, Department of Aviation Technology, Purdue University; the Public Information Office of FAA; Reginald A. Hubley, Publisher of *Aviation Week* and *Space Technology;* Maj. Perry A. Hudel, Instrument Ground School, Andrews AFB, Md.; Maj. David W. Miller and Capt. Murle A. Wilson, USAF, 28th Bombardment Wing (SAC); Col. James E. Anderson, USAF, Beale AFB, California; and to Majorie S. Van Sickle, who patiently did the typing.

NEIL D. VAN SICKLE
Major General, USAF (Retired)

Rapid City, South Dakota
July 1971

Authors of the First Edition

Chapter 1	The Airman's World—The Atmosphere Herbert Appleman and Capt. Charles G. Markham, USAF
Chapter 2	Modern Aircraft Types Col. Neil D. Van Sickle, USAF
Chapter 3	Basic Aerodynamics and the Theory of Flight J. V. Mutchler, Aerodynamics Engineer, Convair
Chapter 4	Airplane Structures Nathan T. Wolkomir, Air Training Command, USAF
Chapter 5	Propulsion Charles S. Tompkins, Boeing Airplane Company
Chapter 6	Aircraft Instruments and Operational Equipment Major John E. Hilburn, Air Training Command, USAF
Chapter 7	Man in Flight Lt. Col. Hugh W. Randel, USAF (MC), School of Aviation Medicine
Chapter 8	Basic Flight Techniques in Light Aircraft Major Harley E. Barnhart, Air Training Command, USAF
Chapter 9	Flying Higher Performance Aircraft Captain John F. Welch, Strategic Air Command, USAF
Chapter 10	Weather Captain Donald J. Smith and Captain Michael A. Titre, Air Training Command, USAF
Chapter 11	Instrument Flying Major John E. Hilburn, Air Training Command, USAF
Chapter 12	Air Navigation Major Harry C. Nuessle, Air Training Command, USAF
Chapter 13	Flight Control Agencies and Flight Rules Major John R. Mattingly, Air Training Command, USAF
Chapter 14	Helicopters Walter M. Morris, Air Training Command, USAF
Chapter 15	Aircraft Maintenance Kenneth E. O'Neil, Air Materiel Command, USAF
Chapter 16	The Arctic Pilot Terris Moore, President, University of Alaska
Chapter 17	Modern Airports Colonel Lester F. Rhodes, USA (Ret.), Engineer, Parsons, Brinkerhoff, Hall, & MacDonald

Contents

MODERN AIRMANSHIP

1

Modern Aircraft

"I've chased the
shouting wind along,
and flung
My eager craft through
footless halls of air.
Up, up the long delirious
burning blue
I've topped the wind-
swept heights with
easy grace,
Where never lark, or
even eagle flew."

High Flight
—JOHN GILLESPIE MAGEE, JR.

Today's "eager craft," in all their diversity of form and purpose, are the heart of flying. They may lift the spirits and speed the business of the individual airman, or carry hundreds in luxury and safety, or hurl missiles in swirling combat.

Whatever the task, only the airmanship of the pilot or crew aboard can satisfy the designer's intent. The numbers, the wide range of speeds and uses, the cost, the nature of the atmosphere in which all this occurs, and the emotional and spiritual nature of human response to piloting have made airmanship a principal profession of the age. It is the soul of an industry whose magnitude was undreamed of even by the most ardent and visionary airmen of only two generations ago.

The statistics of present aircraft active inventories are so vast and so complex that they lose meaning. Certain aircraft are typical of the various broad roles. The aircraft shown here may not be the best, the cheapest, or the most expensive, but they are successful enough to be typical.

Aircraft do fall into three generally accepted categories: *general aviation, airline transports,* and *military.* Each one contributes to some degree to the lore and design of the others, though the stimulus of war is probably responsible for more advances in the art and science of aviation than anything else.

Modern Aircraft Characteristics

Modern aircraft are characterized by cleanness of line. This sleek appearance is found even in the most inexpensive private airplanes and reflects the designer's need to survive in an intensely competitive field. Military aircraft must compete against those produced by the skill and effort of possible enemies; manufacturers of military aircraft in the United States must compete with each other, for the military airman must seek the aircraft which will at the same time provide the greatest range, the highest speed, the greatest maneuverability, the simplest maintenance, and the least cost. In addition, they must be built around the most effective possible system of offensive or defensive weapons, such as bombs, rockets, or missiles.

The civil aircraft is clean because aerodynamic cleanness of line and efficiency of design result in greater range and payload at least operating cost. This is particularly true in the huge airline transports. However, it is also a principal factor when the lightplane buyer decides on a particular aircraft which can come within his means, yet give him as near as possible the performance he observes in the larger civil or military aircraft.

Performance is a term used to describe the ability of an aircraft to accomplish certain things which make it useful for a certain purpose. For example, ability to take off and land with a short roll is an important item of performance to a Canadian bush pilot or an air taxi service; high rate of climb is an essential element of performance in the interceptor fighter; and ability to carry heavy loads long distances economically is essential performance for airline transports.

The chief elements of performance are length of takeoff and landing roll, rate of climb, ceiling, payload, range, speed, maneuverability, stability, ruggedness, and fuel economy. Some of these factors are directly opposed: for example, high speed versus shortness of landing roll; long range versus great payload; and high rate of climb versus fuel economy. It is the preeminence of one or some of these factors which dictates differences between aircraft, and which explains the high degree of specialization found in modern aircraft. As aircraft have been required to do more things, they have been built to do each of them better. Fighters will sacrifice shortness of landing roll for speed, range, and load-carrying capacity; and transports will sacrifice speed for economy of operation, and maneuverability for stability.

Despite this specialization, however, aircraft of all types are widely adaptable—a factor of considerable importance to both civil and military aviation. For example, primary trainers can be used to spray crops, fighters can carry atomic bombs and cameras, and jet transports can convert quickly for passengers or freight.

Civil Aircraft

CIVIL AIRCRAFT CLASSIFICATION

For the purpose of issuing type or airworthiness certificates, the Federal Aviation Agency (FAA) classifies planes as follows.

Normal Airplanes of 12,500 lb or less intended for nonacrobatic, nonscheduled passenger, and nonscheduled cargo operations. Most business aircraft fall into this category. (Cessna 182, Beechcraft King Air, Mooney Mark 21.)

Utility Aircraft intended for normal operations and limited acrobatic maneuvers, not including snap or inverted maneuvers. This may be a business aircraft, such as the Bonanza M35, which has higher stress capability than required for the normal classification.

Acrobatic Aircraft that have no restrictions on maneuvers unless the restriction has been determined as a result of required flight tests.

Restricted Aircraft intended to be operated for agricultural, industrial, and other special purposes. An example would be a Stearman trainer fitted for crop dusting.

Transport Aircraft designed primarily to carry passengers or cargo in scheduled air carrier operations (DC-9, Boeing 707).

GENERAL AVIATION

This category includes all civil aviation except the scheduled airlines. It is the largest user of airspace, flies forty-five times more aircraft and nearly four times more flying hours than the scheduled airlines. It includes business, agriculture, air taxi, air cargo services, instruction, geophysical research, survey and patrol, and pleasure. While its growth is phenomenal, its complexion is also changing.

The aircraft have higher performance and far more communications and instrument flying capability. In the last 10 years, the U.S. general aviation active fleet increased by 72%; the number of multiengined aircraft nearly doubled, four-place and larger increased 140%; while those three-place and less increased less than 11%. Rotocraft increased by 330% to about 1900; and while airports increased nearly 60% to more than 10,000, over 1500 heliports appeared in the United States, Canada, and Puerto Rico.

General aviation aircraft annual deliveries reached more than 13,600 in 1968, reflecting a substantial increase in aircraft specifically designed for air taxi and commuter service. The introduction of new twin-engine aircraft including turbine-powered models was responsible for a large part of the increase in value of the aircraft produced. Nearly 3000 aircraft, representing 24% of the value produced in 1968, were exported.

Because general aviation is representative of airmanship from the new solo student to the research test pilot, flight safety analysis of general aviation flying indicates where we can get the most return for dollars and time spent in pilot improvement, resulting in better utilization at less cost.

In 1968, with 124,237 aircraft flying more than 24 million hours, there were 4968 reported accidents involving 5031 aircraft in the United States for an overall rate of 20.6 accidents per 100,000 flying hours. The fatality rate was 2.9. (For 1970: 4927 accidents; fatality rate, 2.44.)

The National Transportation Safety Board analyses include "those occurrences incident to flight, in which, as a result of the operation of an aircraft, any person receives a fatal or serious injury or any aircraft receives substantial damage." Accident criteria were revised beginning in 1968 to reflect current activity, costs, and aircraft design. For this reason, rates of previous years are not directly comparable.

We have come a long way, but have far to go. During the next year, 1969, the Air Force rate for *new-pilot training* was 2.1!

The human factors obviously predominate. How did pilots err? Above all, they failed to obtain or maintain flying speed. They failed to prepare and plan properly before takeoff (3918 of the 5031 pilots had not filed a flight plan; aerial applicators excluded).

Figure 1.1 The Cessna 150 is presently the most used American trainer, produced in Standard, Trainer, Commuter (shown), and Aerobat versions. It is powered by a Continental 0-200-A 4-cylinder direct-drive engine. Maximum speed is 125 mph; maximum range is 565 mi. *(Courtesy of Cessna Aircraft Co.)*

Figure 1.2 The Cessna Model 172 and its counterpart, the Skyhawk, accounted for nearly 10% of all general aviation flying hours flown during 1967. Its gross weight is 2300 lb, with useful load 1055 lb. This four-place utility airplane has a Lycoming 4-cylinder engine rated at 150 hp at 2700 rpm. Model 172 cruises at 131 mph at 75% power at 9000 ft, with a range of 615 mi, no reserve. Sea level rate of climb at rated power is 645 fpm. Model 172 is the basic design concept for a variety of larger, higher-performance models. The T-41 military primary trainer model is used in USAF, Army, and foreign countries. *(Courtesy of Cessna Aircraft Co.)*

Figure 1.3 The Beechcraft Bonanza has been in production for 25 years. The Model V35B shown weighs 3400 lb, with a useful load of 1373 lb, and room for four to six persons. With a Continental 6-cylinder TSIO-520-D turbo-charged engine rated at 285 hp at 2700 rpm, it cruises 197 mph, 65% power, at 10,000 ft with a range of 512 mi and 45 min reserve. Service ceiling is 29,500 ft, and sea level rate of climb is 1225 fpm, rated power. Gear is fully retractable. *(Courtesy of Beech Aircraft Corp.)*

Figure 1.4 The Piper Cherokee 140 is a two-place, fixed landing gear utility low-wing monoplane, popular as a family, rental, and trainer airplane. Gross weight is 2150 lb; useful load is 937 lb. Powered by a Lycoming O-320 engine rated at 150 hp at 2700 rpm, it cruises 130 mph, at 7000 ft, 75% power, with a range of 525 mi, no reserve. It is produced also with 180 and 235 hp engines. Other models are the retractable-gear Arrow and the six-place Cherokee Six. *(Courtesy of Piper Aircraft Corp.)*

Figure 1.5 The Piper Pawnee PA-25 Agricultural Airplane with a 235 hp Lycoming engine reflects the importance of aviation to agriculture. Designed specifically for spraying and dusting, the B model has a 1200 lb, 150 gal hopper capacity. Pilot safety is stressed. Gross weight is 2900 lb. *(Courtesy of Piper Aircraft Corp.)*

During takeoff and landing, they lifted off prematurely, or leveled off improperly. Other elements of basic technique were also faulty, and many attempted operation beyond their capabilities, including VFR flight into adverse weather. These were the principal errors. They are classic, and are by no means restricted to general aviation pilots.

Figure 1.6 The Alouette II helicopter, simple, rugged, and economical, is famous in wilderness applications. Its Turbomeca Astazou 2A turbine is rated 523 shp for takeoff at sea level. Maximum TO gross weight is 3650 lb. With a useful load of 1300 lb, maximum hovering altitude in ground effect is 8300 ft. Service ceiling is 13,100 ft, normal cruise speed, 114 mph and maximum range, 595 sm. *(Courtesy of Chance-Vought.)*

TABLE 1.1
Selected Causes and Cause Factors, General Aviation Accidents, 1968[a]

Kind of Flying	*Pilot*	*Power*	*Facilities*	*Weather*	*Terrain*	*Personal*
Instructional	89.94	5.69	5.69	19.72	8.43	9.35
Pleasure	85.75	8.64	8.28	21.59	10.37	7.35
Business	80.94	7.28	9.19	26.17	8.84	6.41
Corporation Executive	76.14	7.95	9.09	22.73	4.55	15.91
Aerial Applicators	81.47	16.62	4.36	17.17	11.99	6.27
Air Taxi	68.45	16.67	11.31	27.98	13.69	12.50
All Operations	84.32	9.27	7.26	21.21	10.11	8.12

[a]*NTSB Annual Review,* 1968.

The most dangerous or accident-prone pilot, to make a fictitious composite, was between the ages of 25 and 49, and held a private or commercial license. He had either 100 to 300 hr, or 1000 or 3000 hours. His experience in a particular aircraft was either 6 to 25 hours, or 100 to 300 hr.

The accidents occurred primarily in broad daylight, while VFR, on the airport, in the traffic pattern, or within 5 mi of the airport. Most collisions

Figure 1.7 The Cessna 310, the first designed as a business twin, was introduced in 1954. At a gross weight of 5300 lb, it normally carries four adults and 600 lb baggage, partly in nacelle stowage space. It has two Continental IO-470 VO 6-cylinder fuel-injected engines rated at 260 hp at 2625 rpm with constant-speed, full-feathering, two-bladed propellers. It cruises at 218 mph at 6500 ft at 75% power, with a range of 774 mi, no reserve. Service ceiling is 19,500 ft, for a single engine, 6680 ft. Rate of climb at seal level is 1495 fpm; for a single engine, 327 fpm. The turbo-charged engine model produces full power up to 16,000 ft, with service ceiling 28,200 ft, single engine 17,550 ft, and gross weight 5500 lbs. Air Force version is the U-3, utility aircraft. *(Courtesy of Cessna Aircraft Co.)*

Figure 1.8 The Beechcraft King Air B90 is a six- to ten-place, pressurized, twin turboprop "all-weather" executive transport. Gross weight, takeoff, is 9650 lb. Engines are two Pratt & Whitney PT6A-20 free trubine, rated at 550 shp with three-bladed, hydraulic aluminum alloy, constant-speed, full-feathering propellers. At 8365 lb, 21,200 ft, maximum cruise power, cruises 253 mph, range 1263 mi, with 45 min fuel reserve. At 8000 lb, ceiling is 27,200 ft, for one engine, 21,900 ft; rate of climb, sea level, is 2595 fpm, for one engine, 863 fpm. U.S. Army utility version is the U-21A. *(Courtesy of Beech Aircraft Corp.)*

occurred between small airplanes, in daylight, in or near traffic patterns, in VFR weather during late afternoon, and the pilot had not filed a flight plan. *A startling number of accidents involved the injudicious use of alcohol.*

The rates by kind of flying were also revealing:

Instructional	15.16
Applicator	28.63
Pleasure	30.93
Business, corporate	13.18
Air taxi	8.80

Deficiencies in experience, supervision, and personal flying habits or discipline, as well as the difficulty of the operation, can be deduced from these rates. Though most modern aircraft are forgiving of human lapses, the cost alone today of carelessness or error demands a professional approach, whether the objective is pleasure or profit.

Figure 1.9 The Schweitzer Sailplane 2-33 is a two-seater, with metal wings and ailerons for sport and training. It is 25.75 ft long, has a span of 51 ft, and its weight is 1040 lb. Level-flight high speed is 98 mph; stall speed, dual, is 35 mph. It has a gliding ratio 22.25, and is suitable for airplane or auto-winch tow. *(Courtesy of Schweitzer Aircraft Co.)*

AIRLINE TRANSPORTS

By 1969, world civil airlines, except the USSR and Mainland China, had reduced their operating aircraft from the 1959 peak of 3475 to 2570, of

Figure 1.10 North American Sabreliner (Air Force T-39). The original executive jet aircraft. The Model 60 (not shown) has two Pratt & Whitney JT 12A-8 turbojet engines with target thrust reversers, rated at 3300 lb static thrust each for takeoff. Gross weight is 20,000 lb. With 7100 lb fuel and 10 passengers, range exceeds 1500 nm. Ceiling 45,000 ft. At 38,000 ft cruises Mach .8, TAS 459 knots. Wing leading edge slats, trailing edge flaps, and ventral speed brakes contribute to excellent slow speed response to flight controls. (*Courtesy of North American Rockwell.)*

which 87% were turbine powered. The impact of the jets in the last 10 years has been so great that these airlines carried 168% more passengers, reaching 263 million in 1968. They increased cargo by a factor of 3.7 to nearly 5 billion ton miles, and increased mail carried by a factor of 4.2 to nearly 1.5 billion ton miles.

Jet reliability has made on-time performance a feature to be expected rather than hoped for, though air traffic control and airport limitations have induced delays and severe complications by their inability to handle the aircraft of all types which must rely on them. Nevertheless, in the United States the airlines are the primary and the safest means of scheduled public transportation both at home and to overseas destinations.

As the capacity and speed of scheduled airline transports has increased, the problem of getting to the airports capable of handling them has become more complex. To satisfy this need, there have appeared a number of "third level" or "air taxi" companies which fly planes or helicopters

Figure 1.11 Boeing jet passenger and freight transports were the first in use, and so widely used as to be fairly typical of all jet airline transports. There are, of course, many other fine aircraft in comparable classes.
Top: Model 747B, at 775,000 lb gross weight, largest transport. Length 231.3 ft, span 195.6 ft, height of tail 63 ft. Four Pratt & Whitney JT9D-75 engines, each 47,000 lb thrust. Carries 374 passengers 5750 nm at 543 knots. Loading is fully automatic.
Top Center: Model 707-320B, Intercontinental, gross weight 328,000 lb, up to 189 passengers or quick-change version loads 90,000 lb palletized freight. Four Pratt & Whitney JT3D-3B engines, 19,000 lb thrust, cruises 522 knots, range 5220 nm.
Lower Center: Model 727-200. Medium range, gross weight 170,000 lb. Carries 134 passengers, quick-change version for freight. Three Pratt & Whitney JT8D-9 engines, 14,500 lb thrust, cruises 1480 nm at 522 knots.
Bottom: Model 737-100, short range and designed for relatively short runways, including gravel. Gross weight 111,000 lb, 119 passengers. Cruises 1390 nm at 500 knots. Two Pratt & Whitney JT8D-9 engines, 14,500 lb thrust. *(Courtesy of The Boeing Company.)*

Figure 1.12 The De Havilland Twin Otter is a commuter and utility normal category transport. It is powered by Pratt & Whitney PT6A-27 engines, 620 eshp. Quickly convertible to passengers or freight, it has STOL capability. At a maximum gross weight of 12,500 lb, maximum cruise is at 5000 ft, 208 mph, and a range of 750 mi with 45 min reserve, standard tanks. Service ceiling is 26,700 ft. *(Courtesy of De Havilland Aircraft of Canada Limited.)*

from local communities to the major air terminals. The airplanes used are usually capable of great reliability despite marginal weather, and have very short takeoff and landing requirements.

Military Aircraft

U.S. MILITARY AIRCRAFT DESIGNATION SYSTEM

Because of the wide variety of uses for military aircraft, the system is somewhat complex. However, in its general use, it is simple and logical. The most commonly used elements of the designators are:

Element	*Examples*		
	(a)	*(b)*	*(c)*
Status prefix symbol			
Modified mission symbol		R	U
Basic mission and type symbol	F	C	H
Design number	111	130	1
Series symbol	A	B	D

The *status prefix symbol* indicates experimentation or service test.

The *modified mission symbol* indicates that the aircraft has been modified and is being used for a purpose other than the original one for which the aircraft was designed.

Design number is used to indicate a new design for a particular mission.

The *series symbol* identifies significant changes of a given type and design number.

In the examples shown, the F-111A is a fighter, the 111th fighter design, and the first series of that design. The RC130B is a reconnaissance version of a cargo aircraft of the 130 design, and the second or B series. The UH-1D is a utility helicopter, first design, fourth series.

Some of the more frequently used prefix type codes are shown in Table 1.2.

TABLE 1.2

Prefix Letters		*Type Letters*	
A	Attack	A	Amphibian
C	Cargo	B	Bomber
E	Electronic reconnaissance	C	Cargo
K	Refueling tanker	F	Fighter
M	Missile carrier	H	Helicopter
Q	Drone	K	Refueling tanker
R	Reconnaissance	L	Liaison
S	Search and rescue	P	Patrol
T	Trainer	S	Search and rescue
U	Utility	T	Trainer
V	Staff modified	U	Utility
W	Weather reconnaissance	X	Experimental

The service (Army, Navy, Air Force, Marines) is not shown in the designator, though the aircraft itself is marked with the service operating it. Military aircraft are also identified by popular names, as in the illustrations following.

AIR FORCE BOMBERS

In this atomic age, the missile-carrying heavy bomber (Figure 1.13) is the supreme expression of national military power and airpower. With its long range and flexibility it provides the purest form of airpower employment from one national fortress to the military heart of another. Because of its range, flexibility, and present ability to strike objectives lightly or completely annihilate them, it is the principal military weapon of modern

Figure 1.13 The B-52H Stratofortress, with a gross weight of more than 450,000 lb and eight Pratt & Whitney J-57-43W turbojet engines, has a speed of more than 650 mph, and an unrefueled range of more than 6000 mi at over 50,000 ft. It can attack at high or low level, with air-to-surface atomic missiles, or with nuclear or high-explosive bombs. It is the primary Air Force Strategic Air Command bomber, and was used in accurate close support of ground forces in Vietnam. *(U.S. Air Force photograph.)*

manned strategy. In its ability to be deployed swiftly, to appear in the air over any part of the world at a given time, it is a most significant diplomatic factor and thus a valuable tool in times of uneasy peace.

General Giulio Douhet, the original military prophet of airpower in his book *Command of the Air,* proclaimed in the early 1920s a decisive offensive capability for small bomber forces which was not merited in the light of the explosive power of weapons then available. Only the massive attacks which characterized the last year of the USAF and RAF offensives during World War II, particularly with the use of incendiary bombs, have provided such decisive effects. However, with development of the atomic and hydrogen bombs, a single modern bomber now possesses the capability of delivering at one blow a broad variety of nuclear or nonnuclear weapons tailored precisely to the task at hand. Coupled with this development have been the remarkable advances, based on the experience of the last war, in the technology of navigation and in bombing accuracy, especially from above thousands of feet of cloud. In Vietnam the bomber displayed a degree of accuracy and reliability, bombing blind in close support of troops, that won the praise of all allied forces.

Winston Churchill found in the long-range atomic bomber the "major deterrent" to war after the close of World War II. It is in this deterrent role that the bomber now has its greatest strategic employment.

Great range, flexibility, ability to penetrate enemy defenses, tremendous power, and bombing reliability—these are the factors which have made the bomber so formidable a weapon.

The *medium bombers* are medium only in range, and to a certain extent

Figure 1.14 The General Dynamics FB-111, originally conceived by civilian defense authorities as an all-purpose, Air Force-Navy fighter, never matured in that role. The technology was used to provide a medium bomber, supplementing the B-52. With two Pratt & Whitney TF30P-7 turbofan engines rated at 20,000 lb thrust with afterburner, and pilot-controllable wing sweep from 16° to 72.5°, it is capable of short takeoff and landing. Maximum speed at 60,000 ft, Mach 2; at sea level, Mach 1. Intercontinental range with air refueling. Armament is both nuclear and nonnuclear. *(U.S. Air Force photograph.)*

in load-carrying capacity. However, even these limitations are largely overcome by in-flight refueling and by the increase in effectiveness given to single high-explosive or atomic bombs by the accuracy of navigation and bombing demanded by close support or interdiction requirements and experience, and the capability of new radar and inertial systems.

The medium bombers can be produced in relatively large numbers and therefore can provide a flexibility which the more desirable intercontinental bombers, in relatively smaller numbers, cannot provide. This flexibility is important because it increases the variety of tactics available to friendly forces, and in doing so, it forces a potential aggressor to devote a widespread, highly diversified and extremely costly effort in his own defense. The magnitude of this effort alone may in itself give him cause to pause and reflect on the cost of aggression.

Bombers and other military aircraft are always in a state of change in order to keep ahead of the defenses of possible enemies and to permit using new weapons and techniques. Intercontinental missiles now substantially complement the missile-launching and bomb-carrying bombers as we know them today. As to replacement, the probabilities of manned space flight, and the advantages of human judgment in immediate control, will weigh heavily in the development of future manned bombing aircraft.

FIGHTERS

The versatility of the fighter, its relative smallness, and the individuality and loneliness of its pilot contribute to making it the most romantic of all aircraft, and its crew the symbol of modern knighthood. The very title "ace" describes individual accomplishment; Winston Churchill immortalized the fighter pilots of the Royal Air Force in the Battle of Britain, and thus all fighter pilots: "At the summit the stamina and valour of our fighter pilots remained unconquerable and supreme. Thus Britain was saved. Well might I say in the House of Commons, 'Never in the field of human conflict was so much owed by so many to so few.' "

The fighters have an interesting history: General Henry H. Arnold, Commander of the Army Air Forces in World War II, stated: "It is an historic fact that the first two hostile aviators who met in the air during the World War simply waved to each other and passed on to their reconnaissance

Figure 1.15 The Convair F-106 Delta Dart is the nation's fastest, highest flying, most advanced all-weather interceptor. In 1959 it set a world speed record of 1525.6 mph. Engine is the Pratt & Whitney J75-P-17, developing 24,500 lb thrust with afterburner. Weapons are internally mounted rockets and guided missiles. It can be aerially refueled; when launched into the radar net of an air defense system, interception and attack is assisted by data-link ground control. This view shows open speed brakes, elevons characteristic of delta-winged aircraft, and the "Coke bottle" shaped fuselage characteristic of Whitcombe's area rule. *(U.S. Air Force photograph.)*

missions. Shortly thereafter, when hostile planes met, the aviators shot at each other with pistols and rifles, or tried to drop bombs on the enemy plane. They even tried to ram one another. All of these tactics merely prepared the way for the more potent machine guns on the planes."

The French were the first to fire through the propeller. This was done by fastening small, pointed metal blocks to the propeller where the bullets struck. The development of the synchronized gun followed rapidly. This gun was timed with the engine so that it could not be fired when a blade of the propeller was in front of the muzzle.

The British, during World War II, discarded the synchronous firing guns and mounted much heavier armament in the wings of their aircraft. The advent of jet aircraft since the war, and the development of rockets and air-launched missiles, have resulted in a broad range of methods for carrying and firing weapons of the fighter, all designed to deliver the most potent possible forward firing power.

Modern fighters are roughly divided into two general classes: the *fighter interceptor,* and the *fighter bomber,* or *tactical fighter.* The principal distinction is that the interceptor is highly specialized by performance and equipment to do one task: at night and in any weather, to intercept, identify, attack, and destroy enemy aircraft in the air. The tactical fighter, on the other hand, possesses characteristics which give it a high degree of maneuverability, considerable range, and versatile firepower through both guns and air-to-air missiles. It is also able to attack, with a wide variety of high-explosive, incendiary, and nuclear weapons, hostile airpower either on the ground or in the air at relatively long ranges; to attack and destroy,

Figure 1.16 The F-4E Phantom II (see also Figure 1.25) is the principal and most versatile fighter of the Air Force Tactical Air Command. It carries a pilot and systems operator. Two J-79-GE-17 engines provide 17,900 lb thrust each. With an internally mounted 20mm rapid-fire cannon, externally it carries a variety of bombs, rockets, fuel, and missiles up to 14,000 lb. Gross weight is 58,000 lb. *(U.S. Air Force photograph.)*

Figure 1.17 A Boeing KC-135 refueling F-4's. Originally developed to refuel Strategic Air Command bombers, the KC-135, tanker version of the Boeing 707, now refuels many other aircraft, including fighters on combat sorties. These F-4's, loaded with bombs, are headed for North Vietnam. *(U.S. Air Force photograph.)*

behind the enemy lines, supply sources and lines of communication to enemy armies in the field; and to destroy by direct attack the enemy's fortifications and troops.

The term "day fighter" is now used to refer to aircraft which sacrifice virtually all else to their ability to engage hostile aircraft, both fighters or bombers, visually in aerial combat and to destroy them.

Any fighter, when employed to intercept and destroy enemy aircraft or when being controlled in support of ground forces, operates in an environment of radar and radio direction, both from the ground and from the air. In fact, it is radar vectoring of fighters that makes possible interception at the high speeds and altitudes characteristic of modern air battles.

RECONNAISSANCE

The information essential to intelligent planning and effective execution of military operations is obtained partly by reconnaissance aircraft. They

Figure 1.18 McDonnell-Douglas F-15. Artist's concept of the Air Force's new F-15 fighter. The F-15 will be a single-place, twin-engine jet fighter with supersonic performance over a broad range of altitudes and speeds. In order for it to achieve this superiority in air-to-air combat, it will carry both missile and gun armament. Use of both types of weapons will provide the versatility needed to carry out the typical tactical mission of fighter sweep, escort, and combat air patrol. *(U.S. Air Force photograph.)*

usually are contemporary bombers, fighters (Figure 1.16), or transports which are specially equipped and manned with a highly trained aircrew to permit them to carry out their missions. As a general rule, special reconnaissance aircraft operate singly and rely on deception and speed rather than on firepower for their defense.

MILITARY TRANSPORTS

It is the transport aircraft, from small bush airplanes used in the American Arctic to the modern airliner, which most greatly benefit mankind both in peace and in war. Military and civil transports are highly versatile if available in sufficient numbers. They support far-flung strategic operations with movement of men and materials; they refuel bombers and fighters at remote rendezvous (Figure 1.17); they evacuate wounded so effectively as to save the lives of thousands; they carry mobile ground forces thousands of miles into combat and support them there after their arrival; they have virtually opened the North American Arctic to commerce; and they daily speed along in innumerable ways the commerce and diplomacy of the world.

During World War II, it was considered practicable for only high-priority human and cargo loads to be transported by air. Today air transport has a primary place as one of the reliable, efficient, and economical methods of cargo transport in either peace or war.

The development of transports to their present high degree of efficiency and reliability, regardless of weather, owes much to the commercial airlines; transport flying is a special brand of airmanship in itself. It was the military air transport's versatility and reliability, however, which per-

Figure 1.19 The C-130E Hercules Turboprop Logistic and Troop Transport (Lockheed) has a gross weight of 150,000 lb and range of 2950 mn, and cruises at 350 knots. The engines are Allison T-56, producing 4910 eshp each. It takes a crew of five, and carries 92 troops or 64 paratroops, or 74 litters, with a payload of more than 40,000 lb. The aircraft is shown here in low-altitude parachute extraction cargo delivery at Khe Shan, Vietnam, Sept. 1967. *(U.S. Air Force photograph.)*

mitted President Truman in 1948 to defy the Soviet Union's blockade and keep West Berlin alive by supplying that city by air. For more than a year, despite the Soviet closing of the land corridors available to the Western world into Berlin, the city was supplied with food, clothing, medicine, and fuel. This demonstrated that military air transport can serve as a primary

Figure 1.20 Large military transports. These aircraft are designed for the heavy, outsize capability needed for Army combat matériel and vehicles, concentrated cargo, and passengers, both with and without combat equipment. The C-5 Galaxy: gross weight 764,500 lb; 28-wheel gear gives low footprint pressure; useful load, 151,000 lb from Delaware to England at 450 knots, nonstop is typical; four GE TF-39 engines, rated 41,100 lb thrust. C-141 Starlifter: gross weight 318,000 lb; four Pratt & Whitney TF-33 P-7 turbofan engines, rated 21,000 lb thrust; will cruise 490 knots a distance of 3675 nm carrying 154 troops or 68,500 lb payload. *(U.S. Air Force photograph.)*

Figure 1.21 The HH-3E Rescue Helicopter "Jolly Green Giant," rescuing a pilot from a raft off Vietnam. Note the rotor downwash effect on the water. The current model, HH-53B, has two GE-T64-3 engines, with 3080 eshp. It cruises at 150 knots, and its range unrefueled is 288 nm. At a maximum speed of 169 knots, it carries 38 passengers or 16,000 lb cargo and is fitted with armor plate, hoist, and miniguns. *(U.S. Air Force photograph.)*

Figure 1.22 O-2 Hound Dog. This military adaptation of the Cessna Skymaster is shown in South Vietnam where it serves as a forward air controller to direct strike aircraft to enemy ground targets. It is powered by two 10-360D Continental 6-cylinder 210 hp engines. Rocket launchers are hung under each wing. *(U.S. Air Force photograph.)*

factor in national strategy, as sea blockade runners have traditionally done in the past. In 1948, 426 two- and four-engine transports were required. Roughly, 53 C-141's could do the same task today.

UTILITY AIRCRAFT

In this category are the helicopters (Figure 1.21), the light twins in military use, and the liaison or forward air control (FAC) aircraft (Figure 1.22).

TRAINERS

Air Force trainer aircraft are designed to accomplish two basic missions: (1) to provide efficient and economical training of new fliers, and (2) to maintain the proficiency of fliers on duty with units whose combat aircraft must be in a constant state of readiness or are so expensive to operate that the use of trainers as a training aid is an effective economic measure.

Aircraft for the first mission—training new aircrew members—fall into two categories: the pilot trainers and the navigator trainers.

Pilot trainers At the present time the Air Force pilot trainee is already a commissioned officer, having gotten his commission through one of the Service Academies, the Reserve Officers Training Corps at a college, or from the Officers Training School in San Antonio. He begins flying in a lightplane, the T-41. The T-41 is simply a trainer version of the civil Cessna 172. In it, the pilot becomes familiar with his new environment, and though his training is not extensive, he does receive about 30 hr, and does solo. The principal accomplishment of this phase is the early identification of individuals who, either by desire or by aptitude, should not be continued

Figure 1.23 The North American OV-10A Bronco, a two-place tandem multipurpose armed reconnaissance aircraft, is powered by two Garrett Airesearch T-76 engines of 715 shp. It carries a wide variety of reconnaissance, light bombing, and rocket equipment, and is designed to operate from small forward airstrips. *(U.S. Air Force photograph.)*

Figure 1.24 The T-41 Primary Trainer is a two-place Cessna 172, with a Continental O-300-D engine. Used for new pilot trainee screening, it is operated under civilian contract at military pilot training bases. *(U.S. Air Force photograph.)*

in the pilot training course. This saves both them and the Air Force considerable cost and time.

The next step for the trainee is to fly the T-37 Primary Trainer. In the T-37, he is actually taught to fly, to the extent that it can be done in about 100 hr. He learns to fly the airplane itself and is introduced thoroughly to instrument flying, acrobatics, formation, and elementary navigation. He solos in about 12 hr, although most of the flying is done in intensive dual instruction in conjunction with a comprehensive ground school.

Figure 1.25 The Cessna T-37 Primary Jet Trainer is known as the "Tweetybird" in the Air Force Air Training Command. Student and instructor sit side by side in a primary trainer that has proved very effective. With two Continental J-69 T-25 engines, each with 1025 lb thrust, the T-37 has a ceiling of 35,000 ft, a range of more than 575 nm, a speed of 303 knots, and unlimited acrobatic capability. Gross weight is 6580 lb. *(U.S. Air Force photograph.)*

Figure 1.26 The Northrup T-38A Talon is the two-place Air Force basic trainer. In this superb training aircraft, the instructor, in the aft seat, has excellent visibility. Engines are two GE J-85-GE5's each developing 3850 lb thrust. In Mach 1.2 class, the T-38 has held various world rate-of-climb records. *(U.S. Air Force photograph.)*

At about the half-year point in training, he is ready to leave the primary trainer and move into the basic trainer, the supersonic T-38 Talon. In the T-38 phase, he receives 120 hr of concentrated instruction which begins with instrument instruction even before he has soloed the aircraft. This uses departures and returns from instrument missions for transition familiarization; when he has finished the largest part of his instrument flying, the trainee completes his transition, solos the aircraft, and goes on into high-performance flight maneuvers, most above 25,000 ft. He learns more

Figure 1.27 The McDonnell-Douglas F-4 Phantom II is a carrier-based all-weather fighter. It carries bombs, rockets, missiles, and atomic weapons, and its crew consists of a pilot and a systems operator. Two J79-GE-8B, 17,000 lb thrust engines power it. *(U.S. Navy photograph.)*

Figure 1.28 The McDonnell-Douglas A-4F Skyhawk is a single-place carrier-based attack aircraft, with one J52-P8A Pratt & Whitney 9300 lb thrust engine. *(U.S. Navy photograph.)*

about the characteristics of high-performance aircraft, covering acrobatics, formation, navigation, instruments, and night flying, all in an environment which produces a highly professional military pilot. He has spent a busy flying year.

Navigation training is done in a "flying classroom" version of the familiar twin-engined Convair, the T-29. Equipped with multiple navigator stations, complete with radio and radar, the new navigator learns the techniques of airmanship needed for duty with aircrews of bomber, transport, and two-place fighter units of the Air Force.

Figure 1.29 The Grumman F-14A/B is a two-man tandem air superiority fighter with variable geometry wing; it operates from carriers or austere shore bases. It is powered by a TF-30 P-412 engine, 20,000 lb thrust with afterburner. The F-14B will have a F401-PW-400 engine, which is 550 lb lighter, thrust about 27,000 lb. It uses air-to-air and air-to-ground missiles, cannon, and bomb capability comparable to A-7E. *(U.S. Navy photograph.)*

U.S. NAVY AIRCRAFT

Navy and Marine Corps aircraft operate in support of five major categories of naval missions: antisubmarine warfare, attack, air defense, amphibious,

Figure 1.30 The Ling Temco Vought A-7E "Corsair II" is a subsonic light attack carrier- and land-based aircraft. Its one TF-30 P8 engine delivers 12,200 lb thrust. Six bomb and rocket pylons are shown on the wings, and the speed brake is extended. It has an advanced weapons delivery system and is armed with external missiles and an internal 20-mm Gatling gun. *(U.S. Navy photograph.)*

Figure 1.31 The Grumman A6E Intruder is an all-weather carrier-based two-place attack airplane, with J-52 P-6A, 8500 lb thrust engines. The aircraft pictured above is loaded with thirty 500 lb bombs.

Figure 1.32 The Grumman E-2C Hawkeye provides airborne early warning and control for fleet air defense, to ranges of 200 nm. Operating at normal station position of 25,000 ft, 200 nm from a carrier, it can readily detect low-flying enemy aircraft. Sightings are sent via an air-to-ground data link to fleet for display. A versatile aircraft display permits automatic or voice intercepter control to target from E-2C data link. Rescue aircraft can also be controlled. *(U.S. Navy photograph.)*

Figure 1.33 The Lockheed "Orion" P-3C antisubmarine (ASW) patrol plane has a fully integrated airborne digital computer weapons system with advanced electronics sensors and a variety of ASW weapons. With four T-56-A-10 Allison engines, it has a ceiling of 27,000 ft, and patrol endurance of 8 hr at a range of 1000 nm. Minimum speed (two engines feathered) is 150 knots; maximum diving speed is 405 knots. It carries a crew of 12.

Figure 1.34 The AV-8A Harrier is a Marine Corps V/STOL attack aircraft. Made by McDonnell-Douglas under license from Hawker-Siddeley, it is powered by one Rolls Royce Pegasus 402 engine, and carries a variety of nonnuclear weapons. Ferry range is 1800nm. It uses rotating nozzles to achieve vectored thrust. *(Courtesy of Hawker-Siddeley Aviation Limited.)*

and battlefield close support. These aircraft are designed to operate from aircraft carriers—except for patrol and transport aircraft, which operate from land bases.

The operating environment of Navy combat aircraft requires certain basic design characteristics which differ from those found in other military aircraft. These differences are principally in the structural requirements needed to meet the high landing forces inherent in carrier arrestments; corrosion control; slow-flight characteristics; and operational equipment designed for the navigation, search, and attack problems faced by the naval aviator.

U.S. ARMY AIRCRAFT

The army has significantly expanded in use of aircraft during the past 10 years. Through field maneuvers, experimentation, and employment in Vietnam the Army's air mobile concept has grown to the point that aviation is integrated into every activity on the battlefield. Originally Army aircraft were used for cargo and liaison in the battle area, reconnaissance, artillery fire observation, medical evacuation, and rescue. In addition to these vital functions, cargo helicopter formations carry troops, equipment, and supplies into combat. Considerable study by the U.S. Air Force and Army is being devoted to the coordination of inter-service means which will insure survival of aircraft on tomorrow's battlefields.

Figure 1.35 The Bell AH-1G Cobra, an attack helicopter, is armed with machine guns, rockets, and grenades. One Lycoming T-53-L-13 gas turbine engine of 1400 shp powers it. At a gross weight of 9500 lb, it cruises at 130 knots, with a range of 260 nm with 30 min reserve, carrying a maximum external load of 2200 lb. *(U.S. Army photograph.)*

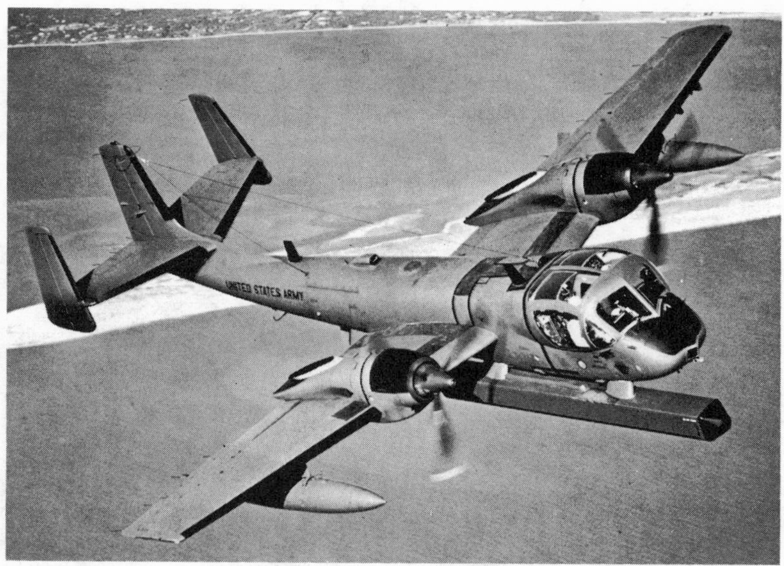

Figure 1.36 The Grumman OV-1D Mohawk is designed for visual, electronic, and photo reconnaisance with interchangeable sensor packages. Its gross weight is 18,109 lb, engines are Lycoming T53-L-701 rated at 1400 shp. Attaining a maximum speed at 10,000 ft of 251 knots, its rate of climb at sea level is 3466 fpm, ceiling is 25,000 ft, and range is 20,000 ft, 820 nm. *(U.S. Army photograph.)*

Figure 1.37 The Bell OH-58 KIOWA is a single-rotor, light observation helicopter designed for visual observation and command control. The armed version performs scouting role. The Allison T-63-A-70 engine develops 317 shp. Its gross weight is 3000 lb, and it cruises at 103 knots, with maximum speed 120 knots. *(U.S. Army photograph.)*

Figure 1.38 The Boeing-Vertol CH-47C Chinook Cargo and passenger helicopter has a gross weight of 33,000 lb and two Lycoming T-55-L11 engines, rated at 3750 shp each, to give a maximum speed of 189 mph. (See Chapter 13.) *(U.S. Army photograph.)*

Figure 1.39 The U-6 De Havilland Beaver is a standard Army fixed-wing utility aircraft. Developed originally as a bush plane, it is very rugged and highly versatile on wheels, skis, or floats. Speed is 97 knots, range, 400 mi. *(U.S. Army photograph.)*

Aircraft Obsolescence

The rate of introduction of new ideas into aircraft design, and the consequent rapid advances in performance, cast the shadow of obsolescence over new aircraft almost as soon as they appear. How fast do modern aircraft actually become obsolete? A valid answer can be found only by considering fleets of aircraft, not individual airplane and helicopter models, for it is only by considering large numbers that aircraft are usefully employed in military or commercial pursuits in which modernness is a principal factor.

Once an Air Force or an airline has committed itself to certain bombers or fighters or transports, a period of years is required for production of the aircraft and for personnel to become proficient in their economical operation and maintenance. The same lengthy cycle is required to replace them with newer and more modern models.

A force of military aircraft is obsolete when its technical inferiority will not permit it to accomplish the combat mission for which it was designed without too great a hazard of defeat. For example, a bomber which flies too low and slow or has too short a range to be able to penetrate a possible enemy's defenses is obsolete even though there is no new and acceptable model which can be built to replace it. This fact, and the time required to develop a new aircraft, result in constant pressure for developments in aircraft for military forces even before the aircraft which a new development is to replace is produced and integrated into the force in usable volume.

The airliner is obsolete when it can no longer produce a reasonable profit for the company that operates it, when it can no longer satisfy the public's needs, and when the aircraft industry expands markets by new developments such as pressurization, jet transports, and the large types such as the Boeing 747. An example is the current demand for safe, high-speed, vibrationless flight which only turbojet or turboprop transports can provide.

Obsolescence is important to the student airman because he may hes-

Figure 1.40 Obsolete Aircraft in Special Operations. With extensive experience in converting obsolescent aircraft for useful roles in air forces with less industrial support than we enjoy, the USAF adapted these from WW II to the needs of Southeast Asia: the C-123 Provider, once a powered glider, to close support transport, jungle defoliation, and civic action pest control; the A-26, a light bomber, to night attack and rescue; the O-1, observation, to forward air control; the A-1, Navy multipurpose, to an attack bomber; the C-47 "Gooney Bird" to every conceivable use plus attacking with three side-firing 7.62-mm "miniguns," each capable of 6000 rounds/min; The Helio U-10 from liaison to a STOL role in psychological warfare and utility; and the T-28, a primary trainer, to an armored attack plane. All of these were highly effective in the environment of Vietnam. *(U.S. Air Force photograph.)*

itate to enter a profession which, because of rapid change in design, may be highly unstable. Of this he need have little worry. The replacement of military, commercial, and particularly private aircraft fleets is a matter requiring many years. A truly radical aircraft is available even to test and research pilots only a few times in a decade. Seldom indeed is an airman confronted with the need to cope with a change so radical as propeller-driven to jet-powered aircraft, subsonic to supersonic flight techniques, or control so automatic as to require no guidance by human skill and judgment.

Instead of being radical, the change in modern air fleets, military and civil, is constant. While costly to the user, this constant change is vital. An obsolete combat aircraft can be used successfully only in a battle setting carefully framed in limited conditions. However, to have to rely on a force which may be used only under those conditions so seriously restricts the flexibility of airpower employment that it dates and crystallizes the possible avenues of national strategy. In the same way, airliners no longer able to compete for the public's favor fall into the essential but less competitive transport routes, or into employment as executive aricraft, or, after years of service, into scrap. The airman lives and works in a fascinating atmosphere of change, but it is also a part of airmanship to be able to put older but serviceable aircraft to dependable and profitable use.

2

*Basic Aerodynamics and the Theory of Flight**

A sound acquaintance with the principles of flight is an essential part of any modern airman's equipment. It is, of course, possible to fly without speaking the language of an aerodynamicist. However, the airman, and particularly the professional airman, will derive much from a careful study of the concepts of aerodynamics and the mathematically expressed relationships found here. The subject cannot be covered in one chapter or even one book; therefore the principal concepts, presented here, are highly condensed and require thoughtful reading.

Basic Principles

Before reading this chapter, an airman should have in mind the questions the chapter hopes to answer. Most basic of all is the question of what holds the airplane up in the sky. The explanation will require a discussion of some simple

*Revised by Professors Daniel B. DeBra and Samuel MacIntosh, Department of Aeronautics and Astronautics, Stanford University.

concepts of airflow which show how a wing produces lift. The breakdown of the flow that produces lift is the explanation of why an airplane stalls.

Why is power needed? What are the controls, and how do they operate and affect the airplane? How do the characteristics and limitations of the aerodynamics influence performance? How does an airplane behave by itself, and how does this natural behavior affect the airman's job as a pilot?

How does the theory change for high-performance aircraft at speeds which approach or exceed the speed of sound?

The airman intuitively recognizes the relevance of these questions and should keep them in mind as he reads this chapter.

FORCES ACTING ON AN AIRPLANE: LIFT AND WEIGHT, THRUST AND DRAG

In Figure 2.1 the airplane is in straight and level flight. There are four net forces—*lift, drag, thrust,* and *weight*—acting on the airplane. By definition the lift forces act perpendicular to the relative wind or the line of flight; the drag forces act parallel to the relative wind; the thrust forces usually act parallel to the line of flight; while the weight always acts in the direction of gravity. *Relative wind* is the remote velocity (speed and direction) of air which strikes an airfoil (Figure 2.11). In level unaccelerated flight the propulsion system must furnish a net thrust force adequate to balance the aerodynamic drag, which is the resistance of the air to the passage of the airplane. The lift force generated by the wing must be large enough to support the weight of the airplane.

VECTORS

For many quantities, both magnitude and direction are significant. They are called vector quantities and are represented schematically as arrows (Figure 2.2 (a)). Velocity and force are the principal vectors of interest

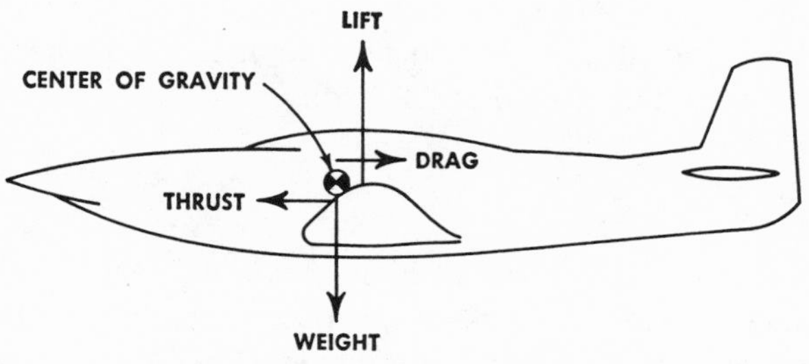

Figure 2.1 Forces acting in straight and level flight.

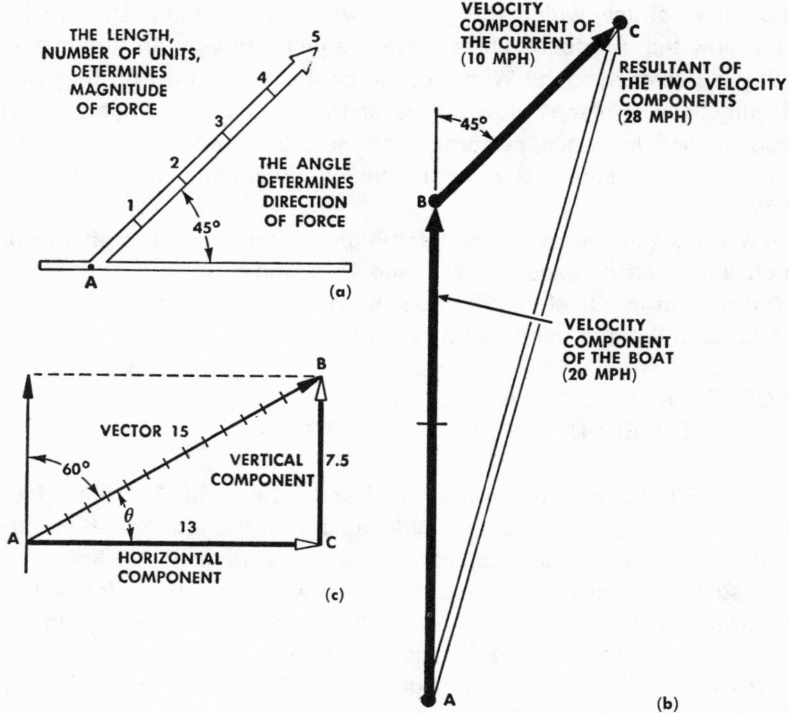

Figure 2.2 Vectors. (a) A force vector where Point *A* is the point of application. (b) Vectors may be added geometrically. For example, a boat whose velocity (speed in a certain direction) is represented by *AB* moves through a current having a velocity of *BC*. The boat's resultant velocity is the geometric sum, *AC*. (c) The vector having magnitude and direction *AB* may be conveniently divided into vertical and horizontal components equal to *CB* and *AC*. In trigonometric terms, $BC = AB\ (\sin \Theta)$, $AC = AB\ (\cos \Theta)$, and $BC = AC\ (\tan \Theta)$.

here. A vector may be the sum of several component vectors. Vectors are added by joining them tail to head. The resultant vector is represented by the line (arrow) from the tail of the first component to the head of the last, as shown in Figures 2.2 (b) and 2.2 (c).

FORCES AND MOMENTS

The effect of a force on an aircraft depends on its point of application. If the line of action of the force does not pass through the aircraft center of gravity, a moment or torque is produced about the c.g., which tends to rotate the aircraft. A moment is given as a product of the force and the shortest distance between its line of action and the reference point about which it acts. The units are therefore those of a force times a distance, such as foot-pounds. When two equal and opposite forces act through separate points, a pure moment or couple is produced which does not change as the reference point is changed. In general, a force system can be represented at a reference point as a force and a moment.

These principles are well illustrated by a mechanic "pulling through" a propeller of a light plane. Consider a propeller 6 ft in diameter with the mechanic pulling at one end. If the mechanic pulls straight down with a 50-lb force, then the moment produced is $50 \times 3 = 150$ ft-lb about the propshaft when the propeller is horizontal. If the propeller is inclined and the man pulls straight down, the moment arm is the horizontal distance from his handgrip to the vertical line through the propeller hub.

THE LAWS OF MOTION

Figure 2.1 shows an airplane in straight and level flight. It represents a condition of balanced forces acting continuously upon the airplane. There are four basic forces: lift, weight, thrust, and drag.

The action and effects of forces are explained by Sir Isaac Newton's three laws of motion:

1. *A body remains at rest or moves uniformly in a straight line unless acted upon by a net force.*

For example, in order to accelerate an airplane, the engine must deliver a thrust greater in magnitude than the existing drag or resistance forces. For unaccelerated flight the net thrust must be exactly equal to the drag. Constant altitude will be held only as long as the lift and weight are equal.

2. *The acceleration of a body is directly proportional to, and in the direction of, any net force acting on the body, and is inversely proportional to the mass of the body.*

This statement is usually expressed in equation form as:

$$F = \frac{W}{g} \times a, \quad \text{or} \quad F = Ma \qquad (2.1)$$

where F = the net force, lb
W = weight of the body, lb
g = acceleration due to gravity = 32.2 ft/sec^2
a = acceleration of the body, ft/sec^2
M = mass of the body defined as W/g, lb sec^2/ft

This equation, when applied to an airplane, explains accelerations and decelerations in flight when thrust and drag or lift and weight are not equal. In addition to the obvious changes in speed, any change in the velocity vector is an acceleration. A horizontal force perpendicular to the velocity vector is required to perform a constant-altitude, constant-speed turn. In an airplane, the force is produced by banking. A component of the lift vector acts horizontally to supply the centripetal acceleration.

3. *For every action there is an equal and opposite reaction.*

The third law explains why a propeller can produce a force sufficient to propel the airplane by pushing against the air, much the same as a rower pushes against the water with his oar to propel his boat forward.

LOAD FACTORS

The term *load factor* is defined as the ratio of the lift developed by an airplane to its weight,

$$n = \frac{L}{W} \tag{2.2}$$

The simplest flight example is one in which lift is exactly equal to weight and is known as "1*g*" flight; that is, the lift is exactly equal to the force needed to overcome the pull of gravity. A load factor of 1 exists in level flight. It is slightly greater than 1 in gentle turns or during the landing flair when the velocity direction is changing slowly. A more severe maneuver can impose a load factor substantially greater than "1*g*" on the airplane and crew.

INTRODUCTION TO AERODYNAMICS

Until the period of World War II the solution of subsonic flight problems was dominant in the field of aeronautics. Most design work was done on the basis of an incompressible air. (That is, the air density was considered to vary with temperature and pressure but not with velocity.) During the latter part of the war, several cases of difficult control and buffeting were encountered at high speeds, especially in dives. It was soon discovered that these and other effects were related to the fact that air *is* compressible.

The range of speeds that must be considered for present-day flight is divided into four regimes. These are denoted successively as *subsonic, transonic, supersonic,* and *hypersonic.* Each regime denotes a speed range within which the aerodynamic design problems are generally similar. The progress made in both theoretical and experimental research to understand the characteristics of flight in these regimes had been phenomenal during the years since World War II.

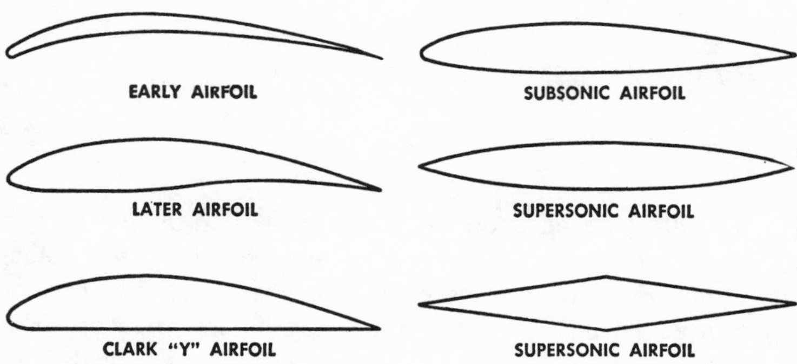

Figure 2.3 Typical airfoil cross sections.

AIRFOILS

An *airfoil* is any surface which is designed to obtain lift upon its surfaces from the air through which it moves. In aerodynamic discussion, "airfoil" means a section of "wing" of infinite span (length); airplane fuselage and wing tip effects may be ignored in study of a simple airfoil. NASA and other research agencies have developed and classified families of airfoils. Studies of the characteristics of these families have done much to increase our knowledge of aerodynamics even though only a relatively small number of these airfoils are efficient lifting surfaces. Figures 2.3 and 2.4 illustrate airfoil terminology and typical airfoil shapes.

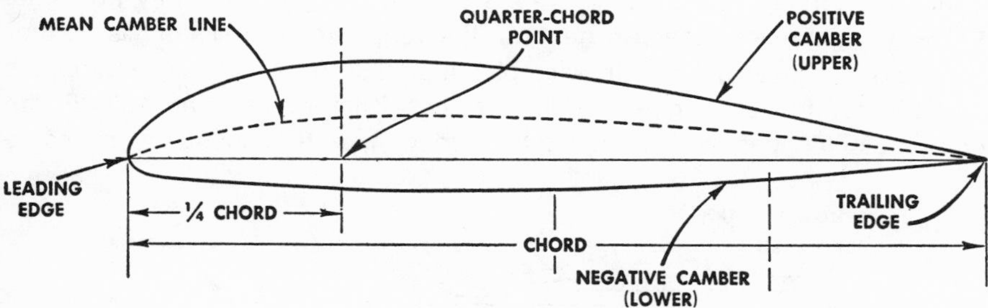

Figure 2.4 Asymmetrical subsonic airfoil cross section. In the symmetrical airfoil, the mean camber line and chord line coincide. Airfoil measurements are made with reference to fractions of chord length. Upper and lower camber are measured from the chord line to the mean camber line at any point, measured perpendicular to the chord line. The sum of the lengths of upper and lower cambers is the profile thickness.

Subsonic Aerodynamics

SUBSONIC FLOW

The theory of lift is based upon the forces generated upon a body and a moving gas in which it is immersed. In subsonic flow, the velocity of particles of the gas never, at any point, exceeds the speed of sound. Air is the gas in which the aircraft is supported by the reaction of airflow around the airfoil and other parts of the aircraft. Air is considered to be composed of a great number of small particles. In steady flow, the path of each particle is called a streamline. Streamlines are everywhere tangent to the gas velocity, and either form closed paths or extend to infinity; no gas can flow across streamlines.

At speeds below about 260 knots, air can be considered incompressible. That is, at a fixed altitude its density remains nearly constant, while its pressure varies. Under this assumption, air behaves no differently from water and is classified as a fluid. If it is further assumed that the effects of viscosity can be neglected, air is classified as an ideal fluid. Even with these seemingly severe restrictions, aerodynamicists have been able to obtain a great deal of practical information. In what follows, we will first concern ourselves with ideal-fiuid aerodynamics and consider some basic principles that apply to this field.

CONTINUITY

The first concept to be considered is one involving a continuity principle. This principle expresses, in general, the requirement that fluid is neither created nor destroyed. For example, if in Figure 2.5 the illustration is considered to be a cross section of a tube with a restriction at *B–B*, the mass of fluid passing through the restriction at *B–B* must be the same

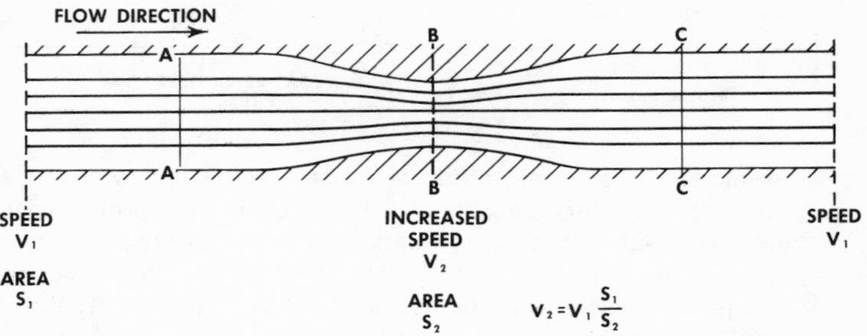

Figure 2.5 Steady flow of an ideal fluid through a restriction.

as the mass of fluid passing through the tube at *A–A* and *C–C*. To maintain continuity with an ideal fluid the speed must therefore vary inversely as the cross-sectional area.

BERNOULLI'S LAW

In 1738 Daniel Bernoulli (1700–1783), a Swiss physicist, found that for an ideal fluid, one could write a very simple relation between the potential energy and the kinetic energy. The potential energy is represented by the pressure, and the kinetic energy is represented by the product of the fluid density and the square of the speed. Bernoulli found that, along a streamline, the sum of these two energies is constant.

Mathematically this is written

$$p + \tfrac{1}{2}\rho V^2 = \text{constant} \tag{2.3}$$

where p = the pressure
ρ = the fluid density
V = the fluid speed

This is a very important result, because it allows the aerodynamicist to calculate the pressure on a body once he knows the speed along the streamlines around the body. From the relation above, we see that *where the velocity is lowered, the pressure must rise, and vice versa.* If we consider a streamline in Figure 2.5, we see that the pressure in the restriction must be lower than the pressure in the other parts of the tube. Furthermore, if flow conditions are such that the speed V becomes zero, the pressure p reaches a maximum, known as the stagnation pressure, and the point where this occurs is called a stagnation point. From equation (2.3) it can be seen that the stagnation pressure is the constant on the right-hand side.

FORCES DUE TO FLUID FLOW

Jean le Rond d'Alembert (1717–1783), a French mathematician and encyclopedist, arrived at a famous quandary of fluid mechanics known as the "paradox of d'Alembert." He studied the forces that an ideal fluid exerts on solid bodies. His calculations showed that no net force would be exerted on the body by the fluid as the fluid moved past the body. For example, the flow past a circular cylinder of infinite length, illustrated in Figure 2.6, produces no net force on the cylinder. D'Alembert recognized that such results were in error, because experiments clearly showed that there was a net force, but he was never able to correct his calculations.

In the next century, Lord Rayleigh (1842–1919), in attempting to explain

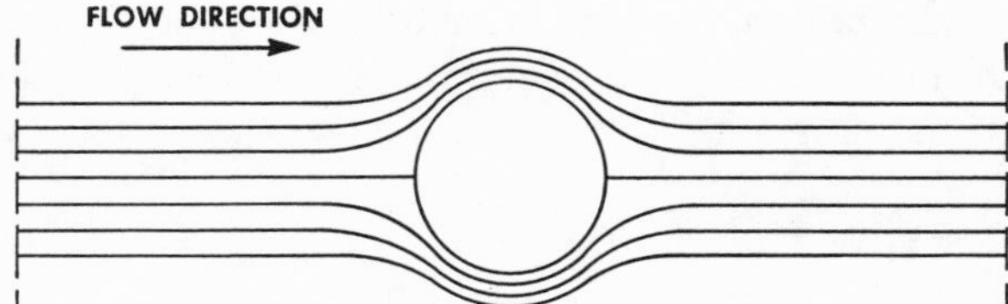

Figure 2.6 Ideal flow past a circular cylinder.

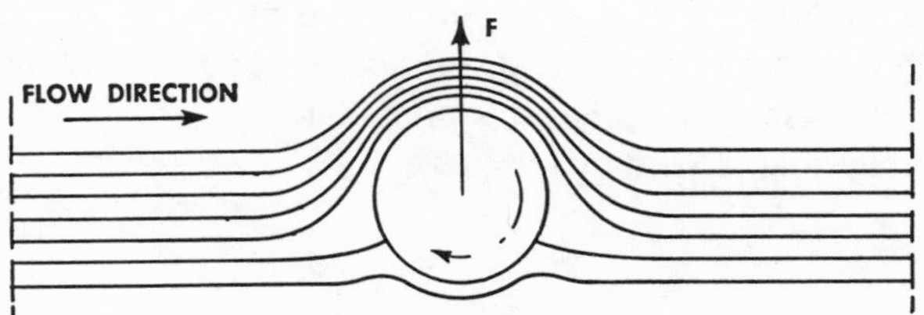

Figure 2.7 Ideal flow past a rotating cylinder.

the swerving flight of a "cut" tennis ball, studied the flow over a rotating cylinder, as illustrated in Figure 2.7. He recognized that a real fluid, which is viscous, will adhere to the cylinder. The rotation thus imparts a circulatory component to the speed at the surface of the cylinder. In comparison with the flow in Figure 2.6, then, there is an increase in speed on the upper surface of the cylinder and a decrease on the lower surface. Bernoulli's law shows that there is a reduction of pressure on the upper surface and an increase of pressure on the lower surface, producing a force F per unit cylinder length normal to the flow direction. A similar, albeit more complicated, flow pattern is caused by the spin of a tennis ball or a baseball; it is the force resulting from this spin that makes them curve.

CIRCULATION

Scientists soon recognized that the circulatory motion caused by the spin of Rayleigh's cylinder was an ingredient that had been left out of the theoretical models. This was pointed out independently by the English engineer, Frederick W. Lanchester (1876–1946), in the late nineteenth century, and early in this century by the German mathematician, Wilhelm Kutta (1867–1944), and the Russian mathematician and professor of mechanics, Nikolai E. Joukowske (1847–1921). Without this circulatory motion, or circulation, the flow about an airfoil would be as shown in Figure 2.8; there is no net force on this airfoil. However, there is also infinite speed at the trailing edge, where the flow is required to round a sharp corner.

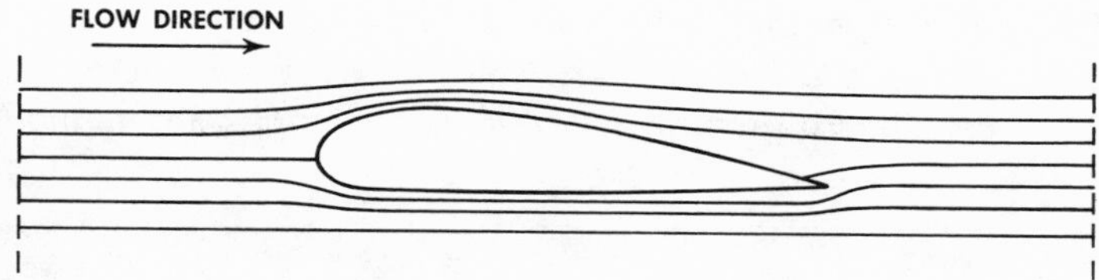

Figure 2.8 Ideal flow about an airfoil without circulation.

Kutta and Joukowske proposed that enough circulation be added to this theoretical model to correct the conditions at the trailing edge. Thus, while the average speed on the upper surface of the airfoil is increased, that on the lower surface is decreased, and the flow over the trailing edge is smooth, as shown in Figure 2.9. Just as in the case of Rayleigh's cylinder, the relative increase in the speed on the upper surface is accompanied by a reduction in pressure, the relative decrease in speed on the lower surface causes a rise in pressure, and a net force F per unit length is calculated. Joukowske was later able to demonstrate a remarkably simple relation between the circulation around a two-dimensional body and the aerodynamic force per unit length produced on it:

$$F = \rho V \Gamma \tag{2.4}$$

where Γ = circulation
ρ = fluid density
V = the speed with which the body moves through the fluid

This relation is useful because it permits calculating the aerodynamic forces directly from the circulation, rather than having to sum up pressure differences over the surface of the body.

Observed Circulation It is interesting to note that the only justification

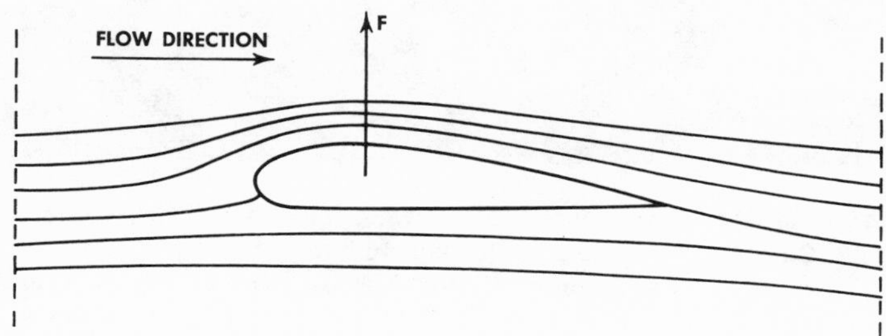

Figure 2.9 Ideal flow about an airfoil with circulation.

for adding circulation to the theoretical model is a practical one—the flow picture of Figure 2.9 agrees very well with experimental observations, as does the calculated force. In a real fluid, the circulation is induced by

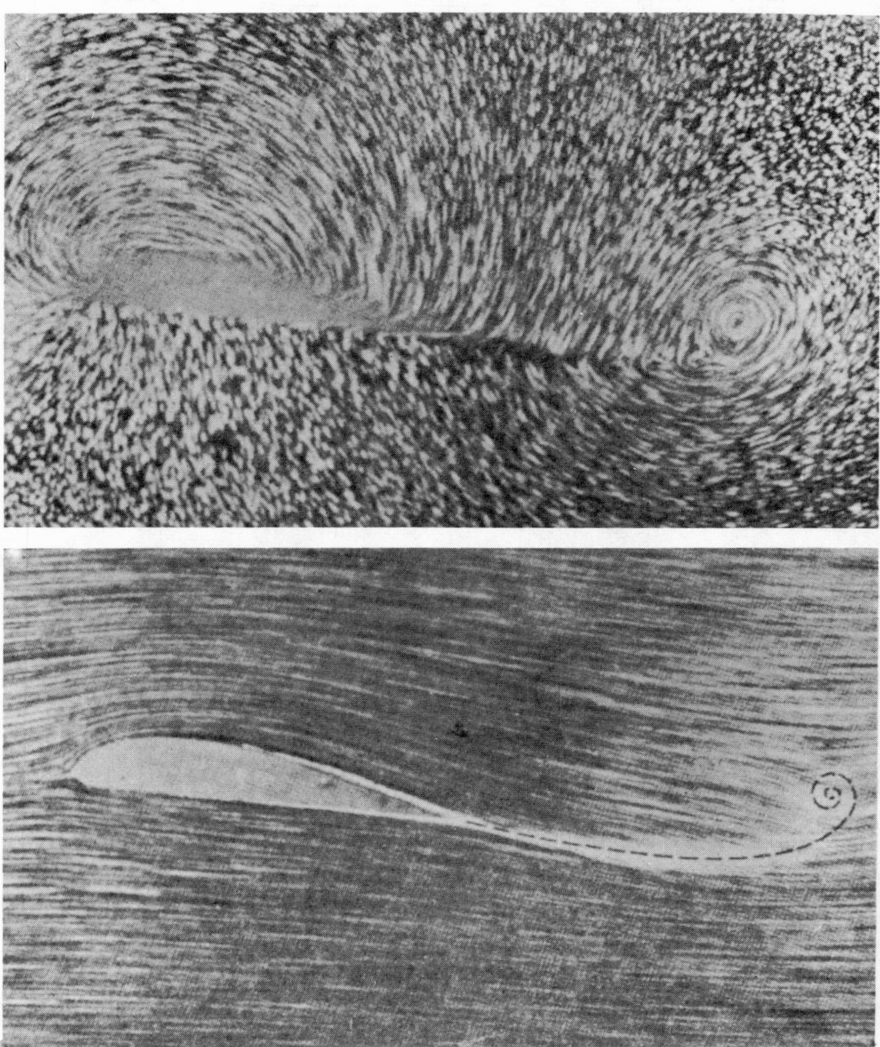

Figure 2.10 Starting vortex. Pictures of water flow around an airfoil. *Lower:* Camera at rest relative to undisturbed fluid. *Upper:* Camera moving with the airfoil. (From T. Von Kármán, *Aerodynamics,* Cornell University Press, Ithaca, N.Y., 1954. By permission from *Applied Hydro- and Aeromechanics,* by Prandtl and Tietjens, copyright by McGraw-Hill Book Company, Inc.)

viscous forces acting near the airfoil surface. We do not have to spin the airfoil, as we had to spin the cylinder; the airfoil is shaped so that its linear motion alone suffices. Nonetheless, there is direct experimental evidence that circulation, or rotatory motion, is produced around an airfoil as it is moved through a fluid. Figure 2.10 shows two views of an airfoil being started from rest in water. In both views, a swirling of the water, called a vortex, is observed being shed from the rear of the airfoil. This vortex causes rotation, or circulation, in the water behind the airfoil. Theodore Von Kármán* has related this flow to the lift generated by an airfoil with unparalleled clarity: "Now we must remember that, according to a fundamental principle of mechanics, a rotation, or more exactly a moment of momentum, cannot be created in a system without reaction. For example, if we try to put into rotation a body, such as a wheel, we experience a reaction tending to rotate us in the opposite direction. Or in the case of a helicopter with one rotor turning in one direction, we need a device to prevent the body of the craft being put into rotation in the opposite sense. Similarly, if the process of putting a wing section in motion creates a vortex, i.e., a rotation of a part of the fluid, a rotation on the opposite sense is created in the rest of the fluid. This rotary motion of the fluid appears as the circulation around the wing section. In a way analogous to what we have seen in the case of the baseball, the circulation creates higher velocity (lower pressure) at the upper, and lower velocity (higher pressure) at the lower, surface of the wing. In this manner a positive lift is produced." This describes the basic principle of the way in which circulation, produced by vorticity, contributes to lift. It is further illustrated on page 49 in reference to airplane wings of finite span.

AIRFOIL FORCES

Conventional Airfoil Notation To simplify discussion of forces acting about an airfoil, standard notation is used as shown in Figure 2.11. The *chord, c,* is the usual reference axis. When written $\bar{c}$, it refers to the mean

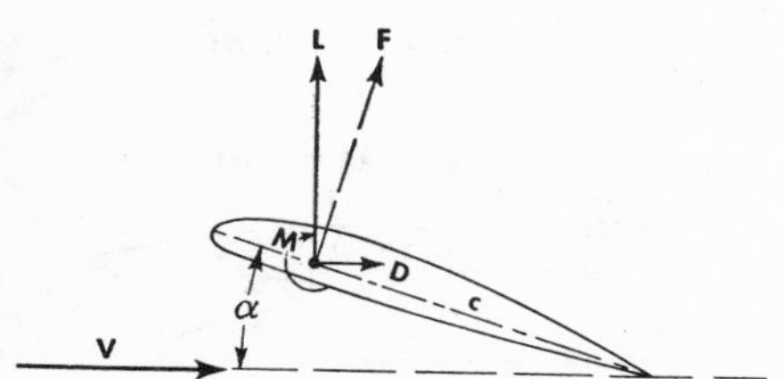

Figure 2.11 Airfoil notation.

*Theodore Von Kármán, *Aerodynamics,* Cornell University Press, Ithaca, N.Y., 1954.

aerodynamic chord from wing root to wingtip. *Angle of attack,* α, is the angle between the chord and the remote relative air velocity *V,* or *relative wind.* The aerodynamic forces acting on the airfoil are resolved into a force *F* acting at some point and a moment *M* acting about that point. The force *F* is further resolved into two components—a lift, *L,* acting perpendicular to the relative wind, and a drag, *D,* acting parallel to the relative wind. If we now refer to the force *F* in Figures 2.7 and 2.9, we see that it acts perpendicular to the relative wind (or flow direction). Thus, the force *F* calculated by Rayleigh, Kutta, and Joukowskii is all lift. In reality, there is also a drag, and to explain it, we must turn to still another effect of viscosity that has heretofore been neglected.

BOUNDARY LAYER

An ideal fluid has no viscosity and therefore no ability to resist deformation due to a shearing force. Since viscosity is the property of a fluid that tends to prevent motion of one part of the fluid with respect to another, it follows that any real fluid, which is viscous, will resist the passage of a body immersed in it. Viscosity may best be visualized by thinking of the difference between a heavy oil and water; the oil is considerably more viscous than water.

The effects of viscosity may be easily seen if one considers a thin, flat plate immersed in a moving fluid. An ideal fluid would stream freely over the surface of the plate. However, any real fluid has a certain amount of viscosity, which will cause it to cling to the surface of the plate. Consequently the layer of particles nearest the plate will come to rest. The next layer of particles will be slowed down but not stopped. Figure 2.12 shows this effect. At the surface of the plate, fluid speed is zero. Some small but measurable distance from the surface the fluid is moving at freestream speed. This layer of fluid within which viscosity induces a varying velocity is called the *boundary layer.* Since it is usually relatively

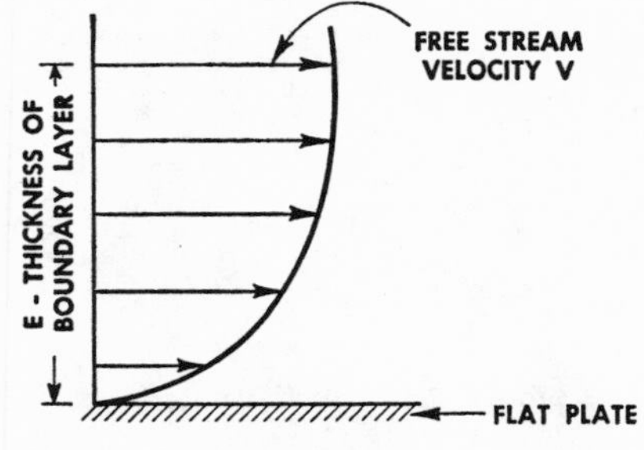

Figure 2.12 Boundary layer on a flat plate.

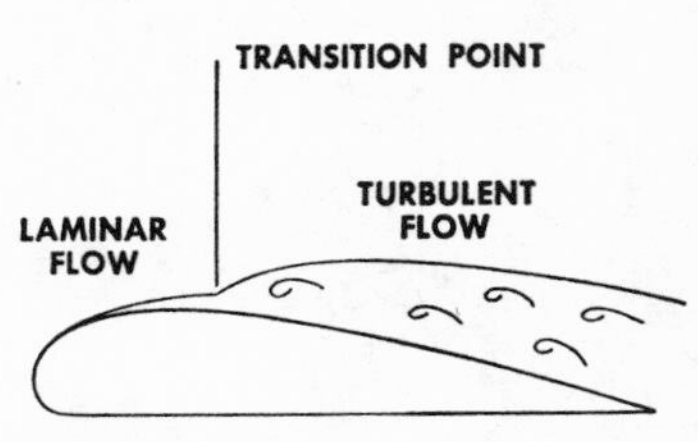

Figure 2.13 Boundary layer characteristics.

thin with respect to the thickness of an airfoil, it does not render lift calculations invalid. Typical boundary-layer thicknesses on an aircraft range from small fractions of an inch near the leading edge of a wing to the order of a foot at the aft end of a large aircraft such as the Boeing 747. This boundary-layer concept was introduced by the German engineer and professor, Ludwig Prandtl (1875–1953).

There are two different types of boundary-layer flow—laminar and turbulent (Figure 2.13). The laminar boundary layer is a very smooth flow, while the turbulent boundary layer contains swirls or "eddies." The English engineer and physicist Osborne Reynolds (1842–1912) developed the basic relationships that enable us to determine which type of boundary layer exists in a given flow. His theories and experiments led to the development of a dimensionless number, called *Reynolds number,* which can be used to determine the nature of flow along surfaces and about bodies. The Reynolds number may be expressed

$$\mathrm{RN} = \frac{\rho V l}{\mu} \tag{2.5}$$

where ρ = fluid density
V = freestream speed
l = a characteristic length
μ = the coefficient of viscosity of the fluid

Examination of flow characteristics indicates that a transition from laminar to turbulent flow along a surface is dependent upon the Reynolds number. As shown in Figure 2.13, the laminar flow breaks down at some critical Reynolds number and becomes turbulent. The transition point depends upon the *surface roughness* and the *degree of turbulence* in the freestream, as well as on the terms making up the Reynolds number. Typical values of the Reynolds number for aircraft range from 3,000,000 for a lightplane to as high as 100,000,000 for the C-5A under certain flight conditions.

Another phenomenon associated with viscous flow is *separation.* Separation is said to occur when the flow breaks away from the body. In particular, this effect is predominant on airfoils at high angles of attack; leading-edge or trailing-edge separation results in extremely high drag and reduced lift. When separation has occurred over the upper surface, the wing is said to have "stalled." When stall has occurred, a further increase in the angle of attack produces a reduction rather than an increase in lift, and a sharp increase in drag. It is important to remember that stall is primarily dependent upon angle of attack (in a particular airplane). High angles of attack come about because of flight at low speeds or because of high load factors, such as occur in certain maneuvers. Thus, an airplane will stall at many different airspeeds, depending upon the flight condition.

The progression from laminar boundary layer to turbulent boundary layer and thence to flow separation gradually increases drag and ultimately destroys lift. Consequently much effort has been expended to control the boundary layer. Depending on circumstances, it may be desirable either to remove the boundary layer, or to reinforce it.

Boundary layer *removal* is accomplished by suction through a porous wing surface; this can serve to reduce skin friction drag and increase lift. Boundary layer *reinforcement* is accomplished by injecting air into the boundary layer through a porous wing surface; this serves to prevent separation, thus increasing lift. The precise location, power and regulation requirements of boundary layer control devices make their application an extremely specialized operation.

Profile Drag The presence of the boundary layer on an airfoil produces two types of drag. *Skin-friction drag* results from the tendency of the fluid to adhere to the airfoil surface, thereby producing shearing forces tangential to the surface in addition to the pressure forces discussed earlier,

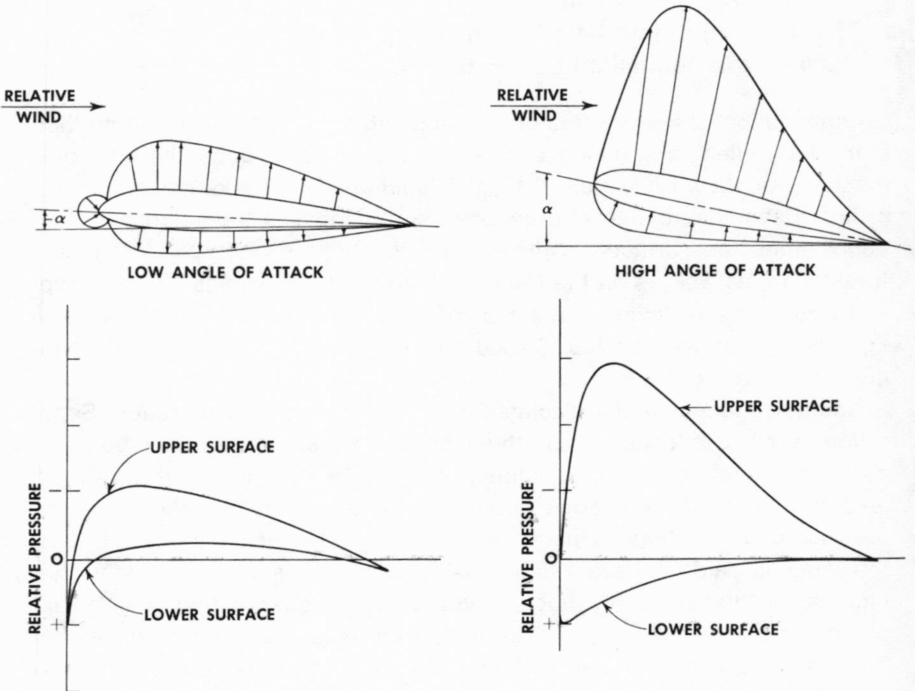

Figure 2.14 Pressure distribution on an airfoil.

which are normal to the surface. *Form drag* results from the wake, a region of fluid of relatively low energy that trails to the rear of the airfoil. The wake and the associated boundary layer on the airfoil surface alter the surface pressure distribution so that the resultant force is not all lift, as in the inviscid model, but also has a component in the drag direction. Separation produces high drag because it increases drastically the size of the wake. In practice, form drag and skin-friction drag on airfoils are lumped together under the name *profile drag.*

Pressure Distribution Figure 2.14 shows typical measured pressure distributions of an airfoil at two angles of attack. In the graphs, "reiative pressure" means the difference between the pressure on the airfoil surface and the pressure in the undisturbed flow far ahead of the airfoil. Above each graph, the pressure distribution is indicated by arrows perpendicular to the airfoil surface. Arrows pointing away from the surface denote a negative relative pressure, or a pressure less than that in the undisturbed flow, while arrows pointing toward the surface denote the opposite effect. The lift developed by the airfoil is proportional to the area enclosed by the pressure-distribution curves, and from them it can be seen that most of the lift comes about from the reduction in pressure on the upper surface of the airfoil.

LIFT AND DRAG, FINITE SPAN WINGS

The discussion of lift and drag has, so far, been confined to the two-dimensional case. From it appears the picture of airflow in the mid-span region of an infinite span airfoil. Now a finite span wing must be considered to see what tip effects exist and how they affect the flow fields so far developed.

Figure 2.15 indicates the pressure distribution over a wing at lift. Because the pressure on the upper surface is less than the pressure on the lower surface, there is a tendency for the air to flow around the tips. This flow is from lower surface to upper surface, from a high-pressure region to a low-pressure region. It was also Prandtl who introduced the proper theoretical model for this situation. The flow of air around the tips pro-

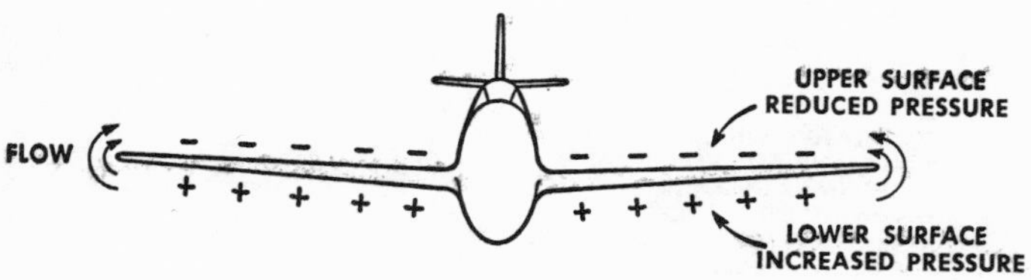

Figure 2.15 Spanwise pressure distribution.

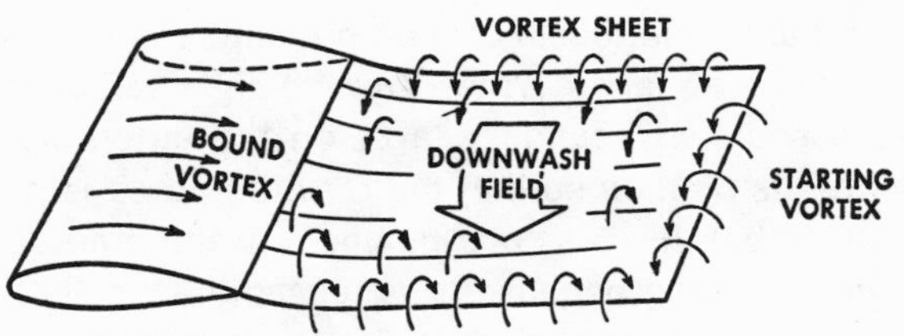

Figure 2.16 Ideal flow about a finite span wing.

duces a system of trailing vortices, strongest at the tips, called a *vortex sheet.* A starting vortex, similar to the starting vortex discussed earlier in connection with the flow over an airfoil, terminates the vortex sheet downstream. A *bound vortex,* so called because it stays with the wing and produces the wing circulation, completes the model, which is sketched in Figure 2.16. The vortex sheet, with rotation in the sense shown by the arrows, induces a downward component of velocity in the flow called the downwash field. Prandtl assumed that at any chordwise cross section of the wing, the force per unit span could be calculated from airfoil theory. The relative wind for the airfoil would be given by the relative wind for the wing combined with the downwash. This is illustrated in Figure 2.17. The resultant wind is seen to be rotated downward by a downwash angle ϵ, and the force on the airfoil, perpendicular to the resultant wind, now has a drag component because lift and drag are defined as perpendicular and parallel to the relative wind. This drag component is called the *induced drag*, because it is induced by the downwash resulting from the vortex

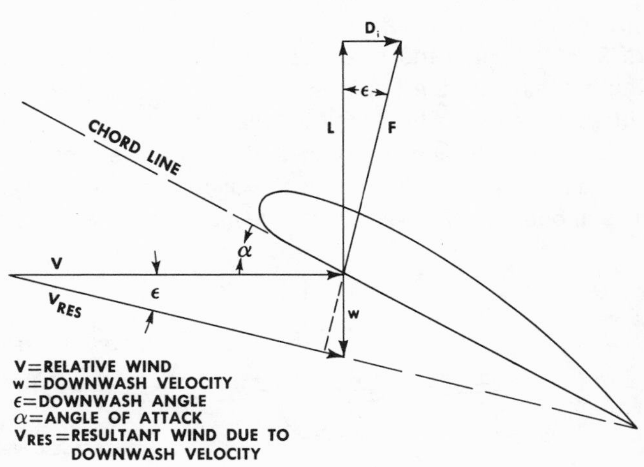

Figure 2.17 The origin of induced drag.

sheet. This drag, combined with the profile drag, gives the total drag for the wing.

WAKE TURBULENCE

The airman flying a light aircraft into an airport served by large commercial aircraft must heed carefully the controller's "Caution, wake turbulence." This extremely strong and dangerous turbulence is primarily caused by the system of trailing vortices behind the aircraft. In actual fact, the vortex sheet soon "rolls up" into two concentrated trailing vortices that originate near the wing tips. These vortices are a particular problem near airports, where large and heavy aircraft are flying relatively slowly.

The lift must always be near the weight of the aircraft. One way of looking at the creation of lift is to view it as the result of a rate of change of momentum imparted to the air by the wing. At slow speeds, the amount of air affected by the wing in one second, for example, is reduced from what it would be at cruising speeds. To provide lift, then, the downwash must be correspondingly greater. This in turn means that the trailing vortices are strongest during this portion of the aircraft's flight. The trend toward larger and heavier aircraft, which land at approximately the same speeds as earlier aircraft, accentuates this problem. Singles and light twins must avoid the 747s!

Airport surface wind is important. A crosswind can blow the turbulence clear of the runway in a short time, but it can also blow it onto a parallel or intersecting runway. The strength and subsistence of wake turbulence cannot be reliably predicted and is quite variable, due in large part to the variability of the weather. The only answer is to leave plenty of room behind the large aircraft.

ASPECT RATIO

Naturally, it is desirable to have the greatest possible lift with the least possible drag, or in other words, to make the ratio L/D_i as large as possible. To see how this may be accomplished, one may look at the vortex pattern in a little greater detail. It is possible to approximate the vortex distribution on a wing as indicated in Figure 2.18. The bound vortex and trailing vortices of Figure 2.18 are shown as a series of "horseshoe" vortices and the strength of the circulation is shown to vary from a maximum at mid-span to zero at the wing tips. The resultant spanwise lift distribution approximates half an ellipse; the minimum induced drag is obtained when the spanwise distribution is elliptical. This distribution results in a constant downwash along the span.

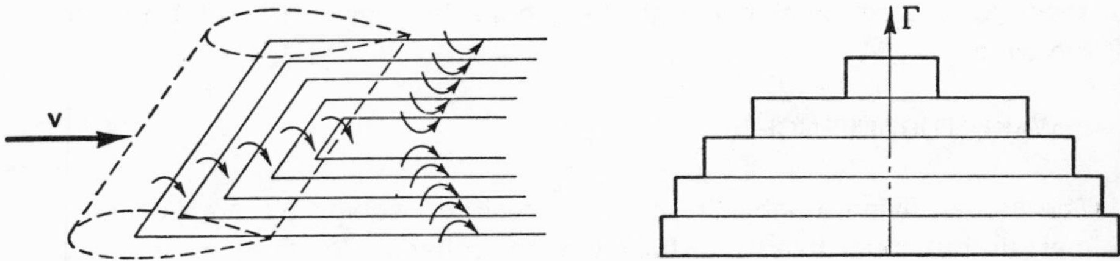

Figure 2.18 Vortex distribution.

One major factor in the determination of wing lift and drag characteristics is *aspect ratio.* Aspect ratio is defined as span squared divided by area:

$$AR = \frac{b^2}{S} \tag{2.6}$$

where AR = aspect ratio
b = wingspan
S = wing area

Generally, the higher the aspect ratio, the smaller the downwash velocity, ω. Hence, L/D_i is improved. The use of high aspect ratio is limited by structural considerations; high strength is more easily obtained with low aspect ratio wings. Proper combinations of wing planform and wing twist can produce nearly elliptic pressure distribution on wings of low to medium aspect ratio.

Current design practice results in aspect ratios of 20 or higher for sailplanes. Some subsonic airplanes have aspect ratios approaching 12, although aspect ratios of 5 to 8 are more common.

GROUND EFFECT

Before continuing in the development of subsonic flight characteristics, we should recognize that the induced-drag characteristics of a wing are not the same near the ground as they are in free air. For operations such as takeoff, landing, or hedgehopping, the induced drag is reduced by the effect of the ground on the flow pattern. The possible drag reduction varies from about 8% with a height above ground equal to semi-span to as much as 50% at a height equal to one-twelfth span.

COMPLETE AIRPLANE DRAG

So far only wing lift and drag have been considered. For a complete airplane, it is necessary to consider the drag produced by the other component parts. The lift produced by components other than the wing is negligible. It is customary to refer to the drag of all parts not contributing to lift as *parasite* drag.

The correct determination of the total drag is an important phase in the design of an airplane since it is the first step in determining the power required to fly the craft.

The total drag of an airplane is obtained by summing up the drag of each part of the aircraft plus the drag resulting from the combination of these components. The airflow at intersections such as that of the wing and fuselage is often disturbed in such a way that the drag in the region of the intersection of the bodies is different from that which can be predicted by simply adding the drag of the parts. This is known as interference drag, a component of parasite drag. Interference effects can be favorable as well as unfavorable.

Exclusive of induced drag and interference drag, the drag of each aircraft component consists of two parts—form drag and skin-friction drag. Although it is usually quite difficult to separate the two, it must be remembered that form drag results from pressures induced on a component by the motion of air about it and depends on the wake characteristics, while skin-friction drag is a result of the viscous properties of the thin layer of air next to the surface of the component. The pressures and hence the form drag are largely a function of component shape as shown in Figure 2.19.

Additional drag may also be caused during flight when control surfaces are deflected.

BUFFET AND FLUTTER

The pressure fluctuations associated with separated flow and turbulent wakes can create a feeling of "pounding" against some part of the aircraft. This effect is known as *buffet.* The separated flow may be due to ordinary stalling over local areas on the airplane, or may be induced by a shock wave caused by the flow reaching sonic velocity locally.

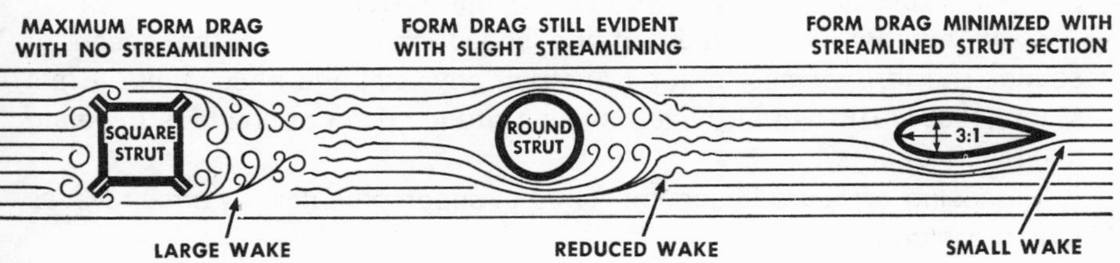

Figure 2.19 Effect of streamlining.

A loss in lifting force and an increase in the drag force are generally associated with buffeting. This lift loss and drag increase may seriously limit the ability of the airplane to perform the mission for which it was designed. Buffeting can further affect the airplane's gun or bomb platform stability, the peace of mind or fatigue of the pilot, crew members and passengers, and, in extreme cases, the structural integrity of the airplane.

Flutter is an aeroelastic instability involving mutual interaction between the airstream and aircraft components such as the wing, the tail, control surfaces, or individual skin panels. When flutter occurs, the airstream interacts with the flexible motion of, say, the wing, such that any oscillation of the wing will rapidly increase in magnitude. Flutter is generally to be avoided at all costs, because it can lead very quickly to catastrophic structural failure. It is a fundamental design requirement that there be a given margin of safety between any flutter condition and the operating limits of the aircraft.

Supersonic Aerodynamics

In the preceding section we were concerned only with subsonic flow. Now we wish to consider flow at speeds greater than the speed of sound. World War II fighters attained speeds which produced, on critical points of the airplane, local flow velocities of Mach 1.0 and higher, although the airplane speed was less than the speed of sound. Many present-day airplanes are capable of exceeding the speed of sound in level flight.

For flight at low speeds, below about 260 knots, air acts as an incompressible fluid. However, as velocity increases, air density changes about the airplane and this effect becomes increasingly important. When flow velocities reach sonic speeds at some point on an airplane, the airplane's drag begins to increase at a rate much greater than that indicated by subsonic aerodynamic theory; subsonic flow principles are invalid at all speeds above this point.

Certain new definitions and concepts are necessary in dealing with air as a compressible fluid and with supersonic speeds:

Mach number is the ratio of the speed of motion to the speed of sound. The term comes from an Austrian physicist and philosopher, Ernst Mach (1838–1916). An airplane traveling at the speed of sound is traveling at "Mach one."

Increasing pressure is accomplished in supersonic flow by *shock waves* (compression waves).

Decreasing pressure is accomplished in supersonic flow by *expansion waves.*

SUPERSONIC FLOW CHARACTERISTICS

When an airplane flies at subsonic speeds, the air ahead is "warned" of the airplane's coming by a pressure change transmitted ahead of the airplane at the speed of sound. Because of this warning, the air begins to move aside before the airplane arrives and is prepared to let it pass easily. If the airplane travels at supersonic speeds, the air ahead receives no advance warning of the airplane's approach because the airplane is outspeeding its own pressure waves. Sound pressure changes are felt only within a cone-shaped region behind the nose of the airplane. Since the air is unprepared for the airplane's arrival, it must move to one side abruptly to let the airplane pass. This sudden displacement of the air is accomplished through a shock wave.

The water-wave analogy furnishes a good physical picture of the subsonic "warning" system and supersonic shock formation. If one drops pebbles into a smooth pond of water, one each second, from the same point, each pebble will produce a water wave moving outward with constantly increasing radius as shown in Figure 2.20A. This is similar to the pattern of sound waves produced by an airplane sitting on the runway before takeoff. Even though one cannot see the airplane, its presence is signaled by these outward-rolling waves of engine noise.

Now suppose we move slowly over the pond dropping pebbles at regular intervals. The picture of the waves is changed to that shown in Figure 2.20B. Each pebble still produces a circular wave, but the circles are crowded together on the side toward which we are moving; the center of each succeeding circle is displaced from the preceding one by a distance proportional to the speed at which we are traveling over the water. This wave pattern is similar to the pattern of sound waves around an airplane flying subsonically. The air ahead of the airplane is warned of the imminent arrival of the airplane and the warning time decreases with

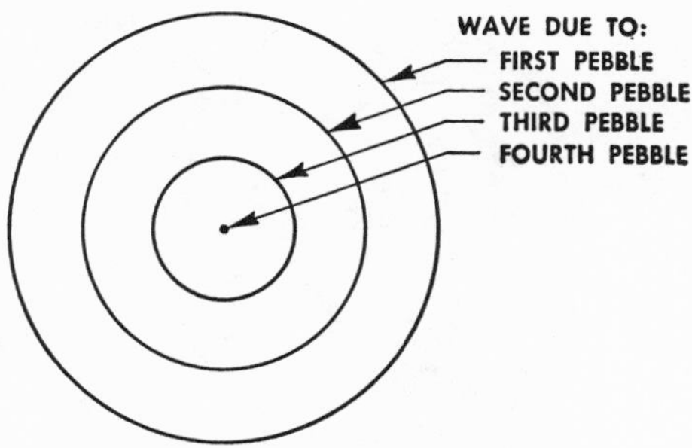

Figure 2.20A Stationary waves.

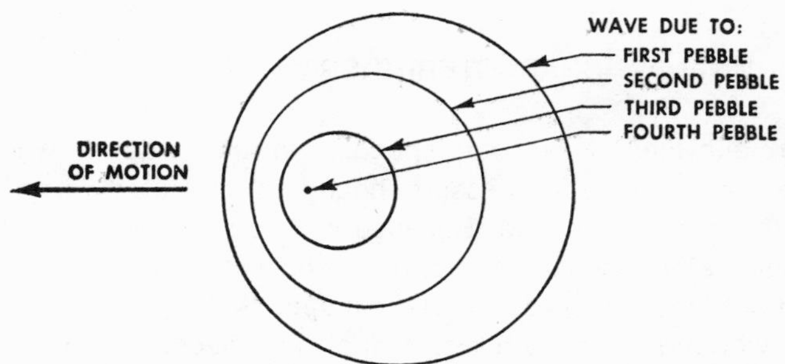

Figure 2.20B Waves for motion at subsonic speed.

increasing airplane speed. The warning time is zero when the airplane is flying at exactly sonic speed. The corresponding water-wave pattern is shown in Figure 2.20C.

If we move across the water more rapidly than the water-wave speed, the wave pattern is markedly different from the patterns formed up to now. The smaller circles are no longer completely inside the next larger ones. Now all the circles are included within a wedge-shaped region as shown in Figure 2.21. This is similar to the sound-wave pattern for an airplane flying at supersonic speed. The airplane is, in fact, a continuous disturbance in the air rather than an intermittent one as the pebbles falling regularly into the pond. Therefore, instead of several circles, there is an envelope surface of countless circles. The wedge on the surface of the pond looks like a section through the cone formed by an airplane in the air. Figure 2.21 indicates that there is considerable overrunning and interference between the wave circles; we might suspect from this that such interference will change the envelope shape for an actual airplane. This is, in fact, the case.

If the airplane is very streamlined and has a long, sharply pointed nose, then the air is not required to move a great distance suddenly in allowing

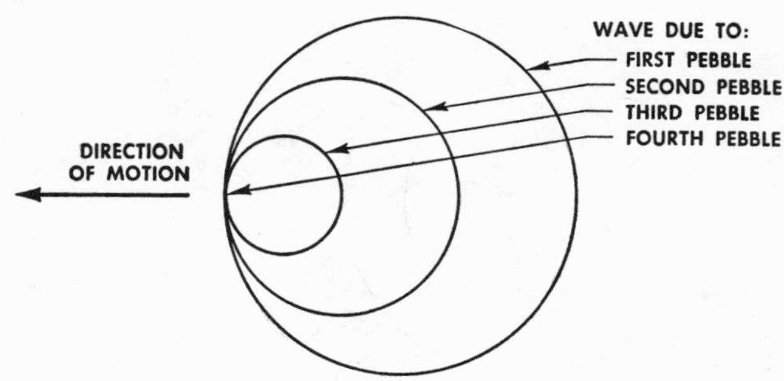

Figure 2.20C Waves simulating Mach 1.0 motion.

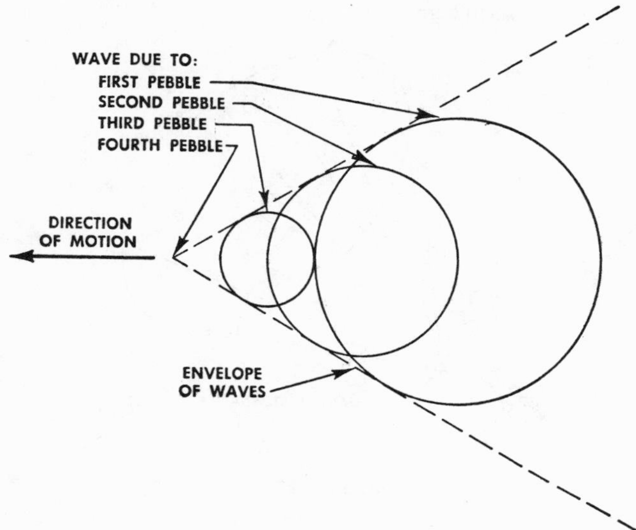

Figure 2.21 Waves simulating supersonic motion.

the airplane to pass. In this case the interference between sound waves is slight; the envelope is defined by the *Mach angle*, μ. Figure 2.22 shows that the Mach angle is the angle whose sine is the speed of sound divided by body speed, or C/V. Thus the Mach angle is 90° at a *Mach number* of 1.0; 30° at a Mach number of 2.0; and 10° at a Mach number of 5.75, for example. This envelope is called a *Mach line* in two dimensions or a *Mach cone* in three dimensions.

TYPES OF SUPERSONIC WAVES

It is now apparent that waves are formed about any disturbance in a supersonic stream of air. The type of wave formed depends on the nature of the disturbing influence. In our case, an airplane is the disturbing influence; its shape determines the location and characteristics of the waves formed. A wave of some type will exist whenever the air is required to

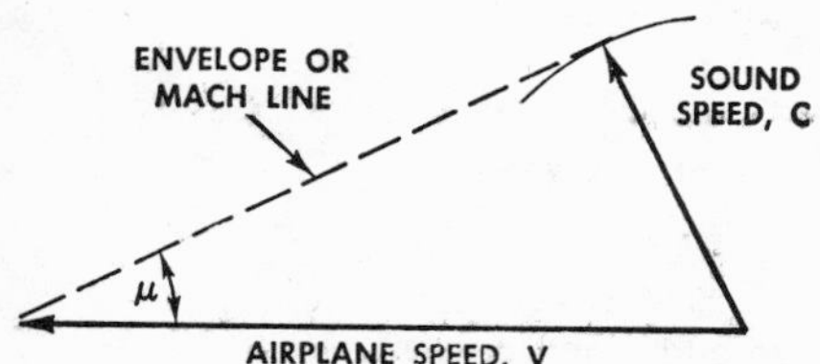

Figure 2.22 Mach angle.

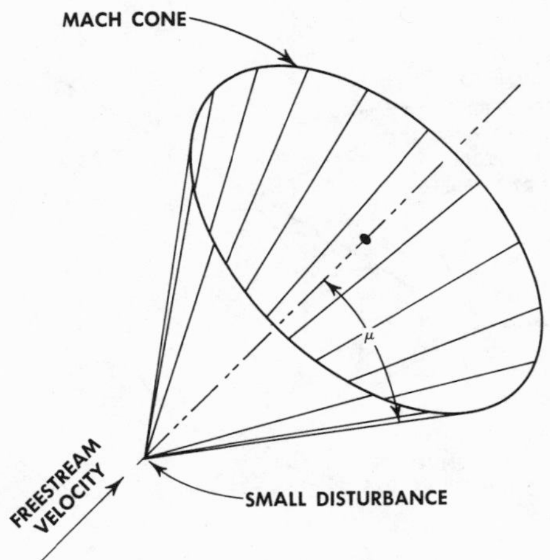

Figure 2.23

change direction. The wave caused by a slight disturbance is defined as a Mach wave. Air passing through a Mach wave undergoes a small increase in temperature and pressure and a small decrease in velocity. The Mach line envelope due to a small disturbance in three dimensions is conical in shape and is called a Mach cone (Figure 2.23). The envelope for a very thin wing is a wedge over most of the span bounded by a Mach cone at each tip as shown in Figure 2.24. The apex angle of these wedges and cones is the Mach angle, μ.

It cannot be overemphasized that Mach waves are associated only with very small or gradual changes in the flow direction of the passing air. The bodies that are small enough to produce Mach waves are in many cases too slender to be incorporated on an actual airplane. Many parts of an airplane must be too blunt and thick for Mach waves to form; instead, shock waves are formed.

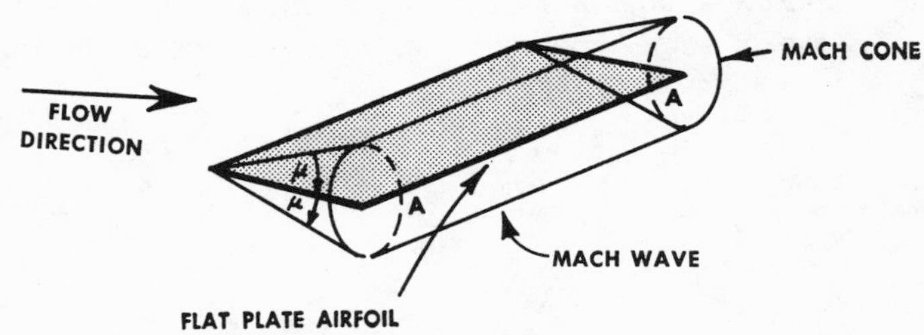

Figure 2.24 Mach wave and Mach cones.

These shocks are formed by the interference of sound waves mentioned during the water-wave discussion. Shocks are like Mach waves in that the pressure and temperature of the air passing through are abruptly increased and the air velocity is decreased. However, the magnitude of these changes through a shock is many times greater than the magnitude of these changes through a Mach wave.

The difference in the magnitude of these changes is the essential difference between a Mach wave and a shock wave. Since the drag of an object is dependent upon the pressure on its surface, the drag caused by a shock is very high compared to that caused by a Mach wave on the same body. Fundamentally a Mach wave may be thought of as a shock of negligible strength, a shock through which air undergoes the smallest pressure, temperature, and velocity changes. The magnitude of the changes in these properties is used to measure the strength of a shock. The strength of a shock is dependent upon its angle with the freestream and the freestream Mach number. Strong shocks are associated with high drag. The strongest shocks are normal shocks, so-called because they stand at right angles to the freestream. All shocks standing at an angle of less than 90° to the freestream are called oblique shocks. Figure 2.25 shows examples of these two general cases.

The Mach wave and shock wave are compression waves. There is also the *expansion wave,* or fan, which has characteristics opposite to the compression wave. In passing through an expansion wave, air velocity increases, while temperature and pressure are reduced. Expansion waves occur where bodies begin to narrow, making more space available for the passing air to occupy. Figure 2.26 illustrates a typical expansion fan, or system of expansion waves. Since compression and expansion waves are opposite in nature, they tend to cancel each other when they intersect, and the shock's strength is reduced accordingly. Figure 2.27 shows a complete wave pattern on a double-wedge airfoil. The airfoil is at zero

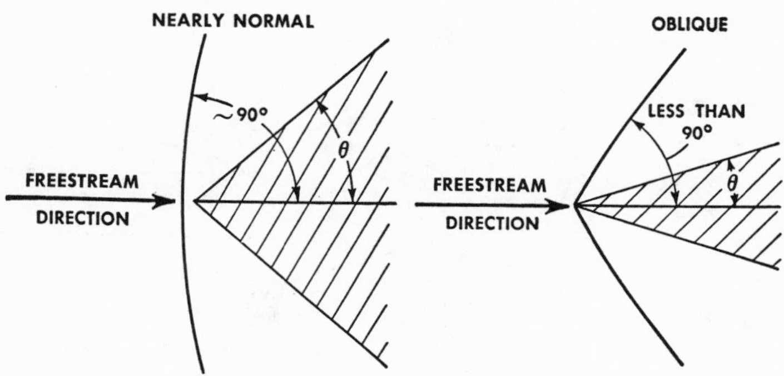

Figure 2.25 Types of shock waves.

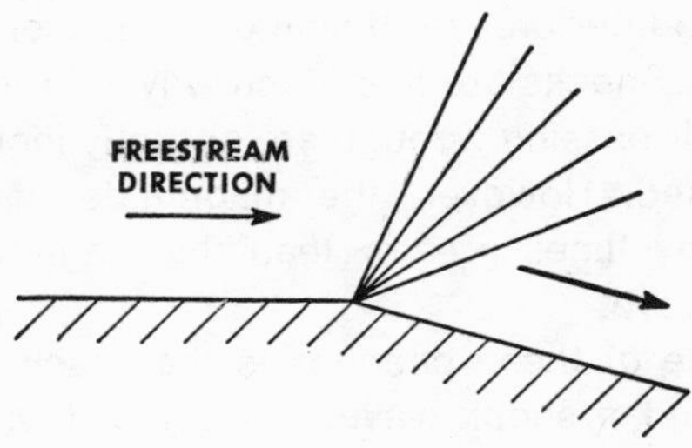

Figure 2.26 Expansion fan.

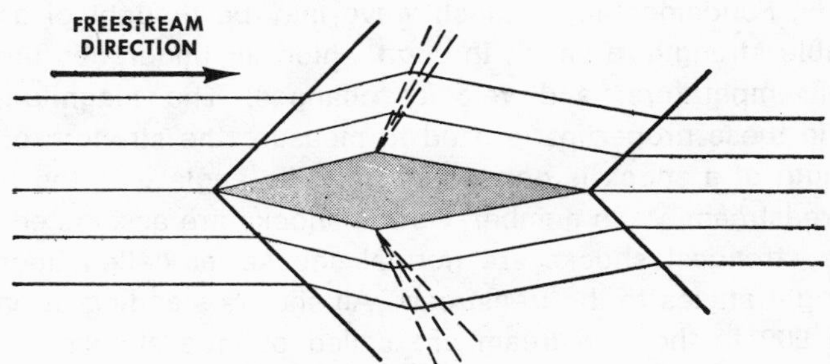

Figure 2.27 Wave pattern on a double-wedge airfoil. Angle of attack = 0°.

angle of attack. Shocks are formed at the leading and trailing edges while expansion fans occur at the surface angles or discontinuities. To obtain lift, the airfoil would have to have some finite angle of attack; the resultant

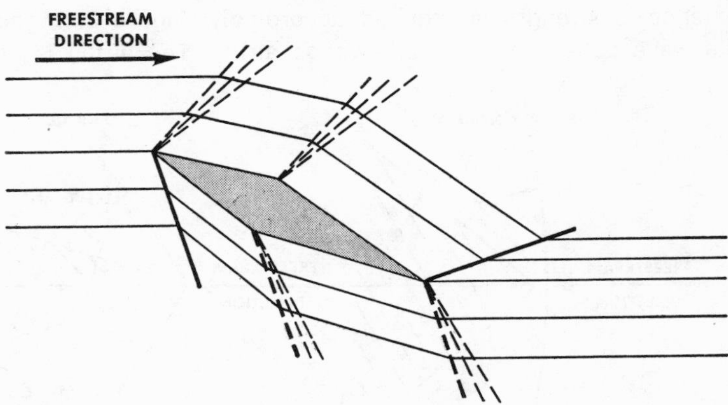

Figure 2.28 Wave pattern on a double-wedge airfoil at angle of attack.

wave pattern is shown by Figure 2.28 when the angle of attack is comparatively large.

The oblique shocks at the upper surface of the nose and lower surface of the tail are replaced by expansion fans in Figure 2.28. This is a graphic illustration of the effect of slope change on wave formation. In Figure 2.27, the turning of the flow required at the upper nose is concave, meaning that a rise in pressure and therefore a shock wave is required. A turning in the opposite, or convex, direction is required at this same point in Figure 2.28; this requires a drop in pressure and therefore an expansion fan. The situation at the lower trailing edge is similar.

AIRFOIL CHARACTERISTICS

The double-wedge airfoil used to illustrate wave patterns is convenient to study because the flow changes direction only at six definite regions. Another typical airfoil section might be as sketched in Figure 2.29. Here there are leading- and trailing-edge shocks, but the expansion is continuous over the entire surface between. The expansion waves intersect the leading-edge shock and progressively weaken it, thus making it a curved shock. The relative pressure, or difference between the airfoil surface pressure and the freestream pressure, is plotted as part of Figure 2.29. The pressure difference is proportional to the local inclination of the airfoil surface with respect to the freestream direction.

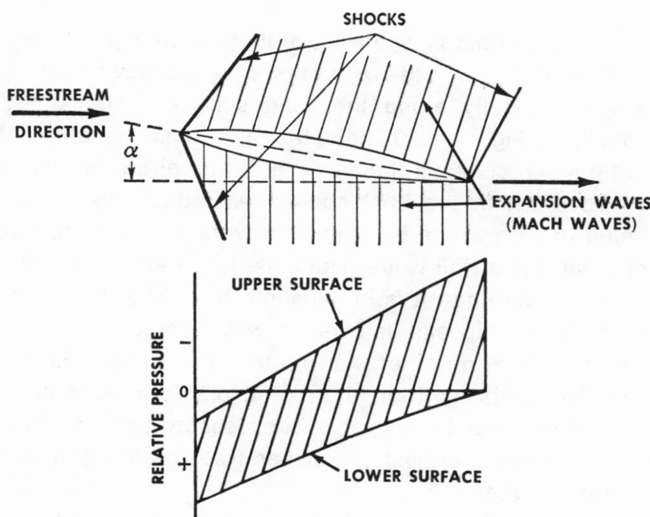

Figure 2.29 Pressure distribution on an airfoil in supersonic flow.

LIFT AND DRAG

As was pointed out earlier, the circulation theory of lift is not applicable in supersonic flow. Here, the upper and lower surfaces of the airfoil are, for all practical purposes, isolated from each other because of the inability of signals in the flow to propagate upstream. The pressure on the airfoil is determined by the freestream Mach number and pressure and the local airfoil inclination to the freestream. The upper and lower surfaces contribute about equally to the lift. This is in contrast to the subsonic case, where most of the lift comes from the upper surface.

The drag of airfoils in supersonic flight is composed of three parts. These are *wave drag, skin-friction drag,* and *induced drag,* or as it is frequently called, *drag due to lift.* Wave drag is the drag at zero lift associated with the creation of shock waves or expansion fans in the flow. It comes from the pressure forces, or forces normal to the airfoil surface, as does form drag in subsonic flow. Skin-friction drag comes from the viscous shearing forces tangent to the airfoil surface, just as it does in subsonic flow. Drag due to lift comes from the alteration of the wave pattern as the angle of attack is changed from its zero-lift value. It is analogous to induced drag in subsonic flow, except that there is no induced drag for (two-dimensional) airfoils in subsonic flow.

WING (FINITE SPAN) CHARACTERISTICS

Remember that in subsonic flow, a wing of finite span experiences a three-dimensional flow which includes a vortex sheet, a downwash field, and induced velocities locally along the wing surface. This is not true in supersonic flow. In Figure 2.30, note that the pressure along the wing between the tip Mach cones is the same as for an airfoil of infinite length. Vortices produced within the tip Mach cones reduce the pressure from the airfoil value to zero at the tip, with the average lifting pressure in the tip region one-half the airfoil value. Thus, the influence of the tips is much less in supersonic flow than it is in subsonic flow. The drag due to lift is increased some by the tip effects over its airfoil value.

If a wing with a planform other than rectangular is used, tip losses can be eliminated. The delta, or triangular, wing planform accomplishes this and can be illustrated by the two possible pressure patterns over a delta wing, depending on the relationship between freestream Mach number and wing leading-edge sweep.

In this case, Figure 2.31, the components of velocity perpendicular to the leading edge are subsonic, even though the freestream flow is supersonic. The lifting pressure is maximum along the leading edge and de-

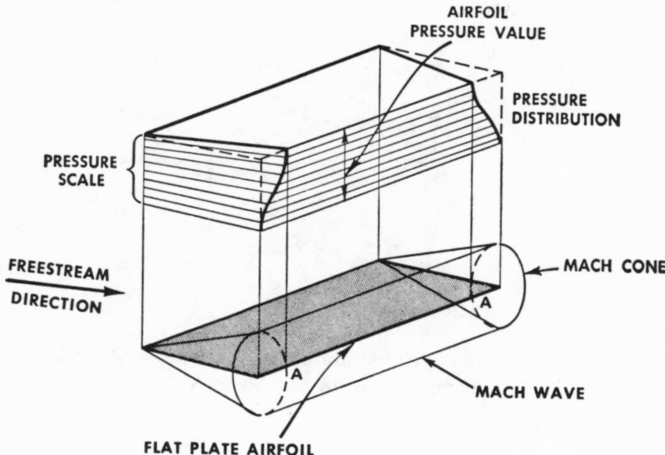

Figure 2.30 Supersonic pressure distribution on a rectangular wing.

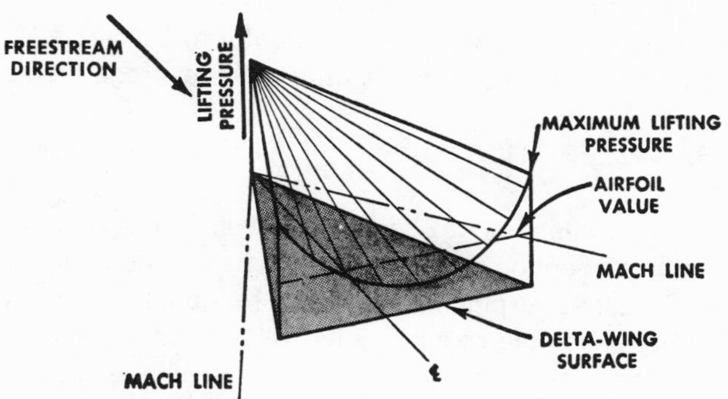

Figure 2.31 Pressure distribution on a delta wing (leading edge inside the Mach line).

creases rapidly toward the center of the wing. The average lift coefficient is less than would be obtained by a similar airfoil in subsonic flow.

In the other pattern, the wing leading edge lies ahead of the tip Mach cone. Figure 2.32 illustrates that the highest lifting pressure still exists along the wing leading edge. In this case, however, the lifting pressure remains constant at this peak value in the region between the leading edge and the Mach cone. Inside the Mach cone, the lifting pressure again decreases, but the wing's average lift coefficient is as high as can be obtained with an airfoil of a similar cross section. When the leading edge

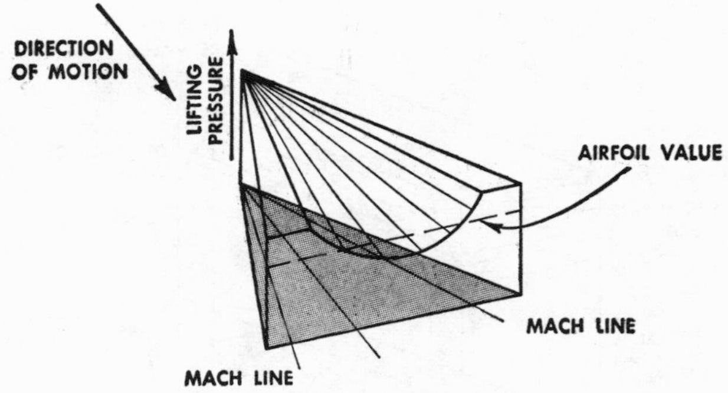

Figure 2.32 Pressure distribution on a delta wing (leading edge outside the Mach line).

is outside, the wave drag is lower than airfoil wave drag. Wing wave drag reaches a maximum when the Mach cone lies along the leading edge.

Consider the effects of modifying the delta planform. If area is added at the trailing edge to make a diamond planform, it is being added where the local lift coefficient is low. In this case, the average wing lift coefficient is less than that obtainable with a delta planform. Conversely, cutting out area to give an arrow planform will increase the average lift coefficient.

BODY CHARACTERISTICS

This discussion pertains only to *bodies of revolution.* A body of revolution is one whose cross section perpendicular to its longitudinal axis is always circular (Figure 2.33). Airplane fuselages are generally as near circular in cross section as volume requirements will permit. All studies, analytical and test, indicate that a parabolic longitudinal shape is desirable. The pressure distribution on a body of revolution at zero angle of attack shows a positive value at the nose lower than for an airfoil of the same "nose semi-angle" (Figure 2.33). Following this, the air finds more room in which to expand than in the case of the airfoil; it can fill the "ring" all around the body. The pressure drops so rapidly that the relative pressure returns to

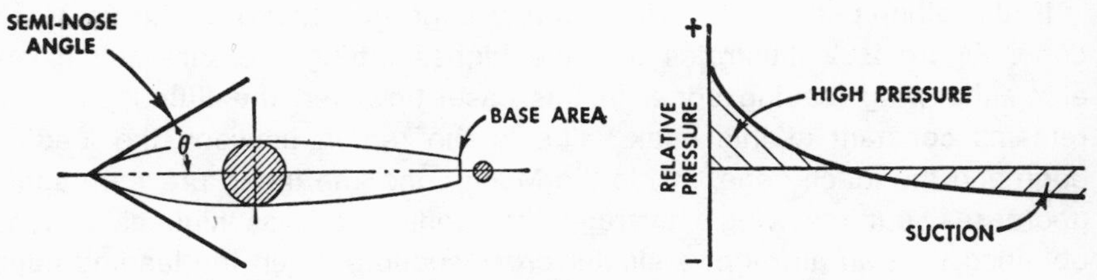

Figure 2.33 Pressure distribution on a body of revolution.

zero before the body slope has returned to zero, that is, before the body contour becomes parallel to the longitudinal axis of the body.

The expansion continues over the aft part of the body and the relative pressure becomes more negative. However, the largest negative value of the relative pressure is limited by the occurrences of a complete expansion to a vacuum. Usually the positive pressure coefficient at the nose is larger than this maximum negative value.

The wave drag of bodies of revolution depends on their shape, angle of attack, and flight Mach number. Angles of attack other than zero usually do not cause a large drag increase, nor will they cause the body to produce much lift. Drag force increases with increasing Mach number just as does wing lift force. Body shape has a strong influence on body drag. The longitudinal lines should be parabolic; the exact equation of the lines is a function of Mach number. A good fineness ratio for low drag is a length to maximum diameter ratio of 8 to 12. Many bodies are designed so that the wave drag coefficient reaches its peak at very low supersonic Mach numbers, then drops rapidly until it begins to approach a minimum value at about Mach 2.

WING-BODY COMBINATIONS

In the study of subsonic drag (page 52), it was apparent that a factor was *interference drag,* resulting from the effect of angles between surfaces, such as wing and fuselage. This drag was reduced by the use of smooth fairings, thus avoiding sharp corners—in effect it was corrected "locally" at the point it occurred.

In supersonic airplanes, the interference problem is a much more critical one and cannot be solved locally.

We have seen that the ideal streamline shape is a body of revolution having a longitudinal parabolic curve. Another way of stating this is that if the cross-sectional areas of the ideal body, taken at even increments along its axis, were plotted, the result would be a parabolic curve.

Studies by Richard T. Whitcomb, NASA, have demonstrated that in supersonic aircraft the parabolic cross-sectional area distribution from nose to tail must be based on the complete airplane cross section, not just the fuselage cross section. This is illustrated in the fuselage design of the F-106, Figure 1.15. The "Coke-bottle" shape of the fuselage is the result of the application of this principle.

LIFT-DRAG RELATIONSHIPS

The preceding sections have discussed the means by which lift may be generated and the types of drag which must be considered in airplane design.

Lift and drag are normally expressed in coefficient form. These coefficients are dimensionless; that is, they are absolute numbers which are not associated with length, mass, or time.

The equations for lift and drag are:

$$L = C_L \frac{\rho V^2}{2} S \tag{2.7}$$

where L = lift, lb
C_L = lift coefficient
ρ = air density, slugs/cu ft
V = speed, ft/sec
S = wing area sq ft
$\frac{\rho V^2}{2} = q$ = dynamic pressure, lb/sq ft

$$D = C_D q S \tag{2.8}$$

where D = drag, lb
C_D = drag coefficient

Lift and drag are commonly plotted on curves similar to those of Figure 2.34. Notice that L/D, or C_L/C_D, reaches a maximum value at some relatively low lift coefficient. Generally, designers attempt to have $(L/D)_{max}$ occur at the lift coefficient associated with maximum-range flight conditions.

PITCHING MOMENT

The pitching moment is the moment, M (Figure 2.11), which tends to rotate an airfoil about the pitch axis (Figure 2.36). As with lift and drag, it can be expressed in coefficient form:

$$M = C_M c q S \tag{2.9}$$

where M = pitching moment, lb-ft
C_M = pitching moment coefficient
c = wing chord length, ft

A moment must be defined with respect to a specific axis. For example, the moments may be summed about a line through the airplane c.g. parallel to the y-axis. In the longitudinal plane a reference point implies an axis so one simply says "about the c.g." A force acting through the reference point produces no moment about it. Given the moment about a point, the net forces can be placed at that point to represent the net force and moment.

Three reference points are of particular interest. The *center of pressure* (c.p.) of an airfoil is the point through which the net pressure force acts; that is, it is the point about which the pressure distribution (Figure 2.14) produces no moments. The *aerodynamic center* (a.c.) is the point at which the moment produced by the pressure distribution does not change with angle of attack. In considering the whole aircraft, the point about which there is no change in pitching moment as a function of angle of attack is called the *neutral point.*

In a cambered airfoil, the center of pressure moves along the chord as a result of various changes in angle of attack and relative wind. The moment of the c.p. about the a.c. is the pitching moment.

Performance

THE NEED FOR THRUST

Thrust is needed for airplane flight for two reasons. The first is to overcome drag so an airplane can fly at a constant height and speed. The second is to change the energy of the airplane as required by the *maneuver* at hand. The energy of the airplane is

$$E = WV^2/2g + Wh \tag{2.10}$$

where E = energy, ft-lb
W = weight of the airplane, lb
V = speed, ft/sec
g = acceleration due to gravity = 32.2 ft/sec^2
h = altitude, ft

The first term is called kinetic energy, and the second, potential energy. As an example of a mission requirement to change the energy, consider the landing of an airplane. The airman must reduce both the kinetic and potential energy. He does this by reducing thrust, T, until drag, D, is greater than thrust. The rate of change of the energy, $\dot{E}$, is power and is given by

$$\dot{E} = (T \cos \alpha_t - D)V \tag{2.11}$$

where α_t is the angle between the thrust and the velocity vector.

The airman may exchange one type of energy for the other without changing the total energy. For example, a shallow dive from straight and level flight increases speed at the expense of altitude. The original flight conditions can be regained with very little change in energy by climbing back to altitude. The excess speed is returned to potential energy as the aircraft climbs.

In the discussion that follows, the relationships between lift and drag will make it possible to discuss the requirements for power under different flight conditions.

POWER REQUIRED

For straight and level flight at constant speed (V and h constant) the energy is constant so thrust equals drag. "Power required" is a convenient way of specifying this equilibrium. It is given by the equation

$$P = \frac{DV}{550} \tag{2.12}$$

where P = power required, hp
D = drag, lb
V = speed, ft/sec

For jet- or rocket-powered aircraft it is most convenient to work with thrust or drag force. In either case the lower curve of Figure 2.35 illustrates a typical speed-power required relationship.

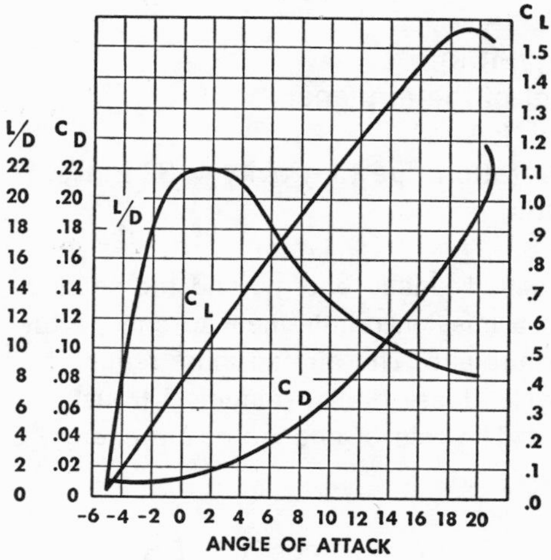

Figure 2.34 Aerodynamic characteristics of a typical airfoil.

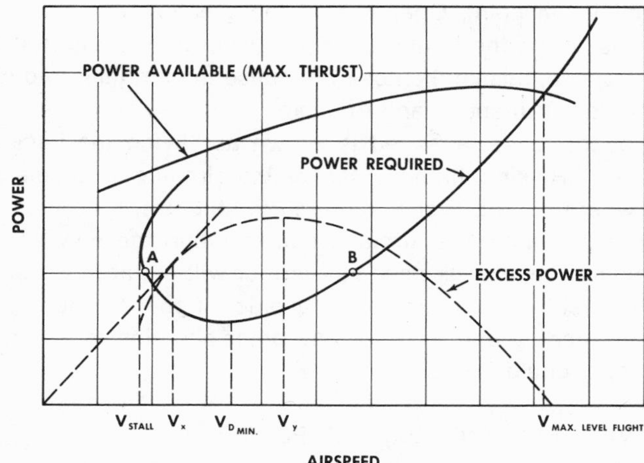

Figure 2.35 Typical aircraft power curve. V_x is the best angle of climb speed, V_y is the best *rate* of climb speed. If the power available curves for a lower throttle setting were added to the graph, it would be lower and would intersect the power required curve at a lower value for the V_{max} in level flight.

Understanding fully the relationship between thrust, or power available, and total drag is vital to safe flying, particularly in large aircraft. Since parasite drag varies directly with the square of airspeed, it is relatively small at low airspeeds. Both lift and induced drag, however, vary directly with angle of attack. If sufficient lift is to be generated at low airspeeds, the wing must be at a higher angle of attack, resulting in a large induced drag as is shown in Figure 2.34.

At low airspeeds, then, induced drag is a more important factor in determining thrust requirement than is parasite drag. As airspeed increases, a smaller angle of attack is required to produce the same lift, and induced drag decreases faster than parasite drag increases; their sum is less, and thrust required is less. Thus the faster the airplane goes, the less power is required up to the point where parasite drag increases faster than induced drag decreases.

The power required at this point is the minimum required for level flight. For an airplane in this condition, it is the lowest point on a curve of power required versus airspeed, the lower curve in Figure 2.35. This minimum-power speed is also the maximum-endurance speed.

It is apparent that at a given level of power, such as line A–B, steady flight at either of two airspeeds is possible—one faster and one slower than at the minimum point. Operation at the greater airspeed is normal and is known as "flying the front side of the power curve." After stabilizing at this greater speed, raising the nose will cause the airplane to decelerate to a somewhat lower airspeed and to climb.

Operation at the lesser airspeed is known as "flying the back side of the power curve." Raising the nose causes the airplane to decelerate to a lower speed where more power is required to stabilize. If no more engine thrust power is available, the airplane can maintain the new speed only by losing altitude. Raising the nose still farther will result in a stall. Flying high on the back side must therefore be avoided if possible during takeoff, low-level flight, landing approach, or any other situation in which loss of altitude or a stall could be hazardous.

POWER AVAILABLE AND EXCESS POWER

Plotting the power available on the same graph gives further useful information. The difference between power available and power required is the excess power and is equal to the rate of change of energy. For constant speed, this change corresponds directly to altitude change. The best rate of climb speed, V_y, is therefore where the difference is greatest. The maximum level flight speed is where the power-required and power-available curves are equal. The best angle of climb speed is V_x, where the tangent to the excess-power curve passes through the origin.

Subsonic Stability and Control

FUNDAMENTAL PRINCIPLES

An aircraft is designed to fly within a range of speeds and altitudes determined primarily by its weight, power, and structural strength. However, the aircraft must be stable and easily controlled to fulfill its design objectives. For stability the aircraft must be capable of holding a given flight condition once equilibrium has been established, and must tend to return to that condition if displaced by an outside force. For controllability, there must be controls that will allow the pilot to maneuver the aircraft safely and precisely. The determination of stability is precise, whereas the handling qualities which determine the controllability are judged subjectively and assigned a score by test-pilot rating.

An aircraft in flight is capable of six different types of motion. It may *translate* (move in a straight line) along any of three axes, or it may *rotate* about any one of these axes. Figure 2.36 shows the conventional stability

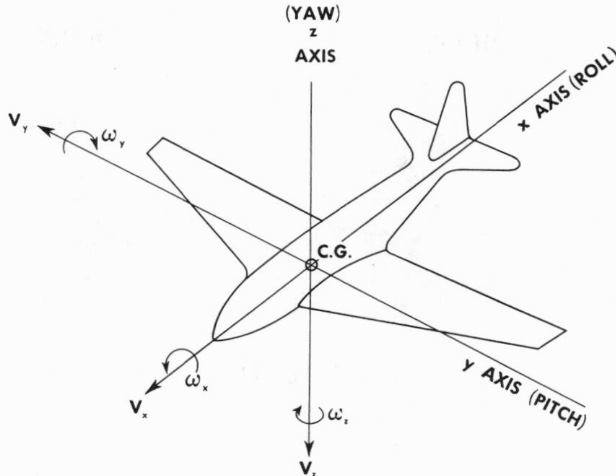

Figure 2.36 Stability axis system. *XZ* is the vertical plane (plane of symmetry), *XY* the horizontal plane, and *YZ* the lateral plane. V_x, V_y, and V_z refer to translation, and ω_x, ω_y, and ω_z refer to rotation with reference to the respective axes.

axis system with its origin at the aircraft center of gravity (c.g.), and indicates the direction of "positive" motion used for mathematical expression. Because of the symmetries of the aircraft, there are two types of motion: *longitudinal* motion and *lateral-directional* motion.

Longitudinal motion is in the plane of symmetry *(X-Z,* Figure 2.36), and involves translation along the *x* and *z* axes, or rotation about the *y* axis. During these motions, the symmetry of the airplane prevents any coupling to the lateral-directional motion.

Lateral-directional motion involves roll and yaw attitude and translation along the *y* axis. These motions are coupled because rotation of the aircraft about either axis induces a moment of sufficient magnitude to cause motion about the other axis, and sideslip (translation along the *y* axis) induces moments about both roll and yaw. (For example, an airplane will not bank without tending to yaw, nor yaw without tending to bank.)

The aircraft controls are designed to be safe and easy to operate so that a pilot can maneuver the airplane as required by the primary task for which it was designed. The purpose of the controls in an aircraft is to make it possible to navigate from one place to another. There is one main force, the lift, with which to perform maneuvers in conventional aircraft. (In VTOL and high-performance aircraft, the thrust may be so great that it is a primary force, too.) The lift magnitude depends on speed

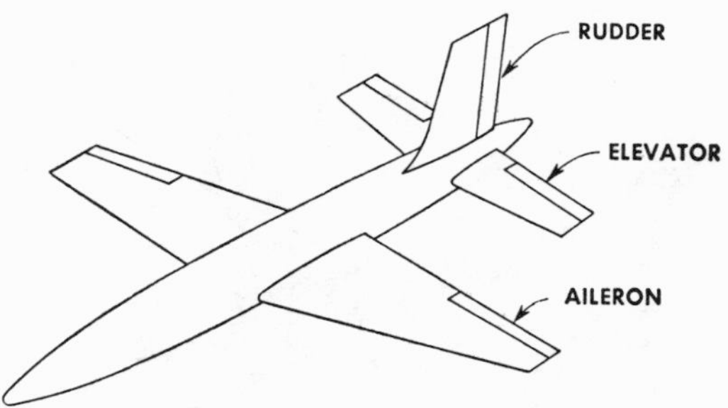

Figure 2.37 Control surfaces.

and angle of attack, while its direction depends principally on the orientation of the aircraft.

The controls which directly affect the lift are referred to as primary controls. These include the elevators and throttle, which are used to control the speed and angle of attack, and the ailerons, which control the angle of bank. A secondary control is the rudder, which controls the angle of sideslip and is used in keeping turns coordinated. Conventional controls are shown in Figure 2.37. The ailerons, elevators, and rudder principally produce moments about the roll, pitch, and yaw axes respectively (although there is some coupling in roll-yaw), and the throttle controls the thrust.

AIRCRAFT CHARACTERISTIC BEHAVIOR

Airplanes have dynamic behavior which is independent of the control an airman exercises over it. These characteristics should be understood to appreciate the task the airman has in controlling the airplane.

Equilibrium is achieved when all of the forces and moments are in balance. In all but very small aircraft, small control surfaces are supplied to trim the aircraft so the pilot does not constantly have to supply control forces or torques to maintain the equilibrium.

An aircraft is said to be *statically stable* if forces and moments are produced to return it to its equilibrium state when it is disturbed.

The airplane is *dynamically stable* if the motion that results from a disturbance dies out and the aircraft eventually returns to its equilibrium state.

A ball perched on top of a smooth hill is in a state of equilibrium that is both statically and dynamically unstable. In a valley, the ball oscillates about its equilibrium position. It is statically stable but unless the oscillations die down due to friction, one cannot call it dynamically stable. Under some conditions of flight, an aircraft which is statically stable may be dynamically unstable, and oscillations that result from a perturbation increase in amplitude. Although static or dynamic instabilities are undesirable, they are not necessarily unacceptable depending upon how fast they occur and what types of motion are involved.

LONGITUDINAL STATIC STABILITY AND TRIM

Gusts, or other changes in the direction or velocity of the relative wind alter the angle of attack. A sudden gust increases the angle of attack, thus increasing lift and drag (Figure 2.34). For static stability the increased lift occasioned by the increased angle of attack must also result in a nose-down pitching moment or the nose will tend to rise and then continue to diverge further and further away from the original equilibrium. Therefore, the static stability of the airplane longitudinally is dependent upon the relationship of lift to pitching moment. The airplane longitudinal static stability is affected by the net contributions from the wing, fuselage, and tail.

First, let us see how the wing affects the static stability, that is, how its pitching moment about the aircraft c.g. (or the corresponding moment coefficient, $C_{M_{cg}}$) varies as a result of a sudden change in angle of attack. This change in angle of attack will cause a change in wing lift (or lift coefficient, C_L). In general, the moment coefficient will also change except if the lift is placed at the wing aerodynamic center. When placed at the wing aerodynamic center, the change in the moment about the c.g. is just due to the change in lift times the moment arm between the a.c. and c.g. A curve that relates $C_{M_{cg}}$ to C_L as in Figure 2.38(a) shows how the pitching moment changes with change in lift. The solid C_L vs C_M curve indicates a stable wing contribution to the overall airplane longitudinal stability, because a positive increment of lift ΔC_L will result in a negative, or nose-down, increment of pitching moment, ΔC_M, as shown in Figure 2.38(b). Hence, moving the wing aft increases the wing's contribution to the aircraft static stability. As a result, in many aircraft the wing is placed so there is a nose-down moment in equilibrium flight that must be trimmed by negative lift on the horizontal tail.

The horizontal tail is well aft of the c.g. so the principal changes in moment about the aircraft c.g. with angle of attack are due to changes in lift. An increased angle of attack produces an increase in lift, and hence a nose-down moment. The horizontal tail therefore produces a stabilizing contribution to the aircraft static stability.

In flying wing and tailless airplanes, special techniques must be used. The a.c. must be behind the c.g. but this leads to trim problems. To obtain the nose-up moment needed for equilibrium, reverse camber on straight

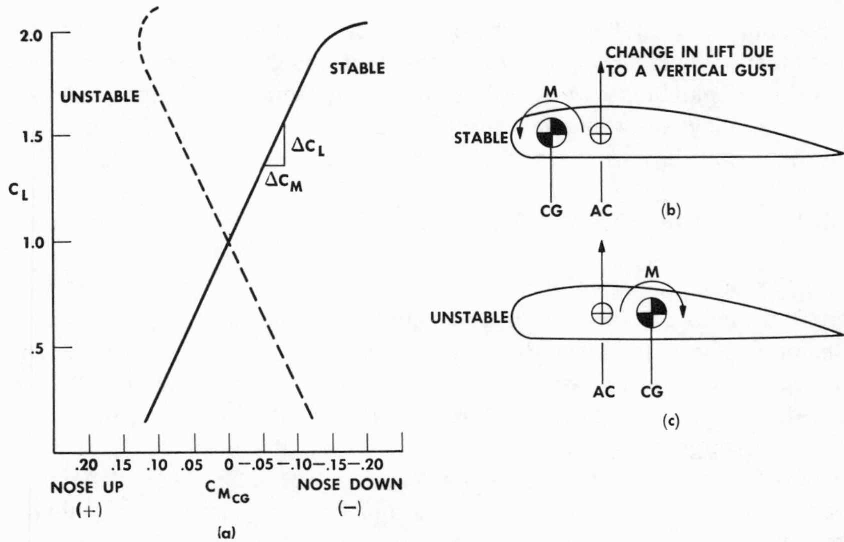

Figure 2.38 Relationship of wing lift and pitching moment to longitudinal stability. In (b) the nose-down pitching moment *M* is evident with the a.c. aft of the c.g. For *changes* in lift, the center of pressure acts generally at the quarter chord point, at the a.c.

wings and wing twist in swept wings (which produces negative lift at the wing tips which are behind the c.g.) are two techniques that can be used to obtain trim after the wing has been located so as to assure adequate longitudinal static stability.

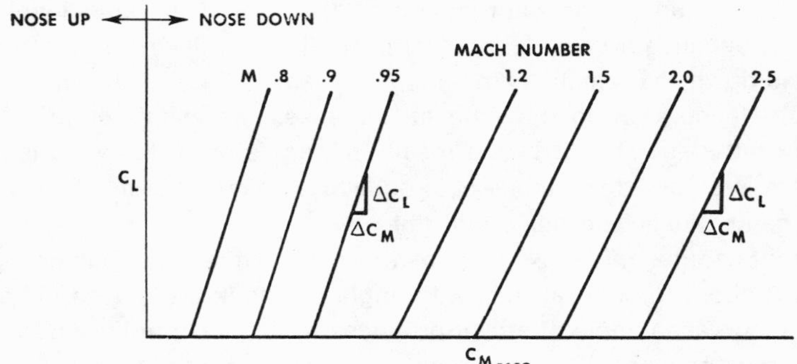

Figure 2.39 Pitching moment. In addition to the large trim changes required, these curves (see Figure 2.43) change slope as speed increases beyond Mach 1.0.

The equilibrium or trim condition changes with airspeed. Supersonic aircraft must be designed to handle large changes in both the trim conditions and the static stability as indicated by the slope of the lift-moment curves (see Figure 2.39).

The reference point for calculating aerodynamic moments is the airplane c.g. The location of the c.g. at which there is no change in moments as the angle of attack changes, is called the *neutral point.* The static stability of an aircraft changes, therefore, with the changes in location of the c.g. due to payload and fuel variations. When the c.g. is in front of the neutral point, the aircraft is statically stable, whereas a c.g. location behind the neutral point would result in the aircraft being statically unstable. The neutral point—c.g. separation can be calculated from the slope of the aircraft $C_{M_{cg}}$ curve (Figure 2.38 (a)) from the equation

$$\text{neutral point—c.g.} = \Delta C_{M_{cg}}/\Delta C_L \tag{2.13}$$

From this expression and the data of Figure 2.39, it can be seen that the neutral point of an airplane moves aft at supersonic speeds.

The range of allowable c.g. locations is an important design and operational consideration. This range is limited by stability and trim consideration. If the c.g. is too far forward, more negative lift than can be produced may be required of the horizontal stabilizer to balance the nose-down moment produced by the wing. The absolute limit is when the horizontal stabilizer stalls but excessive trim increases drag and more importantly, the pilot must have the ability to vary the tail lift if he is to control the aircraft. The amount of this variation is referred to as the *control authority* available. A minimum safe level of control authority, therefore, limits the allowable forward c.g. travel, and stability limits its rearward travel. The airman meets these requirements by insuring that the airplane is loaded so it remains within the airplane's moment and gross-weight envelope at all times.

A complicating factor at supersonic speeds is the change in the C_L vs C_M curve as speed changes (Figure 2.39). The change in slope indicates that the neutral point shifts sharply aft as airplane speed changes from subsonic to supersonic. This means that high elevator deflections must be employed to trim out the increased moment about the c.g. or the pilot must have a way to shift the c.g. aft to minimize trim drag. Presently, a c.g. shift obtained by fuel transfer is the most desirable solution because, as shown in Figure 2.40, not only does the wing a.c. shift aft at supersonic speeds but control-surface effectiveness, C_{L_δ} decreases. Alternatively, variable-geometry aircraft could furnish an automatic method of trim control.

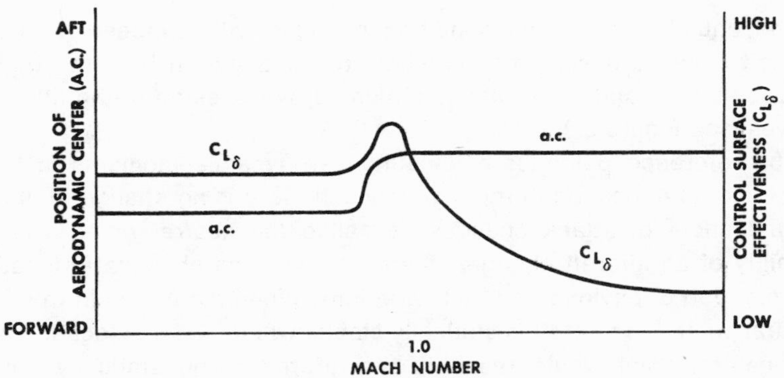

Figure 2.40 Control surface effectiveness.

DIRECTIONAL-LATERAL STATIC STABILITY

The vertical tail provides the keel surface needed for adequate directional static stability, based on moments measured about the c.g. The tail size is not the only factor, however, and too large a tail would add unnecessary weight and drag, detrimental to airplane performance.

The neutral point for directional-lateral stability is analogous to the static longitudinal neutral point just discussed. The tail must be large enough to overcome the typically statically unstable effects of the fuselage and wing (although in lateral motion the wing does not play as important a role as it does in pitch). In directional-lateral behavior, however, the torques about yaw due to roll and sideslip make the discussion more complicated.

The static effects of the coupling mechanisms should be understood to appreciate the types of natural motion that can occur.

The moment about yaw produced by sideslip may be accompanied by a rolling moment. If the moment tends to make the wing headed into the sideslip rise, the aircraft is said to have favorable or positive *dihedral* (see Figure 2.41). For example, if the aircraft lowers its left wing but maintains heading control with the rudder it will slip to the left. The rolling moment produced as shown in Figure 2.41 tends to correct the low wing attitude and return the aircraft to its initial orientation. Positive dihedral is produced by several effects. It corresponds to the lateral neutral point being above the c.g. The aerodynamic center of the tail is usually above the c.g. and contributes positive effective dihedral. A swept wing on the left side of an aircraft slipping to the left meets the air more nearly perpendicular and hence produces more lift, while on the lee side, the right wing meets the air more obliquely and has less lift, thus producing positive effective dihedral. The most obvious effect is the geometric dihedral of the wing.

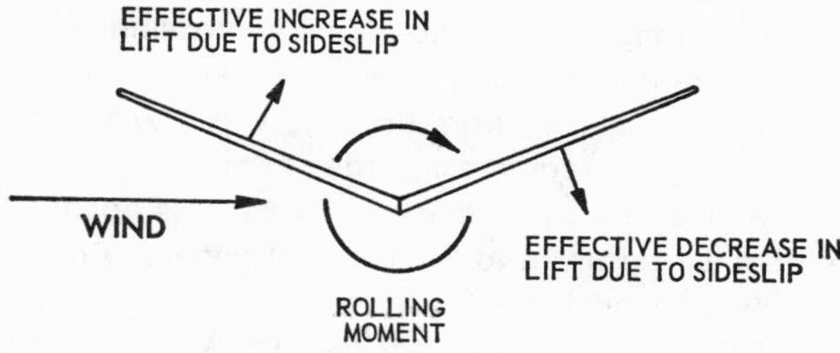

Figure 2.41 Rear view of dihedral effect (in a sideslip to the left).

Not as obvious is the effect of crossflow across the fuselage. In order to pass over the fuselage, the air flows generally upward over the upper part of the windward side of the fuselage and downward over the upper part of the lee side. A straight high-wing aircraft, therefore, experiences flow over its wings that resembles the flow over a wing with the positive dihedral as in Figure 2.4. A straight wing mounted at the bottom of an aircraft similarly has effective negative dihedral.

To obtain the stabilizing effect of dihedral, the whole airplane must be designed with positive dihedral, though the wing design is usually the principal factor.

In addition to these static effects, the angular velocity of an airplane produces moments and forces which are also important to the coupling in the directional-lateral behavior.

A yaw rate causes one wing to go faster than the other. Hence, the lift is increased on the faster wing and reduced on the slower one, causing a rolling moment. The yaw rate also produces a sideslip of the tail due to its tangential velocity perpendicular to the direction of motion. In addition to the side force that results, there is generally a rolling moment of the same sense as the effects of differential wing speed because the aerodynamic center of the tail is above the c.g.

Rolling rates produce similar effects about the yaw axis. A rolling rate increases the angle of attack on the wing which is going down. The lift is increased and it is accompanied by an increase in the induced drag. The opposite is true on the other wing. The difference in drag produces a yawing moment.

POWER EFFECTS ON CONTROL

The location of airplane engines can drastically influence the general control characteristics of an airplane. For a flight condition in which a large amount of excess thrust is available to the pilot, a sudden application of power can be very important to the pilot's impression of controllability. If the airplane is arranged in such a manner that the thrust axis is displaced a considerable distance from the c.g., very rapid and violent control manipulations may be required in order to maintain trim for a steady flight path following a sudden increase in thrust. It is apparent, then, that careful attention must be given to the external geometry of the aircraft in order to insure its manageability.

The torque produced by clockwise-rotating propellers can make an airplane relatively easy to turn left but more difficult to turn right. The Piper Comanche 250 engine, for example, is set at an angle from the airplane center line to compensate for torque effect during takeoff acceleration. On other aircraft, offset vertical fins are used to compensate for these effects.

LONGITUDINAL DYNAMIC CHARACTERISTICS

When there is more than one type of motion that can occur in a dynamic system, the different types are referred to as *modes.* There are two modes of motion that characterize longitudinal dynamics. One is a short-period mode which has been creatively named the *short-period mode.* The airman typically notices this as a fast but well damped oscillation about the pitch axis. He may also be aware of a variation in the g forces on the seat of his pants at the same frequency. There is almost no effect on airspeed during these oscillations. The short-period mode is excited by a sudden movement of the elevators or by a vertical wind gust. Its characteristics are the most important single factor determining the handling characteristics of an airplane.

In Figure 2.42, three aircraft have been disturbed in pitch. The amplitude

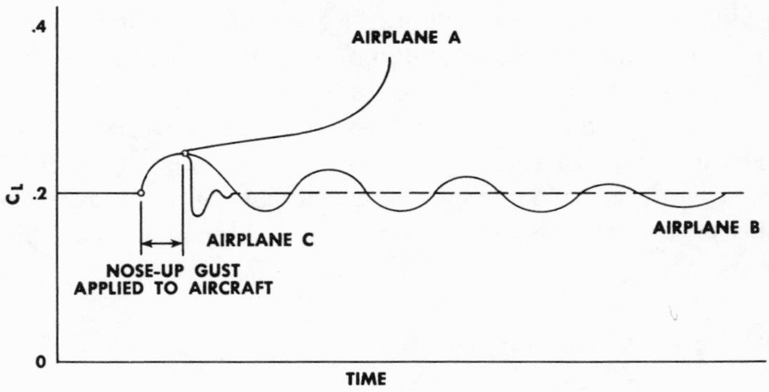

Figure 2.42 Stability in pitch.

of fluctuations through which they return to equilibrium has been plotted against time. Curve A shows how a statically unstable aircraft continually diverges. In curve B, the airplane is both statically and dynamically stable but the return to equilibrium takes too long. It is not adequately "damped" so the pilot is faced with controlling an oscillation with a period of several seconds. Though stable, he may well feel he has a tiger by the tail. If there is too much damping, the pilot is given the impression of sluggishness. Too great a static stability (which makes the oscillations faster) requires excessive control forces to maneuver the airplane. Inadequate static stability makes the aircraft wander in pitch and sensitive to trim. The airplane of curve C is acceptable because it returns to equilibrium in a relatively short time.

The second mode of motion is called the *phugoid mode.* The period of this typically lightly damped oscillation is about 25 sec for light aircraft and increases directly with speed. Even when this mode is unstable, the pilot may be unaware of its existence because it is so slow. The phugoid mode is principally an exchange of potential and kinetic energy. The angle of attack is relatively constant but the airspeed builds up in a shallow dive and increases the lift. The airplane climbs until the loss of lift starts the cycle again. The pitch attitude changes during the dive and climb.

DIRECTIONAL-LATERAL DYNAMIC CHARACTERISTICS

There are three modes that involve roll, yaw, and sideslip. The *dutch-roll* mode is similar to the short period mode in pitch in that the directional-lateral static stability about the yaw axis is the restoring moment that produces the oscillation. The period is slightly longer but there the analogy ends. The dutch-roll oscillations do not need to be as well damped because motions about yaw are not a primary mode of control. The motion is not limited to yaw but is coupled to the other axes so that roll and sideslip respond too. Dutch roll is excited by a sudden application of the rudder or by a lateral gust.

The *rolling mode* describes the rate at which a roll rate dies out. It is very fast, principally involves the rolling rate, but couples into yaw.

A long-period mode that is frequently unstable is called the *spiral mode.* Sideslip causes an aircraft to roll and yaw. If the yawing effect dominates, the aircraft turns into the direction of slip and the nose lowers because the aircraft is banked. This aggravates the situation and the airplane turns and dives at an increasing rate. When there is a lot of dihedral, the corrective rolling moment may right the aircraft and it will return to straight and level flight (albeit at a new heading). The spiral mode is very slow and, as a result, is hardly noticed by the pilot as with the phugoid mode.

CONTROL-SURFACE FUNCTIONS

The function of the elevators to pitch the airplane up or down is quite clear and straightforward, but their use in combination with the throttle deserves some emphasis. We have used the energy of the aircraft as a basis for discussing performance. It is very helpful in understanding the use of controls too. From equilibrium horizontal flight at constant thrust, elevator controls can exchange kinetic for potential energy but cannot change the total energy. Hence one can use the elevator to control speed at the expense of altitude or to control altitude at the expense of speed. The net force acting in the direction of the airplane velocity determines the rate of change of energy or net power (equation 2.11). An increase in thrust from the trim condition increases the energy while a reduction decreases the energy. The energy change can be effected in speed or altitude or both.

Energy management in landing serves as a good illustration. Since the elevators respond more quickly than the throttle, they should be used for tight control of the most accurate measurement available. In the case of a student pilot, this measurement is airspeed, so he is instructed to control his speed with the elevators and then take care of his rate of descent or altitude using the throttle. For the professional pilot flying instruments, his most accurate information is the glide slope, and hence he uses the elevator to maintain glide slope and the remaining control, namely throttle, for speed.

The basic purpose of the ailerons and rudder is to provide the forces and moments necessary for a heading change. The rudder alone affects yaw attitude. Its primary use is to maintain zero sideslip during a turning or rolling maneuver, and to provide yaw control for crosswind landing or similar maneuvers. Lift provides the major turning force. The ailerons bank the aircraft to give a component of lift in the desired direction of turn (Figure 2.43). When deflected, they force the aircraft to roll because the up aileron reduces wing camber, reducing lift, while the down aileron increases lift by increasing camber. *Spoilers* are also used to provide roll control. They are flaps on the top of the wing which are raised to interrupt the smooth flow of air over the airfoil and thereby reduce the lift. When an aileron reduces lift, it also reduces the induced drag. With a spoiler, however, the drag is increased. Ailerons produce adverse yaw because in initiating a left turn, a yawing moment to the right is produced. In some aircraft the effects of aileron and spoilers are combined to balance their yawing effect and to increase the aileron roll control authority at low speeds.

In various aircraft, conventional control surfaces are combined or aug-

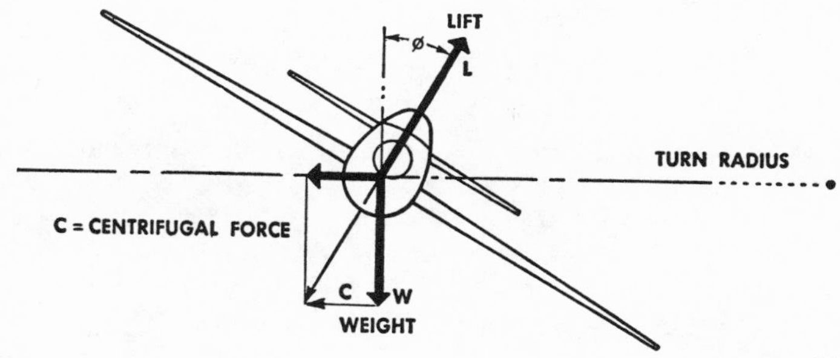

Figure 2.43 Airplane in level turn.

mented. Delta-wing aircraft combine elevator and ailerons, using flap-type surfaces at the wing trailing edge. They move together as elevators, differentially as ailerons. Ailerons and landing-flap controls may also be joined so that ailerons droop as flaps are lowered, improving low-speed control. Aileron and rudder may be interconnected to automatically coordinate the airplane in turns and thereby simplify flying, as in some lightplanes. Aircraft such as the Boeing 707 or Boeing B-52 use spoilers together to reduce lift for rapid descent, and differentially in conjunction with ailerons to enhance ease of lateral control.

CONVENTIONAL CONTROLS

As the speed of the air flowing over a control surface is increased, a given deflection of the surface against the airstream will produce greater and greater forces and moments. Very large and supersonic aircraft have such high forces acting on the control surfaces that designers have been forced to use very elaborate control systems in order to provide the pilot with sufficient mechanical advantage to move the control surface.

Figure 2.44(a) illustrates a conventional type of system in which forces acting on the control surface are transmitted directly to the pilot's control stick. Figure 2.44(b) is another extreme in design in which a hydraulic piston is connected to the aerodynamic control. When the pilot moves the control column he actually positions a valve which allows high-pressure fluid to flow against one side of the hydraulic piston, moving the control surface against the airstream.

Figures 2.44(c) and (d) illustrate two other systems which allow the pilot's control column to be connected directly to an aerodynamic surface. The balance tab of Figure 2.44(c) is linked to the primary surface in such a manner that a displacement of the primary surface moves the small surface in the opposite direction, producing forces which assist the pilot in

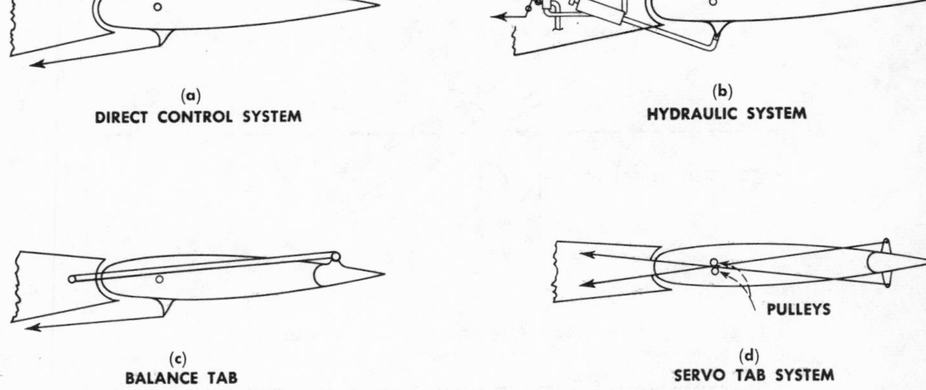

Figure 2.44 Typical control surface mechanisms.

moving the primary surface. The servo tab of Figure 2.44(d) furnishes all the force applied to the primary surface; the control column is linked directly to the servo tab; there is no linkage from the control stick to the main surface.

When aircraft operate at very low airspeeds or very high altitudes, the aerodynamic forces developed by conventional surfaces are too small to provide adequate control. Therefore reaction controls are used. These are either air jets which expel high-velocity air from the engine in variable amounts (Figure 2.45(b)), or miniature rocket engines as used to control the high-altitude research aircraft (Figure 2.45(a)).

In addition to the primary controls, there are other controls which alter

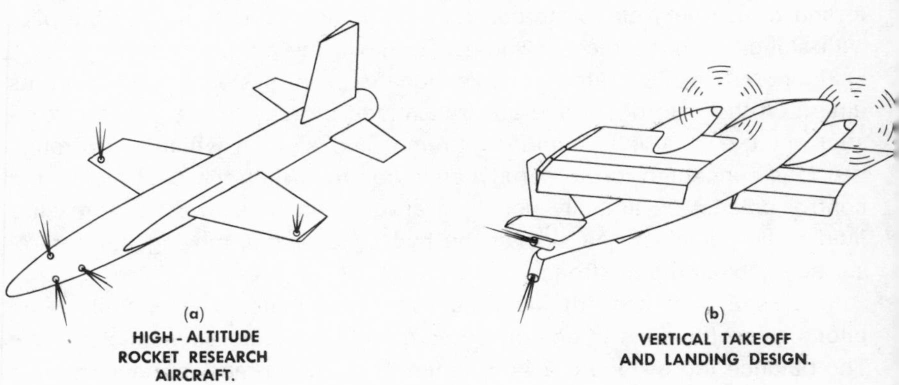

Figure 2.45 Reaction controls.

the aircraft characteristics. These include *speed brakes* and *high-lift devices.*

Speed brakes are hydraulically operated flaps which the pilot can project into the airstream to slow aircraft having the clean characteristics of jets and none of the retarding effects of windmilling props (Figure 1.15).

HIGH-LIFT DEVICES

For high speed and riding comfort in rough air, an airplane should have a high wing loading; that is, for a given gross weight, the wing area should tend to be small. However, for takeoff and landing the airplane should fly slowly and therefore have as large a wing area as is consistent with other factors of design for a given gross weight. Generally the compromise made between these two extremes results in a wing area too small to give satisfactory low-speed characteristics. Consequently, the wing must be modified by adding trailing-edge flaps, leading-edge slots or slats, or other high-lift devices.

Trailing-edge flaps are probably the most commonly used high-lift devices. They increase the maximum lift coefficient attainable, which means that a given airplane can become or remain airborne at lower speeds with flaps extended than it can with flaps retracted. Some types of flap increase $C_{L_{\max}}$ by increasing effective wing camber, while other types increase both area and camber. Flaps are controlled by the pilot and must be used judiciously because they increase drag markedly when extended. Figure 2.46 shows several types of flap.

Leading-edge slots and slats are provided in the leading edge of wings of some aircraft to smooth the airflow over the leading edge of the wing

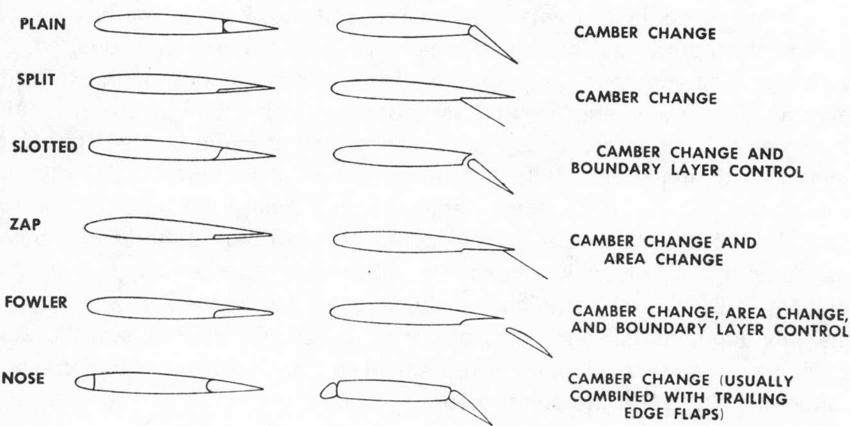

Figure 2.46 Various wing flap designs.

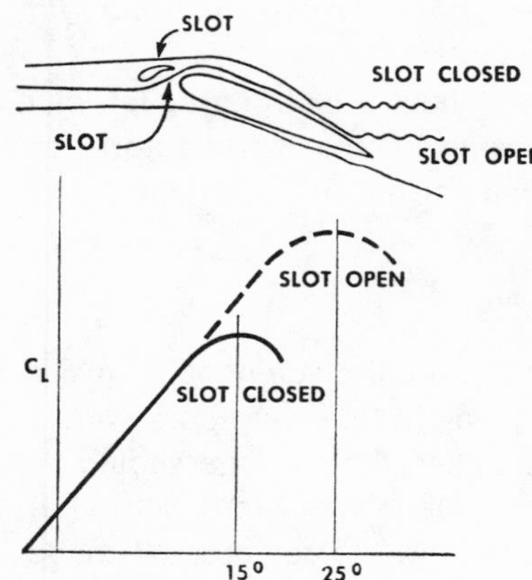

Figure 2.47 Typical aerodynamic characteristics with and without slot. (From *Airplane Performance, Stability and Control,* by Perkins and Hage.)

in such a way as to delay the stall at high angles of attack. Slots are fixed, while slats are mounted in such a way that at high angles of attack the decreased leading-edge pressure permits them to extend into the airstream, effectively increasing wing upper camber. They retract when the aircraft reaches a lower angle of attack. (See Figure 2.47.)

Automatic Controls

Control systems may be designed to augment the natural stability of the airplane or to perform a mission automatically. In an automatic control system, for a quantity such as attitude, angular velocity, speed, or altitude, the signal is compared with the desired state and the error is used to deflect the control surfaces and make the aircraft behave as desired. In stability augmentation, one or more of the natural modes of the aircraft may need improvement. As discussed earlier, each mode involves certain variables but not all. For example, the short period mode involves pitching motion and angle of attack, but not airspeed. To improve a particular mode, one senses one of the variables involved and applies it to a control that also effects the mode. For example, the short-period mode may have its damping improved by measuring pitch rate and applying it to the elevators. Dutch-roll damping can be improved in a similar way with a stability-augmentation system (SAS) that senses yaw rate or sideslip and uses it to control the rudder. A roll signal to the ailerons can overcome a tendency to spiral if the spiral mode is unstable.

In addition to SAS systems, mission-oriented autopilots can be designed to fly the airplane. They frequently work in conjunction with SAS systems and are subject to pilot override. Automatic attitude, heading, and altitude controls are common and automatic landing systems are being developed. For a fighter aircraft, a maximum-performance turn at the limits of the airplane's structural capability can be performed by using an accelerometer to sense and maintain the maximum allowable *g* factor through elevator control. The possibilities are limited only by the ability to sense and the intrinsic aerodynamic and structural limitations of the aircraft.

SUPERSONIC STABILITY AND CONTROL

The analysis of the stability and control characteristics of an airplane capable of flight at supersonic speeds is essentially the same as that used for subsonic aircraft. A supersonic airplane must be statically and dynamically stable; it must have a control system that gives the pilot accurate, safe control of the airplane throughout its flight regime. However, the magnitude of control forces and moments and the changes in these forces and moments resulting from a displacement of the airplane about one or more of the stability axes are much greater at supersonic speeds than at subsonic speeds. Consequently, supersonic airplanes have power control systems to enable the pilot to move the control surfaces. The power control systems used on these aircraft can be designed so that the pilot has the same stick feel for a maneuver of given severity at all speeds despite the variation of control force with speed changes. In general, these airplanes also need 3-axis stability-augmentation systems to provide satisfactory dynamic stability.

STRUCTURAL LIMITS ON PERFORMANCE AND STABILITY

The speed and maneuverability of an airplane are often restricted by structural criteria rather than available power or aerodynamic characteristics. These structural limits are set by the strength and stiffness of the airframe and its components.

Many normal flight maneuvers cause an increase in the loads on an airplane due to accelerations. The limit load factor is imposed to prevent loading any part of the airplane above its design strength. This limit varies from as low as 2 *g*'s for large transports and bombers to as high as 8.67 *g*'s for fighter-type aircraft. Another condition that determines aircraft strength requirements is gusts. A severe gust can impose high *g* loads so suddenly that the speed of airplanes is often limited to prevent structural damage due to gust loading.

Airframe flexibility, airplane weight distribution, and airplane aerodynamics can, singly or in combination, impose other restrictions. Buffet and flutter limits are a typical example of these restrictions. Flexibility can cause aileron reversal and wing divergence. Aileron reversal occurs when wing deformation due to air loads is great enough to nullify the effect of aileron deflection.* Both these effects can make it necessary to impose a high speed limit.

Airframe flexibility problems are compounded by aerodynamic heating at supersonic speeds. At these speeds, skin temperatures are elevated well above ambient temperature. This means that stress analyses must be run on materials at extreme temperatures. To cope with this problem, the designer must resort to high-strength materials and limit high speed because of temperature.

AERODYNAMIC HEATING

Aerodynamic heating results from the conversion of kinetic energy to thermal energy. At the surface of an aircraft, the air is slowed to zero velocity. This means that freestream kinetic energy has been converted to thermal energy. The resultant stagnation temperature is a function of freestream temperature and Mach number. Most of the aircraft surface does not reach this stagnation temperature because the conversion of kinetic energy to thermal energy is not 100% efficient. The maximum resultant skin temperature, known as adiabatic wall temperature, is 85% to 95% as high as the stagnation temperature.† Typical stagnation temperatures are about 260°F at Mach 2.0 and 1550°F at Mach 5. These temperatures serve to explain the structural problems mentioned earlier and the air-conditioning problem to provide a suitable environment for equipment and crew members.

Missile designers have resorted to surface coatings which tend to ablate at extreme temperatures. The energy used to ablate the coating plus the insulating properties of the coating keep the missile primary structure at temperatures well below stagnation temperature.

There is another heating problem that is not due to aerodynamic effects —the effect of high-temperature engine exhaust on structure in the vicinity of the engine exhaust. Piston-engine exhaust location could be altered, but jet-engine exhaust cannot be diverted without a loss of thrust. Consequently, airplane structure must be of a material and design which can withstand this heating.

*Wing divergence occurs when the wing deformation due to air loads causes local wing loading to increase rather than decrease. This effect can be powerful enough to cause local failure in the wing.

†Radiation reduces skin temperature to less than adiabatic wall temperature; this effect increases as altitude and Mach number increase. Adiabatic wall temperature minus heat loss to radiation gives equilibrium temperature: This is the temperature to which an aircraft is designed.

NOISE AND SUPERSONIC "BANG"

The high-thrust jet engines used to power modern aircraft produce a sound level which tends to exceed human tolerance. Users of these aircraft equip their ground crews and mechanics with ear plugs to prevent physical and mental damage due to this noise. In addition to their effect on people, these sounds, or pressure waves, must be considered in the design of any part of the aircraft on which they impinge.

Supersonic flight is now commonplace to the public but an associated phenomenon known as the sonic or supersonic "bang" has not met with the same public acceptance. A bang will occur whenever a shock wave (pressure wave) emanating from an aircraft flying supersonically reaches an observer. According to the water-wave analogy, a supersonic bang is similar to a water wave moving past a floating leaf and causing the leaf to bob up and down.

There are many shocks emanating from an aircraft flying supersonically but these usually interact and coalesce to form two main shocks—one from the nose and one from the aft end of the aircraft. For this reason, the shape of an aircraft has little or no influence on the number of shocks reaching an observer. The bow and tail shock waves gradually diverge as they extend outward from the aircraft. This divergence is due to a slight difference in propagation velocities of the two waves. The observer will hear two bangs if the time interval between the passing of the two waves is of the order of 0.10 sec or greater. If this time interval is much less than 0.10 sec, as would be experienced during a low-level pass of a small aircraft, the ear could not discriminate between the two shock waves and would hear only one bang.

The loudness of the bang is a function of the distance between airplane flight path and observer, Mach number, aircraft size and shape, atmospheric pressure, temperature, and winds. The factor having the strongest influence on loudness is the distance between observer and airplane flight path. The loudness, expressed as an increase in pressure above atmospheric, is inversely proportional to the three-quarter power of this distance.

Atmospheric temperature and wind gradients cause a bending or refraction of shock waves. Other atmospheric conditions, such as clouds, cause a diffusion of the waves. Hence in some cases the shock-wave pattern from the airplane may become so distorted and attenuated that the bang is not even heard on the ground. Prediction of these effects under actual flight conditions is extremely difficult, though by precise control of airplane speed and flight path, shock waves may be focused at a point in space or on the ground. Such conditions can produce a supersonic bang on the order of ten times the normal intensity.

Aerodynamics and Flight

As airplanes have become faster and more complex, the precision required of the pilot has increased correspondingly. Fortunately the expanding knowledge of aerodynamics which has contributed to the design of high-performance aircraft has also come to the aid of the airman. His aircraft can do more than ever for him if he will handle it properly. To handle it properly he needs only two basic tools. One is a conscientious desire to fly his aircraft as efficiently as possible; the other is a basic comprehension of airplane aerodynamics. An airman so equipped will better understand the data in his flight manual; he will use these data properly and thus get most efficient and safe use of his aircraft.

3

Airplane Structures*

An airplane structure is a combination of related parts, frameworks, and assemblies, functionally grouped into a heavier-than-air flying machine. To fly, the airplane's exterior must have an aerodynamic shape. Into this shape must be fitted members having a high strength-to-weight ratio, and capable of sustaining the forces necessary to balance the airplane in flight. Airplanes are designed for some specific purpose that dictates the structural design required. To accomplish any mission, units must be provided to house equipment and payload; to hold the means of propulsion; to support the airplane by reactions obtained from the atmosphere; to balance the airplane in flight; to impart three-dimensional control; and to support the airplane on the ground. The shape, arrangement, and relative size of these members will differ vastly in the various airplane designs, depending on the mission, the specific performance desired, and other factors.

The airplane structure must be capable of withstanding much more force than

*By J. C. Dussault and W. R. Shackelford. Revised by D. J. Ahrens, Cessna Aircraft Co.

that imposed by its weight alone. When the mission of the particular design is established, the designers provide structure according to strict standards established by experience and experimentation to insure safety. In general, airplanes are designed to withstand one and one-half times the maximum expected forces.

The conventional structural elements are: the *fuselage* to house payload, the *wings* to provide lift, the *stabilizers* to provide balance, the *controls* to provide three-dimensional guidance, and the *landing gear* structure. Regardless of the purpose of the airplane, these primary elements must all have high strength, low weight, safety, and an efficient aerodynamic shape.

The forces on an airframe are called *loads.* Actual cargo, crew, and fuel constitute *useful* load, while *payload* is that upon which an actual or theoretical revenue can be realized.

Knowing your airplane's structure will help you as a pilot or mechanic to know what is reasonable and safe to expect of it.

Loads

External loads which act on an airplane come from the air—in the form of turbulence (gusts) or maneuvering loads—and from the ground, which reacts during taxi, takeoff, landing, or ground handling.

For convenience in fixing loads, moments, and directions, structural designers and aerodynamicists both use the coordinate system (Figure 2.36) to depict the various axes of the aircraft. Thus, a rolling moment caused by aileron deflection would be about the *x* axis; a pitching moment caused by elevator deflection would be about the *y* axis; and a yawing moment caused by rudder deflection would be about the *z* axis.

AIR LOADS

Air may be considered a maze of flowing currents which shift in speed and direction. When the airplane departs from one flow and enters another, the resulting change in direction of the airplane results in a load on its structure. The severity of this change will depend upon the *wing loading* (pounds per square foot of wing area) of the airplane, its speed, the speed of the airflow, the relative directions of the airflow, and the path of flight. These factors will be more effective on one type of airplane than another. When you feel these loads inside the airplane in the form of "bumps," the air is turbulent or gusty.

You create maneuvering loads any time you operate the controls in flight. This will be true whether the airplane is changing in attitude or direction, or both. Two or more airfoils may be acting in combination during a maneuver. For example, in a sudden pull-up maneuver, the elevator is deflected upward, causing a down load on the horizontal tail. The nose rotates upward, the wing angle of attack increases, and the up load on the wing will increase. An opposite maneuver, of course, would impose loads in the opposite direction. Rudder deflection will form a sideward load on the vertical tail, resulting in yaw, and ailerons when deflected unbalance the loads on the wings, causing roll. In a well-coordinated maneuver, to change attitude and direction simultaneously, the forces created by all of the control surfaces are acting at the same time, in proportion to their degree of deflection.

Although maneuvering loads may be of approximately the same magnitude as the gust loads caused by turbulent air, the equivalent point of application on the airfoil or the lifting surface will be at a different position. This equivalent point of application, sometimes called the *center of pressure,* is that point on the surface which is the centroid of the distributed air load. If a gust were encountered in level flight, this center of pressure normally would be toward the leading edge of the surface. During maneuvers where the movable surface is deflected, the center of pressure will be at some point close to the hinge line between the movable and fixed surface. In general, gust loads are more concentrated than maneuvering loads.

DYNAMIC LOADS

Air loads, which the designer expects and provides adequate strength for, are not the only problem. Another type of load, for which no practical amount of structure would be adequate, is *flutter.* The designer simply "tunes" the airframe so that this load will not occur. Flutter is an uncontrollable aeroelastic oscillation of a component. It is excited by frequencies or disturbances picked up from the airstream and is, therefore, related to airplane speed. At a certain critical speed the forcing frequency of the airstream will equal the natural or resonant frequency of one of the controls and will cause it to vibrate. Since the vibration occurs at the resonant frequency, the vibrational amplitude will increase rapidly even without an increase in forcing energy. Unless you reduce the speed very quickly, the control will be destroyed. The situation may be aggravated by another control sympathizing with the first—a phenomenon known as *coupling.* Much of flutter prevention is solved by good structural design.

The control is designed so that its natural vibration frequency is either low or very high when compared to its attaching member. This design is accomplished by providing the proper amount of static, dynamic, and aerodynamic balance. If the designer cannot get a satisfactory combination of these three, he uses auxiliary dampeners, usually hydraulic. Because of the extreme importance of this phase of design, be sure you see that the manufacturer's specifications are met any time the control surfaces are modified.

The other factors influencing flutter speed are the natural frequency of the airfoil to which the control is attached, and the natural bending and torsional frequencies of the fuselage. Since safety from flutter depends on avoiding a critical high speed, never intentionally exceed the designer's stated maximum speed. Any airfoil can flutter if the speed is high enough and atmospheric conditions are right. The designer has determined the flutter speed and has kept his highest published speed safely under that value.

Divergence is another type of destructive load. It explains the reasons for some of the structural design shapes.

The resultant wing load is generally far forward on the wing—usually about one-fourth of the chord length aft of the leading edge. This is normally forward of the elastic axis of the wing (the axis where load could be applied without twisting the wing). The load causes the wing to twist in a nose-up direction by an amount proportional to the torsional stiffness of the wing. If the wing lacks torsional stiffness, the twisting would be considerable. Twisting in the nose-up direction increases the angle of attack of the wing and, therefore, the load on the wing. The additional load further increases the angle of attack. If the wing twists easily, the condition above would continue until the limits of the wing were exceeded—a phenomenon called divergence. The designer, therefore, provides adequate torsional stiffness for the airplane's specified operational limits.

Another load resulting from lack of torsional stiffness is *aileron reversal.* This phenomenon could be dangerous close to the ground, but is by no means as serious as flutter or divergence. We have seen that the resultant wing load is usually forward of the elastic axis. When an aileron is deflected downward, it develops a load on its own surface from the airstream. This load is far aft of the elastic axis of the wing and causes a nose-down twisting action on the wing. As the wing noses down, it loses some of the lift gained by deflecting the aileron. If the wing lacks torsional rigidity, it is possible that the nosing down of the wing would cause the loss of more lift than is gained by deflecting the aileron. Then the wing would go downward with a down-aileron deflection—opposite the intended maneuver; hence, aileron reversal.

Load factor seems to be a term which holds interest for all those who fly. It is of prime importance in the design of airplane structure.

As mentioned previously, when an aircraft is in flight and a gust is encountered, a load results which is in addition to the normal weight of the craft. In level, unaccelerated flight the wings support the weight of the craft plus any load needed to maintain equilibrium. A gust when encountered gives rise to an additional force. The gust attempts to change the path of the airplane, but because of its inertia, the airplane tends to remain on its original path. The force of the inertia, which acts so long as the acceleration is taking place, is algebraically added to the force of gravity, and a new total force or apparent weight will result. The ratio of this new force divided by the original weight of the aircraft is a nondimensional quantity called "load factor."

Gust loads in general are of shorter duration than maneuver loads, but their direction change can be much faster and, sometimes, will appear to be almost instantaneous. It is during these times of instantaneous change that the load factors produced will be highest.

The speed and wing loading of the airplane have a direct bearing on the size of the load factor, whether the source of the acceleration be a gust or a maneuver. In general, the gust load factor increases as speed of the airplane or the gust velocity increases, and decreases as the wing loading increases. Thus, when an airplane is below maximum gross weight and encounters a gust, the load factor is higher than when the same aircraft encounters an identical gust at maximum gross weight, assuming speeds and other factors remain constant. In maneuvers, the loads developed increase as the square of the velocity, that is, when the speed is doubled, the loads will increase four times.

In determining load factor by dividing the apparent weight or force by the actual weight, the result is a relative quantity for the particular craft involved. For example, if a plane had a weight of 10,000 lb and developed a load factor of 1.5, the resulting load would be $1.5 \times 10{,}000$ lb or 15,000 lb. The limits which form operational boundaries for aircraft utilization are called *load factors.* Because the speed, weight-lifting capabilities of the airplane, and the atmosphere all play a part in determining the limits to which an airplane is designed, appropriate values are set on these quantities also. Since these are the maximum limits an airplane is ever expected to encounter, they are usually referred to as *limit load factors.* These limits should never be exceeded intentionally.

Recognizing that abnormal circumstances may result in sometimes exceeding these limits and that it is impossible to predict the different elements in nature with complete accuracy, it is necessary that a safety factor be incorporated in all aircraft design. The most common safety factor in use today is 1.5. This safety factor provides a margin for unpredictable elements and insures good service life. Remember that this factor is applied to loads only, and not to the weights, speeds, or other limitations of the airplane. Examples of some of the limit load factors attached to aircraft today are listed in Table 3-1. Notice that the load factors listed are sufficient for the craft to perform the mission or fulfill the purpose for which it is designed.

TABLE 3.1
Limit Load Factors for Various Types of Aircraft

Type	*Performance or Mission*	*Positive Flight Load Factor*
Fighters	Interception, aerial combat, aerobatics	5.3 to 8.7
Bombers	Long-range missions with relatively high payloads	2.0 to 3.7
Trainers	Instruction and practice in flight fundamentals or advanced maneuvers	5.7 to 7.3
Aerobatic	Sudden violent maneuvers, demonstrations	6.0
Utility	Agricultural dressing, training, cargo, general purpose	4.4
Liaison	Observation, transport, rough field operation, photography	3.8 to 4.4
Private	Business flying, training, pleasure	3.8
Passenger Transport	Airlines, large executive or military carriers	2.5
Cargo Transport	Commercial or military freight carriers	2.5 to 3.0

GROUND LOADS

These are the next important loading condition to be considered. Each flight involves at least one takeoff, one landing, and usually some taxiing. Once again the purpose of the aircraft will determine, to a large extent, the amount of time to be spent in the air and on the ground. Usually the landing loads, rather than takeoff loads, govern the design of the gear attachment structure of an airplane, even though the allowable takeoff weight may be higher than the landing weight. Primarily, designers must consider load conditions in level landing, tail-down landing, braked roll, side forces, and, on some special-purpose aircraft, barrier or hook loads for stopping the aircraft roll in a short distance.

Ground handling loads from towing, winching, jacking, and tie-down may present special problems in a particular design and are considered in all designs. Taxiing, turning (with brakes or steering system), and obstructions, such as chocks, curbing, or ground irregularities, also impose many special kinds and magnitudes of loads on the landing gear structure.

Descent velocities of the particular type of airplane, as well as the wing loading in association with the shock-absorption characteristics of the landing gear struts and tires, will determine, in large part, the reaction at ground contact. Total reaction force divided by the weight of the aircraft is called the *landing load factor.*

Two types of inertia loads are involved in landing conditions. The first is *translational inertia*— the force resulting from the aircraft's downward momentum as ground contact is made. The second, *rotational inertia,* is developed when an aircraft touches down on its main landing gear first and begins to rotate toward its nose or tail wheel. The aircraft mass strives to resist this rotation with a counter inertia. The force from rotational inertia can produce airplane structural loads larger than those developed in flight.

MISCELLANEOUS LOADS

These are considered in the structural design of an airplane and come from a host of sources. Most aircraft operating at higher altitudes are pressurized internally, which usually results in a rather large load in the aircraft structure very similar to that of a pressure tank. Structure around doors, windows, and other cutouts becomes particularly critical in these designs. High-frequency vibratory loads have become rather commonplace in the modern airplanes equipped with turbine engines. Loads which are peculiar to transonic and supersonic craft as a result of shock waves have affected the design of military aircraft for some time, but only recently has consideration of these loads been necessary in the design of transports and lighter aircraft. Loads due to buffeting at low speeds are fairly well known and are in the inertia or dynamic load class. Vibratory loads in the frequency range of those produced by piston engines are still present on many aircraft and must be accounted for in a successful design.

Crew and passenger comfort and protection are prime considerations and seats, seat belts, and shoulder harnesses can impose highly concentrated loads which must be adequately absorbed in the structure. Cargo, baggage, and equipment must be satisfactorily restrained and their concentrated mass effects included in the airframe design.

STRESS

Any load applied to a unit area of material is called a stress and will produce a deflection or deformation in the material, termed *strain.* There are *tension, compression, shear,* and *bending* stresses. While there are many other types of stresses, they are special arrangements of these basic ones.

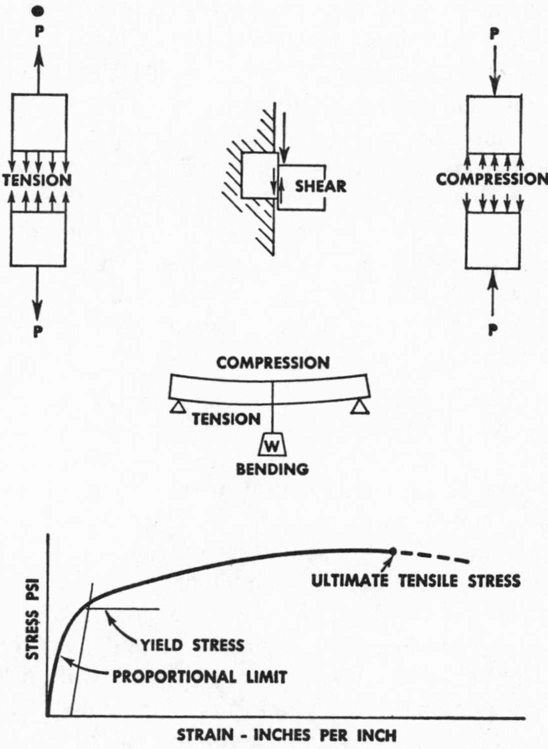

Figure 3.1 Stresses and strain. The lower sketch shows a typical stress-strain curve for aluminum.

Stress is always accompanied by a deformation of material called *strain.* The ratio of stress to strain, within the elastic limit of the material, is constant and is referred to as the *modulus of elasticity.* An example of the stress strain diagram of aluminum is shown in Figure 3.1.

Fatigue loading has become an important design consideration in all classes of aircraft. The increasing performance of modern aircraft and the higher utilization rates have dictated the requirements for primary structure to approach infinite service life. Many structural areas, especially those subjected to highly concentrated cyclic loads, are designed by fatigue requirements. This is accomplished by designing for low stress levels to approach infinite life or by fail-safe techniques which deliberately provide multiple load paths within the structure.

Considerable research in recent years has provided data that are useful in simulating typical load spectra for the type of aircraft being designed. This permits accelerated testing of various airframe components or a complete airframe by subjecting it to repeated loadings simulating the mission profile of the aircraft; from takeoff through flight maneuvers, gusts, and landing. These tests substantiate the design and provide additional data for future designs.

Wings

The primary lifting airfoil of an airplane is the wing. While its planform may be widely varied, its function remains the same. Wings are attached to airplanes in a variety of locations, vertically and longitudinally. The terms *high-wing, low-wing,* and *midwing* all describe both airplane types and methods of wing attachment. Longitudinally, the location of the wing on a particular aircraft will be determined by the size and location of the mean aerodynamic chord of the wing and the center of gravity of the complete airplane. Other descriptive terms applied to wings describe their shape. Examples are "delta wings," "swept wings," "taper wings," "elliptical wings," and "rectangular wings."

TYPES OF CONSTRUCTION

Wings may be either strut-braced or full cantilever, depending on whether (as in many smaller aircraft) an external brace is employed to help transmit loads from the wing to the fuselage. Cantilever wings must resist all loads with their own internal structure.

Wings are designed with one or more main load-carrying members called *spars.* The most common arrangement is two spars where the front spar is generally much more massive than the rear.

The *skin* may be made of metal and used as a primary load-carrying member, or the wing may be covered with plywood or fabric. If fabric is used as a covering, it is saturated with *dope,* a strengthening and filling fluid. Fabric-covered wings have drag wires installed between the spars, running diagonally across the bays of the wing, to prevent fore-and-aft distortion; such distortion is also prevented by orienting the wing ribs diagonally so that they will carry loads normally carried by drag wires.

DESIGN FEATURES

The shape and type of wing used on an airplane are determined by considerations other than structural. The airplane mission will govern in choosing a structural design. Small, low-speed aircraft have straight, nearly rectangular wings. For these wings the main load is in bending of the wing as it transmits load to the fuselage, and the bending load is carried primarily by the spars. In high-speed aircraft, wings are often swept back. Sweepback imposes a very high torsion load because the resultant wing load is located far aft of the wing attachment to the fuselage. Depending upon the degree of wing sweep and its thickness, this torsional load might very well command the most importance in determining the particular structural design. Other items influential in the structural design of the wing are equipment to be housed within the wing, duct work and wiring, fuel cells, nacelles, and external loads. Cost of building and maintenance will also influence structural design. In fact, any existing airplane wing design represents a careful balance of performance, cost, fabrication techniques, weight, and strength.

STRESSED SKIN

Most modern aircraft use sheet metal as wing covering. The sheet-metal skin has high strength and is employed as a primary load-carrying member. The skin is quite strong in tension and shear and, if stiffened by other members, may be made to carry some compressive load. The thickness of wing skins varies widely, depending upon the local stresses encountered in service. Thicknesses vary from as low as .016 in. in small aircraft to as much as .75 in. in the wings of heavy bombers. If weight reduction is of prime importance, the skins may be tapered so that the proper amount of strength is provided for local loads. Metal skins have the additional advantage that they are fairly rigid and hold their aerodynamic shape well.

CELLS

Because of the characteristic way in which loads are developed on the wing, a cell-type construction has important advantages. Ordinarily, wings have two spars which are joined by ribs and covered by metal skin which completes a *box.* Box construction, of course, utilizes the skin as a primary structural member. A cell is quite rigid and resists torsional deformation. The fact that aerodynamic demands limit the shape and space in which structure may be installed adds importance to cell structures. The resultant air load on the wing occurs far forward on the wing chord—usually about one-fourth the distance back from the leading edge. The front spar is placed as close to this line as possible. This center of pressure ordinarily would bend the front spar and leave the rear spar unstrained. The wing must twist if the front spar is to bend alone, but since the box-like cell resists twist, the rear spar is loaded by the deflection of the front spar. Figure 3.2 shows the deflection pattern of the cell beam under the off-center load.

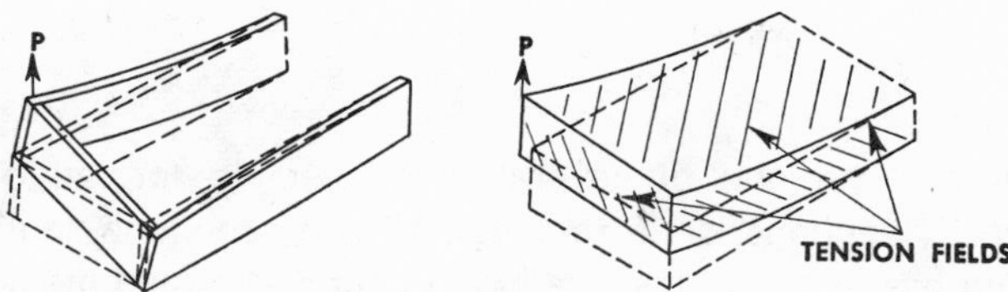

Figure 3.2 Deflection characteristics of a box beam versus a two-spar beam. Note how the tension fields in the skin of the box beam cause it to deflect as a unit.

Because the cell allows a distribution of the load to other areas in the cell, an auxiliary spar added at a convenient location will still help support the bending load. It is therefore unnecessary to design a massive front spar in the limited space available, expecting it to carry the entire bending load. In a conventional two-spar cell-type wing structure, cells are also formed at the leading edge and trailing edges. Cells A and C in Figure 3.3 are important because they, too, resist torsion and bending, and contribute considerable stability to the spars. Since it is possible that creases or dents in the leading or trailing edge cells could cause premature collapse and failure of larger members, leading and trailing edges should always have proper maintenance.

It often becomes necessary to make cutouts in the cell skins to allow access for service or other reasons. These cutouts greatly weaken the cell, especially in its ability to resist twist, and relatively heavy frames or doublers are required around the cutout. If the cutout is exposed to the airstream, or is in a highly stressed area, a cover is installed to complete the cell. The strength desired determines how the cover is attached.

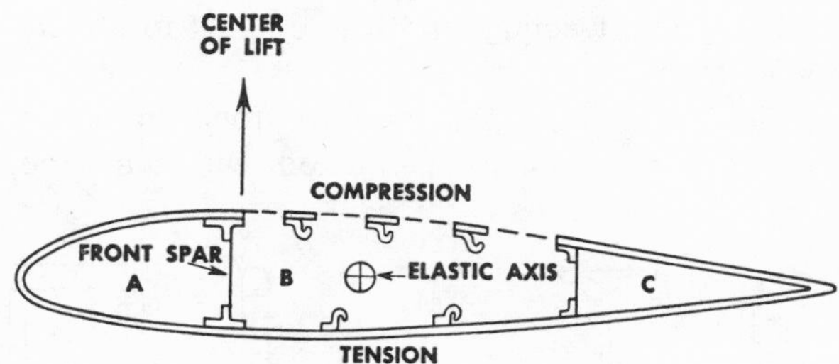

Figure 3.3 Typical wing cross section. Note that the skin on the compression side of the cell is considered ineffective in compression except for that portion attached directly to the stringer.

SPARS

Wing spars may be one of several types: simple formed or extruded channels or "I" sections, solid rectangular wood sections, laminated sections utilizing heavy cap strips attached to simple formed members, truss-type, and semitension field sections.

Simple formed or extruded shapes have the advantage of being easy to build. Load calculations on these spars are well defined. This type of spar has its greatest use in small, low-priced utility airplanes. Though somewhat heavier, they cost less to produce.

Solid rectangular wood spars have much the same features as those listed in the previous paragraph. This type of spar is used today in some small aircraft, although the trend is away from wood and toward greater use of light metals to avoid decay.

Laminated spars are used where the outer flange loads are fairly high in relation to web (center section) loads, and it is necessary to add material to the outer fibers of the section.

Laminated spars permit attaching different sizes of cap strips to the basic spar along the span, thereby forming a lighter tapered effect. Another advantage of this buildup of parts is that a wing may be made to support a heavier airplane model with perhaps no more than fabrication of heavier cap strips, which are attached to the basic spar. This makes a costly redesign unnecessary.

Truss-type spars are occasionally found in larger, transport-type wings using a fairly deep section. These are made up of hollow, rectangular tubing with welded joints, and arranged to form a truss. The truss consists of two large cap strips separated by vertical members, braced rigidly by diagonal members. These spars may be closely designed so that excess weight is not a problem, though they have very little torsional strength unless supported against twisting, and it is difficult to attach other structural members to them.

Semitension field spars are the modern trend in aircraft structural design. The spar types previously mentioned, with the exception of the

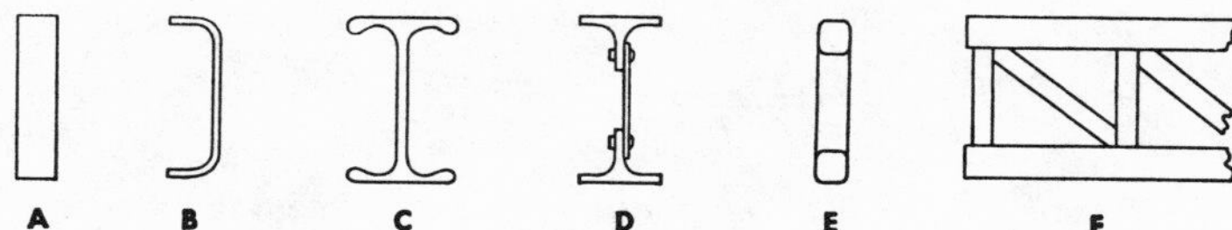

Figure 3.4 Typical spar cross sections. A, rectangular; B, channel; C, I section; D, Built-up I section; E, truss; F, truss spar, side view.

truss type, are called *web shear-resistant beams.* This means that the web material must be strong and stable in shear to withstand the shear load along the beam. The method of handling the beam shear load is what makes the semitension fleld spar differ from others. A semitension field beam is made up of heavy cap strips (usually extruded or milled), with a thin sheet-metal web between them and vertical stiffeners spaced along the spar. As load is applied to the spar, the caps tend to hinge about their end attachments and allow deflection by sliding by each other. To prevent this deflection, a web is provided. The web must then absorb the shearing load caused by the tendency of the spar caps to pass over and under each other.

In a semitension field beam, this shear load is resisted by a tension field set up in the sheet metal web. The tension field runs diagonally across the web material, and if the load is large enough, diagonal buckles will appear in the web material. These buckles occur long before the ultimate spar load is reached and are not an indication of impending failure, since they disappear when the load is reduced. As its stability is not of prime importance, the web may be made much thinner than for web shear-resistant spars. The tension field developed in the web exerts a force that attempts to pull the spar caps together, hence the necessity for vertical stiffeners.

Figure 3.5 shows the similarity between a tension field beam and a truss. The frame is hinged at points *A, B, C,* and *D.* With a load applied as shown, members *AB* and *CD* would rotate about points *A* and *D,* and the frame would not support the load. Member *AC,* however, develops a tension load and prevents this rotation, enabling the truss to support the load. The semitension field beam acts in a similar manner with the thin sheet-metal web replacing member *AC.* The buckle pattern in the thin web would be oriented the same as member *AC* for the same loading. If the load is reversed, the buckle pattern will also reverse. Since the web sheet is flat, it may buckle fairly severely, but, provided the elastic limits have not been exceeded, it will still return to its original flat shape when the load is removed. Semitension field spars are generally the lightest in

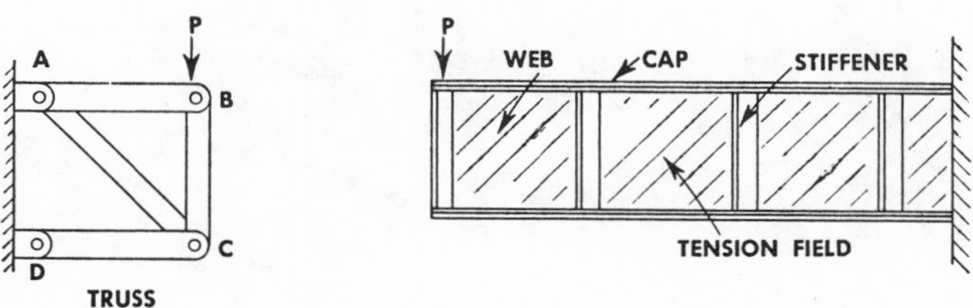

Figure 3.5 Tension field action in a spar.

Figure 3.6 Wing ribs. *(Courtesy of U.S. Air Force.)*

weight, but may be somewhat more expensive than some of the other spar types. To reduce weight further, the heavy cap strips are sometimes milled down to taper toward the wing tips where the spar loads are lower.

RIBS

Ribs are found in some form or another in all airplane wings and serve several purposes. They are placed at appropriate intervals along the wing span and transmit air load from the wing surface to the spars, act as formers to hold the airfoil shape, stabilize the spars against twisting,

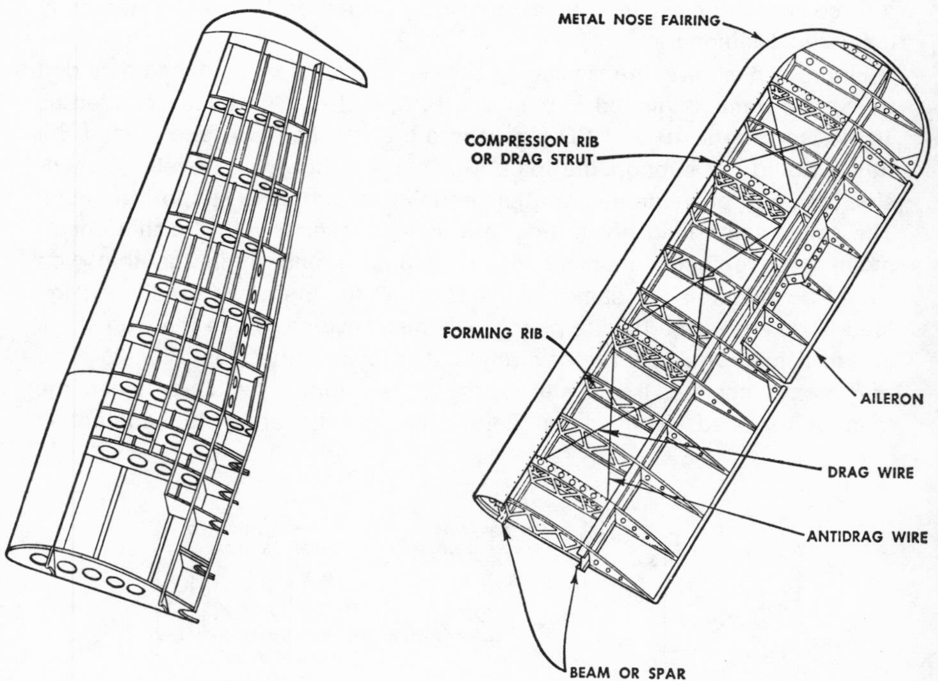

Figure 3.7 Typical light-aircraft wing frames. The frame at left is a stressed-skin style; the frame on the right is a fabric-covered style.

distribute bending loads between the spars, close cells to complete the torque box, form barriers in the internal fuel installation, keep the spars separated when drag wires are used, provide a point of attachment for other components such as landing gears, and for many other needs. Ribs may be made of formed sheet metal, truss work, or a thin sheet-metal web with cap strips attached. Generally, lighter aircraft have thin, formed sheet-metal ribs with large holes ("lightening holes") cut into the web to conserve weight. Heavier aircraft usually have ribs either of the truss type or built-up type.

The particular type of rib will be determined by the purpose it must serve. For example, if a rib is to serve as one side of a fuel cell, it will have a solid web to withstand uniform internal pressure. Another example of a special-purpose rib is shown in Figure 3.7, where the ribs at drag wire attachments are provided with heavy cap strips to prevent the drag wires from pulling the spars together.

STIFFENERS

Where high compressive loads are encountered, or where a shape must be held, stiffeners are attached to the skin. These are usually found fairly closely spaced on the upper wing surface, which normally is in compression, stiffening the compression skin to resist the induced bending loads. Where stiffening demands become extreme, the skin is usually reinforced by a corrugated panel or honeycomb sandwich instead of individual stringers. Typical stiffened panels are shown in Figure 3.8.

ATTACHMENT OF AUXILIARY DEVICES

Wings are usually far more complex than we have seen so far, because to use the space available efficiently, much equipment must be housed within the wing or attached to it. Fuel cells break the continuity of the

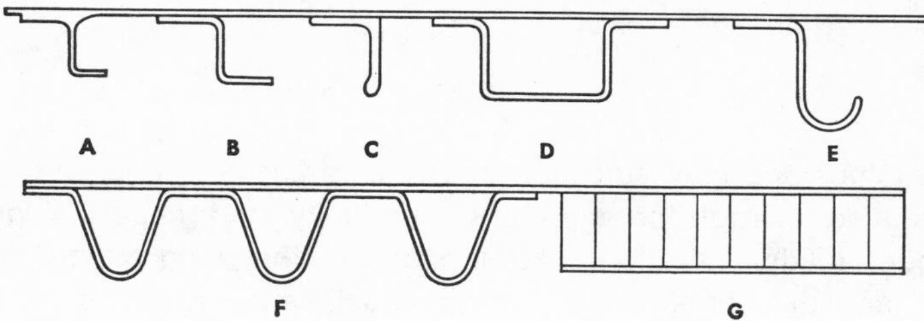

Figure 3.8 Typical methods of stiffening panels. A, integral; B, Z section; C, bulb angle; D, hat section; E, J section; F, corrugation; G, honeycomb core sandwich section.

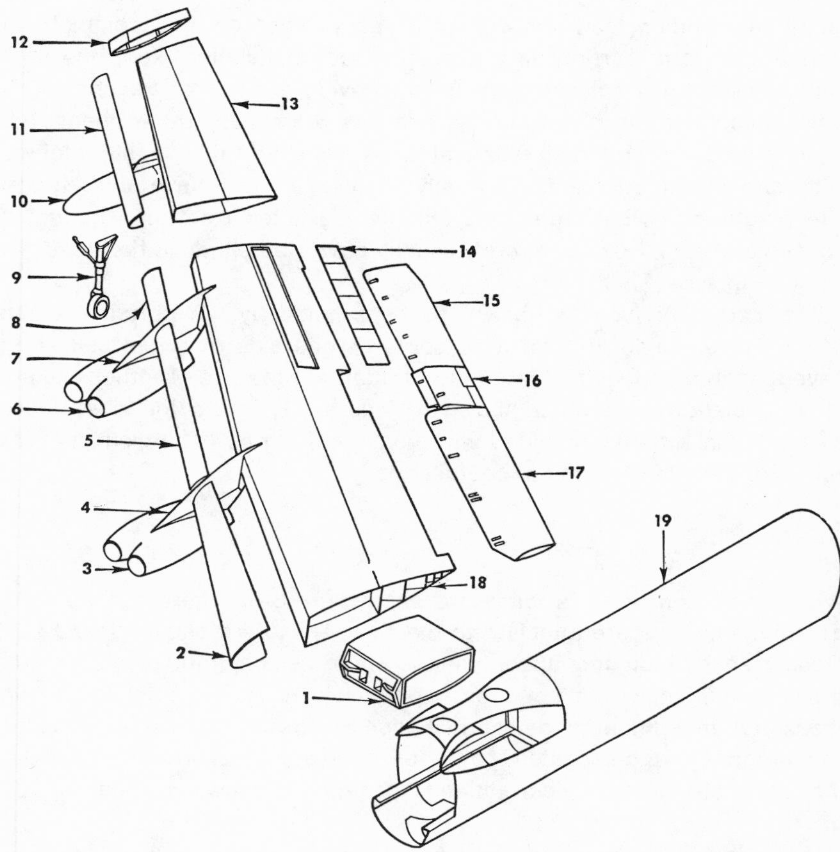

Figure 3.9 Jet bomber wing components. 1, center wing; 2, wing leading edge; 3, inboard power plant; 4, strut nacelle; 5, wing leading edge; 6, outboard power plant; 7, strut nacelle; 8, wing leading edge; 9, wing landing gear; 10, external fuel tank; 11, wing leading edge; 12, wing tip; 13, outboard wing; 14, spoilers; 15, inboard flap; 16, aileron; 17, outboard flap; 18, inboard wing; 19, fuselage.

wing structure and may add high inertia or pressure loads. Engines and nacelles also disrupt the structural continuity and impose high local attachment loads, vibration, and torsion on the wing. Spoilers, flaps, ailerons, and dive brakes create high attachment loads and in addition often require openings or cutouts in the wing. If the landing gear is attached to the wing, provision must be made to support the high local loads. If the gear is retractable, cutouts are necessary but will not allow permanent cover plates as would service access cutouts. Wires, tubes, ducts, controls, and other items must pass through various parts of the wing structure and further complicate the design.

For these reasons, a wing as designed is necessarily heavier than the ideal structure, but adds much to the utility of the completed airplane. Equipment not housed within the wing would have to be placed elsewhere in the airplane, perhaps resulting in even greater weight and performance penalties.

FUTURE TRENDS

The demands on wings both as a lifting device and as a place to house equipment seem to be increasing at a rapid pace. Wings are becoming thinner, more heavily loaded and more multipurpose in design. Several present airplane designs utilize the entire wing as a fuel cell, and have additional external fuel pods or payload pods suspended below them. These increasing demands require a new structural style. To maintain a high degree of structural efficiency, wing structure in the future will make more extensive use of such features as semitension field spars and ribs, strong light metals, tapered spar caps, tapered skins, lightweight but rigid honeycomb sandwich panels, metal bonding, and chemically milled skins and stiffeners. Structural design will keep pace with advancing technology and production capabilities. Strength of materials, fabrication practice, and processes will certainly change in the future, and wing design will change with them.

Data processing and the computer have provided the designer with tremendous new tools. Load, stress, and dynamic analyses can now be performed faster and far more accurately than before. These tools will be more and more an aid in the future to permit the designer to develop stronger yet lighter structure.

Fuselage

The fuselage is the body of the airplane. Some of the features that all fuselages may have in common are provisions for crew, passengers, attachments or carry-through structure for wings and empennage surfaces, instruments, controls, necessary equipment, possible fuel, baggage or cargo, engines, and landing gear. Perhaps the most distinct feature of the fuselage is a result of its purpose: providing space for payloads. The space required creates the need for comparatively large openings within the airframe in relation to its size, whether the airplane is a light four-place craft or a 400-passenger transport. Around this space and function the fuselage structure is designed and built.

Fuselage structures of active aircraft today can usually be divided into the *truss, monocoque,* or *semimonocoque* types. Truss or framework types of construction have wood, steel-tube, aluminum-tube, or other cross-sectional shapes which may be bolted, welded, bonded, pinned, or riveted into a rigid assembly. The exterior is then covered with such materials as impregnated glass fiber, cotton or linen cloth, aluminum, steel, or plywood sheet. Fuselage cloth coverings, as on wings, are usually filled with dope, which makes them taut and airtight, and adds to their strength—although cloth is not a primary structural member. Impregnated glass fiber is a glass cloth or mat reinforced with epoxy or other resins and sometimes is part of the primary structure. Definite progress is being made in the area of total metal bonding of the airframe structure. Some airframe components, that is, fuselage halves and wing and tail sections, are being molded using glass fiber and epoxy. This results in a high degree of rigidity of the structure and very smooth skin surface but with some penalty in weight.

The *monocoque* or *semimonocoque* fuselage structure uses its covering or skin as an integral, structural load-carrying member. Monocoque structure is a thin-walled tube or shell which may have rings, bulkheads, or formers installed within. It can carry loads effectively, particularly when the tubes are of small diameter. As its diameter increases to form the internal cavity necessary for a fuselage, the weight-to-strength ratio becomes more inefficient, and longitudinal stiffeners or stringers are added to it. The result is the most popular type of structure used in structural aircraft design today—semimonocoque. Use of this concept has enabled aircraft designers to use aluminum skins as light as .016 in. in thickness for primary structure on airplanes as large as the modern light twins. Larger semimonocoque aircraft use progressively thicker skins and still maintain an equivalent stress level in the skin along with an equally good weight-to-strength ratio.

Fuselage cross sections may vary widely. While designers keep frontal area as small as possible, most fuselage cross section are a circle or an ellipse. Some light aircraft (as well as some large, unpressurized craft) have a basic square or rectangular shape with large corner radii. Pressurized cabins are almost exclusively of round section, although some have utilized an ellipse whose major and minor diameters are nearly equal. The outer contours of the fuselage along its length must be some form of streamlined shape as described on pages 53 and 65.

Fuselage and wing structural design problems are similar. Because more curvature may, in general, be employed than on the wing—making the skin itself somewhat stronger for compressive or bending loads—and

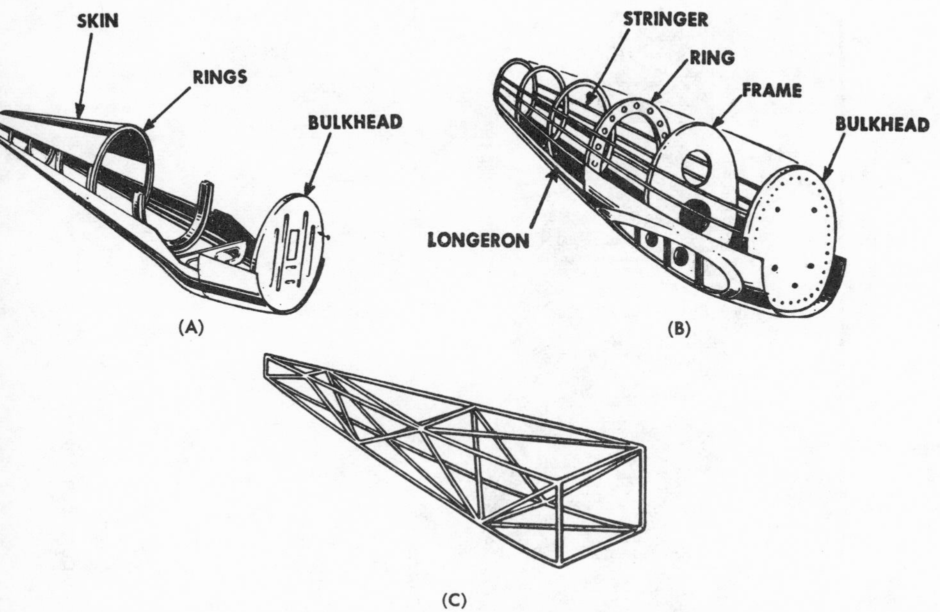

Figure 3.10 Fuselage structural styles. A, monocoque; B, semimonocoque; C, truss-frame. Note stringers used in semimonocoque structure. *(Courtesy of U.S. Air Force.)*

because of the greater cross-sectional area, the fuselage usually does not employ the spar-type structure found in the wing. Most fuselages can be considered a single-cell structure, although when floorboards in multilevel larger aircraft are designed to bear structural loads, the fuselage is a multiple-cell structure.

The skins used in modern aircraft construction are particularly effective in tension but rather ineffective in compression. In addition, the fuselages of these craft are of large diameter or cross section when compared to skin thickness. Accordingly, a unique situation occurs when the structure is subjected to bending loads. One side becomes very much stronger than the other under bending loads, causing the neutral axis of the section to shift toward the strong or tension side. As the neutral axis shifts, the loads or stresses in the weaker side tend to become less, and the loads or stresses become larger in the side that is more capable of withstanding them. Thus, somewhat of an inherent structural equilibrium exists. In addition to this phenomenon, the longitudinal stringers form tension field webs as explained in the discussion of the wing section, further improving its bending-load-carrying capability.

Twisting loads on the fuselage are resisted primarily by the shear stresses in the skin, which are produced directly as well as by the development of tension fields in bays between stringers and formers or bulkheads.

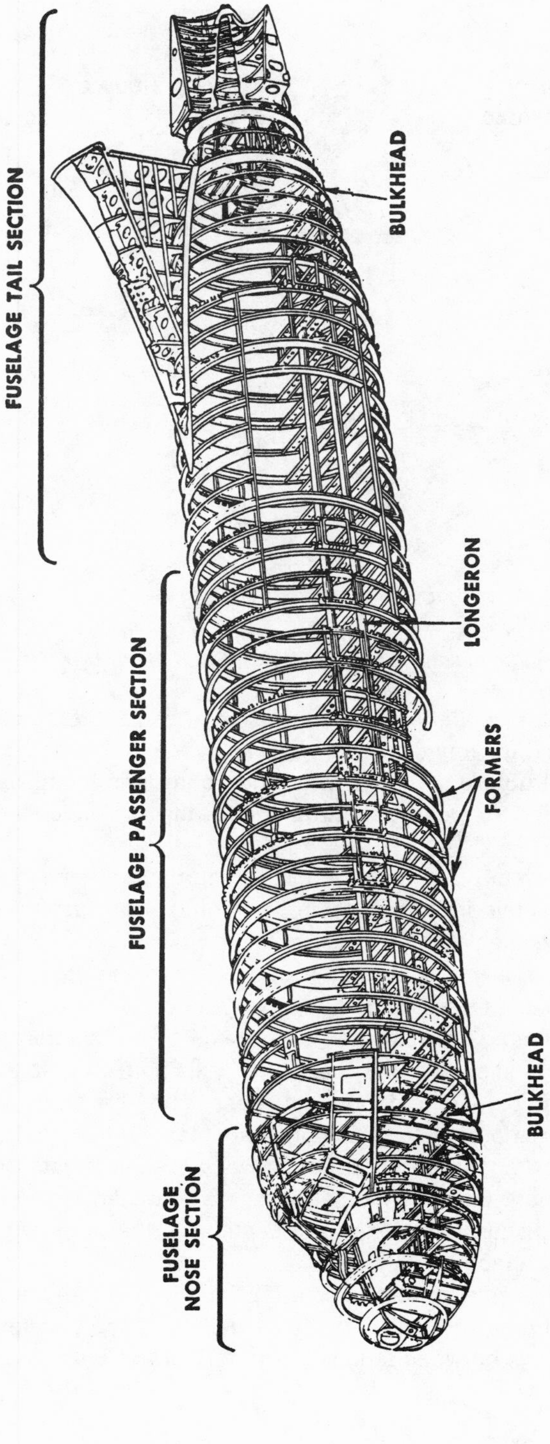

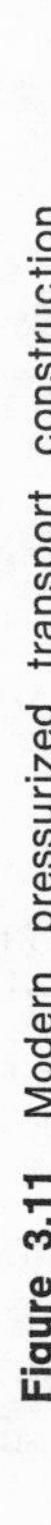

Figure 3.11 Modern pressurized transport construction.

Figure 3.12 Tension field action in a stressed skin structure. The tension field is set up by shear flow in the skin, caused by an extremely high torque on the fuselage tailcone. This semimonocoque specimen is under a load equal to twice the maximum expected load for this particular design. *(Courtesy of Cessna Aircraft Co.)*

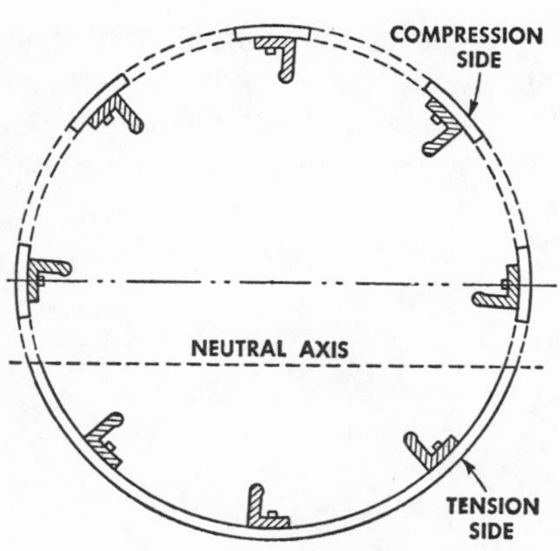

Figure 3.13 Cross section of fuselage under bending load.

Pressurized fuselages must bear an additional load, for the fuselage becomes a pressure tank. Even though the differential pressures are quite low in force per unit area, the quantity of area is large, and consequently so are the forces. Because of the type of construction (semimonocoque) used in most fuselages, each ring or former will develop undesirable stresses, similar to the tension in a barrel hoop. Hoop stresses, which are too concentrated, plus unequal deflections that appear on the outer skin, create a surface that is not aerodynamically smooth. One method of combating this problem is use of "floating skins" in which the ring-to-skin attachment retains its shear capability, but is flexible in tension, allowing the vessel to expand uniformly with pressure. Fatigue of joints due to fluctuating pressures, seals around control systems where they enter or leave the fuselage, door openings and seals, window frames and glass pressures, and—primarily—the need for a "fail-safe" structure to prevent explosive decompression if the skin is punctured from either the inside or outside while under pressure, are important in pressure-fuselage design.

INTERNAL LOADS

High local loads are imposed on the fuselage internally. Seat-attachment loads are quite severe because of their limited area of application and their need to be adjustable. Cargo aircraft floors and tie-downs may be subjected to loads from extremely heavy objects concentrated in a very small area. Floorboard structure used on present-day aircraft may be of the honeycomb variety, sheet-reinforced with corrugations, channels, or stiffeners or other types. On some aircraft plywood is used quite effectively, and while it reduces noise, the weight efficiency may suffer somewhat.

FUTURE TRENDS

Future trends of structural technique in fuselage construction will undoubtedly follow that of development of stronger, lighter metals and synthetic materials, processes of joining cheaply and efficiently, and new methods of forming intricate shapes. The aerodynamic heating resulting from hypersonic speeds may in itself change the structural concepts of fuselage construction completely.

Landing Gear

TYPES

The basic types of landing gears are the *tail-wheel* gear, the *tricycle* gear, and the *bicycle* gear (which utilizes a main gear under both the forward and the rear portion of the airplane). The *bicycle-type* landing gear usually has outrigger wheels to stabilize the aircraft when turning or swerving.

These outrigger supports (Figure 3.9) usually are in contact with the ground when the aircraft is stationary, especially with a fuel load in the wings. Skis, or combination wheel-ski types which will allow the craft to land on or take off from either a snow surface or a dry landing area, are widely used.

Amphibious gears allow the aircraft to operate from a land or water base. Usually the wheels are retractable into the floats, whether the floats be external or a single-hull type amphibian, when the base of operations is water. Special-purpose types of landing gears may be found on experimental aircraft or aircraft which take off or land in an unconventional manner. A skid, or the pedestal-type landing gear on the tail portion of vertical takeoff or landing types of craft, is an example of these special-purpose gears. On aircraft operated at extremely high gross weights, tandem, dual-tandem, or multiple-tandem types of wheel arrangements may be found. Other aircraft designed to operate from soft-surface fields are equipped with this tandem wheel arrangement.

Cessna aircraft use a cantilever single-leaf or tapered tubular spring-type main landing gear which will store the energy in initial impact, thereby producing quite low load factors. Low maintenance, simplicity, and long service life characterize this gear type. Other types are hinged frames or hinged beams which use a shock cord, hydraulic, cylinder, or a coiled or rubber-filled spring to store or absorb the shock. The torsion-bar method of shock absorption has been used successfully on some aircraft.

Cross-wind gears are those in which the wheels are mounted with some degree of castering freedom to allow runway contact when the aircraft is crabbed into the wind.

Aircraft *tires* usually are made of conventional nylon or rayon cord, rubber-filled. Many modern tires on large and small aircraft alike are tubeless and are either the low- or high-pressure type, depending upon the purpose of the aircraft and the space available for storage within the airframe when retracted.

Aircraft *wheel design* is determined by the type of tire desired and the method by which the tire-wheel assembly is attached to the remaining portions of the landing gear.

Static and dynamic impact loads are both utilized in the design of wheel-tire combinations. On supersonic aircraft subject to the effects of high in-flight temperatures as a result of aerodynamic heating, special designs are required.

Brakes used on aircraft are determined by landing speed, thrust, and weight. They are used to assist in steering many types of aircraft. Because of the tremendous heat generated in slowing or stopping an airplane, the brake must be designed for rapid heat dissipation. The most popular type of brake on light aircraft is the single disc-brake block type. In this design

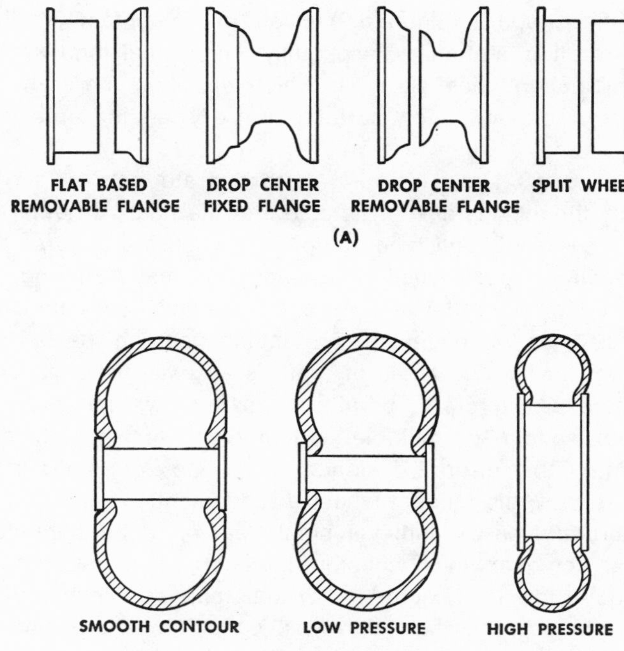

Figure 3.14 Aircraft wheel and tire contours. (A) Wheels; (B) tire contours.

the disc is attached to the wheel by bolts, gear teeth, clips or other devices, and turns with the wheel. Small blocks, usually hydraulically actuated, press on this disc simultaneously from both sides to create the braking friction. As aircraft braking needs increase for different designs, mulitple brake-block assemblies may be added. Segmented rotor brakes have alternately flat rings to which flat discs are attached. These stators and rotors are pressed together to produce the braking action. This type of brake usually is capable of quite rapid heat dissipation. Other types of brakes are the multiple-disc type, which presses discs together to produce friction similar to the principle used in segmented rotor brakes; expander-tube brakes in which an inner tube forces segmented brake blocks against the brake drum to produce friction, and the expanding shoe-type brake in which a shoe is forced against a drum to produce the braking action.

Because of the intense heat developed, brake materials are very important. Brake systems when heated by friction may begin to feel spongy. Although hydraulic fluid pressure is the popular type of actuating force, air, mechanical, and electrical actuation are also used.

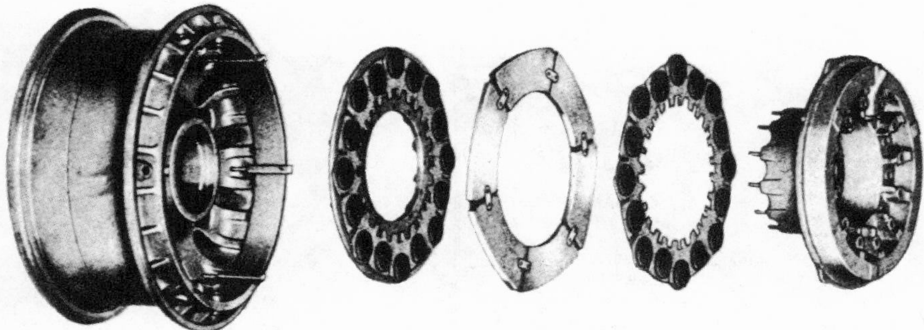

Figure 3.15 Extended view of segmented rotor brake parts. Stators and rotor of a single-rotor brake. Other designs include several rotors with corresponding stators. The segmented rotor allows maximum heat absorption without a tendency to warp. The stators have a lining made of ceramics. Other designs have conventional linings riveted to the stators. *(Courtesy of Bendix Aviation Corp.)*

Aircraft *axles* vary considerably in design. The conventional type for single-wheel installation is similar to the front-wheel spindle axles on automobiles. In the tandem-wheel arrangement, the lower strut axle becomes a trunnion to which is attached the truck upon which the wheels are installed.

SHOCK (OLEO) STRUT

Shock-absorption mechanisms for all larger landing gears are of the air-oil hydraulic type. This type simply dissipates energy by forcing hydraulic fluid through a small orifice. The rate of flow and the length of the stroke determines the efficiency of the shock strut and consequently determines to a large degree the load factor which will be developed when landing. When the aircraft is stationary or taxiing, the weight is supported on a cushion of compressed air inside the upper chamber, above a piston. The pressure in the air chamber can be varied to accommodate varied changes in ground temperature. Oleo strut seals must be kept in good condition; leakage due to contraction is a principal cold-weather problem. On this type of strut, the inner tube must be reasonably free to move inside the outer tube and therefore would be free to turn independently. Consequently, some device must be added to prevent rotation on main or non-steerable landing gears. *Scissors* are used to permit vertical motion only.

The upper trunnion or attachment of the landing-gear strut to the airplane spreads the load out as much as possible to prevent high load concentrations which would require heavy structure or bring about a rather short fatigue life. On wing installations, as shown in Figure 3.17, the

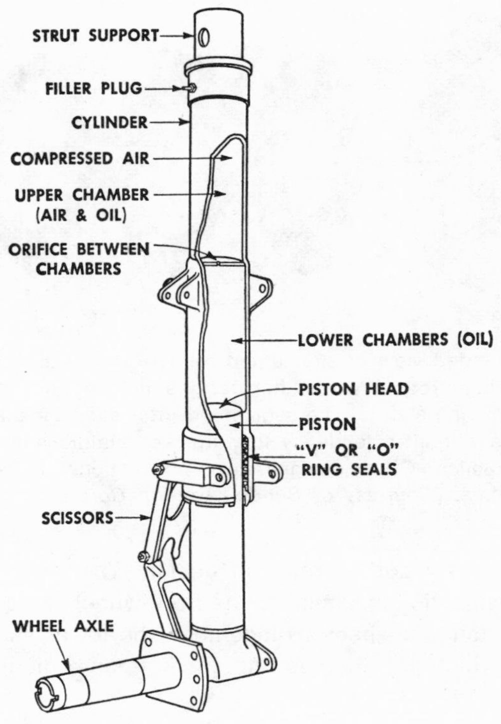

Figure 3.16 Basic landing gear shock (oleo) strut assembly.

trunnion transmits load directly into heavy wing structure installed because of flight loads or for the power plant. This multiple use of aircraft structure increases the weight efficiency of the airplane. Popular trunnion fittings used to day are aluminum, magnesium, or steel forgings. Some aircraft, however, retain the successfully used frame-type weldments.

Most of the design features and the structure of the main landing gear will be applicable to the nose gear of an airplane. Similarities may be noted in Figure 3.17. Brakes are not usually installed on nose gears, and on most aircraft the nose gear carries a much lighter load than the main gear. This is primarily because the main gear is usually located at a position closer to the airplane center of gravity, and normally the nose gear will not make contact until the main gear has suffered the initial impact.

Nose-gear steering is a system which causes the lower strut to rotate within the outer strut or causes the entire strut to rotate in bearings mounted in the nose-gear attachment. Steering systems may be manual, either foot or hand controlled, but usually are hydraulically actuated as in Figure 3.18. Many aircraft utilize positive steering for a limited number of

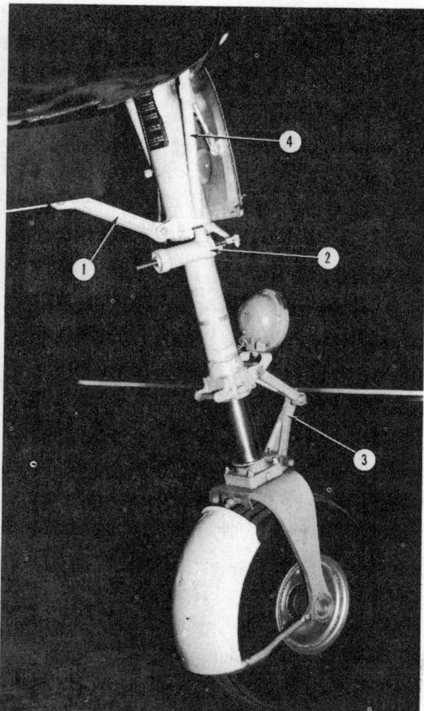

Figure 3.17 Typical tricycle-type landing gear installation on a low-wing airplane. (1) Left, side brace and down lock. (2) Left, drag brace trunnion. (3) Left, retraction link which also acts as down lock. (1) Right, drag brace down lock. (2) Right, shimmy dampener. (3) Right, scissors or torque links. (4) Right, side brace trunnion. This landing gear is retracted by a single electric motor acting through a system of bell cranks and push-pull tubes. *(Courtesy of Cessna Aircraft Co.)*

degrees rotation and then allow free swiveling to enable the aircraft to turn about one main gear. Because of this positive steering and comparatively free swiveling feature, many nose gears would oscillate at some rotational speed of the tire unless equipped with a shimmy damper. The most popular is the hydraulic-type damper. On some craft the power-steering system serves also as the shimmy damper.

RETRACTION SYSTEMS

The performance demanded of modern aircraft requires that the landing gear be retracted in flight to decrease drag. On low-wing aircraft the main landing gear is usually housed within the wing, and the nose gear retracts

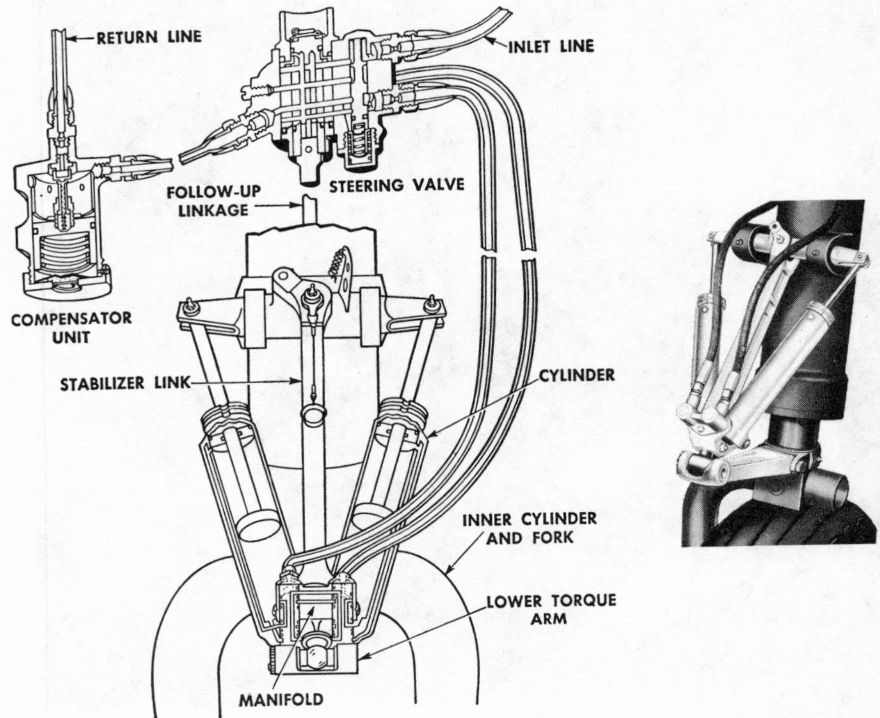

Figure 3.18 Nose-wheel steering mechanism. A schematic diagram of Bendix Torque Link steering, showing the connections to the steering valve, and the compensator which compensates for volumetric changes in the system. The system is in static neutral position with system pressure off. *(Courtesy of Bendix Aviation Corp.)*

into the fuselage forward section. Large, high-performance aircraft—and, in general, most aircraft that cruise faster than approximately 160 kt—are the retractable-geared type.

High-wing aircraft require excessively long gears if mounted on the wing. With longer gears, larger cutouts are required in the structure to permit retraction and extension. As a result, and to eliminate possible weight penalties, the main gear and the nose gear are retracted into the fuselage on most high-wing type airplanes. This has been done successfully on several military aircraft, as well as several amphibian models and on some modern light aircraft. Since many retraction systems require that the gear hinge, it must be fitted with some type of brace to hold the strut stable when down and locked. If so equipped, this brace serves the dual function of a brace when down and a primary retraction system link during the retraction cycle. Many times, the down lock is designed into the brace in the form of a "break over center" device or other mechanical, electrical, or hydraulic lock.

Power source for retraction systems may be hydraulic, electrical, electromechanical, air, or manual. The hydraulic system appears to be the most popular, although many systems have electrical motors for each gear or an electromechanical system to operate more than one gear by utilizing push-pull tubes with a bell crank or torque-tube system.

To realize fully the objective for which a gear is retracted, it is desirable that the opening for the gear in the structure must be closed smoothly and tightly once the gear is retracted. To accomplish this, most retraction systems are equipped with doors that open to allow the gear to enter or exit and remain closed when the gear is up or down and locked. Some designers have eliminated the doors in the interest of saving weight and cost and have successfully used elastomer seals in contact with the retracted tire.

In a few cases some performance loss has been accepted and the wheels simply retracted into the opening. Having the openings closed while the gear is down is advantageous because the tires will not throw foreign matter such as mud, oil, water, or ice into the wheel well during ground movement. The interior of the wheel well should be fairly smooth and reasonably well sealed off to prevent these same objects from becoming lodged on the internal structure should the wheel be spinning when it enters.

Empennages

The conventional arrangement of the empennage group (tail group) is an extreme aft location of a single *vertical fin* and *rudder, stabilizer* and *elevator.* There are many variations in this arrangement; two surfaces mounted in a "V," two or more vertical fins mounted on the horizontal tail, and the stabilizer mounted at various heights on the fin are several examples. Another concept, "flying tails," will be discussed with controls. There may not be a well-defined empennage group, as in delta-wing aircraft where the wing trailing edge must have features to simulate a horizontal tail.

Since the vertical tail must lift to either side and the horizontal tail must lift either up or down with equal efficiency, the airfoils are made symmetrical (upper and lower contours are the same). The control surfaces attached to the empennage are merely large-chord, plain flaps, usually amounting to about half the chord of the airfoil. Some of the more important considerations in determining empennage design are whether the airplane is single or multiengine, the amount of fore-and-aft c.g. and trim range desired, and various stability and recovery requirements.

Structurally, empennages resemble wings, but are normally much less complex and less integrated. They are usually full cantilever, metal-covered airfoils, but some are fabric over a tubular structure with wire strut bracing. Spars are quite often nothing more than formed sheet metal channels. In light, business aircraft the front spars may be formed by the skin. The rear spars are much heavier than the front spars—opposite the general arrangement used in wings—because the larger elevator and rudder flaps cause the center of pressure to be far aft on the airfoil, requiring strength farther aft. Also, the flap loads are quite high and create high attachment loads, and buffeting loads create a need for central rigidity.

Control Surfaces and Systems

Control surfaces are constructed much the same as wings except that they generally have no airfoil shape of their own. Construction of these is far simpler than wings. There is a trend in recent years toward the use of "slab" controls or "flying tails," in which the entire surface moves instead of just a flap. Military airplanes have used this system for some time, but it has only recently been used in light airplanes. These may have two forms, the *flying tail* in which the entire surface is rotated by the pilot, or the *rotating stabilizer* in which the pilot moves a large trailing-edge tab which, in turn, rotates the stabilizer. There are important ad-

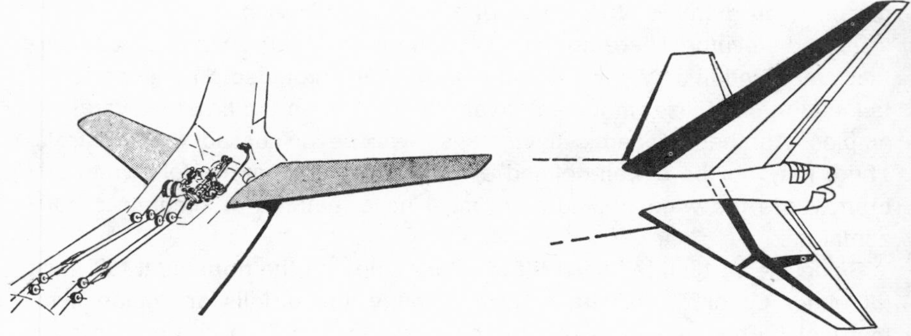

Figure 3.19 A flying tail. *(Courtesy of U.S. Air Force.)*

Figure 3.20 A rotating stabilizer. *(Courtesy of U.S. Air Force.)*

Figure 3.21 T-33 dive recovery flaps. These are located at the head of the wheel wells on the bottom of the fuselage. On other jet aircraft they may be found on either side of the fuselage between wing and empennage. *(U.S. Air Force photograph.)*

vantages to these movable surfaces—good control over stick forces and minimum drag profiles.

Dive flaps or speed brakes must be designed and located so that they will provide high drag but will not appreciably affect the trim of the airplane. As a rule, dive flaps are located on the bottom centerline or on the sides of the fuselage, or on the wing upper surface.

CONTROL SYSTEMS

The various systems that operate the control surfaces of an airplane have considerable influence on the dynamic characteristics of the control surfaces and on the structure of the airplane. Control surfaces are usually connected through a system of bell cranks, pulleys, levers, and cables to the pilot's controls or to the servomechanism used to operate the control. The method of actuating controls is widely varied among airplane designs. Light business and utility airplanes use pilot effort for operation of the controls, and conventional cable arrangements make up the connecting system. Automatic pilots may also be connected into the system. Very large airplanes usually have servomechanisms to amplify the pilot's control forces, or in some cases, the pilot may operate a tab which actuates the control surface. When auxiliary controls such as tabs are installed, it is generally required that they be driven by a system separate from that used to drive the primary control; in case of failure in the primary-control system, the airplane must be maneuverable and controllable by the tab. The tab would be operated in its normal direction when the primary control is free, but in a direction opposite of normal if the primary control is jammed.

The various components of a control system are selected on the basis of the load that they will be expected to withstand in operation. Also, cables must be properly routed and cleared of the structure to prevent their becoming frayed or otherwise damaged. They are always installed with some degree of preload to prevent excessive looseness, to eliminate a portion of cable stretch, and to aid in keeping them on the pulleys. Control-system loads may become quite high and impose severe local loads on the airframe at attachments of bell cranks and pulleys; as a consequence, they affect the airframe design.

Good control system design avoids excessive deflection to reduce control-surface travel and still provide effective control force. All controls, since they are connected by means of elastic systems, have some particular *spring rate* or degree of sponginess. This characteristic could in part determine the flutter speed of the airplane. Preload, or rigging tension, has an influence on this system spring rate and should be checked periodically to see that it is up to the manufacturer's specification. Free play at the surface is another such influence and should be checked for excessive looseness periodically.

Several of the smaller airplanes have interconnecting systems to simplify control of the airplane. Most of these designs have spring-loaded interconnect systems so that the pilot may override the system to execute such maneuvers as slips and flat turns. Quite often, airplanes are equipped with bungee springs or control interconnects to meet certain stability requirements.

Provisions for Power Plants

As noted in other portions of this chapter, the power plant may be located in many different places on or in the airframe. Each location will dictate some particular design feature. Structurally, the power plant is the source of vibration, heat, possible fire, concentrated mass, and sometimes undesirable thrust or drag forces. It necessitates many controls which in turn require cutouts in structure as do fuel lines, oil lines, and electrical lines. All engines require some type of mounting through which its mass, thrust, torque, and vibration are transmitted to the rest of the airplane or are absorbed.

Various types of mounts have been designed. Among them are the welded-tube truss assembly (usually steel) which may be either the *bed* or *ring* type. The sheet-metal built-up type is quite popular on aircraft today and will usually be equipped with some type of steel leg for the final engine-to-mount attachment. With the advent of jet-type power plants where propeller clearance is no longer a problem, the engines on many models of multiengine craft have been suspended below the wings (Figure 3.9) or attached to the fuselage in pods (Figure 1.13). These pods simplify the structural problem somewhat by removing the engine from other primary structure, and offer many other safety advantages as well. The structural problem of pod suspension is largely one of pylon design with well-defined load paths and more straightforward attachment.

Large forgings have been used successfully as mounts for some engine installations. Internal-wing installations have been and are used on many jet-type aircraft. Usually these installations utilize the inboard portion of the wing-to-fuselage attachment area for their location. When this type of installation is used, or if the engine is mounted inside the fuselage, the immediate area around the engine will be covered with stainless steel, aluminized iron, or other materials possessing greater flame- and heat-resistant capabilities than aluminum alloy alone. All openings in this firewall will be sealed to prevent flames from entering adjacent structure or compartments. When engines are located in the proximity of structure that would be affected by temperatures of the engine itself or of its exhaust, the structure must be insulated. Air spaces and insulation materials such as asbestos are common methods in use today.

Piston engines particularly are the source of undesirable, fatiguing vibration in airframes which must be reduced or isolated. Vibration dampers are located at points of engine-to-mount or mount-to-adjacent-structure attachment. When the isolaters are located in the engine-to-mount attachment, much of the vibration is not transmitted into the mount, which is spared this damaging fatigue. Because of the confined space, it is sometimes more convenient to attach the engine to the mount rigidly and attempt to isolate vibration at the mount-to-airframe attachment. Although piston-engine vibration has been considered high-frequency, it is low compared to the frequencies of turbine-powered aircraft—which, fortunately, are usually accompanied by smaller amplitudes. Efficient design must accommodate these high frequencies, sufficiently isolate them, or control the stresses caused by them. The stresses must be below the endurance limit of the material being strained by them, because the frequency developed by power plants creates a tremendous number of cycles in relatively short periods of operational life.

Joints

The large variety of joints found in a structure as complex as an airplane requires many different fastening jobs, each needing some particular type of fastener. The usual joining devices are: bolts, rivets, screws, rivnuts, cams, pins, spot welds, fusion welds, solder, braze, and adhesive bonds. Figure 3.22 shows most of the types of joints, classified generally according to the type of loading to be applied. Bolts are good in either tension or shear and are generally necessary where close tolerance must be held or where moving parts are involved.

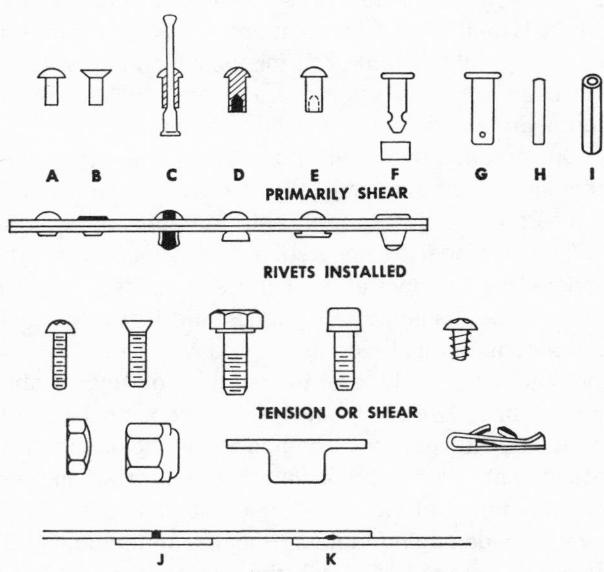

Figure 3.22 Typical aircraft fasteners. *A* and *B* are solid-shank rivets, *C, D,* and *E* are typical blind rivets. *F* is a steel rivet with an aluminum collar. *G* is a steel pin-free fit. *H* and *I* are drive-fit steel pins. *J* is a typical metal-bond joint. *K* is a typical spot-weld joint.

Rivets are very common and are used where shear is the primary load. They are generally much cheaper to buy and install than any other fastener. The ordinary rivet has a button head and solid shank and is made of aluminum alloy. The shank is inserted in a hole and the rivet is driven from the manufactured-head side, swelled into the hole by a bucking bar held at the end of the shank, and upset on the butt end to form another head called the shop head. If the back side of the work is inaccessible to form the shop head on the rivet, one of the several types of blind rivets shown in Figure 3.22 is used.

Screws are used in much the same applications as bolts, but where loads are lower. Two types of screws commonly used are the machine screw and the sheet-metal screw. A machine screw has standard SAE threads and must be installed in a threaded hole or with a nut. Sheet-metal screws, called P-K screws, are tapered, self-tapping screws and may be installed directly in an undersize hole. Generally they are used in full-sized holes with sheet-metal nuts called Tinnerman nuts. They are mostly used where loads are relatively low or when frequent removal is necessary. In all joints secured by bolts or screws, precautions are taken to insure that the fastener will not vibrate or work loose in service. Lock washers, safety wire, cotter pins, fiber lock nuts, expanding nuts, elliptical nuts, tabs, and pal nuts are some of the devices for keeping the fastener at its original setting.

Rivnuts, a development of the B. F. Goodrich Company, may be described as a combination blind rivet and nut plate. They hold two sheets of metal tightly together and also provide a receptacle for a screw so that another removable plate may be installed. They were originally developed for attaching de-icer boots to wings, but are now employed in many other areas, such as attachments of fairings and fillets. There are other types of blind fasteners that act in the same manner as rivnuts, such as the Lok-Screw.

Among the *special rivets* are tubular-steel rivets, used in firewalls because of their superior heat resistance. The high-shear rivets made under the trade names of Hi-Shear and Huck-Bolt have steel shanks with aluminum-alloy collars on the shop head side. The Hi-Shear type is shown in Figure 3.22. These rivets are installed where shear loads are very high, but never where appreciable tension loads are apt to occur. They are less expensive than bolts, both to purchase and to install if proper equipment is available. They are made of carbon steel, heat-treated to 125,000 psi ultimate tensile strength. One disadvantage of high-shear rivets is that they do not swell to fill the hole when driven and must therefore be installed in fairly close-tolerance holes.

Pins are used only in shear applications and are popular because of their low cost, tight fit, and ease of installation. One popular type of pin fastener is the roll pin—a hollow steel pin with a longitudinal gap, driven into a slightly undersize hole. On installation, the longitudinal gap allows the pin walls to spring inward, and the built-in strain then keeps the pin tight in the hole. Shear is the only application where such pins can be used, but they are excellent load-carrying members and are easy and inexpensive to use.

The *cam lock, air lock,* and *Dzus fasteners* are used extensively on cowling or other members which may require frequent removal. A sketch of these types of fasteners is shown in Figure 3.23. This fastener consists of a wire attached to the stationary panel and a latching screw attached to the movable panel. The latching screw has either a wing nut or a slot head, and the other end of the shank is formed into a cam which engages the wire and latches with a quarter turn of the screw. The latching screw is mounted to the movable panel with a grommet, which allows the latch freedom to move while keeping it in position. There are many other types of mechanical fasteners, most of which are similar to those mentioned above.

Welding is, perhaps, the best known of the many nonmechanical fastening methods. Steel parts are particularly well suited for this type of joining. Welding of most steels may be easily accomplished, but other metals usually require special techniques. Aluminum welding is an example. First, aluminum oxidizes easily in the presence of high heat, so that a shield or stream of inert gas may be required to drive off the oxygen. Second, aluminum conducts heat so efficiently that it is dissipated away from the joint out into the part where the high heat could warp the part or remove its hardness.

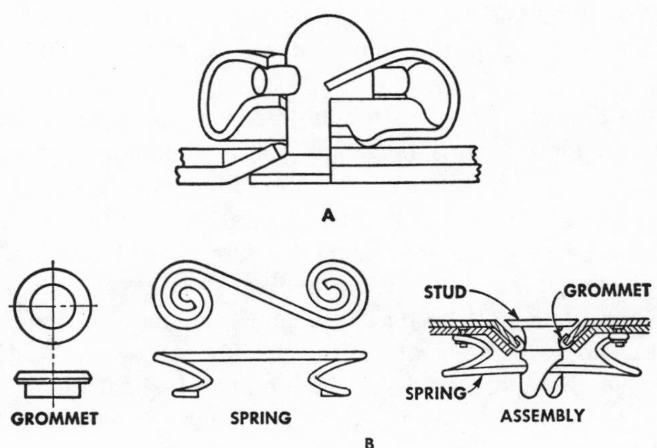

Figure 3.23 Special quick detachable fasteners. (A) Air lock fastener; (B) Dzus grommet and spring.

Brazing and *soldering* are not fusion joints, but rather obtain their strength from cohesion between the weld material and the parent metal. Brazing may be done with silver, coppers, or bronze. Soldering may be done with silver or with the usual solder material made of an alloy of lead and zinc. Soldering and brazing are done with either hot irons or open flame, whereas fusion welding may be performed by flame or an electric arc. Many aircraft fusion welds are made with flame heat.

Spotwelding is a form of sheet-metal welding quite extensively used in aircraft structures. In resistance spotwelding, two or more sheets are joined at a spot by the simultaneous application of electrode pressure and heat from an electric current, which together fuse the sheets at the local spot. Advantages of this type of weld are its low cost and smooth surface appearance. Spotwelds withstand shear load and a lower degree of tension. Since they have a low resistance to peeling loads, rivets are generally installed at each end of a row of spotwelds. If the members must be separated for replacement of parts, the spots may be drilled out as if they were rivets and the parts replaced, using rivets instead of spotwelds. Other methods are ultrasonic and fusion spotwelding, for joining of thin and thick materials, respectively.

Adhesive bonding is a newer method of joining materials, rapidly gaining popularity in aircraft structural design. Bonding materials have been developed which offer a high degree of strength and reliability. There are three general classes of adhesive resins presently in use—*thermoplastic, thermosetting,* and *elastomeric.* Thermoplastic resins soften with the application of heat and must be maintained under pressure to effect a bond. They are low in cost, but also fairly low in strength. Thermosetting resins, when heated, develop full strength and harden. This type usually requires both heat and pressure to effect a bond, which is stronger than that made with the other resin types. Some of the resins in this group are *catalyst-setting,* that is, a catalyst is added to the resin to accelerate curing. Elastomeric resins are polymeric rubber compounds used where a high degree of flexibility is required.

For metal bonding, as in spotwelding, the surfaces must be very clean and free of oxide, grease, and oil. Special inspection techniques may be required to insure safety, and precision equipment is often necessary to obtain structural bonds. Bonded joints, which have very good shear strength, are used in applications where this feature is important. Many of the resins are also good in pure tension. Two types of loads to be avoided are cleavage and peeling. (Opening a book, for example, exerts a cleavage load on the page; the edge stress is quite high.)

Bonded metal joints have many important advantages. First, the stress is distributed over a wide area so that little concentration develops. Second, members are kept free of holes which raise stresses or create concentrations. Third, large panels may be secured by a single bond joint, thus eliminating hundreds of small fasteners. Fourth, the resin between the sheets acts as an insulator to prevent corrosive electrolytic action when electrically dissimilar metals are joined. Fifth, the exterior surface is quite smooth, giving a high degree of aerodynamic efficiency.

Sandwich construction is a special application where metal bonding is very desirable. When resin is used to bond the outer sheets to the core material, it will flow down on the core to form a fillet at each joint. The formation of the fillet yields more contact area for a greater bond strength.

Metal bonding has been discussed more than the other types of joints for two reasons—because the conventional methods are already fairly well understood, and because bonding is rapidly growing in popularity with airframe designers. This type of fastening will appear in greater quantities in the future. With the advent of metal bonding and other new innovations in joint design yet to come, airframes will become increasingly safer, stronger, lighter, and more durable. High-frequency vibrations and fatigue loading require joint designs that distribute load in a favorable manner.

Resins will, undoubtedly, be increased in strength, and fabrication practices will be simplified in the future so that bonding will be available at low cost to every aircraft user.

Materials

In order to obtain a high strength-to-weight ratio and a high degree of safety, materials used in aircraft structures usually are of a higher quality than those found in other types of structures. Some of the materials and alloys commonly found in aircraft structures are steel, aluminum, magnesium, stainless steel, bronze, brass, plastics, wood, and glass fiber. Titanium is being used in increasing quantities, while boron and graphite filament composite structure is a new promising material.

Aircraft structural materials are selected for their particular properties, which vary considerably for each material. A few of the properties that influence selection are: strength, weight, rigidity, hardenability, corrosion resistance, ductility, toughness, resistance to heat (or cold), notch sensitivity, and resistance to abrasion and wear. Certain of these characteristics are very important in aircraft structural design. For example, a ductile material is much more desirable than a brittle material because failure in a brittle material is sudden and complete, whereas in a ductile material the part yields long before the ultimate load is reached and gives warning of the approaching failure. The deformed part could thus be discovered during an inspection of the airplane and replaced. The job assigned to the part in the airplane structure determines which property is most important. Tough material would be used where shock and vibration are encountered; heat-resisting material would be used for firewalls, and a hardenable material would be used where extremely high strength is necessary.

Materials are formed into useful shapes primarily by cutting, bending, forging, extruding, casting, welding, stretching, grinding, machining, and rolling. For making aircraft structural members, materials are usually chosen that will give the greatest strength-to-weight ratio. For this purpose, alloys of two or more metals are used. An alloy is selected which will respond to some of the known methods of hardening by heat treatment. As the hardness of the material is increased, its strength is also increased. Steel responds best of all known alloys to this process. Because of this excellent response, it is possible to strengthen steel so that for a given job it can be "lighter" than aluminum—even though it weighs almost three times as much in equal-volume units—by using very thin-gage stock.

Steel, aluminum, and *magnesium* are the most common aircraft structural materials because they each possess a large number of the desirable properties previously listed. *Wood* is still used in some light aircraft, although the trend is away from wood in favor of metal. Wood is organic and therefore subject to decay in some environments. *Glass fiber, glass cloth,* and *cloth,* when impregnated with a thermosetting resin, are used in wing tips, fillets, ducts, radomes, spinners, and in many other ways—particularly where loads are light or where contours make metal forming difficult. Acrylic *plastics* are made under the trade names of Lucite and Plexiglas. These are used in making canopies, windows, and windshields. They have a fairly high strength, are readily formable when heated, and exhibit excellent optical qualities. The urethanes or foaming plastics have recently come into use in the structure of light airplanes. The plastic is foamed in place between two sheet-metal panels, forming a sandwich structure. Panels made in this way are light in weight, very rigid, strong, and reasonably inexpensive. *Stainless steels* are often used in structure because of their high strength, corrosion resistance, and superior resistance to heat. Although stainless steel is heavy (almost three times an equal volume of aluminum), it is coming into prominence as an aircraft structural material. The weight may not be considered excessive since most types of stainless can easily be made two to three times as strong as aluminum. Many military airplanes have stainless-steel skins and bulkheads. Stainless steel is also used quite extensively in sandwich honeycomb construction.

Paper is a rather unusual aircraft structural material, but is sometimes used as a core material in a sandwich of two sheet-metal panels, to form floorboards or shelves. The floorboards absorb a large amount of high-frequency noise, as well as providing a strong, rigid support for structural furnishings or cargo.

Aluminum alloys are hardenable, quite ductile, and fairly corrosion-resistant. Generally, a thin plate of pure aluminum is rolled onto the outside of the alloy sheet to provide corrosion protection. This "cladding" normally amounts to about 5% of the total thickness of the sheet. Magnesium is one of the lightest of structural metals, but is not as strong as aluminum in equal volume. Magnesium has roughly the same strength-to-weight ratio as aluminum, but is only two-thirds as rigid. It also must be protected from corrosive atmosphere and flames. *Bronze* and *brass* have rather limited use in the actual structure of an airplane. These materials appear mainly in bearings, fasteners, cable turnbuckles, and springs.

Recently, several new materials have appeared in aircraft structures; some to perform special duties not required before, and others as a result of advancing technology in the field. An example of the first category is the new *ceramics;* also called "cemets," "ceramels," "intermetallics," and "refractory" metals. In general, these materials are a combination of ceramics and metals which are combined in a sintering process using powdered materials. The ceramics impart a high heat resistance, and the metals furnish strength. They were developed for special uses where high strength at high temperatures was the goal.

Titanium is being used in increasing quantities, particularly in supersonic aircraft, due to its high strength, light weight, and retentiveness of strength at high temperatures. *Lithium* is proving valuable when alloyed with aluminum by increasing the modulus of elasticity, yet reducing weight when compared to some alloying elements.

Boron and graphite filaments in *composite* structures are moving from the laboratory into practical use and show promise of high strength with light weight. At the present time, however, the cost is prohibitive for general application.

Almost every time aircraft structural materials are mentioned, the question of its resistance to *corrosion* arises. There is good reason for this because, for an airplane to possess utility and have a long, safe life, it must be resistant to ordinary corrosive atmospheres. An airplane, once delivered to the customer, may be flown to any spot on earth; since the parts of the airplane are exposed to the local conditions, they must be protected. Each material has its own needs in this respect. In general, organic materials such as wood or fabric must be protected from moisture and fungus. Metals may be attacked by marine atmosphere and especially by urine, oxygen, chemicals, industrial atmospheres, exhaust gases, and gun smoke. Steels generally tend to rust and must be protected by paint or a plating of a corrosion-resistant metal such as cadmium. Pure aluminum is quite resistant to most types of corrosion, but aircraft structural members made of aluminum alloys will tend to corrode. The plating of pure aluminum on these alloys to impart corrosion resistance has already been mentioned. This "Alclad" material, if heat-treated several times, will lose its resistance to corrosion because the pure aluminum layer will eventually alloy with the core material when subjected to the high heat-treating temperatures. Zinc chromate primer is often applied for corrosion resistance on aluminum and magnesium. Aluminum alloys may also be protected by a process known as anodizing, in which a thin layer of oxide is caused to form on the surface.

Aluminum-alloy corrosion will usually appear in one of the following three ways: First (and least serious) is surface pitting, which does not seriously weaken the material and is easily discovered. Figure 3.24 shows this type of corrosive action. The second type of corrosion is galvanic action, which occurs at a joint between two or more electrically dissimilar metals such as two different alloys of aluminum. Every metal has an electrical potential; if two metals having differing electrical potentials are joined, a partial electric cell is formed. When moisture and acids from the atmosphere enter the joint, the cell is complete and current will flow. This cell eats away the metal and may seriously weaken the joint. This is an insidious type of corrosion since it attacks vital parts and is not readily detectable. A third type of aluminum corrosion is intergranular corrosion, in which the grain boundaries of the core material are attacked. This type of corrosion occurs only when heat-treated aluminum alloy is improperly quenched. As the boundaries are destroyed, the grains lose their bond to each other, and the part loses its strength. Intergranular corrosion is dangerous because of the seriousness of the damage and the difficulty of locating it.

The airplane manufacturer and material supplier are constantly guarding against the possibility of most corrosion and usually help the customer in solving a particular corrosion problem when an unusual use is planned

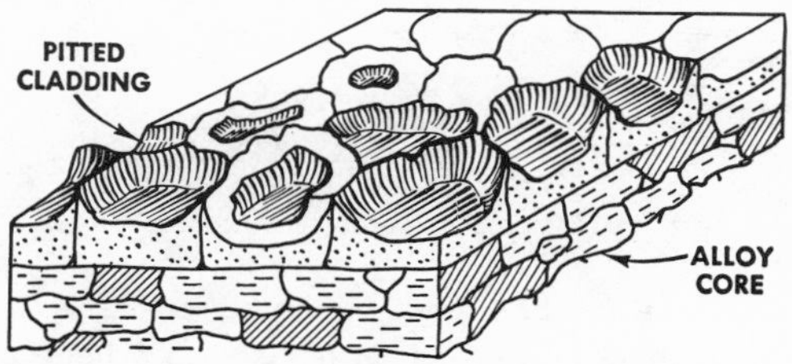

Figure 3.24 Typical surface appearance of superficially corroded unpainted aluminum sheet.

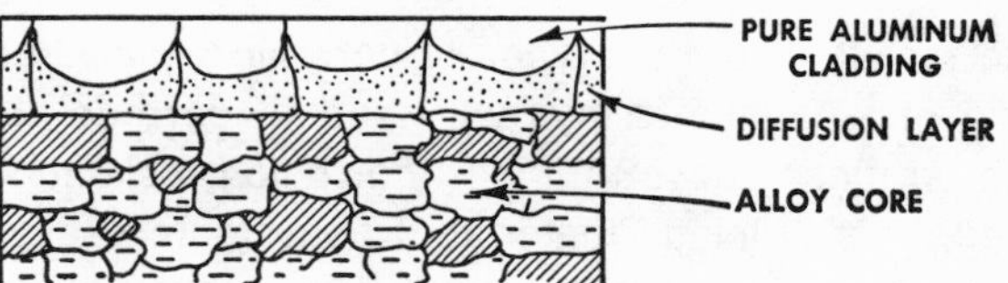

Figure 3.25 Cross-sectional diagram of Alclad.

for the airplane. Corrosion protection, though vital to the airplane, is usually difficult and expensive, so the corrosion properties of a particular material frequently command a major role in the selection of the material.

Plastic components are subject to damage from temperature—either high or low—and from the action of certain solvents. The damage will usually be a progressive embrittlement with subsequent checking at the surface called *crazing.* The transparent plastics may become clouded and lose much of their optical efficiency unless protected from heat and dust.

The future holds much hope in the field of aircraft structural materials. New metals are being applied to structural problems, either alone or alloyed with other metals; new alloys are being discovered, new processes are being developed, and new methods of arranging structural parts are being designed.

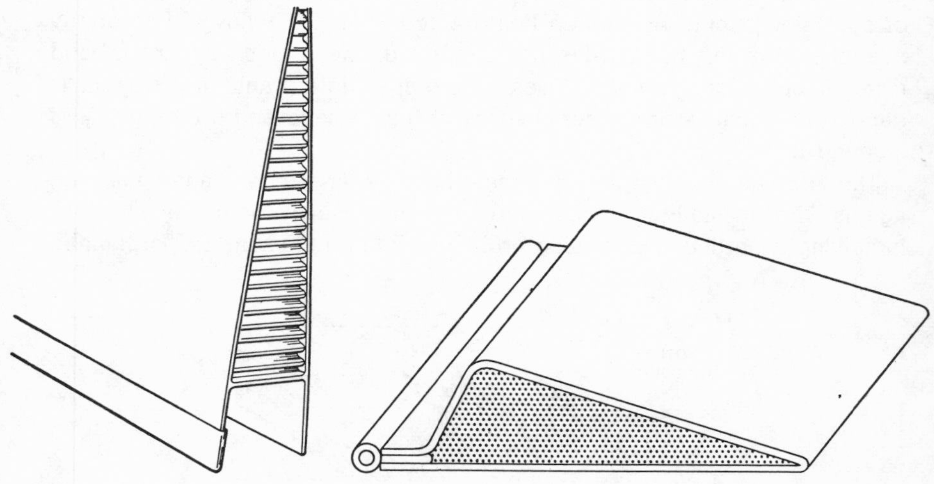

Figure 3.26 Core construction. The sketch at left shows a honeycomb core structure of the stabilizer on the Air Force F-101. The sketch at right shows a plastic-foam core used in some control surfaces.

Strength levels obtained from conventional materials today seem quite ordinary, but 20 years ago they would have been the dream of metallurgists. Conversely, the metallurgist's dream of today will be a reality to designers 20 years hence. At present, aircraft structural steels are being produced which have an ultimate tensile strength of about 350,000 psi. (Structural steel used in buildings has an ultimate tensile strength of about 55,000 psi.) This indeed is a very high strength—but metallurgical technology is already predicting ultimate tensile strengths of 1,000,000 psi in the near future. Theoretically, only 1/100 to 1/1000 of the perfect strength of metals is being used at present; undoubtedly the million-psi level will be achieved. Composite structure, that is, multi-materials, show much promise in permitting the designer to optimize the structure and obtain a better balance of strength to weight. During fabrication, the structure can be assembled by laminations of glass cloth, boron or graphite filaments, epoxy, and similar materials, with both uni- and multidirectional fibers. Thus, the designer can approach ideal structural requirements based on the stress paths in the part or assembly. The stress paths may also be controlled. The use of these materials will increase in the future and result in reducing their cost. Technology in aircraft structural materials has a long, difficult development process ahead, but gains are being made

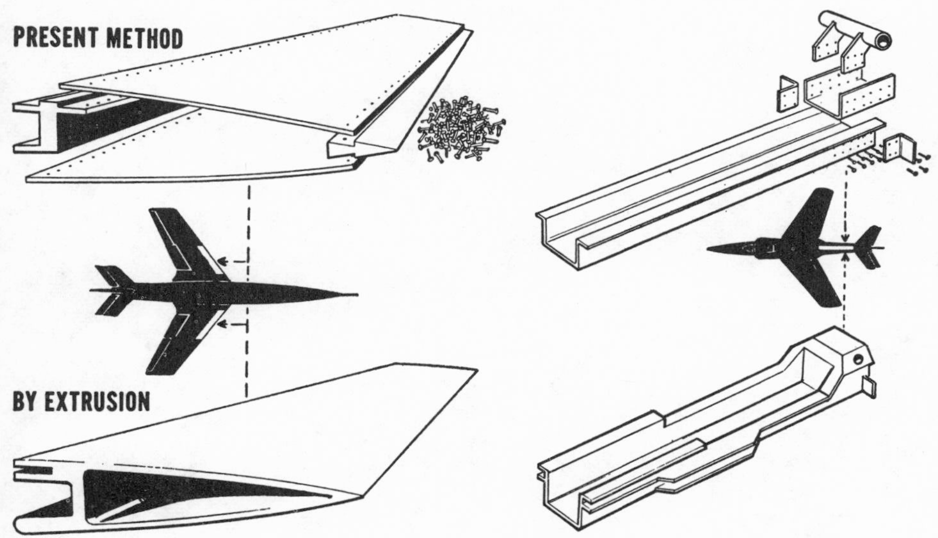

Figure 3.27 Extrusions in airframe fabrication. One-piece aluminum alloy extrusions replace units made by conventional bits-and-pieces build-up. *Left:* Old and new wing leading edges. *Right:* Old and new longerons.

at a gratifying rate. The benefits of these developments are passed on to today's airmen with very little time lag.

"MURPHY'S LAW"
governing aircraft design

1. If it can fail, it will.
2. If it can be hooked up backwards, someone will do it that way.
3. All failures occur at the worst possible point in time and space.

4

Propulsion*

Early desires of man to fly were thwarted for lack of a suitable means of propulsion. The oldest well-authenticated sketches of heavier-than-air flying are those of machines which were designed by Leonardo da Vinci, who conceived of three different flying machines in the fifteenth century. His devices, like most earlier flight ideas, called for human muscles to provide the motive power. It is known now that such plans were doomed to failure since man as an engine is far too weak (for his weight) to sustain dynamic flight. (Dynamic flight requires motive power to stay aloft and to counteract gravitational forces as compared with lighter-than-air devices which float in the air mass as a submarine floats in water.) After Da Vinci, four centuries passed before the Wright brothers developed an engine sufficiently light which could power an airplane built from their advanced aerodynamic theories on propellers and airfoils. Thus in 1903 man succeeded in dynamic flight. In fairness, it should be recognized that dynamic flight was demonstrated successfully by Samuel

*Revised by Charles S. Tompkins, the Boeing Company.

Langley, who launched an *unmanned* model in 1896 which flew half a mile.

During these four centuries many efforts were made to produce engines light enough for dynamic flight. Stringfellow is credited with developing engines of sufficient lightness to support a properly designed dynamic flying machine and exhibited models in London in 1842. Unfortunately, the comprehension of aerodynamic principles had not progressed far enough to permit the trial of his engines in an airplane. By 1875 the lightest engines made weighed over 80 lb per hp. By comparison, the engine designed and built by the Wright brothers for their first flight weighed only 13 lb per hp and developed 12 hp.

Propulsive means were used with limited success in man-carrying balloons long before the first success in dynamic flight. In 1784 a balloon was rowed by a crew of six oarsmen around a closed course of over a mile in diameter in 7 hr. The first dirigible (1852) was powered by a 3-hp steam engine weighing 330 lb. This engine turned a three-bladed propeller, 11 ft in diameter, and made possible the first demonstration of some control over direction of flight.

A 9-hp electric motor weighing 25 lb per hp enabled the airship "La France" in 1884 to demonstrate considerable capacity in powered flight.

Following the success of the Wright brothers in developing the first true airplane power plant, engine development progressed rapidly. The Gnome "monosoupape" air-cooled engine of World War I fame was developed in France in 1909. This engine was unique in that the crankcase and cylinders rotated with the propeller about the stationary crankshaft. Good cylinder cooling was obtained by this arrangement, but engine lubrication was a difficult problem. Later in the war, this engine was producing 125 hp at 900 rpm. Major developments by British and American designers of this period were in liquid-cooled engines. Two famous engines of this type were the 8-cylinder LX 105 which produced 90 hp and the 12-cylinder Liberty engine which developed 400 hp. The latter engine was used in a number of different Allied combat airplanes during the latter part of the war and for several years thereafter.

The 8-cylinder liquid-cooled Hispano-Suiza also powered many World War I airplanes and was the first to incorporate cast aluminum-alloy cylinder blocks with steel liners.

Advancements in aircraft propulsion diminished considerably for a number of years following the close of World War I. However, in the 1930s the development of the controllable-pitch propeller was a tremendous advance and opened many new possibilities for airplanes of greater weight and speed. The next milestone, of course, was the perfection of the gas-turbine (jet) engine into a useful airplane power plant.

By the end of World War II reciprocating engines were producing as much as 3500 hp and weighed less than 1 lb per hp. This was the peak of development for large engines of this type. They could no longer compete with the gas-turbine engine which offered far more power output for each pound of installed weight. Present-day designers are already looking beyond the gas-turbine engine to nuclear power plants which appear to offer untold possibilities.

Theory of Propulsion

A dynamic flying machine must be set in motion by a force called thrust, provided by a propeller, the forward component of the lifting force of rotating helicopter wings, the thrust of gas-turbine engine exhaust, or the thrust of rocket engine exhaust. Gliders and sailplanes are originally set in motion from the thrust provided by a launching or towing device. Continued flight is maintained by descending in rising air currents.

With an airplane, the thrust force must be equal to total airplane drag to maintain level flight at any given speed or altitude. Since airplane drag increases with speed, greater thrust is required for any increase in speed. Thrust force must also be greater than total drag when the airplane is accelerating, as at takeoff, or when the airplane is climbing. Generally, an airplane has reached its maximum speed or altitude when all available thrust is being utilized. However, in many current high-altitude jet airplanes, the amount of thrust available to meet takeoff acceleration and high-altitude requirement is somewhat greater than that required to obtain maximum permissible speeds at lower altitudes because of airframe structural limitations.

In the case of rocket-powered missiles, thrust is utilized in a somewhat different manner. A large thrust force is used for a short initial period to gain a very high speed. After the rocket motor has depleted its fuel, the missile continues on its trajectory by means of the energy imparted to it by the high initial thrust. Once outside the earth's atmosphere, space missiles and satellites will continue in motion indefinitely since there are no friction forces to absorb their energy, until pulled back again by the earth's gravitational field, or "captured" by another heavenly body.

Propellers

The function of a propeller is the conversion of engine shaft torque (turning force) into thrust. In the early days of propeller design, it was thought that thrust was obtained by the rear face of the propeller blade pushing against the air. Later it was learned that propeller blades should be considered as small, rotating airplane wings with the shape of the airfoil being of primary importance. Therefore the upper surface of the airfoil, or the front rather than the back of the propeller blade, should be given primary design consideration.

Propellers may be installed in two different ways. In the "tractor" installation, the propeller is mounted forward of the wing. The tractor propeller "pulls" the airplane through the air and the thrust bearings in the engine are designed for thrust loads in this direction. Nearly all propeller-driven airplanes are designed for tractor-type installations because of the unrestricted air inflow to the propeller. As the terminology implies, "pusher"-type propellers are installed aft of the wing and push the airplane forward. The first Wright airplane and the Cessna Skymaster (Figure 1.22) are examples of the pusher type.

PROPELLER THEORY

Two theories are recognized on the operation of a propeller in converting engine shaft torque to thrust. The momentum theory, developed by R. E. Froude, deals with the energy change to the air mass acted upon by the propeller. The other, and the most commonly used in determining propeller performance, is the blade-element theory developed in practical form by Stefan Drzewiecki.

In the Drzewiecki theory, each propeller blade is considered as being composed of an infinite number of airfoils (called blade elements) joined end to end, forming a shape similar to a twisted airplane wing. Because the propeller is rotating about the engine shaft centerline, each blade element will be rotating in a different arc. The greater the distance of each blade element from the shaft centerline, the larger is the arc it circumscribes and thus the greater the distance it must travel for each revolution. Each blade element, therefore, is moving at a different velocity which is greatest at the blade tip. If each blade element is to operate at maximum L/D, the angle of attack α for each element must diminish as the distance from the hub increases. This gradual decrease in blade angle gives the propeller blade its twisted appearance.

Since the circumference of a circle is $2\pi r$, each blade element rotates through a circular path of $2\pi r$ during each revolution, with r the distance from the center of rotation, expressed in feet. If the propeller is turning at n revolutions per sec, the linear velocity of each blade element in its individual plane of rotation must be $2\pi rn$ fps. In flight, the propeller is moving forward at the same speed as the airplane, as well as rotating about its own axis. This forward velocity must also be expressed in feet

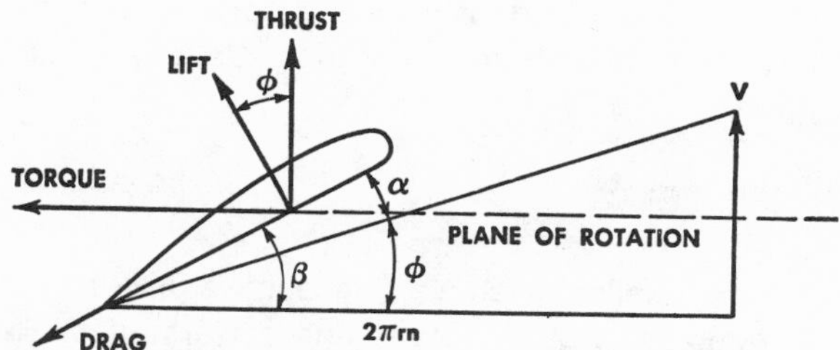

Figure 4.1 Vector diagram of propeller blade element.

per second to keep all terms of the equation in common dimensions. (The conversion is: mph × 1.467 = feet per second, fps; where 1.467 = 5280 ft per mi/3600 sec per hr.) Thus, the total velocity of each blade element is the resultant of the two component velocities, the forward velocity V and the rotational velocity $2\pi rn$, or $2\pi rnV$. This may be shown graphically, as in Figure 4.1, for each blade element.

As shown on the diagram, the angle of attack α is equal to the fixed blade setting angle β, minus the angle ϕ which is determined by airplane velocity V and propeller rotational velocity $2\pi rn$ (or πdn since diameter $= 2r$).

The flow of air about the propeller blade creates lift and drag forces in the same manner as airflow about an airplane wing. The resultant of these forces can be divided into two components, the thrust component acting in the direction of the propeller axis and the torque component. The torque component acting in the plane of rotation resists the rotation of the propeller and is the component that must be overcome by the engine shaft torque. Similar to the airplane wing, the magnitude of the thrust and torque components depends upon angle of attack and velocity.

Coefficients for thrust and torque could be plotted against angle of attack, but since α is equal to fixed blade angle β minus variable angle ϕ, it is more convenient to plot in terms of angle ϕ. The usual procedure is to plot these coefficients against the tangent of ϕ or V/nd. In practice, V/nd is often symbolized by the letter J. Such plotted diagrams, together with the blade angle β of any of the blade elements, define the operating conditions of the propeller as a whole. The blade angle generally given is usually the one for the blade element three-fourths of the distance from the propeller axis to the tip.

Graphs of thrust coefficient C_T, and torque or power coefficient C_P, plotted against V/nd (or J) are prepared by the propeller manufacturers for various families of propellers. With reference to such graphs, values for C_T or C_P may be obtained for any chosen value of V/nd. Power required to drive the propeller and forward thrust delivered can then be determined by multiplying C_T or C_P by air density ρ and certain variables consistent with the method used in the chart preparation. Usually, thrust $= \rho C_T n^2 d^4$, and power required $= \rho C_P n^3 d^5$.

PROPELLER EFFICIENCY

The efficiency of a propeller in converting engine power to thrust is obviously of tremendous importance to airplane performance. The efficiency of a propeller during cruising flight determines the range of an airplane as much as the efficiency of the engine itself in converting fuel energy to shaft power.

Propeller efficiency is expressed as the ratio of *thrust power* delivered to *engine power* required to turn the propeller. Thrust power is thrust force (lb) multiplied by airplane velocity V (fps), or TV (ft-lb/sec). The power required to turn the propeller may also be expressed in ft-lb/sec by multiplying engine shaft horsepower by 550 since one horsepower is 550 ft-lb/sec.

$$\text{Efficiency, } \eta = TV/P = VC_T n^2 d^4 / C_P n^3 d^5 = C_T/C_P(V/nd) \quad (4.1)$$

As noted previously, propeller thrust is expressed in terms of V/nd. Therefore, efficiency may be expressed in terms of V/nd and plotted as shown in Figure 4.2

In the simple fixed-pitch propeller, blade angle β is fixed. Each curve of the chart shown by Figure 4.2 represents efficiency for one angle of β. Since engine revolutions n must be maintained fairly high to obtain a satisfactory power output and only one propeller diameter d can be used at a time, then, for fixed-pitch propellers, maximum efficiency will be

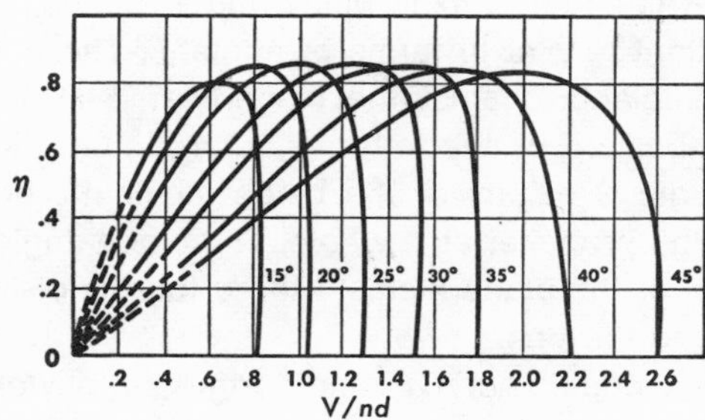

Figure 4.2 Propeller efficiency vs V/nd for various angles of β. (*N.A.C.A. Tech. Rept. 642.*)

obtained within a very narrow range of airspeeds, *V*. The airspeed at which maximum efficiency occurs is called the "design airspeed" for the propeller.

Employing fixed-pitch propellers in high-performance airplane design presents numerous problems. If a wing airfoil section is chosen for a transport airplane that will result in maximum *L/D* at high cruising speeds, a propeller of relatively high angle must also be chosen to yield good efficiency at high cruising speed. As shown by the chart, this propeller will give poor high-speed performance as well as inferior performance at takeoff and climb. A high-speed propeller chosen for a high-speed airplane will have reduced efficiency during cruise and give less than optimum range for the airplane, in addition to reduced climb and takeoff performance.

The advent of the controllable-pitch propeller solved these difficulties extremely well. Provided with a means for varying pitch angle, the pilot could select the optimum angles for takeoff, for climb, for efficient cruising, or for high-speed flight. In fact, modern airplane performance really began with the development of the controllable-pitch propeller.

Fixed-pitch propellers are currently used only on small, light airplanes where cost and lightness of installation are major considerations. The speed range of such airplanes is limited by power output of the engine as well as the propeller.

Propeller Tip Speed The velocity of the blade elements has little effect on efficiency until velocities near the speed of sound are approached. When the velocity of blade elements close to the tip approaches the speed of sound, the effect of compressibility increases power input requirements at no increase in thrust, thereby reducing efficiency. Since compressibility of an airfoil is affected by airfoil thickness ratio, propeller tips are built as thin as possible. Speed of sound is proportional to temperature and, normally, tip speed is limited to 800 to 1000 fps. To prevent tip speeds from exceeding these limitations many engines are equipped with reduction gears. This arrangement permits lower propeller rpm than the engine rpm required for efficient engine power output.

Thrust at Takeoff In addition to providing efficient thrust during cruising conditions, the propeller must be able to convert total engine power to thrust for takeoff. This is necessary to provide rapid acceleration to flying speed and keep takeoff distances within reasonable limits. In Figure 4.2 it will be noted that, when V/nd is zero ($V = 0$), efficiency is also zero. Obviously this is not correct or an airplane would never start in motion. Because of this apparent fallacy in the Drzewiecki theory, the efficiency curves are shown as dotted lines at low values of V/nd, indicating they should not be used in the low-speed range.

Charts of thrust output versus shaft horsepower are provided by propeller manufacturers for use in computing thrust output during the takeoff phase of flight.

PROPELLER TERMINOLOGY

The theoretical advance of the propeller blade per revolution is determined by blade angle β. This advance per revolution is called *geometric pitch.* However, air is not a solid medium and a certain amount of slippage occurs. The *effective pitch* is the actual distance the propeller advances each revolution. The difference between geometric pitch and effective pitch is called *slip.*

Fixed-pitch propeller: A propeller with blade angle fixed.

Adjustable-pitch propeller: A propeller on which blade angles can be adjusted on the ground with propellers not turning. This is especially convenient for a takeoff on a hot day from a high-altitude airport, or for preparing an airplane for float operations.

Constant-speed propeller: A controllable-pitch propeller with a speed governor which maintains selected rpm constant by automatically changing blade angle regardless of airspeed or engine power. Many propellers of this type also provide for full "feathering" of the blades in flight to prevent "windmilling" of the propeller, thus reducing drag when the engine is dead.

Feathering: Mechanically increasing pitch angle until the blade is turned approximately to the direction of flight. Feathering is used most frequently on multiengine airplanes.

Reverse thrust: Thrust in the direction opposite to flight. Nearly all larger multiengine airplanes utilize constant-speed, full-feathering, reversible-pitch propellers. The pitch-change mechanism is designed to permit the pilot to select negative blade angles immediately after landing, thus creating reverse thrust for rapid airplane deceleration. This feature saves brakes on heavy airplanes and permits safe landings on icy runways where wheel braking is extremely ineffective.

Windmilling drag: Perhaps the most undesirable action in the use of propellers as a thrust-producing device is the drag that results from propeller windmilling. If engine power is lost in flight, the airflow over the propeller blades will cause the propellers to rotate and, in turn, rotate the engine. When the blade angle is great enough to be commensurate with the flying speed, propeller efficiency will remain high and the drag will not be appreciably greater than engine load. However, if a failure occurs in the pitch-change mechanism and the blade angle is reduced, excessively high rotational speeds may result. The low blade angle and resultant negative angle of attack of the blade airfoil element cause a tremendous reduction in propeller efficiency. This means the load required to turn the dead engine is supplied by an inefficient propeller, and the resulting windmilling drag can become dangerously high. In such instances it is necessary to reduce airspeed or altitude to reduce propeller rotational speed. However, unless actual failure occurs to the pitch-change mechanism, the propeller speed governor will maintain rpm as it was before engine failure, and the feathering system, if installed, will feather the propeller to stop windmilling rotation altogether.

PROPELLER SELECTION

How much analysis and investigation is required for proper propeller selection depends upon the type of operation of the airplane involved. Airplanes designed to operate at high speed and high altitude require careful investigation to insure that all conditions of takeoff and flight are met with the lightest and most efficient installation. The propeller manufacturer provides charts for propeller performance under all conditions of flight for various families of propellers to be used in the selection analysis. Ideas as to the relative importance of the various factors influencing propeller selection may vary among airplane designers. One may choose a three-bladed propeller for a specific type of airplane to gain a light installation, while another would choose a four-bladed propeller for superior performance at a sacrifice in weight.

The selection of propellers for the smaller airplanes designed to operate at low and medium altitudes and airspeeds under 200 mph is fairly simple by comparison. The propeller manufacturer lists propellers that are designed for use with engines of a given horsepower rating and often lists the make and type of airplane on which the propeller may be used. Fixed-pitch propellers for a specific engine are usually obtainable in a choice of two or more pitch angles. A blade of lower pitch may be chosen for best takeoff and climb performance or a blade of higher pitch may be chosen for better cruise performance. Controllable-pitch propellers for the smaller airplane are selected simply also. The propellers are designed by the manufacturer for application on specific engines. Sufficient pitch change is usually designed into the control mechanism to take care of all speed and altitude conditions of a number of airplanes using the specific engine.

PROPELLER CONSTRUCTION AND INSTALLATION

Propellers made of forged aluminum alloy blades are in general use. The advantages of this type of construction are durability and strength as well as good manufacturing control of airfoil shape, especially important in the large sizes. Small nicks and scratches may be polished out without

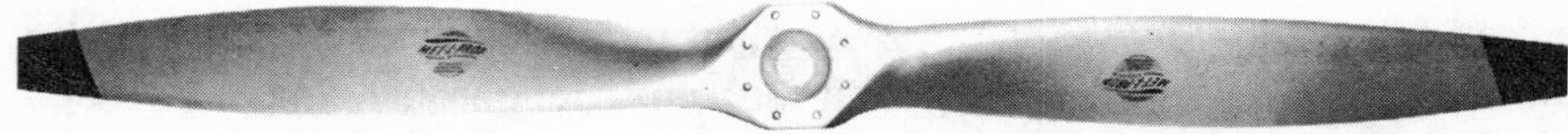

Figure 4.3 Fixed-pitch metal propeller. *(Courtesy of McCauley Industrial Corp.)*

impairing the strength or performance. If the propeller is bent by contact with the ground due to a poor landing, it can usually be straightened by the manufacturer. Figure 4.3 illustrates this type of propeller.

The *simple adjustable-pitch propeller* has rounded blade shanks which are secured by collars to the hub. By loosening the securing bolts in the collar, the blades may be rotated to the desired blade angle (pitch angle) and the bolts retightened.

Constant-speed, controllable-pitch propellers are used on many small and medium-sized personal and executive airplanes of over 80 Hp. Two such installations are shown in Figures 4.4 and 4.5. Both types utilize engine oil under pressure to provide pitch control.

In the type shown by Figures 4.4 and 4.5 the twisting moment of the blade resulting from centrifugal force tends to decrease blade angle and is offset by oil pressure from the governor acting against the forward side of a piston in the hub, the piston being connected through linkage to the blades. The flyball governor is mounted on the front case of the engine and is rotated by gears driven by the engine crankshaft. The gears also drive the governor oil pump. If the propeller tends to increase in speed above

Figure 4.4 Constant-speed propeller installed on a Cessna 180 airplane. *(Courtesy of McCauley Industrial Corp.)*

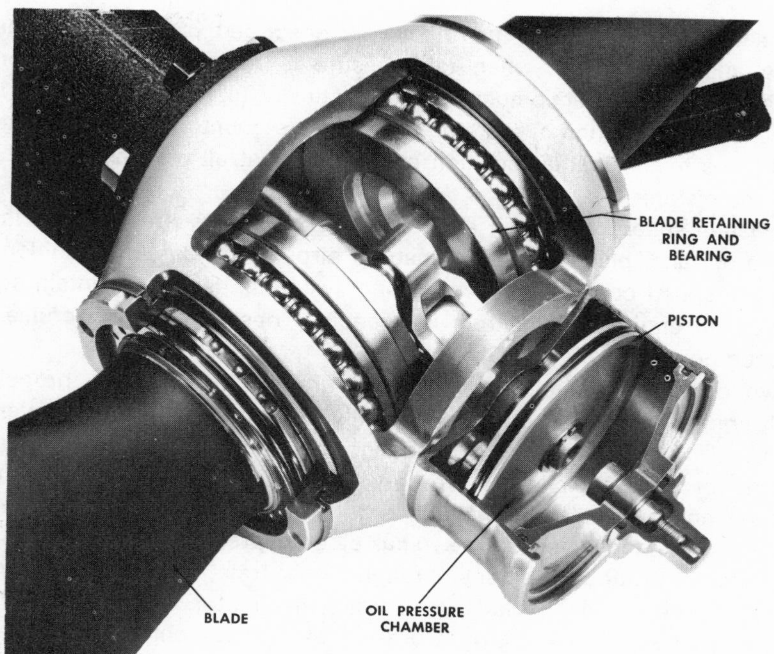

Figure 4.5 Cross-sectional view of one type of constant-speed propeller mechanism. *(Courtesy of McCauley Industrial Corp.)*

the rpm selected by the control in the cockpit, the governor will open the oil passage and admit more pressure to the piston. This action will increase blade angle slightly and restore rpm to the selected value. Conversely, if the propeller tends to decrease in speed, the governor will drain pressure from the piston, permitting the centrifugal twisting movement of the blades to reduce blade angle and increase speed. Changes in engine power (within limits), airspeed, and air density are compensated for by automatic selection of the proper blade angle for the condition, and propeller speed remains constant. The rpm at which constant-speed regulation is desired is selected by the control in the cockpit. This control is directly connected to a spring acting against the centrifugal force of the flyballs in the governor. Increasing or decreasing the spring tension requires a new position for the governor flyballs, which in turn repositions the valve to admit oil to the piston in the propeller hub.

Another type of controllable-pitch propeller is somewhat similar in principle to the propeller described above but different in operation. Counterweights connected to the blade shanks in the hub tend to increase blade angle. The force of the counterweights is offset by oil pressure acting against a piston. Regulation of speed is obtained by controlled oil pressure in the reverse manner to the previously described propeller. Increased blade angle will result when oil pressure is reduced and vice versa. Feathering may be accomplished automatically in some models of this propeller by the action of a spring assisting the counterweights in rotating the blades to the feather position at the time that all oil pressure is bled from the piston.

Constant-speed feathering and reversing propellers are used on large turboprop and piston-engine transport airplanes today. In addition to constant-speed control, a synchronizing system is used to maintain equal rpm on all engines. Equal rpm is especially desirable during cruise for reduced noise and vibration.

Two different principles of operation are employed in the propeller-pitch control systems used predominantly on large multiengine airplanes. Electrical motor power for pitch-change actuation is used in the Curtiss electric propellers while oil pressure is utilized in Hamilton Standard, Hartzell and McCauley propellers. Figure 4.6 shows the details of the pitch-change mechanism of a typical electric propeller.

The motor rotates the blades, through a gear train, by means of segment gears attached to each blade root. When the motor is not running, the blades are held in position by a brake that releases only when power is

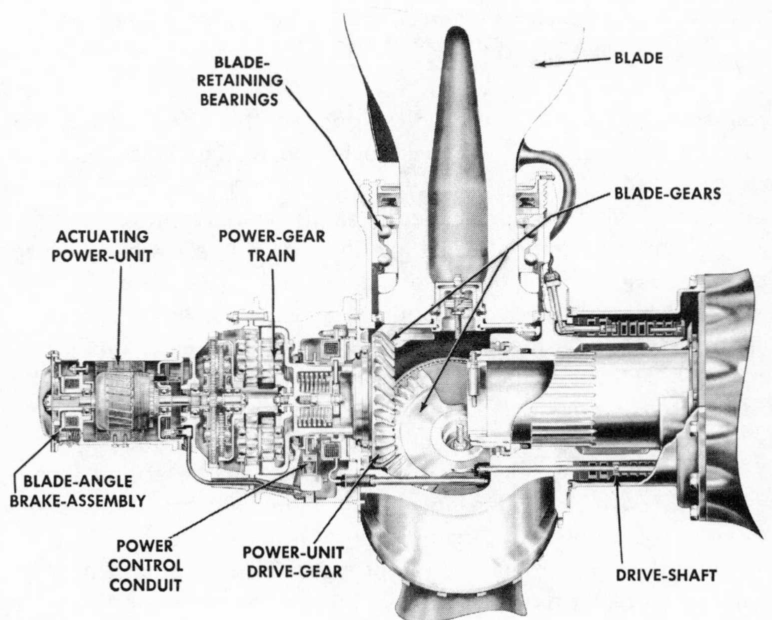

Figure 4.6 Cutaway view of an electric constant-speed, feathering, reversing propeller. *(Courtesy of Curtiss-Wright Corp.)*

applied to the motor. Electrical power is transmitted to the rotating propeller mechanism through slip rings attached to the propeller shaft. Electrical limit switches mounted in the rear housing accurately control the low, high, feather, and reverse blade angle limits. In addition to the electrical low-pitch limit switch, a mechanical low-pitch stop is provided on many models to prevent dangerously low blade angles in event of electrical brake failure. This mechanical stop is retracted when the pilot selects reverse actuation during landing. Constant-speed control is provided by the synchronizer located in the airplane fuselage. The synchronizer provides automatic constant speed by matching all engine speeds with the speed of a synchronous constant-speed motor. The electrical matching of speeds is accomplished by contactors mounted on and driven by the synchronous motor. These units compare the speed of the synchronous motor with the speed of each individual engine by means of the frequency output of three-phase alternators mounted on and driven by the engines. The selected rpm, at which constant-speed operation is desired, is obtained with the pilot-operated master control, which changes the

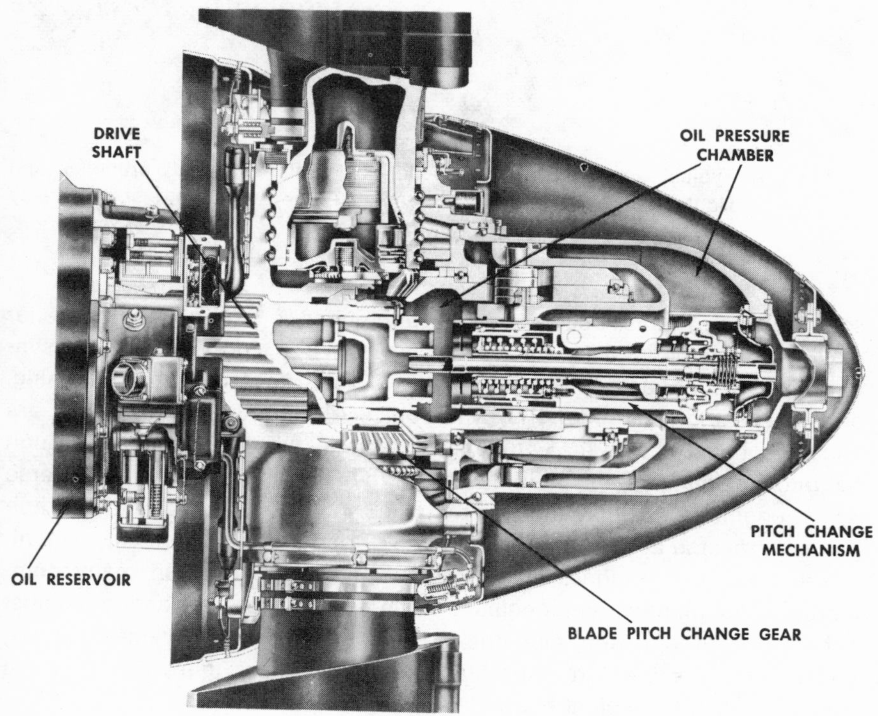

Figure 4.7 Cutaway view of a hydromatic constant-speed, feathering, and reversing propeller.

Figure 4.8 Typical constant-speed propeller installation. Hartzell propeller and Continental tiara engine mounted in Piper Arrow for test. *(Courtesy of Teledyne Continental Motors.)*

speed of the synchronous motor. The pitch-change motor in the propeller may also be operated by manual switches in the cockpit, with the synchronizer disconnected. Manual control is used for feathering, reversing, and in event of failure of the synchronizer. The reversing switches are usually connected with the engine throttles to insure that reversing through flat pitch takes place only at idle power. When the blades are in the reverse angle, engine power may then be reapplied. A pilot-operated safety switch prevents reverse action when not desired during normal throttle movement.

The Hamilton Standard Hydromatic propeller is used on many commercial and military multiengine airplanes. Oil pressure acting against either side of a piston plus the centrifugal twisting movement of the blades provides the force for blade pitch change. Figure 4.7 shows a cutaway view of a typical hydromatic mechanism.

The force of the piston is transmitted through cams and rollers to the drive gear which is meshed with the gears affixed to each blade root.

Figure 4.9 Hamilton standard hydromatic propeller. Constant-speed full-feathering, and reversing, installed on a Lockheed C-130B turboprop transport. *(Courtesy of U.S. Air Force.)*

Constant speed is maintained by the engine-driven, double-acting flyball governor, which meters governor oil pump pressure to either side of the piston as required. As pitch change takes place, oil from the low-pressure side of the piston is returned through passages back to the pump. In some installations engine oil is used by the governor; in others, a self-contained oil system is provided. Rpm selection and synchronization of propellers are obtained by actuation of a three-phase electric stepmotor in each governor head, which varies the tension of the speeder spring acting against the governor flyballs. To obtain synchronization, one governor stepmotor is selected as the "master" motor and all other stepmotors are maintained in phase by the synchronizer in the fuselage. If any propeller tends to underspeed or overspeed, its stepmotor will become out of phase with the "master" one, and electric contactors in the synchronizer will bring the unsynchronized stepmotor back in phase. Rpm selection is obtained by driving the "master" stepmotor to the desired governed rpm. A separate electric-driven pump is provided to assist the governor pump for reversing and feathering operation and is actuated by separate controls in the cockpit. As with the electric propeller, the reversing switches are actuated by the engine throttles.

Jet Propulsion

The principle of jet propulsion is very familiar and very simple. The jet or rocket engine moves the airplane or missile forward by reacting to the momentum of a mass of air or gaseous matter accelerating out the rear (nozzle) of the engine. The recoil of a rifle and the reactive thrust of a fire hose are typical examples of this principle. Sir Isaac Newton explained jet propulsion in 1690 when he propounded the third law of motion: "Every action produces a reaction, equal in force and opposite in direction." Thus the reaction to the momentum of the gases escaping from the jet engine nozzle creates the thrust force which propels the airplane or missile. From Newton's law it can be seen that the thrust force is *not* the result of the jet gases pushing against the air behind but instead is the *reaction* to the momentum of the escaping gases. This fact is demonstrated by rocket motors, which produce full thrust in outer space beyond the normal atmosphere. (Unlike air-consuming turbojet and ramjet engines, rockets carry their own oxygen supply for combustion and do not depend upon the oxygen in the atmosphere.)

ENGINE TYPES

All engines employing the principle of jet propulsion are jet engines. However, common terminology denotes jet engines which carry their own oxidizing agent as rocket motors. Engines which draw in air, heat it by burning fuel, and expel it from the nozzle are commonly termed jet engines. The various types of jet engines and rocket motors with their principles of operation are discussed later in the chapter. The following symbols, followed by the model number of the engine, are used by the Armed Services to identify the various types of jet propulsion engines.

J = Turbojet R = Rocket
PJ = Pulsejet T = Turboprop
RJ = Ramjet TF = Fan

POWER MEASUREMENT

Jet thrust force is measured in pounds as is the thrust force of a propeller.

The magnitude of jet gross thrust force is determined by the mass flow of air or gaseous matter multiplied by the velocity with which it escapes from the nozzle. This may be expressed by:

$$F = \frac{W_a}{g} V_J = MV_J \tag{4.2}$$

where F = thrust force, lb
M = mass flow rate = W/g
V_J = jet velocity, fps
W_a = weight flow, lb/sec
g = gravity acceleration = 32.2 ft/sec/sec

Because aerodynamic equations require thrust to be expressed as a force, to equate thrust requirements against drag and acceleration forces, there is no purpose in attempting to express jet-engine output in terms of horsepower. Though it is relatively meaningless, jet-engine "power" can be determined by multiplying thrust force times true airspeed in feet per second and dividing by the horsepower constant.

$$\text{hp} = (\text{jet thrust} \times \text{TAS} \times 1.467)/550 \tag{4.3}$$

Therefore, when true airspeed is 550 fps or 375 mph, the jet thrust and jet "power" are the same. At speeds below this value, jet "power" is less than jet thrust in pounds. In the case of the turboprop engine, where both propeller thrust and jet thrust are utilized, it is sometimes desirable to convert jet thrust into horsepower. By adding this value to the horsepower rating of the engine, the total propulsive output of the engine can be expressed as "equivalent shaft horsepower" (eshp). Jet horsepower must be multiplied by propeller efficiency to convert to shaft horsepower. Assuming a propeller efficiency of 80%, we have

$$\text{eshp} = (\text{jet thrust} \times \text{TAS} \times 1.467 \times 0.80)/550 + \text{shaft horsepower} \tag{4.4}$$

Propulsive Efficiency

PRINCIPLES AND LIMITS

The efficiency with which a propulsion system is utilized in propelling the airplane or missile is called "propulsive efficiency." A thorough understanding and investigation of propulsive efficiency are necessary for successful design when comparing one propulsion system with another. This is especially true when comparing propeller propulsion with jet propulsion.

Propulsive efficiency may be expressed very simply by

$$\text{Efficiency} = 2V_a/(V_J + V_a) \tag{4.5}$$

where V_a = airplane velocity, fps
V_J = jet velocity (or propeller slipstream velocity), fps

In the case of propeller-driven airplanes, propulsive efficiency very closely approximates propeller efficiency (Figure 4.2) because the propeller moves a large mass of air at relatively slow speeds. During cruising conditions, the air behind the propeller is moving at approximately the same speed as the airplane; hence, V_a and V_J are approximately equal. In contrast, the thrust-producing gases escaping from the jet engine nozzle are extremely high in velocity, relatively smaller in mass flow, and cannot be varied extensively in flight.

It is not presently possible to design a pure jet engine that would have satisfactory fuel economy and light weight without high jet velocity. For this reason, all jet-powered airplanes are designed for high-speed flight to obtain maximum propulsive efficiency.

High-altitude operation must be considered in propulsive efficiency analysis. Because of compressibility effects on the propeller airfoil, propeller efficiency decreases with both airspeed and altitude. This factor limits current subsonic propellers to approximately 500 mph true airspeed and 40,000 to 45,000 ft altitude.

Since jet thrust is accomplished at high jet velocities, the higher the airplane speed, the greater is the propulsive efficiency. Current turbojet engines are limited to approximately 2000 mph and 90,000 ft altitude. Turbofan engines provide an extremely good compromise between propeller and turbojet engines. Higher propulsive efficiency is available for takeoff and is maintained to speeds and altitudes far greater than is possible with propellers. The ramjet engine is limited to possibly 3000 mph and 100,000 ft altitude. Because the rocket engine carries its own oxygen supply, it suffers no atmospheric compressibility effects internally. The jet

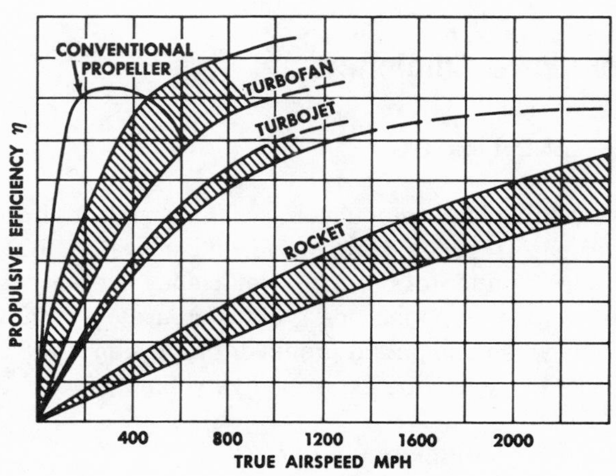

Figure 4.10 Comparison of propulsive efficiency. *(Courtesy of Hamilton Standard.)*

velocity is limited only by nozzle design and propellant (fuel plus oxidizer) burning rate.

A comparison of propulsive efficiency for the various propulsion methods is shown by Figure 4.10.

TAKEOFF PERFORMANCE

During takeoff, the propeller offers some advantage compared with the pure jet. Not only does the propeller move large masses of air at a more advantageous velocity for greater propulsive efficiency, but the slipstream of the propeller flowing over the wing increases the effective lift of the wing. A turboprop engine, comparable in physical size to a pure jet engine, will develop shaft horsepower approximately equal in rating to the thrust rating of the pure jet engine. Using an approximate conversion factor of 2.0 to convert shaft horsepower to thrust for takeoff, it can be seen that the turboprop engine will develop about 2.0 times as much takeoff thrust. The newer high-bypass-ratio turbofan engines approach the performance of propellers for takeoff and, in the larger sizes, provide thrust levels far greater than is possible with propellers of any reasonable diameter.

Increased takeoff thrust for pure jet airplanes is obtained by several methods. A method used extensively in fighter airplanes, called *afterburning,* is the burning of additional fuel in the engine tailpipe. While this method requires a high fuel consumption during operation, it can result in as much as a 50% increase in takeoff thrust. Water or water-alcohol mixtures injected into the engine compressor or burners on turbojet and turbofan engines also provide increased thrust for takeoff: as much as 15% to 25% increase can be developed by this method. The use of afterburning or water injection for increased takeoff thrust is termed *augmentation.* Further details of augmentation are discussed later in the chapter.

The normal propeller-driven or turbojet airplane requires a thrust force great enough to accelerate it until the wings provide sufficient lift for flight. A helicopter is set in motion by the lifting force of its rotating wing (rotor). Forward velocity is obtained by tilting the aircraft to provide a forward component of the lifting force. In an effort to obtain the speed and lift force advantage of the fixed wing, coupled with the vertical takeoff and landing advantage of the helicopter, the VTOL (vertical takeoff and landing) aircraft is being developed. Several design conceptions are undergoing study and test. With the turboprop-powered tilt wing and tilt engine, either the entire wing (or sections thereof) with the engines is tilted, or the engines only are rotated to the vertical position for takeoff and landing. The thrust force provided must be greater than the entire weight of the airplane. Separate turbofan lift engines and vectored main engine jet exhaust are also used on some experimental aircraft.

Reciprocating Engines

Reciprocating aircraft engines operate on the same principle as the crude engine which powered the Wright brothers' airplane. The advancement to present-day, high-powered engines has been the result of improved efficiency, construction, and reliability. The vast improvement in these factors is clearly evident. The Wright brothers' engine weighed 13 lb per hp, whereas many modern engines weigh less than 1 lb per hp. Each cylinder on a large modern engine will produce more than ten times the horsepower of the entire Wright brothers' engine, and do it for many hundreds of hours before overhaul is necessary.

PRINCIPLES OF OPERATION

The term *reciprocating engine* is derived from the action of the pistons moving back and forth within the cylinders in a reciprocal motion as the crankshaft rotates. The term *internal combustion* denotes the action of burning fuel within the engine to provide the forces that develop the engine power output.

The basic power-producing elements of a reciprocating engine are the *cylinder, piston, crankshaft,* and *connecting rod.* (See Figure 4.11). The piston receives the force of the expanding gases within the cylinder and transmits the force to the crankshaft by means of the connecting rod. The crankshaft is caused to rotate by the force of the connecting rod and transmits the turning effort (torque) to the propeller. Further details are given later in the chapter.

All reciprocating engines in general use for airplane propulsion are internal-combustion engines operating on the *Otto cycle* (Figure 4.12). Reciprocating engines operating on the *diesel cycle* have been used in the past to a minor extent for airplane propulsion but have never been developed with a reliability and lightness comparable to Otto cycle engines.

The Otto cycle principle is named for Nicholas A. Otto, who built the first successful engine operating on this principle in 1876. Another description commonly applied to engines operating on this principle is "four-stroke, spark ignition." As implied by the latter description, one complete cycle consists of four strokes of the piston—two inward strokes (toward the crankshaft) and two outward strokes. The completion of one cycle, therefore, requires two complete revolutions of the crankshaft. On multicylinder engines, the pistons are connected to the crankshaft in a manner such that each cylinder completes its cycle at a different time relative to propeller position. This results in smoother operation, since the power stroke of each piston occurs at a different time.

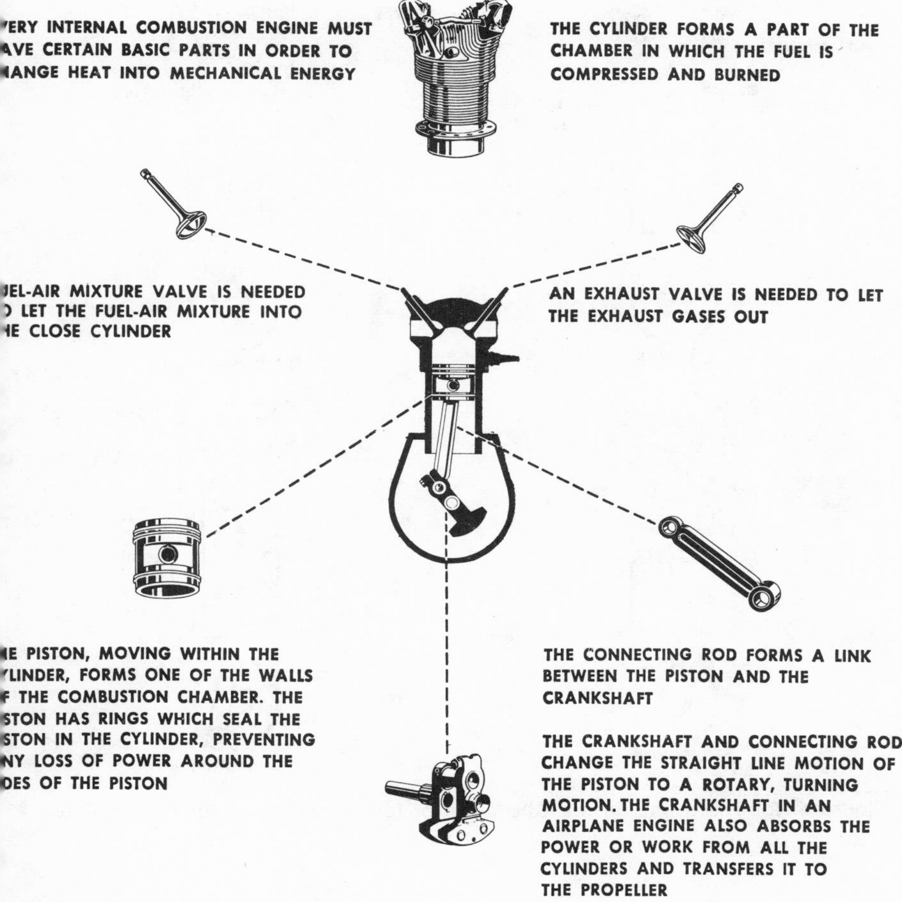

ERY INTERNAL COMBUSTION ENGINE MUST
VE CERTAIN BASIC PARTS IN ORDER TO
ANGE HEAT INTO MECHANICAL ENERGY
THE CYLINDER FORMS A PART OF THE CHAMBER IN WHICH THE FUEL IS COMPRESSED AND BURNED
JEL-AIR MIXTURE VALVE IS NEEDED
LET THE FUEL-AIR MIXTURE INTO
IE CLOSE CYLINDER
AN EXHAUST VALVE IS NEEDED TO LET THE EXHAUST GASES OUT
IE PISTON, MOVING WITHIN THE
LINDER, FORMS ONE OF THE WALLS
F THE COMBUSTION CHAMBER. THE
STON HAS RINGS WHICH SEAL THE
STON IN THE CYLINDER, PREVENTING
NY LOSS OF POWER AROUND THE
DES OF THE PISTON
THE CONNECTING ROD FORMS A LINK BETWEEN THE PISTON AND THE CRANKSHAFT
THE CRANKSHAFT AND CONNECTING ROD CHANGE THE STRAIGHT LINE MOTION OF THE PISTON TO A ROTARY, TURNING MOTION. THE CRANKSHAFT IN AN AIRPLANE ENGINE ALSO ABSORBS THE POWER OR WORK FROM ALL THE CYLINDERS AND TRANSFERS IT TO THE PROPELLER

Figure 4.11 Elements of a reciprocating engine.

The four strokes of the Otto cycle are called *intake, compression, power,* and *exhaust.* The relationship is shown by Figure 4.12. When the piston is at the very end of the stroke, away from the crankshaft, it is said to be at "top dead center." The term "bottom dead center" means the opposite end of the stroke or the one closest to the crankshaft.

The intake stroke begins with the piston at (or near) top dead center. At this point, the intake valve is opened by the valve mechanism and the intake stroke of the piston draws the fuel-air mixture into the cylinder from the intake manifold. (In supercharged engines the fuel-air mixture is forced into the cylinder under pressures greater than atmospheric.) When the piston reaches the end of the intake stroke, the intake valve closes and the compression stroke begins. (Fuel-injection engines operate similarly

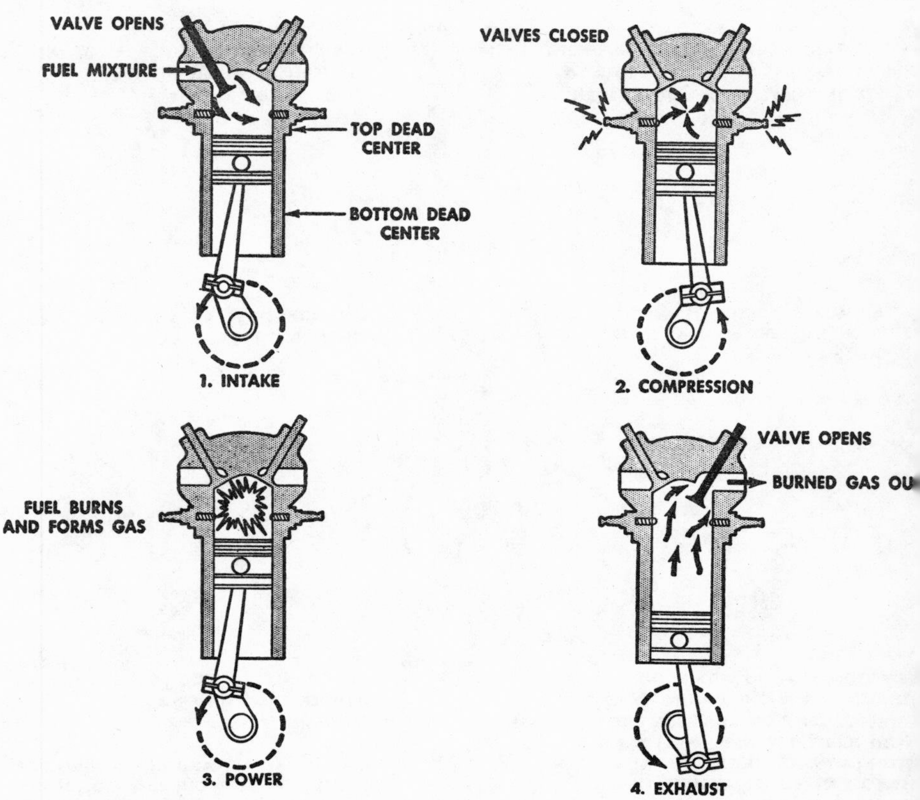

Figure 4.12 The events in the Otto cycle or four-stroke spark ignition engine.

except that the fuel is injected in the proper amount under very high pressure directly into the cylinder during the compression cycle.) As the piston moves toward the top of the cylinder, the enclosed combustible mixture is compressed to a small volume. An instant before the piston reaches top dead center, the spark plug is energized, igniting the fuel-air mixture. While burning takes place, the piston passes top dead center and the power stroke begins. The burning of the fuel-air mixture greatly increases the temperature and pressure of the gases. These high pressures act against the piston which transmits its force by means of the connecting rod into the crankshaft, creating the turning torque of the crankshaft. When the piston reaches the bottom of the cylinder, at the completion of the power stroke, the exhaust valve opens and the upward movement of the piston in the exhaust stroke expels the burned gases from the cylinder. At the completion of the exhaust stroke, the intake valve opens and a new cycle begins.

Valve Timing Because the intake and exhaust valves open and close only once for two revolutions of the crankshaft, the mechanism which actuates the valves is driven at one-half crankshaft rpm. The time at which each valve opens and closes, relative to piston and crankshaft position, varies with different engines. The amount of supercharging and the rpm at which the engine is to derive its greatest power or efficiency determine the inertia and velocities of inrushing combustible mixture and outgoing burned gases which, in turn, determine the valve timing for which optimum engine power is realized. On some supercharged engines, the intake valve is opened before the exhaust valve is completely closed to insure complete expelling of the burned gases. This timing is called "valve overlap." During the development of an engine, a great deal of testing is performed to determine optimum valve timing, among other considerations.

Spark Advance This term is applied to indicate the angular position of the crankshaft, relative to top dead center, at the moment spark ignition is applied to the combustible mixture. A 15° spark advance means the spark is applied when the crankshaft is 15° from reaching top dead center on the compression stroke. The spark is nearly always applied before top dead center, as this results in better engine performance.

Compression Ratio The ratio of the cylinder volume at the end of the intake stroke to the cylinder volume at the end of the compression stroke is called *compression ratio.* The greater the ratio, the smaller is the relative volume to which the air-fuel mixture is compressed. Greater compression (within limits) results in higher engine power output for a given engine size, but opposed to this are other factors such as spark ignition timing and fuel burning rate.

Detonation will occur if the burning rate of the fuel is not compatible with compression ratio and spark advance, or vice versa. It is necessary to control the burning rate of the fuel so that complete burning takes place during several degrees of crankshaft rotation. If the burning rate is too fast, the pressure in the cylinder will build up too rapidly and the entire remaining mixture will explode instantaneously, causing *detonation.* When applied to automobile engines, detonation is often referred to as "pinging" or "knocking."

Preignition will occur with an effect similar to detonation if a "hot spot" (improperly cooled valve, carbon particle, etc.) in the cylinder causes ignition of the unburned portion of the fuel prior to the normal burning rate.

Octane Rating Fuels for Otto cycle engines are rated according to their ability to burn without causing detonation by comparing them with a pure hydrocarbon called *octane.* This hydrocarbon has an assigned rating of 100. Thus, a fuel with an octane rating of 80 has inferior detonation characteristics compared to pure octane, while a fuel rated at 130 has better characteristics. The comparison tests are conducted in a special single-cylinder engine in which the compression ratio may be varied.

FUEL-AIR MIXTURE

After fuel and air are mixed in the desired proportions in the carburetor,* the mixture is forced into each cylinder through pipes or passages in the intake manifold. With fuel injection, the airflow through the carburetor signals the injection pumps to meter the proper amount of fuel directly into the cylinder. The ratio of fuel mixed with the air is called "fuel-air ratio" (F/A) and has a very pronounced effect on the operation of the engine. If the mixture is extremely "lean," low in fuel content, the mixture may not burn at all or may cause "backfiring." Backfiring is caused by incomplete combustion in the cylinder so that, the next time the intake valve opens, the still burning fuel will ignite the fresh mixture in the intake manifold. If the mixture is moderately lean, but still not the proper ratio, detonation may result at high power settings from too rapid burning. Excessively rich mixtures cause loss of power as well as uneconomical fuel consumption. However, excessively rich mixtures are sometimes employed on supercharged engines for short-period operations at high power, such as is used for takeoff. Power loss due to the rich mixture is more than offset by forcing a greater weight of fuel-air mixture into the cylinders. The objective of the overly rich mixture in this instance is slower combustion at the higher pressures within the cylinder and the attendant prevention of detonation. The effect of fuel-air mixture on power is shown by the curve in Figure 4.13. The mixture entitled "best economy" is the mixture that yields the most horsepower per pound of fuel burned. On some supercharged engines, the fuel-air mixture is *not* enriched during high-power operation. Instead, the engine is operated with "best power" fuel-air ratio and detonation suppression is obtained by

*For the operation of the carburetor see page 165.

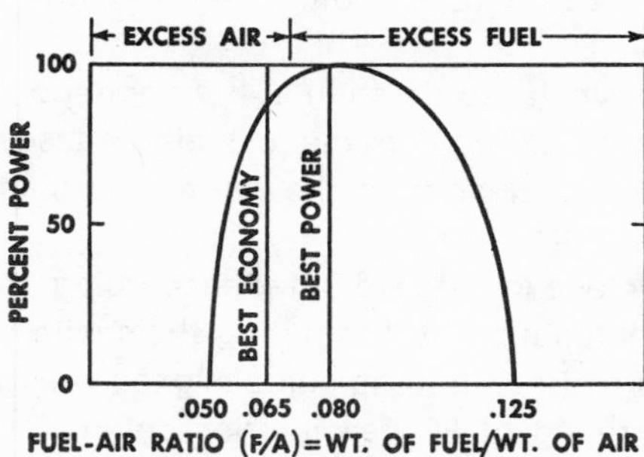

Figure 4.13 Effect of fuel-air mixture on power output.

substituting a mixture of water and alcohol for the normally excess fuel. This practice is done only on very high-powered engines and is called "anti-detonant injection," or ADI.

PERFORMANCE

Only a fraction of the total heat energy of the fuel burned is converted to useful horsepower. The remainder of the heat energy is lost through the exhaust gases, the engine cooling system, and the friction of the moving engine parts. The ratio of useful energy to total energy of the fuel consumed is called *thermal efficiency.* Reciprocating engines are generally about 34% thermally efficient. In some instances, discussed later, utilization of some of the energy in the exhaust gases has resulted in higher values. Approximately 10% of the total fuel energy is lost to engine friction, 10% to 15% to cooling, and the remainder of the loss to the exhaust gases. Friction loss is the difference between actual horsepower developed, called *indicated* horsepower (ihp), and useful shaft horsepower, called *brake* horsepower (bhp). The ratio of brake horsepower to indicated horsepower is called *mechanical efficiency.* (Mechanical efficiency = bhp/ihp.) As shown by later discussion, all of the brake horsepower is not used to drive the propeller. A portion may be used to drive pumps, generators, superchargers, etc., depending upon installation.

The indicated horsepower developed by a reciprocating engine may be expressed simply as the foot-pounds of work performed by all pistons in one minute divided by 33,000. (The value 33,000 ft-lb/min, or 550 ft-lb/sec is an established standard for one horsepower.)

$$\text{ihp} = PLAN/33{,}000 \tag{4.6}$$

where P = mean effective pressure, psi*
L = length of stroke, ft
A = area of piston, sq in.
N = number of power strokes per minute

The horsepower expressed by the above equation is indicated horsepower and does not account for friction losses of the moving engine parts.

Because friction losses and mean effective pressure would be very difficult to calculate, actual engine horsepower is determined by operating the engine while coupled to a measuring device called a *dynamometer.* The dynamometer does not measure horsepower directly; instead it measures the turning force of the crankshaft. This turning force is called *torque* and is measured in pounds-foot. Thus, if an arm were connected to

*Average cylinder pressure during the power stroke.

the crankshaft, 200 lb-ft of torque will exert a force of 200 lb at a right-angle distance of 1 ft from the centerline of the crankshaft. At a distance of 2 ft, the force would be 100 lb, etc. (The expression *pounds-foot* for *torque* should not be confused with *foot-pounds* for *work* which is the product of force times distance in the direction of force is acting.)

Once torque is determined, the useful horsepower delivered by the engine shaft is easily calculateed. Since $2\pi r$ is the circumference of a circle, the work per revolution is 2π times torque, and

$$\text{hp} = \frac{2\pi \times \text{torque} \times \text{rpm}}{33{,}000} \tag{4.7}$$

The horsepower output thus determined is called *brake* horsepower.

For the purpose of comparing the relative performance of various engines, the original equation, hp = $PLAN/33{,}000$, is used. Since all parts of the equation are known except mean effective pressure P, this value is calculated. The resulting pressure is now called *brake mean effective pressure* (bmep), since it is calculated from measured or *brake* horsepower.

$$\begin{aligned} \text{hp} &= (\text{bmep})LAN/33{,}000 \\ \text{bmep} &= \text{hp} \times 33{,}000/LAN \end{aligned} \tag{4.8}$$

Since N is the number of power strokes per minutes and one power stroke occurs for every two revolutions, N = rpm/2. Converting the power stroke L to inches and multiplying by piston area and the number of cylinders, the total piston *displacement* in cubic inches is determined. The equation now becomes

$$\begin{aligned} \text{bmep} &= \text{hp} \times 33{,}000/(L/12) \times A \times \text{no. of cylinders} \times \text{rpm}/2 \\ &= \text{hp} \times 792{,}000/\text{rpm} \times \text{piston displacement} \end{aligned} \tag{4.9}$$

Thus, engines (especially the larger sizes) are compared according to total piston displacement and maximum allowable bmep.

POWER REGULATION

From the last equation it is apparent that only two variables determine the power output of a particular engine. These factors are bmep and rpm. The magnitude of bmep for an engine, at any constant rpm, will be determined by the amount of fuel-air mixture pumped into the cylinders during the intake stroke. The greater the weight of mixture charge, the greater is the internal cylinder pressure resulting from the burning fuel. The weight of the mixture charge will be determined by the density of the air in the charge, assuming the carburetor maintains the proper fuel-air ratio. Therefore, all the factors that influence charge air density will also influence the engine horsepower output. The density of the charge air is determined by atmospheric pressure and temperature, position of the throttle valve in the carburetor, and if supercharging is used, the amount of air compression in the supercharger. The throttle valve provides the basic control for charge air density and is regulated by the throttle lever. When the throttle is wide open, the charge air density is determined only by atmospheric pressure and temperature and the amount of supercharging. Since air density decreases with altitude, engine power will also decrease as the airplane climbs to higher altitudes. The effect of altitude on engine power output and the effect of supercharging are shown in Figure 4.14. All curves below the top line reflect wide-open throttle. Partial closing of the throttle has the same effect on the density of the air charge as an increase in altitude.

Charge air density not only varies with altitude pressures, but varies considerably with temperature and humidity. On small airplanes, the effect of these variables on engine power is usually ignored. However, on large airplanes where gross weight and takeoff distance must be carefully balanced, power corrections must be made to the manufacturers' "standard day" horsepower charts. Engine power output varies as the square root of the ratio of standard day temperature to observed temperature where both are converted to absolute temperature.

$$\text{corrected hp} = \text{chart hp}\sqrt{(460 + T_s)/(460 + T_a)} \qquad (4.10)$$

where T_s = standard day temperature = 60°F
T_a = observed temperature, °F

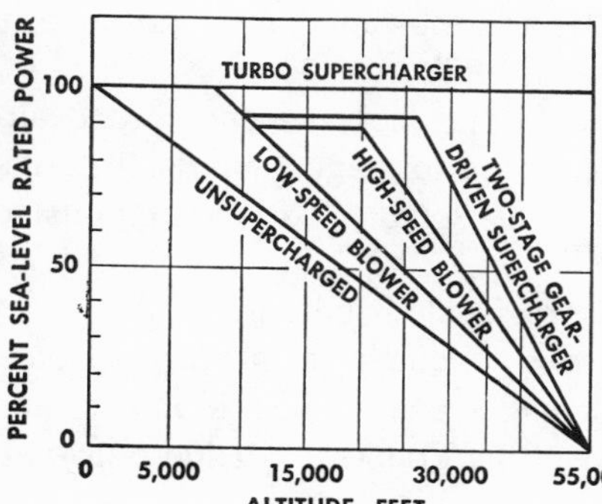

Figure 4.14 Engine performance at various altitudes for several methods of supercharging.

A fairly accurate approximation that may be used is 1% correction for every 10°F temperature variation from standard day.

Humidity corrections are made by determining *absolute* humidity (not relative humidity) of the atmosphere at the particular moment and using the manufacturers' power correction charts.

The engine manufacturer designates various power settings at which each type of engine may be operated for short periods and at which the engine may be operated continuously. For large-engine operation, *takeoff* or *emergency* power may be held for a period of only five minutes. The designation *rated power* on military engines, or *METO power* (maximum except takeoff) on commercial engines, is the maximum power permitted for continuous operation. Both of these powers require a rich fuel-air mixture. The maximum cruise power permitted under lean fuel-air mixtures is called *maximum cruise.* The altitude at which rated or METO power requires wide-open throttle is called *critical altitude.* Above this altitude engine power will reduce because of reduced atmospheric density. Obviously, the amount of supercharging will determine the critical altitude as shown by Figure 4.14.

POWER INDICATION

Rpm and bmep are the primary variables affecting horsepower output of any particular engine. Rpm may be readily indicated to pilot or flight crew by means of the engine instrument called the *tachometer,* which measures the rotating speed of the crankshaft. On small airplanes this is often the only power-indicating instrument. (Figure 5.11.)

The other variable, bmep, cannot be measured. However, the pressure of the fuel-air mixture in the inlet manifold can be measured on a pressure gage. Since this pressure is the primary influence on bmep, its measurement serves the purpose well. The pressure in the intake manifold is called manifold pressure (mp or map), and the measuring instrument is called *manifold pressure gage.* The manifold pressure gage always registers total pressure above absolute zero (vacuum) since the function of the gage is the indication of air density in the manifold. (Figure 5.2.)

With the two main variables indicated to the pilot, the engine and airplane manufacturers can prepare airplane performance charts in terms of rpm and map for maximum power limitations, a variety of cruising powers, and other operating conditions.

Another power-indicating instrument, previously used only on the larger engines but now available on medium-size engines, is the *torquemeter.* This is a torque-measuring device built into the nose of the engine, and it measures the amount of turning effort of the crankshaft being delivered directly to the propeller. The advantage of this direct indication is that all factors which affect power output will be reflected in the torquemeter reading. Such factors as malfunctions in the valve mechanism or ignition system and reduction in air density due to temperature and humidity will not necessarily be reflected in manifold pressure indication. However, power losses due to these causes will result in reduced torquemeter indications. This instrument is extremely valuable in determining allowable takeoff gross weight for high-performance airplanes under adverse conditions.

SUPERCHARGERS

Supercharging increases power output by compressing more fuel-air mixture into the cylinders than would be induced by atmospheric pressure alone, thereby creating burning pressures. Because superchargers increase the weight and cost of the engine, they are seldom used on engines below 200 hp. Also, airplanes utilizing engines of smaller horsepower generally operate at altitudes that do not require supercharging. The compressor in nearly all the makes of superchargers operates on the centrifugal principle. This type of compressor permits high-speed operation and attendant lightness of construction relative to airflow delivery.

Superchargers may be designated by two categories: single-stage and two-stage (or auxiliary stage). Single-stage denotes a single compressor; two-stage signifies two compressors in series. The single-stage compressor is usually contained within the engine case and is driven by a system of gears directly from the crankshaft at several times the rotating speed of the crankshaft. It is usually the engine *blower.* The total pressure at the outlet divided by the total pressure at the inlet is called *blower ratio.*

Auxiliary-stage supercharging is supplied by a separate gear-driven supercharger or by an exhaust-gas-driven *turbosupercharger.* Its chief advantage is its use of exhaust gas energy to provide the large power requirements for air compression at high altitudes rather than taking this power from the engine crankshaft.

Auxiliary-stage supercharging generally requires the employment of an *intercooler* to remove some of the heat of compression from the supercharged air. The intercooler exchanges the heat of compression with atmospheric air directed through passages in the intercooler. Cooling of the air not only increases its density, assisting the compressor, but prevents excessively high temperatures of the fuel-air mixture entering the cylinders, thereby controlling detonation.

A number of engines in the 250-hp to 500-hp class are now using single-stage turbosupercharging to provide high engine power up to 20,000 ft altitude. In some installations intercooling is provided and a portion of the turbosupercharge output is used for cabin pressurization.

PERFORMANCE CHARTS

Charts furnished by engine manufacturers show power output for various operating conditions. Performances of smaller engines used with fixed-pitch propellers are usually shown, for sea-level operation only, by charts similar to Figure 4.15. A *propeller load* curve represents the power that will be absorbed by a specific fixed-pitch propeller at any given rpm. In Figure 4.15, curve *A* is a propeller chosen (the usual case) to provide full power at takeoff rpm. If full engine power is not needed for acceptable takeoff performance a propeller of greater blade angle may be chosen resulting in full throttle before maximum allowable rpm is reached. This propeller, which will permit higher cruising speeds, is shown by curve *B*. The curves marked *full throttle* indicate maximum output of the engine at any given rpm and would require a controllable-pitch propeller of extensive blade angle variation to absorb the power. Normally, the blades of a controllable-pitch propeller will contact the high-pitch stops at an inter-

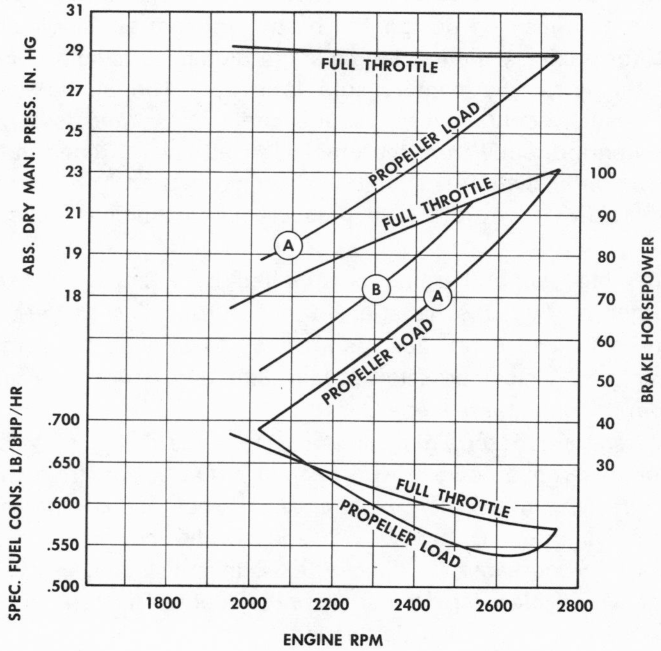

Figure 4.15 Typical sea-level engine performance chart.

SEA-LEVEL PERFORMANCE

TO FIND ACTUAL HORSEPOWER FROM ALTITUDE, RPM, MANIFOLD PRESSURE, AND AIR INLET TEMPERATURE.

1) LOCATE "A" ON ALTITUDE CURVE FOR GIVEN MANIFOLD PRESSURE AND ALTITUDE AT RPM, SHOWN
2) MODIFY HORSEPOWER AT "A" FOR VARIATION OF INLET AIR TEMPERATURE TO THE TURBOCHARGER T_A FROM STANDARD ALTITUDE TEMPERATURE T_S BY FORMULA:—

$$(\text{HP AT "A"}) \times \sqrt{\frac{460 + T_S}{460 + T_A}} = \text{ACTUAL HP}$$

(APPROXIMATELY 1% CORRECTION FOR EACH 10° F VARIATION FROM T_S)

BRAKE HORSEPOWER AT STANDARD TEMPERATURE AND PRESSURE
+350
+300
+250
+200
+150
+100
+50
0
−50
NORMAL RATED POWER
310 HP, 38.6" HG MAP
ENGINE RPM
2575 RPM
18 20 22 24 26 28 30 32 34 36 38 40
ABSOLUTE MANIFOLD PRESSURE, IN. HG

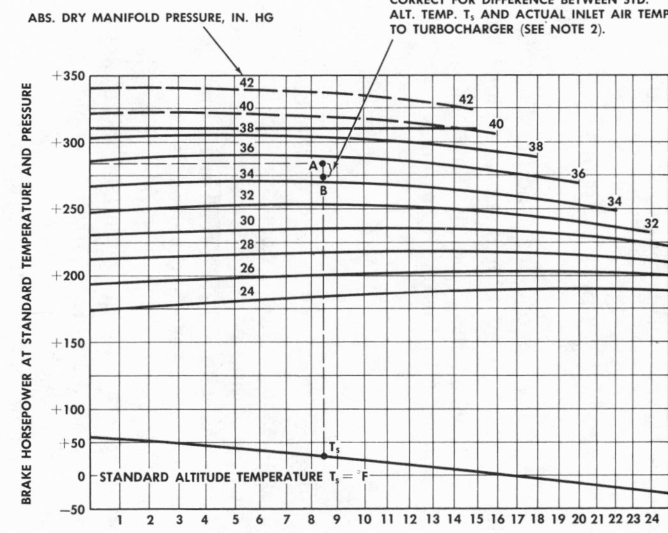

Figure 4.16 Typical turbosupercharged engine performance chart. *(Courtesy of Avco Lycoming.)*

mediate rpm and follow a prop load curve to idle rpm. The power absorbed by a fixed-pitch propeller increases as the cube of the rpm change.

$$hp_2 = hp_1(rpm_2/rpm_1)^3$$

The performance charts for engines incorporating superchargers, and to be used with constant-speed propellers, are plotted to show altitude performance as well as sea-level performance. A typical chart of this type is shown by Figure 4.16 for one rpm line.

ENGINE COOLING

A substantial portion of the total energy of the burning fuel is lost as heat within the engine. In addition, considerable heat is created by the friction of the moving engine parts. This heat must be removed to maintain metal temperatures within structural limits. Engine heat dissipation, especially from the cylinder head and valves, is also necessary for proper control of the fuel-air mixture burning rate. Heat is removed by the cylinder cooling system and by the circulating oil system which removes internal engine heat and then the oil itself is cooled.

Air-cooled engines, which are used almost exclusively today, are cooled by passing air directly over the cylinders and bringing it into contact with the cooling fins. The cooling fins are necessary to present a large surface area for transfer of heat to the cooling air since air (or any gas) is not as efficient as liquids in absorbing heat. The size and location of the cooling fins and the amount of air circulation required about the various parts of the cylinder play a very important part in the success of the air-cooled engine as an airplane power plant. To direct the cooling air around each cylinder for uniform cooling, a system of *baffles, dams,* and *hoods* fabricated from sheet metal is closely attached to portions of the cylinders. These baffles can be seen on some of the engine illustrations on the following pages. Note the greater depth of the cooling fins on the cylinder heads inside of which the combustion takes place.

A portion of engine heat is dissipated through the circulating oil system. Besides providing lubrication, the oil removes heat from the bottom of the pistons and absorbs the heat caused by friction. The oil is then pumped through oil coolers where the heat is transferred to atmospheric air. On some small engines, the lower part of the crankcase, or oil *sump,* provides sufficient heat transfer without requiring a separate oil cooler.

Cooling Drag Because heat loss represents a substantial portion of total thermal energy output of the engine, the drag imposed on the airplane to provide adequate cooling airflow must be carefully considered.

The larger the engine, the greater is the cooling requirement. Thus cooling drag receives considerable attention from both the engine manufacturer and airplane manufacturer, and flight tests are accomplished to determine the most satisfactory installation.

Cooling drag is equal to the loss in velocity energy of the air mass required for cooling. This may be expressed as:

$$\text{cooling drag (lb)} = M(V_a - V_E) \tag{4.11}$$

where M = mass airflow = W/g
V_a = airplane velocity
V_E = exit velocity of cooling air leaving airplane
W = weight of airflow, lb/sec
g = gravitational acceleration = 32.2 ft/sec/sec

This equation represents total drag loss to the airplane and includes the aerodynamic losses of the ducting system that conducts the air to and from the engine.

The manufacturers of air-cooled engines, principally in the larger sizes, provide charts of cooling air requirements. These charts usually show required *weight flow* of cooling air and the *baffle pressure drop* required to force the airflow through the cylinder-cooling baffles.

Oil cooling requirements are usually expressed by the manufacturer in terms of oil flow, maximum allowable oil temperature, and Btu of heat to be rejected per minute.

Regulation of Cooling Airflow In small airplane installations, the cooling air inlets and exits are usually fixed. The inlet area can be seen directly behind the propeller in Figure 4.4 The cooling air exits from the engine compartment through the flap openings on the bottom of the nacelle. Optimum areas are determined during flight testing by measuring cylinder temperatures and oil temperatures. In larger airplanes where speed ranges and power variations are greater, the cooling air exit areas are adjustable from the cockpit for control of cooling airflow. The adjustable portions of the exit on air-cooled engines are called *cowl flaps* since they form part of the engine cowling.

CARBURETION

The measurement of airflow for combustion and the metering of the proper amount of fuel to obtain the desired fuel-air ratio are called *carburetion.* As discussed previously, if the cylinders are not supplied with proper fuel-air mixture for each operating condition, engine performance will be penalized. For this reason, carburetors have become rather complex, especially on high-power engines.

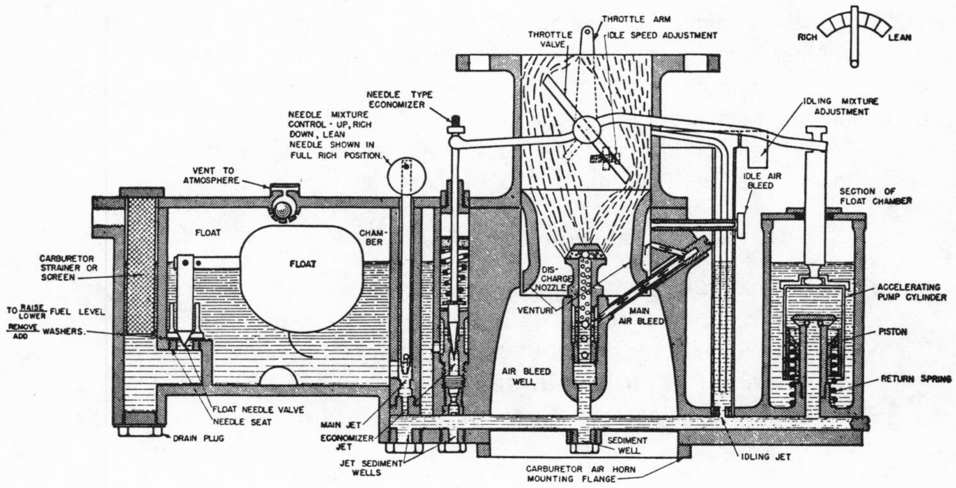

Figure 4.17 Float-type aircraft carburetor.

Principle of Operation Although detailed operation varies considerably, every carburetor operates on the same basic principle, that is, the measurement of airflow and the metering of fuel. Every carburetor contains an *air venturi* as the airflow measuring device (or part thereof) and a *throttle* for regulating the amount of airflow. The principal differences in carburetors are the methods employed for metering fuel.

Types of Carburetors The *float-type carburetor* (Figure 4.17) of most small-horsepower engines is similar in operation to automobile carburetors. The fuel is led from the float chamber, in which a constant fuel level is maintained by the float mechanism, through the fuel metering jets to the *throat* of the air venturi. When air is flowing, the static pressure in the throat is less than the atmospheric pressure in the float chamber with the amount of static pressure reduction being proportional to the airflow. As the airflow increases, the static pressure decreases, which in turn causes increased fuel flow. By proper design of the air venturi and the metering jets, the proper fuel-air mixture will be obtained for most engine operating conditions. During *idle operation,* the airflow through the venturi is not sufficient to provide the rich mixture needed for idle. To overcome this, additional fuel is added through an idle enrichment jet below the throttle. This jet is ineffective at higher airflow. To provide the *power enrichment* required for high-power operation, an auxiliary jet is opened by a linkage connected to the throttle admitting additional fuel at higher throttle angles. An *accelerating pump* is also connected to the throttle linkage to provide an additional charge of fuel during rapid throttle opening. *Altitude compensation* is provided on some float-type carburetors to reduce metered fuel flow commensurate with reduced atmospheric air density and maintain desired fuel-air ratios. This additional control is required because the air venturi does not measure true weight flow of air. Manual mixture control for cruise economy is often provided.

Pressure carburetors, sometimes called automatic carburetors or injection carburetors, are used on most of the large radial engines. The larger fuel flow requirements of high-power engines do not permit the simple metering system employed in float-type carburetors. Fuel is pumped under constant pressure into the pressure carburetor, and the utilization of this pressure to force fuel through the metering jets in proportion to airflow provides the principal means of fuel-air mixture control. The fuel pressure on the metering jets, called *unmetered fuel pressure,* is regulated in proportion to airflow by means of a valve connected to diaphragms which are positioned in accordance with airflow through the air venturi. After passing through the metering jets, the fuel is led through discharge nozzles below the throttle. On some engines the metered fuel is directed through hollow passages in the supercharger impeller before escaping to be mixed with the air.

These carburetors generally provide two mixture settings, auto rich and auto lean, which may be used for the richer fuel-air mixtures for cruising powers. *Manual leaning* is permitted at lower cruise powers for additional fuel economy. Altitude compensation, an acceleration pump, and power enrichment are always provided on the pressure carburetor.

Direct fuel injection is used on most of the horizontally opposed engines over 150 hp today. A very simple low-pressure system is shown diagrammatically in Figure 4.18. Fuel is fed from the supply tank, usually by an electric fuel booster pump, to a positive displacement engine driven fuel pump which supplies fuel flow in proportion to engine speed.

By arranging a calibrated orifice and a relief valve in the pump discharge, pump delivery pressure is also maintained proportional to engine speed. Fuel is then fed through the fuel-air control unit which is linked directly to the throttle where fuel flow is properly proportioned to airflow for correct fuel-air ratio. From the control unit, fuel is delivered to the fuel manifold valve which provides a central point for dividing fuel to the individual cylinders. In the fuel manifold valve, fuel pressure raises and lowers a diaphragm and plunger to open or close the individual fuel supply ports simultaneously.

A ball check valve under the plunger serves to insure that the plunger fully opens the outlet ports before fuel flow starts. Thus there is no unbalanced restriction to flow in the fuel manifold valve.

From the fuel manifold valve, individual lines carry the metered fuel to the fuel discharge nozzles, one for each cylinder. These are installed

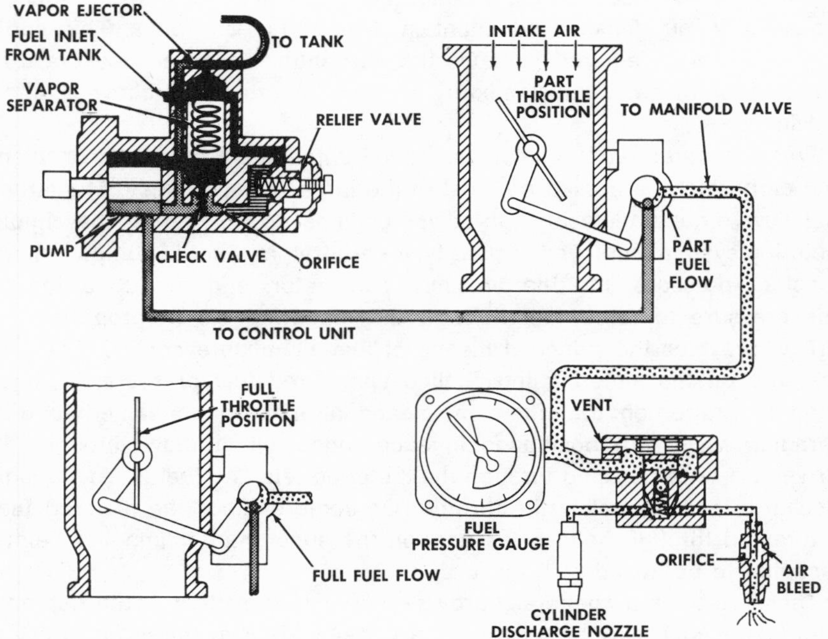

Figure 4.18 Schematic diagram of fuel injection system. *(Courtesy of Teledyne Continental Motors.)*

in the cylinder heads outside each intake valve. An air "bleed" or vent arrangement is incorporated in each nozzle. This helps to vaporize fuel and, by breaking the high vacuum which exists at idle speed, maintains the fuel lines solidly filled for instant acceleration of the engine.

For high-altitude operation with turbocharged engines, an aneroid bellows is added to the fuel pump to control orifice calibration and the fuel nozzles are fed with ram air.

Ice. Carburetor icing has always been feared by the airplane pilot. It may stop the engine completely or seriously restrict the power output. The float-type carburetor has the worst icing characteristics, since the fuel is evaporated immediately above the throttle valve in the narrowest air passage. In moist air, the cooling effect of the evaporating fuel will cause ice to form at atmospheric temperatures considerably above 32°F. The pressure carburetor eliminates this type of icing. However, under normal atmospheric icing conditions, impact ice will form on the throttle valve and on the air pressure tubes leading to the fuel control diaphragm. Carburetor icing is prevented by heating the induction air or obtaining the air from an alternate unrammed source.

TYPES OF ENGINES

The air-cooled, horizontally opposed engine is used exclusively in new normal and utility category aircraft today. Larger aircraft in production rely almost entirely on turbine engines for their propulsion.

Horizontally Opposed Engines The smaller air-cooled engines, up to 500 hp, are now constructed with opposed cylinders similar to the engine shown in Figure 4.19.

This cylinder arrangement lends itself to compact, rigid construction with small frontal area. Four-, 6-, and 8-cylnder engines are used with various horsepower ratings from 100 to 500. Many of the medium and larger sizes employ single-stage turbosupercharging and propeller speed reduction gearing. Magnetos are used for ignition, and electrical starting is customary. The oil systems are usually self-contained. Cylinders may be replaced individually for easy and low-cost maintenance.

Engines of advanced technology and design have been developed to combat the encroachment of turboprop engines in this power range. These engines utilize a much higher operating rpm (4000 to 5000) resulting in reduced engine weight per horsepower, greater operating smoothness, and reduced noise, both in the cabin and outside. Engines of the newer design have achieved weight ratios of slightly above one pound per horsepower in the 4- and 6-cylinder size to slightly less than one pound per horsepower in the 8-cylinder class.

Figure 4.19 Utility aircraft engine. Continental Model IO-520-A 6-cylinder, direct-drive, weight 475 lb, fuel injection, uses 100/130 fuel. Rated 285 hp at 2700 rpm for t.o. at sea level. Displacement, 520 cu in. *(Courtesy of Continental Motors Corp.)*

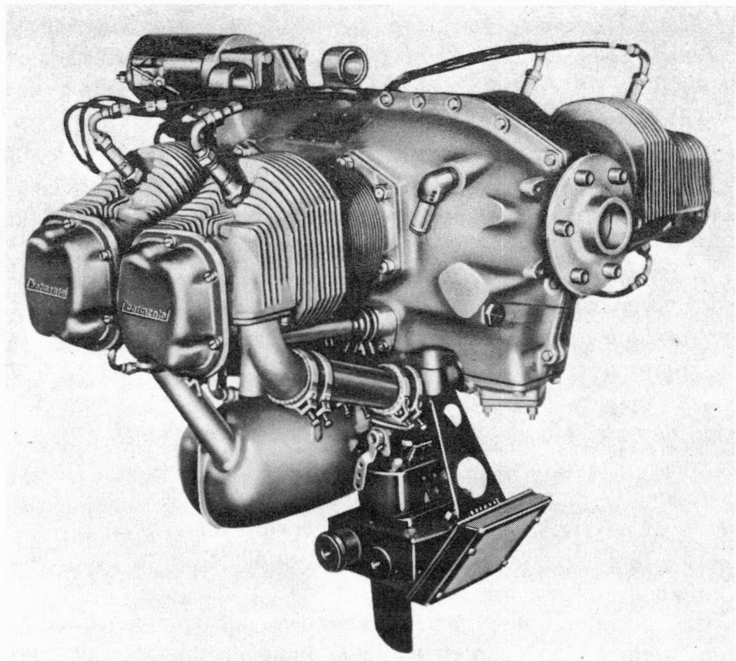

Figure 4.20 Four-cylinder, direct-drive, 100-hp aircraft engine. *(Courtesy of Teledyne Continental Motors.)*

Many design features are used to reduce engine complexity, weight, and cost. One manufacturer has developed a system of torsional vibration control, eliminating the need for pendulum crankshaft dampers thereby sharply reducing vibratory torque in the crankshaft, propeller gearing, propeller, and accessory drives. This also permits the use of lighter, slower, and quieter propellers. Perhaps most significant, it reduces stresses in all engine components permitting lighter weight in all structural members (Figure 4.23).

Reduction gearing for propeller drive is accomplished by spur gears which also drive the camshafts. While this limits the range of reduction to one-half engine speed, the resulting 2000 to 2500 rpm is about right for the power range and propeller diameter.

An additional significant feature of these engines besides reduced weight is a reduction of 25% to 30% in cooling air pressure. Since cooling drag in light twin-engine airplanes is a large percentage of total drag, the improvement is significant.

These horizontally opposed engines rely more and more on turbosupercharging ("turbocharging") for high-altitude performance providing a greater selection of cruise altitudes and higher true airspeeds.

Figure 4.21 Six-cylinder opposed aircraft engine. Teledyne Continental Model Tiara T6-285, geared drive dual turbocharged. Rated 285 hp at 4000 rpm for takeoff at sea level. Displacement 406 cu in., weight 402 lb. *(Courtesy of Teledyne Continental Motors.)*

Figure 4.22 Twin-row radial engine—R-2800. *(Courtesy of Pratt & Whitney Aircraft Co.)*

Radial Engines The larger radial aircraft engines which have served aviation so long and faithfully became famous with the Wright "Whirlwind" J-5 which powered the *Spirit of St. Louis* from New York to Paris with Charles A. Lindbergh in 1927. These engines have the cylinders arranged radially about the engine case to accommodate the greater number of cylinders required.

The horsepower ratings range from 300 hp to about 3700 for takeoff. They have from one to four rows of cylinders and 7 to 28 cylinders. Although the radial engine presents a rather large frontal area (an aerodynamic disadvantage), the short crankshaft coupling results in great strength and lightness, and the arrangement of cylinders in this manner permits greater utilization of cooling air.

The largest radial engine in use today is the 28-cylinder R4360, which produces 3500 hp for takeoff with water injection. The cylinders are arranged in four rows of seven cylinders each. The R4360 was developed toward the close of World War II and was chosen for a number of late-war and post-war multiengine airplanes. It is the last and largest of the large aircraft reciprocating engine.

ENGINE CONSTRUCTION

Horizontally opposed engines are constructed with a single case split at the centerline for access to internal parts—crankshaft, bearings, gearing, etc. The cylinders are bolted to the case and may be removed and replaced individually.

One of the new generation high-speed fuel-injection engines with rear mounted turbosuperchargers is shown in Figure 4.23. Accessories are side mounted for ease of removal for maintenance. An additional 20-bhp for driving other accessories such as air conditioning or spray pumps is available from the two four-bolt pads shown at the rear of the engine.

Radial Engines The major parts of radial engines are *power section, nose section,* and *rear section* or *accessory case.* The power section contains the crankshaft, valve mechanism, pistons, and cylinders. The cylinder assemblies, composed of cylinder barrels and cylinder heads containing the valves, are often called "jugs."

Similar to the opposed engines, intake pipes and exhaust stacks are connected to each cylinder head. Valves are actuated by *rocker arms* housed in rocker boxes atop each cylinder head. The rocker arms are actuated in turn by *push rods* actuated by means of the lobes of cam rings (camshaft in horizontally opposed engines).

In a radial engine, there is only one "throw" or crank on the crankshaft for each row of cylinders. Therefore all connecting rods are connected to the base of a "master" or articulating rod attached by a main bearing to the crankshaft.

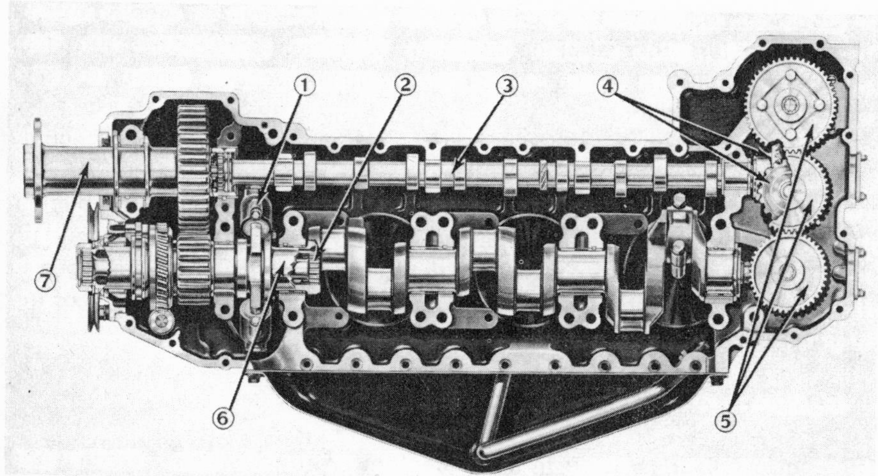

Figure 4.23 Cross section of 6-cylinder, horizontally opposed, high-rpm tiara engine. 1, Vibratory torque control unit (VTC); 2, quill shaft; 3, camshaft; 4, hypoid gears (2); 5, accessory drive train (3); 6, propeller driver shaft; 7, propeller shaft. *(Courtesy of Teledyne Continental Motors.)*

The front case or nose section contains the reduction gears for driving the propeller shaft at speeds lower than crankshaft rpm, and also the drive gears for the magnetos mounted on the outside of the case, the propeller governor drive, and the torquemeter, if used. The rear section contains the engine blower (previously described) and the diffuser for distributing the supercharged fuel-air mixture to the intake pipes. It also contains the air passage from the carburetor to the blower inlet and provides mounting for the carburetor. The rear case also houses the drive gears for the accessories mounted on the case exterior. These consist

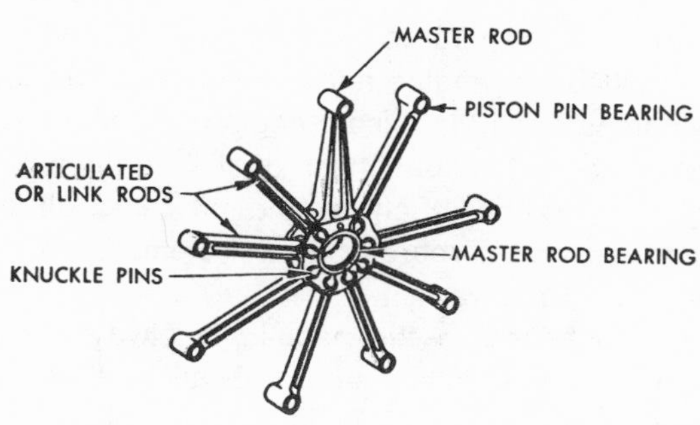

Figure 4.24 Radial engine articulating rod assembly.

of additional equipment requiring rotative power—some for engine operation, some for other airplane functions. Common accessories are: fuel pump, hydraulic oil pump, air pressure pump, vacuum pump, ac and dc electric generators.

A separate oil tank is required for radial engines, since an oil supply cannot be carried in the crankcase. The oil is fed from the supply tank (usually located close to the engine) into a pressure pump or pumps. These pumps force it under pressure to all parts of the engine requiring lubrication and internal cooling. As the oil escapes from the passages in the engine, it falls into sumps where scavenge pumps force it out of the engine, through the oil cooler, and back to the supply tank.

POWER-PLANT INSTALLATION

Engine installations aside from helicopters are of two types: *tractor* and *pusher.* In Figure 1.22 the front engine is a tractor mount, and the rear one a pusher.

Engine mounts play an extremely important part in the successful engine installation. Not only must they be light in weight, yet carry the vibrational and gyroscopic loads of the engine and propeller, but they must afford access to the engine and accessories for maintenance. Also, they must be designed to permit easy engine removal and replacement. Except for very small installations, engines are attached to the engine mount by means of rubber-bushed mounting brackets to isolate some of the engine vibration. In the very large engine installations, careful attention is given to the design of the mounting brackets (called *vibration isolators*) to insure that certain harmful engine and propeller vibration frequencies are not absorbed into the airplane structure. The engine mount is usually a welded structure fabricated from high-strength steel tubing. In single-engine airplanes it is attached to the main fuselage members, and in multiengine installations it is bolted to supporting structure on the wing spars.

Engine Nacelles The compartment housing the engine and protruding from the wing is called the engine nacelle. On occasion the term applies to the engine compartment in single-engine installations. The nacelle contains not only the engine but most of the additional equipment required for engine operation, such as the oil tank, oil coolers, superchargers, intercoolers, and carburetor heat system. A typical small-engine installation is shown in Figure 4.8.

The equipment contained in the nacelle is always isolated from the rest of the airplane by a stainless steel firewall in accordance with civil or military safety specification. This is a reuirement for single-engine installations as well. All cutouts in the firewall for passage of controls, tubing, wiring, etc., must be sealed according to the specifications for each different engine installation.

Cowling Engine cowling design is extremely important to the satisfactory cooling of air-cooled engines. Earlier installations exposed the entire cylinder to the airstream. Not only did this preclude any control of cylinder-head temperature, but the turbulence thus created caused unnecessary drag. The addition of baffles around the cylinders and the enclosure of the entire engine within the cowling greatly improved engine cooling while reducing drag as well. A typical example of small engine cowling is shown by Figure 4.4

Power Package Designs of multiengine airplanes generally provide for removal of the entire power-plant assembly rather than the engine alone. The engine mount is unbolted at the firewall, and the entire nacelle is removed including oil tank, oil cooler, auxiliary supercharger, etc. By means of quick-disconnect fittings at the firewall for all controls, fluid lines, and wiring, an entire power package may be changed in a few minutes.

Turbojet and Turbofan Engines

The principle of jet propulsion was recognized very early in aviation development as possibly the best method for obtaining greater and greater speeds. The practical application of the principle proved very difficult, however, because of the extreme inefficiency of early engine design. Early developments centered around the turbojet and turboprop engines, patterned to some extent upon developments in stationary gas-turbine and steam-turbine engines. In 1930, Frank A. Whittle was granted an English patent for a turbojet engine design, but it was not until 1937 that intensive work was begun on his design in England. The Germans initiated turbojet development in 1936 along with other jet engine and rocket motor programs. This work was carried on in an intensified manner, and the first turbojet-powered airplane flight took place in Germany in 1939. The airplane was a Heinkel HE178 powered by a Heinkel HE 53B engine. Meanwhile, the Whittle engine program progressed rapidly in England. In 1941 the fourth Whittle engine, Model W1 delivering 855 lb of thrust, propelled a Gloster E-28 airplane to 339 mph at 20,000 ft. In this same year, the General Electric Company agreed to develop turbojet engines for the U.S. Army Air Forces from plans of the Whittle W-2-B engine. The first American flight took place in 1942 when a Bell Aircraft P-59, powered by two General Electric IA engines of 1300 lb thrust each, flew successfully. By 1944, production was started

Figure 4.25 The first turbojet engine built in the United States. *(Courtesy of General Electric Co.)*

on the 4000-lb thrust J-33 engine for the P-80 airplane. During 1944, the first axial-flow compressor turbojet engine was successfully tested by General Electric. The first turbojet engine built in the United States is shown in Figure 4.25.

PRINCIPLES OF OPERATION

The operating principle of the turbojet engine is quite simple. There are only three basic parts: the air compressor, combustion chambers, and a turbine wheel (or wheels) for driving the compressor. The compressor in the forward part of the engine draws in large quantities of air, compresses it to high pressure, and forces it through the combustion chambers. Fuel is forced through spray nozzles into the combustion chambers where it is mixed with part of the air. This mixture is then burned in a continuous combustion process and produces a very high temperature, around 4000°F, which heats the entire air mass to 1600 to 2400°F. The hot gases then pass through the turbine wheel (or wheels) directly behind the combustion chambers. Part of the energy in the hot gases is used to rotate the turbine wheel, which in turn drives the compressor by means of a direct shaft. The hot gases then expand and blast out of the tailpipe nozzle at high velocity. The reaction to the momentum of the escaping gases is the thrust force which propels the airplane.

The efficiency with which the three basic parts of the turbojet engine operate, particularly the turbine wheel and compressor, is very important to thrust output. Since approximately two-thirds of the energy available in the hot gases is absorbed by the turbine wheel to drive the compressor, one can easily see the necessity for high efficiency of both the turbine wheel and the compressor. All early models failed because of inefficient turbine and compressor design coupled with inferior materials for construction. Since thermodynamic laws reveal that the energy available in hot gases increases with both temperature and pressure, design development constantly strives for compressors that will provide even greater pressures and turbine wheels that will withstand higher temperatures. It is the improvement in these two regions that has led to the tremendous development in turbojet engines since the first flight in 1939. Perhaps most outstanding has been the improvement in materials for turbine wheel blades.

MAJOR PARTS

Turbojet engine construction is relatively simple compared to a reciprocating engine. The major parts of typical turbojet engines are shown by the cutaway drawing in Figure 4.26.

Compressor The *centrifugal* compressor was used in early engines but is seldom used in new designs except in combination with axial flow on some turboprop engines. In the centrifugal compressor, air enters the rotating *impeller* at the center through the inlet guide vanes. Rotating at high speed, the impeller compresses the air by centrifugal action. The air passes from the rim of the impeller through a *diffuser,* which retards the tendency of the air to rotate with the impeller, into the combustion chambers.

The *axial-flow* compressor is on nearly all turbojet and turboprop engines today. The distinct advantage of this type of compressor is its small diameter. As can be seen in Figure 4.26, many "stages" can be added together without increasing the diameter of the engine. As shown by the illustration, the compressor blades are very similar in appearance to the blades on the turbine wheel. In front of each row of rotating compressor blades is a stationary row of "stator" blades fixed to the engine case. The stator blades are provided for the purpose of stopping rotation of the air and directing it at the proper angle (similar to angle of attack of the airplane wing or propeller) into the succeeding row of compressor blades. As the air passes through each stage, the air compression pressure and temperature are increased. The air passes from the last stage of compression through a *diffuser* section which serves the purpose of reducing velocity of the air and increasing static pressure. From the diffuser, the compressed air passes into the combustion chambers where heat is added prior to entering the turbine wheels.

The engine shown in Figure 4.26 employs two compressors, each driven independently by its own set of turbine wheels and at different speeds. This has been accomplished by making the drive shaft for the rear compressor hollow and rotating the shaft for the forward compressor within. An advantage claimed for this arrangement is higher speeds and attendant smaller size for the rear compressor, since the higher temperatures at the later stages of compression permit greater blade tip speeds before Mach limitations are reached. Engines of this type are often called "two-spool," "dual rotor," or "split compressor" engines. Present production engines employ seven or nine stages on the low-pressure compressor and seven stages on the high-pressure compressor.

A single-rotor, axial-flow compressor, as the name implies, utilizes one compressor. Up to 17 stages of compression have been successfully designed and built.

Combustion Chamber The performance of the combustion chamber, often called "burner," is very important to satisfactory engine operation. The fact that the burner must operate properly over a wide variation of airflow adds to the complication of design.

As shown in Figure 4.26, these combustion chambers surround the engine with equal portion of airflow directed into each chamber. Com-

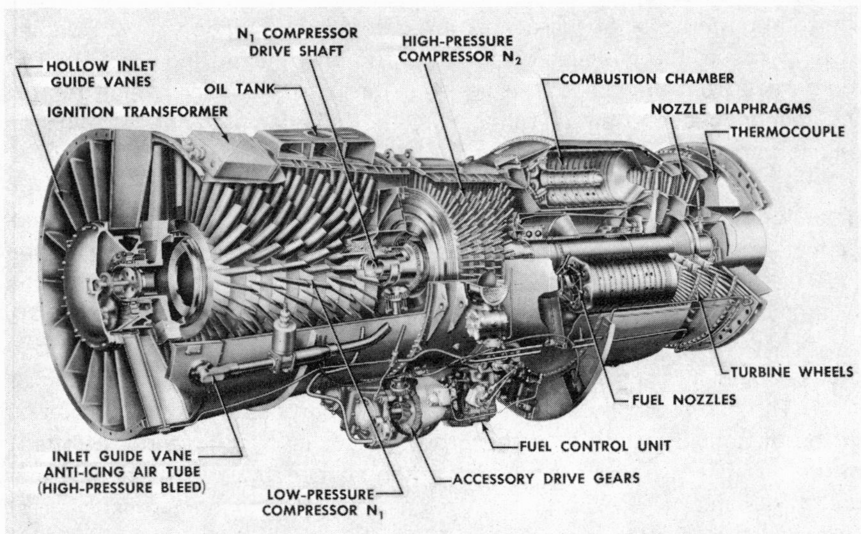

Figure 4.26 Principal parts of a dual-rotor axial-flow turbojet engine. *(Courtesy of Pratt & Whitney Aircraft Co.)*

bustion takes place within the "liner," which is perforated to permit the entry of the portion of air used for combustion. The remainder of the airflow passes between the liner and the jacket to cool the liner and then enters the liner toward the rear. At the aft end of the combustion chamber the two air masses have been thoroughly mixed and are passed through the turbine wheel. Fuel is sprayed into each liner at the forward end through individual nozzles installed in flameholders. Spark plugs for starting combustion are usually installed in two opposite chambers, and all chambers are interconnected with tubes for flame propagation. When combustion is thoroughly underway, the sparking of the plugs is usually discontinued. For this reason, any interruption in fuel flow thereafter will cause the engine to "flame-out," requiring restarting in flight, an "air start."

Turbine Wheels Perhaps one of the most outstanding achievements in turbojet engine progress is the development of alloys to withstand the temperature and stresses encountered in turbine wheels. Not only is the turbine wheel required to withstand high stresses due to centrifugal and axial loads, but it must do this at temperatures of 1600 to 2400°F.

As shown in Figure 4.26, the turbine wheel is composed of a number of individual blades. The blades, which provide the turning force, are individual parts keyed or slot-mounted to the heavy rim of the wheel. The turning force of the turbine wheel is imparted to the compressor by a shaft suitably supported by ball or roller bearings. The ability of the turbine wheel to withstand the high gas temperatures is enhanced by cooling air that is bled from the compressor and piped in a manner to blast on the rim of the wheel. The turbine-entrance guide vanes (turbine-nozzle diaphragm in the illustration) are usually hollow so that a portion of the cooling air may be directed through them to facilitate cooling. New high-performance engines also have cooled hollow first- and second-stage turbine wheel blades.

Large compressors may require more than one turbine wheel to provide sufficient power to drive the compressor. Split compressor engines likewise require more than one turbine wheel. If more than one turbine wheel is required, a row of stationary guide vanes, often called the nozzle diaphragm, affixed to the engine case is positioned between each wheel and the next.

Exhaust Cone The exhaust cone and the inner cone aft of the turbine wheel play an important part in engine performance. By controlling the relative diameters of the inner and outer cones at each station moving aft, a predetermined area for exhaust gas passage is established.

Tailpipe and Nozzle The tailpipe is attached to the end of the exhaust cone. Frequently the entire tailpipe is called the nozzle, but the nozzle actually is the opening in the end of the tailpipe. Tailpipes will vary in length dependent upon the installation. In pod installations where the engines are mounted on struts below the wing, a very short tailpipe suffices. Engines installed in the fuselage or wing root may require tailpipes of some length. Special tailpipes are required for engines using afterburning. This is discussed under *augmentation.*

Sound-Suppressing Nozzles Special nozzles are used on several turbojet transports to reduce the disturbing noise intensity of the jet blast during takeoff over populated areas surrounding commercial airports. This low-frequency, high-intensity noise is caused by the turbulent mixing of jet exhaust gases with the atmosphere. Nozzles providing more surface area to the airstream reduce the formation of large-scale eddies, lowering the intensity of the lower "rumbling" frequencies and changing the character of the sound. Also, by permitting a more rapid mixing of the jet gases with surrounding air, they increase the rate of sound-energy dissipation.

Thrust Reverser Thrust reversal to assist wheel braking during the landing roll is accomplished by stopping the aft flow of the jet and directing it partially forward in the direction of airplane movement. This feature is provided on all large commercial transports. It is almost a necessity when landing on extremely wet runways on which wheels can hydroplane, or on icy runways. It greatly reduces brake wear when used during normal runway conditions.

To prevent the hot gases from entering the compressor inlet, of the same or adjacent engines, the reverser directs the jet blast outward at a suitable angle from the nacelle. Because of this angle, and losses due to turning of the gases, thrust available in the reversed direction is about 40% to 50% of forward thrust for the same engine rpm.

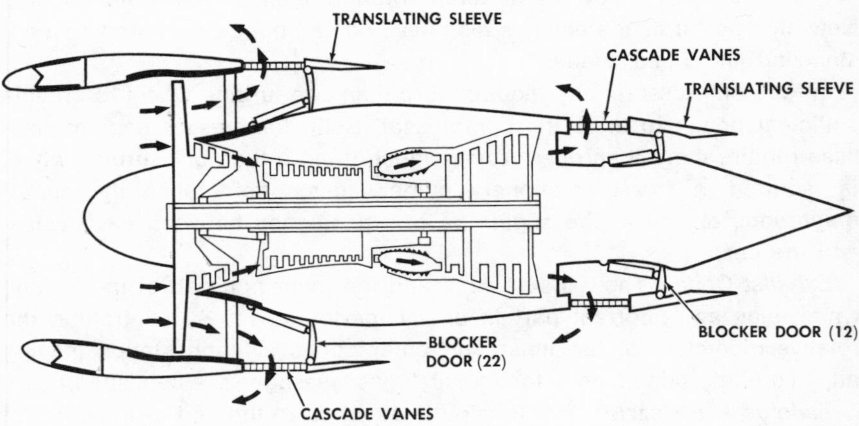

Figure 4.27 Short-duct turbofan thrust-reverser principle utilizing turning vanes and blocker doors. *(Courtesy of The Boeing Company.)*

Figure 4.28 Target-type thrust reverser used on single-nozzle and coplanar-nozzle installations, such as the Boeing 737. *(Courtesy of The Boeing Company.)*

Two major types of thrust reversers are in general use. In one type the primary exhaust gases and fan air are directed forward by means of turning vanes. Aft direction of the gases is blocked by means of clamshell doors or segmented blocker doors swung into position when the cowling is translated to expose the turning vanes. A diagrammatic sketch is shown in Figure 4.27. This type is used on Boeing 747, McDonnell Douglas DC-10, and Lockheed L-1011.

The other main configuration is the target type, which swings a portion of the cowling aft and outward to direct the gases forward. This system is used on engine installations where the fan air and the primary air are mixed inside the engine or tailpipe and exit through a single nozzle or exit through separate coplanar nozzles. "Coplanar nozzles" are those in which fan air and primary air exit at the rear but through separate nozzles. The fan-air nozzle usually surrounds the primary nozzle. A diagrammatic sketch of this type, used on the DC-9, the Boeing 737, and the C-141 is shown in Figure 4.28. The Boeing 727 also uses a target type but the aft direction of the gases is blocked by an internal set of clamshell doors. (See Figure 4.29.)

Accessories The accessories, such as fuel pumps, ignition coils, or transformers used for engine operation, are mounted on the outside of the engine or in the mounting strut and driven by the engine shaft

Figure 4.29 Target-type thrust reverser. Boeing 727 with Pratt and Whitney JT8D engine. Side panels are open exposing engine for maintenance. *(Courtesy of The Boeing Company.)*

through gear trains. Other accessories necessary for airplane operation, such as electric generators and alternators, hydraulic pumps, and vacuum pumps, may also be mounted on the engine and driven by gear trains.

Another method for driving airplane accessories mounts the accessories in the airplane wing or fuselage where small turbines drive them by means of compressed air bled from the engine compressor. On most engines they are mounted below and on the sides of the engine-compressor case.

Oil System A very simple oil system is required since there are few moving parts in the turbojet engine. The circulating oil provides lubrication for the shaft bearings and accessory drive gears as well as being used to remove heat from the bearings. Fairly low pressure is required to force the oil into the bearings and gears. After passing through the bearings and gears, the oil is collected and scavenge pumps direct it back to the oil tank. Before it reaches the tank it is pumped through heat exchangers to remove the heat picked up in the bearings. On some engines, the heat in the oil is exchanged with incoming fuel (before the fuel reaches the nozzles) in the heat exchanger provided for this purpose. Larger engines may require an air-oil heat exchange in addition, since a fuel-oil heat exchanger may not remove all the heat as required.

Fuel System With the exception of the fuel control system, the fuel system (fuel supply) is quite simple. Fuel is pumped from the airplane supply tanks into an engine-driven fuel pump where the pressure is raised to several hundred pounds to insure adequate atomization in the nozzles. After pressurization, the fuel enters the distribution manifolds to which the nozzles are connected. Some American engines employ a dual manifold system and a double nozzle to control atomization at starting rpm. During starting, a spring load valve called a *flow divider* directs the fuel into the smaller manifold until rpm and fuel pressure rise above predetermined values. In this interval, fuel is fed from the small manifold to the smaller orifice in the nozzle to provide adequate atomization at low fuel flow. As fuel-pump pressure builds up and fuel demands increase, the flow divider changes position, permitting fuel to enter the large manifold and be atomized through the large orifice in the nozzle. On other engines, low flow atomization is controlled by means of valves in the nozzle itself. British engines often obtain atomization in quite a different manner. Fuel enters the nozzle at relatively low pressure and is atomized within the nozzle by jet of air.

At engine shutdown, the fuel supply from the pump is quickly cut off by shutoff valves actuated when the throttle is closed. However, the residual pressure in the fuel manifold will still cause a small flow of fuel until the pressure bleeds off. To prevent this fuel from entering the combustion chambers and creating an uncontrolled fuel-air mixture, a relief valve in the manifold opens and the residual fuel is drained overboard.

PERFORMANCE

The magnitude of thrust output of turbojet and turbofan engines is determined by the mass airflow through the engine and the velocity of the mass leaving the jet nozzle and fan. This has been expressed earlier in the chapter as

$$F = \frac{W_a}{g} V_J = MV_J$$

This equation represents the thrust output when the engine and airplane are at rest. When the airplane and engine are in motion, air is being rammed into the engine compressor inlet, tending to retard the forward motion. This retarding force is called *ram drag* and its magnitude is determined by the mass airflow through the engine and the airplane velocity:

$$\text{ram drag} = \frac{W_a}{g} V_a = MV_a$$

The net thrust (F_n) for the engine in motion is, therefore, the *gross* thrust output minus the ram drag:

$$F_n = \frac{W_a}{g} V_j - \frac{W_a}{g} V_a$$

$$F_n = \frac{W_a}{g} (V_j - V_a) = M(V_j - V_a) \tag{4.12}$$

and

$$V_j = \frac{gF_n}{W_a} + V_a$$

Equation (4.5) may be reexpressed as

$$\text{Propulsive Efficiency} = \frac{2\,V_a}{gF_n/W_a} + 2\,V_a$$

In other words, net thrust is equal to the product of mass airflow and the change in velocity through the engine. Actually, the mass flow of gases from the nozzle is increased by the amount of fuel added for combustion. However, since the airflow is about 70 times greater than fuel flow, the mass of the added fuel is neglected in basic equations.

Airflow Factors that determine compressor airflow will also affect

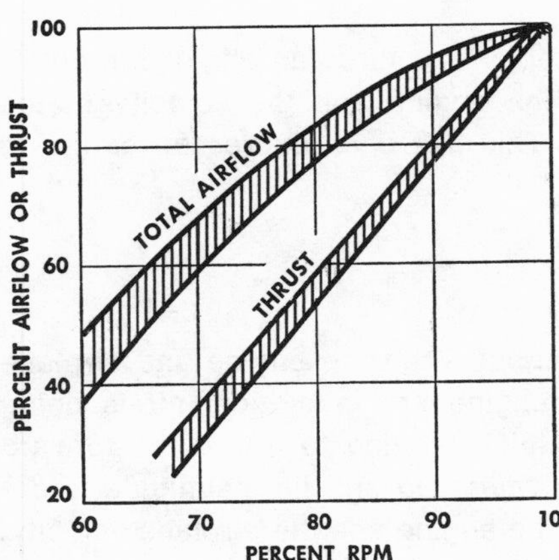

Figure 4.30 Compressor airflow and thrust vs rpm at zero airspeed.

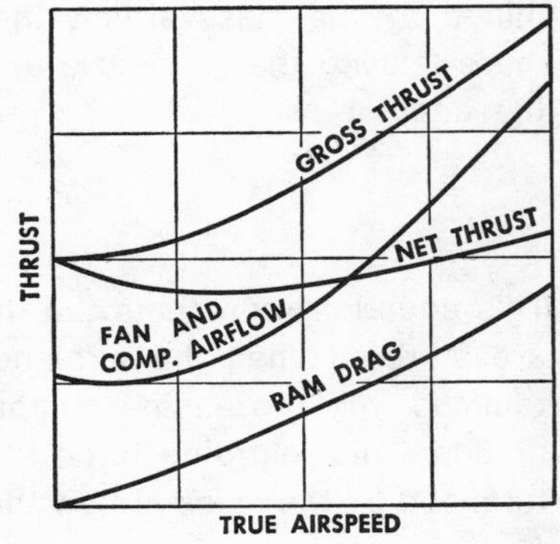

Figure 4.31 Thrust and ram drag vs airspeed.

thrust output. For turbofan engines, the discussion applies to *total* airflow (fan + compressor.) Compressor airflow, measured in pounds per second, is determined by the size of the compressor (and fan if turbofan), compressor rpm, airspeed, and air density. Compressor airflow varies extensively with rpm, as exemplified by the fact that thrust output at idling speeds is only 6% to 10% of thrust output at maximum rpm. Figure 4.30 shows the relationship of rpm with compressor airflow and thrust. Compressor airflow also increases with airspeed because more air is rammed into the compressor inlet. This increases the *gross* thrust output of the engine but also increases the ram drag. The effect of airspeed on gross thrust, ram drag, and net thrust is shown by Figure 4.31.

The design of airplane ducting systems leading the air into the compressor plays an important part in compressor airflow. Multiengine airplanes with the engines mounted in the wing or in pods below the wing will have relatively short inlet ducts. Fighter-type aircraft with engines mounted in the aft portion of the fuselage may require relatively long inlet ducts. With both types of installation, great care, usually requiring extensive testing, is required to insure that the maximum amount of air will enter the engine with a minimum of duct losses. This is particularly true at takeoff speeds and high-speed flights. The efficiency with which the compressor inlet ducts scoop in the air and conduct it to the compressor is designated by several terms—ram recovery, ram efficiency, or recovery factor. The effects of ram efficiency on engine performance are shown by Figure 4.32.

Because air becomes less dense as ambient air temperature rises and decreases in density with altitude, compressor airflow and engine thrust

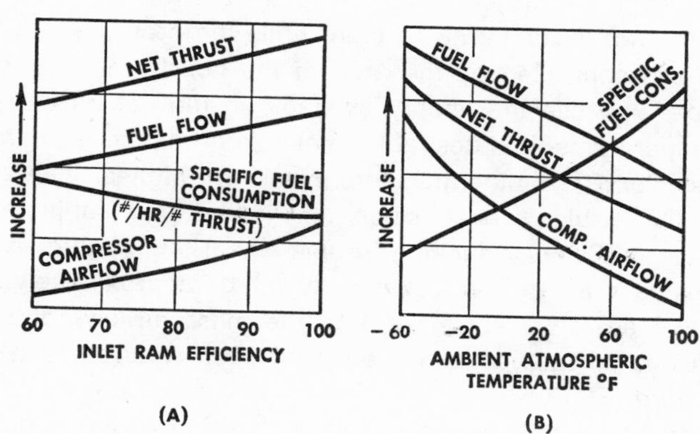

Figure 4.32 Effect of (A) inlet ram efficiency, and (B) atmospheric temperature on engine performance at constant airspeed.

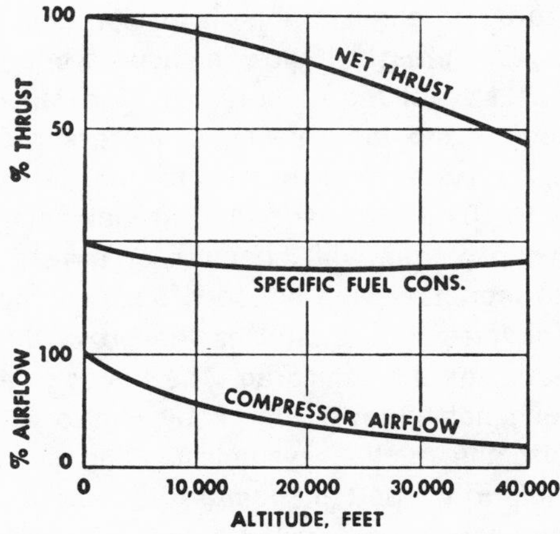

Figure 4.33 Effect of altitude on engine performance at constant airspeed.

also decrease. The effect of reduced air density and the resulting reduction in engine thrust must be considered carefully by the designer for performance at takeoff and performance at high altitude when selecting the proper size engine for a given airplane. Figure 4.32 shows the effect of atmospheric temperature on engine performance. The effect of altitude on engine performance is shown by Figure 4.33. An increase in atmospheric temperature at altitude from the standard-day conditions used for the plot in Figure 4.33 will further decrease altitude performance.

Primary jet velocity (V_J), is determined during the design of the engine. At any given engine rpm, jet velocity results from the pressure and temperature of the hot gases in the tailpipe, while the pressure and temperature in turn are controlled by the area of the nozzle through which the gases escape. Because the energy available in the hot gases is greater at higher temperatures, it is desirable to maintain tailpipe temperatures as high as possible. The factor that determines the highest allowable temperature is the turbine wheel, since this is the part subjected to the greatest stresses. Because limiting turbine wheel temperature is approximately the same in all engines, jet velocity will be approximately the same and jet nozzle area will correspond to the mass airflow for any given engine at full rpm. Tailpipe temperature is often referred to as *exhaust gas temperature* (EGT).

Fan air velocity is determined during the design of the engine by the number of stages desired and the pressure rise across each stage. The nozzle area is generally fixed to result in supersonic flow at a given altitude, airspeed, and compressor rpm.

Primary jet nozzle area is adjusted on some engines prior to takeoff to obtain maximum tailpipe temperature and jet velocity on engines that operate at fixed maximum compressor speed. Since air density decreases with increase in ambient air temperature, compressor airflow will decrease. Therefore, a smaller nozzle area is required to maintain maximum tailpipe temperature and pressure. Some engines, particularly two-spool engines, correct for thrust loss due to high ambient temperatures by adjusting the compressor speed control, permitting an increase in rpm to maintain airflow. Although jet velocity decreases with reduced compressor airflow, resulting from lower rpm or higher ambient air temperature, it does not diminish appreciably as altitude is increased, even though compressor airflow by weight does diminish.

When airspeed and rpm are held constant, compressor and fan airflow diminishes with altitude as shown in Figure 4.32. However, the reduced atmospheric pressure that causes the reduction in compressor airflow also acts on the nozzle. The reduced atmospheric pressure behind the nozzle tends to increase the velocity of the gases escaping from the nozzle by permitting greater gas expansion within the tailpipe. The reduced compressor airflow and the greater expansion of the hot gases tend to offset each other, and jet velocity remains substantially constant.

FUEL CONSUMPTION

Turbojet engines have higher fuel consumption, relative to their output, than have reciprocating engines. However, the cost per gallon of jet fuel is substantially less than reciprocating engine gasoline, and the higher fuel consumption of the turbojet engine as an airplane range factor is greatly offset by its light weight compared to a reciprocating engine and propeller installation. Also, jet airplanes are able to cruise at much higher altitudes and take advantage of reduced airplane parasite drag.

Current intermediate turbofan engines consume about 20% to 30% less fuel than the best axial flow jet engines. The new generation turbofan engines of very high bypass ratio (5 to 6) yield fuel economies 50% to 60% better than the best turbojet engines. These engines approach the ultimate reached in the large reciprocating engine specific fuel consumption. These increased bypass engines have been made possible by improved compressor design and by the use of turbine wheel cooling and materials capable of withstanding higher temperatures.

AUGMENTATION

This term applies to methods for increasing thrust during takeoff in addition to that delivered by the basic engine. Two such methods are in

Figure 4.34 Supersonic low bypass ratio axial-flow engine with afterburner. Pratt and Whitney TF-30 used on F-111A and F-14A fighter aircraft. Develops 20,000 lb thrust with afterburner. *(Courtesy of Pratt & Whitney Aircraft Co.)*

common use. *Afterburning* is used predominantly on fighter airplane and supersonic transport installations for thrust augmentation. As the term implies, fuel is added to the hot gases in the tailpipe after they have passed through the turbine wheel. The burning of this additional fuel greatly increases the gas temperature and correspondingly the jet velocity, resulting in as much as 50% increase in thrust. Because the hot gases pass through the tailpipe at high velocity, it is necessary to introduce the fuel through flameholders in the tailpipe similar, in some respects, to the flameholders employed in the combustion burners. The increase in gas temperature from afterburning causes the gases to expand, which tends to increase tailpipe pressure and turbine wheel temperatures.

To take care of this additional expansion and maintain turbine wheel temperatures within limits, a variable-area nozzle is used. When the afterburner is turned on, the nozzle is automatically opened to the wide-open position. When afterburning is turned off, the nozzle returns to the area required for normal engine operation. To permit complete combustion of the afterburning fuel, a greater length of tailpipe is required than for a normal engine without afterburning. A typical afterburning engine is shown in Figure 4.34. Note the length of the tailpipe and the variable-area nozzle.

Another method for obtaining augmentation is *water injection.* This method has produced up to 25% additional thrust. One desirable feature of this method is the small increase in engine weight over the basic engine compared with considerable weight increase for afterburning. Also, water injection equipment causes little or no change in normal engine performance, whereas afterburning equipment causes a slight increase in fuel flow during normal (afterburner off) operation because of the blocking effect of the flameholders in the tailpipe. To obtain the augmentation created by water injection, the water is introduced into the compressor or is forced through nozzles into the combustion chambers, or both. When introduced into the compressor, the water cools the air by evaporation, permitting the compressor to deliver more mass flow of air at maximum rpm. To offset the additional airflow, a signal is sent to the fuel control, increasing fuel flow slightly to heat the additional air. Thrust is increased by the increased mass airflow, plus the mass of the added water and fuel.

When water is introduced into the combustion chambers (or diffuser section), the resulting increase in compressor airflow is less than by direct compressor injection. However, large amounts of water injected into the combustion chambers, plus the slight increase in compressor airflow, result in a substantial gain in thrust. The injection water must be very highly distilled to prevent mineral deposits from forming on the compressor or turbine blades, which will seriously reduce their efficiency.

TURBOJET CONTROLS

Since the fundamental operating principle of the turbojet engine is to increase the velocity of air passing through it by increasing the temperature of the air, the fundamental requirement of the engine control is to provide the correct amount of fuel for heating the air. This must be accomplished in a very precise manner for the wide range of airflows influenced by rpm, altitude, airspeed, and ambient temperatures. In addition, the control must meter in the proper rate to provide controlled acceleration from low to high rpm. Some early engines, particularly British, required the pilot to perform some of the control functions when a change in airflow was experienced. This was particularly true for changes in altitude and control of engine acceleration rate. All modern turbojet controls now are designed to relieve the pilot of all duties except the movement of a single lever to select the desired thrust output of the engine regardless of airspeed, altitude, or ambient air temperature.

The modern turbojet control meters fuel at any selected rpm by measuring compressor airflow. This is done by slightly different methods by various engine manufacturers. One system measures compressor discharge total pressure (static pressure plus velocity pressure) only; another measures compressor discharge pressure but also measures compressor inlet temperature. A third system measures the difference between compressor inlet temperature and pressure and combustion chamber pressure (which is substantially the same as compressor discharge). By any of these means, changes which influence the compressor airflow, such as ambient temperature, airspeed, or altitude, automatically call for a corresponding change in fuel flow. Rpm is maintained constant at each selected speed by a mechanical governor directly driven by the engine shaft.

For any tendency of the engine to exceed or drop below the selected rpm, the governor will reduce or increase fuel flow to keep rpm constant. Selected rpm does not necessarily remain constant as altitude is increased, however. At higher altitudes, the reduced air density has an adverse effect on the burning characteristics of the fuel-air mixture as well as affecting compressor and combustion chamber operation. To prevent the burning process from suddenly blowing out, either during rpm acceleration or sudden changes in airspeed, an altitude bias is integrated into the governor control. This bias causes the governor to call for higher and higher idle rpm as altitude is increased, regardless of sea-level idle throttle position. Idle rpm, therefore, will be considerably higher at altitude than it is at sea level.

Engine acceleration rate from a lower to a higher rpm must be carefully regulated automatically by the control at all altitudes. Compressors, particularly axial-flow compressors, have a characteristic known as "surge" or "stall." This condition results from air separation on the compressor blades in a manner similar to stall and separation on an airplane wing. During rpm increase, usually in the medium speeds, stall and separation will occur if compressor discharge pressures are built up too rapidly for the corresponding airflow.

The control, therefore, must be designed to meter the exact amount of fuel which will permit the engine to accelerate as rapidly as possible but not so fast as to cause a stall. This rate of change of rpm also varies with altitude, being much slower at high altitude. On some engines an additional control is added to reduce compressor stall tendencies and increase acceleration rate. This control opens bleed ports in the compressor which "waste" some of the compressor air by dumping it overboard during acceleration through the critical rpm region. As soon as the critical rpm region is passed, the control automatically closes the bleed ports.

Compressor stall on some very high pressure ratio compressors is controlled by varying the angle of stator vanes between several stages of the compressor. This control is usually used in combination with compressor bleed. Figure 4.26 shows four stages of variable stator vanes in the N_2 compressor.

TURBOJET AND TURBOFAN OPERATION

Turbojet and turbofan operation is relatively simple. An individual throttle lever and starting switch for each engine are the only controls necessary in the cockpit. Movement of the throttle positions the mechanism within the automatic control on the engine, which then regulates fuel flow to establish an rpm in relation to the throttle position. In installations where augmentation is used, a separate switch may be employed to "arm" the afterburning or water injection electrical control circuit. Operation of the circuit is then controlled by switches actuated when the throttle reaches near to the wide-open position. A fixed "detent" position of the throttle is usually provided to facilitate setting of the throttle at the proper ground idle position. In some installations, another throttle position below the idle detent is marked for engine starting. Moving the throttle to the fully closed position closes a fuel cutoff valve on the engine. A separate start lever provides this function on some engines.

On many engines, thrust output is indirectly indicated to the pilot by the tachometer which measures engine rpm. Because different engines will operate within different rpm ranges, the tachometer indicator is usually graduated in percent of maximum rpm for the particular engine. The tachometer permits the pilot to select cruising thrust engine speeds and adjust the engines for equal thrust on multiengined airplanes. On dual-rotor engines, where the two compressors rotate at different rpm, each tachometer indicates the speed of only one rotor. This does not provide a satisfactory indication of relative thrust output since the ratio of the two compressor speeds (hence the thrust output) may vary from engine to engine.

Thrust output is determined on some dual-rotor installations by measuring tailpipe total pressure (PT_7). This pressure may be shown on a gage in the cockpit, or, as in most installations, PT_7 is divided by compressor inlet total pressure (PT_2) and the ratio PT_7/PT_2 presented on a gage in the cockpit. The latter system, called *Engine Pressure Ratio* (EPR) has the advantage of eliminating altitude density effect on the indication.

The only other engine instruments used in turbojet installations are fuel pressure, oil pressure, oil temperature, exhaust gas temperature, and in some cases, fuel rate of flow. Exhaust gas temperature indication is especially necessary during maximum engine rpm operation and certain other operating conditions to insure that excessive temperatures are not imposed on the turbine wheel. If limiting exhaust gas temperatures are reached before maximum rpm is attained, the pilot must not advance the throttle further since serious damage to the turbine wheel can result.

Compared to reciprocating engines, starting of turbojet and turbofan engines is relatively simple. The starter motor on turbojet engines is geared to the engine rotor shaft. On some engines the starter is electrically powered, on others it may be operated by compressed air. In the last-mentioned starter, the turbine wheel shaft is connected to the main engine starting gears. To start the engine, the starter is engaged, which commences rotation of the compressor (high-pressure compressor on dual-rotor engines). When the compressor has reached an rpm at which it will deliver sufficient airflow for combustion, the throttle is opened to admit fuel, and combustion takes place. The starter continues to operate

Figure 4.35 Small turbojet engine. The General Electric CJ 610 (J-85) produces 2950 lb takeoff thrust. The J-85 produces 4300 lb thrust with afterburner and eight-stage compressor to 5000 lb thrust with nine-stage compressor. This basic engine powers the T-38, Aero Commander, Lear Jet, F-5A, and several foreign aircraft. *(Courtesy of General Electric Co.)*

until self-acceleration speed is obtained. At this point, the starter disengages automatically, at the same time shutting off the spark ignition system. The ignition system can be switched on in flight for in-flight restart or operation in icing conditions which might cause flameout.

Types of Engines Because jet propulsion requires high-speed, high-altitude flight for greatest propulsive efficiency, the major jet engine design effort has been concentrated on the larger thrust output machines. However, several smaller models, with 2000 to 4000 lb thrust, have been developed for use in high-speed target airplanes, business aircraft, and jet training airplanes. A majority of the larger turbojet engines developed in recent years fall within the 10,000 ot 25,000 lb thrust class (without augmentation).

Larger turbojet engines of the 38,000 to 40,000 lb thrust class are being developed for the Anglo-French *Concorde* and the Russian TU-104 supersonic transports. The General Electric GE-4 engine will provide 70,000 lb thrust with afterburning for the Boeing 2707 supersonic transport.

The axial-flow JT-3C engine (J-57) is used on several commercial and many military airplanes. Thrust ratings vary from 12,000 lb unaugmented ("dry"), 13,500 lb with water ("wet"), to 18,000 lb with afterburning.

The J-79 (CJ-805) engine is unique because it uses a single 17-stage

Figure 4.36 Single-rotor J179 turbojet engine. This engine uses 17 stages of compression with stator vane angle control. The J-79 is used on a number of subsonic and supersonic fighter aircraft and develops 18,000 lb thrust with afterburner. (Afterburner not shown in illustration.) *(Courtesy of General Electric Co.)*

compressor developing 16,000 to 18,000 lbs thrust with afterburning. Seven stator vane stages in the compressor are variable. This engine is used on several supersonic fighter airplanes. A picture of this engine without afterburner is shown in Figure 4.36.

The foregoing are typical examples of turbojet engines in use today. Generally, new development is centered around the turbofan or bypass engines with the GE-4 supersonic engine being an exception.

Turbofan engines are being used exclusively today on all later commercial and military subsonic transports. As noted previously, these engines were developed to provide greater propulsive efficiency than turbojets by increasing total airflow and reducing velocity of the combined jets. The additional airflow does not pass through the combustion chambers and turbine wheels but is ducted aft around the engine case. The fan air may be exited at the forward part of the nacelle through a separate nozzle as shown by Figure 4.40 or may be conducted around the entire engine case and exited through a common nozzle as in Figure 4.29, or exited through separate coplanar nozzles at the rear as on the C-141.

Medium bypass ratio engines are in widespread use today on a number of large transports. The JT-3D (TF-33) was developed from the J-57 engine. This turbofan powers the Boeing family of 707 and 720 fanjets, the later McDonnell Douglas DC-8 series, and the C-141 Starlifter. Takeoff thrust is rated at 18,000 and 19,000 lb for the 15-stage commercial engines to 21,000 lb for the 16-stage military TF-33 version.

The 13-stage JT-8D-5 developing 12,500 lb thrust and the JT-8D-7 developing 14,500 lb thrust are used on the Boeing 727 and 737 airplanes and the McDonnell Douglas DC-9. In this engine the fan air is conducted

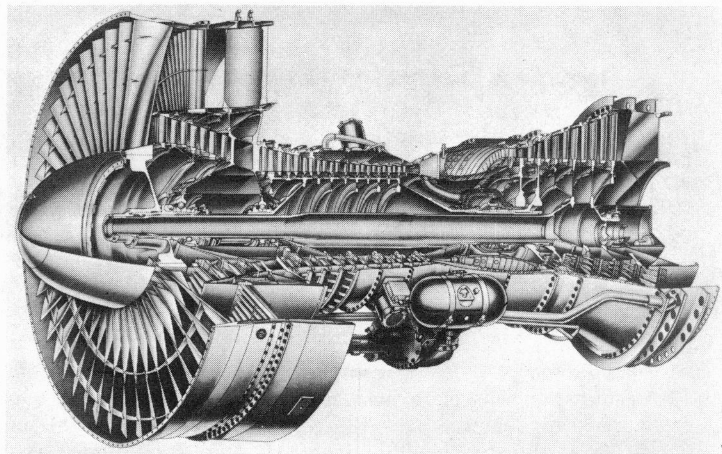

Figure 4.37 Cutaway view of the JT-9D high bypass ratio dual-rotor turbofan engine. The two rotors have 15 stages of compression and a seven-stage turbine is used. It produces 47,000 lb thrust at takeoff and has a weight-to-thrust ratio of .187 lb per pound of thrust. *(Courtesy of Pratt & Whitney Aircraft Co.)*

Figure 4.38 Front view of JT-9D turbofan engine showing eight-foot-diameter fan. Installed on Boeing 747. *(Courtesy of The Boeing Company.)*

around the main engine case by an outer case and exits with the primary gases through a common nozzle.

The new generation high bypass ratio turbofan engines are exemplified by the Pratt and Whitney JT-9D. A cutaway view of this engine is shown in Figure 4.37, and a front view of the eight-foot-diameter fan is shown in Figure 4.38.

Takeoff thrust is 47,000 lb with water injection. The 15-stage compressor operates at a compression ratio of 24 and the single-stage fan has a pressure rise of 1.56. The specific fuel consumption is 0.36 lb per lb of thrust and the dry uninstalled weight ratio is 0.187 lb per lb of thrust. All values are for a standard day at sea level. This engine powers the Boeing 747 and some models of the DC-10. The GE-6 (TF-39) engine which is used on the McDonnell Douglas DC-10 and the C-5A are somewhat similar in design and performance as is the Rolls Royce RB-211 used on the Lockheed 1011 airbus. Growth versions of these engines in the 55,000 lb thrust range are under development.

Smaller high bypass ratio engines (5000 lb and under) are in developmental stages but have severe competition from new turboprop engines in this power range.

TURBOJET AND TURBOFAN POWER-PLANT INSTALLATION

The simplicity of these engines permits correspondingly simple installations. The near absence of vibration allows rigid engine mounting, and good aerodynamic cleanness is afforded by the small diameter of the engine. Engine cooling drag, which is a large performance penalty in reciprocating-engine installations, is insignificant in turbojet and turbofan installation.

Common terminology has classified turbojet engine installations into two types, the "buried" and the "pod." As suggested by the title, a buried installation is the enclosure of the engine (or engines) within the body or wing structure or immediately adjacent thereto and enclosed by fairing. When the engine is mounted in a closely cowled nacelle and separated from the wing or body by a supporting strut, the term "pod installation" is applied. One of the advantages of the pod installation is the exposure of the entire engine for maintenance by simply removing the cowling. The pod installation also provides safety in case of engine fire since the engine is remote from basic airplane structure. Buried installations are used predominantly on fighter airplanes in this country, whereas most large multiengine airplanes now utilize the pod installation with exceptions being the body-mounted engine in the tail of three-engined airplanes such as the Boeing 727, the Lockheed 1011, and the McDonnell Douglas DC-10.

Figure 4.39 Submerged J-57 engine installation in the F-100. *(U.S. Air Force photograph.)*

Figure 4.40 Turbofan engine nacelle. JT-9D engine installation on the Boeing 747 airplane. *(Courtesy of The Boeing Company.)*

A typical buried engine installation in a fighter airplane is shown in Figure 4.39. A pod-mounted installation with the engine mounted below and forward of the wing is shown in Figure 4.40. This is a short-duct turbofan installation with the fan exhaust at the forward end of the nacelle. A typical side mounting at the tail section of the fuselage as used on the Lear Jet, DC-9, BAC-111, and the Boeing 727 is shown in Figure 4.29.

Turboprop Engines

Turboprop engine development actually began in 1926 when the English scientist Griffith proposed an axial-flow compressor and turbine engine for driving a propeller. After wind tunnel tests, development was discontinued because of the economic depression and scientific reluctance to accept the engine as having any practical significance. Following the successful development of the turbojet engine, interest was again directed toward the turboprop engine and successful flights in England and the United States were made with turboprop installations in 1945. For several years following these flights, the majority of effort was devoted to improving turbojet design in the United States, and turboprop development lagged. More emphasis was placed on turboprop development in England and France during this period and the turboprop-powered English Viscount 630 was placed in commercial passenger service in 1950. Turboprop engine development during recent years in the United States has been directed toward smaller engines of a few hundred horsepower. These engines are now appearing on numerous medium-weight twins such as the Beech King Air.

PRINCIPLES OF OPERATION

Basically, the turboprop engine is a turbojet with most of the heat energy converted to shaft power by the turbine wheels, leaving very little for jet reaction. The basic parts of the engine compressor, combustion chambers, and turbine wheels are the same in both engines, except that larger or a greater number of turbine wheels are used.

In most turboprop (called gas turbine engines when installed in helicopters) engines of recent design, separate turbines are used to drive the compressor and power output shafts. This type of design is called "free turbine." In the cutaway picture shown by Figure 4.41, the two turbines, each with two stages, are indicated. In all of the earlier larger turboprop engines the compressor and propeller gearing were driven by a single

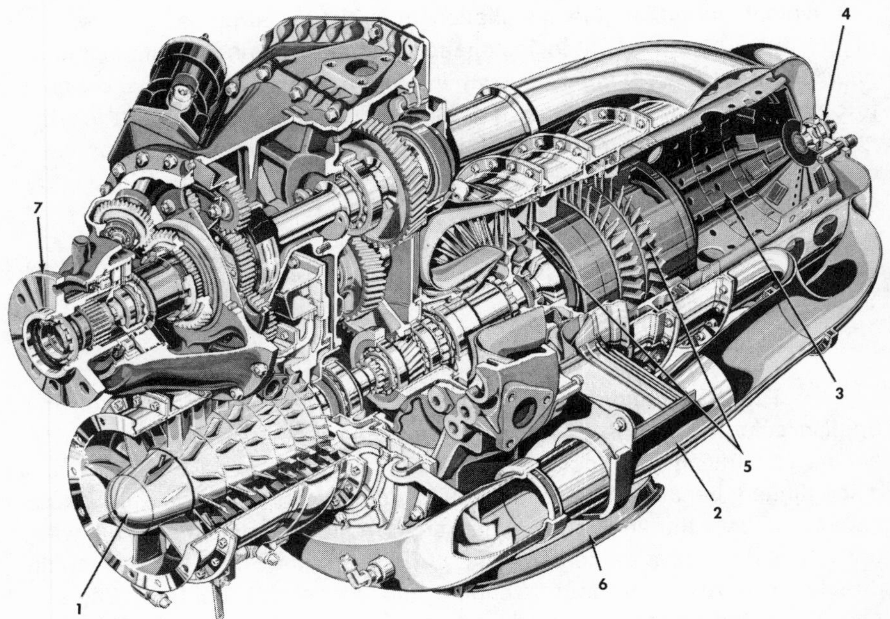

Figure 4.41 The Allison Model 250 turboprop engine. This engine utilizes six stages of axial-flow compression coupled with a single-stage centrifugal compressor. It develops 418 eshp. 1, Compressor: six axial stages and one centrifugal stage of the compressor. 2, Air transfer tubes: air from compressor to combustion section through two air transfer tubes. 3, Combustor: single combustor. 4, Fuel nozzle. 5, Turbines: two-stage axial turbine, which drives compressor; second two-stage axial turbine, which drives power-output shaft. 6, Exhaust: twin exhaust ducts. 7, Propshaft flange: accessories gear case and propeller reduction gearbox. *(Courtesy of Allison Division of General Motors.)*

shaft, losing a great amount of flexibility and efficiency offered by the free turbine design.

Turboprop Controls A significant difference exists between turboprop and turbojet engine controls. In the turbojet engine, fuel is metered by the control as required in proportion to airflow to maintain constant rpm, or is metered in the proper amount to effect changes from one rpm to another. As mentioned previously, the control must be designed to meter fuel within precise limitations to prevent overheating of the turbine wheels, compressor surge, or burner blowout. The control must also correct for varying conditions of altitude, air temperature, and airspeed for a given power lever position.

All of the control requirements of the turbojet are present in the turboprop engine with additional requirement imposed by the propeller. By means of the blade pitch-angle control, the speed and power absorption of the propeller can be varied independently of the normal engine control. Propeller controls are generally different for the free-wheel engine and the direct-drive engine. Usually the propeller rpm control and engine speed control are separate for the free turbine installations. The windmilling drag with flameout for this type of engine is only about 25% that for the direct drive. In addition, power section acceleration is extremely rapid since the propeller mass is not directly connected to it.

For direct-drive turboprop controls, the engine is operated within a narrow range in the high-rpm region for all flight conditions. This operation minimizes the effect of propeller inertia on power changes. Fuel is metered into the engine in relation to blade angle and desired power output. The propeller rpm governor is integrated with the fuel control and monitors fuel flow to cause rpm to remain within the established limits. With this type of control, flight idle rpm is generally quite close to maximum rpm. Thus during landing approach conditions, engine rpm will be high and propeller blade angle low. In some instances the blade angle is so low in proportion to flight speed that negative thrust will result and the propeller will windmill, feeding a small amount of power into the engine shaft. This action makes the turboprop installation substitute as an air drag brake.

Since idle rpm is only slightly less than maximum rpm, a rapid increase in power requires extremely rapid change in blade pitch. This is accomplished on one type of propeller by a system of clutches and gears which obtain the large power requirements directly from the engine shaft.

Windmilling drag in direct-drive turboprop installations is much more severe than with reciprocating and free turbine engines. If flameout should occur in the engine, the large power requirements of the compressor will be absorbed by the propeller, creating a serious airplane control condition, especially during low blade angle settings during approach. To prevent this condition, a device is incorporated in the propeller drive which immediately clutches in the propeller feathering drive (pitch increase) when negative thrust rises above a preset value. The blades are then driven at a very high pitch change rate toward the feather position.

TYPES OF ENGINES

Because of light weight and simplicity of construction, turboprop engines are being developed in a wide variety of power ranges. Experimental use of turboprop and turbine engines ranging from 200 to several hundred hp in small airplanes and helicopters are in widespread use. Continued im-

Figure 4.42 A 3750-shp turboprop engine. Gas turbine versions of this engine are used in several helicopter installations. *(Courtesy of Lycoming.)*

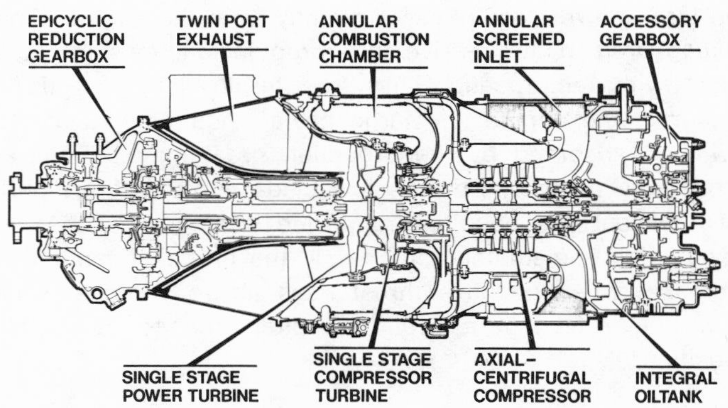

BASIC CONFIGURATION RETAINED THROUGH TO PT6A-50

Figure 4.43 PT-6A engine. This engine is available in several power ranges including twin pack with a single reduction gear assembly. It powers a large number and variety of aircraft throughout the world. *(Courtesy of United Aircraft of Canada Limited.)*

Figure 4.44 Allison 501-D13 turboprop engine with separately mounted reduction gearing. This engine is used in the Lockheed Electra transport; it develops 3750 eshp at takeoff. T-56 version at 4900 eshp powers the C-130. *(Courtesy of Allison Division of General Motors.)*

provement in design is resulting in engines with fuel consumption rates approaching the reciprocating engine. Examples of the smaller turbine engines widely used today are shown by Figures 4.41, 4.42, and 4.43.

The engines shown in Figures 4.42, 4.43, and 4.44 induct air at the front through multiple-stage axial-flow and single-stage centrifugal compressors. Reverse-flow annular combustion chambers feed the compressor and the free turbine for power output. In the PT-6A engine, shown in Figure 4.43, the air intake is at the rear of the engine supplying a typical axial-centrifugal compressor. Reverse-flow annular combustion chambers are used with the turbine wheels forward. Exhaust gases are discharged through twin ports at the forward end just aft of the propeller drive gear box.

Design development of large turboprop engines for heavy multiengine aircraft has been discontinued. The simplicity, reliability, and improved performance of turbojet engines, particularly with the advent of the turbofan engine, has made large turboprop airplanes somewhat obsolete from a new design standpoint.

TURBOPROP POWER-PLANT INSTALLATIONS

Similar to the turbojet, the simplicity and small diameter of turboprop engines permit light and aerodynamically clean installations. A representative installation is shown in Figure 1.19.

Rocket Motors

Rocket motors are the oldest man-made propulsion devices, having been used by the Chinese to propel incendiary weapons in A.D. 1232. The *propellant* fuel used in these early rockets is believed to have been some form of slow-burning black powder which predated the later invention of explosive black gunpowder.

Rocket development for the next several hundred years was devoted to purely military application, except for some use in later years to propel lifelines to ships in distress. Slow-burning black powder was used in all rocket motors during this period. Toward the close of the 19th century, the possibility of rocket motor power for aircraft propulsion led a number of investigators throughout the world to propose various types of rocket motor power plants. In the United States, Dr. Robert H. Goddard conducted intensive studies in rocket motor development from 1909 until his death in 1946. Early experiments with rocket motors made Dr. Goddard realize that desired speed and endurance could not be achieved with solid propellants of the types used in earlier motors. He therefore devoted most of his efforts toward the development of liquid-propellant motors, and a successful flight of a liquid-propellant machine was made in 1926. The fuel used in this motor was liquid oxygen and gasoline. The American Rocket Society, formed in 1932 by a group of amateurs interested in Dr. Goddard's work, perfected a number of new types of motors and flew various models.

Similar experimentation with liquid-propellant rocket motors was carried on in other countries during this period, much of it inspired by Dr. Goddard's writings. In Germany, intensive research in rocket propulsion just prior to World War II culminated in the development of the V-2 rocket-propelled bomb launched in large numbers against England later in the war. This machine had a total weight of 28,500 lb of which 10,800 lb were liquid oxygen and 8400 lb fuel (alcohol). The fuel was consumed in approximately one minute, producing 56,000 lb of thrust which accelerated the machine to supersonic speed in a high-altitude trajectory. The range of the V-2 was 150 to 180 mi. Design details of the V-2 rocket motor were important reference materials in later liquid-propellant rocket motor development in this country.

PRINCIPLES OF OPERATION

Rocket motors produce thrust by ejecting a mass of hot gases at high velocity from a nozzle in a similar manner to the jet engines described earlier in the chapter. The principal difference is that jet engines ingest air continuously, heat it by utilizing the oxygen in the air to burn fuel, and eject the hot mass of gases out the nozzle. Since oxygen constitutes about 23% of the air mass, a relatively larger mass of air is heated by the combustion process. As noted previously in the chapter, the air-fuel ratio of a turbojet engine is approximately 70 to 1. This means that only one seventieth of the total mass flow need be carried with the aircraft.

In rocket motors, the mass of gaseous material ejected from the nozzle is composed entirely of the products of combustion of the oxidizing agent and fuel, both of which are carried with the aircraft. The weight penalty involved in transporting the entire jet mass limits the duration of combustion in rocket motors to a relatively short period. Since thrust is the product of jet mass and jet velocity, it is extremely desirable to obtain very high jet velocities. Therefore, rocket fuels are used that burn at extremely high temperatures, resulting in high combustion-chamber pressures and very high jet velocities.

Rocket motors have been classified generally according to the two types of propellants used—*solid propellants* and *liquid propellants.*

Solid-Propellant Rocket Motors Solid propellants contain a mixture of oxidizer and fuel in one substance. Usually the constituents are pressed into a dense solid form with the shape of the form being a factor in the burning rate of the charge. Various types of nitrocellulose smokeless powders are often used to form solid-propellant charges. Combinations of other chemicals are also used.

Solid-propellant charges are usually classed into two types—*unrestricted burning* or *restricted burning.* The unrestricted burning charge will burn from all exposed surfaces with the geometrical shape of the charge determining the burning area. Usually the burning time is quite limited. The restricted burning charge has some surfaces coated with a burning inhibitor to limit the burning area and provide a longer burning period.

In solid-propellant rocket motors, burning of the charge is started by a pyrotechnic igniter which is set off with electric current.

The storage area for the charge forms the combustion chamber and the gases resulting from combustion are discharged through a nozzle at the aft end. Jet velocities range up to 7000 fps.

Liquid-Propellant Rocket Motors Liquid propellants are carried in tanks separate from the combustion chamber and are fed into the chamber at a controlled rate during the combustion process. A *monopropellant* contains an oxidizing agent and a fuel as a single liquid. A *bipropellant* system carries the fuel and oxidizing agent in separate tanks and provides for controlled mixing within the combustion chamber. The latter type is the principal system in use today. In the bipropellant system, the fuel and oxidizing agents are forced through feed lines, by means of pumps or tank pressure (or a combination), into suitable nozzles in the combustion chamber where burning takes place. Because of the extremely high combustion temperatures, the fuel is normally circulated through a jacket or lines surrounding the combustion chamber to provide cooling of chamber surfaces before entering the nozzles. Several combinations of liquid propellants are in general use. Common among these are liquid oxygen and gasoline (or jet fuel), nitric acid (oxidizer) and gasoline, and liquid oxygen and alcohol. Combustion-chamber pressures are usually about 300 psi, jet velocities 7000 to 10,000 fps, and combustion-chamber temperatures range from 4000 to 5500°F. Some propellants such as nitric acid and analine (fuel) are extremely toxic and require special handling precautions reducing the practicability of their use. Ignition may be spontaneous as with nitric acid and gasoline (or analine or jet fuels); with other combinations, spark or other types of ignition may be required to start combustion.

Impulse To compare rocket motor size and relative performance, a rating of *impulse* is used. This value is the product of thrust times firing duration. *Specific impulse* is used to denote the impulse from a single pound of propellant, usually for comparison of solid-propellant rocket motors. *Specific thrust* for liquid rocket motors is defined as pounds of thrust per pound of propellant burned per second.

5
Aircraft Instruments and Avionics

The efficiency and utility of modern aircraft are largely dependent on the ability of instruments to depict accurately what the aircraft is doing in flight, and how well its power plants and components are functioning. In addition to instruments, a variety of radio equipment is required to permit efficient navigation. The combination of these two, and the use of electronics in instrument design, is called *avionics.* To understand the roles of flight instruments, regard them in these categories: *control instruments, performance instruments, and navigation instruments.*

Control Instruments

These instruments permit the pilot to control how the aircraft flies by showing him directly and immediately both the *attitude* of the aircraft with respect to the natural horizon, and the *power* being delivered by the propulsion system. In other words, they permit him to control its performance. They are the *attitude indicator* (or horizon indicator), and a power indicating instrument—in propeller aircraft usually the *manifold pressure gage and tachometer;* in turboprop aircraft, the *torquemeter;* in turbojets, the *tachometer,* the *exhaust pressure ratio indicator,* or the *exhaust total pressure indicator.*

ATTITUDE INDICATORS

The attitude indicator is mounted directly in front of the pilot. There is good reason for this location. It is the only instrument which serves as a direct substitute for the natural horizon, and shows immediately whether the aircraft is straight and level, climbing, diving, or banking. It exactly duplicates the natural horizon seen through the windscreen.

SUCTION-DRIVEN ATTITUDE INDICATORS

This instrument, though less accurate and versatile than electrically driven instruments, is nevertheless the one which permitted the development of attitude instrument flying as it is known today. It has served well all over the world in thousands of aircraft for millions of hours and is still widely used in general aviation aircraft.

The attitude indicator may be considered a small horizontal metal bar, visible through the glass face of the instrument. It is kept parallel to the earth's horizon by the *rigidity in space of a universally mounted vertical gyroscope.* The base of the universally mounted gyroscope may be repositioned at will, without changing the relationship between the plane of the rotor and the earth's surface, once the gyro is spinning at the proper speed.

Suction System Power to spin the rotor of air-driven instrument gyros is provided by the aircraft suction system.

The vane-type pump, consisting of sliding vanes on an eccentrically mounted rotating shaft in the pump case, is driven from the engine accessory section. At 1000 rpm or more, it gives a maximum suction pressure of 10 in. of mercury (Hg). The suction relief valve is adjusted to the required suction pressure, usually 3.8 to 4.2 in Hg. The gate check valve protects the system from engine backfires, and the pressure relief valve releases the pressure which would be built up in such cases. Most multi-engine aircraft have suction pumps on more than one engine; either can be selected in the event of failure of one.

Attitude Indicator In the attitude indicator in Figure 5.1, the air sucked out of the case is replaced by air channeled through the instrument in such a way that it is eventually forced against buckets carved in the rotor, spinning it at about 15,000 rpm.

Figure 5.1 Instrument panel, Beechcraft, Bonanza Model 35. Top row, left to right: clock, airspeed indicator, attitude indicator, altimeter, manifold pressure gage, tachometer. Second row: ADF indicator, turn and slip indicator, directional gyro, vertical speed indicator. Radio equipment, top to bottom: Narco ADF, dual COM/NAV radios, and DME. The suction gage and VOR course direction indicator are behind the control arm. Compass and free air temperature gage are mounted on the center windscreen frame. *(Courtesy of Beech Aircraft Corp.)*

The air spilling off the rotor is channeled down through the cylindrically shaped rotor housing and out through four vertical slits cut 90° apart in the wall of the housing. After the air departs from the housing, it is drawn out of the case, thus completing the cycle. If air under pressure were forced in and against the rotor, the effect would be the same. Thus the man-made horizon is gyroscopically kept parallel to the earth's horizon. One has but to attach the rear view of a miniature aircraft in front of this horizon, with its wings fixed horizontally in the case (parallel to the actual aircraft's wing), and any rolling motion of the aircraft will be detected by the miniature aircraft appearing to dip its wing into the horizon.

Figure 5.2 Flight and engine instruments, Cessna 310. Top row, left: Airspeed, attitude, altitude, course indicator. Second row, left: clock (below ILS marker beacon lights), turn and slip direction indicator, vertical speed, course indicator. Third row: exhaust gas temperature, ADF indicator. Center; top to bottom: dual NAV/COMM receivers, ADF control head, transponder. Right center: DME. Right top: dual manifold pressure, LE oil pressure, temperature, and cylinder head temperature, RE ditto. Second row: dual engine tachometers, fuel quantity gages, outside air temperature, and suction pressure. *(Courtesy of Cessna Aircraft Co.)*

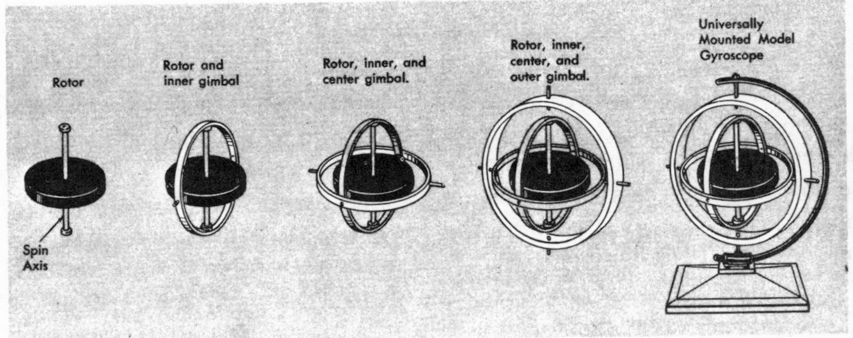

Figure 5.3 Mountings of the gyroscope. Great density, high spin rate, and the least possible friction in bearings and mountings are determinants of gyroscopic efficiency. *(Courtesy of U.S. Air Force.)*

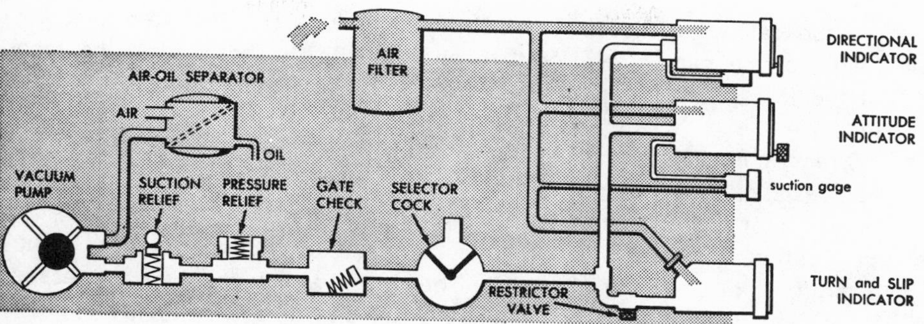

Figure 5.4 Typical aircraft suction system. *(Courtesy of U.S. Air Force.)*

Figure 5.5 Suction-driven attitude indicator. The instrument indicates a level 30° bank to the left. The center knob adjusts the height of the reference "airplane." Most current suction driven attitude indicators are commercial or milittary indicators remanufactured, deleting the caging knob at lower right. *(U.S. Air Force photograph.)*

In order to determine bank precisely, a scale is provided on the upper half of the circular instrument face, and is marked at 30°, 60°, and 90° increments from top center.

The horizon will displace above or below the miniature aircraft to reflect the respective nose-high or nose-low pitch attitude of the aircraft.

A knob below the face of the instrument permits the pilot to adjust the height of the miniature aircraft to align it with the horizon on the face of the instrument for continuous flight reference at different pitch attitudes.

Precession, the term given to any tilting or turning movement of the spin axis of a gyroscope, is the result of friction in the gyro mounting bearings, or the deflection of the spin axis by an externally applied force. In flight instruments, this force is the result of friction, of turning the aircraft, or of changing airspeeds. The rate at which the gyro precesses varies inversely with its speed of rotation, and directly with the applied force. As shown in Figure 5.6, a force (A) which attempts to *tilt* the spin axis will cause it to *turn;* one which attempts to *turn* the spin axis (B) will cause it to *tilt*. Gyroscopic *drift* is precession caused by internal friction in the gyroscope assembly.

Friction, however small, will cause the gyro in an attitude indicator to precess away from vertical. An automatic erection device is installed to counteract precession error. Hanging from above the four vertical slits through which air leaves the bottom of the rotor housing are four pendulous vanes, which half cover the slits when the gyro is erect (Figure 5.7). Should the gyro's spinning axis tilt away from vertical, that is, no longer

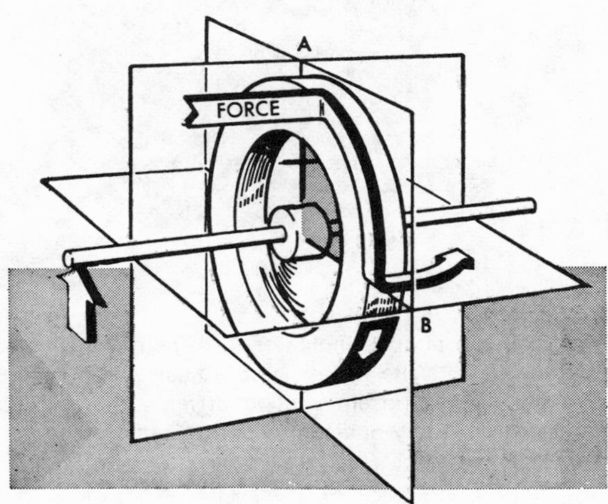

Figure 5.6 Effect of precession. An external force applied to the rim of a spinning gyro will cause it to precess in a direction 90° ahead in the plane of rotation and in the direction of the applied force. *(Courtesy of U.S. Air Force.)*

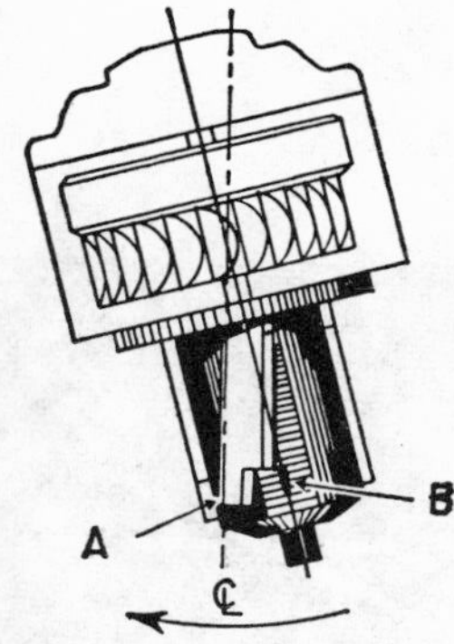

Figure 5.7 Action of pendulous vanes. The vane *A* is uncovering the slit *B*. On the opposite side, the vane is covering the slit. As the gyro erects from the force of the air jet, the vanes cover the slits equally, equalizing the jet force. *Courtesy of U.S. Air Force.)*

be perpendicular to the earth's surface, the gyro housing would tilt with it. But since the vanes hang vertically under the influence of gravity, their relative movement causes the greater opening of one slit and a corresponding narrowing of the slit located on the opposite side of the housing. The unequal escape of air which results is, in effect, a jet blast from the largest opening, which drives the bottom of the gyro housing away from the force of the blast. The resultant movement or precession of the bottom of the gyro forces it back to an erect position. When erect, the air escapes equally and no unbalanced force exists.

Centrifugal force in turns, and acceleration or deceleration will displace the vanes and introduce a false precession. Thus, during turns (coordinated or otherwise) and during periods of acceleration and deceleration, the horizon bar will be displaced slightly in pitch or bank. These errors are seldom greater than 3° or 4° and are of minor concern to the pilot who is adept at using the instrument.

Operating Limits The safe operating limits of the instrument are 60° of pitch and 100° of bank. Exceeding the limits of the instrument will cause it to strike against its limitations and "tumble." As explained above, this is a violent and uncontrolled precession and can result in cracked, flattened, or loosened bearings, any of which causes excessive friction and increased precession.

ELECTRIC ATTITUDE INDICATORS

The inherent limitations of suction-driven attitude indicators made essential the development of indicators which could cope with wider performance ranges in acceleration, speed, temperature, altitude, and maneuverability as the capabilities of modern aircraft expanded. The first widely used electrically driven attitude indicator was a self-contained unit, the J-8.

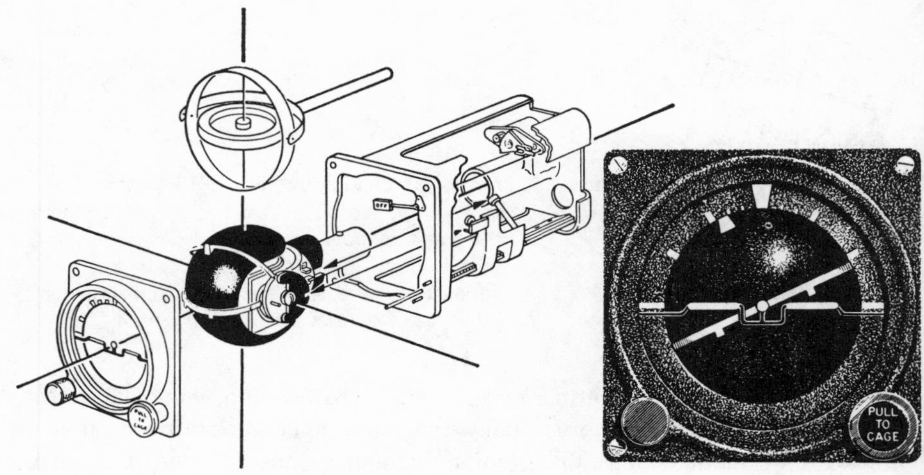

Figure 5.8 J-8 self-contained attitude indicator. *(Courtesy of U.S. Air Force.)*

The vertically mounted gyro is an electric motor, driven at 21,000 rpm by 115-volt, 400-cycle ac current. The gimbal mounting, a yoke and pivot assembly, supports the horizon bar, which can move up and down through an arc of 27°. A kidney-shaped partial sphere forms a black background for the instrument face. On the upper lobe is painted a black bullseye and the word DIVE; on the lower lobe is painted a white bullseye and the word CLIMB. These words, when under the nose dot of the miniature aircraft reference bar, represent about 60° pitch. The bank index pointer is attached to the yoke and pivot assembly and is free to rotate through 360°.

The dial face of the attitude indicator is marked with 0°, 10°, 20°, 30°, 60°, and 90° of bank and is used with the bank index pointer to indicate degrees of bank left and right.

The J-8 incorporates an erecting mechanism which maintains the gyro's spin axis vertical. Errors due to false erection in turns, acceleration, and deceleration can be as much as 5° of pitch or bank; however, they are usually less than 5°. As soon as the sensing device senses true gravity again after a maneuver, the errors are corrected rapidly.

Designed originally for fighter-type aircraft, the gyro is nontumbling, and the instrument has a "pull to cage" knob with which the pilot can erect the gyro in 30 sec after power is available, with enough rigidity for an instrument takeoff. An "off" flag appears whenever current to the instrument is interrupted; it disappears whenever the current flow is adequate. It is spring-loaded down and its appearance in flight includes current failure only.

Operation The J-8 permits 360° rolls and loops without tumbling the gyro, and the expanded motion of the horizon bar provides sensitive pitch indications in near level flight attitudes. When the aircraft attitude exceeds 27° of pitch up or down, the horizon bar is held in extreme position, and the reference changes to the painted bullseyes. At 90° of pitch, as in going inverted at the top of a loop, the sphere rotates quickly through 180°. As soon as the aircraft departs the vertical, the instrument again indicates the true attitude of the aircraft. This rapid rotation of the ball is controlled precession, not tumbling.

Both the angle between the horizon bar and the miniature aircraft, and the bank index pointer, show the bank attitude of the aircraft.

SYNCHROS

A *synchro* is an electrical motor system which controls electrically the angular position of one shaft by the angular position of another remotely located shaft (Figure 5.22A). Simple synchros have two components: the transmitter and the receiver. The transmitter, often called a synchro generator, consists of a rotor which has a single winding, and a 3-pole stator made up of windings displaced 120°. The rotor is supplied from an ac source and is coupled directly to the controlling shaft, as in a small electric motor. The voltages induced in the stator windings by the alternating field set up by the windings of the rotor are representative of the rotor position at any instant.

These voltages are carried by cable to the field windings of the synchro receiver, a similar synchro motor. Its rotor, free to turn, is coupled to a shaft, similar to that which positions the needle in an instrument face. The receiver rotor assumes an angular position depending on the voltages from the transmitter. The entire system is called a *servomechanism* if the torque has to be increased or amplified to turn the receiver rotor and its shaft.

REMOTE VERTICAL GYRO ATTITUDE INDICATORS

By separating the gyro assembly from the cockpit indicator, the designers were able to eliminate the restrictions imposed by mechanical connection between the two and the space limitations behind the instrument panel. For high-performance aircraft, the remote gyro attitude indicator is currently used, with its greater flexibility of mounting and greater accuracy. These systems consist of a displacement gyroscope, a rate gyroscope, and one or more amplifier-indicator combinations.

The displacement gyro, usually called the *control assembly,* is a hermetically sealed, gas-filled unit, displayed in Figure 5.9(A), which con-

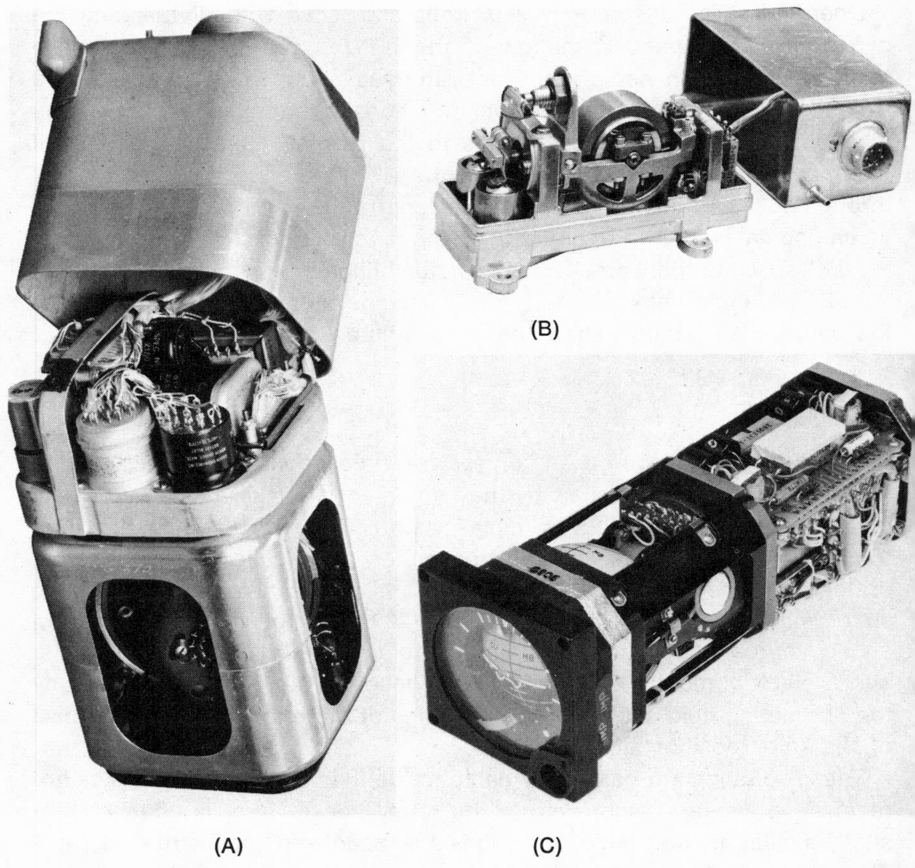

(B)

(A) (C)

Figure 5.9 Remote attitude indicator components. The control assembly, opened, is at (A); the rate switching gyro is at (B), and the indicator is at (C). The amplifier is not shown. In a sealed case, it is about the size of the control assembly. *((A) and (B) courtesy of Lear Instrument Division. (C) courtesy of Bendix Corp.)*

tains a 2°-of-freedom vertical gyro element, an automatic starting cycle circuit, an internal gravity erection system, roll and pitch erection cutout switches, and a provision for external application of fast erection when desired. The vertical gyro establishes the vertical reference line from which roll or pitch deviations of the aircraft are measured. Driven by 400-cycle, 3-phase 115-volt ac, it turns about 22,000 rpm and is mounted in gimbals which give 360° of freedom in roll and 82° of freedom in dive or climb.

The erection mechanism, which holds the spin axis of the gyro vertical, consists of torque motors and rings on the gyro gimbals. These motors are engaged by the switching system whenever the gyro is not vertical, and the appropriate motor acts on the gimbal ring to return the gyro to vertical.

The separate rate switching gyro, or *rate gyro,* Figure 5.9(B), which is mounted with its spin axis parallel to the aircraft lateral axis, senses turns; when the turn is more than 15° per minute, the erection mechanism is interrupted so that no false erection of the vertical gyro takes place during a normal turn. The time delay eliminates nuisance switching in and out of the erection system due to rough air and during small turns faster than 15° per minute.

When ac and dc power are applied simultaneously, as when aircraft power is turned on or a "fast erection" switch is activated, a thermal relay or fast erection switch allows faster operation of the torque motors, and the gyro is erected in 2 min. There is no manual erection device. Without the fast erection switch, erection requires up to 15 min.

The *amplifier* is also a sealed, gas-filled unit, which amplifies the error and rate signals from the indicator, and produces an output to run the servo motor in the indicator which responds to the servos in the control assembly. The amplifier has two independent amplifier channels, one for the roll axis and one for the pitch axis. Amplifiers may be separate units, or may be in the same case with the indicator.

The *indicator,* Figure 5.9(C), hermetically sealed and gas-filled, contains two transistorized amplifier channels and two servo assemblies, one for the roll and one for the pitch axis.

The attitude indicator consists of the instrument face, calibrated in degrees of bank, a fixed miniature aircraft reference, an "OFF" flag which shows whenever the control unit is getting insufficient current, the reference bar and sphere, and a pitch trim knob which adjusts the horizon reference electrically by vertical placement of the reference bar.

Attitude indicators are now being widely used such as that in Figure 5.10, in which the attitude of the aircraft is indicated by orientation of the movable sphere with respect to the fixed miniature aircraft. The horizontal center line of the sphere moves below the aircraft symbol for climb, and above it for dive. Pitch angle is indicated by reference marks on the sphere, and bank angle by the bank angle scale around the upper face of the instrument and a movable bank index or "sky pointer" which rotates with the sphere.

The pitch trim knob electrically positions the sphere to provide for pitch trim corrections relative to the fixed miniature aircraft.

Turn and acceleration errors have been reduced from that experienced in the J-8 to the point where turn error is virtually eliminated, and acceleration error is generated at the rate of .8° to 1.8° per minute versus the 3° to 6° error of the J-8.

Figure 5.10 MM-3 attitude indicator. Pitch trim knob is in the lower right corner of the indicator. The "OFF" fiag indicates no power. *(U.S. Air Force photograph.)*

Future Trends Remote gyro systems have the greatest opportunity for development for application to all aircraft. At present, scales, lighting, and symbols are simplified and improved. Color is being used to make them more natural and easier to use without error and with reduced fatigue. They are incorporated into integrated flight director systems, page 259. Gyro inputs from inertial guidance systems are being used, and video displays of complete instrument systems are being evaluated.

POWER INDICATING INSTRUMENTS

The *tachometer* is the basic power indicating instrument in lightplanes having fixed-pitch propellers; it is also basic in many jets, with the only difference being that the jet engine tachometer measures percent of maximum rpm rather than actual rpm.

There are two basic types of tachometer system: mechanical and electrical.

The *mechanical* instrument consists of flyweights working against a spring, in either tension or compression. The flyweights are mechanically connected to the engine so as to revolve at a speed proportional to the engine speed. The collar to which the weights are attached is free to move up and down the shaft against the force of the spring. As the weights revolve around the shaft, centrifugal force causes them to move away from the shaft. This movement away from the shaft is proportional to the speed of rotation and is resisted by the compressing of the spring. For each speed there will be a state of equilibrium when the centrifugal force is exactly equal to the spring compressive force. For a given speed there will be a certain displacement of the collar up the shaft. As the collar is connected to the indicator, this displacement, acting through a lever and gear train, shows the speed of the engine in revolutions per minute. In tachometers for lightplanes, a counter is added which records engine time in hours and minutes. It is calibrated by assuming an average rpm.

The *electrical tachometer* consists of an ac generator and a dc indicator. The generator is a simple inductor-type generating mechanism. The speed of the engine determines the frequency output of the generator.

The indicator on the instrument panel is a small millivoltmeter. A small transformer, built into the case, is designed so the core saturates at the voltage output of the generator when the engine speed is less than 100 rpm. Thus the voltage in the secondary coil is dependent on the frequency of the primary coil. The ac voltage is rectified to dc by a small

Figure 5.11 Color in engine instruments. Tape instruments shown here for a twin jet are colored in the usual green for operating range, yellow for caution, and red for danger. Exhaust Pressure Ratio, Exhaust Gas Temperature, Tachometer, Fuel Flow, Oil Pressure, and Oil Quantity are all shown. Red flag on Fuel Flow indicates the instrument is inoperative. Instant readability is provided by color-contrasting the tapes. *(Courtesy of U.S. Air Force.)*

unit placed in the indicator. The displacement on the millivoltmeter then indicates the speed of the engine in revolutions per minute. (See Figure 5.1.)

Jet engine tachometers are primary power indicating instruments. They indicate the speed of rotation of the turbine rotor, and, because of the high turbine speeds between 15,000 and 20,000 rpm, they indicate *percent of* maximum speed. These tachometers are electrical instruments consisting of two units, the indicator and generator, connected by electrical cables. Large turbine engines having two rotors use two tachometers, N1 for the front rotor and N2 for the rear rotor. (Figure 4.26.) The scale on the indicator ranges from zero to 110%. Indication is by two needles, one a vernier of the other to facilitate accurate readings at slow speeds for engine starting, and to enable the pilot to adjust power with greater precision.

The generator that actuates the tachometer is located on the engine accessory section and is driven by the main engine rotor shaft through a gear train.

The tachometer generator is coupled to the jet unit through a drive unit which drives the generator at a speed proportional to the turbine shaft speed. When the shaft of the generator rotates, it supplies a three-phase electric current, the frequency of which is directly proportional to shaft speed. This current is conducted to synchronous motors in the tachometer indicator which indicates the related speed in percent of rpm.

In the event of aircraft electrical failure, the tachometer will continue to function since it generates its own electricity. The scales are marked in green and red, with the upper operating limit normally set at 100% rpm.

MANIFOLD PRESSURE GAGES

The most accurate measure of power in piston-powered aircraft equipped with variable-pitch propellers is the manifold pressure gage. It measures the pressure under which the fuel mixture is supplied to the intake manifold. In conjunction with the engine tachometer which indicates the engine speed (constant for a given takeoff, climb, cruise, or approach power range set by the propeller control) the manifold pressure gage is the most easily read and accurate measure of engine power change. It is calibrated in inches of mercury (Figure 5.1).

There are many types of manifold pressure gages manufactured. One type uses a curved, flexible, hollow tube (Bourdon tube) which is flexed by changes in pressure. It measures pressure in the engine blower section or the carburetor air intake and transmits it to the indicator by a capillary

Figure 5.12 Exhaust pressure ratio indicators. *Left:* Round-dial indicator. The set knob permits setting in the digital readout a desired referenced value, as for takeoff or climb, with which the index marker coincides. *Right:* Tape-type instrument, showing the exhaust pressure ratio for all four engines. This is used on the Air Force C-141. *(Courtesy of U.S. Air Force.)*

tube. A second uses a bellows or evacuated chamber, one end of which is sealed with a diaphragm which electrically or mechanically indicates pressure on an indicator.

Manifold pressure gages indicate the station ambient air pressure when engine and airplane are stopped. In flight, they indicate air pressure at the flight level plus the pressure induced in the engine intake manifold by the ram air effect of airspeed. For this reason, when an engine fails, the manifold pressure gage will not go to zero, but will generally indicate

Figure 5.13A Boeing 747 control cabin. Safety dictates simplicity, cleanness, and physiological accessibility. All but pilots' control, performance, and navigation instruments, and pilot-essential controls and COM/NAV, lighting, and engine switches are located on the flight engineer's panel in the TWA cockpit. *(Courtesy of The Boeing Company.)*

Figure 5.13B Boeing 747 Flight engineer's panel. Fuel, heat, electrical power, air con tioning, cabin pressure, and engine condition instruments and controls a here, aft of the co-pilot. Circuit breaker panel is overhead. *(Courtesy The Boeing Company.)*

about 30 in. Hg. Note the reading in the upper left-hand dial on the copilot's panel in Figure 5.2. The engines are stopped.

TURBINE ENGINE POWER MEASUREMENT

The two most sensitive indicators of power change in turbojet engines are the tachometer, previously described, and the *exhaust pressure ratio (EPR) indicator.* The EPR is described on page 191. The ratio is mechanically computed and transmitted electrically to the indicator, which is calibrated in nondimensional units. A set knob on the instrument face permits a limit index to be set to maximum allowable or desired EPR reading, as for takeoff.

Turboprop engine power output is measured by the *torquemeter.* The torquemeter measures power available at the propeller shaft in pounds per square inch of torque oil pressure. This pressure is developed by pistons of the torque measuring system which reflect the changing pressures as engine reduction gears advance along the propeller shaft. A pressure transmitter, through synchronous motors, transmits the pressure indication to torquemeters, one for each engine, to the pilot's instrument panel.

Performance Instruments

The performance of an aircraft in a given attitude and with a certain power is indicated by the *airspeed indicator, Mach indicator, heading indicator, altimeter, vertical velocity indicator,* and *turn and slip indicator.* In high-performance aircraft, the *angle of attack indicator* is coming into general use.

PITOT-STATIC SYSTEM

Altimeters, airspeed indicators, and vertical velocity indicators all operate by sensing differential air pressures around the aircraft. Ram air, that is, air flowing by at aircraft speed, compared with static air, actuates airspeed indicators. Static, or still air at the pressure existing at the aircraft altitude actuates altimeters. Changes in static air pressure actuate vertical velocity indicators.

Ram air is sensed by the *pitot head*, or *"pitot tube."* Impact pressure is taken from the pitot head through pressure lines either to the instrument or to the air data computer. The pitot head is located on the leading edge of a wing, the vertical stabilizer, or the nose section, on a shaft which projects it into undisturbed air. On supersonic aircraft, it is mounted

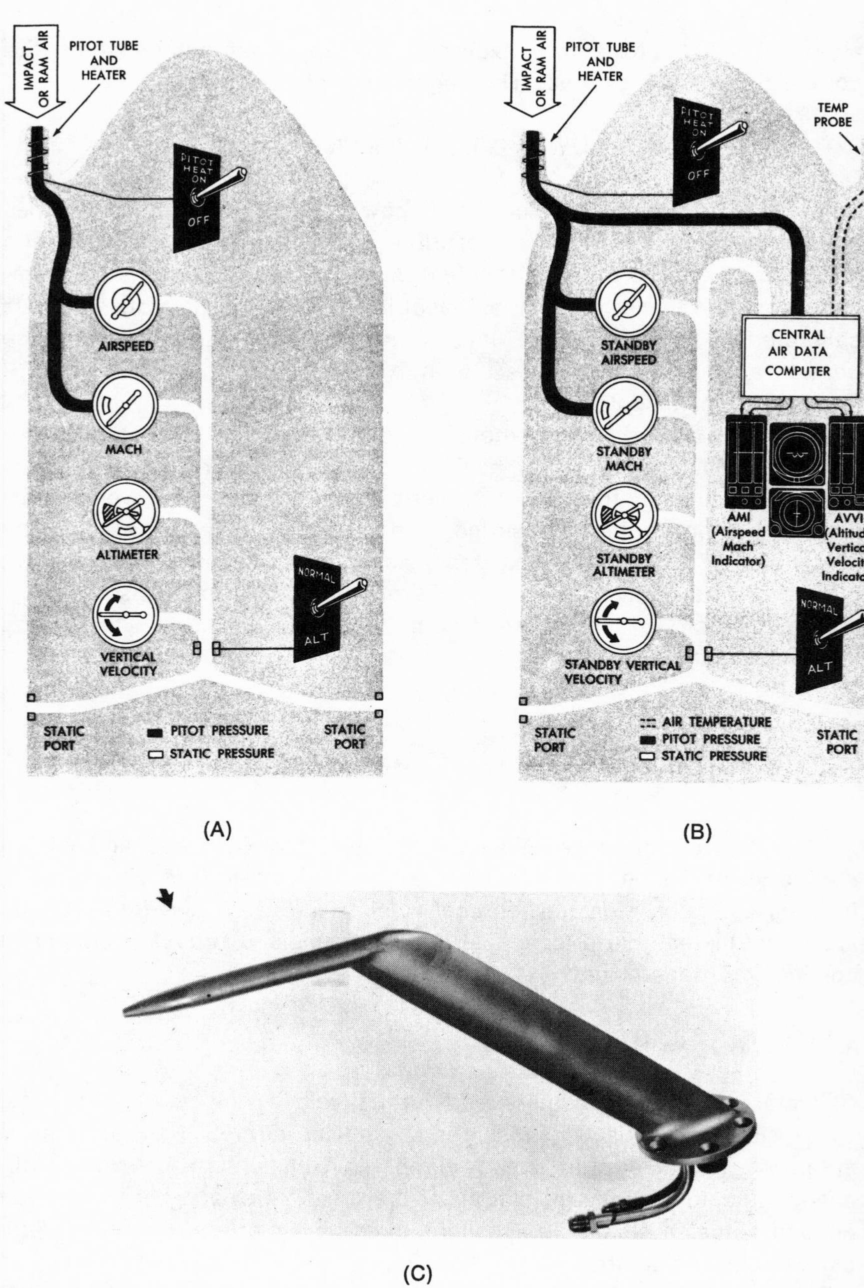

Figure 5.14 Pitot-static system. (A) Conventional round-dial instruments. (B) Integrated flight instruments. (C) Compensated pitot-static tube as used in the C-141. *(Courtesy of U.S. Air Force.)*

on a shaft or "boom" of sufficient length to project ahead of the nose shock wave.

Static pressure is vented through small holes in the side of the fuselage and led through lines to instruments or to an air data computer. On most aircraft using a flush-mounted static source, there are two vents, one on each side of the fuselage. They are connected by a Y-type fitting to compensate for any possible impact pressure that might occur on one of the vents from rapid changes in attitude such as slips, skidding turns, and rolls. A new pitot tube for transonic aircraft is in use with an aerodynamic shape such that the airflow at any speed insures static air pressure over ports in the tube head, about 2 in. aft of the tip. This system eliminates the installation error described below.

The pitot chamber is affected by the impact pressure of the air on the open pitot-tube tip as the aircraft moves in flight. The static chamber, if it is contained in the pitot head, is vented through small holes on the top and bottom of the tube to free, undisturbed air. The accumulation of ice and water are prevented by a heating element in the pitot head which the pilot turns on before entering areas of visible moisture; clogging of the static ports may be offset by an alternate source in the cockpit. The alternate source is usable only when aircraft are unpressurized.

When switching to "alternate source," one should expect to observe the altimeter and airspeed move slightly higher than normal, and the vertical speed indicator momentarily indicate a climb as the slightly lower in-flight pressure in the cockpit is registered.

AIR DATA COMPUTERS

Higher-performance aircraft are now customarily equipped with flight and navigation instruments which do not take information directly from outside air sources, but receive electrical impulses from a *central air data computer.* The computer receives ram air, static air, and temperature information and converts it to electrical signals. Airspeed, vertical velocity, altitude, and outside air temperature all use this source. (Figure 5.14). While all the errors introduced in instrument aneroids and bellows are present in the Central Air Data Computer, they are reduced to a minimum by the elimination of mechanical linkages in electrically operated instruments. The "CADC" is designed or selected for a particular aircraft installation, further minimizing error.

AIRSPEED INDICATOR

The airspeed indicator measures the difference between static air pressure and ram air pressure. Ram air is led to the inside of a hollow flexible bellows. Static air is vented into the instrument case and surrounds the bellows. The pressures are equal on the ground at rest, but as the aircraft accelerates as, for example, on takeoff, the ram air pressure increases. The relatively greater pressure in the bellows expands it, and through a system of gears and levers, moves the airspeed indicator needle or drum in the face of the instrument, registering airspeed in knots or in statute miles per hour.

Jet aircraft airspeed indicators also have a maximum allowable airspeed needle. It is used in a manner similar to the "red line" marking on airspeed indicators in piston aircraft to show the maximum safe speed of the aircraft in which it is installed. The difference is that the maximum allowable needle is a movable "red line" and points out the maximum safe indicated airspeed for that aircraft at all altitudes, whereas the stationary red line marking is accurate only for sea level on a standard day. A second sealed bellows expands under the lighter atmospheric pressures of higher altitudes. This expansion is linked to the maximum allowable needle to cause it to decrease its indications with an increase in altitude. The higher the altitude the farther it descends, constantly showing the maximum allowable indicated airspeed at increasing altitude.

There are three general errors characteristic of airspeed indicators:

Installation error is the error caused by the difference between the actual and the theoretical pressure differential developed by the pitot-static system.

Compressibility error results from "packing" of air in the pitot tube at high airspeeds, and results in indications of higher than normal airspeeds. This error is usually not more than one or two knots, but increases sharply to as much as 10 knots just below the speed of sound, about Mach .96. It decreases rapidly after the aircraft is slightly above the speed of sound.

Air density error is a gradual increase in actual speed through the air resulting from the effect of changes in altitude and temperature. It is determined and corrected by the use of a flight computer, or a true airspeed indicator which in addition to the normal bellows contains aneroid and temperature diaphragms which compensate for changes in air density.

As a result of these errors, various types of airspeed are identified as follows:

Indicated airspeed (*IAS*) is that read directly from the face of the indicator.

Calibrated airspeed (*CAS*) is IAS corrected for installation error. It is found for different airspeeds on calibration cards posted in the cockpit, and differs for each aircraft.

Equivalent airspeed (*EAS*) is CAS corrected for compressibility error; it may be taken from aircraft performance charts, or from an aircraft performance computer for the particular type.

Figure 5.15 Airspeed indicator. The present wide range of airspeed performance requires a drum or other vernier device to permit precise airspeed readings during slow flight for approach and landing. The small figures are Mach numbers. The striped needle is the variable Mach limit needle. *(U.S. Air Force photograph.)*

True airspeed (*TAS*) is CAS (or EAS in transonic aircraft) corrected for air density at flight level, and determined from outside air temperature and indicated pressure altitude, either by using a computer (Figure 11.14) or by a true airspeed indicator which must then be corrected for installation error and compressibility.

Ground speed is TAS corrected for wind effects (page 665).

MACH INDICATOR

This instrument indicates the ratio of aircraft speed to the speed of sound in the air at flight altitude. It is essentially an airspeed indicator which has an aneroid diaphragm to sense static air pressure. No temperature diaphragm is necessary because both true airspeed and Mach are dependent upon air temperature, and in the ratio, air temperature values are cancelled. By mechanical means, the differential air pressure of the airspeed indicator and the static pressure of the aneroid are combined to provide an indication of Mach number on the face of the instrument.

Combined airspeed-Mach indicators are provided for aircraft in which panel space is at a premium. Airspeed, Mach, and limiting Mach are displayed. A knurled knob is provided to permit setting a desired reference speed.

ALTIMETERS

The altimeter measures the height of the aircraft above a given reference, both for maintaining terrain clearance and for aircraft separation. The pressure altimeter is a simple barometer which measures atmospheric pressure and displays indicated altitude in feet above a preselected reference. As an aneroid barometer, it actually measures the weight of air lying above it at any given altitude.

Because atmospheric density at various altitudes is constantly changing from the lapse rates of Figure 6.4 due to changes in temperature and pressure, the altimeter must be designed to some arbitrary standard. The standard is the lapse rates in Figure 0.0.

Altimeter Setting In order to account for deviations from the standard day at the surface, the altimeter has a knob by means of which the pilot can set barometric pressures from 28.10 to 31.00 in. Hg into the *Kollsman window* (Figure 5.17). If 29.92 were set in the Kollsman window, and the aircraft were on an airport at the seashore on a standard day, the altimeter would read 0 ft, the elevation of the airport above sea level. But if it were not a standard day, and the barometric pressure were, for example, 30.20, the altimeter—reading altitude above a standard datum plane of 29.92—would show the aircraft to be 250 ft lower than sea level. If the pilot then turned the setting knob until the altimeter indicated 0 ft, 30.20 would appear in the Kollsman window.

Indicated altitude is that shown by the instrument. It is altitude above sea level when the current barometric pressure, or *altimeter setting* is in

Figure 5.16 Combined airspeed-Mach indicator. *(Courtesy of U.S. Air Force.)*

Figure 5.17 Sensitive three-pointer altimeter. Instant and accurate readability is essential with current high altitudes and high rates of climb and descent. The cross hatch is visible below 16,000 ft and the triangular index indicates each 10,000 ft. *(U.S. Air Force photograph.)*

the Kollsman window. *Pressure altitude* is altitude above the standard datum plane. The datum plane is at sea level only on a standard day, when the barometric pressure is 29.92.

True altitude is indicated altitude adjusted for temperature. It is determined by use of the computer but assumes the standard lapse rates.

Density altitude is pressure altitude corrected for nonstandard temperature. It is used for high-performance engine calibration, and is also determined from the computer (Figure 11.13) or from charts.

Absolute altitude is the height above the surface of the terrain over which the pilot is flying. It can be determined only by a radio altimeter (Figure 11.50). One can estimate it fairly closely by subtracting the height of the ground, read from the map, from true altitude; however, the reading will err by the amount of error in the map and by the degree to which the air (through which the pilot is flying) deviates from the standard lapse rates. It can vary so greatly due to pressure systems aloft and wind effects that the FAA requires 2000 rather than 1000 ft clearance above the highest terrain in mountainous areas.

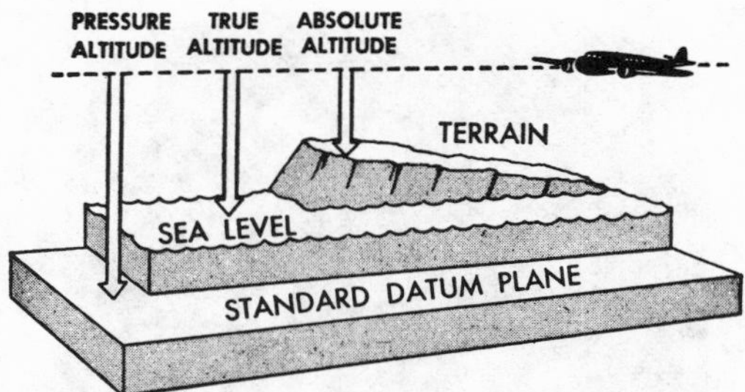

Figure 5.18 Types of altitude. Sea level and the standard datum plane are the same only when barometric pressure equals 29.92 Hg. *(Courtesy of U.S. Air Force.)*

In international flight, there are three distinct altimeter setting symbols. They may be measured in inches of mercury or in millibars:

QNH Standard altimeter setting as known in the United States, measuring existing surface pressure reduced to sea level at that point. (Pressure altitude above sea level "MSL.")

QNE Always 29.92 in. or 1013.2 mb.

QFE Actual surface pressure, not reduced to MSL. This causes the altimeter to read altitude above the reporting point.

Because the altimeter is affected by temperature and pressure both in the air and on the ground, a study of deviations from the standard shown in Figure 6.4 will show that:

When flying from an area of higher pressure to one of lower pressure, the altimeter, if not reset, will place the aircraft at an altitude LOWER than indicated.

When flying from an area of higher temperature to one of lower temperature, the altimeter will place the aircraft at an altitude LOWER than indicated.

Altimeter Error Air traffic density, high rates of climb and descent of modern aircraft, and instrument approach procedures which require precise altitude all make altimeter error of vital importance. These errors consist of *mechanical errors* in the instrument itself, which are compensated for by those altimeters which derive their information from a Central Air Data Computer, *installation error,* which is error introduced by faulty airflow around the static ports, and *reading error,* in which the pilot misreads the altimeter.

Installation error is corrected by the design of compensating pitot tubes (Figure 5.14), and by compensation provided by the CADC. Reading error is reduced by the design of the altimeter presentation. The three-pointer altimeter, Figure 5.17, is the most difficult to read. To reduce error, it has a rotating disc on the face which uncovers a brightly hash-marked sector, as shown in Figure 5.17, when below 16,000 ft.

The vertical scale type (Figure 5.43) is the easiest to read. Among round-dial altimeters, the "counter-drum-pointer" type is the easiest to read (Figure 5.28). It derives its information from a CADC and presents it on counters which indicate 10,000 and 1000 ft, a drum which indicates 100 ft, and a pointer which indicates tens of feet. It is based on a servo-pneumatic mechanism in which the pneumatic portion is based on evacuated bellows which expand and contract under different pressure altitudes, as in the customary altimeter. This system acts as a standby system. Normally the drum, counter, and pointer are driven by servos from the CADC. These altimeters are also capable of transmitting encoded information to the aircraft transponder and thus to Air Traffic Control.

VERTICAL SPEED INDICATOR (VSI)

This instrument indicates the rate of climb or descent in feet per minute by measuring the rate of change of atmospheric pressure.

The VSI employs a thin metal bellows similar to the one in the airspeed indicator, one side of which is connected to the static pressure line. The airtight case of the indicator is also vented to the static pressure line, but through a restricted passage called the "calibrated leak." This opening is extremely small and of a uniform specific size. With the opposite or free side of the bellows connected by levers and gears to the indicator needle, any expansion or contraction of the bellows will cause a corresponding downward or upward movement of the needle. In level flight, the same static pressure fills the case and bellows; there is no movement of the bellows and the indicator needle zeroes. In a climb or descent, however, a differential pressure is created and there is a corresponding expansion or contraction of the bellows, with the corresponding indications by the needle.

In a descent, for example, the aircraft descends into greater atmospheric pressure; the denser air fills the bellows instantly. This denser air would also fill the instrument case instantly, but the calibrated leak restricts free flow and in effect traps lighter pressure in the case. The relatively greater pressure in the bellows causes it to expand and the indicator needle registers a descent. But the instrument is also measuring the rate of descent because the faster the descent is made, the harder it is for pressure to exchange through the calibrated leak. This naturally

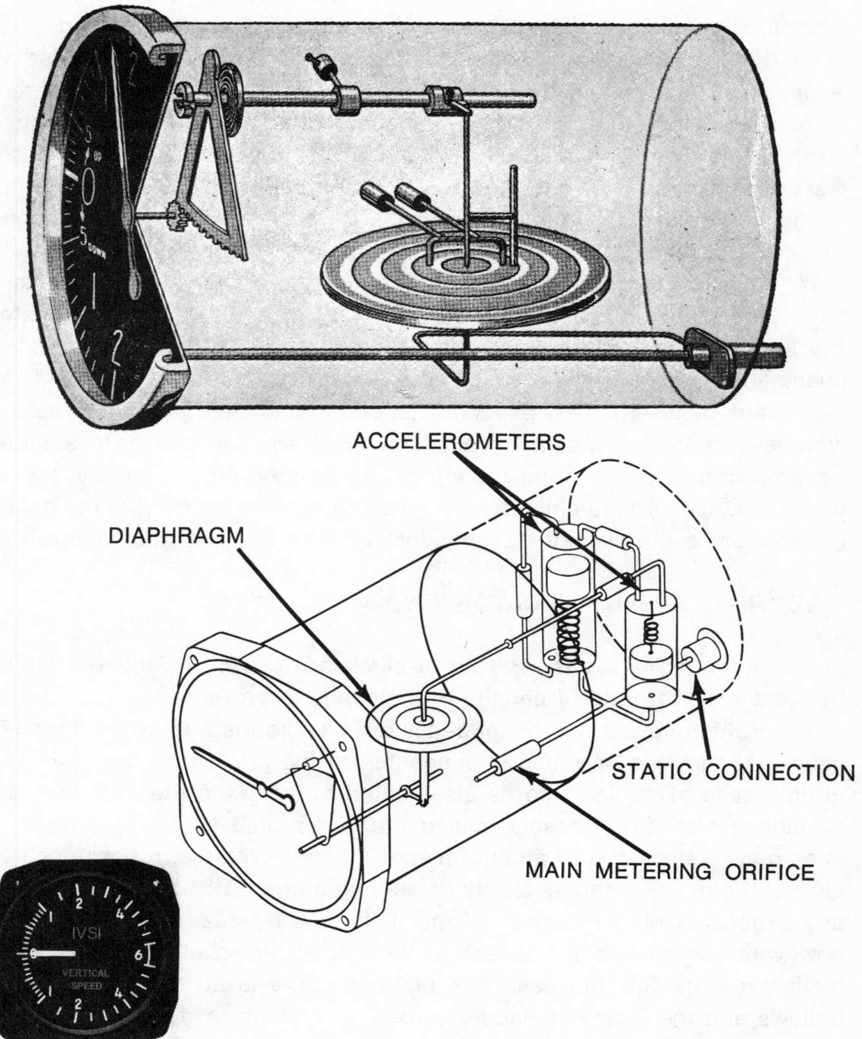

Figure 5.19 Cutaway view of vertical speed indicators. *Upper:* The standard model. *Middle:* The "instantaneous" or "inertial" model, employing accelerometers. *Lower:* A full-face photo. *(Courtesy of Teledyne.)*

creates a greater pressure differential and greater travel of the indicator needle.

So long as the aircraft is descending at a constant rate, the pressure differential will be constant and it is merely a matter of scaling the instrument dial in feet per minute correspondingly. When the aircraft levels off from the climb or descent the indicator needle lags behind. This is the result of the time interval that it takes for the pressure to equalize again through the calibrated leak. Experienced instrument pilots expect the lag and disregard the indicator during this settling down period.

The primary use of the vertical speed indicator is determining rate of climb or descent. However, it is also an excellent trend instrument for maintaining level flight since entry into climbs and descents from level flight is indicated instantly.

Inertial-Lead Vertical Speed Indicators (IVSI) These instruments are designed to reduce VSI lag. In them, two small accelerometers (Figure 5.19) sense the initial acceleration in climb or descent. They provide a response before the indicator can respond to static pressure change, giving an "instantaneous" reaction, and enhance vertical speed control when used properly with the attitude indicator, during wings-level climb and descent. Because the accelerometers turn with the aircraft, they induce an error during turn entries. Outside .7*g* to 1.4*g* load factor, the accelerometers are inhibited, and the IVSI acts as a normal VSI.

HEADING INDICATORS

This term is applied to any gyro-stabilized heading reference instrument. A *directional gyro* is a heading indicator which is gyro-stabilized, its gyro spun by either suction or electric power. It is not magnetic, but may be aligned to the heading of a magnetic compass or any other directional reference. The term is also used to mean a gyro in a gyro-stabilized magnetic compass system which provides "short-term" directional stability, preventing compass oscillations, and connected by synchros to a cockpit indicator. Such a system is said to be in the "directional gyro mode" when it is detached, or unslaved from the magnetic reference and set to an independent reference such as a standby magnetic compass or a runway heading.

Directional gyros of any type depend upon the gyroscopic property of rigidity in space. They are subject to errors caused by gyro drift, by real precession caused by aircraft maneuvering forces, and by apparent precession. *Apparent precession* affects universally mounted gyros which are translated rapidly over long distances at high speed. As the earth rotates, or as the gyro is translated long distances, the plane of rotation changes from the viewpoint of an observer on earth. For example, a gyro rotating in a horizontal plane at the pole would appear to be rotating in the vertical plane at the equator, since its plane of rotation in space does not change as it is transported through 90° of earth curvature.

SUCTION-DRIVEN DIRECTIONAL GYRO

The rotor spins in the vertical plane. Fastened to the vertical gimbal, at right angles to the plane of rotation, is a circular compass card. The case of the instrument, and the airplane, simply turn about the compass card. The aircraft suction system draws air from the case of the instrument; air coming in to replace it is directed at buckets on the periphery of the gyro rotor, turning it at about 18,000 rpm. Precession is corrected by two parallel jets which strike at the center of the rotor when it tilts from the vertical; the precessive force returns it to vertical. A caging and heading set knob is provided which permits rotation of the card to a desired heading indication by means of gears and a friction clutch.

The limits of this instrument are 55° of pitch and roll. The gyro, striking stops, will tumble and the compass card will spin when these limits are exceeded. The aircraft must then be returned to level flight, and the gyro caged and reset. The gyro should be caged during maneuvers which exceed its limits, in order to avoid undue wear on rotor and gimbal bearings.

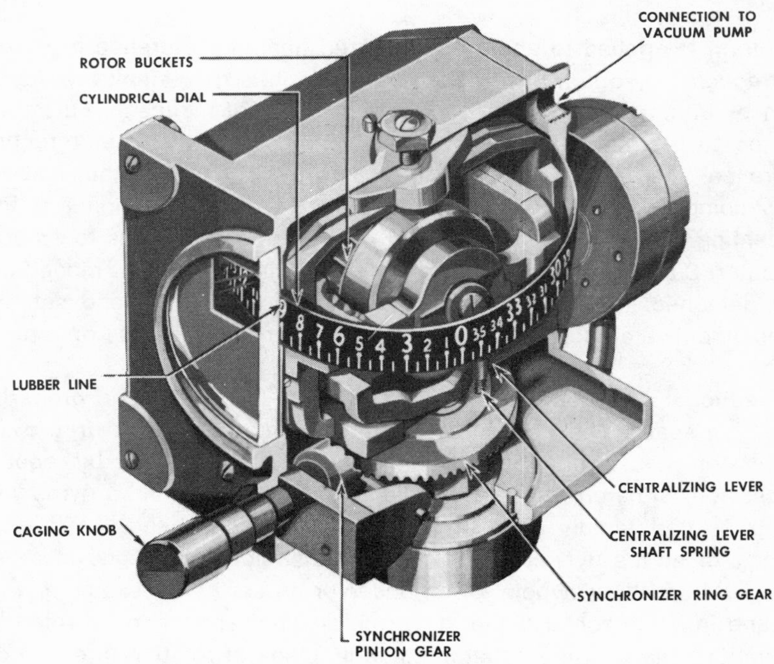

Figure 5.20 Cutaway view of suction-driven heading indicator. *(Courtesy of U.S. Air Force.)*

REMOTE INDICATING GYRO-STABILIZED COMPASSES

These compasses, known also as *gyrosyn compasses,* have been developed for a wide variety of applications, but all have four basic components: the *remote compass transmitter,* the *directional gyro,* an *amplifier,* and the *heading indicator.*

The remote compass transmitter is the direction-sensing device of the system. It is usually located in a wing tip or other magnetic interference-free location.

It contains a *flux valve,* which is an iron core shaped like a three-spoke wheel with a heavy rim, broken between spokes. Each spoke of this wheel is wound with primary and secondary coils. Alternating current from the compass inverter creates a reversing magnetic field through the primary coil. This wheel is suspended horizontally from its hub in pendulous fashion so that as the aircraft banks it remains horizontal; an oil bath restricts its fluctuation. It cannot rotate in its housing, and turns with the aircraft. As long as the aircraft is on a fixed course, the earth's

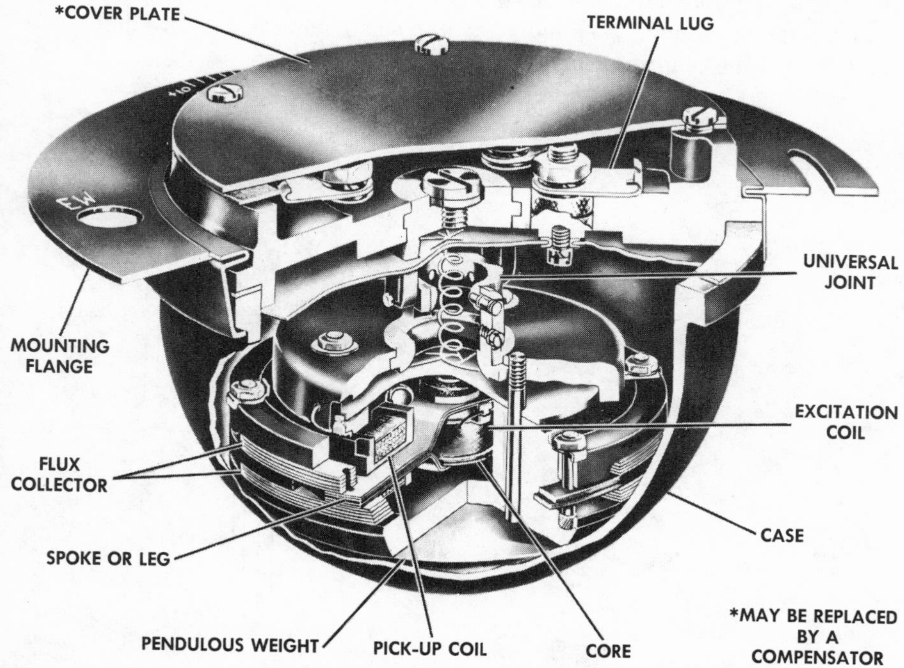

Figure 5.21 Gyrosyn compass flux valve (flux gate.) As the magnetic direction-sensing element, the flux valve is the heart of the remote indicating-type compass. *(Courtesy of Sperry Gyroscope Co.)*

magnetic lines of flux have a constant effect, and the field of the primary coil is constant. When the aircraft turns, the field changes, and a current is induced in the secondary coil. These signals from the secondary coil are amplified in the amplifier, and by synchronous motors align the *heading indicator* with the magnetic heading of the aircraft.

The heading indicator is stabilized by the directional gyro, which may be either a remote unit or integral with the heading indicator.

The gyro compass systems have operating limits of 85° of pitch and roll, and are free of northerly turning error, oscillation, or swinging. Since inherent gyro drift is continuously being corrected by being slaved to the magnetic compass transmitter, no resetting is required unless the system is one which can be unslaved for operation in the directional gyro mode.

When a slaving cutout switch is provided for "DG mode" operation, a setting switch is provided; there is also an *annunciator,* a left-right needle which, when centered, indicates that the compass transmitter and gyro are properly synchronized when reslaved.

In today's era of specialized flying, it is impossible to expect a single type of compass system to satisfy the many varied commercial, general aviation, and military operational requirements. Specialized models are available to meet the needs of auto-pilots, high-performance aircraft, and trans-polar operation. Very high accuracy and automatic corrections for latitude are the features of the more advanced systems.

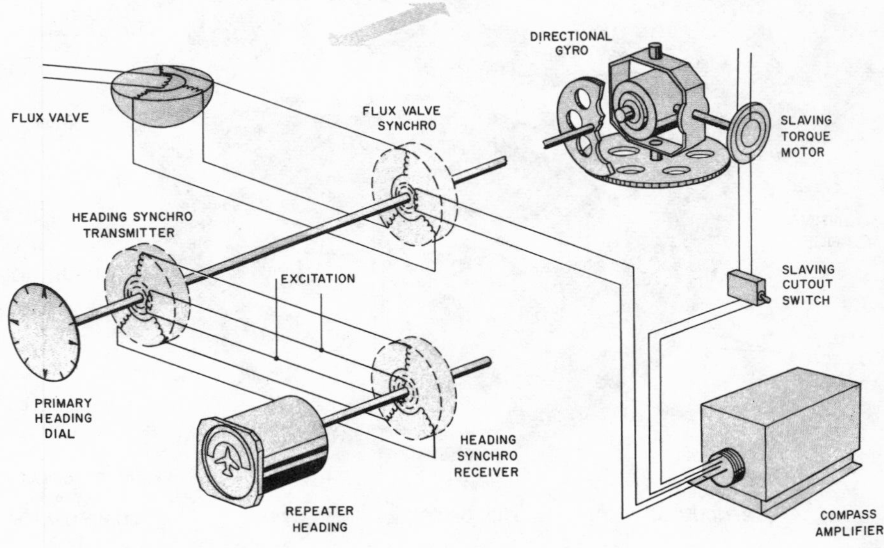

Figure 5.22A Schematic of basic components of the gyrosyn compass system. *(Courtesy of Sperry Gyroscope Co.)*

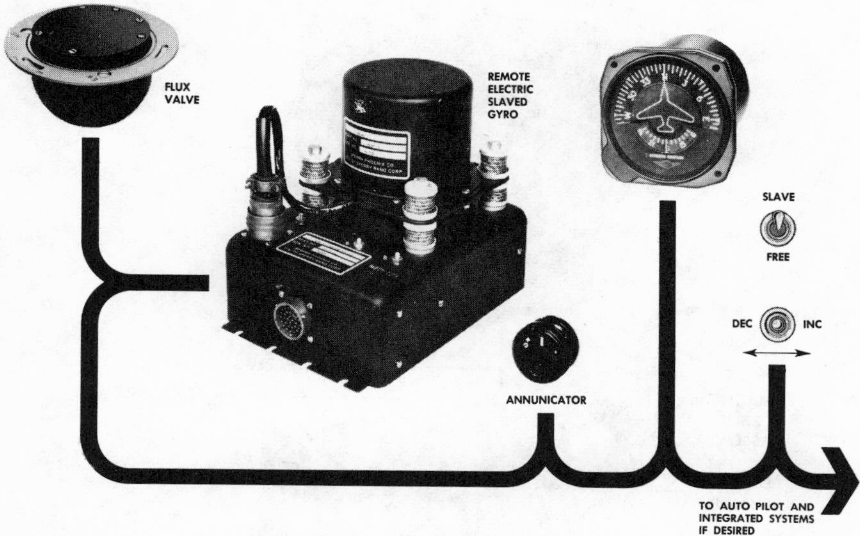

Figure 5.22B Gyrosyn compass system designed for business and executive aircraft. This system uses a solid-state amplifier, may be operated in the DG mode, and can provide for more than one indicator, or for directional reference for an autopilot system. It provides a drift-free heading reference, self-maintained to $\pm 1°$. Self-erecting in the slaved mode. *(Courtesy of Sperry Phoenix Co.)*

MAGNETIC COMPASS

This old and familiar instrument is the simplest and least precise aircraft heading reference. It serves primarily as a heading source for emergency use, and for checking large errors in other systems. The panel-type magnetic compass consists simply of two steel bar magnets mounted on a float around which the compass card is placed. The magnets are parallel, with their north-seeking ends pointed in the same direction. The compass card has letters for cardinal headings, and every 30° is represented by a number, the last zero of which is omitted. Between these numbers the card is graduated for each 5°. The float assembly (which consists of the bar magnets, compass card, and float) is housed in a bowl filled with acid-free white kerosene, which dampens out excessive oscillations of the compass card and relieves by buoyancy part of the weight of the float from the bearings. The liquid also provides lubrication and prevents rust within the case of the instrument. The glass face of the compass is an integral part of the bowl and has a lubber line or reference line mounted behind it on which compass indications are read. If the face is broken, the fluid is lost and the compass is unusable.

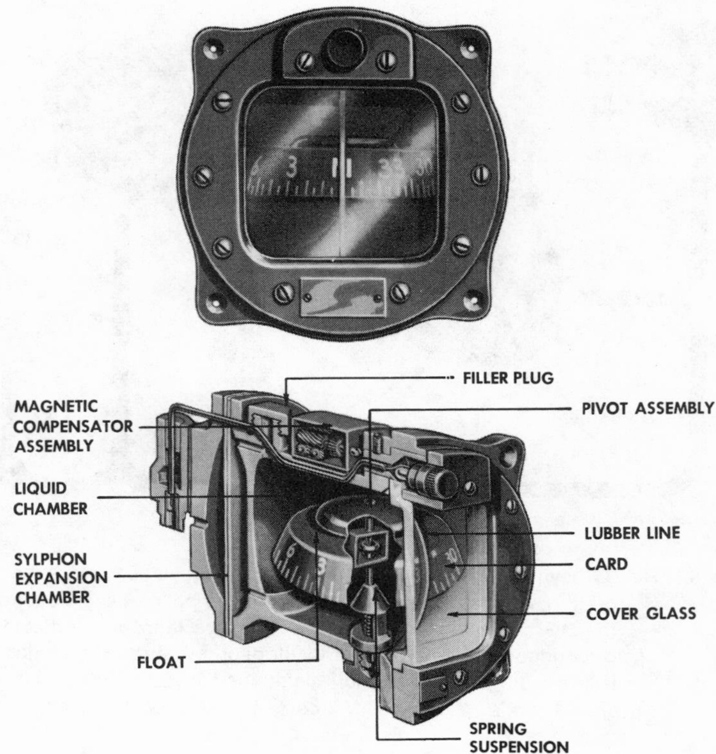

Figure 5.23 Cutaway and front view of panel-type magnetic compass.

Magnetic needles tend to point downward in middle and high latitudes, aligning themselves more completely with the earth's magnetic lines of force (flux) as they flow downward to the surface at the magnetic pole. This tendency, called *magnetic dip,* induces fluctuating errors in the compass during acceleration or deceleration, and during turning.

Acceleration-deceleration errors are most evident on east-west headings, and turning errors most evident on north-south headings. Errors are also caused by aircraft electrical equipment, radios, or even by a camera lightmeter placed near the compass.

TURN AND SLIP INDICATOR

The first gyroscopic instrument, it now serves primarily to indicate a need for yaw trim, though it is a primary instrument in sailplanes and of value as backup bank control in airplanes.

Figure 5.24 Electric turn and slip indicator. Mounted in a single degree of freedom gimbal. When aircraft turns, gyro rotor is turned, causing it to tilt left or right an amount proportional to the rate of turn. Mechanical and damping linkage is located between rotor and instrument face. *(U.S. Air Force photograph.)*

It consists of two parts, a turn needle and an inclinometer, or "ball." The turn needle indicates a turn when the gyro, horizontally mounted with its spin axis parallel to the aircraft lateral axis, tilts in precessive response to a turn or yaw of the instrument case. The gyro is usually electrically driven, and as a rate gyro, by a mechanical mechanism causes the turn needle to deflect according to the rate of turn of the aircraft about its vertical axis.

The *turn needle* indicates the rate (number of degrees per second) the aircraft is turning, regardless of bank. It is calibrated for a single needle width deflection to indicate a "*standard rate*" of either 2 or 4 min for the aircraft to turn through 360°. With a full-needle-width deflection, the 2-min needle indicates a rate of 3° per sec, and the 4-min needle indicates a rate of 1½° per sec.

The inclinometer or *ball,* restrained only by a stabilizing fluid in its tubular race, shows whether the aircraft is slipping or skidding; that is, the relationship between the angle of bank and the rate of turn.

Gravity and centrifugal force only act on the ball. During a coordinated turn these forces are in balance and the ball remains centered. In a skid,

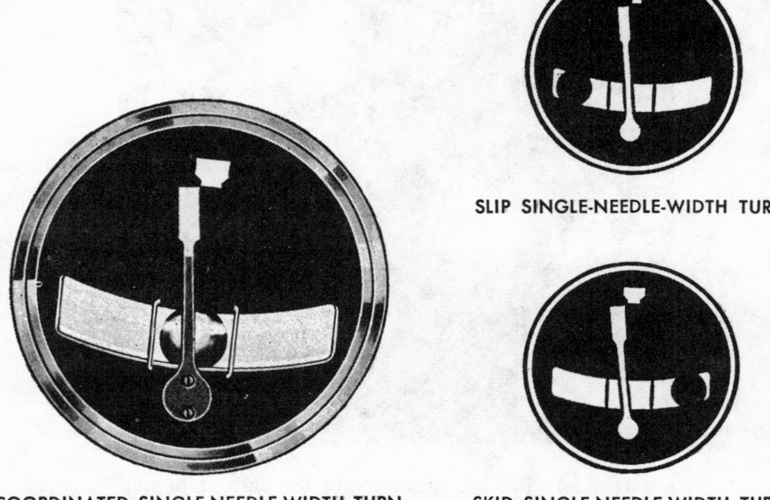

Figure 5.25 Three indications of turn and slip indicator in a left turn. *(Courtesy of U.S. Air Force.)*

the rate of turn is too fast for the angle of bank, and excessive centrifugal force moves the ball toward the outside of the turn. In slips to the inside of the turn, the cause and effects are reversed. In a properly coordinated turn, the ball will be centered.

When the aircraft is flying level but out of trim longitudinally, the ball will be off center; a rudder trim adjustment is needed, and will center it.

ANGLE OF ATTACK INDICATOR

This instrument has become of primary importance in maneuvering high-performance aircraft, particularly those which experience violent maneuvers or great changes in gross weight.

Angle of attack is defined as the angle formed between the chord line of the wing and the relative wind (Figure 5.26). In its simplest form, the small stall warning vane which actuates a buzzer or light on the instrument panel of lightplanes is essentially an angle of attack indicator. Called a "stall warning" device, it operates when the airspeed is so low related to load and relative wind that airflow gets under the vane, lifts it, and closes the warning circuit.

At some angle of attack, every wing will stall. This stall angle will always remain the same for that particular wing, regardless of the gross weight,

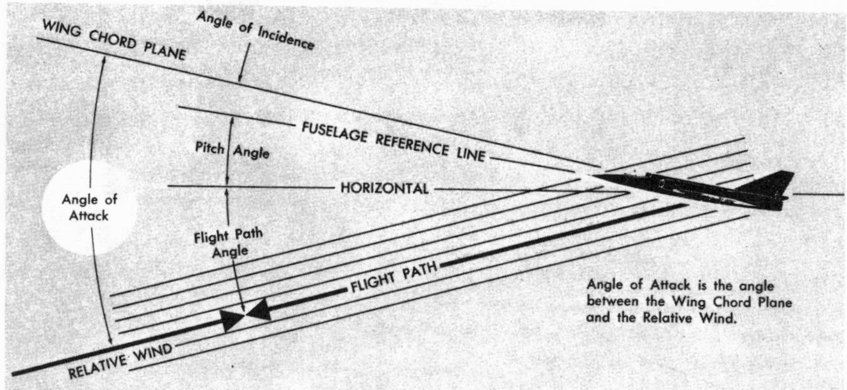

Figure 5.26 Angle of attack.

attitude, airspeed, or "G" load. High-lift devices such as flaps in effect change the wing, changing the wing area and chord line, so their use results in a different wing and a different stall speed.

When you consider that each wing has the same angle of attack for each maneuver, regardless of gross weight, that is, final approach, climb, maximum range, maximum endurance, steep turns, etc. it is apparent why angle of attack is valuable information, eliminating the guessing associated with differing airspeeds for these maneuvers under different weight conditions and "G" loading. Since a lift requirement results from weight supported by the wing, the airspeed must be increased to maintain the

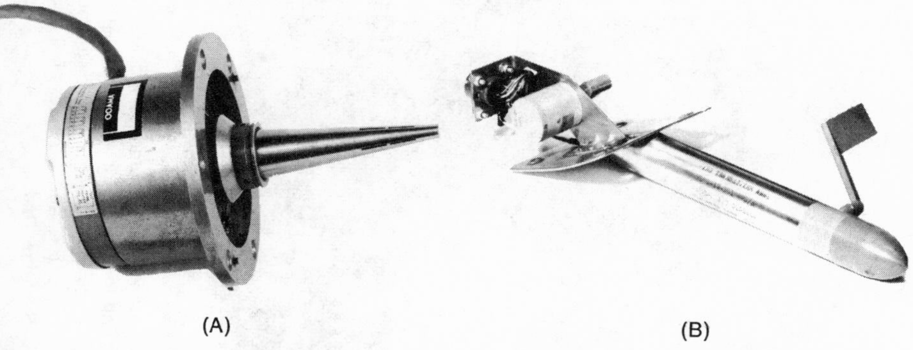

Figure 5.27 Angle of attack sensors. (A) From F-4. Parts 90° around probe sense local pressures, and lead to compartments of a paddle chamber. The paddle rotates until pressures are equalized. Potentiometers transmit signals to cockpit indicators. (B) From C-130 and C-123. The vane aligns itself with local airflow. *(U.S. Air Force photographs.)*

Figure 5.28 Standard instruments, Lockheed 1011 Airline Transport. Left group: Dual-pointer radio magnetic indicator (RMI), altitude director indicator (ADI), and horizontal situation indicator, (HSI). Right group: Counter-drum-pointer encoding pneumatic-servo altimeter, combined airspeed-Mach indicator, true airspeed indicator, vertical speed indicator, and outside air temperature indicator. All air data derived from a CADC. *(Courtesy of Sperry Flight Systems Division.)*

same angle of attack at higher gross weights and at "G" loading. The only exception is that angle of attack indications may not be accurate during takeoff roll and at liftoff while in ground effect.

ANGLE OF ATTACK SENSORS

Both vanes and slotted probes which sense differential pressures are used along the fuselage where airflow disturbance is a minimum (Figure 5.27). Both may transmit a signal either directly to the instrument or to the central air data computer.

Cockpit indicators of angle of attack vary. They may be graduated in actual angles, units, symbols, or percent of lift being used, or as a "fast-slow" indication. Both round dials and vertical tapes (Figures 5.43 and 10.3) are used.

The third group of instruments include the VOR course indicator, the radio magnetic indicator (RMI), the range indicator, the "radio compass" or ADF (automatic direction finder), transponder, and marker beacon. Flight director systems are a combination of attitude, performance, and navigation instruments.

They complete the picture by showing you the position of the aircraft relative to the fixes it passes en route, and to its destination. In essence, then, they tell you what control and performance indications you must establish and maintain to navigate where you want to go. These instruments are all dependent upon radio, and operate according to the characteristics of radio ground stations of various types.

Aircraft Radio

Radio is so essential to modern aircraft that it is literally as much a part of the aircraft as the power plant. Modern air traffic control has developed to meet the needs of increased traffic congestion of high- and low-performance aircraft under all kinds of weather. It has, of course, been entirely dependent upon the flexibility and efficiency of air-to-ground radio communications equipment, radio aids to navigation, and the skill of the airmen using them.

RADIO ENERGY CHARACTERISTICS

While most people have some notion of radio theory, it is important for airmen to understand the following basic ideas:

Radio waves, although lower in frequency, are similar to light and heat waves and can be reflected, refracted, and diffracted. The velocity of travel is approximately 300,000 meters (186,000 mi) per second in free space. When the wave amplitude is plotted against angle or time, the curve is normally a sine function (Figure 5.29).

A *cycle* is the complete process of starting at zero, passing through two maximums of opposite direction, and returning to zero again.

Frequency is the number of cycles completed in one second. One cycle per second is the basic unit of measurement, the *Hertz.* The terms *kilohertz* (1000 cycles, abbreviated kHz) and *Megahertz* (1000 kilohertz, abbreviated MHz) are applied in discussing radio frequencies.

Wavelength is the distance traveled by a wave during one cycle. This distance is normally expressed in meters.

Modulation is the process of creating a variation in the amplitude, frequency, or phase of the radio wave with another waveform, such as speech, to transmit intelligence.

Bandwidth is the amount of frequency spectrum required to transmit the desired intelligence. For example, a television signal, which transmits both visual and audio information, has an average bandwidth requirement of 6 MHz. Other types of information, such as voice or music, require a bandwidth of 3 to 30 kHz, depending upon the quality or fidelity desired.

Audio waves and the associated frequencies are those detectable as sound by the average human ear. The velocity of travel is approximately 1180 ft per sec or 663 knots. The frequency range extends from 20 to 15,000 Hertz (Hz), subject to variation in hearing of different individuals.

Radio communications of many types are conducted in a frequency

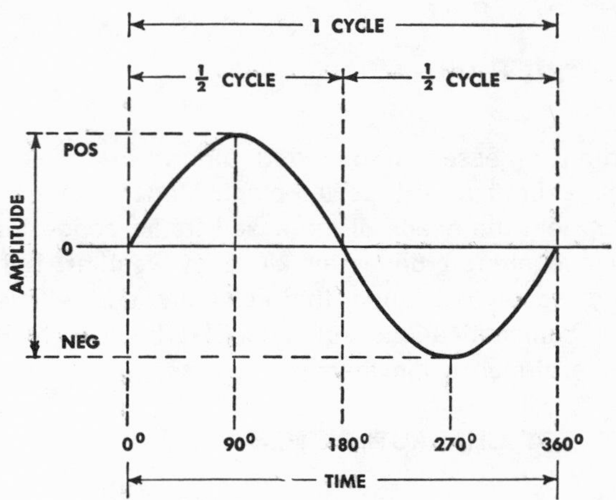

Figure 5.29 Radio wave characteristics.

range of 10 kHz to 30,000 MHz. This overall frequency range is divided into bands which assists in identifying general frequency characteristics and the equipment which applies. These bands are classified as follows:

VLF	Very low frequency	10 to 30 kHz
LF	Low frequency	30 to 300 kHz
MF	Medium frequency	300 to 3000 kHz
HF	High frequency	3 to 30 MHz
VHF	Very high frequency	30 to 300 MHz
UHF	Ultrahigh frequency	300 to3000 MHz
SHF	Superhigh frequency	3000 to 30,000 MHz

Basically, radio frequency signals or waves are generated by equipment known as the transmitter. This signal is then coupled to a suitable antenna which in turn radiates the energy into space. Once radiated, the signal is detected or intercepted by equipment known as the receiver.

A radio signal that is not modulated is known as a "continuous wave" (cw). In order to transmit intelligence, however, the signal must be altered in some manner and these alterations decoded at the receiver. One of the most simple methods of transmitting intelligence is to interrupt the signal at different rates and sequences to conform to a code for letters, numbers, and punctuation. The Morse code is, of course, an excellent example of this method of transmission.

Once some form of modulation is applied to the "continuous wave," it then becomes known as a "carrier." If the modulating signal varies the amplitude of the carrier, this is called "amplitude modulation" (AM). "Frequency modulation" (FM) indicates that the carrier is varied in frequency. "Phase modulation" (PM) indicates that the phase of the carrier is varied. The most common form of modulation used in aircraft radio transmitters in AM.

To intercept a signal and reproduce the transmitted intelligence, the receiver must be capable of being tuned to the correct radio frequency, amplify an overall bandwidth equivalent to that of the transmitted signal and provide for the appropriate type of demodulation. "Demodulation" is the reverse process of modulation and performs the task of extracting the intelligence from the carrier.

General Characteristics of Propagation A nondirectional radiator (antenna) in free space will radiate radio frequency energy in all directions. Part of the energy travels along the earth's surface and is called the "ground wave." The balance of the energy is radiated into space and is referred to as the "sky wave." Particles in the atmosphere, the earth itself, terrain features, and structures all act to absorb or attenuate radio frequency energy. The amount of attenuation increases with distance from the radiating source.

Ionospheric Reflection The ionosphere is composed of a number of ionized gas layers that exist above the surface of the earth. The height and density of these layers vary with the amount of radiation received from the sun. Thus a pattern of variations arises between daylight and darkness, with the changing seasons of the year, and during periods of sunspot maxima. Certain radio frequencies, particularly those in the HF band, are subject to reflection by one or more of the ionosphere layers with only slight attenuation. This creates a condition where the sky wave of an HF radiator is reflected back to the earth at some distant point with appreciable strength. The distance from the transmitting location to the first point of return to the earth is called the "skip distance." Since the earth is also a reflective surface, multiple skips are not uncommon.

Interference Anything that acts to degrade the quality or intelligibility of a signal at the receiver location may be classed as interference. However, the term is normally limited to *man-made interference* such as that caused by poor power connections or an arcing motor brush; *natural interference* caused by thunderstorms, charged rain or snow particles, and general atmospheric noise; and *mutual interference* caused by other transmissions on or closely adjacent to the same frequency. When deliberate, this is called "jamming."

General Characteristics of Various Frequency Bands There are many variations within a designated band, and the range or direction of transmission may be limited or enhanced by factors of power, antenna configuration, and type of modulation. However, general characteristics may be summarized as follows:

VLF Almost entirely ground wave. High power and large efficient antennas can provide worldwide coverage. Very limited application to aircraft radio.

LF Primarily ground wave. Used for homing beacons. Subject to sky-wave reflections during dark hours and unstable sky-wave reception at dawn and dusk. Vulnerable to natural interference.

MF Primarily ground wave. Standard broadcast stations are included in this band and can be used as homing beacons. Subject to medium- and long-range sky-wave reflections during hours of darkness, especially during winter.

HF Ground wave attenuates rapidly. Reflected sky wave normally employed and useful for communications up to 12,000 mi or more, depending on ionospheric conditions. Used mostly by long-range aircraft for position reporting, receipt of weather information, change in flight plans, etc., to and from distant ground stations. Also employed by light aircraft operating beyond VHF and UHF facilities. Bush pilot operations are an excellent example.

VHF Practically no ground wave. Line-of-sight range via sky wave.

TABLE 5.1
Characteristics of Radio Waves

Frequency	3 kHz	30 kHz	300 kHz	3 MHz	30 MHz	3 kMHz	30 kMHz 300 kMHz
Designation	VLF	LF	MF	VHF	VHF	UHF	SHF
Maximum range (miles)	Worldwide	3000	5000	12,000	Line-of-sight (sporadic long ranges)	Line-of-sight	Line-of-sight
Propagation	Ground wave and D-layer reflection	Ground wave and D-layer reflection	Ground wave and E-layer reflection	F-layer reflection	Sporadic ionosphere reflection	Sporadic atmospheric reflection	Sporadic ducting, some atmospheric absorption
Applications	Communication, experimental	Communication, navigation	Communication, navigation	Communication, navigation, control, medical	Communication, navigation, television, control, relay, radar, industrial, medical	Communication, navigation, television, control, relay, radar, medical	Communication, navigation, control, relay, radar, industrial, nuclear resonance

Normally penetrates ionosphere as opposed to strong reflection. This is the principal air-to-air and air-to-ground frequency band in use today. Voice communications and navigational aids are included. Since line-of-sight is a basic restriction, the useful range increases with an increase in aircraft altitude.

UHF Frequency characteristics closely parallel those of VHF. Utilization of this band for air-to-air and air-to-ground communications was brought about by the need for more channels and the severe congestion existing in the allotted portion of the VHF band. Most airport facilities and virtually all FAA stations now have both UHF and VHF capabilities.

SHF Very little application to aircraft radio at the present time. Line-of-sight characteristics subject to some atmospheric absorption.

ASSIGNMENT OF AERONAUTICAL FREQUENCIES

In the United States, VHF communications and navigation frequencies are assigned generally as follows:

VHF Communications	118.00 to 135.95 MHz
Instrument Landing System (ILS)	
Glide Slope	328.60 to 335.40 MHz
VOR and ILS Localizer	108.00 to 117.90 MHz

All odd-tenth MHz frequencies beginning with 108.1, that is, 108.3, 108.5, etc., through 111.9 are localizer (LOC) frequencies. The even-numbered-tenth frequencies from 108.00 through 112.00 and all frequencies higher through 117.90 are VOR only. Seventy-five megahertz is used solely for marker beacons and Z markers (page 582).

UHF frequencies between 225.0 and 400.2 are used for air traffic control, and are assigned differently from time to time depending upon the development of air traffic control facilities and traffic loads. They are assigned and changed so as to provide the least likelihood of mutual interference between nearby stations.

Radio ranges and radio beacons use low frequencies between 200 kHz and 550 kHz.

Radio frequency assignment details are found in the FAA-published "Airman's Information Manual" described on page 757.

VHF OMNIRANGE (VOR)

VOR is the primary instrument navigation system because its frequencies avoid the effects of static, and because it can give a detailed, precise display of the aircraft's position by easily read instruments.

Principle of Operation Two VHF radio signals are transmitted from the same facility. One is constant in phase throughout 360° of azimuth, while the other, a variable-phase signal, is transmitted in a rotating signal pattern. Rotating at 1800 rpm, this variable phase combines with the constant phase to provide a signal which varies uniformly throughout 360°. The phase differential is oriented with magnetic north, so that aircraft receivers can measure the phase differential electronically and present it visually to the pilot in the cockpit.

The infinite number of courses which radiate from the VOR station are called radials. They are identified by their magnetic bearing outbound from the station. Thus, regardless of your heading, if you were momentarily due

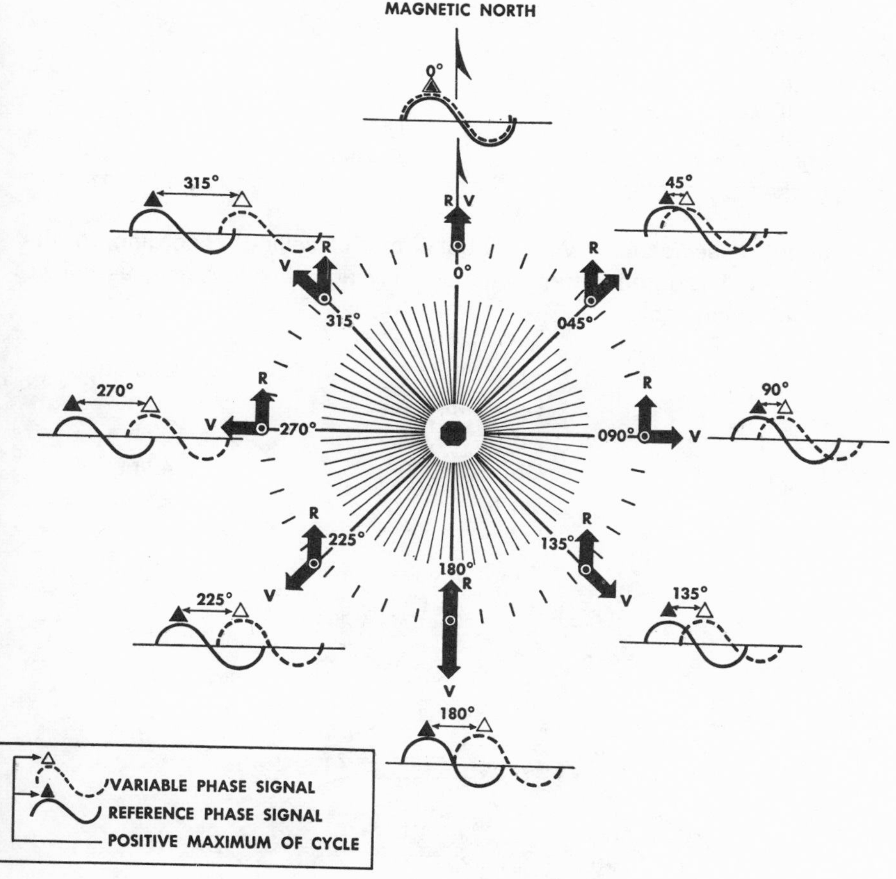

Figure 5.30 VOR phase angle relationship. Signals are in phase at magnetic north and vary elsewhere around the station. *(Courtesy of U.S. Air Force.)*

east of the station, you would be on the 90° radial. If inbound on this radial, your course would be 270°. Because VOR uses frequencies in the VHF band, signals are limited to line-of-sight reception, and the usable range varies with altitude.

TABLE 5.2
Line-of-Sight Distances for VHF Reception

Aircraft Altitude (ft)	*Approximate Transmission Range (nautical miles)*	*Aircraft Altitude (ft)*	*Approximate Transmission Range (nautical miles)*
100	12	4,000	70
200	15	5,000	80
400	25	8,500	100
600	30	10,000	115
800	35	12,500	125
1,000	40	15,000	135
2,000	50	17,500	145
3,000	65	20,000	160

Station Classification VOR stations are classified according to the altitude and interference-free distance they are able to serve, as shown in the following table:

Class	*Altitude*	*Distance*
H	Up to 45,000	130 nm
H	Above 45,000	100 nm
L	Up to 18,000	40 nm
T	Up to 12,000	25 nm

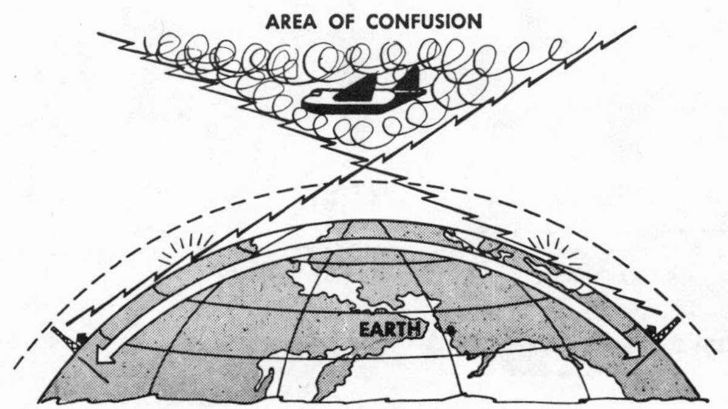

Figure 5.31 Area of confusion resulting from co-channel interference.

Identification VOR stations may be identified by a coded three-letter station identifier, a voice identifier, or a combination of both. Stations on the same frequency are spaced to avoid interference. However, with the increased density of installations, it is possible, at certain locations and altitudes, to receive two stations with approximately equal signal strength. The resulting "area of confusion" is shown in Figure 5.31. You can recognize it by oscillation of the instrument panel indicator and by an aural whistle. Eliminate it by selecting different stations along the route.

TACAN, VORTAC, AND VOR-DME/T

The need for more precise all-weather navigation for both civil and military flying has required the development of equipment to give the pilot a direct picture of his bearing and distance from a station. The result is TACAN (tactical air navigation) equipment and its near relatives, VORTAC (co-located VOR and TACAN) and VOR-DME/T, a co-located VOR and DME portion of TACAN.

TACAN-equipped aircraft can receive both bearing and distance information from TACAN stations, and distance information from the DME (distance measuring equipment) portion of VORTAC stations. An aircraft equipped with VOR and DME equipment can receive bearing and distance information from VORTAC stations, and distance information from TACAN stations.

Flight procedures for using VORTAC are generally the same as those used for VOR and TACAN. TACAN ground equipment consists of receiver-transmitter combinations (transponders) and rotating-type antennas for transmission of bearing and distance information. TACAN stations, called beacons, have a practical receiver-limited range of 195 nm, and are identified by a coded signal which is repeated every 30 sec. TACAN and VORTAC information appear in the cockpit on the navigation instruments shown in Figure 9.2, and flight director systems.

TACAN BEARING INFORMATION

So far as the pilot is concerned, the information might be coming from a VOR, except that TACAN's signal pattern is somewhat more complex and gives greater bearing accuracy. In addition, the use of UHF frequencies makes it less vulnerable to terrain effects. Using UHF frequencies, TACAN requires a much smaller ground-station antenna. TACAN antennas consist of a vertical wire omnidirectional signal transmitter around which rotate two concentric cylinders. These cylinders have embedded in their walls "parasitic elements" (vertical wires), which distort the signal pattern into fine and course phases as the cylinders rotate. One

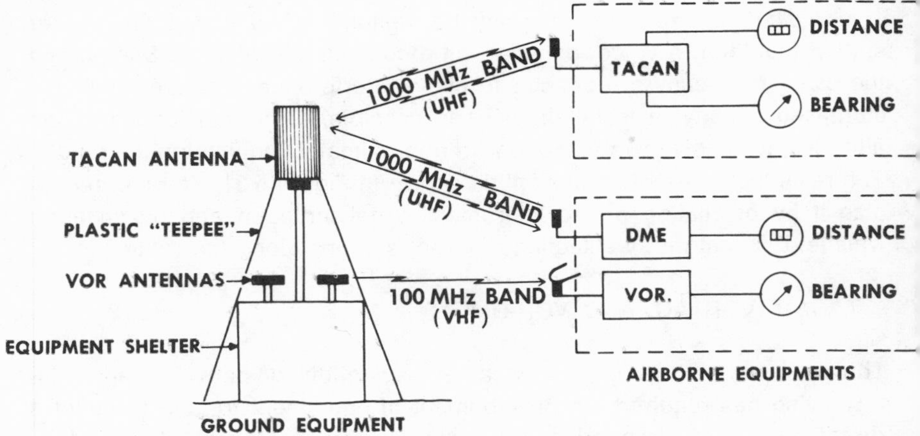

Figure 5.32 Utilization of VORTAC equipment and frequencies. *(Courtesy of U.S. Air Force.)*

stage of the phases is oriented with magnetic east. The airborne receiver measures the time differential between the phases of the signal, giving bearing information which is accurate to within $\pm 1°$.

Aircraft Radio Equipment

The versatility of modern aircraft, and the necessity for a high order of navigation precision and communication clarity and reliability have resulted in the development of the extensive airways and traffic control systems which now exist worldwide. To use this system, aircraft communications and navigation equipment has been developed in a pattern which follows aircraft cost and use. It may be grouped generally into systems for utility and pleasure aircraft, executive or business aircraft, and airline transports. Military equipment embraces all classes, depending upon the complexity of the mission. There is a wide variety available for each class. The distinction between classes is a matter of versatility, reliability, precision, and cost.

COMMUNICATIONS AND NAVIGATION EQUIPMENT

Because the selection of this equipment depends so much on the locale of aircraft operations, the aircraft use, and the probable pilot capability, a precise list is inappropriate. However, the network of airways in the United States is such that even while not following airways, reliance

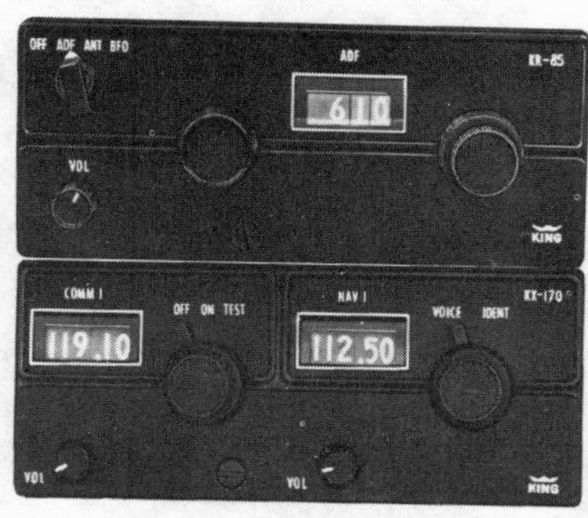

Figure 5.33 Typical basic communications/navigation equipment for general aviation aircraft; using primarily VFR. COMM/NAV has 360 communications, and 200 navigation channels. It is fully transistorized, with automatic squelch (interference reduction). The VOR/LOC (localizer) converter indicator (Course Indicator) is transistorized and lighted. ADF is crystal-tuned from 200 to 1699 kHz in 1 kHz increments. Compass card is manually rotated. *(Courtesy of King Radio Corp.)*

upon VHF omnirange-type stations for the principal VFR radio aid to navigation is adequate. An ADF is helpful in areas (Canada, Alaska, Mexico, mountainous terrain) where VHF stations are unavailable, or where HF nondirectional beacons and radio broadcast stations are generally used. A popular and typical VFR installation is shown in Figure 5.33.

For IFR capability the installation shown in Figure 5.34 is considered minimal. It is not only essential to be able to communicate easily and navigate precisely. One must be able to do so efficiently in the Air Traffic Control environment if the aircraft is to provide acceptable utility in most parts of the United States.

Combined COMM/NAV equipment consists of the COMM transceiver (transmitter and receiver), and the NAV receiver. Both receive voice broadcasts, using either headsets or cockpit speakers.

From this basic idea, in which VHF communications and navigation are combined, grows the concept of separate and dual NAV/COM receivers and control units. The more versatile units have refinements which increase their reliability and utility: Manual and automatic squelch circuits improve readability by reducing background noise. Transistors instead of vacuum tubes are used to reduce heating and size, and to lengthen

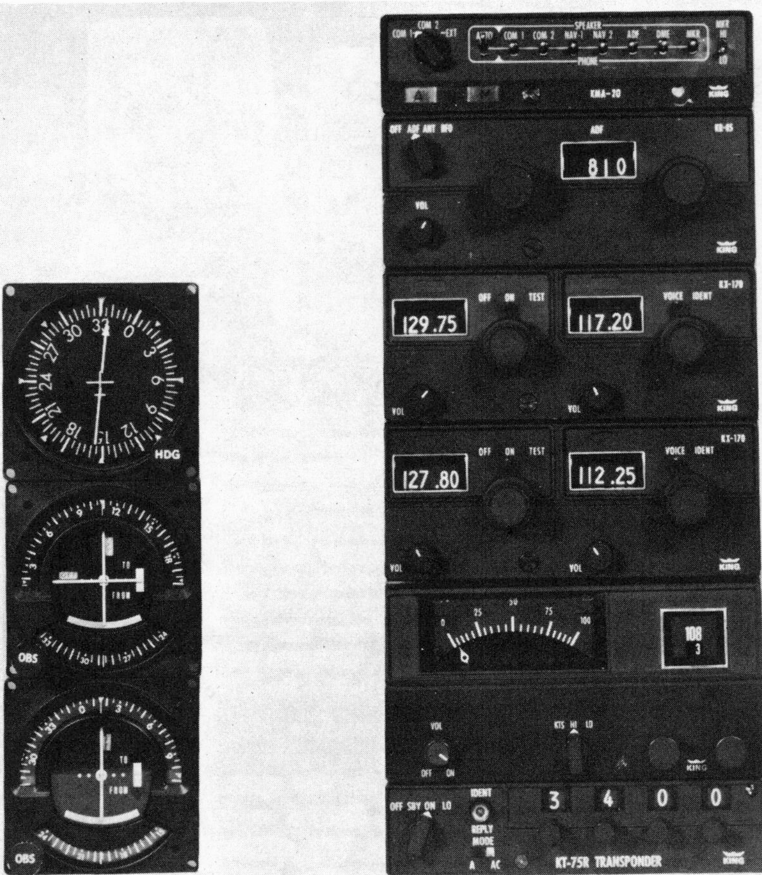

Figure 5.34 Minimal IFR communication and navigation installation. Top to bottom, right: control console, audio amplifier, and three-light marker beacon; ADF receiver; dual 360-channel COMM, 200-channel NAV receivers; DME with ground speed; transponder. The DME, while not vital in basic minimal installations, is so convenient where many diverse instrument approaches and precise positioning are required, that it is included. *(Courtesy of King Radio Corp.)*

service life. Remote controls and indicators permit dual installation, and use by multiple crew members. Modular design permits quick removal for test and repair of circuits. Frequency controls are designed into the circuits to prevent audio frequency distortion and to limit interference caused by unstable radio frequencies. Selectivity is increased; many more crystal channels are available and they can be tuned faster.

UHF radios are used for communications to expand greatly the fre-

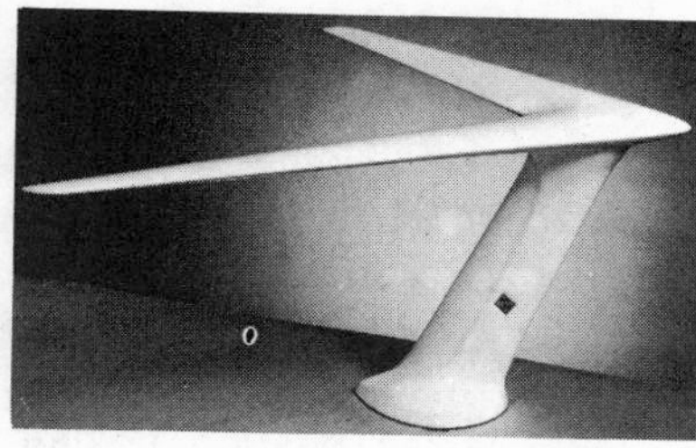

Figure 5.35 Typical NAV/COMM antenna. Communications are received on vertical shaft; navigation signals on wings. *(Courtesy of National Aeronautical Corp.)*

quencies and to reduce static. Separate audio control panels permit the pilot to receive or transmit on more than one radio at a time, or to select various receivers for monitoring or tuning.

Long-Range Communications The ground-to-air needs of airlines and commercial firms are handled by Aeronautical Radio, Incorporated. In addition, the airlines themselves have HF nets as do the military and FAA. Long-range transports, long-range military aircraft, and bush aircraft which operate beyond the range of line-of-sight VHF and UHF, carry HF receivers and transmitters. While the variety available can fit any simple or complex need, the trend is toward crystal-tuned transmitter-receivers. With this equipment, the aircrew has access to long-range flight control and assistance, emergency communications, weather forecasts, and connections into commercial telephone circuits.

Figure 5.36 HF voice transceivers. *Left:* panel-mounted, 5-channel, 9-lb crystal-tuned unit for small aircraft. *Center and right:* remote-controlled, 22-channel 15-lb crystal-tuned unit for a wider variety of aircraft. Both are used with trailing wire antennas whose variable length improves signal strength. They operate at 2.0 to 13.5 MC on 12- or 24-volt power supply. *(Courtesy of Sunair Electronics, Inc.)*

Navigation receivers and indicators are more complex and have more positive test and warning flag systems, and are combined with directional indicators. The indicators also give more stable indications of bearing and ILS position. They are combined with glide slope receivers to permit full ILS use. Indicator and control head dials are designed and illuminated with greater emphasis on human factors affecting error.

Figure 5.28 shows the *RMI,* which consists of a rotating compass card, a double-barred bearing pointer, and a single-barred bearing pointer. The rotating compass card operates from the aircraft's master compass system and is independent of the VOR receiver. The compass card rotates as the aircraft turns so that the magnetic heading of the aircraft is always under the index at the top of the instrument.

The double-barred bearing pointer gives magnetic bearing from the aircraft to the VOR station to which the receiver is tuned. If the aircraft is headed directly toward the station, the head of the double-barred pointer and the magnetic heading of the aircraft will both be directly under the index at the top of the instrument. Should the aircraft be turned 90° to the right, the compass card will rotate 90° to the left and the double-barred pointer will also rotate 90° because it always points toward the station. Thus, the magnetic bearing from the aircraft to the station is always shown under the head of the double-barred pointer.

The single-barred pointer operates in the same way. It is usually connected to an ADF, or may be used with a dual VOR receiver installation, or a TACAN receiver.

The course deviation indicator of Figures 5.32 and 5.33 has a course set knob, the course selector window, and the reciprocal course window, a TO-FROM indicator, and a course deviation indicator (the vertical needle). It may also have OFF warning flags, a marker beacon light, and a glide slope indicator (horizontal needle). Some instruments also have a heading pointer, which shows the heading of the aircraft with respect to the selected course.

With the course knob you can select any desired course, which appears in the course window. The TO-FROM indicator shows whether the course selected, if intercepted and flown, will take you directly *to* or *from* the station. The course deviation indicator (CDI) shows the position of the selected course in relation to the aircraft. Regardless of the heading of the aircraft, unless the aircraft is on the radial in the window, or its reciprocal, the CDI will be off center toward the radial.

The four dots in a horizontal plane on the face of the instrument represent 20° of azimuth. If the CDI indicates a full-scale deflection, it shows that you are 10° or more from your selected course. The inner dots represent 5° from the selected course.

The glide slope indicator is operative only when an ILS frequency is selected; it will be centered with the alarm flag displayed when the receiver is tuned to VOR frequencies.

The two red alarm flags on the CDI and glide slope indicators are spring loaded to the OFF position and operate independently of each other. When the flag disappears from an individual indicator, it shows you that the appropriate indicator is receiving a strong enough signal for reliable indications.

When a VOR is transmitting an abnormal or erroneous signal, the station identification is not transmitted. In this case the receiver may be receiving an erroneous signal strong enough to keep the alarm flag from showing. Therefore, the indicator is reliable only when the alarm flag is not showing *and* the station identification is being received.

DISTANCE MEASURING EQUIPMENT (DME)

To determine distance, an airborne set transmits an interrogation pulse which the ground station receives and answers with a pulsed reply. The airborne equipment measures the time interval between the interrogation and reply; this interval is in proportion to the airplane's distance from the station. In order to prevent an airborne receiver from mistaking ground replies intended for other aircraft, the repetition rate of each airborne transmitter is wobbled or varied slightly to give it an instantaneous repetition rate which differs from that of other aircraft in the area.

When the receiver is tuned to a station, it first must go through a "search mode," in which it looks for ground-station replies which are

Figure 5.37 DME cockpit indicators. *Left:* distance-ground speed indicator. Set knob permits duplicating distance readout from drums on lower dial. Minutes to station is then shown under the pointer, which shows ground speed continuously with reference to the station. *Right:* distance indicator shows up to 200 nm. Bars appear when the distance reading is not valid *(Courtesy of RCA.)*

effectively synchronized with its own repetition rate. This searching process may take up to 20 sec, and during this time the range indicator distance drums rotate rapidly through the whole range. When a synchronized signal is found, range-gate circuits lock onto it, the set goes into its normal operating "track mode," and the distance drum stops at the distance to the station. If the TACAN DME signal is momentarily cut off, as when the aircraft banks and screens the receiving antenna, the range indicator will show the same distance for 10 sec; beyond that time, the receiver reverts to the search mode and starts a new search cycle.

DME is accurate within ±600 ft, plus 0.2% of the distance being measured. Because DME measures slant range, the error is greater close to the station. At 12,000 ft and 10 nm, the error would be only 720 ft. If the aircraft crossed the station 12,000 ft above it, however, the minimum distance indication would be 2 mi (6,080 ft per nm).

THE AUTOMATIC DIRECTION FINDER (ADF)

The ADF is a homing and direction-finding instrument which can utilize the transmissions of commercial broadcast stations, radio range stations, or nondirectional HF radio beacons. Information on the geographical location, identification, frequency, and power output of these stations is readily available in aeronautical publications and on aeronautical charts.

Equipment While there are many manufacturers of reliable ADF equipment designed for a wide variety of installations, the one in Figure 5.38 is typical, and is used as the basis for this discussion. It consists of a power unit, a control unit, a receiver, a bearing pointer, and a loop antenna. It uses in addition an LF fixed antenna. It receives either CW or amplitude-modulated signals from 190 to 1750 khz.

Figure 5.38 Automatic direction finder components. *Left:* control unit. *Middle:* bearing pointer; set knob permits setting desired bearings under the top index. *Right:* loop antenna: the receiver and power unit are not shown. This equipment, not including the necessary connecting cables, weighs less than 20 lb. *(Courtesy of Aircraft Radio Corporation.)*

The Control Unit This unit contains the *band selector* and *tuning crank, volume control* coupled with the ON-OFF switch, and the *tuning meter.* The tuning meter helps to make tuning more accurate for ADF operation. The station is properly tuned when the needle is deflected to its maximum right-hand position. When the set is turned on, it will move from right to left, swinging back to the right as you tune the station with the tuning crank. The degree of its deflection for any station increases or decreases with the volume control setting, increasing with greater volume.

The *function switch* determines whether the receiver is connected to the LF fixed antenna (ANT), the loop antenna (LOOP), or both (COMP). In the ANT position, the set is a simple LF receiver. In LOOP position, the set has directional characteristics, but the loop must be manually oriented by the *LOOP left-right switch.* Being a shielded antenna, this position is useful for reception through precipitation static, or for RDF (Radio Direction Finder) operation, with direction finding by manual loop rotation.

The *ON-BFO switch,* on many sets marked *Voice-CW,* selects either amplitude-modulated or carrier-wave reception, by the use of a beat-frequency oscillator. It provides a clear and uninterrupted tone for RDF operation.

The Bearing Indicator may be of the type shown, having a fixed card, or may have a movable card as an RMI (Figure 5.28). In either case, the needle is driven by an autosyn receiver mechanism which causes it to show the angular position of the loop antenna in relation to the longitudinal axis of the aircraft. Zero degrees or the top index represents the nose of the aircraft, and the bearing indicator always indicates relative bearing and points to the station. Because the procedures for using the RMI bearing indicator are the same for both ADF and VOR, this discussion is limited to the fixed-card type.

The Loop Antenna This is the directional element of the system. A loop receiving antenna gives maximum reception when the plane of the loop is parallel to the direction of wave travel. As the loop is rotated from this position, volume gradually decreases, and reaches a minimum when the plane of the loop is perpendicular to the direction of wave travel.

The loop antenna behaves in this manner because the input from a loop antenna to a receiver is the resultant of the opposing voltages in the two halves of the loop. When the current flows in a looped conductor, it must flow in opposite directions in each half of the loop. This occurs when the plane of the loop is in line with the station. When one side of the loop is closer to the transmitter, a slight delay results between the time the radio wave reaches one side and the time it reaches the other. There is, therefore, a phase difference between the voltages induced in

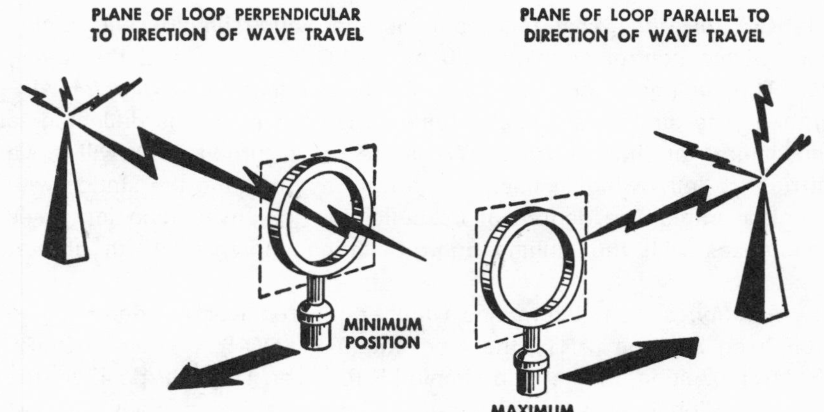

Figure 5.39 Minimum and maximum positions of the loop antenna.

each half of the loop. This causes the signal strength arriving at the receiver to vary according to the position of the loop.

When the plane of the loop is parallel to the direction of wave travel, a maximum voltage is induced in the loop, and you hear the loudest signal in the headset. Conversely, when the plane of the loop is perpendicular to the direction of wave travel, both sides of the loop are equidistant from the station, the wave reaches both sides at the same time, the signal strength is zero, and you hear nothing in the headset. This position of the loop is called the *null position.*

The null position is used for direction finding—that is, the needle of the bearing indicator points perpendicular to the plane of the loop. The null position is used because it can be determined more exactly than the maximum. While signal strength changes less than 10% during a 25° rotation from the maximum position, it changes 50% during the same rotation from the null position.

180° Ambiguity When you rotate the loop to a null position, you know definitely that the radio station is being received on a line perpendicular to the plane of the loop. However, it may be on either side. The inability of the loop to determine which of the two possible directions is correct is called the 180° ambiguity of the loop.

180° ambiguity is resolved by the use of an internally or externally installed nondirectional *sensing antenna.* Both the loop and sensing antenna are connected to the ADF receiver. When the signal strength pattern of the sensing antenna is superimposed on that of the loop antenna, the result is that there is only one null position of the loop.

The ADF loop antenna is automatically rotated to the null position when signals are being received over both the sensing and loop antennas. The combined signals energize a phasing system which operates a motor on the loop drive. As the motor turns, the loop is rotated. The bearing pointer, being synchronized with the loop, indicates the bearing to the station when the set is properly tuned and the loop has stopped in the null position.

Advanced Navigation Instrument Systems

PICTORIAL-SYMBOLIC PLAN VIEW SYSTEMS

This system, a combination of the course indicator and the gyro compass, presents in visual planform the position of the aircraft with respect to the selected course. It greatly simplifies the pilot's computation and orientation problems, giving a clear and instant orientation at all times.

With the VOR receiver tuned to a VOR station, the NAV flag disappears. The course select knob is rotated to position the course arrow on the desired radial heading.

The lateral deviation bar represents the VOR radial, and indicates its position with respect to the aircraft by reference to the miniature airplane symbol etched on the instrument face. Each dot of deflection from center indicates 2° aircraft displacement from the radial, and the expanded scale bar an additional 6°.

To intercept a radial, the pilot turns the aircraft until the miniature aircraft is headed toward the bar an acceptable interception angle; in Figure 5.40 the aircraft is heading 330° to intercept a course of 300°. With no drift, the aircraft would be flying along the radial when the bar was centered and the miniature airplane aligned over it on a heading of 300°. The TO-FROM pointer points to the course which, if selected and flown, will lead to the selected station.

While the bar is centered, the difference between the selected heading under the course arrow and the actual heading under the lubber line is the correction for wind drift.

With a glide slope receiver, glide slope information is shown on the left of the instrument by a glide slope arrow.

INTEGRATED FLIGHT DIRECTOR SYSTEMS

The attitude indicator gives the pilot a forward looking view of his aircraft's position. The RMI and CDI combined in the pictorial-symbolic plan view system gives him a downward-looking, or planform view of his position relative to a VOR radial. By putting these instruments one above

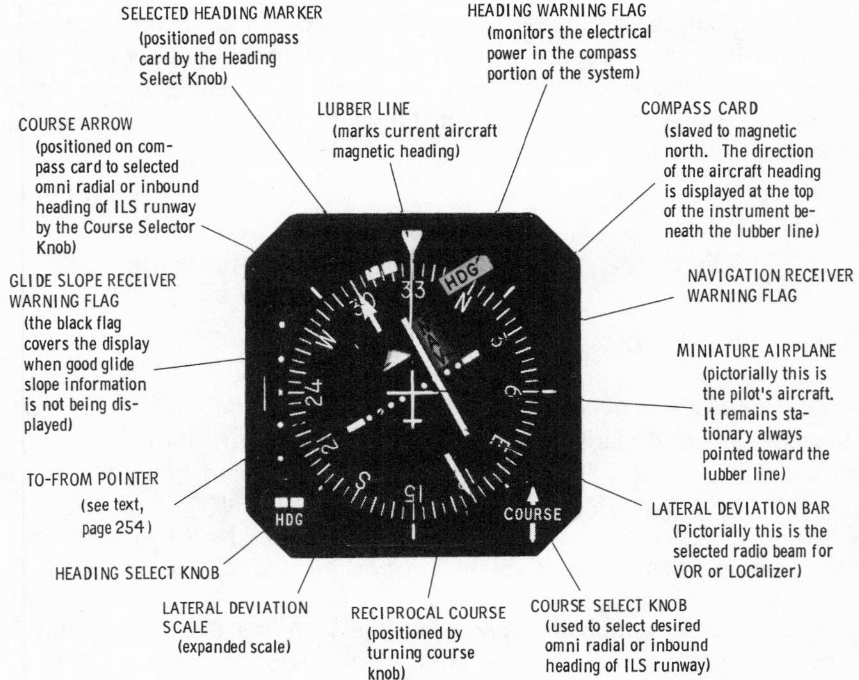
SELECTED HEADING MARKER
(positioned on compass card by the Heading Select Knob)
HEADING WARNING FLAG
(monitors the electrical power in the compass portion of the system)
LUBBER LINE
(marks current aircraft magnetic heading)
COMPASS CARD
(slaved to magnetic north. The direction of the aircraft heading is displayed at the top of the instrument beneath the lubber line)
COURSE ARROW
(positioned on compass card to selected omni radial or inbound heading of ILS runway by the Course Selector Knob)
GLIDE SLOPE RECEIVER WARNING FLAG
(the black flag covers the display when good glide slope information is not being displayed)
NAVIGATION RECEIVER WARNING FLAG
MINIATURE AIRPLANE
(pictorially this is the pilot's aircraft. It remains stationary always pointed toward the lubber line)
TO-FROM POINTER
(see text, page 254)
LATERAL DEVIATION BAR
(Pictorially this is the selected radio beam for VOR or LOCalizer)
HEADING SELECT KNOB
HDG
COURSE
LATERAL DEVIATION SCALE
(expanded scale)
RECIPROCAL COURSE
(positioned by turning course knob)
COURSE SELECT KNOB
(used to select desired omni radial or inbound heading of ILS runway)

Figure 5.40 Pictorial-symbolic course indicator. *(Courtesy of Collins Radio Co.)*

the other, the cross-check problem is greatly simplified, but he still must practice to retain the fine judgment which will tell him *how much* of a correction to make to remove a displacement from his desired position and altitude or rate of climb or descent.

The "director" portion of the system determines this for him. In the flight director mode, a symbolic airplane as in Figure 5.42 (or in other models, cross bars) derives its displacement from center from a computer which computes the rate of return to a desired or command flight condition. The pilot merely changes pitch or bank attitude to center the symbol. By keeping it centered, the aircraft is gradually flown back to the desired condition.

Components The flight director system consists of four basic parts: a horizon deviation indicator (HDI), a course deviation indicator (CDI), a flight instrument amplifier, and the flight steering computer. These components receive inputs from the aircraft's radio navigation (VOR-LOC) system, from its vertical and rate gyros, and from its compass system.

Figure 5.41A
Horizon director indicator. The computed steering commands of the command bar indicate needed corrections in both pitch and roll. When the flight director mode is not used, the command bar is recessed out of view, leaving a conventional attitude indicator. *(Courtesy of The Bendix Corp., Eclipse-Pioneer Div.)*

Figure 5.41B
Course deviation indicator. The CDI indicates displacement from the planned position and selected altitude or glideslope, compass heading, omnibearing selection, TO-FROM indication, and altitude-hold indication. Warning flags indicate malfunction of power off in compass system, and navigation and glideslope receivers; or that receivers are not tuned to the ILS frequency. *(Courtesy of The Bendix Corp., Eclipse-Pioneer Div.)*

Commands may be put into this system in level flight by setting an "altitude hold" function on a given altitude and setting the course arrow on a desired course. During an ILS, the commands are put in by tuning the ILS frequency, and by switching to the ILS mode of the system. Because the command steering indication of the command bar in the HDI is more sensitive than the displacement information presented by the attitude indicator and the CDI, a relatively small attitude change will center the command bar, correcting the displacement at a smooth rate.

The Flight Instrument Amplifier, a transitorized unit, amplifies the attitude, heading, and command signals to operate the servomechanisms in the HDI and CDI.

The Flight Steering Computer is the "brain" of the system. It contains the transistorized computer circuits needed to use input signals from the gyros and radio receivers for computation of a combined command for display on the HDI.

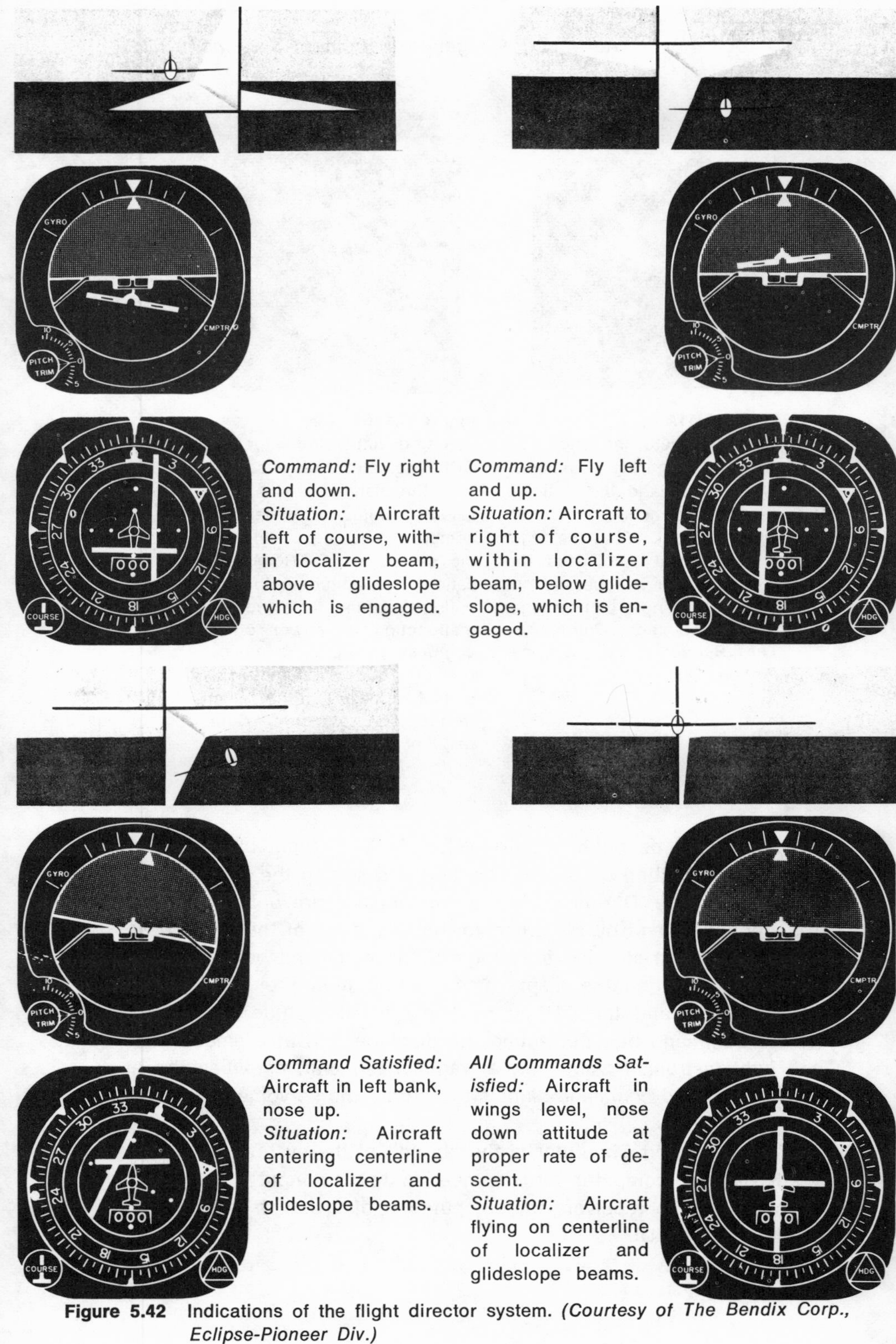

GYRO
CMPTR
PITCH TRIM
COURSE
HDG
Command: Fly right and down. *Situation:* Aircraft left of course, within localizer beam, above glideslope which is engaged.
Command: Fly left and up. *Situation:* Aircraft to right of course, within localizer beam, below glideslope, which is engaged.
Command Satisfied: Aircraft in left bank, nose up. *Situation:* Aircraft entering centerline of localizer and glideslope beams.
All Commands Satisfied: Aircraft in wings level, nose down attitude at proper rate of descent. *Situation:* Aircraft flying on centerline of localizer and glideslope beams.

Figure 5.42 Indications of the flight director system. *(Courtesy of The Bendix Corp., Eclipse-Pioneer Div.)*

HIGH-PERFORMANCE AIRCRAFT INSTRUMENT PANELS

The flight director system is coupled with vertical reading performance instrument tapes in Figure 5.43. The result is a system in which the pilot is concerned with matching only horizontal and vertical lines. "Command" means the value used as a guide for some flight condition, as takeoff, climb, or cruise. The pilot sets this value. The vertical scale indexes show the degree to which the aircraft is meeting the desired values. Developed originally for supersonic fighters, this system is now used also in high-performance subsonic aircraft such as the C-141.

Vertical-Tape Engine Instruments With the multitude of engine power and condition data that is vital to modern multiengine aircraft, and the

Figure 5.43 High-performance integrated flight instrument panel. This panel appears in the F-105 and F-106, and the F-111. (A) Angle of attack-airspeed indicator. (B) Standby airspeed indicator. (C) Attitude director indicator. (D) Horizontal situation indicator. (E) Vertical speed-altimeter indicator. (F) Standby altimeter. Note that in this HDI, the turn and slip indicator is mounted in the lower rim, and that the steering bars are the cross-pointer type. The attitude indicator horizon is tipped because there is no power on the instrument.

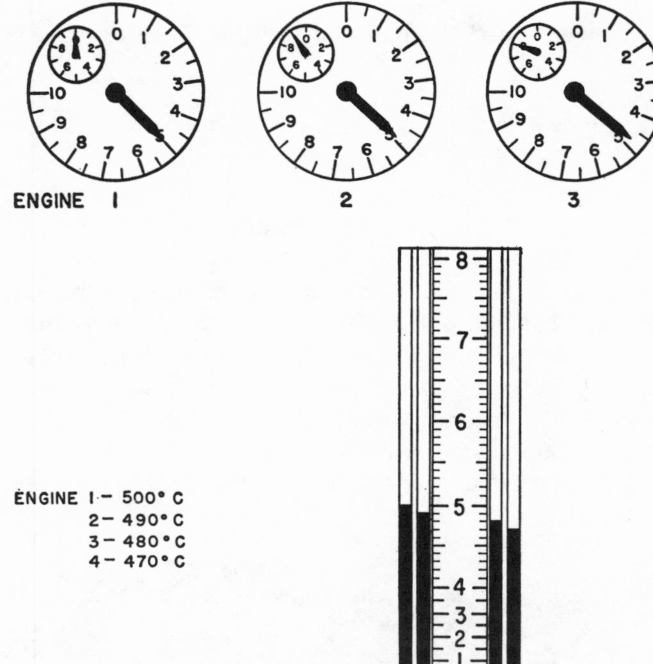

Figure 5.44 Comparison: round dial vs vertical scale display. This illustration shows only one element of the complex information shown in the jet engine panel of 5.13. The simplicity and clarity of multiple critical indications are evident. *(Courtesy of The Bendix Corp., Eclipse-Pioneer Div.)*

Figure 5.45 Engine parameters displayed on vertical tape showing malfunction takeoff. Engine 3, egt is + 10° error; rpm for engine No. 3 is showing 1.0% error. *(Courtesy of The Bendix Corp.)*

relatively limited time in which a pilot must make critical judgments based on readings of those instruments, the vertical-tape presentation is considered superior. This is clearly illustrated in Figure 5.44, in which the eye immediately detects the difference in values in the vertical instruments, while the round dials, even though all appearing alike, are reading quite differently.

The test instrument panel model shown in Figure 5.43, when compared with the instrument panel in Figure 5.2, demonstrates the application of this system very clearly. In the C-141, Figure 1.20, the horizontal line principle is applied to both flight and engine instruments, combining Figure 5.42 and Figure 5.43 in one panel.

LOW-ALTITUDE PRECISION ALTIMETERS

Safe scheduled airline operation into airports under low ceilings has in the past been limited to a minimum of 200 ft because of the possible errors in barometric-type altimeters close to the ground. To lower this landing minimum to 100 ft, and to provide precise low-altitude information for automatic approach and landing, the radio altimeter has been developed in a refined form.

Operating below 2500 ft, the radio altimeter has accuracy on the order of ±1% below 80 ft, and ±2% between 80 and 500 ft. A frequency-modulated transmitter sends continuous wave energy to the ground through a wide-beam antenna. An equally wide beam antenna receives the reflected signal returned from the ground. Because the reflected signal has undergone a frequency change proportional to the altitude of the aircraft, the frequency difference, or error, can be measured and converted into signals which drive the altitude indicator on the pilot's panel.

THE AUTOMATIC PILOT

In large aircraft, automatic pilots are essential to relieve the pilot from the task, frequently full-time, of maintaining course and altitude. In higher-performance aircraft, the automatic pilot can do a better job of flying under normal circumstances than can the human pilot, because it can sense changes in heading, pitch, and trim faster than he can, and can apply a more precise correction.

In small aircraft, autopilots perform the same role; they also make flying more pleasant and safer by providing relief for the single pilot, who, in congested areas, can be quite busy with navigation and radio.

Operation The basic idea of autopilot operation is this: A vertical gyro, such as the remote gyro for the attitude indicator, provides a stable reference platform for pitch and roll axes; a directional gyro, as for the heading indicator, provides a stable directional reference. To each of the three flight surfaces, elevator, aileron, and rudder, there are attached servo motors capable of moving the control surface. When the aircraft deviates from the attitude and heading in which the pilot placed it when he engaged the autopilot, synchros in the gyros signal the servo motors through a central coordinating computer to correct the deviation by a movement of the control surface. This is the basic autopilot. It may be designed around any or all of the three axes, and some lightplane autopilots are designed to maintain only the yaw, or directional axis, stable.

There are complications. First, a trim servo is required to insure that the elevator trim reflects shifting loads in the aircraft under various flight conditions. Without it, the elevator could gradually become held out of alignment under great stress, and a sudden disengagement of the servo could mean violent dive or climb.

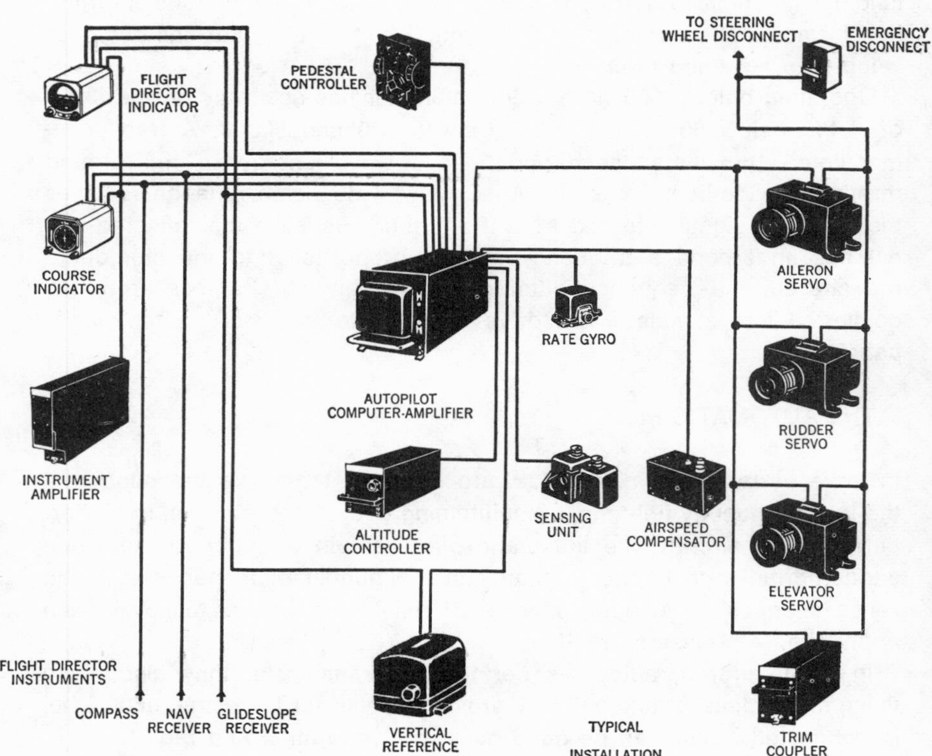

Figure 5.46 Autopilot system schematic. *(Courtesy of Collins Radio Corp.)*

Second, in order to provide smooth operation, rate gyros (sensors), are required in the pitch and roll, and the yaw axes, to detect the *rate* at which the aircraft is deviating from its set attitude. This permits the autopilot to govern the *rapidity and force* of the correction, and prevents over- and undercontrolling.

Third, controls have to be provided to the pilot so that while the autopilot is engaged, he can make smooth turns to selected headings, and can remain level, climb, or descend.

Fourth, the basic autopilot can sense only attitude, not altitude. Therefore, an *altitude control* may be introduced to signal the elevator servo and elevator trim servo whenever the aircraft deviates from a selected altitude. This is a sensitive barometric sensor which is in a null (no-signal) condition as long as the aircraft is on altitude within the limits of the sensor; usually less than ± 40 ft.

Fifth, when the pilot wants to follow a certain course, as an OMNI radial, a computer can be introduced which signals the autopilot to turn, to intercept, and to follow the radial. This function is expanded in many

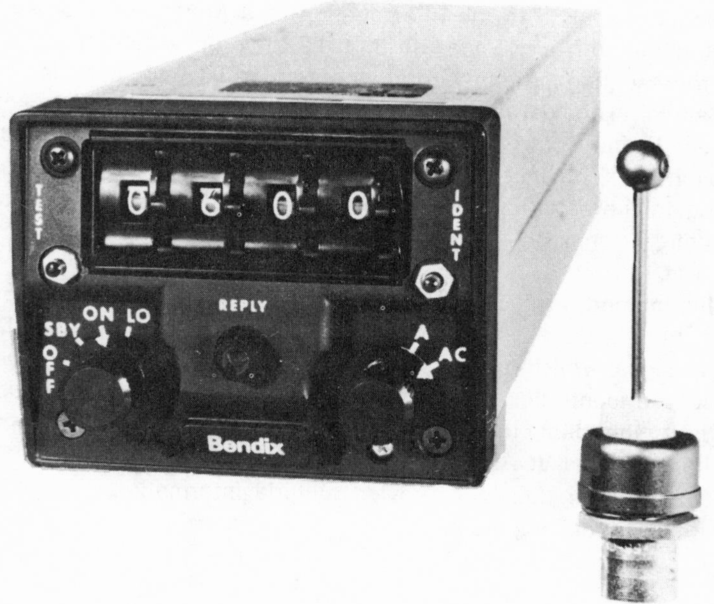

Figure 5.47 Transponder Head and Antenna. The Air Traffic Control Radar Beacon System (ACCRBS) requires transponders in all positive control area. Normal mode is "A." "AC" includes altitude reporting. *(Courtesy of Avionics Division of The Bendix Corp.)*

autopilots to permit automatic low approaches with ILS and glide slope receivers.

Using the Autopilot There is more to flying the autopilot than just turning it on. A good pilot who practices and studies the autopilot in his aircraft can get a good deal more out of it than the casual user. He will trim the aircraft properly before engaging it, and will pay attention to the aircraft trim during autopilot flight. He will be aware that in strong downdrafts and updrafts, an excessively low or high airspeed can result from using the altitude hold function. He will know the limits of the autopilot, and its effect on passenger comfort, in turbulence. Autopilots in turbulence try to maintain too fixed an attitude, with the result that the flight becomes excessively rough or oscillating; a strain on aircraft, crew, and passengers.

TRANSPONDERS

The present trend of development of Air Traffic Control leans more and more heavily on the airborne radar safety beacon or transponder. The transponder responds to the interrogation of a ground interrogator used in conjunction with ATC radar so that the blips on the controller's radar scope representing certain aircraft are reinforced and identified by the coded signal. This particular signal, transmitted as a reply, is selected by the Air Traffic Controller, who assigns to aircraft by voice a mode and code such as "Transmit on Mode A, Code 1234." Individual aircraft responding to the same mode and code may be identified by transmitting an identifier signal on the controller's request, or by flying identifying maneuvers.

By this method, also, a small aircraft whose surface will not provide a suitable radar reflection on the controller's scope can be identified by its reply signal which appears on the scope at the aircraft's location. Because the controller then knows the aircraft's precise location, he can advise the pilot, thus providing an even more precise instrument navigation aid than VOR with DME.

The transponder does not provide altitude information, though this is the next step in development.

6

*The Atmosphere and Its Weather**

The atmosphere is defined by Webster's Dictionary as "the whole mass of air surrounding the earth; . . . a surrounding influence or environment." This is the airman's world. In this world of surrounding air, thinness and bouyancy permit measuring distance in minutes rather than miles, and beauty, enchantment, and freedom are the pervading influence. Only in the airman's world can one view horizons encompassing land and sea, mountain and prairie, storm and calm, even peace and war, at a single glance.

Chemical Structure of the Atmosphere

The ancient Greeks considered air to be one of the four basic "elements" —the others being fire, earth, and water. As we know, air is not an element in the chemical sense but a complex mixture of gases, like apples, oranges, and bananas thrown together in a fruit bowl.

*Revision by Lt. Col. John S. Perry, and Mr. Herbert S. Appleman, Air Weather Service, USAF.

The basic unit of each gas is the molecule, far too small to be seen even through the most powerful electron microscopes yet developed. The molecules of oxygen, nitrogen, and other atmospheric gases maintain their separate identities as they exist side by side.

In the lowest 40 to 50 mi of the atmosphere the relative proportion of each gas in the mixture stays remarkably constant. Nitrogen and oxygen, by volume 78% and 21%, are the most abundant gases. Argon, an inert gas, makes up about 1%. Only 0.03% is carbon dioxide, yet this part is vital to life, since plants require it for photosynthesis. In addition, carbon dioxide, like water vapor, is a powerful absorber of the sun's radiation, thus moderating temperature. Traces of helium, krypton, and neon are also present. Water vapor is the most variable part, ranging from values as high as 5% in moist tropical air to almost 0% in regions of intense cold and great heights. In addition to its gaseous parts, the atmosphere contains various types of small, solid particles, such as sea salt and dust. Since the condensation of moisture in the atmosphere occurs on these solid particles (*condensation nuclei*), they are nearly as important as the gases.

Although nitrogen and oxygen compose 99% of the atmosphere up to altitudes of a thousand miles or more, the form of the bases does not remain constant. At some distance above the earth, ultraviolent radiation from the sun causes some of the molecules to dissociate from the molecular state to the atomic state. At lower levels where the atmosphere is relatively dense, the atomic state is rare because recombination takes place about as rapidly as dissociation.

When an atom and a molecule of oxygen combine, ozone is formed. Most of the ozone occurs in a layer about 15 mi thick between 10 and 25 mi from the surface of the earth, although it extends from as low as 5 to as high as 35 mi. This layer is frequently called the ozonosphere.

While there is only a minute quantity of ozone present, it so efficiently absorbs certain ultraviolet wavelengths that it greatly warms the upper part of the ozone layer. This makes the temperature at 30 mi altitude about the same as that at the earth's surface. Ozone also protects the lower layers from excessive shortwave radiation which would kill nearly all forms of life on the earth.

Above the ozone layer, air density decreases until recombination eventually does not occur, leaving both oxygen and nitrogen in atomic form.

Physical Properties of the Atmosphere

While the airman should understand the atmosphere's chemical structure, he deals more directly with its physical properties and structure. The primary physical properties which determine structure are pressure, temperature, humidity, and radiation.

PRESSURE

Atmospheric pressure at any point is equal to the weight of the air column of unit cross-sectional area above that point. It can be expressed either in terms of actual weight, such as pounds per square inch (psi), or in terms of the height of a column of some other fluid, such as inches of mercury, which exerts the same pressure. At sea level the average pressure of the air is 14.7 psi. The same pressure is exerted by a column of mercury 760 mm (29.92 in.) in height. In meteorology the unit of pressure most commonly used is the millibar (mb), which is the pressure exerted by a force of 1000 dynes/cm^2. These equivalents are shown in Table 6.1.

TABLE 6.1
Standard Atmospheric Pressure at Sea Level Expressed in Various Units

1013.25	millibars (mb)
14.70	pounds per square inch (psi)
760	millimeters of mercury (mm Hg)
33.90	feet of water
29.92	inches of mercury (in. Hg)

TEMPERATURE

While the temperature of a substance may be considered the degree of its hotness or coldness, measured on a relative scale, the kinetic theory better explains this physical property of gases.

The molecules of a gas move constantly. Their average speed is high at higher temperatures, low at lower temperatures. The temperature at which all motion of molecules stops is defined as absolute zero.

The two thermometer scales in common use today are the Fahrenheit and centigrade. Gabriel Daniel Fahrenheit, a German physicist, developed a scale which selected as 0° the temperature on a particular winter day in Danzig. This gave a boiling point of 212°, a freezing point of 32° and an absolute zero of -459.69°.

A French scientist, Rene Antoine de Reaumur, devised a more scientific scale in 1731, using alcohol as his liquid and the freezing point of water as 0°. From this idea was developed the centigrade (also called Celsius) scale, with the freezing and boiling points of water equal to 0° and 100° respectively, and an absolute zero of -273.16°. This scale is now in common use in all but the English-speaking countries, where it is employed only in scientific and technical measurements. For example, all upper-air temperature measurements in the United States and Canada are reported in degrees centigrade. The relationship between the Fahrenheit and centigrade scale is expressed by this formula: degrees Fahrenheit = 9/5 degrees centigrade + 32.

HUMIDITY

The quantity of water vapor contained in the atmosphere is relatively small, ranging from a trace to a maximum of 4% or 5%. Without this moisture, however, most life as we know it could not exist. Moisture is the basis of rain, snow, thunderstorms, clouds, fog, frost, and dew; by its absorption of solar and terrestrial radiation it affects the temperature of the air.

The capacity of air for holding moisture increases with increasing temperature. Air is termed *saturated* when it is in equilibrium with a flat water surface at the same temperature and pressure as the air. In other words, such a water surface will neither evaporate into nor gain water from saturated air. The actual water vapor content of an air parcel can be described in a number of ways. Most commonly used by meteorologists are *mixing ratio, dew point,* and *relative humidity.*

Mixing ratio is the ratio of the mass of water vapor to the mass of dry air in the parcel, usually expressed in parts per thousand. Dew point is the temperature to which air must be cooled to reach saturation at its original pressure and mixing ratio. It is also the temperature at which a smooth surface would first show traces of condensation or dew. Further cooling would cause condensation of a part of the vapor as dew—hence the name dew point. Relative humidity is the ratio of the actual mass of water vapor in the air to that which would exist if air at the same temperature and pressure were saturated. It is expressed in percentage. The difference between the actual temperature and the dew point temperature is called "spread," and is an indication of relative humidity. A 0° spread corresponds to 100% relative humidity.

The ability of air to hold moisture falls off rapidly with decreasing temperatures. Assuming a surface pressure of 1000 mb, the mixing ratio of saturated air at a temperature of 20°C (68°F) is 15 parts per thousand. This value falls 50% with a cooling of only 10°C. At a temperature of −37°C, the saturation mixing ratio is down to 1/100 of its original value.

Water vapor is added to the air mainly through evaporation from wet surfaces and transpiration from plant life. Since these are low-level sources, the amount of moisture, like temperature, tends to decrease with altitude.

RADIATION

All motions in the earth's atmosphere, all forms of weather, and even life itself owe their origin to energy received from the sun. This energy is transmitted to the earth in the form of electromagnetic waves. Electromagnetic radiation occurs over a wide spectrum of wavelengths. At one end of a complete spectrum are the extremely short waves, including the cosmic rays, gamma rays, and X rays. Next come the ultraviolet, visible light, and infrared rays. Finally at the other end of the spectrum are the longer waves used in radar, television, and radio broadcasting. Solar radiation is concentrated in only part of this spectrum: visible light and parts of the ultraviolet and infrared bands.

The quantity of solar radiation received at the outer layers of the earth's atmosphere on a unit of surface in a unit of time is called the *solar constant.* Its value has been calculated to be 1.94 calories/cm^2/min. After this radiation is absorbed, heat is liberated. A small fraction (about 5%) of the incoming solar radiation (*insolation*) is absorbed by the ozone layer. The next barriers are the cloud layers, which cover about half the sky. The *albedo* (reflecting ability) of the clouds is about 0.80, so 40% of the total insolation is reflected back to space without releasing its heat. Another 15% is absorbed by the various atmospheric constituents, especially by water vapor in the lower levels; most of the remaining 40% is absorbed by the earth.

These figures include the small amount of insolation reflected either back to space or down to earth by the process known as scattering. Light waves are scattered, or reflected in all directions, when they strike very small particles. If the particles are smaller than the wavelength of light, as is true for molecules of air and many condensation nuclei, the shorter wavelengths (blue light) are scattered most. This selective scattering gives the sky its characteristic blue color. At very high altitudes, where the molecules of air are widely separated, scattering becomes negligible and the sky appears black. Particles larger than the light waves, such as fog, cloud, and precipitation droplets, scatter nonselectively and give the sky a whitish appearance.

All this absorbed radiation must necessarily be radiated back to space, since otherwise the earth would be growing progressively hotter. The average wavelength of radiant energy varies inversely with the temperature of the emitting body. The earth, which is relatively cool, radiates principally in the long-wave infrared band. The atmosphere is not nearly so transparent to these long waves as it is to the short-wave solar radiation. Water vapor, clouds, and (to a smaller degree) carbon dioxide are all good absorbers of rays in the infrared spectrum. Thus the energy is trapped and the lower layers of the atmosphere are warmed. Glass has the same property of being transparent to short waves and absorbing long waves; the resulting temperature rise is known as the *greenhouse effect.*

Although for the earth as a whole the terrestrial radiation must equal the absorbed insolation, there is a marked discrepancy between income and outgo at certain latitudes. In equatorial regions, where the sun is most nearly overhead, there is an excess of insolation, while in polar regions there is a deficiency.

Physical Structure of the Atmosphere

Atmospheric structure may be seen as comprising a series of layers, each with its own characteristics. Several nomenclature systems have been devised for identifying the various layers. Perhaps the most common, and certainly the simplest, divides the atmosphere into four layers of alternately decreasing and increasing temperature—the troposphere, the stratosphere, the mesosphere, and the thermosphere—plus a boundary layer between the atmosphere and space called the exosphere (Figure 6.1). The layers in which the temperature decreases with height tend to be unstable and turbulent, while those in which the temperature increases with height tend to be stable and smooth. Within the thermally bounded layers are two regions that have unique physical properties—the ozonosphere, which coincides with the stratosphere, and the ionosphere, which overlaps the mesosphere and thermosphere (Figure 6.1).

THE TROPOSPHERE

The lowest layer and the one most familiar to man is the troposphere. The name is derived from the Greek *tropos,* meaning "turn" and refers to the great amount of overturning of the air in this layer. Convective currents rapidly and continuously carry air parcels upward and downward. Nearly all of the varied activity termed weather takes place within this layer. The troposphere is characterized by a decrease in temperature with height at the rate of about 3½° F per 1000 ft until a leveling-off point is reached at the tropopause. The change in temperature with height is called the *temperature lapse rate.* If the temperature within a layer is constant, the lapse rate is said to be *isothermal.* An *inversion* is a layer in which the temperature increases with height.

The troposphere extends to greater elevations in warm regions than it

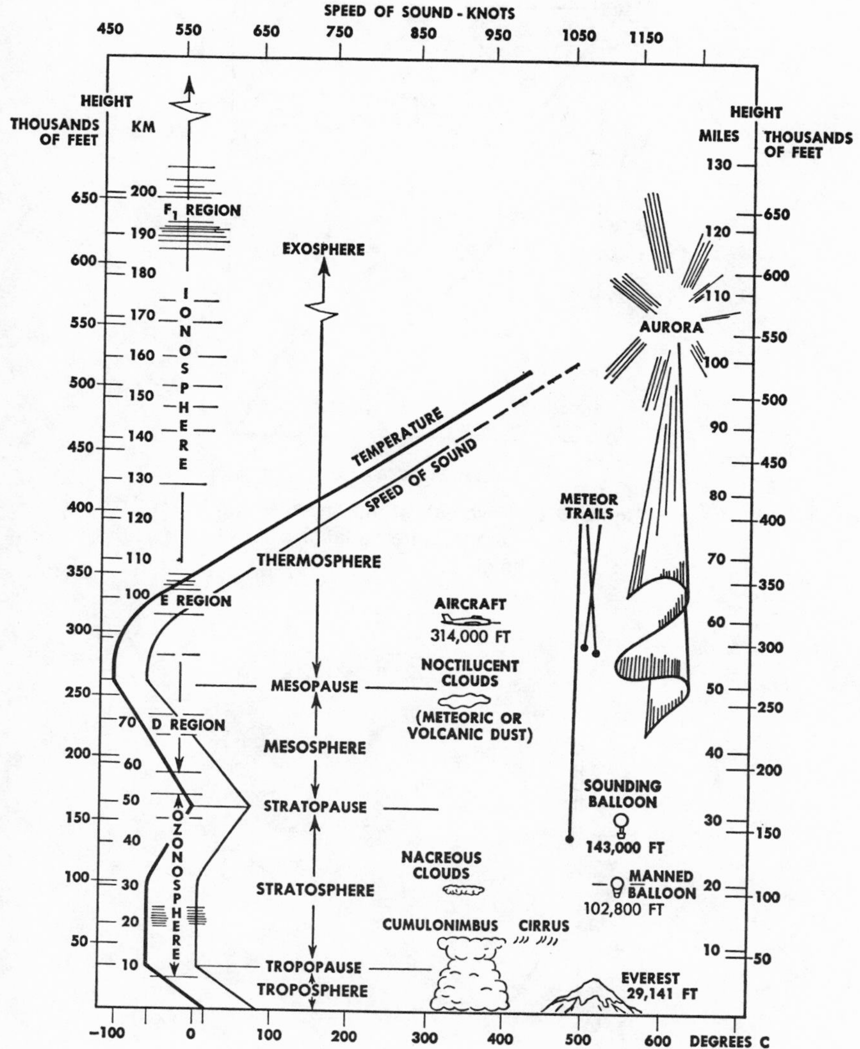

Figure 6.1 Phenomena and structure of the atmosphere. Radio waves are, in general, absorbed in the *D* region, and refracted at the *E* region.

does in cold, reaching 50,000 ft or more at the equator, and only 25,000 ft at the poles. This difference results in the phenomenon of temperature reversal at high altitudes. At the surface of the earth, polar air is much colder than tropical air. However, the temperature of polar air decreases with height only up to its low tropopause, while that of tropical air continues falling until its much higher tropopause is reached. At some alti-

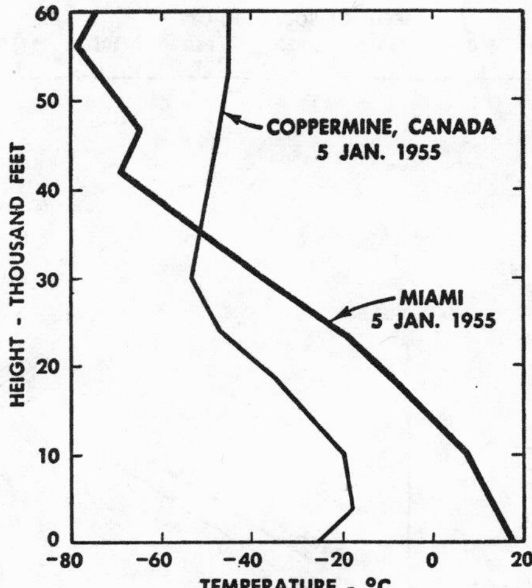

Figure 6.2 Reversal of the north-south temperature relationship at high altitudes.

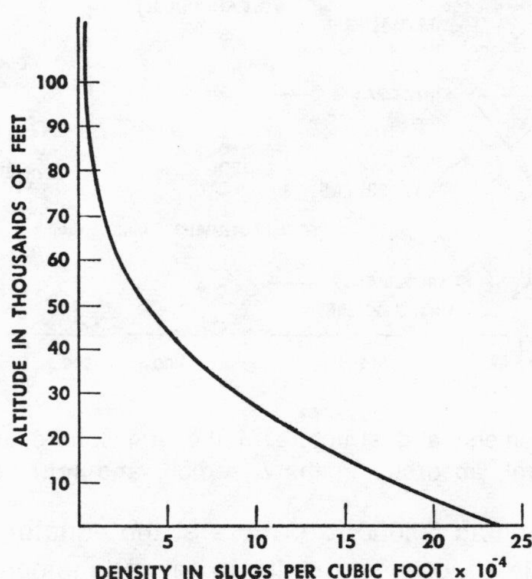

Figure 6.3 Decrease in density of the atmosphere with altitude. Density in slugs per cubic foot $\times 10^{-4}$.

tude, therefore, tropical air becomes colder than polar air. Typical temperature-altitude soundings for polar and tropical air are shown in Figure 6.2. Here the north-south temperature reversal occurs near 35,000 ft.

Another important characteristic of the atmosphere, particularly noticeable in the troposphere, is its decrease in density with altitude (Figure 6.3). Though the troposphere contains less than 1% of the total volume of the atmosphere, it contains over 75% of the total mass. In fact, half of the total mass is contained in the lowest 18,000 ft. Similarly, the pressure exerted by the air decreases with altitude.

The distinction between air pressure and air density is important. As described in other chapters, the two have independent effects on aircraft engine operation and on the human body. Density is a measure of mass contained in a unit volume, and is often expressed in the number of slugs in a cubic foot. Pressure is a measure of force exerted on a surface of unit area, and may be expressed in pounds per square foot (lb/ft^2) or pounds per square inch (psi).

THE STRATOSPHERE

Above the troposphere, extending to great altitudes, lies the stratosphere. An isothermal layer usually extends from the tropopause to perhaps 10 or 20 mi, at an average temperature of −56.5°C. Above this point the temperature increases, reaching a maximum value at about 30 mi.

Scientists estimate that the average peak temperature is −2.5°C, not far below the earth's average surface temperature. This temperature peak near 30 mi altitude is called the *stratopause*. It is close to the top of the ozone layer. Even though the total quantity of ozone in the atmosphere is small and the great bulk lies at lower levels, its great ability to absorb short-wave radiation is the primary cause of the high temperature at this level.

Since the source of moisture is at the surface of the earth, one would expect to find few clouds in the stratosphere. In general, this is true. However, it is not unusual for the tops of large "thunderheads" to be found there also. More surprising is the fact that clouds have been found at altitudes ranging from 70,000 to 90,000 ft above ground. These rare mother-of-pearl clouds, so called for their iridescence, are believed to be composed of tiny globules of ice.

THE MESOSPHERE

Above the stable stratosphere is a turbulent layer called the mesosphere, in which the temperature falls rapidly with height. It reaches an average minimum value of −92.5°C near 50 mi. The upper boundary of the mesosphere is called the mesopause. The rare noctilucent "shining-at-night" clouds, which are probably composed of meteoric dust and ice crystals, occur near the mesopause.

THE THERMOSPHERE

Like the stratosphere, the thermosphere is a region of increasing temperature with height. Here are found the aurorae and most of the meteor trails. The high temperatures in the thermosphere are at least partly due to the absorption of some of the shortest ultraviolet waves by oxygen molecules. There is still sufficient air in the lower part of the thermosphere to cause significant drag and frictional heating on vehicles passing through it. As shown in Figure 6.1, there is no temperature boundary to the top of the thermosphere.

THE EXOSPHERE

The very high temperatures existing above 350 mi result in a very rapid movement of the atoms and molecules, some of which achieve sufficient velocity to overcome the force of gravity and escape into space. This fringe region between the atmosphere and outer space is termed the exosphere. Both the lower and upper boundaries of the exosphere are diffused and poorly defined. Generally the limits are considered as lying roughly between 350 and 600 mi, although some authorities put the upper limit above 1000 mi.

THE IONOSPHERE

An important effect of radiant energy from the sun is to ionize air. That is, electrons are dissociated from neutral air molecules and atoms producing positively charged ions and free electrons. The most effective agent for this process is solar ultraviolet radiation. Most of the ultraviolet is blocked from reaching the lower atmosphere by the stratosphere's ozone. Also, at lower altitudes the density of the air is so great that ionized particles rapidly meet and recombine. In the mesosphere and above, however, solar ultraviolet radiation acts with full force, and density is so low that charged particles have a long lifetime. This deep layer in which substantial numbers of freely moving charged particles are present is termed the ionosphere. It extends between about 35 and 300 mi altitude.

The main effect of the ionosphere upon the aviator is its ability to refract, reflect, or absorb radio waves. This property makes long-distance radio communication possible through reflection of radio waves between the earth and the ionosphere. Since the ionosphere is created and maintained by solar radiation, its characteristics vary markedly with the passage of day and night and with varying solar activity. Predictions of its radio propagation activities are routinely made by the National Oceanic and Atmospheric Administration (NOAA) of the Department of Commerce, which contains the National Weather Service (formerly Weather Bureau.)

THE STANDARD ATMOSPHERE

Atmospheric properties at any level vary greatly with location and time of year, and because of moving weather systems. But for many practical purposes it is desirable to have a universally accepted model atmosphere. For example, altimeters which depend upon pressure should all behave the same. Such uniform standards are also essential for aircraft design.

The latest, and most generally accepted standard atmosphere is the ICAO Standard Atmosphere shown in Figure 6.4. This is the U. S. Standard Atmosphere adopted in 1962. Supplementary standards for higher altitudes and varying seasons and latitudes were published in 1966. These

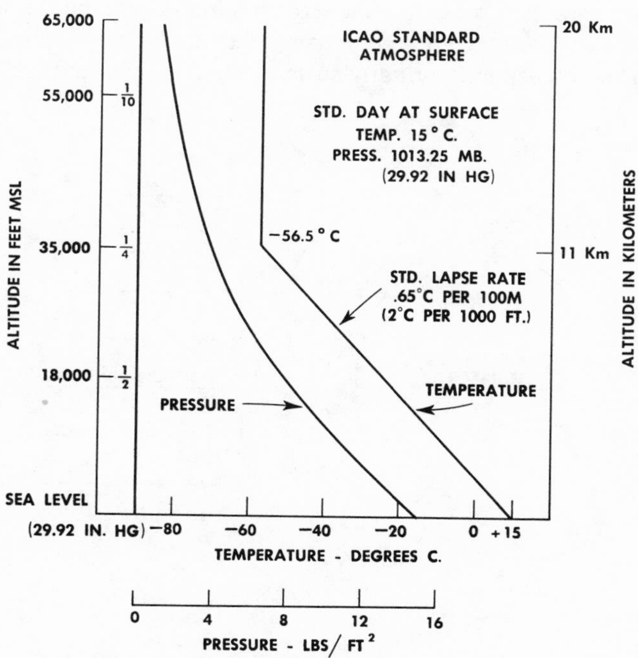

Figure 6.4 The standard atmosphere, lower levels, with standard day at the surface.

give the aircraft designer and operator valuable guidance on the nature of his environment.

Circulation of the Atmosphere

The most striking feature of the atmosphere to airmen is its unceasing motion and change. Clearly this constant activity requires some outside source of energy to maintain it. This is provided by the sun, whose radiant energy acts most effectively at low latitudes where the earth's surface is perpendicular to the sun's rays. Conversely, the sun illuminates the polar regions at low angles so that each unit of energy is spread over a larger area. Because both tropics and poles can lose heat to outer space equally well, the net effect is a constant input of heat to the earth and atmosphere near the equator and a compensating deficit near the poles.

GENERAL CIRCULATION

If the earth were not rotating, unequal heating would cause a simple system of convection currents with rising motion in the tropics, sinking motion over the poles, and northerly surface winds in mid-latitudes capped

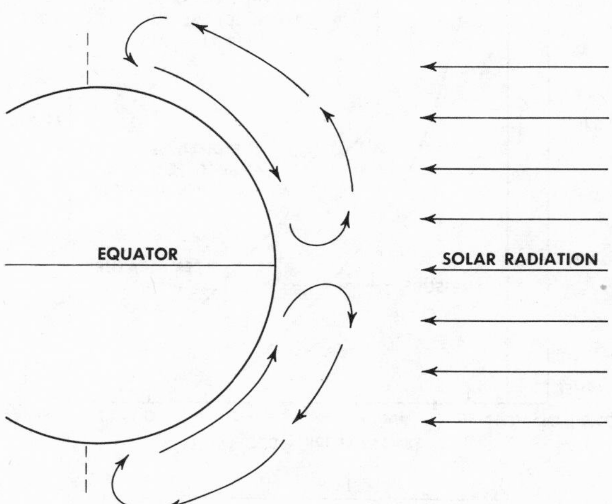

Figure 6.5 Atmospheric circulation on a nonrotating earth.

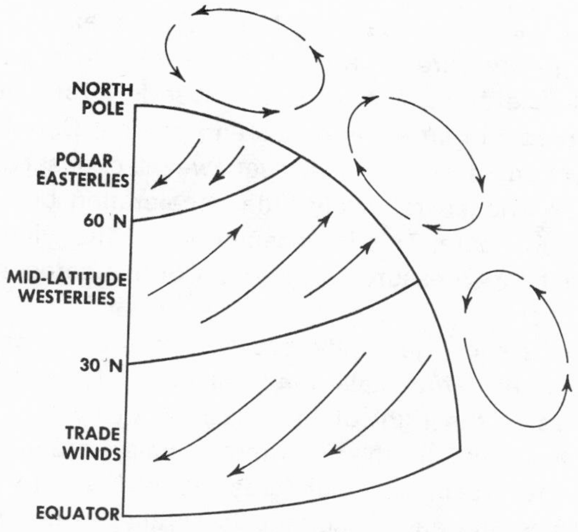

Figure 6.6 Observed general circulation of the atmosphere.

by southerly winds aloft. (See Figure 6.5). Such a circulation would efficiently transfer heat from equator to pole.

The rotation of the earth significantly complicates this simple picture. Air set in motion by heat-generated pressure forces attempts to follow a straight course as viewed from space. However, the earth rotates under this moving air, so that to an earthbound observer the air currents appear to deviate to the right (in the Northern Hemisphere). To us it appears as if a force is pulling the air to the right. This apparent force is termed *Coriolis force.*

Coriolis force induced by the rotation of the earth makes the simple one-cell circulation of Figure 6.5 impossible. Instead, a far more complex circulation is used by the atmosphere to transfer heat from south to north. Near the equator and pole, prevailing easterly winds are found. The subtropical easterlies are termed trade winds and are among the steadiest winds on earth. In mid-latitudes the prevailing wind is westerly, but the dominant circulation feature is the continual series of vortexes or eddies which move from west to east in the westerly winds. For this reason, any depiction of the average circulation, such as Figure 6.6, bears little resemblance to the weather of any individual day.

GEOSTROPHIC WIND

Another remarkable and useful consequence of the earth's rotation is a relationship between the pressure distribution and the wind known as the *geostrophic wind law.* Any parcel of air always experiences a force directed from high pressure toward low pressure. When we increase the pressure in a bicycle pump, the air in the hose is forced out. But on the earth a moving parcel of air experiences an apparent Coriolis force to the right of its direction of motion. However, we also observe that moving streams of air experience relatively little acceleration or deceleration in the course of a few hours. This is possible only if the wind and pressure cooperate so that the pressure force and Coriolis force almost exactly balance each other.

This state of balance generally prevails in the atmosphere. In the Northern Hemisphere, large-scale winds almost universally blow so that high pressure lies to the right of the direction of motion, balancing the deviating Coriolis force. In the Southern Hemisphere, the direction of Coriolis force is reversed, and high pressure is found to the left of the wind. In the tropics, the earth's surface is parallel to its axis of rotation, Coriolis force is virtually absent, and the winds are poorly related to the pressure distribution. Near the earth's surface, the force of friction is also significant and winds turn somewhat toward low pressure.

Figure 6.7 Average pressure and wind distribution from 20,000 to 40,000 ft.

LOW-LEVEL CIRCULATION AND PRESSURE

The distribution of average pressure on the earth is consistent with these rules and the average air circulation we mentioned above. A "trough" of low pressure lies over the equator between the two trade wind belts, while to the north and south large subtropical high-pressure areas mark their northern boundary. The polar high-pressure area suggested by the polar easterlies is much less pronounced, but the stormy mid-latitudes are marked by traveling low- and high-pressure systems in which wind and pressure behave much as suggested by the geostrophic wind relationship.

WINDS ALOFT

These migrating low-pressure areas (or cyclones) and high-pressure areas (or anticyclones) are associated with the bulk of the weather experienced in mid-latitudes where most of the world's flying is done. But to aviators, the winds above the earth's surface are of almost equal interest. The typical wind flow in the troposphere can be represented by a ring of subtropical highs bounded to the north by a belt of westerlies surrounding a weak polar low. (Figure 6.7.) The westerlies are by no means constant. They meander around low-pressure troughs and high-pressure ridges which are generally associated with the surface cyclones and anticyclones mentioned above. A typical relationship is shown in Figure 6.8.

THE JET STREAM

A remarkable feature of the upper air was discovered during World War II when high-flying bombers encountered westerly winds of several hundred knots on bombing attacks over Japan. Systematic observations later showed that these winds were organized into a semicontinuous narrow band which encircled the globe, as shown in Figure 6.7. This narrow current of fast-moving air is termed the *jet stream.*

The jet stream is typically found just below the tropopause at about 35,000 ft and generally lies above a zone of strong temperature contrast (a front). A schematic cross section of a jet stream is shown in Figure 6.9. As indicated, the maximum winds are located in a core perhaps 100 mi wide and a few thousand feet in depth. Wind speeds fall off rapidly to the north, or cold side of the flow, and much less rapidly to the south. Horizontal wind changes can be as great as 100 knots per 100 mi to the north or as little as 25 knots per 100 mi to the south. In the vertical, the most rapid change occurs above the core. Thus a pilot seeking to avoid adverse headwinds should head north or toward colder air.

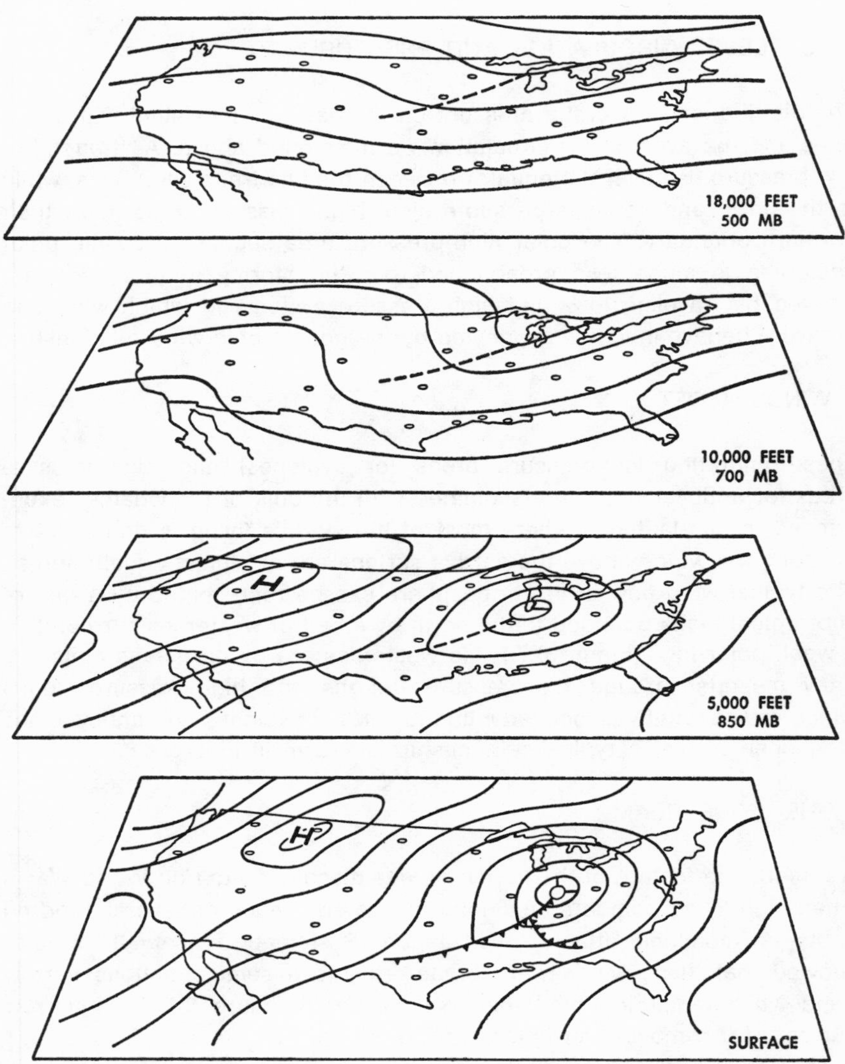

Figure 6.8 Relationship between winds aloft and surface pressure patterns.

A major by-product of the jet stream and its associated wind shears is clear air turbulence (CAT). Analysis of turbulence reports shows a high frequency in the regions of strongest wind change surrounding the jet stream. Since the actual structure of the jet stream consists of many narrow fingers of strong wind, it is no easy task to locate exactly the

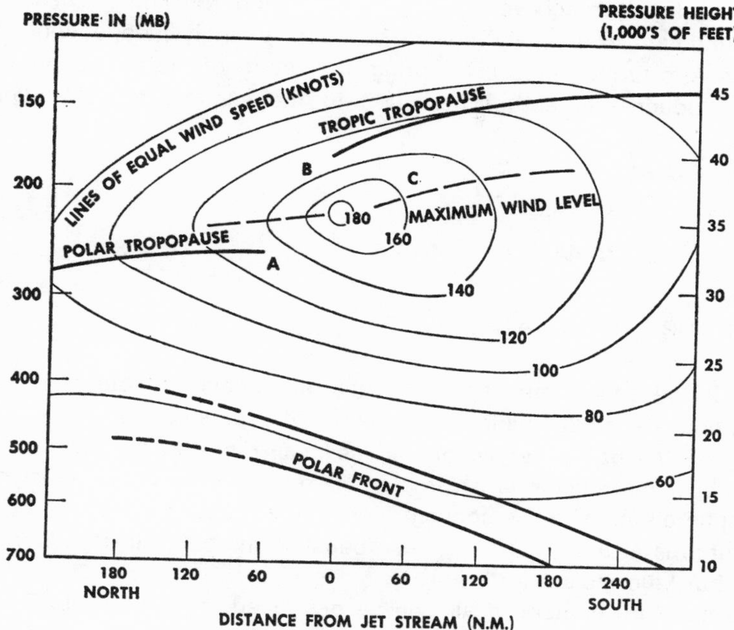

Figure 6.9 Polar front and cross section of a jet stream looking downwind. Most probable CAT is at *A, B,* and *C.* Cirrostratus cloud frequently found in area *C.* *(Courtesy of U.S. Air Force.)*

regions of strongest shear. Hence pilots traversing the high-altitude jet stream should be prepared for turbulence at all times.

STRATOSPHERIC WINDS

With the advent of supersonic transports, the weather of the stratosphere becomes of increasing interest. Above the tropopause, the effect of the small weather-producing disturbances of the troposphere rapidly dies out. At SST altitudes of 70,000 ft or more, atmospheric pressure and density are less than 3% of their surface values.

The circulation alternates between radically different summer and winter situations. The summer stratosphere is dominated by a warm high-pressure area over the pole surrounded by a broad, weak belt of easterly winds. In fall, this pattern gradually reverses itself, and by winter the polar high has been replaced by an intense low with temperatures of −80°C or lower. This low is bounded by intense polar night westerlies which frequently reach velocities of several hundred knots. These westerlies undulate in a slowly moving fashion seemingly independent of the tropospheric turmoil below. In spring, the return of the sun to polar latitudes produces an abrupt transition to the summertime stratospheric circulation.

The Growth of Clouds

MOISTURE IN THE ATMOSPHERE

Water is the only compound which naturally occurs on our planet in all three phases—solid, liquid, and gas. In the atmosphere, it is present chiefly as the gas water vapor, but its occurrence in the form of water droplets or snowflakes is of greater interest to the aviator. Most of the atmosphere's moisture is concentrated in the lower troposphere because its source is at the ground and also because the cold air at higher levels holds but little moisture.

The moisture content of air can be described in many ways. The concept of *saturation* is essential to understanding these measures. Air is saturated when it is in equilibrium with a water surface. That is, the air contains sufficient water vapor that no more can be evaporated into it at the existing temperature. The saturation water content varies strongly with the temperature. For approximately every 20°F (11°C) increase in temperature the water-holding capacity of the air is doubled. Relative humidity and dew point, described on page 272, are measures of saturation.

CONDENSATION PROCESSES

In order for the water vapor in the air to condense into cloud or rain drops, the air must be brought to its saturation point either by cooling or by adding water. There must also be present a suitable particle or surface to serve as a base for condensation. In absolutely clean air (which is never found in nature) water molecules in the air would coagulate together only by accident, and water vapor concentrations many times "saturation" would be required for condensation.

In the real atmosphere, however, small particles of dust or salt are always present, and condensation starts to build cloud droplets on these when the air's water content only slightly exceeds saturation. The number and kind of these "condensation nuclei" have a great effect on the char-

Figure 6.10 Formation of clouds due to expansion and cooling of air lifted over terrain features. *(Courtesy of U.S. Air Force.)*

acter of clouds. Over the continents dust particles are plentiful and clouds consist of quite small droplets. On the high seas, the air is clean and moisture condenses on a small number of large salt particles, forming clouds with large wet drops.

The majority of clouds and fogs are produced by cooling the air to its saturation point, that is, reducing the temperature to the dew point. This can occur by passage over a cooler surface or by loss of heat through radiation. The most important cooling process, however, is lifting. As will be discussed later, rising air cools at a steady rate but keeps its moisture content. Eventually saturation is reached.

On occasion clouds or fog form without cooling by addition of moisture. For example, rain falling from higher clouds can saturate lower layers, producing low clouds or fog. Sometimes dry air moves over warmer moist surfaces and "steam fog" is formed.

The development of precipitation is a complex and imperfectly understood process. Droplets, falling at different speeds, probably collide and coalesce into larger drops. These grow further and break apart, starting a chain reaction. In continental air the presence of ice crystals appears to be crucial in forming condensation nuclei for the requisite large drops. In any event, continual influx of moist air and cooling by rising motion are essential to produce any significant amount of precipitation. An individual cloud at any instant holds a surprisingly small quantity of water.

Stability

To a pilot, the stability of his aircraft is a major concern. A stable aircraft, if disturbed from its intended altitude or flight path, will return to normalcy of its own accord. An unstable aircraft, however, will continue to deviate ever more dangerously away from level flight. (Figure 2.42.)

The same phenomenon is observed in the atmosphere. Air normally flows in horizontal paths because any deviation up or down is resisted by strong buoyant forces. When these forces diminish or vanish, the air is said to become unstable, and vertical air currents are possible with little input of energy. The pilot experiences these vertical currents through turbulence or the clouds and weather they produce.

ADIABATIC LAPSE RATE

We have seen that temperature decreases with altitude at a normal lapse rate of 2°C (3½°F) per 1000 ft.

If a parcel of air is forced to rise (is *lifted*) in the atmosphere, it encounters lower pressure and expands. If no heat is added or removed (adiabatic conditions), it will cool as it rises. This *adiabatic lapse rate* (adiabat) is about 3°C (5½°F) per 1000 ft of ascent.

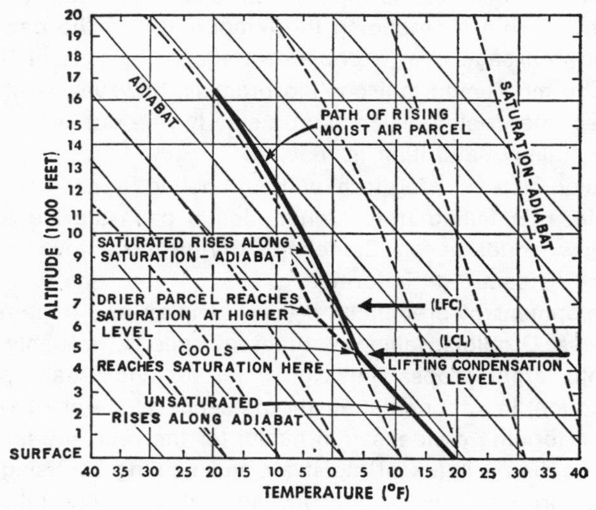

Figure 6.11 Adiabatic diagram showing stability calculations.

If the air contains water vapor, it will eventually cool to a temperature at which the air is saturated, and condensation will begin. The level at which this first occurs is called the *lifting condensation level* (LCL). Upon condensation, the heat which was required to evaporate the water originally is released. Hence rising air cools at a much slower rate when condensation is taking place. This rate is termed the "moist" or *saturation adiabatic lapse rate* and is about 1½°C per 1000 ft.

These processes can be best studied and depicted on an adiabatic diagram such as shown in Figure 6.11. Different versions of these charts are used by the various meteorological services, but all have coordinates of temperature and pressure (or altitude) and are over-printed with a pattern of lines showing the dry and saturation adiabatic lapse rates.

STABILITY AND INSTABILITY

The density of air depends upon its temperature and pressure. At constant pressure, a parcel of cold air is denser than the warm air around it and will tend to sink. If lifted, it will tend to return to its original level as long as it cools faster than surrounding air. The air is then *stable.*

If the cooling rate of a lifted air parcel is less than the temperature lapse rate of the surrounding air, the lifted parcel will become warmer and lighter than its surrounding air. It will then continue to rise spontaneously. When this condition prevails, the air is said to be *unstable.*

Frequently such a comparison will show a sounding whose slope lies between the dry adiabat and the saturation adiabat. This represents *conditionally unstable air,* because a lifted parcel will be stable until it reaches the LCL, and then will become unstable. The point at which it becomes unstable is the *level of free convection* (LFC). If the parcel were lifted a small distance above the LFC it would become warmer than the surrounding air and be accelerated freely away from its original location. Lifting action which sets off this free acceleration might result from forced ascent over a hill (orographic lifting) or from a warm air mass riding over a cold, dense air mass (frontal lifting). If lifted above the level of free convection, cloudiness and precipitation usually result. (Figure 6.11.)

The concept of moisture and stability is very important to those who fly, as Table 6.3 will show.

EFFECTS OF STABILITY AND INSTABILITY

The atmosphere's stability helps to determine what type of clouds will form. For example, gradual ascent of stable moist air up a sloping surface will produce layered, or *stratus* clouds with little vertical development or turbulence. Conversely, clouds forming in unstable air show a puffy, turbulent character. In them, release of latent heat adds to the intensity of vertical motion.

Highly stable air greatly inhibits the exchange of low-level air with the free-flowing air at higher levels. Pollutants generated at low levels can thus accumulate, producing haze or smog. Thus poor visibility is common in areas where large-scale descent of air produces warm layers aloft. Some of the effects mentioned are conveniently summarized in Table 6.2.

TABLE 6.2
Characteristics of Air According to Moisture and Stability

	Dry Stable Air	*Moist Stable Air*	*Dry-Unstable Air*	*Moist Unstable Air*
Visibility	Poor in haze	Poor in haze and fog	Good	Good except in precipitation
Cloud type	None	Clouds in stratified layers—*stratus*	None	Clouds of vertical development—*cumulus*
Precipitation	None	Steady	None	Showers
Flying conditions	Smooth	Smooth	Turbulent	Turbulent
Type of icing	None	Mainly rime	None	Mainly clear

Cloud Types

Clouds are significant to the flyer as obstructions to vision and as sources of potentially hazardous weather. However, they also aid him by acting as sensitive indicators of air motion, turbulence, and weather.

Although dozens of cloud types are recognized by meteorologists, a much smaller number of categories is sufficient for practical aviation. Four general classes are: low clouds (below 6500 ft), middle clouds (6500 to 16,500 ft), high clouds (above 16,500 ft and generally below 45,000 ft), and clouds with extensive vertical development. Within these families, we can distinguish two main subdivisions: lumpy or *cumiliform* clouds formed by turbulent local air motions in unstable air, and smoothly layered or *stratiform* clouds produced by gradual uplifting of whole layers of fairly stable air.

Dark clouds which produce precipitation are modified by the word "nimbus." Middle cloud types are denoted by the prefix "alto," while high clouds which are generally formed of ice crystals are prefixed by "cirro." Thus a puffy, fair-weather, low cloud is termed "cumulus," and a thunderstorm is "cumulonimbus." Smooth-layered clouds at different levels are called "stratus," "altostratus," and "cirrostratus."

Cloud forms offer valuable clues to flying conditions inside them. As we mentioned earlier, lumpy cumiliform clouds suggest turbulence, while smooth-layered stratus clouds indicate smooth air. Dark clouds, particularly those with considerable vertical extent, have a high liquid water content. Above the freezing level, these water droplets will be supercooled, ready to freeze on contact with any foreign body such as your aircraft.

Air Masses

Although the atmosphere is in constant motion, there are large regions where the air is relatively stagnant for a number of days. In these conditions air can take on quite uniform properties over a large area. Such a body of homogeneous air is termed an *air mass.*

SOURCE REGIONS

The geographical area in which an air mass acquires its characteristic properties is termed its source region, and the air mass generally carries

TABLE 6.3
Summer Flying Weather Conditions in Various Air Mass Types

Air Mass	*Clouds*	*Ceilings*	*Visibilities*	*Turbulence*	*Surface Temp. (Degrees F.)*
cP (near source region)	Scattered cumulus	Unlimited	Good	Moderate turbulence up to 10,000 ft	55 to 60
mP (Pacific coast)	Stratus tops, 2000 to 5000 ft	100 to 1500 ft	1/2 to 10 mi	Slightly rough in clouds, smooth above	50 to 60
mP (east of Pacific)	None except scattered cumulus near mountains	Unlimited	Excellent	Generally smooth except over desert regions in afternoon	60 to 70
mT (east of Rockies)	Stratocumulus early morning; cumulonimbus afternoon	500 to 1500 ft a.m.; 3000 to 4000 ft p.m.	Excellent	Smooth except in thunderstorms, then severe turbulence	75 to 85

the name of this region. The two principal types of air mass are *polar* and *tropical*. Further significant classifications are *maritime* and *continental* because of the importance of the differing moisture content.

TABLE 6.4
Winter Flying Conditions in Various Air Mass Types

Air Mass	*Clouds*	*Ceilings*	*Visibilities*	*Turbulence*	*Surface Temp. (Degrees F.)*
cP (near source region)	None	Unlimited	Excellent (except near industrial areas, then 1 to 4 mi)	Smooth except with high wind velocities	−10 to −60
cP (southeast of Great Lakes)	Stratocumulus and cumulus tops, 7000 to 10,000 ft	500 to 1000 ft, 0 over mountains	1 to 5 mi, 0 in snow flurries	Moderate turbulence up to 10,000 ft	0 to 20
mP (on Pacific coast)	Cumulus tops above 20,000 ft	1000 to 3000 ft, 0 over mountains	Good except 0 over mountains and in showers	Moderate to severe turbulence	45 to 55
mP (east of Rockies)	None	Unlimited	Excellent except near industrial areas, then 1 to 4 mi	Smooth except in lower levels with high winds	30 to 40
mP (east coast)	Stratocumulus and stratus tops, 6000 to 8000 ft	0 to 1000 ft	Fair except 0 in precipitation area	Rough in lower levels	30 to 40
mT (Pacific coast)	Stratus or stratocumulus	500 to 1500 ft	Good	Smooth	55 to 60
mT (east of Rockies)	Stratus or stratocumulus	100 to 1500 ft	Good	Smooth	60 to 70

In the Northern Hemisphere, polar air masses are formed in northern region where the air is cooled from below. Typically, large-scale sinking motion is also present. Hence these air masses are cold, stable, and dry. In contrast, tropical air masses are warmed from below, producing less stable lapse rates. If they form over the ocean, convection can carry surface moisture high above the ground. Tropical air masses are thus fertile sources of clouds and weather. In middle latitudes mixing of air by the action of moving weather systems prevents the formation of unique air mass types. These regions are the meeting place of air masses from north and south, as we shall see.

AIR MASS WEATHER

The weather changes associated with moving systems are complex and difficult to forecast. There still are many occasions in which an identifiable air mass overlies a large area of the United States producing characteristic and fairly uniform weather. These characteristic weather types are summarized in Tables 6.3 and 6.4. Air mass types are indicated in the tables as c for continental, T for tropical, P for polar, and m for maritime origin.

Fronts

The circulation of the atmosphere moves air masses from their source region and brings them into contact. Thus the differences in temperature, moisture, and stability which distinguish one air mass from another tend to be concentrated in narrow transition zones. These lines along which air masses meet are termed *fronts.*

THE POLAR FRONT

The boundary between the two principal air masses—polar and tropical—is known as the *polar front.* We can roughly describe this as a continuous transition zone encircling the globe. It is by no means uniform in character. In some regions terrain features obscure the transition. In others, the circulation tends to disperse the temperature gradient, producing a gradual transition between polar and tropical air.

For much of the year a picture rather like Figure 6.12 could be drawn. This chart, typical of winter conditions, illustrates a number of frontal characteristics. Polar air, colder and heavier than tropical air, pushes underneath it and extends further south at the surface than aloft. Also evident are a number of areas where polar air bulges to the south or warm air pushes north. These waves are created by air circulation around moving high- and low-pressure systems in the westerlies.

Although the polar front is the dominant feature of weather charts in mid-latitudes, other fronts may be found between air masses of the same general source region. The necessary conditions for front formation are simply the existence of dissimilar air masses and a wind pattern which concentrates their differences into a narrow zone.

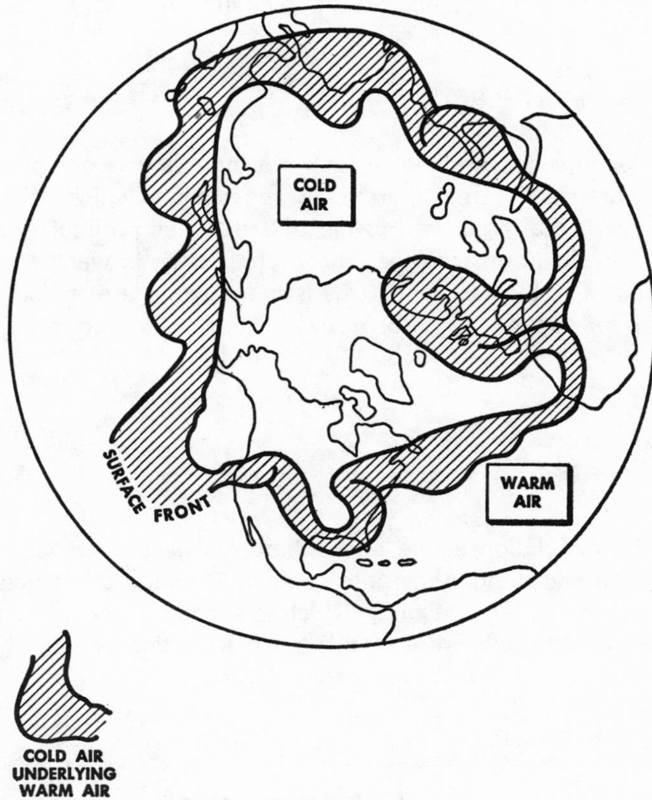

Figure 6.12 An example of the position of the polar front.

COLD FRONTS

Fronts are classified by their motion. A front which moves so that cold air replaces warm air at the ground is called a *cold front.* The leading edge of the advancing cold air has a fairly steep slope of 1:50 to 1:150. A slope of 1:50 means that at a point 50 mi back from the surface position of the front, the front would be found one mile high.

Because of this steep slope, rapidly moving cold fronts are associated with rapidly rising warm air in a narrow band. This produces clouds of considerable vertical development in a narrow strip with frequent showers and thunderstorms. The weather pattern classically associated with cold fronts is shown in Figure 6.13(A).

In the Northern Hemisphere, cold fronts are generally oriented from northeast to southwest and move to the southeast. Ahead of the front,

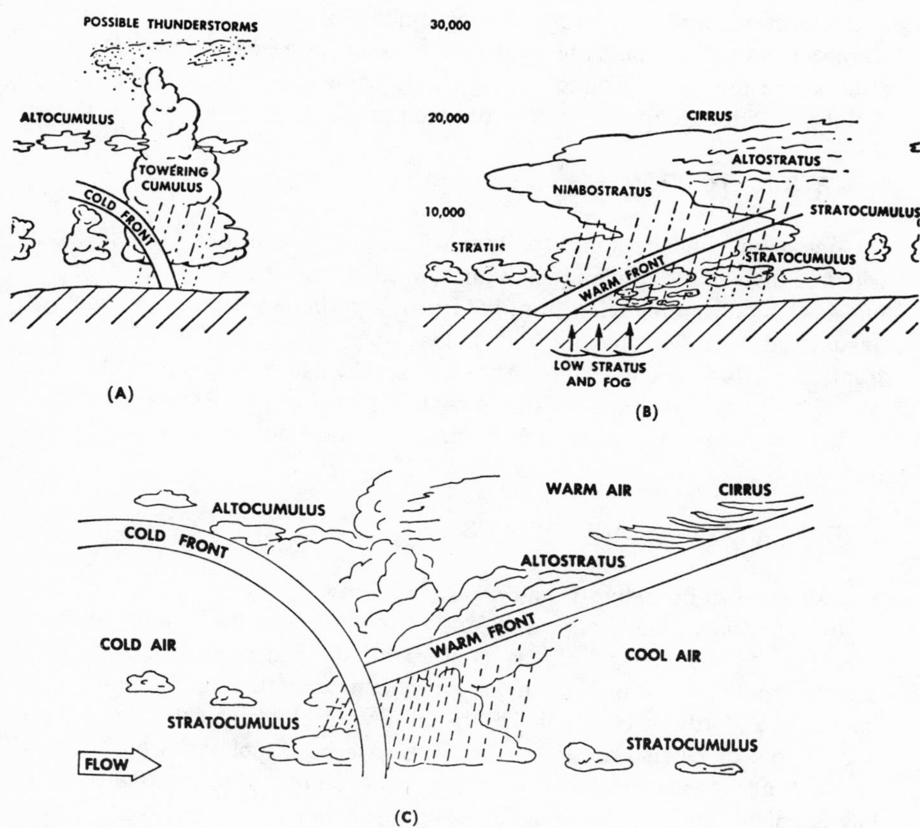

Figure 6.13 Classical concept of frontal weather. (A) Cold front. (B) Warm front. (C) Occluded cold front. In an occluded warm front, the cool air would be riding up on the slope of warm air.

winds are southerly and fair-weather clouds are prevalent. As the front approaches, clouds thicken, the pressure falls, and the wind increases. Showers and thunderstorms are encountered around the time of frontal passage, which is signaled by a shift of the wind to the northwest, a drop in temperature, and a marked rise in pressure. With a strong, fast-moving cold front, clearing is rapid after frontal passage.

WARM FRONTS

A *warm front* is the leading edge of an advancing mass of warm air. The slope of the frontal surface is generally much flatter than in a cold front. The warm air rises over the cold air mass much more gradually, producing a widespread area of clouds and precipitation. Rain falling out of the warm air mass into the lower cold air may saturate it, causing widespread stratus and fog. With ground temperatures below 32°F, freezing rain may result. A model picture of warm-front weather is shown in Figure 6.13(B).

STATIONARY FRONTS

On occasion, the circulation pattern will maintain a front's intensity, but will not give it a significant motion toward either the warm or cold air masses. Such a nonmoving front is termed a *stationary front.* The weather associated with it typically resembles warm-front weather. Stationary fronts are often produced on the trailing southwestern ends of cold fronts which advance into the Gulf Coast region of the United States and stagnate. Persistent fog, drizzle, and stratus are found on the cold side of the front.

FRONTAL WAVES AND OCCLUSIONS

The air masses bounding fronts are set into motion by moving circulation systems in the westerly wind patterns of middle latitudes. These systems are seen on weather charts as centers of high and low pressure with winds circulating around them in agreement with the geostrophic wind law. In the Northern Hemisphere, the airflow is clockwise around a high and counterclockwise around a low. The reverse directions are observed in the Southern Hemisphere. In either hemisphere, circulation around a low is called *cyclonic,* around a high *anticyclonic.*

Low-level air tends to spiral inward in lows and outward in highs. Thus lows are regions of converging and rising air, while highs are characterized by diverging and sinking air. As a result, strong fronts and massive cloud systems are primarily found in low-pressure areas.

Lows and their associated frontal systems go through a typical life cycle as shown in Figure 6.14. In the figure, the dark line indicates a front. In standard meteorological practice, pointed pips on this line pointing toward warm air indicate a cold front, rounded pips pointing into cold air show a warm front, while alternating pointed and rounded symbols denote a stationary front. When circulation around a low-pressure area on the front begins, cold air is forced south to the west of the low and warm air is moved north to the east, forming cold and warm fronts. Deepening of the low continues this process, producing the frequently observed pattern shown in Figure 6.14(C).

The cold front generally moves faster than the warm front, and eventually overtakes it near the low-pressure center. (Figure 6.14(D).) There is generally sufficient air mass contrast along this line of convergence to

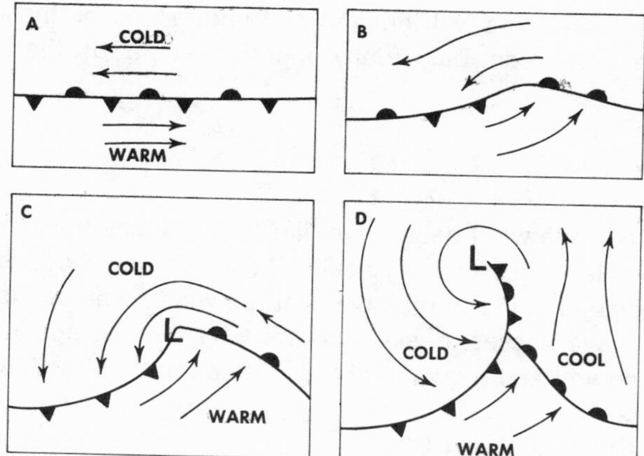

Figure 6.14 Life cycle of a frontal wave. (A) Undisturbed front. (B) Initial wave. (C) Fully developed wave. (D) Occlusion.

define an *occluded* front (denoted by mixed pointed and round pips on weather charts). A cross section of an idealized occluded front viewed from the south is shown in Figure 6.13(C). In this example, the air behind the cold front was colder than the air ahead of the warm front. The cold air thus slides in under the cool air, lifting a tongue of warmer air aloft and forming a *cold-front occlusion.* The opposite situation is also possible: Air to the east of the low may be colder than that to the west. The occlusion then appears as a continuation of the warm front and is termed a *warm-front occlusion.*

Occluded fronts are generally accompanied by an extensive band of clouds and precipitation curving back into the low-pressure center.

Tropical Weather

While the weather of middle latitudes is dominated by the effects of traveling cyclones and anticyclones, tropical weather generally follows a rather routine course. In place of the violent alternations between northerly and southerly winds with accompanying weather and temperature changes, we find in general a simple daily cycle of clouds and weather superimposed on a cycle of wet and dry seasons. For this reason, a close study of local and regional climatology is particularly rewarding to the aviator in tropical regions.

The weather systems which disturb the regular course of events in the tropics are not nearly as well defined and understood as those of middle latitudes. Here we can but briefly mention some of the outstanding features.

EASTERLY WAVES

In the easterly trade wind belts wave-like disturbances traveling from east to west are often observed. Typically these are preceded by northerly winds and some clearing of the normal trade-wind cumulus clouds. As the crest of the wave passes, heavy showers with tops rising to 15,000 ft or more are observed and the wind shifts to a southerly direction.

THE EQUATORIAL TROUGH

The trade winds of both hemispheres converge toward a band of low pressure near the equator. This equatorial trough, sometimes known as the *intertropical convergence zone,* is a region of increased cloudiness and weather. It is generally displaced from the equator toward the summer hemisphere and is subject to north-south oscillations.

HURRICANES

The most spectacular features of tropical weather are the intense cyclonic storms called hurricanes in the Atlantic or typhoons in the Pacific. These storms originate over warm tropical waters in the late summer and early fall.

Initially, they appear as a cyclonic air circulation around a weak low-pressure center. These tropical depressions may increase in intensity as they drift eastward, and may intensify until winds reach hurricane force (65 knots). On reaching the western Pacific or Atlantic, the storms generally curve northward, where they bring extensive rain, winds frequently over 100 knots, and great damage. Although these storms are far less frequent than the cyclones of middle latitudes, their immense strength and unpredictable shifts in direction make them the most feared weather disturbances of our earth.

Weather Services

Aviation weather needs the world over have made observation, reporting, and analysis of weather one of the truly international activities of man. Not even the Iron and Bamboo Curtains stop the flow of this vital, mutually needed information, though only Communist China is not a member of the World Meteorological Organization.

In the United States, the National Weather Service provides basic weather service. Supported by the weather information networks of the Air Force, Navy, NASA, Coast Guard, and FAA, it operates the World Meteorological Center (WMC) near Washington, D.C. This is the analysis center for all data, and issues the basic analyses and forecast charts which are used by civil and military forecasters as source material for their briefings. Forecasts for individual terminals are produced by regional centers or the terminal stations themselves, where WMC's output is also interpreted by local forecasters for individual flights.

Through Flight Service Stations (FSS) and Weather Bureau Airport Stations (WBAS) pilots can obtain the information and guidance necessary for safe and efficient flight. Knowing how to obtain and use this information is an absolutely essential element of modern airmanship.

WEATHER OBSERVATIONS

While there are many diverse sources, the most abundant and useful weather reports are those recorded regularly by professional weather observers throughout the world. At active airfields, observations are taken every hour or whenever significant changes occur. These aviation-oriented reports are distributed rapidly by teletype circuits, principally those of FAA, to other aviation terminals. Observations for major international airports, for example, are distributed world-wide in but a few minutes.

The pilot is most likely to encounter the Aviation Weather Reports transmitted on regular schedules over civil and military circuits to teletype units in airfield weather stations. A little study of the typical example given below, and queries in the local weather station should enable the aviator to understand the bulk of these reports. Understanding the terminology used is important because, for example, the difference between an *estimated* and a *measured* ceiling could be critical in pilot decision making.

MIA 8 ⦶ E 15 ⦶ 50 ⊕ 2R-F122/54/52 0910/989/BINOVC

MIA *Station identification symbol* It identifies the reporting station on all weather teletype transmissions.

The sky condition group Cloud heights are reported to the nearest 100 ft are transmitted in hundreds (8 = 800 ft, etc.). Cloud amounts are determined in tenths of sky cover and encoded as:

○ Clear
⦶ Scattered—not more than 5/10 total sky cover
⦶ Broken—more than 5/10 but not more than 9/10 sky cover
⊕ Overcast—more than 9/10 sky cover
× Obscuration—interference to vision such that the sky cannot be seen

A (–) sign may precede any of the above to denote thin coverage.

The method by which the cloud cover height is determined is indicated by one of the following letters:

M Measured
B Balloon
A Aircraft report
E Estimated
P Clouds obscured by precipitation. This is estimated vertical visibility
W Indefinite cloud bases
R Radar or RAOB
D Persistent cirroform ceiling
U Indeterminate cirroform ceiling

The group in the example

8 ⦶ E15 ⦶ 50 ⊕ 2R-F

indicates the following multiple cloud layers: scattered clouds at 800 ft; a broken layer of clouds estimated at 1500 ft; an overcast cloud condition at 5000 ft.

It is important to recognize that clouds are reported *as seen by the ground observer.* The coverage reported at a level reflects all the clouds the observer can see *between the surface and that level.* A report of 15 ⦶ 30 ⦶, for example, could represent 4/10 of clouds at 1500 ft and 6/10 coverage at 3000 ft. On the other hand, the same report could result from a judicious arrangement of 4/10 at 1500 ft and only 2/10 at 3000 ft.

2R-F *Visibility in miles and the observed weather* This visibility is 2 mi and the weather is coded as R-F, light rain and fog. Some of the common weather symbols are:

T Thunderstorm
RW Rain showers
L Drizzle
ZL Freezing drizzle
S Snow
A Hail
GF Ground Fog

H Haze
K Smoke
D Dust
BN Blowing sand, etc.

There are many of these symbols and they may be found listed in any weather station. They may be grouped together to show multiple weather conditions.

Other symbols are:

122/ *The sea level pressure* This is the barometer reading in the weather station reduced from the station elevation to standard sea level. It is a pressure reading in millibars. This example, 122, decodes as 1012.2 mb.

54/52 *The temperature and dew-point temperature in degrees Fahrenheit* (54°F temperature/52°F dew point in this example).

0910 *The surface wind* The first two digits indicate the true (not magnetic) direction from which the wind is blowing. The last two digits indicate speed in knots. In the example, the wind is blowing from 90° at 10 knots. Variations in the wind report might be:

00 Calm
G Gusts (followed by the peak speed)
Q Squalls (followed by the peak speed)

989/ *The altimeter setting in inches of mercury* This example is decoded as 29.89 in. of mercury.

The remainder of the report might carry special cloud data, maximum or minimum temperatures, radar reports, NOTAMS (notices to airmen) in coded form, abbreviated remarks descriptive of the weather (such as BINOVC—breaks in the overcast), coded forecast groups from Navy stations, etc.

Only a small part of the weather report has been covered here. The most essential items to the flyer are clouds, visibility, precipitation, surface temperature, wind, and temperature-dew point spread.

Pilot Reports Surface-based observations give valuable information on conditions at and near airports. However, conditions between observing stations and weather phenomena aloft can best be observed by the pilot himself. Because of this, flight controllers and weathermen eagerly solicit weather reports from aircraft.

On teletype summaries, pilot reports are indicated by the code word PIREP, and contain the following information:

1. Originating station designator
2. The word PIREP and the filing time (GMT)
3. Location or extent of the reported weather

4. Time of observation (local time)
5. Weather condition (turbulence, icing, cloud tops, weather, etc.)
6. Altitude
7. Type of aircraft

Weather Radar Observation Water droplets in clouds reflect radio waves and hence can be "seen" by radar. Large raindrops reflect much more energy than cloud droplets. These large drops require strong updrafts to generate and support them. Hence the brightest radar echoes are associated with hazardous convective storms, making radar an invaluable aid to the aviator.

Airborne radar will be discussed in later parts of this chapter. The weather services, however, operate over a hundred weather radars throughout the United States. They permit local forecasters to detect and track thunderstorms in an area of as much as 250 mi radius. Verbal descriptions of radar echoes are regularly transmitted to a Weather Bureau unit at Kansas City, Missouri, where summaries and maps are

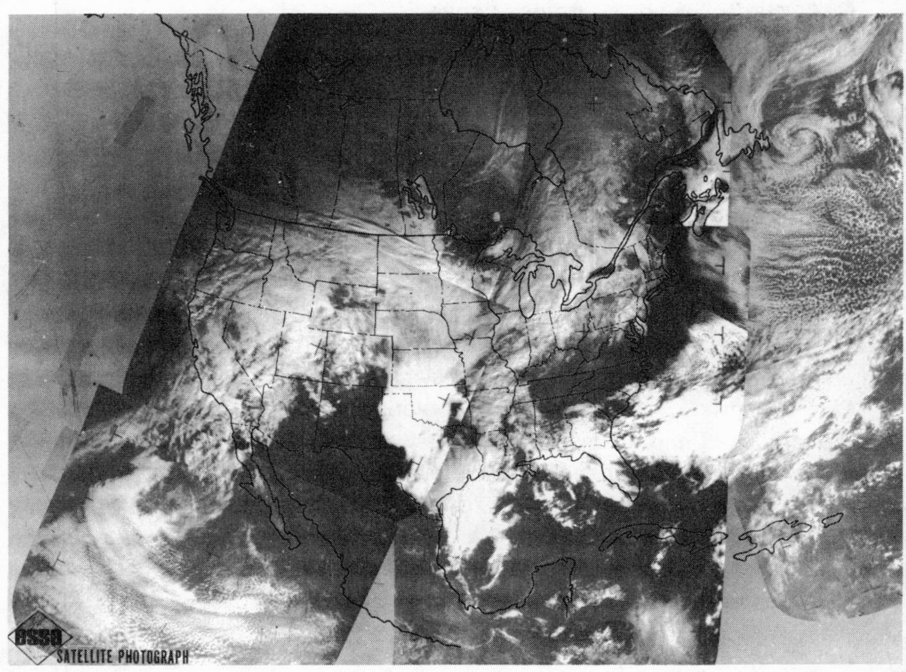

Figure 6.15 Mosaic of APT weather satellite pictures. *(Courtesy of National Environmental Satellite Center.)*

prepared. These are transmitted to weather stations nationwide and give a quite complete picture of significant weather throughout the nation.

Weather Reconnaissance Air Force, Navy, and Weather Bureau all operate specially instrumented aircraft in their respective areas of interest to obtain detailed current reports of the existence and intensity of adverse weather. This is particularly important in coastal storm and hurricane warning, where frequent, precise, specific information is essential.

Weather Satellites Both the United States and the USSR have launched a number of weather satellites. These circle the earth at an altitude of several hundred miles in orbits designed to be sun-synchronous. That is, they pass over each part of their path at the same local time.

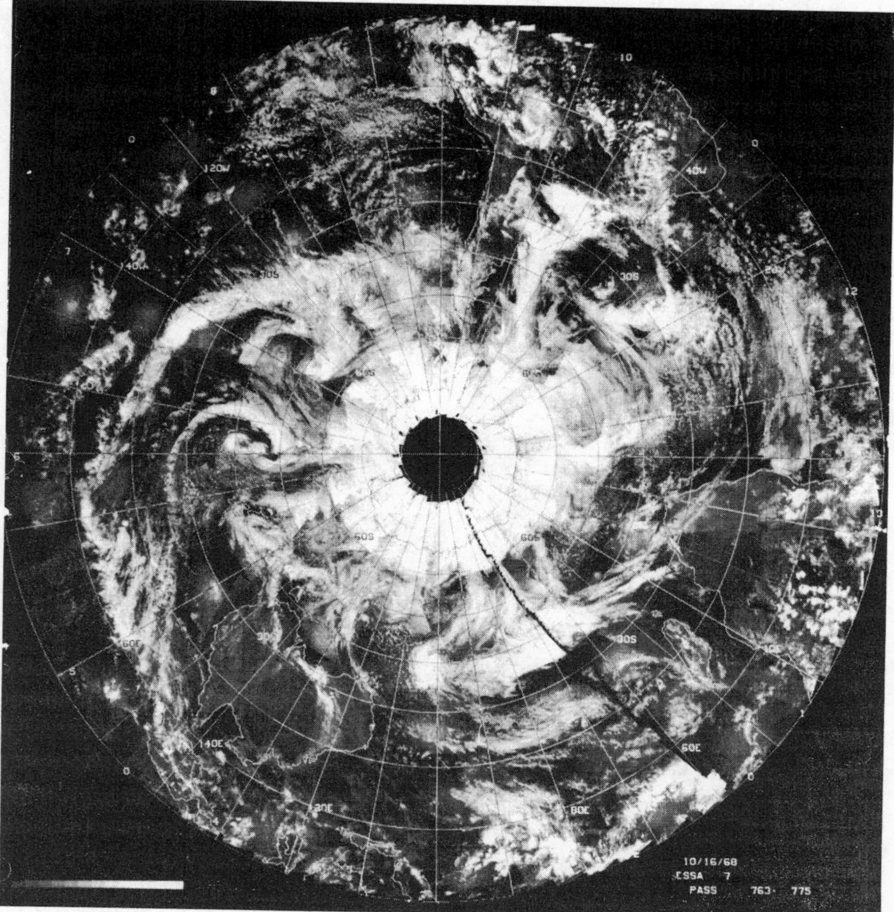

Figure 6.16 Satellite cloud patterns. Computer-processed pictures of cloud patterns over the Southern Hemisphere. Composite of data observed by Essa-7 in several orbits. *(Courtesy of National Environmental Satellite Center.)*

Two basic types of pictures can be received from weather satellites. Certain satellites will transmit their latest picture whenever interrogated by a ground station. At present, about 500 facilities throughout the world can receive pictures from these Automatic Picture Transmission (APT) satellites. A mosaic of a number of these pictures is shown in Figure 6.15. The light areas are cloud masses, while land and sea are about equally dark. These pictures are particularly valuable in forecasting weather for transoceanic routes or for isolated island stations.

Other weather satellites store a number of pictures in on-board tape recorders and transmit a large volume on demand to special NASA installations. These data are then processed by computer at the National Environmental Satellite Center at Suitland, Maryland, to form global pictures of cloud distribution. For example, Figure 6.15 shows weather systems over most of the United States, information obtainable from no other source.

Weather Analyses and Forecasts

Weather observations are of maximum use to the meteorologist and his customers only after a coherent picture of the weather has been drawn from them. A knowledge of the recent past, climatology, forecasts, and judgment all are used to produce these analyses. From them, the future course of events can be projected by a mixture of scientific knowledge, empirical rules, and experience.

METHODS OF PREPARATION

In addition to the basic NMC analyses and forecasts, specialized analyses and forecasts for worldwide military operations are made by the Air Force Global Weather Central at Offut Air Force Base, Nebraska, and the U. S. Navy's Fleet Numerical Weather Central at Monterey, California. All three centers are supplied with data by teletype and by the Air Force's Automated Weather Network which furnishes overseas weather data collected worldwide. AFGWC and NMC also receive satellite data from the national satellite system.

The weather centrals use electronic computers to decode, edit, and sort these data. Computers also analyze the upper-air data in preparation for "numerical" forecasting. This comparison of data characteristic of selected vertical atmospheric columns at a given time with typical models, is the simulation of the atmosphere's behavior through numerical calculation based on physical laws.

WEATHER SERVICES FOR AVIATION

The NMC is the source of information, analyses, and forecasts, principally used by other weathermen. These, in turn, can serve the pilot. Aviation weather specialists in the Weather Bureau's Flight Advisory Service Centers (FAWS) prepare and distribute terminal and area forecasts. They are responsible for areas roughly coinciding with Air Route Traffic Control Centers of FAA.

In the WBAS (Weather Bureau Airport Station) most pilots find their weather information. The briefer here is not necessarily only a briefer. He has observing and forecasting duties, too, and it is likely that his experience in the area can be of considerable assistance in solving local problems. In addition, he can request and expedite the occasional greater-than-normal requirements which pilots may have. He is also responsible for distributing FAWS-issued hazardous weather warnings, known as SIGMETS and ADVISORIES FOR LIGHT AIRCRAFT.

High-Altitude Forecast Centers, which still serve mainly airline jet operations, provide forecasts, mostly in graphic form. Seven of these centers cover the area from the Philippines and Japan east into Europe, and from the North Pole to the equator. Much of the product of the United States center, located with NMC, goes directly to airline operations offices, though some FAWS offices receive them also.

These Severe Local Storm Forecast Center (SELS), is located in Kansas City, Missouri. The Air Force's Air Weather Service has a hazardous weather office at Offut Air Force Base. It furnishes similar products for military operations; the two provide mutual support, and are fully cooperative.

The National Hurricane Center in Miami, Florida, uses information from Air Force and Navy aerial reconnaissance, satellites, and surface observations to locate, track, and forecast the movement of hurricanes. They distribute forecasts and warning bulletins by aviation weather circuits, and by any other available means, including news media.

With the aid of weather satellites it is almost impossible for a tropical storm to reach damaging size without detection. When one is located, it is christened with a suitable name and regular bulletins are disseminated on its progress. If it approaches land, reconnaissance aircraft of the Air Weather Service and the U. S. Navy are regularly dispatched to determine its exact location and intensity.

This system obviously requires an extensive distribution system. The FAA distributes weather and aviation information on a series of circuits to more than 500 terminals; the Air Force COMET system, consisting of three circuits, collects information from pilots and distributes it and other weather information to military installations and operations. The Navy operates radio circuits from shore bases to ships at sea, both sending and receiving weather information. All of these systems have facsimile networks used to send a wide variety of charts, discussed later, throughout the system.

AIRCREW BRIEFING

Military and airline operations offices insure that their aircrews use all the information available, presented in the form most useful for the flight program they conduct. The individual pilot or other interested airman has a briefing service available to him through the WBAS nearest him, by telephone, and by radio via FSS.

He will find information available on almost any aspect of flight in the form of charts, reports, forecasts, or prognostications, in chart form and in writing; nevertheless, it is important to know what to ask for, and what to expect:

Chart or Report (Observed Data)	*Time of Data Frequency of Publication*
1. Hourly and Special Reports	Every hour
2. Pilot Reports in icing, turbulence, cloud tops, flight conditions	Regularly as available
3. Weather Depiction Charts	Every 3 hr, beginning 0100Z
4. Surface Weather, Charts, Continental United States	Every 3 hr, beginning 0000Z
5. Surface Weather, North America	Every 6 hr, beginning 0000Z
6. Constant Pressure (Upper-Air) Charts	Twice daily, 0000Z, 1200Z
7. Winds Aloft Charts	Every 6 hr, beginning 0000Z
8. Radar Summary Charts	Every 3 hr
Forecasts	
1. 12-hr Terminal Forecasts	Every 6 hr
2. Amended Terminal Forecasts	As needed
3. 24-hr Area Forecasts, 50 states	Every 6 hr
4. Amended Area Forecasts	As needed
5. 12-hr Winds Aloft NMC	Twice daily, 0550Z, 1750Z
6. 12-hr Winds Aloft FAWS	Twice daily, 1150Z, 2350Z

EGOANALYSIS

This term, coined by the editor, describes that peculiar combination of conceit, bravado, and inexperience which will make pilot after pilot enter the WBAS, say nothing or a gruff "Hello," and head for the hourly weather reports. There he proceeds to brief himself, either being expert in reading and understanding the reports and their predecessors which might indicate trends, or somehow feeling that he ought to be. How much easier it would be if he would simply ask the briefer or forecaster what he can expect to encounter during the flight he has in mind!

By not doing so he immediately deprives himself of the expertise of a man whose business it is to know the weather and to help. Most forecasters and briefers intuitively—or cynically—recognize a case of ego-analysis when they see it, and will not volunteer their aid unless asked. The pilot is as a result unaware of most of the information available to him, and does not know the things which he, as a taxpayer, has paid for that could affect significantly the pleasure and efficiency, if not the safety, of his flight.

WEATHER DEPICTION CHART

One of the most popular briefing aids, this chart is prepared at NMC every three hours beginning with data observed at 0100Z. Because the data are at least 1 hr 20 min old by the time the chart is posted in the WBAS, and because these charts are based on *observed* data only, pilots should check local conditions.

Weather Depiction Charts contain precipitation and other important phenomena, sky coverage, visibility if less than 6 mi, cloud bases in hundreds of feet above terrain up to 20,000 ft. Using this chart in conjunction with the hourly reports and the Surface Weather Chart is excellent briefing technique for shorter flights.

SURFACE WEATHER CHARTS

This is the most informative single chart available to the pilot or forecaster. The data are observed almost simultaneously for the entire area of the chart, and with NMC's computer methods, is no more than 1½ hr old when it reaches the weather office over the facsimile system. For the contiguous states, it is based on observations taken at 0000Z, 0003Z, 0006Z, etc. and transmitted every three hours. Charts covering smaller areas are frequently made by local weathermen to show local detail and influences. A chart covering the United States including Alaska and Hawaii, and extensive ocean areas, is published every 6 hr.

The pattern of pressure systems is of most interest to the pilot. All lines are *isobars,* which are lines connecting points having equal barometric pressure. Regarding the chart in Figure 6.18, it is interesting to note:

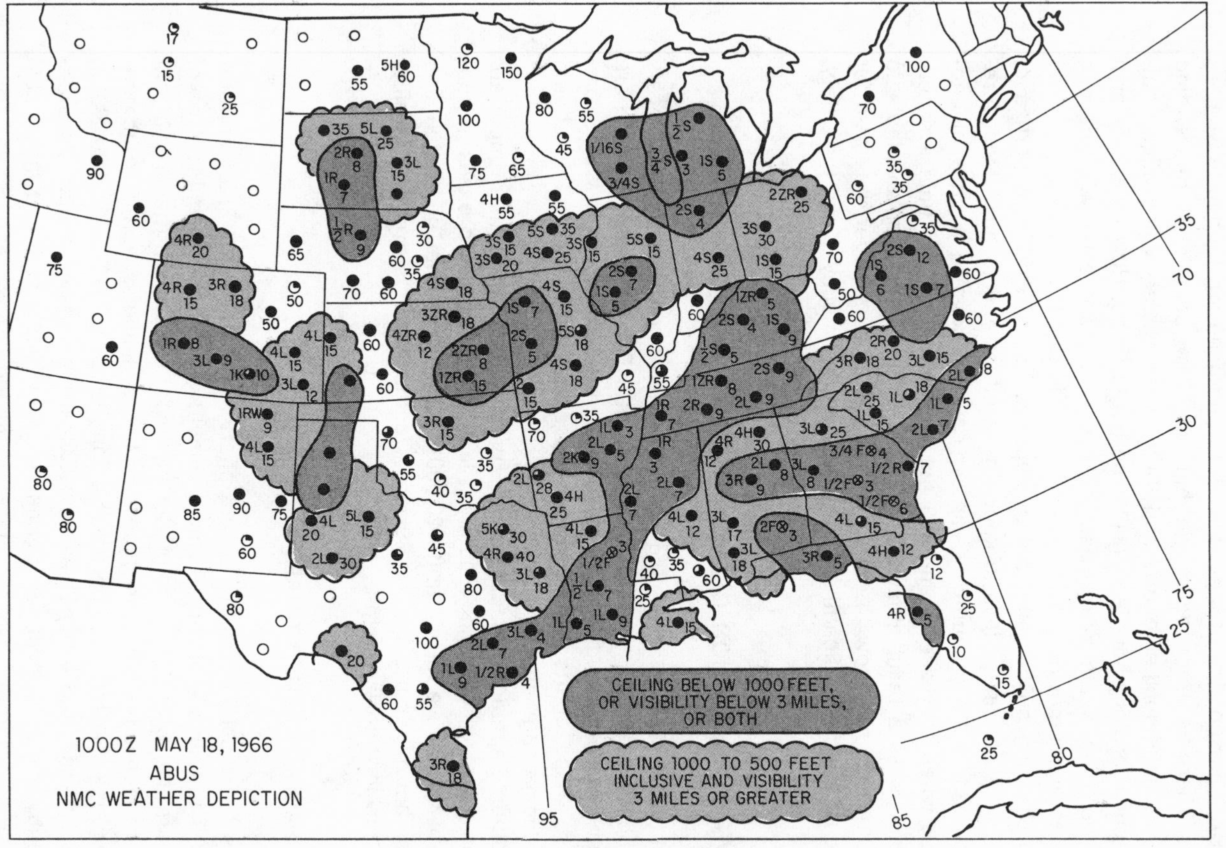

Figure 6.17A Weather Depiction Chart.

STATION MODEL	TOTAL SKY COVERAGE	SIGNIFICANT WEATHER
gnificant weather Total sky coverage s mi 3RF 15 Ceiling height (to 10,000)	Clear Scattered Broken Overcast Obscured	T Thunderstorm ZR Freezing rain ZL Freezing drizzle R Rain S Snow E Sleet L Drizzle W Shower H Haze K Smoke F Fog GF Ground fog Clouds topping ridges
NALYSIS:		
iling and visibility classes:	Outline:	Color code:
Ceiling below 1000 ft. or visibility below 3 miles, or both.		Red
Ceiling 1000 to 5000 ft. inclusive and visibility 3 miles or greater.		Blue

NOTES:

(1) Precipitation will always be entered when reported as occurring at the station at the time of observation, except that no more than two symbols for significant weather will be entered.

(2) Obstructions to vision other than precipitation will be entered when visibility is reduced to 6 miles or less, except that if two forms of precipitation are reported, the other obstructions to vision will not be entered. Haze and smoke will be omitted if precipitation is reported.

(3) Visibility values of 6 miles or less will be entered in miles and fractions.

(4) All ceiling heights will be entered in hundreds of feet.

(5) The analysis of the ceiling-visibility classes will be based on the reports themselves and is not meant to include possible between-station orographic effects, or even systematic interpolations between stations.

ure 6.17B Symbolic notation used on Weather Depiction Charts. *(A and B reprinted from M. W. Cagle, "A Pilot's Meteorology," Third Edition, Van Nostrand Reinhold, New York, 1970.)*

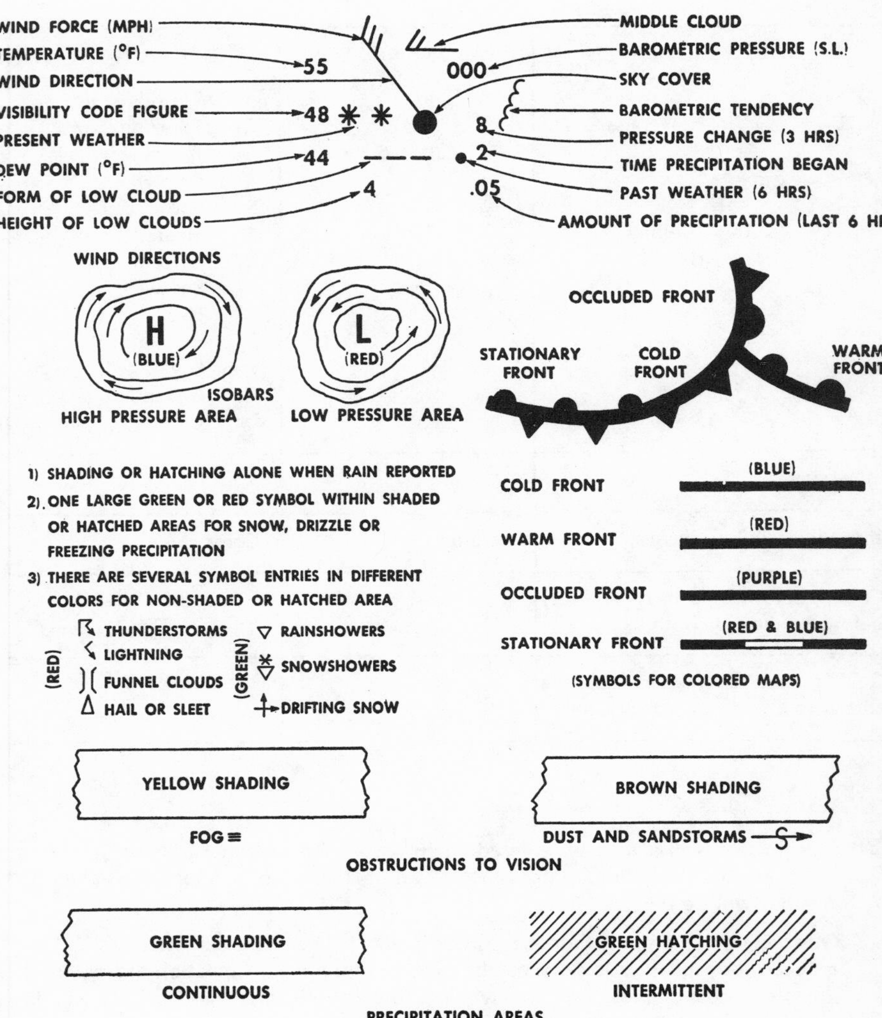

Figure 6.18A Legends and symbols found on weather map.

(a) Following the geostrophic wind law mentioned earlier, the winds generally blow so that low pressure is to the left looking downwind. Winds are strongest in areas of strong pressure gradients, identified by closely packed *isobars,* or lines of constant pressure.

(b) The high-pressure areas have generally clear skies, indicated by unshaded station circles, while clouds and weather accompany the low and its fronts.

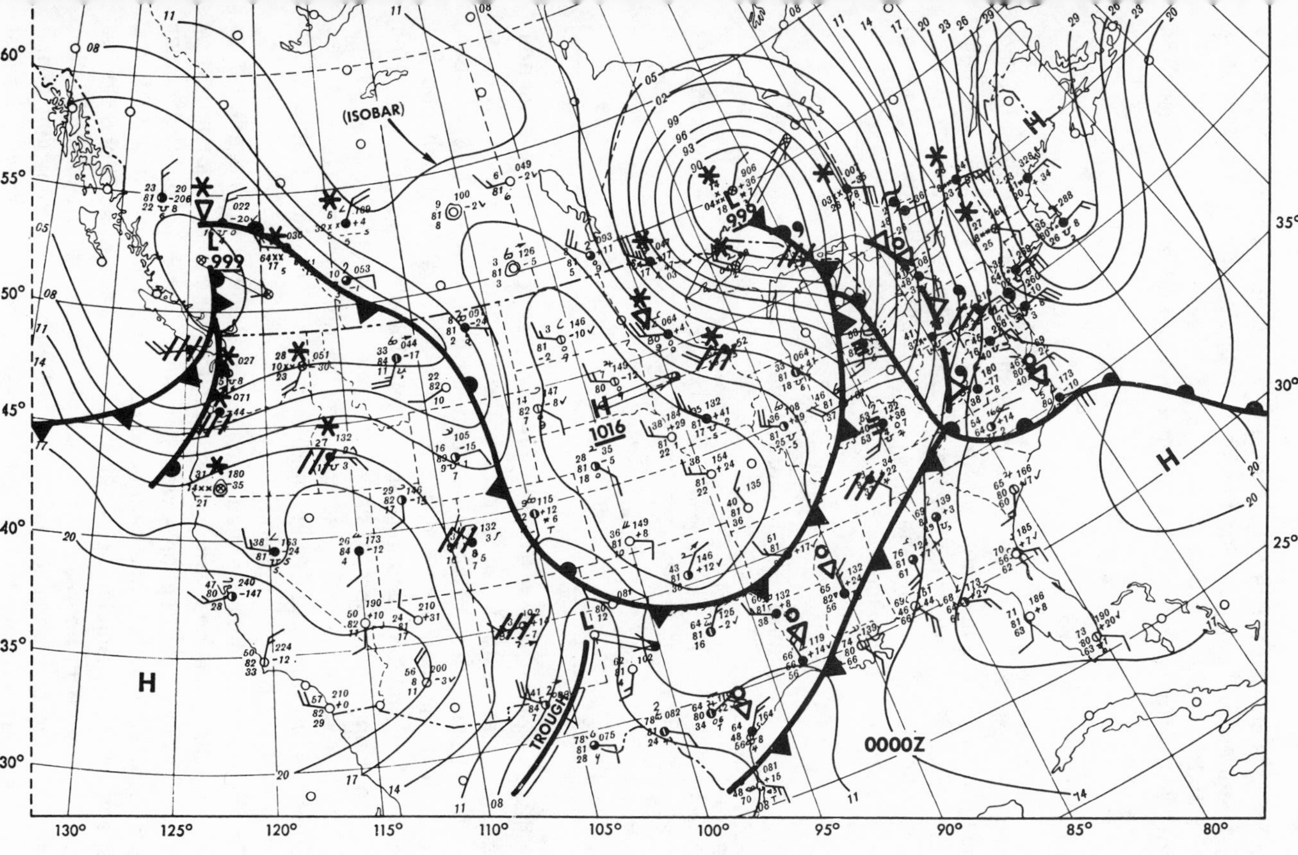

Figure 6.18B Surface weather map.

(c) Winds shift as fronts pass. In Kentucky we find southerly winds and temperatures in the 50s. Behind the front in Illinois there are northwesterly winds and temperatures below 40.

(d) Weather phenomena are indicated by colored shading (not shown on the map).

UPPER-AIR CHARTS

Constant-pressure charts reveal the circulation of air aloft by indicating, among other things, the variations in height above mean sea level (msl) of certain selected "standard" pressure levels. The levels usually chosen are 850, 700, 500, 300, 200, and either 150 or 100 millibars (mb). Standard charts and their approximate relative altitudes are:

TABLE 6.5
Altitude of Standard Upper-Air Charts

Pressure	*Height*		*Pressure*	*Height*	
(mb)	*(feet)*	*(meters)*	*(mb)*	*(feet)*	*(meters)*
850	5,000	1,500	300	30,000	9,000
700	10,000	3,000	200	40,000	12,000
500	18,000	5,500	100	53,000	16,000

Although some weather stations prepare their own high-level charts, these are normally produced for each of the standard levels by WMC every 12 hr and transmitted via facsimile. Upper-air charts (Figure 6.18) not only give current information on winds and temperatures at flight altitudes, but also serve as vital forecast tools for the meteorologist. Circulation patterns aloft are simpler and more easily extrapolated in time than those of the surface layers. Small-scale weather systems are steered by the broad currents of the upper air, and the life cycles of individual storms are closely tied to upper-air patterns.

On these charts, data are plotted at the locations of rawinsonde (radar wind sounding) stations. Winds are indicated by the shaft of an arrow pointing in the wind direction toward the station circle. A dark triangular flag indicates 50 knots, while barbs and half barbs indicate 10 and 5 knots respectively. For example, a plot of shows a west wind of 65 knots. The temperature in degrees Celsius is plotted to the left of the station circle, and the dew-point spread is plotted below it. To the right of the station appears the height of the pressure surface in meters with the first or last digit omitted to save space. The lines used in analysis, called *isolines* (lines of equal value), represent pressure, temperature, moisture, and wind speed.

Contour lines Contour or height lines connect points which represent equal altitudes above sea level based on the pressure level of the constant-pressure chart. These are drawn for intervals of 60 meters on charts below the 300-mb surface, and for intervals of 120 meters on the 300-, 200-, and 100-mb charts. Winds blow parallel to the contour lines with lower heights to the left and higher heights to the right.

Isotherms These short, dashed lines connect points of equal temperature. They are normally drawn for even 5°C intervals.

Moisture Lines Isolines of dew point, usually called moisture lines, connect points of equal dew-point temperature. On the higher-level charts, generally 500 mb and higher, moisture lines are not drawn since the low temperatures at these higher levels not only prevent much moisture existing, but tend to make measuring difficult.

Isotachs On the higher level charts, generally 500 mb and higher, dotted lines of equal wind speed, called isotachs, are often drawn. They relate only to speed, and do not indicate direction. Heavy broken lines with arrowheads are indicative of jet-stream locations.

Fronts Fronts are indicated in the same symbolic manner as they are on surface charts, provided that the frontal surfaces extend to the pressure levels involved. It is important to remember that fronts are practically always displaced geographically at different levels because of frontal slope.

PROGNOSTIC CHARTS AND SEVERE WEATHER SERVICES

The atmosphere is subject to the same natural laws which govern all other material bodies. If we know its state at one moment and know all the forces acting upon it, its future behavior should be as well determined as that of the sun and moon. This capability has been partly realized today with the aid of modern data-gathering and analysis systems, and global analyses of the atmosphere can be produced in reasonable time. Computers produce useful forecasts out to five days once each day by numerically simulating the behavior of the atmosphere. Numerically produced prognostic charts for most of the standard analysis levels are transmitted by facsimile to weather stations. All stations receive NMC products, while Air Force and Navy stations also receive products from the military weather centrals.

Prognostic charts are similar in content to actual analyses. Contours of pressure or height, isotherms, isotach, etc., are presented, but station data are naturally absent. The surface forecast charts are produced manually, because of low-level weather's local influences, although the forecasters rely heavily upon numerical forecast guidance.

Severe Weather Forecasting Special analysis and forecast techniques are required to predict the probability of occurrence of small severe weather phenomena such as thunderstorms and tornadoes. For this reason, both the National Weather Service and the Air Weather Service of the U.S. Air Force have established specialized centers for severe storm prediction. The National Weather Service's National Severe Storms Forecast Center at Kansas City, Mo., prepares advisories on severe weather for public and aviation use. These are issued by local field offices which also disseminate local warnings based on radar, public observations, pilot reports, and similar sources.

The AWS Military Weather Warning Center, formerly located with the Weather Bureau at Kansas City, has joined the Air Force Global Weather Central at Offutt Air Force Base, Nebraska. It issues warnings on hail, gusty winds, severe thunderstorms, and tornadoes both for areas and for certain individual military installations. Its principal product is a daily teletype map showing areas of expected severe weather.

Severe weather forecasts have become increasingly reliable over the years, and now merit the most careful attention of pilots and others considering the traverse of an area in which severe weather is forecast.

WINDS ALOFT CHARTS

Efficient, safe, and economical flight planning requires the use of winds aloft in predicting ground speed, determining fuel required, and in flight, being able to determine practicable alternate routes and destinations. Because the winds aloft are determined more by the pressure systems than by terrain effects, they are generally more reliable, either as observed, or in forecasts.

WMC plots the data it receives at 0000, 0600, 1200, and 1800Z using the barb and pennant arrows described for the constant pressure charts. In facsimile form, these reports are transmitted in three sets of four charts for Lower Levels (second level above the surface to 10,000 ft), Intermediate Levels (14,000 to 30,000 ft), and Upper Levels (35,000 to 60,000 ft). Here again, remember that this is *observed* data, and may be 2 to 9 hr old.

RADAR SUMMARY CHARTS

These summaries of all radar reports in the contiguous states are transmitted every three hours by facsimile. They include severe weather warnings as well, and are an essential briefing aid during the thunderstorm season.

FORECASTS

Forecasts may be mental, by the pilot looking at the weather office reports or the sky, or may involve the most sophisticated skills of the

Weather Bureau's Flight Advisory Weather Service (FAWS), and the centers of the armed services.

They are much more detailed and specific than 12- to 36-hour prognostic charts, and thus, while more valuable in flight planning, are more vulnerable to error in details. They may relate to terminals, area, and to specific routes on request.

12-Hour (FT1) and 24-Hour (FT2) Terminal Forecasts Containing height and amount of cloud, visibility, precipitation, surface wind, and specific weather remarks, these forecasts are valid for 12 or 24 hr, and are prepared each 6 hr. They are transmitted in a code basically similar to that used for hourly weather observations.

For example:

FT1 084 121645 Z } Heading.
17Z Sun -05Z Mon }
RAP C4X ½ S-BS 3425G35 23Z
C 8 ⊕/IS-BS 3420G30

The heading, which may introduce a forecast for many stations, is read "24-hour forecast issued by Minneapolis FAWS (084) on the 12th at 1645Z. It is valid from 1700 Sunday to 0500Z Monday. Rapid City will have ceiling obscured, visibility one-half mile in light snow and blowing snow, wind from 340° at 25 knots, gusts to 35 knots. At 2300Z this will change to ceiling 800 ft overcast one mile in light snow and blowing snow, winds from 340° at 20 knots, gusts to 30 knots.

Because this transmission requires special weather teletypewriters, the World Meteorological Organization and the United States military weather services use the Meteorological Aviation Report (METAR) code, which any teletypewriter can transmit. The same report in METAR code would read:

RCA 1414 KRCA 34025/35 0800 71SN
38BL SN 9/104 QNH 2970 INS CIG 04

GRADU 2301 34020/30 1600 71 SN
38BL SN 8 ST08 QNH 2975/NS CIG 08 BS

This code in addition provides greater flexibility, and the forecasts include the forecast altimeter setting (QNH). Weather reports as well as forecasts are sent by METAR.

Amended Terminal Forecasts are issued by FAWS when changes are important to planning, dispatching, flying, and in flight assistance. The forecaster considers the minimums of the specific terminal, plus pertinent changes in forecasts of thunderstorms, wind, freezing precipitation, ceiling, and visibility.

Area Forecasts may be considered generalized route forecasts. They include a definition of the area, clouds and weather, icing and various freezing levels, turbulence, and an outlook. These forecasts are sent in abbreviated plain language, though symbols are used where convenient. The outlook describes briefly what may be expected in the 12 hr following the forecast period.

Amended Area Forecasts, except in Alaska, are sent as In Flight Advisories, transmitted through FAA Flight Service Stations by FQWS.

Winds Aloft Forecasts These are produced twice daily by computer as two 6-hr forecasts, good for 12 hr, by NMC. They are transmitted at 0550 and 1750Z. The FAWS centers produce manually prepared forecasts twice daily, good for 12 hr, at 1150 and 2350Z.

Each forecast predicts true wind direction and speed in knots at 2000 or 5000 ft (depending on field elevation), 10,000, 15,000, 20,000, and 25,000 ft.

ADVISORIES

In Flight Weather Advisories, produced by FAWS centers, serve both civil and military aircraft. They are sent out according to standard criteria for adverse weather warning. They may be tabulated as follows:

Item	*Contents*
Significant Meteorological Advisory (SIGMET)	Intended for large aircraft. Tornadoes, squall lines, large hail, severe or extreme turbulence, heavy icing, dust storms, or sandstorms.
ADVISORIES For Light Aircraft	For small singles and twins. Sent whenever following expected within 2 hr: moderate icing, moderate turbulence, winds of 40 knots or more within 2000 ft of surface, and the possibility of low ceilings and visibilities.
Hurricane Advisories	Whenever hurricane threatens.
Severe Weather Outlook	Primarily thunderstorms, during appropriate seasons.

Fog

Unlike other weather hazards a pilot is likely to encounter, fog presents little or no hazard during the en-route portion of the flight. Fog, however, is a hazard during takeoffs and landings, since it restricts the visibility near the surface of the earth.

FOG FORMATION

The three factors that favor the formation of fog are high relative humidity, very light wind, and condensation nuclei.

Since fog is composed of liquid water, condensation is necessary, so high relative humidity is obviously of prime importance. In fact, the relative humidity must be very near 100%. The natural conditions which bring about high relative humidity (or saturation) are frequently cited as being fog-producing processes: evaporation of additional moisture into the air, or cooling of the air to its dew point. A high relative humidity may be noted on the Hourly Teletype Reports by observing the spread (difference in degrees) between temperature and dew point. Fog rarely occurs when the spread is more than 4°F and occurs most frequently when the spread is less than 2°F. A very light wind or no wind is generally favorable for fog formation. Light winds provide a mixing action which extends the depth of cooling near the surface and thereby increases the depth of the fog. Finally, there must be condensation nuclei suspended in the air. These nuclei provide a base around which moisture condenses. Smoke and salt particles are the most common forms of nuclei found in the atmosphere. Although almost all regions of the earth contain sufficient nuclei to permit fog formation, certain regions (such as industrial areas) have a marked abundance of them (smoke particles and sulfur compounds). These regions frequently have fog with greater than normal spreads between temperature and dew point, and the resulting fogs tend to be more persistent (Figure 6.19).

FOG DISSIPATION

Turbulence, resulting from strong winds, causes fog to dissipate by mixing warmer or dryer air from higher layers of the atmosphere with that of the surface, thus widening the temperature-dew point spread. Dissipation may also be accomplished by heating of the fog layer, either from the radiation of solar heat or from adiabatic downslope motion, both

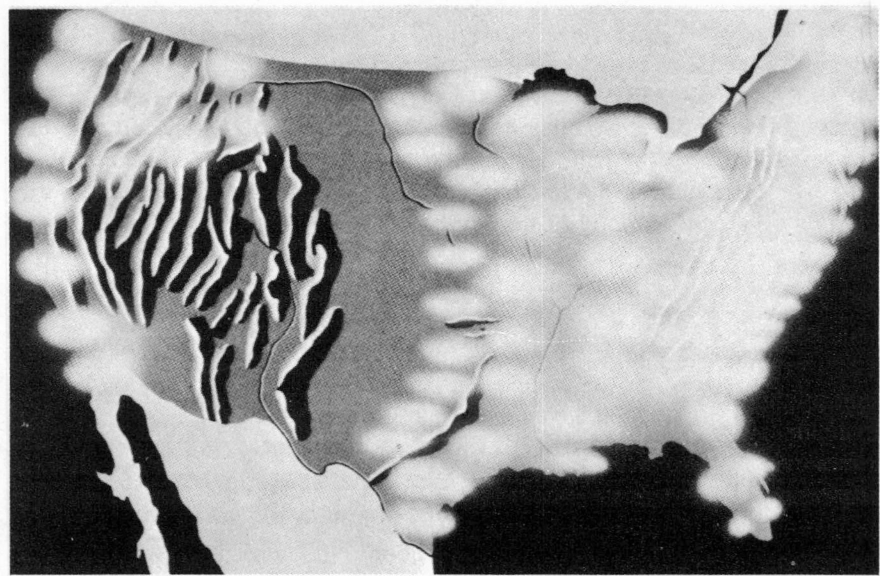

Figure 6.19 Areas in the United States most affected by fog. *(Courtesy of U.S. Air Force.)*

of which result in a widening of the temperature-dew point spread. It is apparent that an increase of the temperature-dew point spread is a manifestation of decreased relative humidity so that the fog evaporates or "burns off."

FOG TYPES AND CHARACTERISTICS

One common type of fog encountered by the pilot is *radiation fog,* which is formed by radiational cooling. After sunset, the earth radiates heat, gained during daylight hours, to the atmosphere, and by early morning the temperature at the surface may drop as much as 20°. Since the dew point normally changes only a few degrees during the night, the result is a decrease in the temperature-dew point spread. If the radiational cooling is great enough and other conditions are favorable, radiational fog forms. This type of fog is most likely to form under the following conditions:

1. Clear skies (maximum radiational cooling).
2. Sufficiently high dew point (so that temperature may cool to it).
3. Low, steady wind less than 10 mph.

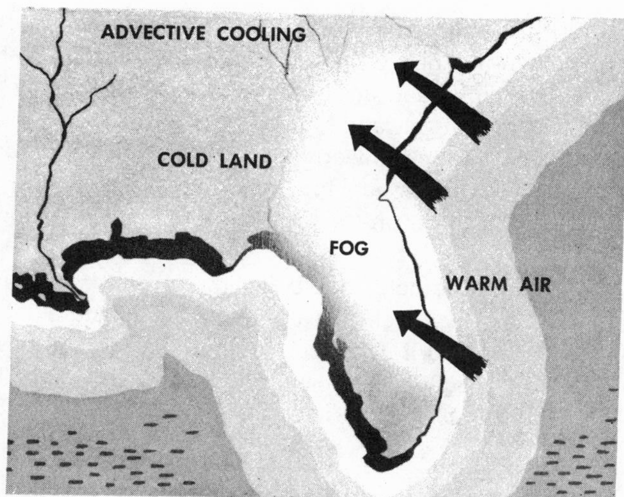

Figure 6.20 Advection fog is formed as warm moist air moves over cold ground. *(Courtesy of U.S. Air Force.)*

These conditions are most frequently realized when a land region is under the influence of a high-pressure cell.

A second type of fog is called *advection fog* (Figure 6.20). Advection fog is very common along coastal regions and is formed by the movement of moist air over a colder surface. One example of this fog is sea *fog,* which is formed (as the name implies) over water. Cold ocean currents, such as are present off the coast of San Francisco, serve to cool and condense warm moist air which comes from seaward. This fog may be carried inland by the wind and is frequently intense. Advection fog frequently forms during periods of relatively strong winds despite the apparent dissipating effects of the turbulence generated by strong winds.

Advection fog is also very common in the Gulf States area during the winter when warm, moist air moves inland over cool land surfaces.

A third type of fog, which is called *upslope fog,* is formed by the transport of air up a rising land surface. As the air rises, it cools by expansion (adiabatic cooling) as a result of the decrease in pressure. Fog results when the cooling is sufficient to bring the temperature down to the dew point. The most common fog of this type is formed on the eastern slope of the Rocky Mountains by the westward flow of air from the Missouri Valley. Sufficient wind to support continued upslope motion is a necessity for this type of fog formation. However, if the wind is too strong, the fog may be raised from the surface and occur as low stratus.

All other types of fogs are classified under the general term *evaporation fogs.* Included within this group are the frontal fogs which are fairly common in the winter months and are associated most commonly with slow-moving systems. They are always found in a cold air mass under warm, moist air. Precipitation from the warm air falls through the colder air, and evaporation sufficient to produce fog may take place. In the case of a warm front, such fog will be prefrontal; postfrontal fog is associated with a cold front.

Steam fogs occur where cold, stable air flows over a water surface several degrees warmer; the intense evaporation of moisture into the cold air results in fog when and if saturation is produced. Conditions favorable for this type of fog are light winds, clear nights, and stable air. These conditions are common around lakes and rivers in the fall of the year.

ICE FOG

Ice fog is in a separate category and is formed of tiny ice crystals that have sublimated directly from the vapor state—frozen water vapor. It is very fine, misty, and dangerous. Its danger is in the speed of formation (extremely rapid) and in the fact that it is encountered primarily just where one doesn't want it, near centers of habitation.

This type of fog is a hazard in the Arctic regions. It may be expected to form from clear, cold air at temperatures between −20°F and −50°F. The trigger action for this type of fog is a great deal like others, a nucleus of some impurity upon which the ice will gather. In the Arctic regions, these condensation nuclei are not too prevalent and are found downwind of towns, highways, and (most unfortunately) around airports.

It is not unusual for an entire airport to fog in within 10 min after an aircraft engine has disturbed the fine balance between fog and no fog. Vertical visibility in ice fog is usually good; horizontal visibility may be zero.

Thunderstorms

Since approximately 44,000 thunderstorms occur daily over the surface of the earth, a pilot can expect to encounter thunderstorm areas frequently. A knowledge of how to avoid them in planning and flying, or how to penetrate them as a last resort, is basic airmanship.

A certain combination of atmospheric conditions is necessary for the formation of a thunderstorm. These factors are: unstable air of relatively high moisture content and some type of lifting action.

Thunderstorms generally have the same physical features. They do differ, however, in intensity, degree of development, and associated weather phenomena such as hail, turbulence, and electrical discharges. They are generally classified according to the manner in which the initial lifting action is accomplished. Two general classifications are currently used—*frontal* and *air-mass*.

1. Frontal types
   - Warm front
   - Cold front
   - Prefrontal (squall line)
2. Air-mass types
   - Convective
   - Orographic
   - Nocturnal

FRONTAL THUNDERSTORMS

The *warm-front thunderstorm* is caused when warm, moist, unstable air is forced aloft over a colder, denser shelf of retreating air (Figure 6.21). Owing to the extreme shallowness of the warm frontal slope, the air is lifted gradually. The level of free convection will normally be reached at isolated points along the lateral surface of the front aloft, and therefore warm-front thunderstorms are generally scattered.

Warm-front storms are extremely difficult to identify because they are

Figure 6.21 Warm-front thunderstorms. *(Courtesy of U.S. Air Force.)*

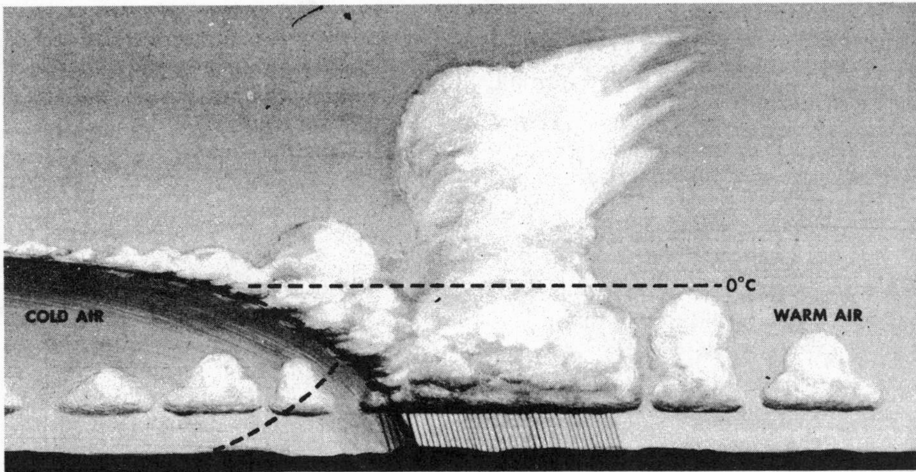

Figure 6.22 Cold-front thunderstorms. *(Courtesy of U.S. Air Force.)*

obscured by other clouds. The warm-front thunderstorm is dangerous because the pilot may fly from an area of relatively smooth instrument flight into an area of great turbulence in a matter of seconds. A thorough preflight study of the stability chart with the weather forecaster forewarns the pilot of the existence of possible thunderstorm areas. Presence of showery precipitation in the warm-front weather pattern also is an indication of cumulus or thunderstorm activity.

The cold-front thunderstorm is caused by the forward motion of a wedge of cold air into a body of warm, moist, unstable air (Figure 6.22). Cold-front storms are normally positioned along the frontal surface aloft in what appears to be a continuous line. The problem of recognition is negligible because most cold-front storms are partly visible to the pilot approaching the front from any direction. The bases of these storms are usually closer to the surface than the bases of warm-front thunderstorms.

Prefrontal or squall-line thunderstorms are the result of the lifting action that takes place at a squall line, normally great enough to force the warm air up to the level of free convection, thereby producing a line of thunderstorms along the squall line (Figure 6.23). These thunderstorms are normally similar to but more violent than the cold-front thunderstorms. Tornadoes are normally associated with the most violent of squall lines.

AIR-MASS THUNDERSTORMS

Air-mass thunderstorms have two things in common: They form within an air mass and they are generally isolated or scattered over a large region.

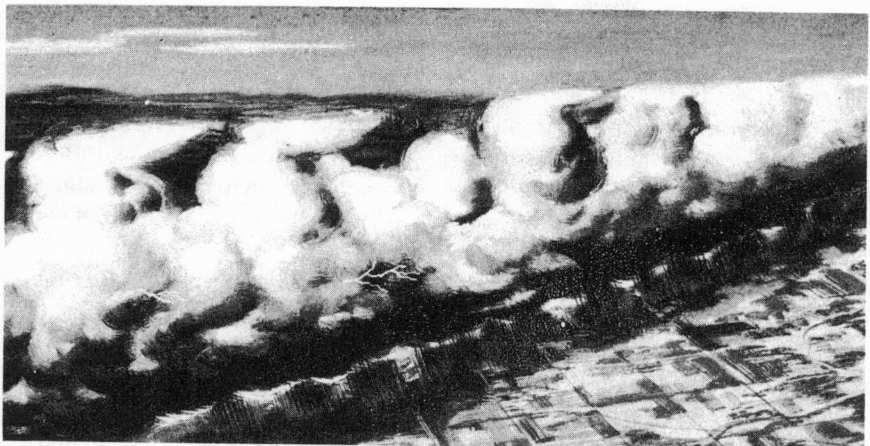

Figure 6.23 Squall-line thunderstorms. *(Courtesy of U.S. Air Force.)*

Convective Thunderstorms Convective thunderstorms may occur almost anywhere in the world, over land or water (Figure 6.24). Formation of these storms is caused by solar heating of areas of the land or sea, which in turn provides heat to the lower layers of the air and results in rising currents of the warmed air. Land-type convective thunderstorms normally form during the afternoon hours at about the time the earth is receiving maximum heating from the sun. If the circulation is such that relatively cool, moist, unstable air is passing over the land area, heating from below will cause convective currents and result in towering cumulus which may continue to develop into thunderstorm activity. Dissipation normally occurs during the night or early morning hours after the land has lost its heat to the atmosphere.

Sea-type convective thunderstorms form in the same manner but at different hours. They generally form during the night after the sun has set and dissipate during the later morning hours. Examples of both types of convective thunderstorms may be found around the Gulf States. Clock-

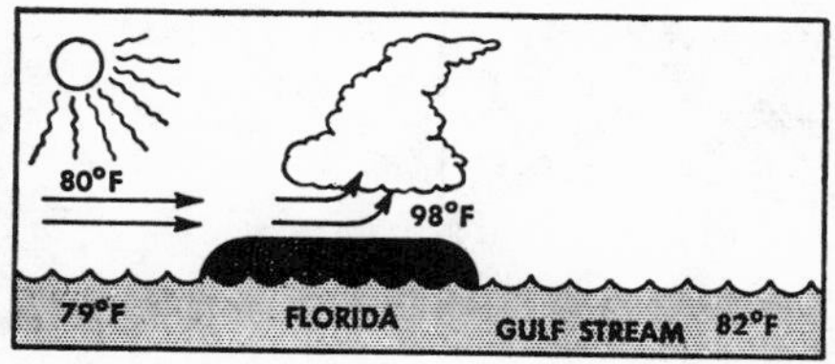

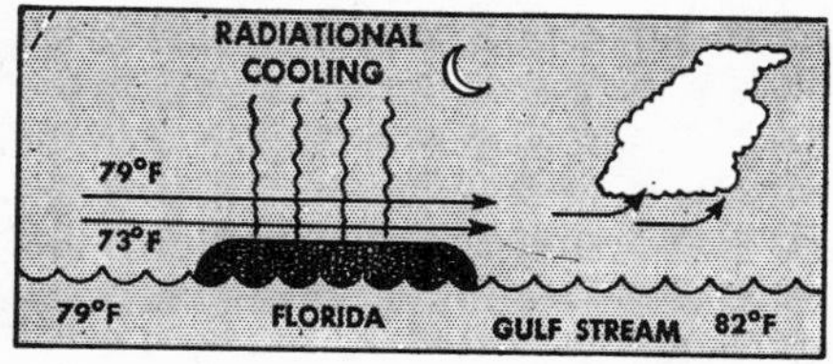

Figure 6.24 Convective-type thunderstorms.

wise circulation around the Bermuda high-pressure cell transports moist air over the land surface of these states during the entire day. The flow is off the water and across the land during the hours of sunlight. Since the land surface is considerably warmer than the air, the air is heated from below. Convective currents result, and the common afternoon thunderstorm follows after continued convective activity. Toward sunset, the land surface gives off heat rapidly to the air and a balance between the land and the air is gradually reached.

At about the same time that the thunderstorms which have formed over land begin to dissipate, new ones begin to form over the sea surface. Thus it may appear that the thunderstorms move from land to sea. Although this may occur to a limited extent, basically the daytime and nighttime thunderstorms form as a result of the different heat-retaining properties of water and soil. Water is not subject to such rapid temperature changes as is land and therefore does not give off sufficient heat to the air to produce extensive convective activity until after sunset. During the night, however, a large-scale loss of heat from the water surface to the atmosphere occurs, and thunderstorms are formed by essentially the same process that transpires during the formation of late afternoon thunderstorms over land.

Orographic Thunderstorms As the name implies, orographic thunderstorms form in mountainous regions where the air traverses a long or steep slope (Figure 6.25). A good example of this type of storm is frequently found in the northern Rocky Mountain region. When the circulation of the air is from the west, moist air from the Pacific Ocean is transported to the mountains and forced upward by the slope of terrain. If the air is unstable, the upslope motion may cause thunderstorm activity on the windward side of the mountains. Such thunderstorms frequently form in a long, unbroken line similar to the cold-front type and persist as long as the upslope circulation continues. From the windward side of the mountains, identification of orographic storms may sometimes be difficult because they are obscured by other clouds, usually somewhat

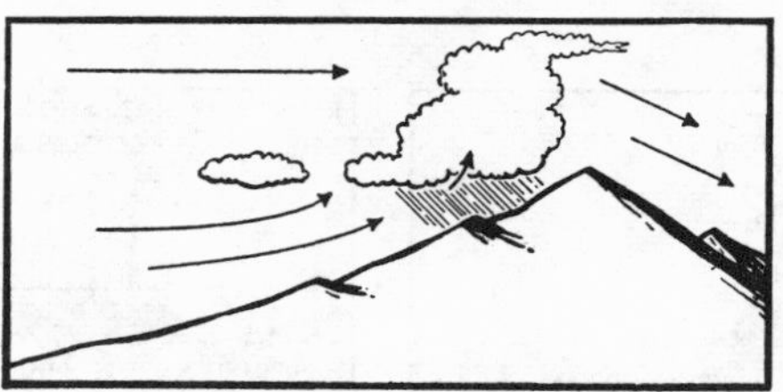

Figure 6.25 Orographic thunderstorms. *(Courtesy of U.S. Air Force.)*

stratiform. From the lee side, identification is positive; the outlines of each storm are plainly visible. Don't fly through an orographic thunderstorm because this type of storm, almost without exception, enshrouds a mountain peak or a hill. For the same reason, don't fly under this storm unless the opposite side of the area is clearly visible, and then have plenty of terrain clearance.

Nocturnal Thunderstorms This is a type of thunderstorm which occurs later at night and in the early morning hours in the Central Plains area of the United States from the Mississippi Valley region westward. Its occurrence is explained as follows: A weak warm frontal surface overlies the area affected in such a manner that a relatively moist layer of air exists aloft. Nighttime radiation from the moist layer causes extreme cooling of the air at this level. The layer of air which has cooled settles in the early morning hours and forces unstable surface air aloft to initiate thunderstorm activity.

STRUCTURE OF THUNDERSTORMS

The fundamental structural element of the thunderstorm is the unit of convective circulation known as a convective cell. A mature thunderstorm contains several of these cells, each varying in diameter from one to five miles. By radar analysis and measurement of drafts, it has been determined that the circulation in each cell is generally independent of that in surrounding cells in the same storm. Each cell progresses through a cycle which usually lasts several hours. In the initial stages of cumulus development, the cloud consists of a single cell, but as the development progresses, new cells may form and older cells dissipate in a continuous and unbroken process. The life cycle of a thunderstorm consists of three stages: (1) the *cumulus stage,* (2) the *mature stage,* and (3) the *dissipating* or *anvil stage.* It should be noted that the transition from one stage to the next is not an abrupt one, but that the borders (with respect to time) of each stage blend gradually into the next.

STAGES OF A THUNDERSTORM

Cumulus Stage The common cumulus cloud is the initial stage of all thunderstorm formation. Actually, only a very small percentage of cumulus clouds ever become thunderstorms, but the ordinary cumulus activity is always the basic or initial stage of the storm (Figure 6.26(A)). The chief distinguishing feature of the cumulus, or building stage is the updraft that prevails throughout the entire cell. The speed of the updraft may vary from a few feet per second to as high as 100 fps in well-developed cumulus clouds. As the updraft builds a cumulus cloud to higher altitudes,

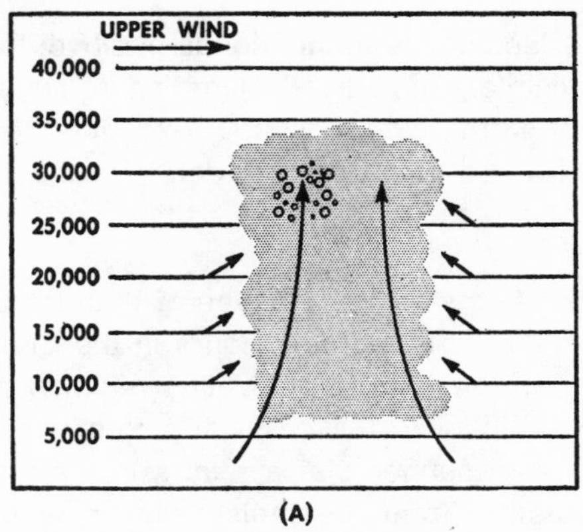

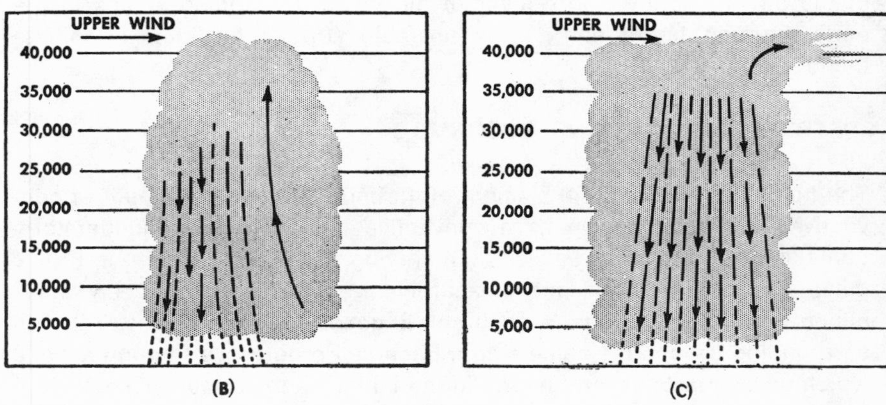

Figure 6.26 (A) Cumulus stage of the thunderstorm. (B) Mature stage of the thunderstorm. (C) Anvil of dissipating stage of the thunderstorm.

small water droplets are formed. The greatest number of droplets form near the freezing level and grow in size by collision with other droplets. Usually rain does not fall during the cumulus stage because the raindrops are carried upward or remain more or less suspended by the upward air currents which exist throughout the cloud.

The Mature Stage The occurrence of rain at the ground generally indicates the transition from the cumulus stage to the mature stage. By this time the cell has usually attained a height of 25,000 ft or more. After the number of raindrops has increased to such an extent that they can no longer be supported by the updrafts, they begin to fall from the cloud and exert a drag on the air within the clouds. Such a drag is a major factor in the formation of a downdraft which characterizes each convective cell in the mature stage. The downdraft is evident at the surface as strong and gusty horizontal outflow which results when the downward flow of air is forced to move horizontally because of the solid lower barrier presented by the earth (Figure 6.26(B)). Downdrafts begin to form in the middle region of the cloud and gradually increase in both horizontal and vertical directions. Downdrafts in thunderstorms tend to be less gusty and smaller in speed than updrafts, but frequently are as strong as 40 fps. In contrast, updraft speeds of 100 fps are not uncommon early in the mature stage. When one considers that the downdraft is immediately adjacent to the updraft in each cell, and that several cells are continuously forming and dissipating, it is apparent that severe turbulence may be expected when flying through a thunderstorm.

Mature cells generally extend to altitudes of 30,000 to 50,000 ft. It is in this stage of the formation process that hail is frequently formed when a cell extends to great heights and/or has very strong updraft speeds. The "hard" rains which are often characteristic of thunderstorms also occur during the mature stage of each cell. In contrast to the life span of 10 to 15 min of the cumulus stage of an individual cell, the mature stage usually lasts for 15 to 30 min. Again, one must remember that a given thunderstorm is composed of several cells which continuously form and dissipate so that the life of an entire thunderstorm is usually much longer than these figures would tend to indicate. When there is increasing wind with height, the updraft axis may tilt and rain fall out of the updraft without impeding it. Such storms spawn hail and other severe weather; they are often found on the great plains.

Dissipating or Anvil Stage Throughout the life span of the mature cell, the downdraft continues to develop both horizontally and vertically as a result of momentum and the drag effect of the falling precipitation. At the same time, the updraft is in a stage of dissipation. As this process progresses, the entire lower levels of the cell become an area of downdraft, and the upper levels become an area of little or no vertical motion. A downward current throughout the cell is the chief characteristic of the dissipating stage of a cell (Figure 6.26(C)).

Since the source of air necessary to maintain a downdraft is gradually reduced by the dissipation of the updraft, and since the descending motion effects a drying process, the entire structure now begins to dissipate. The dissipation stage may be identified at the surface by the gradual abatement of precipitation and finally complete cessation. At the same time the lower levels of the cloud frequently tend to become stratiform in appearance. A further identifying feature of this stage of the development process is the formation of the characteristic anvil top which results from the strong horizontal winds aloft blowing the upper portions of the cloud forward of the main portion. The life span of the dissipating stage is considerably more variable than that of the other stages and is dependent upon the strength of the original updrafts and the amount of moisture which the air contains.

VERTICAL DEVELOPMENT

The height of thunderstorms is a primary concern of pilots whose responsibility it is to determine an optimum flight altitude. Prior to the advent of radar analysis, it was difficult to give accurate estimates of cumuliform cloud tops, because of the general presence of more or less stratiform clouds in the lower levels.

Measurements of the vertical extent of thunderstorm activity were made by personnel of the original Thunderstorm Project in 1946 by using radar equipment with a range-height indicator. It was found that the closest correspondence between the radar-measured top and the actual top occurs during the cumulus stage, because ice crystal tops in the mature and anvil stages do not give good radar echoes.

Storms with heights of 50,000 ft or more were measured in less than 10% of the cases observed. The greatest frequency of storms measured had heights between 25,000 and 29,000 ft. The average of all heights measured was 37,000 ft; the maximum height recently observed was 66,000 ft.

Another factor indicated by draft research was the relative strength of updrafts and downdrafts. Updrafts appear to be of consistently greater magnitude than downdrafts. Thus, a good general rule with regard to flight is that an aircraft making a penetration of a thunderstorm will emerge at a higher altitude than that at which the penetration was started. Although this may not hold true for the dissipation stage of the development, the ability to maintain a given altitude is relatively easy in this stage because of the lesser speed and lesser gustiness which characterized the downdrafts.

Turbulent motion (gusts) within the cellular circulation pattern of thunderstorms has a considerable effect upon an aircraft in flight. In fact, the actual severity of a storm, so far as flying is concerned, is dependent upon the intensity and frequency of these gusts.

Gusts are both vertical and lateral, and all contribute to the dangers of turbulence to be expected. Gusts have been measured as high as 260 fps up and 160 fps down. The absolute value of gusts is not as significant as the frequency, which has been recorded at 40 fps up and 40 fps down in $\frac{1}{10}$ sec. The evidence indicates that gust intensity increases with altitude clear to the top of storms.

The forecast or observed tops of thunderstorm cells give the most important single indication of the severity of the storm. The greater the vertical development, the stronger will be the up and down drafts and turbulence, and the chance for hail.

Flight techniques in severe turbulence are discussed on page 336.

WEATHER WITHIN THE THUNDERSTORM

Rain The pilot, upon entering any thunderstorm, may expect to encounter considerable quantities of liquid moisture which may not necessarily be falling rain. Liquid water in a storm may be ascending if it is encountered in a strong updraft; it may be suspended seemingly without motion, in extremely heavy concentrations; or it may be falling to the ground. If it is falling, it is rain in the usual sense of the word. Rain, as normally measured by surface instruments, is associated with the downdraft. This does not preclude the possibility of the pilot's entering a cloud and being swamped, so to speak, even though rain has not been observed at the surface. Rain will be found in almost every case of penetration of a fully developed thunderstorm. Liquid water, in heavy concentration, has been encountered at 40,000 ft, at temperatures far below freezing. There have been instances in which no rain was reported, but in these the storm probably had not developed into the mature stage. Altitudes above the freezing level showed a sharp decline in the frequency of rain of any intensity.

Hail Hail can be found virtually anywhere near or within a thunderstorm or its overhanging anvil. Although the likelihood of hail is closely related to the vertical development and intensity of the storm, there is no infallible method of forecasting hail or determining whether an individual storm contains hail. Because wet hailstones reflect radio energy very strongly, bright radar echoes are well correlated with hail.

Lightning According to pilot reports substantiated by subsequent ground inspection during the project, lightning strikes occurred in less than 2% of all thunderstorm penetrations. In general, damage was minor, being limited to small punctures in the aircraft skin. Radio failure caused by lightning occurred only when the antenna was damaged. This was rare. A maximum frequency of strikes occurred at the 16,000-ft level, and the next highest frequency was at 26,000 ft. However, strikes may occur at any level, if conditions are favorable.

Icing On more than 50% of all traverses in the Thunderstorm Project, icing was encountered at 20,000 ft. Mostly rime ice, it never accumulated to the degree that it impaired safety, but this is attributed to the short exposure time in these traverses. Icing is considered most likely at or above the freezing level; the strong vertical currents and water at high levels indicate it should be expected at any level.

Snow The maximum frequency of moderate and heavy snow occurred at the 20,000- and 21,000-ft levels. Snow, in many cases mixed with supercooled rain, was encountered at all altitudes above the freezing level. This was apparently of considerable concern to the pilots, for it presented a unique icing problem; wet snow packed on the leading edge of the wing and resulted in the formation of rime ice. This was particularly true close to the freezing level, and on occasion this altitude had to be abandoned because of the rapidity at which ice accumulated on the aircraft.

First Gust A significant surface hazard to approach, landing, and takeoff associated with thunderstorm activity is the rapid change in wind direction and speed immediately prior to thunderstorm passage. Strong winds at the surface accompanying thunderstorm passage are the result of the horizontal spreading-out (divergence) of the downdraft currents from within the storm as they approach the surface of the earth. The total wind speed is a result of the downdraft divergence plus the forward velocity of the storm cell. Thus, the speeds at the leading edge, as the storm approaches, are ordinarily far greater than those at the trailing edge, and the effect of the approach of a thunderstorm is to cause a sudden and marked increase in the surface winds at a station. This initial wind surge as observed at the surface is known as a "first gust." The speed of the first gust is normally the highest recorded during storm passage and may vary in direction as much as 180° from the surface wind direction which previously existed. First-gust speeds increase to an average of about 15 knots over prevailing speeds, although gusts with a total speed of more than 90 knots have been recorded. The average change of wind direction associated with the first gust is about 40°; this value is not considered particularly significant, as the wind shifts occurring with thunderstorms over a station may be as much as 180° in direction, depending on the orientation of the thunderstorm with respect to the station.

Altimeter Errors Rapid and marked surface pressure variations generally occur during the passage of a thunderstorm. The typical sequence of these variations is for an abrupt fall as the storm approaches, an abrupt rise accompanying the rain, and a gradual return to normal as the rain ceases. The importance to a pilot of such pressure fluctuations is that they may result in significant altitude errors even though the altimeter setting which he uses is current almost to the minute. In the investigations by the Thunderstorm Project, it was found that, if a pilot had landed during the rain, in approximately 24% of the storms studied, he would have been approximately 60 ft higher or lower than his altimeter indicated, using an altimeter setting given him a few minutes earlier. *Two cases of the altimeter reading more than 140 ft too high were noted.* A pilot should realize that any altimeter setting given him during or immediately before a thunderstorm is highly unreliable.

WEATHER RADAR RETURNS

Airborne radar has become a vital tool in avoiding severe weather because the water, snow, and hail within turbulent clouds cause strong radar returns which vary with their density. Thunderstorms, which are essentially areas of high moisture concentration, appear on the radarscope as bright returns with fuzzy edges. Clouds with moisture content in liquid

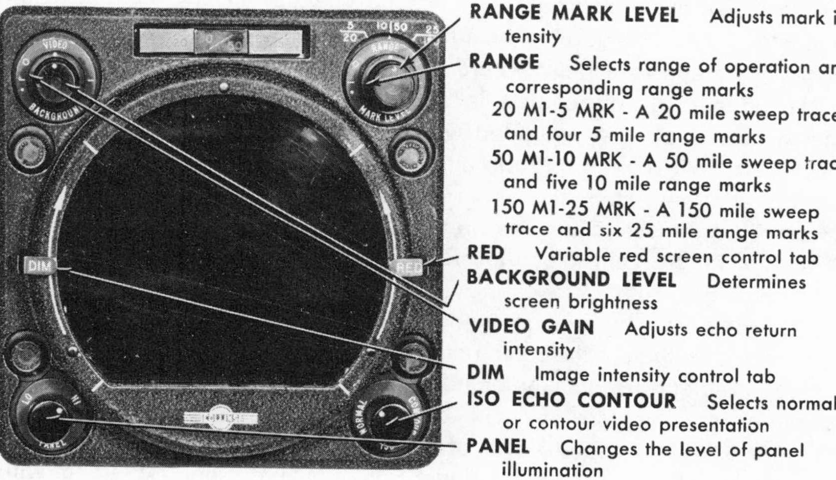

(A)

(B)

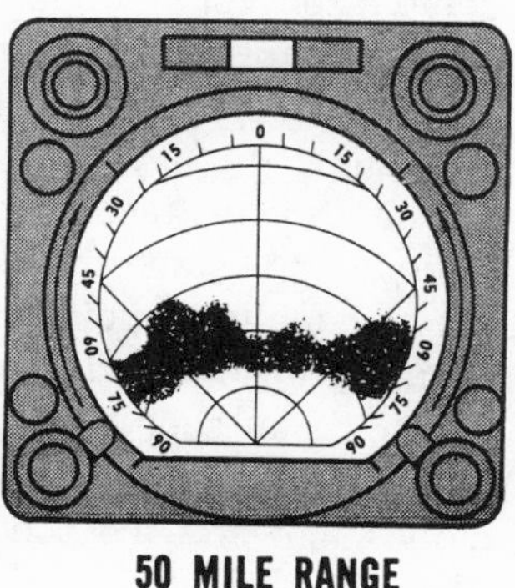

(C)

Figure 6.27 Typical weather radar components. The indicator (A) and cockpit control (B) operate from a transmitter-receiver, a synchronizer, and a parabolic rotating or oscillating radar antenna. The drawing shows a typical display on this equipment, which represents the sector forward of the aircraft nose, in which the antenna is mounted. *(Courtesy of Collins Radio Co.)*

form are much more accurately located than those which have their moisture concentration in crystal form. In general, rain gives a brighter echo than snow since water particles reflect about five times as much radio energy as snow crystals of the same size and shape. The echo brightness from dry hail is also about one fifth that of rain. Hailstones covered with water reflect signals as if they were entirely composed of water.

Contouring and Determining Turbulent Areas The regions of more intense moisture concentration—hence turbulence—in any storm can be delineated with considerable accuracy by reducing the receiver gain by successive steps to a point where only the strongest echo signals show on the scope. This procedure is called "contouring" the region. Many current radar sets are equipped with a contour function or "iso-echo." These sets have contouring circuitry. By switching to the contour function the radar set automatically blanks out returns above a fixed degree of power or brightness. Then the areas of strongest echo-signal power remain dark in the center of the storm cell presentation as illustrated in Figure 6.27(B).

Areas of heavy turbulence tend to lie where the contour gradient is steepest rather than in the region of most intense echo signal. These areas of steep gradient are quickly located on a set with contouring circuitry by comparing the "contour-off" with the "contour-on" picture as illustrated in Figure 6.28(B). Accurate evaluation of severe weather requires a comparison of "off" and "on" depiction; therefore do not fly along with contour left "on." Without the contour function, delineating the areas of heaviest turbulence is more difficult and time consuming. One must reduce the gain control by successive steps and determine the areas of steepest gradient.

Establishing Standard Gain Settings It is important in weather radar operation to establish a standard maximum gain setting. Do this by turning the gain up to the point where the static just disappears. Mark this setting. By using this method for establishing a maximum gain setting and returning to it after such procedures as that outlined for contouring, you will be able to evaluate storms on the basis of comparative returns. However, storms that produce echo returns of similar intensity are not necessarily of equal strength.

Antenna tilt setting is also important in weather interpretation. Proper tilt setting will change with the flight altitude and the radar range setting. Initially adjust the tilt until ground targets just begin to appear at the maximum distance desired for surveillance. Since the bottom portion of the beam has just touched the ground, its natural spread upward will take care of any storm in the vicinity. When thunderstorms or other severe weather are observed, tilt the antenna up occasionally to determine levels

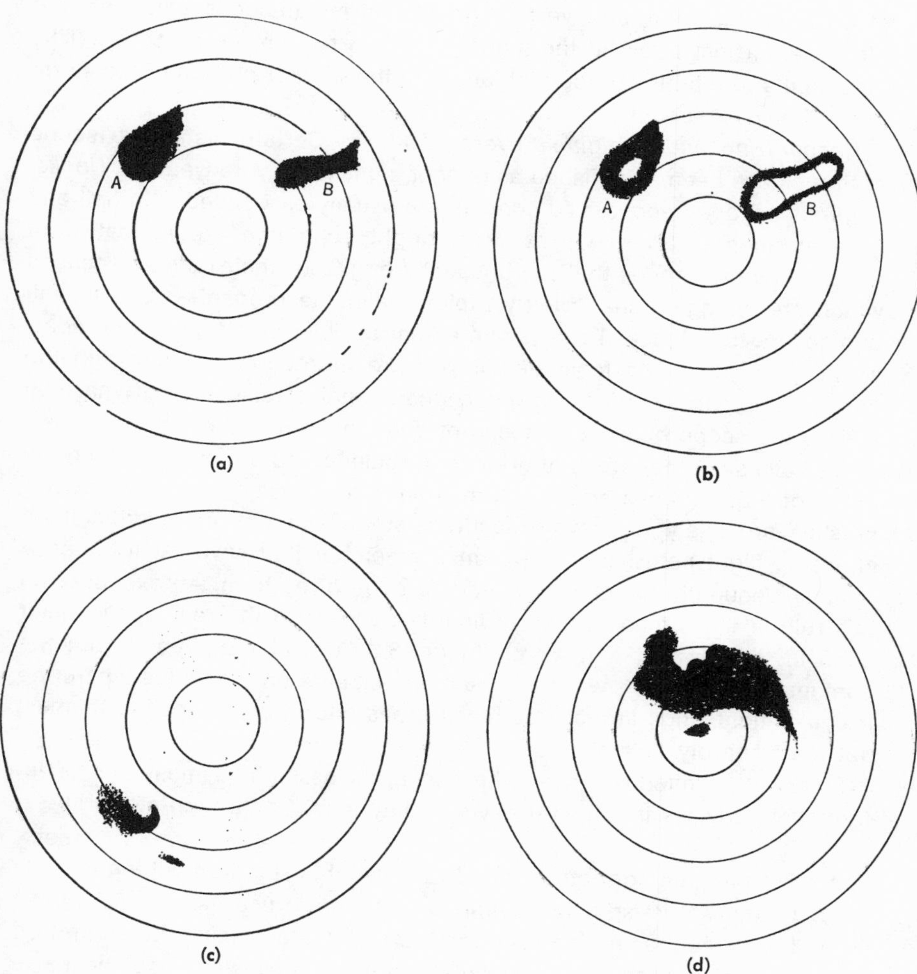

Figure 6.28 Airborne radar indications of weather. Contour circuitry. Figures (a) and (b) illustrate the employment of contour circuitry. In (a) the contour circuitry is off. In (b) with "contour on," the intense moisture concentrations and storm cells have been delineated. Note that Cell *B* has the sharpest gradient, particularly to the lower right, and would therefore be expected to be more turbulent than *A*. The same effect can be achieved on sets not equipped with contour circuitry by successively reducing gain.

Severe weather danger signs. Figure (c) illustrates the hooked finger indicating hail and possibly a tornado. Figure (d) illustrates scalloped edges and nodules.

of most intense returns or vertical growth. In mountainous areas, set the tilt to permit just a few of the higher peaks to remain on the scope. This insures that the tilt is not too high and that the weaker portion of the storm is not being observed.

Recognizing and Avoiding Severe Weather Certain distinctive scope patterns have been established as danger signs for severe weather. *Hooks, fingers, scalloped edges,* and *nodules* are usually associated with hail and high turbulence. *Sharp waves* on a bright echo line are indicative of violent squalls. Echoes that are unusually bright for their range or echoes which are changing shape fairly rapidly delineate probable areas of hail and severe turbulence. To a certain extent the interpretation of the radar-scope presentation is facilitated if you are thoroughly familiar with the current synoptic situation. However, guard against discounting what you see on the scope because it does not conform to the forecast.

We have seen that areas of greatest turbulence do not coincide with the areas of most intense scope return. Above the freezing level, where ice crystals are likely to prevail, accurate storm fixing is more difficult. In choosing flight paths through storms, remember that severest turbulence is most frequently found on the leading edge of a storm. An exception to this rule is the tornado which ordinarily appears to the rear of the radar echo in the form of a hook or "figure-6." On radar equipped with the contour function, the severest turbulence appears on the scope where the irregular light rings around the black areas (storm cells) are the thinnest but most sharply defined.

Summary United Airlines, whose experts assembled most of this information, advises its pilots that when they must fly through storm areas:

"1. Set the gain correctly, then always use this standard setting.
2. If your set is iso-echo equipped (contoured) use it.
3. If your set has no iso-echo feature and you are using the suggested low-gain procedure to stimulate contouring, always use the same low-gain settings.
4. Use ground clutter to help you adjust the tilt.
5. Be sure to tilt the antenna to see the region you are about to fly through.
6. Sharp rainfall gradients are indicative of sharp shear areas (turbulence).
7. Watch for and avoid hail echoes:
   - Hooked fingers
   - Pointing fingers
   - Scalloped edges.
8. Avoid any "figure-6" echoes.

9. Fly at least 5 mi from storms below the freezing level and at least 10 mi from storms above the freezing level exhibiting the characteristics discussed.
10. Avoid by at least 10 mi any storm which is changing shape rapidly.
11. Monitor the scope constantly, if possible, when in storm areas.
12. Fly well clear of rapidly developing storm echoes.
13. Never fly under an overhang from a thunderstorm cloud—unless you are asking to be hit by hail."

The experience of the U.S. Air Force is combined with these precepts to produce the rules summarized in Figure 6.29. The avoidance distances given are minimums. Whenever possible, one should stay 20 mi away from any thunderstorm. Rules based on the use of radar assume that the radar is in good condition, and is designed specifically for weather use. Such radars have a narrow beam of about 5° vertically and horizontally. Navigational and Air Traffic Control radars are relatively poor guides to weather activity because of their vertically broad beams. Severe storms may fill only a portion of their pulse volume, producing spuriously weak returns.

AVOIDANCE DISTANCES FOR AIRCRAFT EQUIPPED WITH NARROW BEAM RADAR

Flight	Echo Characteristics			
Altitude (1000s of Ft)	Shape	Intensity	Gradient of Intensity*	Rate of Change
0-20	AVOID BY 10 MILES ECHOES WITH HOOKS, FINGERS, SCALLOPED EDGES, OR OTHER PROTRUSIONS.	AVOID BY 5 MILES ECHOES WITH SHARP EDGES OR STRONG INTENSITIES.	AVOID BY 5 MILES ECHOES WITH STRONG GRADIENTS OF INTENSITY.	AVOID BY 10 MILES ECHOES SHOWING RAPID CHANGES OF SHAPE, HEIGHT, OR INTENSITY.
20-25	←	AVOID ALL ECHOES BY 10 MILES		→
25-30	←	AVOID ALL ECHOES BY 15 MILES		→
ABOVE 30	←	AVOID ALL ECHOES BY 20 MILES		→

* APPLICABLE TO SETS WITH ISO-ECHO. ISO-ECHO PRODUCES A HOLE IN A STRONG ECHO WHEN THE RETURNED SIGNAL IS ABOVE A PRE-SET VALUE.

1. IF FLIGHT IS OVER STORM CLOUDS, ALWAYS MAINTAIN AT LEAST 5000 FT VERTICAL SEPARATION FROM CLOUD TOPS.
2. IF AIRCRAFT IS NOT EQUIPPED WITH RADAR, OR RADAR IS INOPERATIVE, AVOID BY 10 MILES ANY STORM THAT BY VISUAL INSPECTION IS TALL, GROWING RAPIDLY, OR HAS AN ANVIL TOP.
3. IF AIRCRAFT IS EQUIPPED ONLY WITH WIDE BEAM RADAR, AVOID ALL STORMS BY THE SAME DISTANCES RECOMMENDED FOR NARROW BEAM RADAR, EXCEPT THAT STORMS SHOULD BE AVOIDED BY 10 MILES IN THE ALTITUDE RANGE 0-20,000 FT.
4. INTERMITTENTLY MONITOR LONG RANGES ON RADAR TO AVOID GETTING INTO SITUATIONS WHERE NO ALTERNATIVE REMAINS BUT THE PENETRATION OF HAZARDOUS AREAS. AVOID FLYING UNDER A CUMULONIMBUS OVERHANG. IF SUCH FLIGHT CANNOT BE AVOIDED, TILT ANTENNA FULL UP OCCASIONALLY TO DETERMINE IF HAIL EXISTS IN OR IS FALLING FROM THE OVERHANG.

Figure 6.29 USAF Air Weather Service flight procedures near severe storms.

Flying in Severe Turbulence

Pilots of piston airplanes are concerned with turbulence in storms at lower levels, and with Clear Air Turbulence (CAT) in mountainous areas. Jet transport pilots are also concerned with CAT in jet-stream areas. While CAT is considered generally less severe than thunderstorm turbulence, both are highly dangerous, can come as a surprise, and have resulted in the loss of bombers, transports, and utility aircraft flying at all altitudes.

CLASSIFICATION OF TURBULENCE

Though adjectives describing turbulence are highly subjective and therefore imprecise, Table 6.6 is the generally accepted classification.

Low-Level Turbulence This turbulence may be considered random eddies in the air, caused by convection from ground heating, from wind over rough terrain, and from the wake of large aircraft. The Boeing 747 and the Air Force C-5 are aircraft that create extremely strong and long-lived wing-tip vortices. These extend in long parallel rolls along and below the aircraft's flight path and present severe hazards to other aircraft. A cross wind is very helpful in blowing the wake of a large aircraft to one side of the approach and landing path, or to one side of the takeoff runway. With no wind, wake turbulence, either prop or jet wash, can be very persistent and treacherous.

The least low-level turbulence occurs in the early morning, in stratus cloud conditions, and in light winds.

Clear Air Turbulence CAT is the turbulence in clear air, usually associated with high altitude, that can produce a violent "chop" or washboard-like effect. It is frequently a surprise. Remote thunderstorms and dry convection can contribute to its presence. It is patchy and transitory; these patches average 2000 ft deep, 20 mi wide and 50 mi long; they are elongated in the direction of the wind, and are difficult to locate.

CAT is likely near mountain waves (Figure 6.30) and jet streams. The intensity of mountain-wave CAT will vary directly with wind speed across a mountainous area. The most intense CAT is found in a strong jet stream oriented perpendicular to a mountain ridge; this produces a very strong mountain wave. Most frequently, it is found at 30,000 ft in winter and 34,000 ft in summer, whether in relation to mountain waves or jet-stream wind shear. CAT is a winter hazard, with three or four times more occurrences in winter than in summer, and more than twice as many occurrences with a cirrus overcast than with a broken condition.

TABLE 6.6
Classification of Turbulence

DEFINITION: ALTHOUGH AIRCRAFT REACTIONS TO A GIVEN TURBULENCE CONDITION VARY WITH AIR SPEED, WING LOADING, ATTITUDE, PILOTS EXPERIENCE AND ABILITY, ETC., THE DESIGN CRITERIA OF ALL TRANSPORT, NORMAL, UTILITY, AND ACROBATIC CATEGORY AIRCRAFT REQUIRE ESSENTIALLY IDENTICAL LIMIT GUST LOADS, EXPRESSED IN TERMS OF POSITIVE AND NEGATIVE ROUGH AIR GUSTS.

THE CLASSIFICATION OF TURBULENCE IS BASED UPON AIR MOVEMENT ALONE, NOT UPON AIRCRAFT SIZE OR TYPE.

CLASS OF TURBULENCE	TYPICALLY FOUND IN ASSOCIATION WITH THESE CONDITIONS	EFFECT
EXTREME (Gusts ± 50 fps)[1]	RARELY ENCOUNTERED. USUALLY CONFINED TO THE STRONGEST FORMS OF CONVECTION AND WIND SHEAR. +50 KT. IN OR NEAR THE ROTOR EFFECT OF A STRONG MOUNTAIN WAVE. IN SEVERE THUNDERSTORMS (LARGE HAIL 3/4", ALMOST CONTINUOUS LIGHTING, ETC.) USUALLY IN SQUALL LINES RATHER THAN ISOLATED THUNDERSTORMS.	AIRCRAFT IS VIOLENTLY TOSSED ABOUT AND IS PRACTICALLY IMPOSSIBLE TO CONTROL. MAY CAUSE STRUCTURAL DAMAGE.
SEVERE (Gusts ± 35–50 fps)[1]	IN ASSOCIATION WITH EXTREME TURBULENCE. + 50 KT. FOUND UP TO 150 MILES LEEWARD OF THE RIDGE. 25 TO 50 KT. FOUND UP TO 50 MILES LEEWARD OF THE RIDGE, FROM RIDGE LEVEL UP TO SEVERAL THOUSAND FEET ABOVE. IN AND NEAR MATURE THUNDERSTORMS AND OCCASIONALLY IN TOWERING CUMULIFORM CLOUDS. NEAR JET STREAMS.	AIRCRAFT MAY BE MOMENTARILY OUT OF CONTROL. OCCUPANTS ARE THROWN VIOLENTLY AGAINST THE BELT AND BACK INTO THE SEAT. UNSECURED OBJECTS ARE TOSSED ABOUT.
MODERATE (Gusts ± 20–35 fps)[1]	IN ASSOCIATION WITH EXTREME AND SEVERE TURBULENCE. + 50 KT. FOUND AS MUCH AS 300 MILES LEEWARD OF THE RIDGE. 25 TO 50 KT. FOUND AS FAR AS 150 MILES LEEWARD OF THE RIDGE. IN, NEAR AND ABOVE THUNDERSTORMS AND IN TOWERING CUMULUS. NEAR JET STREAMS, IN UPPER TROUGH, COLD LOW, AND FRONT ALOFT SITUATIONS. AT LOW ALTITUDE (USUALLY BELOW 5000 FT.) WHEN SURFACE WIND EXCEEDS 25 KNOTS, WITH STRONG THERMALS, AND COLD AIR ADVECTION.	OCCUPANTS REQUIRE SEAT BELTS AND OCCASIONALLY ARE THROWN AGAINST THE BELT. UNSECURED OBJECTS MOVE ABOUT.
LIGHT (Gusts ± 5–20 fps)[1]	IN MOUNTAIN AREAS EVEN WITH LIGHT WINDS. IN AND NEAR CUMULUS CLOUDS. AT LOW ALTITUDES WHEN WINDS ARE NEAR 15 KNOTS OR WHERE AIR IS COLDER THAN UNDERLYING SURFACE.	OCCUPANTS MAY BE REQUIRED TO USE SEAT BELTS, BUT OBJECTS IN THE AIRCRAFT REMAIN AT REST.

[1] Furnished by the editor.

U.S. Weather Bureau

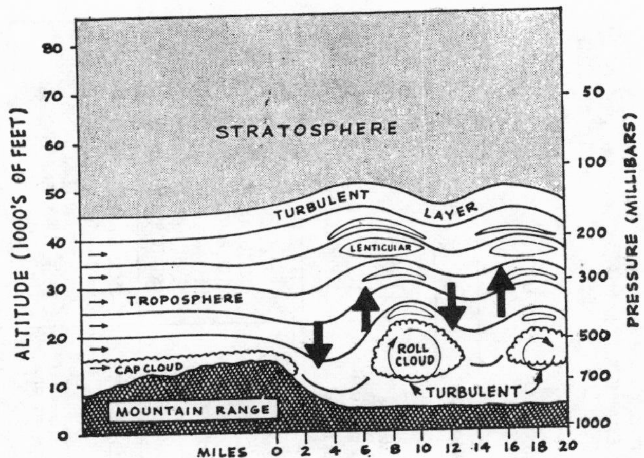

Figure 6.30 Mountain-wave turbulence. *(Courtesy of U.S. Air Force, Aerospace Safety.)*

Remember that mountain waves and their turbulence are found not only in high mountains and high-alittude flying. They occur downwind of *any* obstacle, including an isolated hill a few hundred feet high. The stronger the wind, the larger the effect, and while there are a variety of other meteorological conditions which affect the strength of the wave and its turbulence, this is a good rule of thumb: *If the wind at the altitude of the top of the obstacle is 20 knots or more, there will be a noticeable wave turbulence.* This turbulence will be greatest in the rotor zone downwind from the obstacle, as shown in Figure 6.30, and will be at a maximum at about the same altitude as the top of the obstacle.

Avoid flying downwind of peaks at about their altitude. This point of maximum turbulence will be at the same place no matter what the wind speed. The rotor zone gets larger in diameter as the wind speed increases, and more severe turbulence will be encountered, but it does not change position. In extreme cases it can reach the ground. This will be indicated by blowing dust clouds.

The rotor zone will be indicated by a roll cloud looking like wispy cumulus if there is moisture in the air, and this can be used to help avoid it. However, waves can be just as strong when the air is very dry, with no roll clouds or lenticular clouds to mark their position.

You can avoid wave turbulence by keeping in mind the picture in Figure 6.30 and adjusting your flight path to avoid the turbulent areas. Fly well above or below the altitude of the obstacle, or if this is not possible, turn upwind or downwind to get out of the turbulent zone. The rising or descending air between the rotor zones is usually very smooth.

FLIGHT PROCEDURES IN SEVERE TURBULENCE

Straight-Wing Aircraft The most important principle is to fly *attitude.* Allow the altitude and airspeed to deviate within reasonable limits, correcting with small or moderate attitude changes. Slow the aircraft to its best penetration speed, which is usually 40% to 60% above stalling speed for the gross weight at the time. Slow to desired speed before entering the turbulence if possible, and in piston aircraft use a higher RPM than normal cruise to provide power flexibility in the event of strong down gusts of long duration. Because of the relatively low aircraft speed, up or down gusts may be felt for a relatively long period of time, which could result in undesirable changes in altitude. *Don't "chase" the performance instruments.*

It is generally best to fly manually, particularly the elevators, and do not try to maintain attitude by trimming. Be sure the "altitude hold" function of the autopilot is OFF. The autopilot corrects attitude and holds altitude with the trim tabs. In turbulence, the autopilot can establish excessive tail loads and severe out-of-trim conditions for level flight.

High-Performance Swept-Wing Aircraft There are two general concerns: imposing excessive structural loads, and allowing the aircraft to get into undesirable extremes of attitude. It has long been generally accepted that a rough airspeed limit slower than cruising is less likely to result in structural damage. Experience indicates, however, that structural damage has not occurred unless there has been a severe change in attitude and a subsequent combination of stresses resulting from both the recovery maneuver and the severe turbulence.

Flexible wings and high wing loadings, considered with the effect of strong, frequent, longitudinal, lateral, and vertical gusts, all of which affect the angle of attack of the wing, make the importance of severe maneuvers much more significant.

In large swept-wing aircraft, it is now considered essential to penetrate turbulence at higher than cruise speeds, because the aircraft at low speed is closer to the stall buffet and high drag, tempting the pilot to make undesirable thrust changes; trim changes due to thrust changes at low speed are greater, compounding control problems; and the airplane can be laterally and directionally upset at low speeds in severe turbulence. In these aircraft, higher speeds are now specified, and pilots should fly to the high rather than the low side of the target speed. Refer primarily to the specific speeds prescribed in the operating instructions for the specific aircraft.

Attitude is all important, but it is better to do nothing than to attempt control attitude too rigidly, exceeding moderate control inputs.

Control pitch solely with the elevator, *never* with trim. As a general rule, do not change thrust. It is much better to accept large variations in altitude.

Disengage the autopilot to avoid excessive out-of-trim conditions. If equipped with a yaw damper, keep it engaged. Do not "chase" performance instruments.

THUNDERSTORM PENETRATION

While the principal problem in thunderstorms is severe turbulence, the following items are also essential:

Anti-Icing Be sure this equipment is full ON.

Seat Belts and Loose Items Be sure all are are secured.

Cockpit Lights Turn them high to avoid blindness by lightning contrast.

Power Set at whatever is desired before entry. Then use this as a basic value. Higher rpm provides power flexibility in piston aircraft, and reduces the rate of prop ice accretion.

Gear and Flaps. Do not extend them. They serve only to make the airplane less efficient aerodynamically.

Turns Avoid turns if possible. Then make them shallow.

Expect the experience to be an upsetting one with many surprises. Have yourself and your airplane prepared as far in advance as possible.

Icing

This hazard has long been most dreaded, particularly in slower aircraft flying at lower and intermediate levels. Icing hazards dictate constant alertness and substantial respect at all times, and in all aircraft. *Structural* ice forms externally and reduces aerodynamic efficiency; ½ in. of ice on some airfoils can reduce lift by 50%. Ice can also completely mask outside vision, reduce effectiveness, and limit operation of gear, flaps, and brakes, disrupt the pitot-static system, and destroy radio communication.

Internally, ice forms in jet intakes and carburetors, seriously restricting airflow, or accumulating, then breaking off and damaging turbine blades.

RESULTS OF ICE ACCRETION ON AIRCRAFT STRUCTURES

The presence of ice on an airfoil disrupts the smooth flow of air over the airfoil and thus decreases lift and increases drag, with a resulting increase of the aircraft's stalling speed. Ice on the propeller results in a loss of thrust. The addition of ice to the various structural parts of the aircraft results in vibration, causing added stress on these parts. This is especially true in the case of the propeller, which is very delicately balanced. Even a very small amount of ice, if not distributed evenly, can cause great stress on the propeller and engine mounts. The danger of added weight is not too great under ordinary circumstances, if too much of the lift and thrust are not simultaneously lost. Weight does become an important factor, however, in critically loaded aircraft.

FACTORS NECESSARY FOR ICE FORMATION

Free-air temperatures of freezing or lower are necessary for the formation of ice on an aircraft in flight, although observations have shown that ice may form on a static object when the free-air temperature is as high as +4°C, as a result of evaporational and adiabatic cooling. When an aircraft is in flight, the heating from skin friction and the impact of water droplets cause the temperature of the skin to rise. For most purposes, the heating and cooling effects cancel each other; thus, structural ice can be considered possible at 0°C or below.

At temperatures less than about −2°C or −4°C, the frequency of ice formation decreases gradually with lowering temperature, and the most severe icing is encountered generally between 0°C and −15°C; however, under unusual circumstances dangerous icing conditions have been encountered at temperatures less than −15°C.

The free-air thermometer is not too accurate and in some aircraft, it has been mounted improperly. A record, therefore, should be kept of the error in this instrument (and the pilot should be aware of this error), or else the instrument should be calibrated correctly.

In addition to freezing temperatures, the second factor necessary for structural ice formation is the presence of liquid moisture visible to the naked eye.

FORMS OF VISIBLE LIQUID MOISTURE

Clouds are the most common form of visible liquid moisture; however, not all clouds at temperatures below freezing give rise to ice formation. The pilot does not have any way of knowing which clouds will present an icing situation, but he must be aware that the possibility exists if the temperature is below 0°C.

Freezing rain may be encountered in otherwise clear air below a cloud deck. When warm moist air is forced to rise over a colder air mass, a frontal inversion will exist. Below this inversion, icing dangers are frequently encountered. In being forced aloft, the air may be sufficiently cooled to produce saturation and precipitation. The raindrops falling into the cold air may freeze upon contact with the aircraft if the temperature is at freezing or below. Freezing rain is probably the most dangerous form of ice because it can build to great proportions in a matter of minutes and is extremely hard to break loose.

TYPES OF STRUCTURAL ICE

The type of ice that will form on any moving structure usually depends on four factors:

1. The free-air temperature.
2. The skin temperature of the structure.
3. The surface characteristics of the structure (configuration, roughness, etc.)
4. The size of water droplets.

Clear Ice (Glaze) Clear or glaze ice is considered to be the most serious of the various forms of structural ice. It is most often encountered in regions of large, supercooled (liquid at below-freezing temperatures) water droplets or in an area of freezing rain. This condition most often presents itself over mountainous terrain and in regions of unstable weather conditions, in and below cumuliform clouds (Figure 6.31). Clear ice is dangerous because of the great amount of freezing water available and the freezing high rate of accretion—in addition to this, it is very tenacious. Moreover, in many instances water droplets do not freeze immediately upon impact, thereby causing airfoil deformation as clear icing occurs.

Figure 6.31 Icing over mountains. *(Courtesy of U.S. Air Force.)*

Rime Ice Rime ice is generally encountered in stratiform clouds, that is, stable weather conditions. The small water droplets of a stratus cloud freeze immediately upon impact with the aircraft surface. Rime ice builds up slowly by comparison to clear ice. The greatest resultant danger is the added drag caused by the very rough ice surface created. Rime ice is relatively easy to break loose by conventional methods. It should be realized that the various icing forms and attendant hazards may often occur in any and all combinations if the weather situation allows. For instance, ice resulting from freezing drizzle is usually a combination of rime and clear ice.

Frost Frost is a hazard very often underestimated. Frost may form on the ground or in the air. On the ground, frost is likely to form during the night when surface temperatures are below freezing. Frost forms in clear air by sublimation (change of state directly from gas or vapor to solid ice) when the moist air comes into contact with a very cold surface.

Frost may form in flight when descending into warmer (but still freezing) more moist air, or when flying from a very cold air mass to a warmer air mass. Frost causes added drag and offers a very real hazard at lower, critical air speeds. For this reason, the aircraft should be checked thoroughly and frost should be removed prior to takeoff. *Any* frost is too much frost. It *must* be removed before takeoff. Another frost hazard is the restriction to visibility caused by frost on windshield surfaces.

ANTI-ICING AND DEICING AIDS

An anti-icer is an item of equipment which prevents the formation of ice, and a deicer is an item of equipment which eliminates ice after it has already formed. Anti-icing and deicing equipment can be divided into three general classes:

1. *Mechanical* (deicing boots which are used on wings, tail assembly, and radio mast).
2. *Chemical* (anti-icing fluid and paste). Anti-icing paste is used on propellers and anti-icing fluid is used on the propeller, windshield, carburetor, and jet engine accessory section.
3. *Thermal* (electrical heat and exhaust or compressor heat). Electrical heat is used on the Pitot tube, electrical wingboot, and wing-tip tanks. Exhaust or compressor heat is used on the wings and tail assembly, windshield, intake air, canopy, and carburetor.

Anti-icers should be used before or immediately upon entering an icing zone and operated continuously until the aircraft is out of the icing zone.

Deicing boots should be used intermittently and only after an appreciable thickness of ice has accumulated upon the boot. Deicing boots are most useful in eliminating rime ice, but are not so reliable in removing clear ice. They should not be used during takeoff or landing.

The "hot-wing" or exhaust-heated wing may be considered as either an anti-icer or deicer, depending upon the time at which the unit is put into operation. It is usually most effective as an anti-icer.

FACTORS INFLUENCING THE RATE OF DEPOSIT OF ICE ON AIRCRAFT

The concentration of liquid water is a definite factor determining the rate of deposit; the more liquid available, the more pronounced and rapid the deposit.

Diameter of the Droplets of Water When a wing moves through the air, the air is deflected at the leading edge. If water droplets are present in the air, they tend to move with the airstream. The smaller the drops, the greater their tendency to follow the airstream; and the larger the drops, the more they resist this deflecting influence. Therefore, the large drops (small deflection) are collected more easily than the small drops (large deflection).

Airspeed Airspeed is a factor to be considered because, as airspeed is increased, the rate of deposit is increased. However, at high subsonic speeds and above, the situation is reversed because skin friction at these speeds actually provides enough heat to melt structural ice. At true airspeeds of above 575 knots, it is expected that structural ice will cease to be a problem.

The critical airspeed of frictional heating for ice removal will vary with aircraft (type, configuration, surface characteristics, etc.) and outside air temperature. A pilot who finds a safe airspeed for ice removal should expect that a higher airspeed would be necessary at lower temperatures.

Other Factors Research has added another group of factors that affect the structural icing rate of an aircraft. The shape of the airfoil is important. The thinner the cross section of the airfoil, the less tendency there is for drops to bypass the surface under certain conditions. The smoothness of the airfoil surface also serves to affect the rate of icing. An airfoil that is physically or aerodynamically unclean presents a greater surface area to catch the freezing droplets. Another important factor is the temperature difference between the airfoil and the surrounding (ambient) air. The latter factor is not fully understood and is being investigated further.

PRECIPITATION ICE FORMS THAT MAY BE ENCOUNTERED

Hail Hail develops in highly turbulent thunderstorms. Water drops, which are carried upward by vertical currents, freeze into ice pellets, start falling, accumulate a ring of water, and are carried upward again; the newly added water freezes. A repetition of this process increases the size of the hailstone. Hail is a warm-weather phenomenon and can be produced only by strong vertical currents. It does not lead to the formation of structural ice, but it can cause serious physical damage to the aircraft skin. Hail is frequently encountered in clear air, falling from the anvil cloud in front of a thunderstorm.

Sleet The initial stage of sleet formation results from water passing directly from the vapor to the solid state (sublimation), and forming very small grains or pellets of ice. This early stage of the formation process usually occurs at a considerable distance (approximately 8000 to 10,000 ft) above the freezing level. As these minute ice particles begin to fall from the cloud, they grow by impact with the supercooled water droplets contained in lower levels of the cloud. Variations in the height of the freezing level will result in variations of the altitude through which the sleet particles will fall before reaching this level. This results in varying sizes and textures of the sleet particles which may be encountered. Sleet is essentially a cold-weather phenomenon which results in the formation of structural ice only when it is mixed with supercooled liquid water. When sleet is encountered in flight, it is not wise to climb because frequently there are associated freezing rain areas above.

Snow When condensation takes place at temperatures below freezing, water vapor sometimes changes directly into minute ice crystals. These crystals grow to form a single snowflake. Dry snow does not lead to the formation of structural ice, but wet snow frequently does.

INDUCTION SYSTEM ICING

Carburetor ice constitutes a very real problem that results from a process quite different from that by which structural ice is formed. It can, in fact, be formed under conditions in which it is impossible for structural ice to be formed. If the humidity of the free air is high, carburetor ice may occur with temperatures as high as 21°C. The ice results from the marked cooling due to two separate processes which occur during carburetion: (1) vaporization of the gasoline and (2) the decrease of pressure in the venturi shaped throat of the carburetor. The greatest temperature drop is caused by the first of these.

Induction system ice may form in various places and on various parts of the induction system. It may form in the air scoop, in curves of the induction system, at the discharge nozzle, in the venturi, or on the throttle (butterfly) valve. One of the best indications of induction system icing is an otherwise unexplained loss of manifold pressure which disappears when carburetor heat is applied, if it is applied early enough after the indication is detected.

JET AIRCRAFT ICING PROBLEMS

Ice formation on airframes of turbojet aircraft differs from that on piston-engined aircraft, mainly because of the cleaner design and much higher speeds of jets.

As the operational speeds of aircraft increase, there is an associated increase in the importance of aerodynamic heating in the prevention of airframe icing. Airspeed and altitude are the primary factors to be considered in determining the amount of aerodynamic heating.

For a constant airspeed, the amount of aerodynamic heating decreases with increasing altitude. Also, at a constant altitude, the amount of aerodynamic heating is greater for higher airspeed. Aerodynamic heating also varies with position on the wing; it is greatest on the wing's leading edge and decreases to a minimum just behind the wing shoulder or mid-chord. For this reason, it is quite possible for an aircraft to experience *runback-icing* on the wing at slightly higher temperatures and speeds than permit icing on the leading edge.

It is not always true that the high speeds and altitudes which characterize turbojet performance keep them out of icing conditions.

When operating above 30,000 ft, aircraft are not likely to encounter icing. However, during operations at lower altitudes, jet aircraft may experience icing weather while climbing, cruising, descending, or making final approach. The amount of ice accretion will depend upon the attitude and true airspeed when in an icing situation.

JET-ENGINE ICING

Because any surface which is subjected to the direct flow of air may collect ice, jet engines experience icing both externally and internally. Inlet lips, accessory housing domes, islands and island fairings, compressor inlet screens, inlet guide vanes, and compressor blading are all vulnerable. Other surfaces—such as duct-splitter plates and openings for boundary-layer bleed-off and accessory cooling purposes—may experience icing, though not directly in the air stream.

Compressor-inlet screens, once a considerable hazard, are now retractable, removable, or heated both before takeoff and during flight in most jet aircraft. The inlet guide vanes of an axial-flow jet engine are also critical icing components. When the inlet screen has been removed, the centrifugal flow-type engine is, by contrast, relatively unsusceptible to icing. Rear screens of centrifugal type engines are not susceptible to icing because of their proximity to warm portions of the engine.

Ice accumulation decreases the performance efficiency of turbojet engines. As ice accumulates, there is a reduction in the total pressure at the compressor inlet which results in reduced airflow, reduced thrust, and an increase in fuel consumption. Although the tail-pipe temperature may rise when airflow decreases due to ice accumulation, it is unwise to depend upon tail-pipe temperature rise as an indication of icing in turbojet engines.

While damage due to icing in centrifugal flow-type engines is unknown, it may occur in axial flow types. Structural damage does result from the shedding of large ice accumulations from components ahead of the compressor inlet when no screen is used. Small pieces will pass harmlessly through the engine but a large piece of ice may lodge in the space between rotor and stator blade stages or may strike a rotor blade and be deflected into the guide vanes or stator blades, causing damage. Ice formed in the compressor during outside parking or storage of an aircraft may result in damage if the ice is not removed before attempting to start.

Prolonged operation of jet engines in supercooled fog (fog composed of water droplets at below-freezing temperatures) can result in intake icing with possibly hazardous consequences.

Although not directly associated with existing atmospheric conditions other than low temperatures, fuel-screen icing may occur in turbojet engines. Jet fuel can contain a large amount of water. When supercooled, the water will form ice on the fuel screen as the fuel passes through it. Ice may occur even in relatively dry weather if the jet fuel has a high water content.

Icing problems in the axial flow (induction icing) are being met by direct heating of the critical components of the engine inlet. The general practice for jet-engine anti-icing is:

1. Use of retractable screens which can be retracted before icing conditions are encountered.
2. Use of hollow-heated vanes utilizing heated compressor discharge air or combustion chamber hot gas as the heat transfer medium.
3. Use of hollow-heated construction similar to guide vanes or the use of electrical surface heating.
4. Use of double-wall construction with hot air, hot gas, hot oil between the walls, or use of electrical surface heating.

Although heating the engine air inlet will overcome icing, it does cause some loss of thrust, and can present carbon monoxide problems when engines are used as a source of pressurized air.

The most efficient and successful method of wing anti-icing is the thermal system of hot air heating the wing with a chordwise flow of heat. This system prevents ice by completely evaporating water droplets by the heating of the leading edges back to about 15% of the chord.

The heat is obtained by use of compressor bleed, air taken off the last compressor stage which has the necessary operating heat of 121°C to 260°C (250°F to 500°F), and pressure of from 20 to 100 psi. This air is channeled through ducts to the internal leading edge and flows back inside the wing to dissipate out the trailing edge.

Loss of power thrust during the thermal heating operations is approximately 8%, with a corresponding percentage of increase of specific fuel consumption. Also there is an increase in tail-pipe temperature, due to the extra fuel used and the loss of compressed air which is going into the wings.

POLAR ICING REPORTS

A summary of 14,843 pilot reports indicates the following conditions exist in operations north of 60° north latitude at medium and low altitude:

1. Only 1409 pilot reports of the total of 14,843 mentioned icing of any type.
2. The month of maximum occurrence of severe icing was December.
3. The month of maximum total of cases of all types of icing was February.
4. The month of least icing was September.
5. Of all types of icing reported, rime—especially moderate rime—was the predominant type found at lower temperatures in all seasons.
6. In winter the following types of ice were found at the temperatures indicated:

Rime ice	6°C to −40°C
Clear ice	5°C to −26°C
Mixed ice	2°C to −25°C

Max. no. cases at 36°C and 0°C

7. One case of severe rime was reported at a temperature of −40°C. (Since this summary was made, cases of severe icing have been reported at temperatures as low as −55°C.
8. In summer the following types of ice were found at temperatures indacted:

Rime ice	7°C to −23°C
Clear ice	5°C to −12°C
Mixed ice	2°C to −15°C

Max. no. cases at −6°C

9. Severe ice in summer was reported at temperatures from 0°C to −8°C.

10. Severe ice in the winter was reported at temperatures from 2°C to −8°C.
11. When observation was possible, icing appeared least at a temperature of −11°C. (Greatest difference in vapor pressures over water and ice occurs near −11°C.)

Light icing was classified as an accretion of a trace to 0.2 in. per 5 min, moderate icing as an ice build-up of 0.2 to 1.5 in. in 5 min. Severe icing was reported where the rate of accretion was greater than 1.5 in. per 5 min.

The temperatures above are free-air temperatures as reported by standard aircraft instruments. The flight altitudes ranged from 7000 ft to 12,000 ft, and the reports were for the Alaskan Region.

WEATHER STATION AIDS FOR DETERMINATION OF ICING REGIONS

Whenever a pilot plans a flight, he should utilize the weather charts and other facilities, including the knowledge of the qualified forecaster on duty, to aid in anticipating possible icing regions. Some of these facilities are listed and explained below.

Weather Maps The various surface and constant-pressure weather maps indicate the positions of fronts, thus indirectly marking regions of possible aircraft icing. For example, the region of the cloud system of any warm front (Figure 6.18) presents a potentially dangerous icing situation. This region may extend over a great area, vertically and horizontally, and severe icing conditions may be present at any point in it. In the smooth or stratiform clouds, icing tends to be predominantly rime in character.

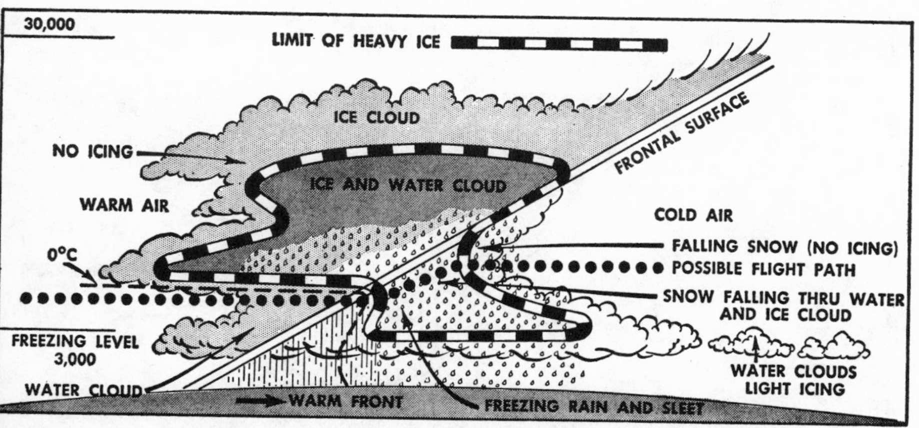

Figure 6.32 Icing under a warm front. *(Courtesy of U.S. Air Force.)*

In cold fronts, prefrontal squall lines, and air-mass thunderstorms, clear ice usually is formed as a result of the turbulence and the presence of large water droplets (Figure 6.33).

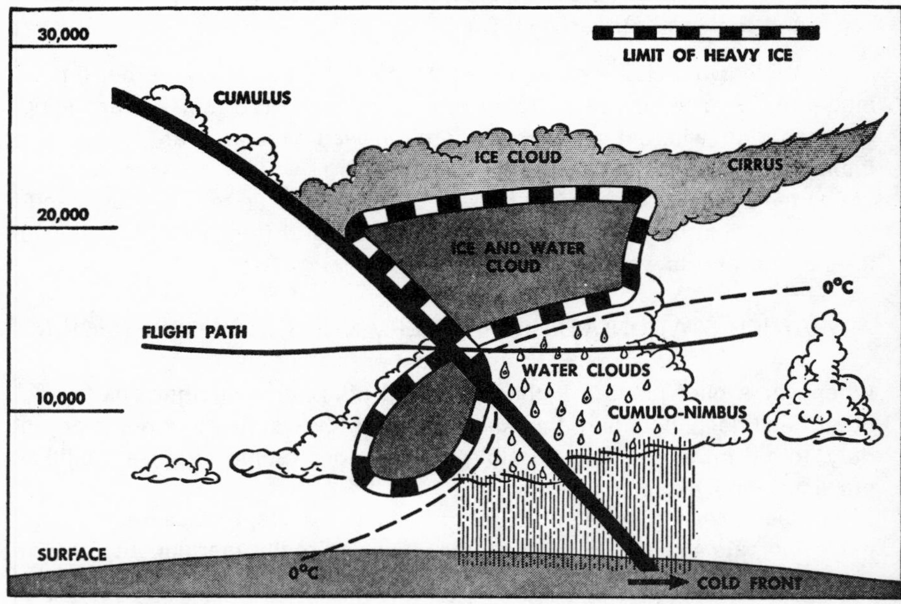

Figure 6.33 Icing zones along a cold front. *(Courtesy of U.S. Air Force.)*

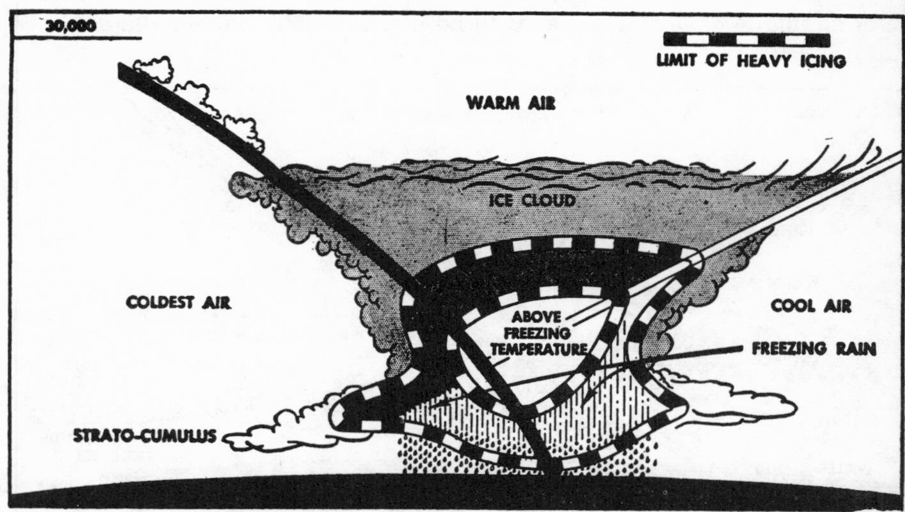

Figure 6.34 Icing zones along an occluded front. *(Courtesy of U.S. Air Force.)*

Occluded fronts (Figure 6.34) present an icing hazard which may be considered to be about the same as in a warm front—particularly in northern regions such as Alaska and the North Atlantic. The extensive cloud cover may necessitate considerable flying time in clouds, with the type, severity, and zones of icing determined by considering each case separately.

AIR WEATHER SERVICE AND NATIONAL WEATHER SERVICE WRITTEN FORECASTS

Both types of weather forecasts give information on the height of the freezing level and regions in which the pilot can expect ice formation. Since it is often possible to fly in clouds at temperatures below freezing and not pick up any ice, the forecast may seem to be in error. These forecasts, then, simply indicate regions where conditions are favorable for ice formation. The pilot should be prepared to encounter ice and consider himself fortunate if he does not encounter it.

TELETYPE WEATHER REPORTS

Pilot reports (PIREPS) of icing will often be included in teletype weather reports—PIREPS collection or individual special reports—and may be used as a source of much useful preflight planning information by other pilots.

The pilot planning a flight should note areas where the free-air temperatures are favorable to ice formation and where clouds are expected.

7

Medical Aspects of Flight*

Since earliest times man has been involved in a constant struggle to adapt to his environment.

The most significant environmental conditions in aviation, other than the aircraft itself, are the extreme atmospheric pressures and temperatures as altitude increases. While these naturally occurring phenomena of the atmosphere have, of course, remained constant, their effects have become more pronounced as aircraft have reached greater heights.

In the aircraft itself the flyer is surrounded by an increasingly complicated man-made environment within the greater natural one of the air. Because of increased performance and operational complexity of modern aircraft, man's problems in flight are increasing every year. Despite the ability of the human body to make some physiological adjustment for all types of environmental changes, aircraft have tended to "outgrow" the aircrew. The performance of powerful, present-day aircraft exceeds that of relatively frail man unless he is supported by elaborate equipment such

*By Col. Hugh W. Randel, USAF, MC, Deputy Director, Space Medicine, NASA.

as oxygen masks, pressurized cabins, anti-*g* suits, ejectable seats, and at very high altitudes, pressure suits. The problem of adapting the aircrew to the demanding environment of a high-performance aircraft is a field of study of aviation medicine. How well this adaptation is made depends upon proper selection of flying trainees, the adequacy of their equipment, and how well they are trained to understand and use it. To perform effectively within his environment the flyer must be fully aware of his own physiological and psychological limitations and the functioning and use of his equipment. To this end, this chapter will discuss some of the more important medical aspects of flight.

Hypoxia

Oxygen, essential to human life, is even more critical than food or water. Man literally lives from one breath to the next in that death rapidly occurs if he is not constantly supplied with oxygen by the process of respiration. Complete lack of oxygen, known as *anoxia,* is promptly fatal. It is seen in such conditions as suffocation, drowning, strangulation, and certain types of poisoning. Much more common, however, is partial lack of oxygen, which is termed *hypoxia.* The threat of hypoxia is a serious and constant hazard at high altitude. The early symptoms are insidious, and the victim may actually have a feeling of well-being even as more serious effects are developing. Because its onset is without pain or other warning symptoms, hypoxia is the most important physiological hazard of high-altitude flying. During World War II, for the first time large numbers of aircraft operated routinely at altitudes of 15,000 to 30,000 ft. Through military necessity aircrews were hurriedly indoctrinated in the use of their oxygen equipment, and cases of hypoxia occurring during the stress of combat became fairly common. The following account describes one such episode involving five members of a bomber crew.

While on a combat mission early in February 1944, five members of a combat crew were victims of hypoxia. At 1010, at an altitude of 27,000 ft, prior to reaching the target, the ball turret gunner, beginning to feel that he was not getting enough oxygen, discovered that one of the fittings on the quick-disconnect coupling had pulled loose from the hose. He attempted to put it back together but, becoming more and more nervous, failed and lost consciousness.

The navigator called all stations on the interphone at 1015 to make an oxygen check. When the ball turret gunner failed to answer, the navigator ordered the left waist gunner to check up on the ball turret gunner. The left waist gunner disconnected his own oxygen supply hose from the main line, and connected up with an A-4 special walk-around bottle. As he reached the ball turret, he felt that he was not getting enough oxygen, so he returned to his own station in order to reconnect his hose to the main outlet in the oxygen system.

When the radio man saw this difficulty, he tossed the right waist gunner a D-2 cylinder for use as a walk-around bottle, and the right waist gunner disconnected his own oxygen supply from his station outlet, plugged into the D-2 cylinder, and went to the ball turret. Here he disconnected his own hose and tried to connect the walk-around bottle with the ball turret gunner's hose, but because of a faulty connection at the quick-disconnect junction, it did not work and the right waist gunner lost consciousness. The radio man, viewing this procedure, tried to help both unconscious men (the right waist gunner and the ball turret gunner) by walking down with his long hose remaining connected to his station outlet, but by doing so he stretched the hose, shutting off his oxygen supply, and lost consciousness.

The bombardier then picked up two A-4 walk-around bottles from the nose and started back through the bomb bay to help the crewmen. He was changing his oxygen hose from one bottle to the other in the bomb bay just as the ship was nearing the target, and the bomb-bay doors began to open. He dropped both walk-around bottles and ran toward the radio room where he lost consciousness.

As soon as the bombs were released over the target, the pilot dived the ship from 25,000 to 5000 ft, and the copilot, going back in the ship to try to assist the men suffering from hypoxia, gave artificial respiration and emergency oxygen to the ball turret gunner for approximately 20 min., or during the time the plane was descending to 5000 ft. All of the men regained consciousness after the plane began to lose altitude. Although it was impossible to obtain accurate time intervals from the men because of the number of persons unconscious and the high degree of excitement, it is believed that the ball turret gunner was unconscious for about 1 hr 10 min., about 40 to 45 min. of which was at 27,000 to 28,000 ft; the right waist gunner was unconscious for about 20 min. at 28,000 ft; the left waist gunner was not totally unconscious but was hypoxic for a period of about 15 min. at 28,000 ft; the radio operator was unconscious for approximately 15 min. at 28,000 ft; and the bombardier was unconscious for 10 min. at 28,000 ft.

Today both military and civil aircraft are equipped with pressurized cabins and oxygen breathing equipment to maintain sufficient oxygen pressure for the crew and passengers at any flight altitude attained thus far. If this equipment is maintained and used properly, the flyer is adequately protected against hypoxia. To insure that they appreciate the need for this equipment, aircrews must understand something of human physiology and how respiration takes place.

CHARACTERISTICS OF THE ATMOSPHERE

The air was described in Chapter 6 as a mixture of gases, nitrogen and oxygen being the principal components. Up to extremely high altitudes these two gases, with minute amounts of several others, are present in constant proportions. It can be seen in Table 7.1 that nitrogen constitutes nearly four-fifths and oxygen about one-fifth of the total volume of dry air. At sea level and for about 10,000 ft upward the 20% of oxygen in the air is adequate for human breathing because the total pressure of the air

TABLE 7.1
Components of the Air and Percentages at Sea Level

Nitrogen	77.14	Neon	.0012
Oxygen	20.69	Helium	.0004
Argon	.93	Water vapor	1.2
Carbon dioxide	.03	Hydrogen	.01

(and hence the partial pressure of oxygen) is relatively high. With increasing altitude, however, there is a corresponding decrease in atmospheric pressure, and as a consequence there is a much thinner concentration of oxygen at 30, 40, or 50,000 ft than at sea level. The pressure varies from 760 mm of mercury at sea level to about one-half this amount at 18,000 ft (379.4 mm of Hg) and less than one-eighth this amount at 50,000 ft. The second column in Table 7.2 illustrates the progressive decrease in pressure as altitude increases. One of Dalton's gas laws states that *the sum of the partial pressures of a mixture of gases (including water vapor) is equal to the absolute total pressure of the mixture.* Therefore, the atmospheric pressure at any altitude is the sum of the pressures of the various component gases. Since the atmosphere is 20% oxygen, the partial pressure of oxygen at sea level is 20% of the total atmospheric pressure, or 160 mm Hg as shown in Table Table 7.2. Thus at 50,000 ft the oxygen partial pressure is 20% of the total pressure at that altitude and amounts to only 18 mm Hg.

TABLE 7.2
Total Atmospheric Pressure and Oxygen Partial Pressure at Various Altitudes

Altitude (ft)	*Atmospheric Pressure (mm Hg)*	*O_2 Partial Pressure (mm Hg)*
Sea level	760	160
5,000	632	126
10,000	523	105
15,000	429	85
20,000	349	70
25,000	282	56
30,000	225	45
35,000	179	36
40,000	141	29
45,000	111	23
50,000	87	18

HOW MAN BREATHES

During the process of respiration, oxygen is extracted from the air which passes in and out of the lungs. That part of respiration during which there is muscular expansion of the chest is called the *active* phase. In this phase the volume of the chest is increased and air is inhaled to fill the lungs. Air is exhaled by relaxation of the chest muscles and diaphragm and this is known as the *passive* phase of respiration. With each breath, oxygen must be extracted from the inspired air and absorbed by the blood, and carbon dioxide must be given up by the blood to the lungs to be exhaled. Both of these exchanges are accomplished through the membranous walls of innumerable minute lungs sacs adjacent to tiny, equally thin-walled blood vessels. Pressure differences across these thin walls cause the required oxygen to pass in, and waste carbon dioxide to pass out—air in the lung sacs thereby losing its oxygen and gaining carbon dioxide.

Oxygen is carried to the tissues and carbon dioxide returned to the lungs by the red cells of the blood. Oxygen in the inspired air is under higher pressure than the oxygen in the blood, so it passes through the lung and blood vessel walls by diffusion. On the other hand, carbon-dioxide pressure in the venous blood in the lungs is greater than in the inspired air, so it diffuses in the opposite direction. Gaseous exchange between the blood and the lungs is thus accomplished by physical diffusion in accordance with basic gas laws whereby a gas diffuses from a region of higher partial pressure to a region of lower partial pressure. From this it is seen that the important requirement for the transfer of oxygen into the blood is *sufficient oxygen partial pressure in the air.* The partial pressure of oxygen in the air at sea level (160 mm Hg) is more than adequate to force oxygen out of the lungs and into the blood.

OXYGEN REQUIREMENTS AT ALTITUDE

As altitude increases above sea level, atmospheric pressure steadily decreases, so oxygen pressure decreases and the amount of oxygen available for absorption by the blood becomes proportionately less. For example (Table 7.2), at 20,000 ft, where atmospheric pressure is less than half its sea-level value, oxygen partial pressure is diminished accordingly, and only a small amount of oxygen passes from the lung air into the blood. It is important to remember that the atmosphere, regardless of altitude, contains 20% oxygen. Hypoxia is caused by the decrease in oxygen partial *pressure* rather than any decrease in the percentage of oxygen.

MANIFESTATIONS OF HYPOXIA

As hypoxia develops with increasing altitude, the blood carries decreasing amounts of oxygen to supply the body tissues. Because of its considerable adaptability, the body is able to compensate fairly well for this oxygen lack for the first several thousand feet of altitude. Going higher, mental and motor coordination deteriorate steadily until collapse occurs.

The most important feature to remember about hypoxia is that its onset is usually unnoticed by the affected individual. There is no pain or discomfort mental processes and judgment are quickly impaired and the individual has no insight into his deteriorating condition.

The lowest altitude at which hypoxia is of practical importance to the flyer is 5000 ft, at which level night vision is measurably diminished. Except for this effect, the mild hypoxia experienced up to 10,000 ft has little practical significance. Above 10,000 ft, however, the results of hypoxia rapidly become serious. These effects include loss of visual acuity, mental dullness, confusion, loss of judgment, failure of muscular coordination, and eventually unconsciousness. There is no pain or discomfort and there may even be a misleading sense of exhilaration.

With the onset of hypoxia, the impairment of vision appears to the victim to be due to diminishing light. This may be graphically demonstrated when an individual under mildly hypoxic conditions reads from a test card (Figure 7.1). As the hypoxia is relieved by the administration of oxygen, visual acuity improves dramatically. This effect is most noticeable under conditions of poor illumination. The reading card shown in Figure 7.1 becomes progressively indistinct as it is read downward because of the gradual darkening of the background which produces an effect of diminishing illumination. There is a marked increase in the number of lines that can be read immediately after the hypoxic reader is given oxygen. A handwriting test is also frequently used to demonstrate to aircrews the extent to which hypoxia produces mental confusion and loss of muscular coordination (Figure 7.2).

DURATION OF CONSCIOUSNESS

A convenient and practical way to evaluate the risk of hypoxia at any altitude is in terms of the average time of consciousness for subjects without oxygen, that is, the interval during which the subject can perform some purposeful activity such as handwriting, after being deprived of oxygen. Man's performance at different altitudes without oxygen has been studied by means of controlled experiments in low-pressure chambers wherein high-altitude flights are simulated (Figure 7.3). Under these hypoxic con-

HOW MUCH CAN YOU SEE WITHOUT OXYGEN?

The purpose of this chart is to demonstrate to you the effects on your vision of oxygen starvation at relatively low altitudes. You will read the chart first while breathing chamber air at altitude, and then while breathing 100% oxygen at the same altitude. Record in the proper place on the sheet given you the point on the chart at which it becomes impossible for you to read under each condition. Notice how much easier it is to read when you start taking oxygen. In reading this chart do not touch the print.

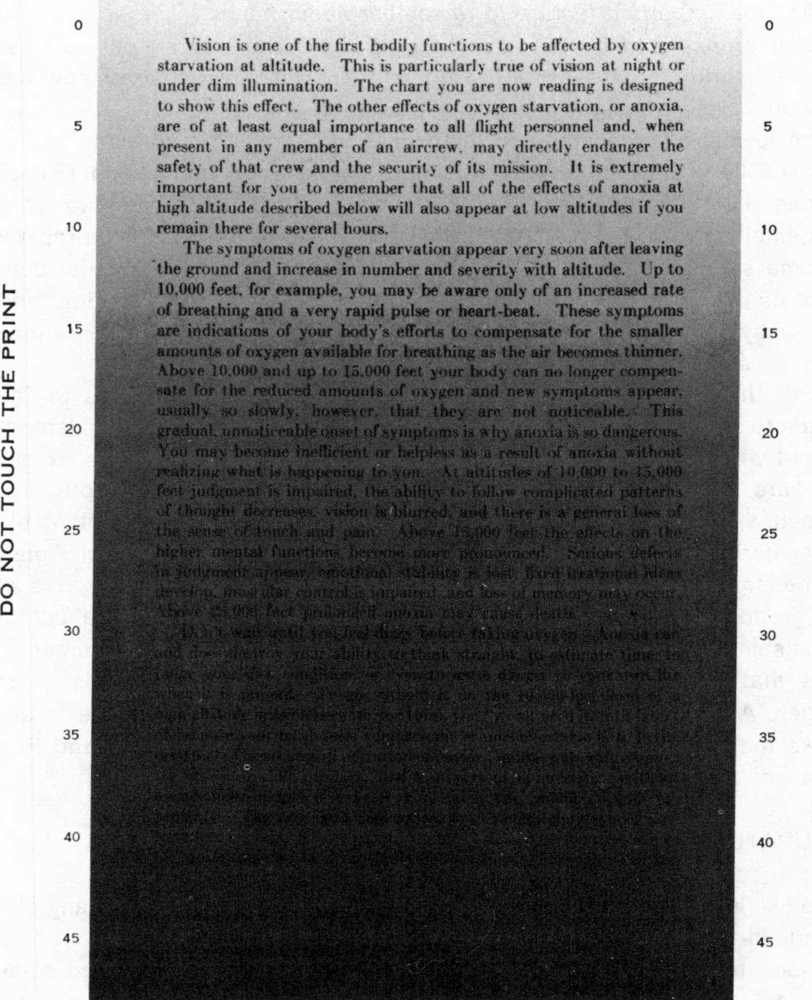

DO NOT TOUCH THE PRINT

Vision is one of the first bodily functions to be affected by oxygen starvation at altitude. This is particularly true of vision at night or under dim illumination. The chart you are now reading is designed to show this effect. The other effects of oxygen starvation, or anoxia, are of at least equal importance to all flight personnel and, when present in any member of an aircrew, may directly endanger the safety of that crew and the security of its mission. It is extremely important for you to remember that all of the effects of anoxia at high altitude described below will also appear at low altitudes if you remain there for several hours.

The symptoms of oxygen starvation appear very soon after leaving the ground and increase in number and severity with altitude. Up to 10,000 feet, for example, you may be aware only of an increased rate of breathing and a very rapid pulse or heart-beat. These symptoms are indications of your body's efforts to compensate for the smaller amounts of oxygen available for breathing as the air becomes thinner. Above 10,000 and up to 15,000 feet your body can no longer compensate for the reduced amounts of oxygen and new symptoms appear, usually so slowly, however, that they are not noticeable. This gradual, unnoticeable onset of symptoms is why anoxia is so dangerous. You may become inefficient or helpless as a result of anoxia without realizing what is happening to you. At altitudes of 10,000 to 15,000 feet judgment is impaired, the ability to follow complicated patterns of thought decreases, vision is blurred, and there is a general loss of the sense of touch and pain. Above 15,000 feet the effects on the higher mental functions become more pronounced. Serious defects in judgment appear, emotional stability is lost, fixed irrational ideas develop, muscular control is impaired, and loss of memory may occur. Above 25,000 feet prolonged anoxia may cause death.

DO NOT TOUCH THE PRINT

Figure 7.1 Hypoxia test card. *(Courtesy of Lighting Research Laboratory, General Electric Company, and Aeromedical Laboratory, Wright Air Development Center, USAFO.)*

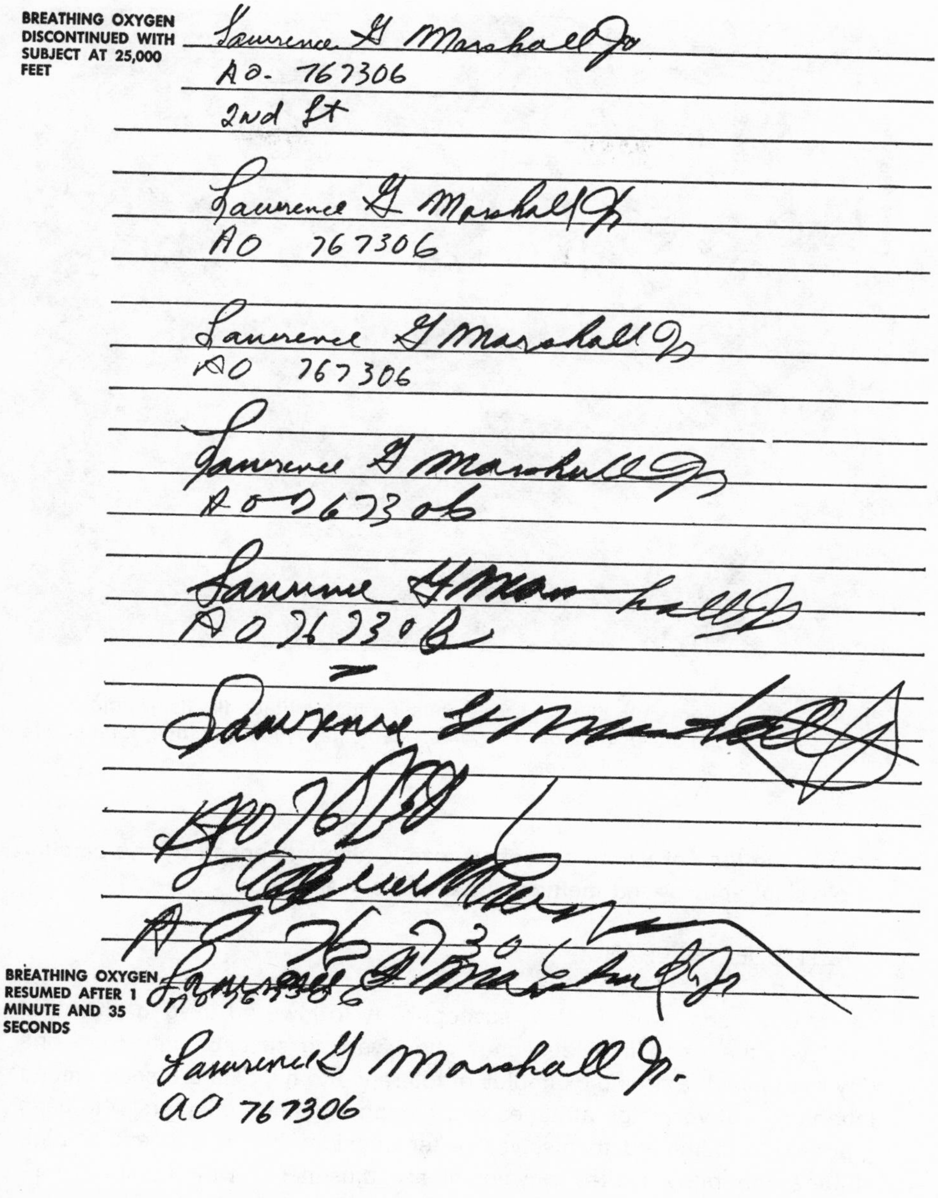

BREATHING OXYGEN DISCONTINUED WITH SUBJECT AT 25,000 FEET

BREATHING OXYGEN RESUMED AFTER 1 MINUTE AND 35 SECONDS

Figure 7.2 Effect of hypoxia on handwriting. At a simulated altitude of 25,000 ft in low-pressure chamber the subject's oxygen supply was disconnected for 1 min 35 sec while he continued to write his name and military serial number. The fourth signature shows beginning deterioration of writing and seventh is completely illegible. Oxygen was resumed just prior to the writing of the eighth signature.

Figure 7.3 Low-pressure chamber for simulating high-altitude flights. *(Photo taken at the USAF School of Aviation Medicine, Gunter Branch, Gunter Air Force Base, Alabama.)*

ditions, the time of useful consciousness is also influenced by the amount of physical activity and method of exposure (Table 7.3).

ALTITUDE TOLERANCE

Flyers differ somewhat in their susceptibility to lowered oxygen pressure, and even the same individual may show varying susceptibility from one day to the next. Extreme examples of tolerance to hypoxia are seen among inhabitants of very high altitudes and among mountain climbers who have gradually conditioned themselves. After considerable time spent at high altitude the body makes physiological adjustments which allow more effective use of the available oxygen. In Asia and South America entire communities are found at altitudes well above 10,000 ft. One of the highest permanent settlements in the world is a sulfur-mining community in Chile at an elevation of 17,500 ft. The miners and their families live there throughout the year, and the men go each day to work in the mine at 19,000 ft. In attempts to scale Mount Everest in the Himalayas, mountain climbers have spent periods of several days as high as 25,000 ft without oxygen. On the successful British expedition in 1953, Sir Edmund Hillary removed his oxygen mask on the summit of Everest at an altitude of 29,002 ft for 10 min. These examples show that under special conditions some men are capable of considerable adaptation to altitude.

TABLE 7.3
Time of Consciousness Under Various Conditions of Hypoxia and Physical Activity[a]

Altitude (ft)	*O_2 Rapidly Disconnected, Sitting Quietly*	*O_2 Rapidly Disconnected, Moderate Activity*	*Rapid Decompression, Sitting Quietly*
22,000	10 min	5 min	—
25,000	3 min	2 min	2 min
28,000	1½ min	1 min	1 min
30,000	1¼ min	¾ min	¾ min
35,000	¾ min	½ min	½ min
40,000	30 sec	18 sec	23 sec
65,000	12 sec	12 sec	12 sec

[a](Adapted from Air Force Manual 52-13).

The intensive physical training necessary to produce this high degree of physiological conditioning of aircrews has not been feasible. Although peak physical condition is highly desirable in all flyers, it still does not permit them to fly safely at high altitude without oxygen equipment. For practical and safe flying operations, 10,000 ft is the upper limit, above which some type of oxygen breathing equipment (or cabin pressurization) must be used.

PREVENTION OF HYPOXIA

The several devices used to prevent hypoxia in flight are all designed to increase the amount of oxygen absorbed by the blood in one of the following ways:

a. By increasing the percentage of oxygen in the inspired air (constant-flow or demand oxygen mask).

b. By increasing the pressure of oxygen in the inspired air (pressurized aircraft cabin).

c. By combinations of *a* and *b* (pressure breathing oxygen mask, high-altitude pressure suit).

As seen in Table 7.4, man may raise his physiological altitude "ceiling" in flight by using these different types of equipment. As altitude increases, the equipment required to give adequate protection becomes more complex.

TABLE 7.4
Oxygen Breathing Equipment Required for Various Altitudes

Altitude (ft)	*Atmospheric Pressure (mm Hg)*	*Required O_2 in Inspired Air (%)*	*Required O_2 Equipment*
Sea level	760	21	—
20,000	349	49	Demand system
25,000	282	62	Demand system
30,000	225	81	Demand system (safety pressure)
34,000	187	100	Demand system (safety pressure)
40,000	141	100	Pressure breathing (safety pressure)
42,000	128	100	Pressure breathing, 12 mm Hg
43,000	122	100	Pressure breathing, 18 mm Hg
45,000	111	100	Pressure breathing, 29 mm Hg
47,000	100	100	Pressure suit
50,000	87	100	Pressure suit
63,000 and above	47	100	Pressure suit

The Demand Oxygen System Up to an altitude of 34,000 ft adequate oxygen from the aircraft supply is provided by a demand-type mask, which supplies oxygen to the user only when he inhales. This is accomplished by means of a special valve which opens to deliver the mixture of oxygen and air when the user inhales. Expired air escapes through a flapper valve in the mask facepiece. With each altitude increase, a regulator automatically increases the percentage of oxygen in the breathing mixture until eventually, at 34,000 ft (Table 7.4), it becomes pure oxygen. In this way, during normal conditions, oxygen is made available as needed. For emergencies the regulator may be adjusted to deliver a constant flow of 100% oxygen at any time. Another function of the regulator is to control the pressure of oxygen as it flows from the aircraft supply. In conventional gaseous oxygen systems, oxygen is carried in cylinders at a pressure at 450 psi in low-pressure systems or 1800 psi in high-pressure systems and must be reduced to the pressure of the outside air before it reaches the mask. The protection afforded by the demand system is adequate, provided the mask is properly fitted to the face to prevent serious leaks. Even meticulous fitting of the mask does not completely eliminate leakage, but, up to 30,000 ft, this small amount is usually insignificant. Above this altitude, minute leaks around the mask-to-face seal become unduly hazardous. This type of equipment, which was developed during World War II, has been improved and is still in use for altitudes up to 40,000 ft (Figure 7.4).

The Pressure Breathing System Above 40,000 ft, breathing pure oxygen is no longer sufficient to maintain the flyer's normal state of alertness and reaction. To prevent hypoxia, oxygen in the mask must be at a pressure greater than that of the outside air so that the partial pressure of oxygen is raised. The breathing of oxygen at sufficiently increased pressures thus makes more oxygen actually available to the blood. In this way, man's physiological ceiling can be raised from 40,000 to 45,000 ft. Table 7.4

Figure 7.4 Demand oxygen mask (USAF type A-13A) and flying helmet (USAF type P-4A.)

shows the amount of breathing pressure required for altitudes of 40,000 to 45,000 ft. Breathing against pressure requires the subject to reverse his normal respiratory cycle in that expiration, normally the passive phase of the cycle, becomes an active phenomenon. Since oxygen is forced into the lungs by the breathing pressure, inspiration is entirely passive. Some practice is necessary to adapt to this breathing sequence. Most flyers readily learn this procedure and can breathe the pressure required to ascend to 42,000 ft for several hours. Pressures in excess of this are tiring if breathed for more than an hour. Because of the fatiguing effect and other more serious physiological limitations, 45,000 ft is the upper limit to which this system may be routinely used. In emergencies, for short periods only, pressure breathing may be used up to 50,000 ft.

For routine operations above 25,000 ft, a pressurized aircraft cabin is required. A high-altitude pressure suit must be worn above 50,000 ft. Regardless of the type of oxygen equipment used, it must be carefully fitted to the individual flyer. It is vitally important to check oxygen equipment for leaks and proper function prior to each flight.

Liquid Oxygen Systems Liquid oxygen, a blue transparent fluid produced by fractional distillation of liquid air, is now in extensive use. It is maintained in the liquid state by insulated double-walled containers which also serve to convert the liquid to gaseous oxygen for breathing. The required temperature of −297.4°F is maintained in these containers by the insulating effect of the near-perfect vacuum between their metal walls.

While the internal design of a liquid-oxygen system differs considerably from that of a conventional system, it is used in the same way. Because the volumetric ratio of liquid to gaseous oxygen at standard conditions is about 1 to 800, liquid-oxygen systems provide more oxygen with great savings of space and weight.

OXYGEN EQUIPMENT IN CIVIL AIRCRAFT

The jet airline passenger since 1958 flies routinely in pressurized aircraft at high altitudes formerly used only in military flying. At these altitudes, oxygen equipment must be immediately available to protect the crew and passengers should cabin pressure be lost. FAA regulations require that at least one of the pilots wear an oxygen mask in the operative condition at all times above 25,000 ft—except that this may be delayed until flight level 410 if each crew member has a quick-donning mask which can be secured and sealed in place with one hand within five seconds. For this purpose, airline crews wear or have access to lightweight masks in the "ready position" for quick donning in an emergency.

These masks, which may be individually fitted, provide respiratory support up to 45,000 ft with demand or pressure-demand oxygen. Passengers too must be protected against such emergencies by continuous-flow oxygen masks.

FAA regulations require that certificated aircraft flying above 25,000 ft be equipped with an oxygen dispensing unit for each passenger. For aircraft flying above 30,000 ft individual masks will be presented to the user automatically. In the latter case, if cabin-pressure altitude exceeds the 14,000-ft equivalent level for any reason, a barometric control causes automatic dispensing of simply designed masks from the overhead compartment. Constant flow of oxygen starts immediately when the passenger applies the mask to the face.

Although many small private and business aircraft now in use do not operate at extremes of altitude, it is often desirable for them to fly above 10,000 ft to get maximum performance and to take advantage of more favorable weather and traffic conditions. For these aircraft, diluter-demand or constant-flow oxygen equipment is available for crew and passengers as either installed or portable units. One type of portable unit with masks for pilot and passengers is shown in Figure 7.5.

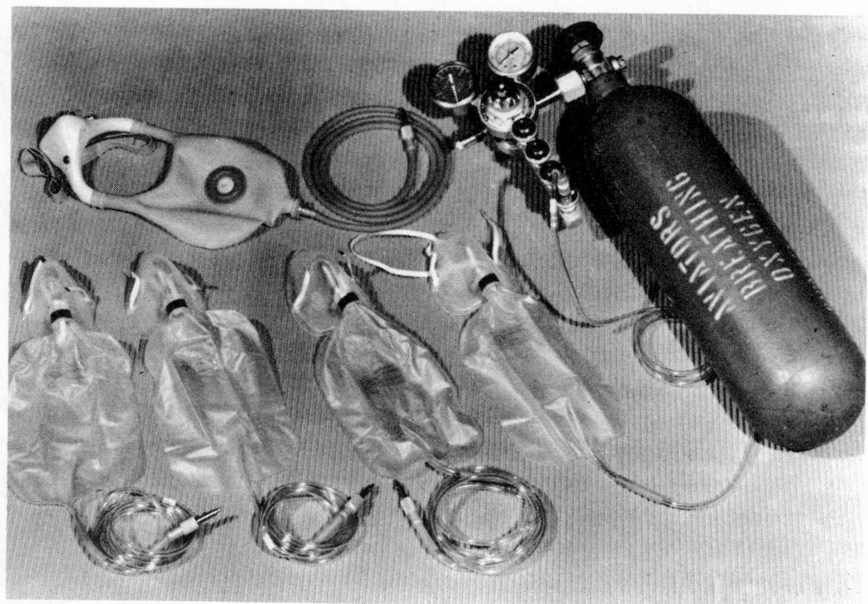

Figure 7.5 Portable oxygen unit for small private or business aircraft. The pilot's nasal-type mask pictured here is adequate for the altitudes flown. The passenger masks of very lightweight plastic are disposable and inexpensive. Adjusting the small regulator mounted on the oxygen container to the correct aircraft altitude insures the appropriate flow of oxygen to each mask.

Further amplification of oxygen requirements in civil aircraft may be found in Federal Aviation Regulations Part 25.1447 and Part 121.333.

Effects of Undissolved Body Gases

Although generally considered to be a mass of solids and liquids, the human body also includes a significant amount of gas, largely air and its component gases. Some of these are dissolved in the body fluids, as, for example, nitrogen, oxygen, and carbon dioxide in the blood. In addition, air is found as a free gas within the gastrointestinal tract, the middle ear, and the sinuses. These gases, dispersed throughout the body, react to variations in atmospheric pressure (resulting from altitude changes) according to well-known physical laws.

During changes in pressure, the behavior of free gas, such as the air in the body cavities, is determined by Boyle's law. This law states, that, *when the temperature remains constant, the volume of a gas varies inversely as the pressure.* This characteristic of a gas is readily demonstrated in a low-pressure chamber by observing a partially inflated balloon which gets larger in proportion to the decrease in pressure. Thus at 18,000 ft, where atmospheric pressure is one-half its sea-level value, gas volume is doubled. Table 7.5 indicates the approximate relative increase in dry gas volume at different altitudes:

TABLE 7.5
Increase of Volume of Dry Gas with Altitude

Altitude (ft)	*Number of Atmospheres of Pressure*	*Relative Gas Volume*
Sea level	1	1
18,000	½	2
28,000	⅓	3
33,000	¼	4
42,000	⅙	6
48,000	⅛	8

GASTROINTESTINAL GAS

The intestinal tract normally contains gas derived from swallowed air and from the action of the digestive process. The amount of this gas is variable among individuals, and from day to day in the same person. Like all other gases, it conforms to Boyle's law and so expands with ascent of the aircraft. Flyers are familiar with the sensation of abdominal bloating which is sometimes experienced during fast ascents to high altitude. Normally, this is not noticeable until an altitude of 15,000 to 20,000 ft is reached, but the onset of distress will be determined, to some extent, by the amount of gas and the rate of ascent. In 110 low-pressure chamber flights above 35,000 ft, severe abdominal discomfort was experienced in 5.5% of the subjects, moderate discomfort in 3.6% and slight discomfort in 19%. Usually the healthy flyer is able to expel enough of the expanded gas to relieve the condition. In larger aircraft where space permits, this may be helped by mild exercise.

Flyers should avoid gas-forming foods in meals taken before and during flight. Although certain foods such as beans, cabbage, and fresh bread are notorious in this respect, there is considerable individual variation from person to person. Any type of irritation within the gastrointestinal tract may produce discomfort which is not necessarily directly proportional to the amount of gas present. For this reason foods difficult to digest or those which are highly seasoned should be avoided.

BAROTITIS

Consistent with Boyle's law, air in the cavity of the middle ear expands and contracts with changes in atmospheric pressure. During altitude changes, if pressure in the ear is not readily equalized with the outside air pressure, inflammation, with pain and temporary deafness, is produced in the affected ear. This condition has been given the name of *barotitis* because of its frequent occurrence in persons who fly. It is one of the most common medical complications seen by flight surgeons and occurs in experienced aircrews as well as passengers.

In order to understand how barotitis develops it is necessary to have some knowledge of the anatomy of the ear and eustachian tube (Figure 7.6). Structurally, the organ of hearing and equilibrium is composed of three parts, an *outer ear,* a *middle ear,* and an *inner ear.* The outer ear includes the external cartilaginous portion and the *auditory canal.* The latter extends inward and terminates at the thin, membranous *eardrum.* The auditory canal, the middle ear, and the inner are surrounded by bones of the skull.

The middle ear is a small air-filled cavity separated from the auditory canal by the eardrum. It contains three small bones which serve as sound conductors. Barotitis involves this small inclosed cavity of the middle ear. The inner ear is composed of delicate, membranous structures occupying a small chamber within the temporal bone. It has the dual function of

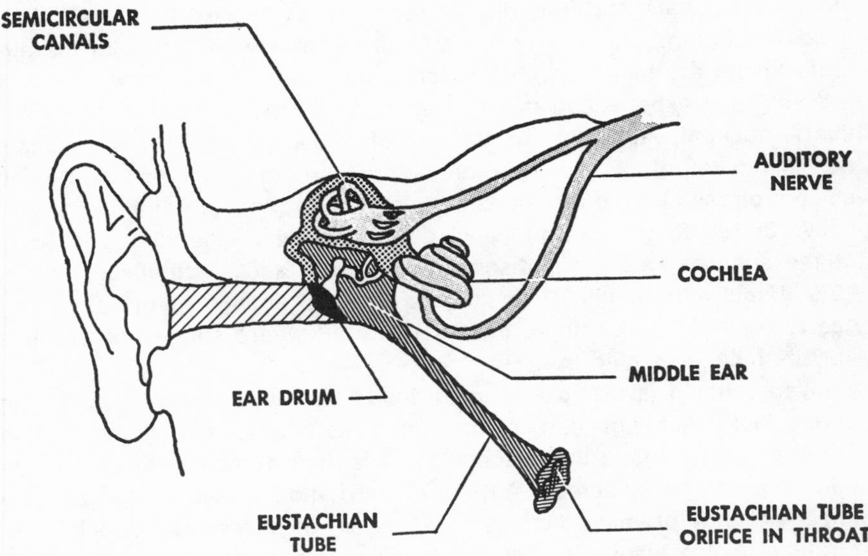

Figure 7.6 Structure of the ear and Eustachian tube. *(Drawn by Charles J. Shaw, Chief of the Gunter Branch Graphics Section, Air University Library, Gunter Air Force Base, Alabama.)*

hearing and assisting in the maintenance of balance. The narrow duct leading from the middle ear to open into the back of the throat is called the *eustachian tube* (Figures 7.6 and 7.7). By this means the middle ear communicates with the outside air so that, normally, any pressure difference between the middle ear and the atmosphere is equalized. This tube remains collapsed except at intervals when it is briefly opened by the act of swallowing or yawning. At such times, small throat muscles come into play causing it to open momentarily.

As the air in the middle ear expands during ascent, a small bubble is forced out through the eustachian tube at frequent intervals of altitude. A pressure differential of approximately 15 mm Hg in the middle ear cavity is sufficient to produce this effect. This is manifested by the familiar faint popping sensation in the ears during ascent. Ordinarily no difficulty is encountered on ascent because pressure equalization occurs automatically. On descent, however, the situation is reversed and air in the middle ear decreases in volume. When this happens there is a tendency for the opening of the eustachian tube in the throat to react like a flutter valve so that ventilation of the middle ear is much more difficult.

Normally, ventilation of the middle ear during descent can be accomplished by frequent swallowing or yawning. Experienced flyers often re-

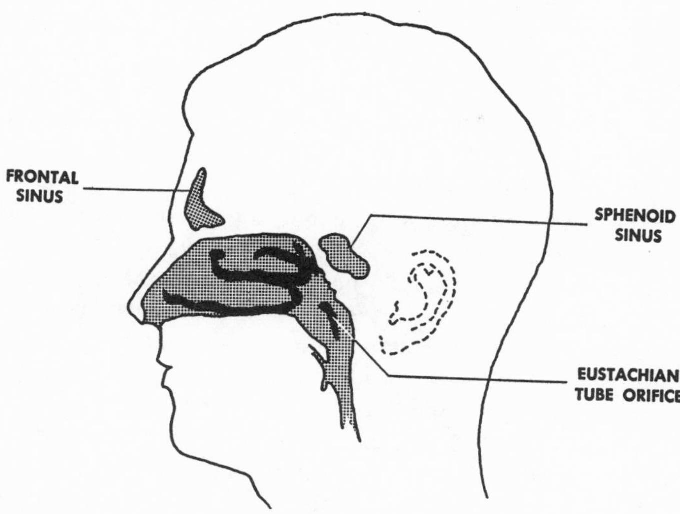

Figure 7.7 The sinuses. The maxillary and ethmoid sinuses are not shown in this drawing. *Drawn by Charles J. Shaw, Chief of the Gunter Branch Graphics Section, Air University Library, Gunter Air Force Base, Alabama.)*

lieve such an "ear block" by a maneuver resembling a stifled yawn which becomes very effective after practice. All of these measures produce contraction of the small throat muscles, thus briefly opening the eustachian tube. If these methods fail, air may be forced through the eustachian tube by the *Valsalva maneuver,* which consists of closing the mouth, holding the nose and blowing steadily with moderate force.

As descent progresses, if ventilation does not occur, pressure in the middle ear becomes relatively lower than in the outside air and the eardrum is forced inward. A sensation of fullness, pain, and deafness is produced. As the pressure differential increases between the ear and the outside air, there is a critical point (approximately 90 mm Hg) beyond which this pressure cannot be overcome by any of the above methods for opening the eustachian tube. For this reason, it is important to ventilate the ears actively at frequent intervals during descent.

Inability to open the eustachian tube properly is usually due to the common cold or other upper respiratory infection. The resultant swelling of the tissues in the throat and nose closes the small orifice of the tube. Other frequent causes of such interference are nasal allergy and overgrowth of tissue around the orifice. The eardrum is retracted to varying degrees and fluid collects within the middle ear, producing temporary deafness. Under unusual conditions when a very high pressure differential develops, there may be rupture of the eardrum. In the majority of cases recovery is complete after several days under proper medical management. This, of course, includes the avoidance of flying during the convalescent period.

In order to prevent the development of barotitis, airmen should not fly while suffering from upper respiratory infections or other conditions which interfere with ventilation of the middle ear. If there is difficulty in equalizing pressure, the aircraft should be brought down at as slow a rate of descent as possible. In severe cases, reascent followed by very gradual descent may be necessary. Veteran pilots in interceptor-type aircraft are able to descend at rates in excess of 5000 fpm without any difficulty because of their highly developed ability to ventilate their ears.

Descents as slow as 500 fpm may cause trouble in inexperienced persons who are not familiar with the phenomenon. For this reason, unpressurized passenger aircraft should descend at 250 to 500 fpm, and sleeping passengers are awakened prior to landing so that their swallowing reflexes will function normally. Swallowing takes place only about every five minutes while the subject is asleep as compared to an average of once every minute while he is awake. Chewing gum may be distributed to stimulate more frequent swallowing. In pressurized aircraft this problem has been largely eliminated because cabin pressure is maintained at ground level.

BAROSINUSITIS

Barosinusitis is an inflammation of the sinuses caused by the same mechanism as barotitis, that is, by changes in pressure. Like the middle ear, the four paired sinuses are air-filled cavities each with a single opening and are similarly affected by pressure differences. Though less common than barotitis, it is equally painful, and relief is more difficult because of structural differences. The sinus cavities, located within the bones of the face and skull, are grouped about the nasal passage, one of each pair on either side of the midline (Figure 7.7). Each drains into the nasal cavity by a narrow opening through which equalization of pressure takes place during altitude changes. The mucous membrane lining of the sinuses is continuous with that of the nose and throat. If the openings are closed by inflammation and swelling of the membrane, a pressure differential develops within one or more of the sinuses. Pain is most common in the forehead, but may be felt in the face or even in the back of the head, depending upon which of the sinuses is involved.

As with the eustachian tube, obstruction is much more likely to occur on descent than on ascent. Unlike the eustachian tube openings, however, the small sinus apertures cannot be controlled by the individual, since they are merely rigid openings in bone. Failure to ventilate the sinuses is more likely during rapid descents. When pain occurs, descent should be stopped if possible, and level flight maintained until the pressure is equalized. If severe pain persists, reascent is necessary to relieve it. Relative negative pressure causes fluid to be drawn out of the mucous membrane linings and to collect in the cavities.

Under appropriate treatment the inflammation of barosinusitis usually subsides within a few days. The same precautions should be followed as for the prevention of barotitis.

Decompression Sickness

Decompression sickness is a condition developed at reduced atmospheric pressure and manifested by pain in the joints, abdomen, or chest. When it affects flyers at high altitudes, it is sometimes called *aeroembolism,* or *bends.* It is caused by the formation of gas bubbles (mostly nitrogen) in the tissues and body fluids. The same conditions prevail and similar symptoms result when deep sea divers are suddenly decompressed by being brought to the surface too rapidly. Before the use of pressurized cabins in aircraft, decompression sickness was a frequent occurrence among aircrews flying above 30,000 ft. It is still a potential hazard in the event of loss of cabin pressure at high altitude. Also it is seen occasionally in individuals undergoing high-altitude indoctrination in low-pressure chambers or in aircraft. The following account describes a typical case which occurred in flight at 35,000 ft.

> In order to simulate combat conditions, each passenger was required to do standard exercises every five minutes. Some time after reaching peak altitude, the subject developed occasional shooting pains from the left hip down the anterior thigh to the left knee. After the eighth exercise, he experienced nausea and dizziness. Although he started to cough, he noted no chest pain. Because of his extreme pallor and lack of response to questions and commands, the plane was sent into a fast dive. During the first five minutes of the dive his respirations were 60 to 90 per minute, and he could not swallow. At 12,000 ft his color was ashen and his face was covered with perspiration. After regaining full consciousness at 10,000 ft, he was perspiring and aware of extreme cold. He had no recollection of any events during the dive. The cough continued for one-half hour after he reached ground level. At the hospital he was given hot coffee and wrapped in hot blankets. Hot water bottles were applied and he recovered fully.

It has been estimated that about 29% of flyers would develop incapacitating decompression sickness during a 3-hr flight at an altitude of 35,000 to 38,000 ft in unpressurized aircraft. Decompression sickness is more dangerous in flight than in low-pressure chambers because the latter can be quickly recompressed if symptoms develop.

EVOLVED BODY GASES

To understand the mechanism of decompression sickness, further consideration of the behavior of gases is necessary. Because of constant absorption of oxygen and release of carbon dioxide in the lungs, these dissolved gases are maintained at relative equilibrium within the body. These two gases occur in both physical and chemical combination and actively enter into the body metabolism. This is not true of nitrogen, which is inert and is therefore found only in physical combination. Physically combined nitrogen makes up about 80% of the gas that is dissolved in the tissues. Since it is held in solution solely by physical pressure, its amount varies according to the atmospheric pressure.

This is in accordance with Henry's gas law which states that, *with a constant temperature, the quantity of gas which goes into solution is proportional to the partial pressure of the gas concerned.* Therefore, at any altitude, dissolved gases are present in the body in the same percentage as they occur in the air at that altitude. As altitude increases, gases tend to come out of solution in proportion to the alteration in pressure and to maintain equilibrium with the atmosphere.

If ascent is slow and the altitude attained is less than 30,000 ft, these *evolved gases* do not collect as excess but are utilized (oxygen) or released via the lungs (carbon dioxide, nitrogen) as rapidly as they come out of solution. If, however, the ascent is rapid and pressure is decreased to at least one-half its sea-level value, gases may be released at such a rate that they cannot be completely eliminated by the lungs and thus tend to collect as bubbles in the tissues and body fluids. Because it is inert, nitrogen is the principal component of such bubbles. As these bubbles enlarge, they may obstruct the very small blood vessels and produce various symptoms because of interference with the circulation in local areas of the body. There is considerable evidence that symptoms are also due to the direct pressure of bubbles around small nerves. Bubble formation is more likely to occur in tissues of the body where circulation is poor and where nitrogen is most abundant. Fat has a greater affinity for nitrogen than does any other tissue, and fat people are most likely to have decompression sickness.

The most frequent symptom of decompression sickness is pain in the joints or abdomen known as *bends.* Any joint may be affected, but the knee and shoulder are most often involved. Onset is usually fairly sudden and pain tends to become worse as long as the individual is at high altitude. Pain is often severe enough to force the flyer to descend. Symptoms occurring in the chest are known as *chokes,* referring to a sharp burning pain accompanied by shortness of breath and coughing. Skin symptoms include itching, burning, warm or cold sensations and a mottled appearance of the skin. The nerves may be temporarily affected so that the individual has partial loss of vision, inability to speak, or partial paralysis.

Very rarely, decompression sickness may be fatal. Most cases, however, are painful and temporarily incapacitating, but leave no permanent effects. The pain of bends usually subsides shortly after descent. Chokes and manifestations of nerve involvement, although rare, are of much more serious import. Decompression sickness is unusual below 25,000 ft, but above 30,000 ft it becomes common. On a flight of 50 unpressurized, single-place interceptor aircraft at 30,000 ft for 2 hr, it is estimated that 30 pilots would have symptoms of varying severity and three of them would have to abort their flight because of severe decompression sickness.

PREVENTION OF DECOMPRESSION SICKNESS

Even apparently mild cases of decompression sickness must be considered potentially serious. The only satisfactory treatment is immediate recompression. In low-pressure chambers this is easily done, but in actual flight, rapid descent may not be feasible for operational reasons. The incidence of decompression sickness increases directly with the following factors:

a. The pressure altitude.
b. The rate of climb.
c. The total time spent at altitude.
d. The amount of exercise performed.
e. The age of the subject.
f. The degree of overweight of the subject.

Experience indicates that the faster the ascent, the higher the altitude, and the longer the flight, the greater will be the incidence and severity of symptoms.

Subjects who perform active physical exercise at altitude are more likely to develop symptoms. Analysis of data on aircrew trainees in low-pressure chambers shows that susceptibility to decompression sickness increases directly with advancing age. Studies made during the same period have indicated that overweight individuals are at greater risk than those of slender or medium build. This then is an added reason for air crewmen to maintain themselves in good physical condition.

Other than pressurization of the aircraft cabin, the best prophylactic measure against decompression sickness is *denitrogenation.* By breathing 100% oxygen for a period of time, the dissolved nitrogen is removed from the tissues prior to the subject's reaching high altitude. Since the partial pressure of nitrogen in the lungs is greatly diminished by this procedure, nitrogen diffuses outward from the blood and tissues and is exhaled. In this way the dissolved nitrogen stored in the tissues is depleted.

If as much as one-half the body nitrogen is lost by denitrogenation, significant protection is afforded. This amount can be removed by prebreathing 100% oxygen for one hour prior to flight. After the first hour, nitrogen is lost at a much slower rate. Prebreathing oxygen at ground level can be done only for scheduled missions. Denitrogenation prior to takeoff is not feasible for interceptor crewmen who must fly at any time with little warning. These crews get some protection by breathing oxygen from the ground up so that denitrogenation is at least begun before a critical altitude is reached.

In view of the value of recompression in the treatment of decompression sickness, the U.S. Air Force and Navy have in operation a number of strategically placed positive-pressure chambers. Treatment with overcompression is reserved for the more serious cases. The Air Force has a medical treatment team at the School of Aerospace Medicine, Brooks Air Force Base, Texas. It is available on 24-hour call, and will provide advice, or actually travel to the site of the emergency to assist in the treatment of affected airmen.

SCUBA DIVING

If one has participated in scuba or other diving with the associated increased pressure before flying, decompression sickness may occur at relatively low altitude. The additive effect of the further decrease in pressure when flying soon after surfacing from a dive may be sufficient to cause symptoms. Under such circumstances decompression sickness may occur at altitudes well within the capabilities of light aircraft. After surfacing from a dive sufficient time should be allowed to reestablish ground-level nitrogen equilibrium before flying. For maximum safety after a dive to a depth of 25 ft or greater, individuals should not fly for at least 12 hr except in pressurized aircraft in which cabin pressure is maintained at or below 8000 ft.

Pressurized Cabins and Rapid Decompression

The use of pressurized cabins in aircraft has partially solved the problems of hypoxia, barotitis, barosinusitis, and decompression sickness by reducing the peak-pressure altitude of flight and by avoiding rapid pressure changes. The flyer is surrounded by an artificial atmosphere under greater pressure than the outside air. The oxygen partial pressure is thus also raised so that more oxygen is made available for absorption by the lungs. For example, when the true altitude of the aircraft is 30,000 ft, the cabin pressure altitude may be only 8000 ft so that breathing oxygen is not necessary. Since the entire body is pressurized, it is protected against the effects of free and evolved gases as well as hypoxia. Pressurization up to a cabin altitude of 10,000 ft may be used in lieu of oxygen breathing equipment. For cabin altitudes from 10,000 to 42,000 ft oxygen equipment must be used in conjunction with cabin pressurization. Oxygen equipment is also required to offset the hazard of sudden loss of cabin pressure, that is, rapid decompression.

PRESSURIZED CABINS

Isobaric control of pressure is a system in which the cabin is maintained constantly at a fixed pressure throughout the flight, regardless of flight altitude. In *differential control* of cabin pressure the cabin altitude varies with the flight altitude according to a given ratio. Isobaric control may be used until the aircraft reaches the altitude where its maximum allowable structural pressure differential exists. Above this critical altitude, differential control is required.

In most present cargo-type aircraft the cabins are relatively large as compared to the surface area which is likely to undergo mechanical rupture or perforation by gunfire. This feature minimizes the hazard from rapid decompression. The pressure differential for this type of aircraft is 6.55 psi. The most recent interceptors are provided with a pressure differential of 5 psi. In the latter, up to 31,000 ft the cabin altitude is maintained at 12,500 ft by isobaric control. Above this flight altitude the constant differential of 5 psi is used. Under combat conditions this is reduced to 2.75 psi as a precaution against sudden decompression (over a wide pressure differential) which is more likely to occur in combat. Because of the relatively small size of the cabins in some of the jet bombers, the same precautions are necessary and a similar pressurization schedule is used.

In FAA-certificated aircraft with pressure systems, the occupied cabin areas must be maintained at an altitude of 8000 ft or below at the maximum operational altitude of the aircraft.

RAPID DECOMPRESSION

If pressure is suddenly lost in flight, there is a forceful equalization of cabin pressure with that of the outside air as cabin air is rapidly expelled. The magnitude of this decompression, and hence the physiological effect on the flyer, is determined by:

a. The size of the cabin defect.
b. The altitude of the aircraft.
c. The volume of the cabin.
d. The amount of pressure differential.

The smaller the cabin, the larger the defect, and the greater the pressure differential, the more rapid is the rate of decompression. Extremely rapid loss of cabin pressure is termed *explosive decompression.*

Physiological Effects With the sudden equalization of pressure there is a forceful blast of air outward through openings and passages in the aircraft. At such times, crewmen near these openings have been swept out of the aircraft. For this reason personnel at their stations in pressurized cabins should always have their seat belts fastened when flying in combat.

In addition, the free gases within the body cavities suddenly expand and are partially expelled. The decompression which occasionally occurs in flight is usually relatively slow so that body gases escape without dangerous internal pressures being developed. The middle ear and the sinuses are ventilated without difficulty because the greater pressure inside the cavities forces open the eustachian tube and the sinus orifices.

If excessive, expanding gases within the intestinal tract may cause pain, but since this organ is normally capable of considerable stretching, serious injury is not likely to occur. The same is true of the lungs; the lung gas is normally expelled through the trachea with little resistance. Decompressions of the magnitude usually experienced in aircraft are not great enough to produce lung damage. Immediately following decompression, the flyer is exposed to the risk of decompression sickness and hypoxia. As previously discussed, these two hazards are in direct proportion to the flight altitude. As shown in column four of Table 7.3, the time of consciousness is unusually brief following rapid decompression, that is, hypoxia develops more quickly than after simple deprivation of oxygen.

Aircrews should maintain oxygen masks in a state of readiness at all times when flying in pressurized aircraft. In case of rapid decompression, oxygen equipment will be needed immediately (if it is not already being used) and, if the altitude is above 43,000 ft, descent of the aircraft will be necessary. A practice rapid decompression in a low-pressure chamber is carried out as part of the altitude indoctrination of all military aircrews.

Very-High-Altitude Emergency Equipment

For aircrews flying above 43,000 ft some type of emergency protection must be available in case of cabin decompression. Up to 43,000 ft a well-fitted face mask with 100% oxygen at 18 mm Hg pressure gives adequate protection for a short time, even if cabin pressure is lost. Above this altitude, the breathing pressure required to prevent hypoxia is too high for routine use. Breathing oxygen under pressures greater than 18 mm Hg rapidly becomes prohibitive because of leakage around the mask, respiratory fatigue, and interference with the circulation of blood to the heart and lungs. By the time 63,000 ft is reached, atmospheric pressure has diminished to 47 mm Hg (Table 7.4). At this altitude water boils at 98.6°F (man's normal body temperature).

Since the body is approximately 70% water, its gases come out of solution at 63,000 ft and the blood is said to "boil." In order to survive at such altitudes if cabin pressure is lost, the flyer must have a garment which will give him some degree of pressurization. Breathing pressures required for this necessary pressurization exceed the limits of human tolerance unless counterpressure is supplied to the surface of the body by a tightly fitted suit. Such a suit also prevents the interference with circulation and supports the chest against the required high breathing pressures. At present the Air Force has three items of equipment which are used together to give this protection at very high altitudes: the high-altitude partial-pressure suit, the pressurized helmet, and the automatic oxygen assembly.

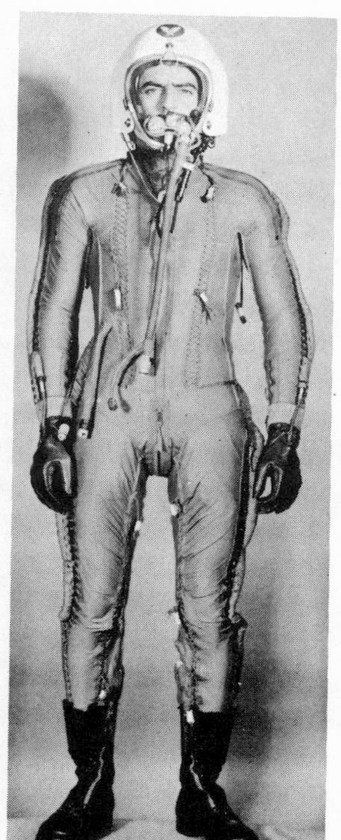

Figure 7.8 High-altitude partial-pressure suit, helmet, and gloves. Note snug fit of suit even though capstan tubes are not inflated. *(Taken at School of Aviation Medicine, USAF Aerospace Medical Center, Brooks Air Force Base, San Antonio, Texas.)*

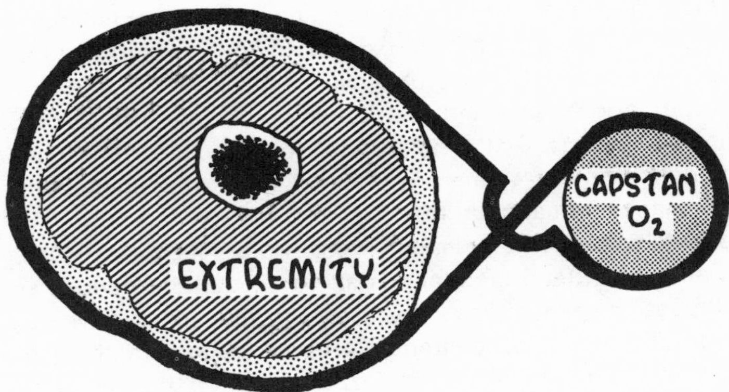

Figure 7.9 Capstan principle employed in the high-altitude partial-pressure suit. Inflation of the capstan tubes causes tightening of the closely placed straps which are attached to back, arms, and legs of the suit. This provides uniform counterpressure over the limbs and body. (From Randell and Ward, *J. Aviation Med.,* **25** (6) (Dec. 1954.)

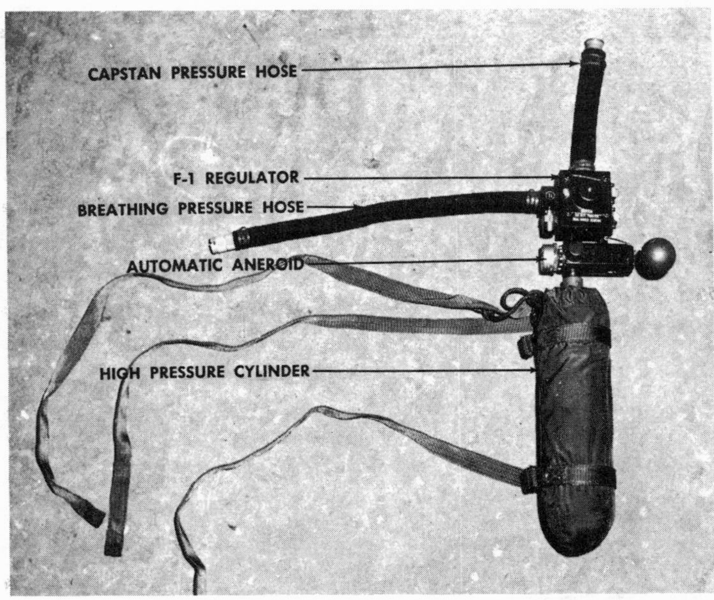

Figure 7.10 Automatic oxygen assembly (USAF type C-1). By means of this equipment, oxygen is automatically supplied to the helmet and to the partial-pressure suit if cabin pressurization is lost above 43,000 ft. *(U.S. Air Force photograph.)*

THE PARTIAL-PRESSURE SUIT (FIGURES 7.8, 7.9, AND 7.10)

This suit is a tightly fitted garment which completely covers the body and limbs. It is worn uninflated and inflates automatically when cabin pressure is lost. Each suit is carefully fitted to the individual flyer by means of laces and zippers. *Capstan* tubes are attached to the back, arms, and legs by a series of small straps. When these tubes are inflated, the closely placed straps are tightened, thus tightening the suit to give pressure over the body and limbs (Figure 7.8).

THE PRESSURIZED HELMET (FIGURE 7.8)

A large glass-fiber helmet containing an inner rubber bladder must be worn with the partial-pressure suit. The helmet is sealed off as a separate pressurized compartment by inflation of the inner rubber bladder, and

Figure 7.11 High-altitude partial-pressure suit and accessories. The late Captain Iven C. Kincheloe, USAF, is shown wearing equipment with which he flew to a manned aircraft altitude record of 126,000 ft in 1956. The aircraft is the rocket-powered Bell X-2 in which the flight was made.

100% oxygen under high breathing pressure is forced into it. Incorporated within the facepiece is an oxygen inlet, microphone, inflight feeding valve, and a 24-volt heating circuit for defrosting.

THE AUTOMATIC OXYGEN ASSEMBLY

Following sudden loss of cabin pressure above 55,000 ft, the time of useful consciousness is 8 to 12 sec. Therefore, if cabin pressure is lost, breathing pressure must be supplied and the suit must be pressurized immediately. The oxygen asembly automatically provides an instant supply of oxygen under pressure to both the helmet and the capstan tubes if decompression occurs above 43,000 ft. The amount of pressure delivered to both the suit and the helmet is proportional to the altitude. Under normal operating conditions, oxygen flows to the helmet from the aircraft supply in the routine way.

Figure 7.12 Full-pressure suit, helmet, boots, and gloves. A ventilation-insulation garment is worn next to the pilot's body beneath the suit. Curved facepiece of helmet extends laterally to afford maximum visibility. *(U.S. Air Force photograph.)*

At present, the partial-pressure suit and its accessory equipment are for emergency use only. They were developed as a means of preserving life for the short time required for the aircraft to descend following a very-high-altitude decompression. Also, if a bail-out is necessary above 43,000 ft, the emergency use of the suit allows time for a free fall to a safe altitude. This equipment has been successfully used up to 105,000 ft in the low-pressure chamber. In 1956 Capt. Iven C. Kincheloe of the United States Air Force wore this equipment on his high-altitude record flight in which he reached a peak altitude of 126,000 ft (Figure 7.11).

THE FULL-PRESSURE SUIT

Although adequate as high-altitude emergency protective equipment, the partial-pressure suit has certain limitations for prolonged wear. The wearer has some restriction of movement, limitation of vision, and discomfort when the suit is worn for long periods. The ideal system for overcoming these difficulties and furnishing the flyer with a livable atmosphere is a full-pressure suit in which the wearer is surrounded by a layer of pressurized oxygen or air. In developing such a suit, further problems of overheating, weight, and lack of mobility are encountered. The full-pressure suit used by USAF crews is shown in Figure 7.12. This suit, with helmet, gloves, and boots is a complete full-pressure outfit which insures safety, mobility, and comfort of crewmen at very high altitude. It maintains a complete envelope with ventilation, pressurization control, breathing oxygen to the helmet, and communications.

Vision in Flight

From the earliest days of aviation, the flyer's vision has been regarded as a most vital part of his physical equipment for flights. In flying, constant demands are made on the vision in order to avoid obstacles, to judge distance, to read colored signals and maps, to study the terrain, and to read flight instruments within the cockpit. Elaborate and careful tests of vision are a prominent part of every physical examination for military and commercial flying, and failure to meet these high visual standards is the most common cause for rejection of candidates for flight training. It is absolutely necessary that a candidate starting his flying training have perfect vision. In later years some defects of vision will inevitably develop with increasing age. This loss of visual ability is expected and is acceptable after the flyer has accumulated considerable flying experience which compensates, to some extent, for visual defects.

Not only must flying candidates have perfect vision, but they must be taught to understand certain principles of efficient vision and practical means by which they can use their eyes more effectively. The flyer's vision may be adversely affected by accelerative forces, hypoxia, and decompression sickness. Some knowledge of the structure and function of the eye is basic to an understanding of these and other visual phenomena of flight.

STRUCTURE AND FUNCTION OF THE EYE (FIGURE 7.13)

When an object is seen, it means that an image has been formed at the back of the eye and then transmitted to the brain. To be seen, objects must, of course, be illuminated in some way. This light is reflected from the object to enter the eye through the *cornea,* the outer transparent layer of the eyeball. Behind the cornea is the *iris,* an opaque layer with a central opening, the *pupil,* through which light enters. The *lens* is a semisolid, transparent disc behind the iris. A delicate muscle regulates the size of the pupil, enlarging it in dim light and contracting it in bright light. As light enters the eye and passes through the lens, it is focused by the latter to produce an image on the *retina.* The retina is the receiving portion of the *optic nerve* which is arranged to form a layer over the back of the eyeball. This is the nerve of vision which transmits the image to the brain. The multiple, minute nerve endings making up the retina are of two different types, differentiated by their structure and function (Figure 7.14).

The small central area of the retina is composed largely of tapered nerve endings called *cones.* These are most effective when illumination is good, and they are required for maximum visual acuity. They are also

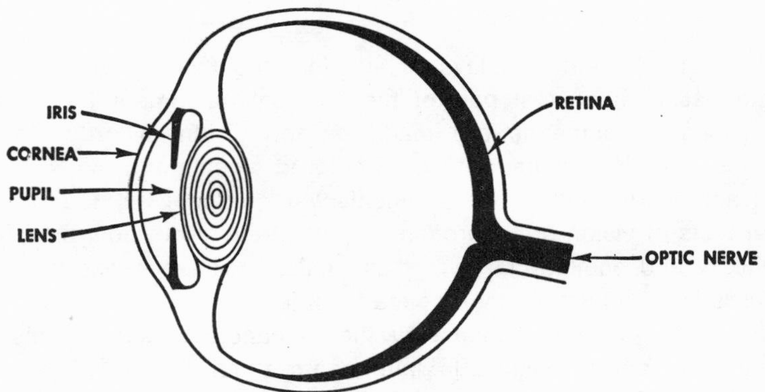

Figure 7.13 Diagrammatic section of the eyeball.

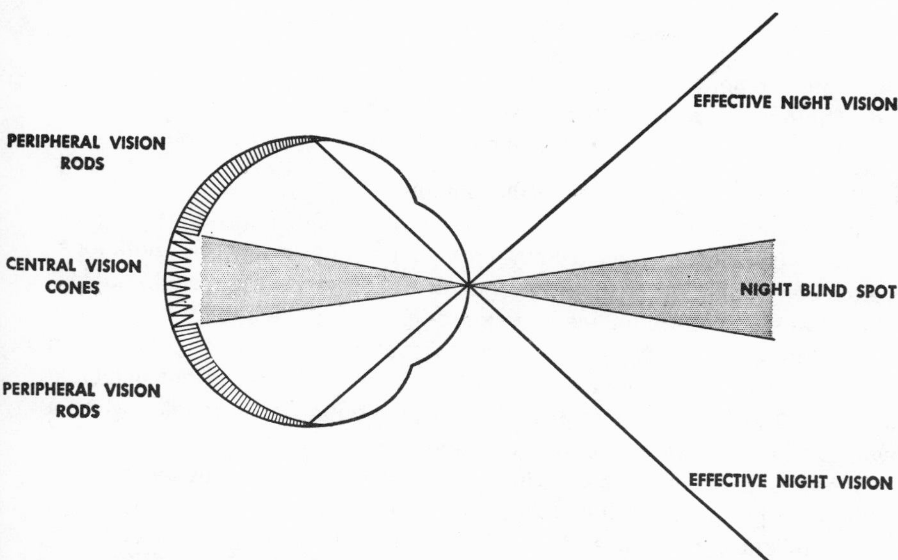

Figure 7.14 Diagram of retinal nerve endings for central and peripheral vision.

necessary for the discrimination of color, but function very poorly under low illumination. They account for what is called *central vision* which is effective only in good light. In the outer or peripheral portion of the retina, the nerve endings are mostly long, cylindrical *rods* which give less effective visual acuity. These rods give us our *peripheral vision* upon which we depend for seeing at night or in very dim light.

VISUAL ACUITY

Visual acuity is the ability to perceive the shape and detail of objects. It is measured by having the subject read a series of progressively smaller test letters at a distance of 20 ft. The smallest letters that can be read correctly indicate the visual acuity. If the subject is able to read letters of a prescribed size at a distance of 20 ft, he has 20/20 visual acuity, which is considered to be normal. This visual test is the single most common cause of failure of the physical examination for military flying. Studies on military pilots of World War II indicate that, of all visual factors, visual acuity is most closely related to success in air-to-air combat.

Regardless of whether an individual's visual acuity is good or poor, the clarity of his vision will be influenced by several characteristics of the object viewed, such as:

a. Its distance from the viewer.
b. Its size and contour.
c. Its movement.
d. The amount of light it reflects.
e. Its contrast with the environment.

Also of obvious importance are the amount of light and the condition of the intervening atmosphere in the field of vision. Our knowledge of these factors is used every day to improve visual acuity in specific situations: We turn on lamps to increase the amount of light or hold a needle against a light background so that we can see to thread it more easily. The central part of the retina, which gives maximal visual acuity, requires illumination of at least 0.001 candlepower. Often this amount of light is not available at night. Bright moonlight provides illumination of 0.02 candlepower, a level at which central vision can function.

Since visual acuity is best with central vision and diminishes steadily toward the periphery of the retina, everything in the field of vision is not seen with equal clearness. At a few degrees off center, visual acuity is significantly diminished, and so we see objects most clearly by looking directly at them. Also, if the eye is in motion, nothing but an indistinct blur is seen. As a pilot constantly scans the sky for other aircraft he must carefully examine small, individual patches of sky rather than sweeping his gaze over wide areas. In this way, for search of any particular area of the sky, the gaze is immobile and directed at the area being scanned.

To combat eye fatigue caused by glare sunglasses should be worn while scanning from aircraft. The most desirable lenses are those which are tinted to eliminate most of the ultraviolet and infrared light, but not light within the visible spectrum. This is best achieved by tinting sunglasses and helmet visors a neutral shade such as currently used by the U.S. Air Force.

DEPTH PERCEPTION

Depth perception is the ability to judge distance. It is required in making landings, in formation flying, and in avoiding obstacles in flight. Several factors enter into an estimation of distance, and an idea of distance may be obtained by employing one or more of these factors. In any given situation the individual is not usually aware of just how he makes his judgment of distance; he does it subconsciously. Some depth perception factors involve only one eye, and others require both eyes, the value of the latter deriving from the fact that the two eyes are at slightly different angles from the object. In flying situations most of the distances are so great that this angle is too small to be of importance. Therefore, an experienced flyer with only one eye may rely upon other objects and characteristics within the visual field to give him his concept of distance.

NIGHT VISION

Man does not see at all in the absence of light, but such conditions of total darkness are rare. If there is any light at all from the moon or stars, it can be picked up by peripheral vision since the rods in this part of the retina are sensitive to light intensities as low as 1×10^{-6} candlepower. Under most conditions moonlight provides enough illumination for central vision, but starlight alone is rarely bright enough. The ability to see at night can be greatly improved by understanding and applying certain techniques. The individual flyer's night visual ability can actually be increased by practice. If the rods of peripheral vision are exposed to strong light even briefly, their sensitivity is temporarily destroyed. For this reason, avoidance of strong light must begin well in advance of a night flight, since several minutes are required to regain rod sensitivity after it is lost.

Dark Adaptation After rod function is destroyed, the period during which sensitivity is slowly regained is known as the period of dark adaptation. This process takes place in each eye independently. The eyes become partially dark-adapted very quickly, as when one enters a darkened theater; only a brief period is required before the aisle and seats can be clearly seen. Dark adaptation is nearly complete after 30 to 40 min. Rod function is destroyed most quickly and completely by white light, and dark red light exerts the least amount of influence on dark adaptation.

By wearing dark red goggles before a night flight, flyers whose mission requires effective night vision can continue to read or work in a lighted room without interfering with their dark adaptation process. Otherwise they must stay in darkened surroundings for 30 min prior to flight. During the preflight check of the aircraft, as little light as possible should be used. Red flashlights, red cockpit lights, and red luminous instrument dials are used in aircraft for this reason. However, one disadvantage of red light is its interference with color perception. Some white light may still be required for certain uses such as the reading of colored maps. An instant of exposure to white light makes it necessary to start over with dark adaptation. If such exposure is unavoidable, as when caught in a searchlight beam, one eye should be closed to preserve the function of its rods.

Eccentric Vision Normally we look directly at an object, utilizing central vision in order to see it more clearly. For night vision this habit must be altered. Since central vision is ineffective under low illumination, the flyer should not look directly at objects at night. They are seen much more clearly if vision is directed slightly away, rather than directly toward them. Eccentric vision, that is, gazing about 10° off center, should be practiced as a valuable means of improving night vision. In this way, the peripheral rods are used instead of the central cones. This effect can be demonstrated by counting a cluster of very faint lights in the distance at night. By looking slightly away from center, more lights can be clearly seen than by looking directly at them.

At night, objects are seen by contrast with their background, that is, they must be darker or lighter than their surroundings. Aircraft are more easily seen if they are above and silhouetted against the lighter sky. Since rod vision is not sensitive enough to see small objects, aircraft at night are seen best from above or below where they present a larger outline. Other handicaps to night vision are the lack of color discrimination and depth perception, for which the rods are of little use. Without colors, normally familiar objects may be difficult to identify. Also, because of poor depth perception, a small aircraft near at hand may be mistaken for a larger one far off. Thus at night it is important to interpret properly such visual clues as are available. The ability to do this improves with practice and night-flying experience.

Effects of Hypoxia Night vision is reduced by lowered oxygen tension, exposure to carbon monoxide, and deficient diet. As previously mentioned, night vision is unusually sensitive to hypoxia. When flying at night at an altitude as low as 5000 ft, instrument dials may blur slightly if oxygen is not used. At 12,000 ft there is a marked reduction, and at 16,000 ft nearly complete loss of night vision can occur because of hypoxia. Exposure to carbon monoxide reduces the oxygen-carrying capacity of the blood and so has an effect on night vision similar to that of the hypoxia of altitude.

Blood has a much greater affinity for carbon monoxide than for oxygen, absorbing it over 200 times more readily than oxygen. The presence of carbon monoxide, therefore, tends to limit the number of red blood cells free to absorb oxygen. Carbon monoxide may penetrate the cockpit from the aircraft engines or small amounts may be absorbed by the flyer who smokes excessively. Incomplete combustion of tobacco produces small but significant amounts of carbon monoxide. Once absorbed by the blood, it is given up very slowly over a period of several hours. A flyer who smokes steadily during or even prior to flight is certain to impair his night vision.

The ability of the eyes to dark adapt depends upon an adequate amount of vitamin A in the diet. This vitamin is found in many commonly consumed foods such as green vegetables, milk, eggs, and cheese. Therefore, vitamin A deficiency is not likely to occur under normal conditions. Taking excessive amounts of vitamin A (above the normal requirement) is of no benefit to night vision.

VISUAL ILLUSIONS AT NIGHT

The night flyer has very few available visual references with which he can orient objects outside the aircraft. For this reason he is susceptible to certain visual illusions.

If one stares at a stationary light in a darkened room it will soon appear to be moving about from side to side in wide, irregular arcs. This phenomenon, in which a fixed light appears to be moving, is called *autokinetic* movement, or "stare vision." It may also occur during night formation flying. This has been offered as an explanation for certain night accidents in which an aircraft is seen to break away from a formation, go into a steep dive, and crash without any apparent attempt to recover. It seems likely that a pilot who can see nothing but the taillight of the lead aircraft and stares fixedly at it may leave the formation and even lose control of his aircraft because he tries to follow the apparent movement of the taillight. The exact cause of autokinetic movement is not known. It can be prevented by constantly shifting the gaze from the light to some reference point on the aircraft.

COLOR VISION

The discrimination of color is entirely dependent upon the cones of central vision. Individuals who have below-average ability to differentiate color are said to be "color blind." A better term is "color defective" inasmuch as total color blindness (caused by an absence of retinal cones) is rare. Defective color vision is usually hereditary, and both eyes are involved, but the condition is not related to other visual defects. About 10% of the male population has some degree of defective color vision. In females the incidence is 2%. The most common type of defect is red-green blindness, wherein these colors cannot be discriminated and are seen as a neutral shade. In partial red-green blindness, red and green can be identified, but they are seen as a darker shade. Good color vision is essential in aviation in order to interpret colored navigation lights on aircraft, airdromes, and obstructions; for the reading of maps and the recognition of terrain features; and for colored emergency signals such as flares or smoke grenades. All degrees of defective color vision are disqualifying for military flying. Persons who normally have only mild color blindness have increased difficulty in color determination if they become excited or nervous.

VISION AT HIGH SPEED

A very brief but significant interval elapses between the time when something is seen and appropriate action is taken. This interval is called the *reaction time* and may be divided into three phases:

a. Latent perception phase.
b. Recognition and decision phase.
c. Decision transmission phase.

In the perception phase a retinal image is formed and transmitted to the brain via the optic nerve. This requires about one tenth of a second. In the recognition and decision phase the image must be analyzed and a decision made as to action required. In the transmission phase the decision is passed down to the muscles which will execute the action. At modern high flying speeds, this short delay for the elapse of reaction time is a potential hazard which is intensified in aerial combat. At flying speeds of 600 knots, two aircraft approaching each other have a closing speed of 1200 knots. Even if another aircraft is recognized at the maximum range of the pilot's vision, little time is left for decision and action. On several occasions during the Korean War, formations of hostile aircraft flew through each other before either was aware of the other. A pilot with perfect visual actuity can see and identify a fighter approaching from in front at a distance of 4 mi. Anything that lengthens the three phases of reaction time is a flying hazard. Mental dullness, fatigue, or inattention will quickly extend reaction time beyond the limits of flying safety.

Effects of Acceleration

SPEED, VELOCITY, AND ACCELERATION

Speed may be defined as the numerical value of the rate of motion. It merely means that something is moving rapidly and does not necessarily include the idea of direction. At one time it was feared that man would eventually reach a critical speed of flight which, if exceeded, would cause serious bodily damage. It now appears that this fear was unfounded—at least for speed in straight and level flight, as long as the rate remains constant. However, if the rate of speed is increased or decreased or if the direction of flight is altered, there may be significant physiological effects. *Velocity* is the time rate of motion in a given direction and so it includes both *speed* and *direction.* When velocity is changed in any way, *acceleration* takes place. A decrease in velocity is negative acceleration, or *deceleration.* Therefore, acceleration in flight is produced by either a change in the speed or the direction of the aircraft. This happens when speed is gained or lost, as in takeoffs and landings, or if there is a change in direction, as during turns, dives, or recovery from dives.

In modern aircraft, because of their great speeds and maneuverability, acceleration is frequent and may be extreme. When this occurs, accelerative forces are brought to bear upon both the aircraft and the flyer. Flyers know that every aircraft has a limit to the accelerative forces which it can safely sustain. If this acceleration limit is exceeded, there may be structural failure of the aircraft and it is said to have been "overstressed." As might be expected, flyers themselves can be physiologically overstressed, if accelerative forces are excessive. In modern, high-performance aircraft the limit of man's tolerance to these forces is frequently approached and sometimes exceeded.

MEASURING ACCELERATION

Because of these critical limits of accelerative forces, it is important that we have some means of measuring them. For this purpose there is a standard acceleration unit called the "gravity," or "*g*." It is convenient to think of acceleration or *g* effects as similar to the force of gravity, which is equal to 1*g*. The actual force of 1*g* for any object is therefore equivalent to the weight of the object. A man at rest, weighing 200 lb, is subject to the normal pull of gravity (1*g*), but if he accelerates by a change in speed or direction, this original *g* force of 200 lb may increase to 2*g* (2*g* would be equal to 400 lb in this instance) or more. For example, in a pull-out from a dive a flyer sustains 3 to 6*g* and at that moment weighs 3 to 6 times his normal weight. The magnitude of an accelerative force is appropriately measured in *g*'s, or multiples of the force of gravity.

TYPES OF ACCELERATIVE FORCES

In addition to its magnitude, an accelerative force may be described in terms of the *means by which it is produced,* its *direction* relative to the axis of the human body, and the length of *time* during which it acts. The following outline shows these three different systems for classifying accelerative forces and certain aircraft maneuvers which produce each type:

I. MEANS BY WHICH ACCELERATION IS PRODUCED

A. Linear Acceleration	aircraft takeoff, upward seat ejection
B. Linear Deceleration	aircraft landing, aircraft ditching, parachute opening

C. Radial Acceleration	pull-out from a dive, push-over into a dive
D. Angular Acceleration	aircraft in a spin

II. DIRECTION IN WHICH ACCELERATION ACTS WITH REFERENCE TO BODY AXIS

A. Vertical Acceleration	
1. Positive	pull-out from a dive, banked turn
2. Negative	push-over into a dive; buffeting in turbulent air, downward seat ejection
B. Sagittal Acceleration	landing or takeoff with subject facing forward
C. Transverse Acceleration	takeoff and landing with subject facing laterally

III. DURATION OF THE ACCELERATIVE FORCE

A. Prolonged Acceleration	pull-out from a dive
B. Sudden Acceleration	parachute opening, aircraft crashes

Means by Which Acceleration Is Produced *Linear* acceleration is produced if only the rate of movement changes, as when there is an increase or decrease in speed along a straight line. A decrease in speed is sometimes called *linear deceleration. Radial* acceleration is produced by a change in the direction of movement, as when an aircraft pulls out of a dive. When there is a simultaneous change in both speed and direction of movement, this is called *angular* acceleration. A dramatic example of this is an aircraft in a spin.

Direction of Accelerative Forces with Reference to Body Axis When the direction of action of an accelerative force is parallel to the long axis of the body, it is said to be *vertical* acceleration. This type may be called *positive* if the force acts in a head-to-foot direction or *negative* if in the foot-to-head direction. In *sagittal* acceleration the force is exerted in either a front-to-back or back-to-front direction. When the force acts from left-to-right or right-to-left, it is said to be *transverse.*

Duration of Accelerative Forces Sudden accelerations are those which act for less than one second. *Prolonged* accelerations are those in which the force acts for one second or more.

In considering the foregoing classification, it should be remembered that the accelerative forces in a given flying maneuver are not limited to one of these types. In flight, in a single maneuver several types of accelerative forces may occur. Thus several combinations of terms from this classification will usually be required to describe accurately the accelerative force of any given flying maneuver. For example, in pulling out of a linear dive the flyer is subjected to *g* forces which may be described as radial, vertical, positive, and prolonged.

BODY REACTIONS TO ACCELERATION

The effects of a *g* force on the individual depend not only on the magnitude of the force (the number of *g*'s), but also on its duration and its direction, that is, the axis of the body on which it acts. Colonel John P. Stapp, an Air Force flight surgeon, demonstrated man's capacity to withstand very high *g* forces when he was experimentally subjected to a force of 46.8*g* without serious injury. This was done on a special deceleration sled which was suddenly stopped while moving at 175 mph so that the subject experienced sagittal acceleration for only .008 sec. This sudden deceleration was equivalent to driving an automobile into a brick wall at 120 mph. He was uninjured because of adequate body support, proper positioning, and the very brief time during which the force acted. However, for forces acting in a foot-to-head direction, only 3*g* for 5 sec is the upper limit of man's tolerance.

Tolerance to sudden acceleration or deceleration of less than 1 sec duration is much greater than for prolonged acceleration. The latter produces relatively gradual physiological changes such as loss of vision or consciousness over a period of seconds. These effects are manifest at *g* forces of relatively low magnitude and they increase proportionally with acceleration. Since sudden acceleration or deceleration is too brief to alter physiological function materially, forces of great magnitude may be tolerated, as demonstrated by Col. Stapp. Only when such forces are extremely high, as in aircraft crashes, does structural damage to the body result. This short-duration, high-*g* acceleration is not routinely experienced by the flyer but represents a stress to which he may be exposed in emergency situations. As such, sudden acceleration or deceleration is of primary concern to the flight surgeon and the aeronautical engineer in designing aircraft cockpits, seats, safety belts, crash helmets, and other protective equipment.

Prolonged acceleration, on the other hand, is a daily experience of every flyer and hence he should thoroughly understand its effects. Figure 7.16 illustrates the duration and magnitude of accelerative forces produced by various flying maneuvers. Most of the accelerations experienced in flying are caused by a change in the direction of the aircraft. Usually the pilot's head is toward the center of the flight curve, and so vertical acceleration with the force acting in a head-to-foot direction is the most common type encountered.

The principal physiological effects are due to disturbances of the heart and blood supply, the temporary molding of soft tissues, and increase in the weight of all parts of the body. During the pull-up from a 70° dive (Figure 7.16) a pilot experiences 4 to 6*g* for 3 to 1 sec. He is forced down

Figure 7.15 Human tolerance to sudden deceleration. Lt. Col. John P. Stapp, USAF (MC), at the completion of a test ride on a special deceleration sled at Aero Medical Field Laboratory, Hollman Air Development Center, New Mexico. *(U.S. Air Force photograph.)*

into the seat, his face sags, his limbs become heavy, and all his movements are markedly restricted. Manipulation of controls is difficult because of the immobility of arms and trunk. The most important effect, however, is that produced on the blood vessels and heart. The blood supply requires a fairly constant pressure for its normal function, and this is maintained by the pumping action of the heart. This pressure may be considerably disturbed in local areas of the body during acceleration. With positive *g,* the force acting in a head-to-foot direction tends to force the blood away from the head and into the lower parts of the body. The heart is unable to pump enough blood upward against this unusual force, and the blood supply to the head becomes inadequate. As the effective blood

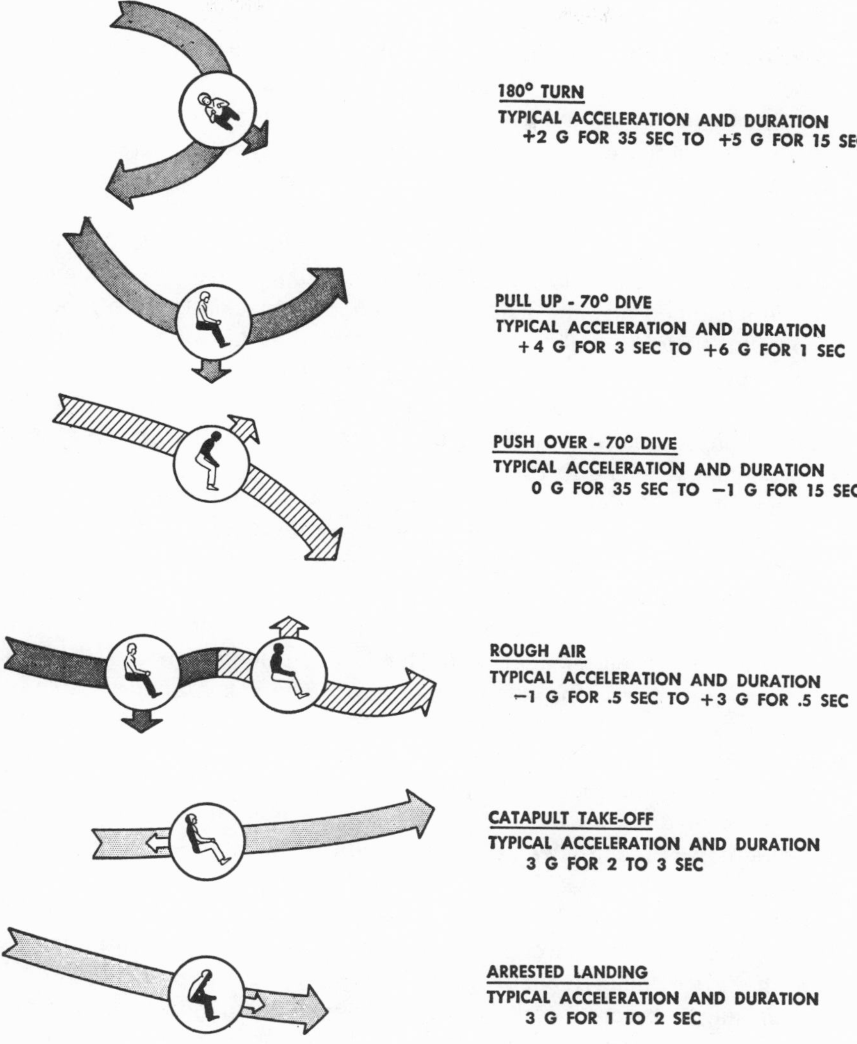

Figure 7.16 Accelerations produced by flying maneuvers. The dark-stippled portions of the arrows indicate that part of the maneuver which produces positive acceleration, the cross-hatched portions indicate negative acceleration, and the light-stippled portions indicate sagittal acceleration. *(Courtesy of Engineering Department, Douglas Aircraft Company, Inc., El Segundo, California.)*

pressure in the brain (and hence the oxygen supply) is reduced, the first symptom is a progressive loss of vision. The sequence of changes is as follows:

a. Dimming of vision or "grayout" at 3.5 to 4.0*g*.
b. Loss of peripheral vision so that the individual develops "gun barrel vision," that is, vision limited to the central area of the visual fields directly in front of the eye as if looking down a gun barrel.
c. At 4.0 to 4.5*g*, complete loss of vision—"blackout."
d. At 4.5 to 6.0*g*, loss of consciousness.

It should be remembered that *"blacking out" indicates only loss of vision and not loss of consciousness.* Between the time when the maximum *g* force is sustained and the actual occurrence of blackout, there is a time lag of 2 to 3 sec so that vision is lost just at the start of the climb after pulling out of a dive. Consciousness is retained and the flyer can carry out most required actions. Vision will return within a few seconds after acceleration ceases. If there is loss of consciousness, then there may be some confusion for 20 to 30 sec.

Going into a 70° dive from level flight, the accelerative force is in a direction opposite to that of gravity (foot-to-head) and thus briefly neutralizes the normal force of gravity. For this short time the flyer is in a state of "weightlessness" or 0*g*. Performance is not adversely altered during weightlessness if the pilot's seat belt is tight. Following this, the effects of negative *g* prevail, so that blood tends to be forced toward the head and blood pressure in the head is increased. The small blood vessels become distended, the face is flushed, and there is a sensation of fullness in the head and eyes. If negative *g* becomes excessive, there may be minute hemorrhages in the face and eyes.

Because of this, the limit of tolerance to accelerative force acting in this direction is much lower than for positive *g* forces. Some pilots have reported a "red-out" of vision during negative acceleration. Since this has not been demonstrated experimentally, the exact cause is not known. It may be due to the lower lid being forced up, to act as a reddish veil over the eye. Unlike the effects of positive *g,* which progress through several stages before becoming serious, negative *g* effects are sudden in onset and quickly become serious. Fortunately, sustained negative acceleration is infrequent in controlled flight. As shown in Figure 7.16, it occurs in a push-over into a steep dive and during buffeting in rough air. It will be considered again in connection with downward seat ejection from high-speed aircraft.

Hence, like many biological phenomena, the effect of *g* forces on man, as well as his tolerance to them, is a function of *time* and *magnitude* (number of *g*). A third critical factor is the *direction* in which these forces act on the body. Human tolerance to various *g* forces for a given time period is shown in Figure 7.17. It is seen that the average flyer can safely withstand an acceleration of 10*g* for 1 sec if it is in a positive or sagittal

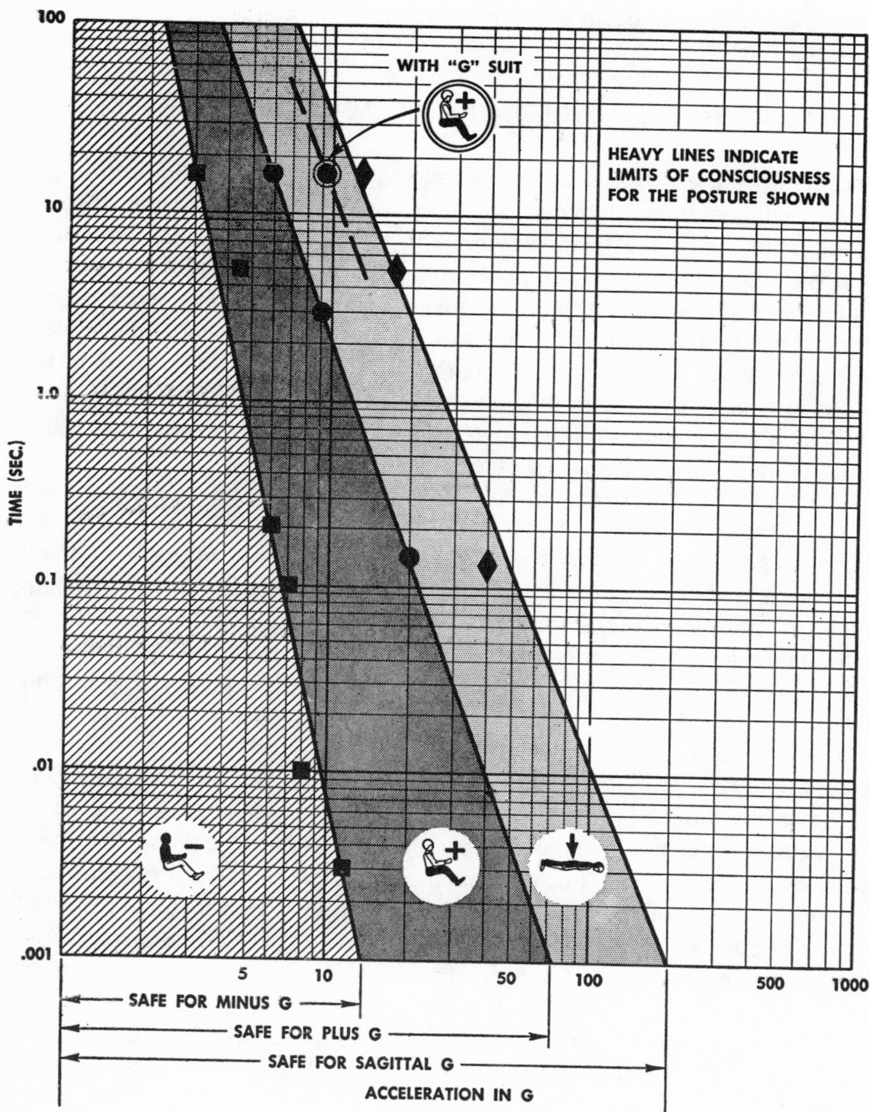

Figure 7.17 Human tolerance to acceleration. The average man's time limit of consciousness under acceleration is plotted on a logarithmic graph. The cross-hatched area indicates tolerance to negative *g;* the cross-hatched plus the dark-stippled areas, tolerance to positive *g*; the cross-hatched, plus the dark- and light-stippled areas, tolerance to sagittal *g*. *(Courtesy of Engineering Department, Douglas Aircraft Company, Inc., El Segundo, California.)*

direction, but would be in danger if this force were applied in a negative direction.

INCREASING HUMAN TOLERANCE TO ACCELERATIVE FORCES

The most frequent and troublesome effects of acceleration in aircraft are those resulting from sustained positive *g* by its reduction of the effective blood pressure in the head. Anything that increases blood pressure and opposes the tendency of blood to collect in the lower part of the body will raise the flyer's tolerance for these positive *g* forces. Short, stocky individuals generally have a higher tolerance than tall individuals. One possible reason for this is the diminished distance from the heart to the brain in shorter people. In the same individual *g* tolerance may vary from day to day because of fatigue, the emotional state, overindulgence in alcohol, hypoxia, temperature, and probably many other factors.

Emotional reactions such as fear or anger will raise blood pressure and hence *g* tolerance. Also, if the flyer is cold, his tolerance will be raised because constriction of the small vessels at the surface of the body tends to keep blood from pooling in the abdomen and legs. Conversely, high temperatures reduce tolerance. It is well known that an individual is somewhat more resistant to acceleration after having eaten a heavy meal.

In general, blood flow and blood pressure are beyond any sort of conscious control. To a limited extent, however, movement of blood toward the lower portions of the body and the fall in blood pressure can be retarded by performing certain *body maneuvers,* assuming *special postures,* or by wearing *anti-g suits.* A straining maneuver which increases pressure in the abdomen and chest has the effect of raising the blood pressure in the head. The abdominal and chest muscles are contracted to force air out of the lungs through the partially closed glottis every 3 to 4 sec so that a slow, forceful exhalation results. This effectively raises the blood pressure in the head for several seconds. By this means, tolerance to positive acceleration can be raised by about 2*g*. This procedure will not increase tolerance to negative *g* because here the requirement is for a reduction, rather than an increase, in blood pressure in the head region.

Crouching Since an important factor in human tolerance is the direction of the force relative to the body's long axis, altering body position will readily increase tolerance. From the upright sitting position, a change in posture which reduces the vertical distance from the heart to the brain tends to support the blood pressure in the head and so to increase significantly human *g* tolerance. If the pilot leans forward from the waist as much as 35°, and at the same time raises his knees, his tolerance is raised by 2 to 3g. The effectiveness of crouching in this way was well demonstrated by pilots during World War II.

Prone Position Assumption of the full prone position places the head at approximately the same level as the heart and hence the gain in tolerance is considerable. In this position, in the pull-out from a dive, the accelerative force acts sagitally in a back-to-front direction and 10 to 12g can be endured. One practical limitation to the use of this position is the restricted forward vision of the pilot and the neck strain involved in elevating the eyes for forward vision. The prone position is used only in space flight launches.

For present aircraft, the conventional upright (seated) position is most comfortable and practical. Alteration of this position to increase g toler-

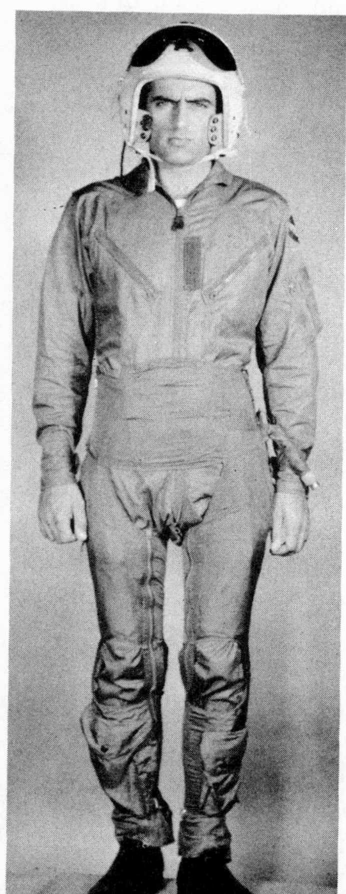

Figure 7.18 U.S. Air Force anti-g suit. The tightly fitted suit has an abdominal bladder and paired bladders over thighs and calves. As the wearer experiences g forces, these bladders inflate automatically to supply counter-pressure to legs and abdomen, thus raising g tolerance. *(U.S. Air Force photograph.)*

ance is subject to the important limitations of cockpit design, pilot comfort, and vision.

Anti-g Suits A closely fitted anti-*g* suit which operates automatically during high accelerations will materially increase man's tolerance. The limbs are constricted and the abdomen compressed by means of air bladders which are inflated in proportion to the magnitude of the accelerative force. Inflation takes place by means of air supplied automatically from the aircraft whenever acceleration exceeds 2*g*. The effect is to prevent pooling of blood in the lower extremities and abdomen and to raise blood pressure. The higher the pressure in the suit, the greater is the increase in the arterial blood pressure. One simple model consists of a pair of leggings and a wide belt which are snugly fitted to the individual by means of laces and may be worn beneath or over the flying suit (Figure 7.18). Incorporated within the suit are five bladders which inflate to exert pressure over the calves, thighs, and abdomen. The degree of inflation provided varies in direct proportion to the magnitude of the *g* force.

Tolerance to positive acceleration can be raised by as much as 3*g* by using some anti-*g* suits, but bladder pressure required to give this much protection is so high as to be uncomfortable. The lower pressures, which are commonly used, raise the blackout level by 1 to 2*g*. Contrary to popular belief, wearing these suits does not raise human tolerance to prolonged acceleration to a point where it exceeds the stress limits of the aircraft. Maneuvers which result in sudden short-duration acceleration, however, may damage the airplane without injury to the pilot. A flyer may increase the protection offered by his suit by straining or crouching. It has been found that, if the crouching position is assumed while wearing the suit, the gain in tolerance is greater than the simple addition of the gains produced by the suit alone or by crouching without the suit. Anti-*g* suits give no protection against negative *g*.

VIBRATION

This accelerative force is similar to noise in many ways. It is a wave which is too low to be heard but can be felt. Direction, amplitude, and frequency of the wave, are all important in determining its effect on the pilot. These effects may range from mild fatigue to complete incapacitation and severe pain. Helicopters are more apt to produce continuous, low-frequency, large-amplitude vibrations that will produce significant fatigue in pilots and passengers. Military pilots on high-speed, low-level flights in moderate to severe turbulence have experienced fatigue with accompanied deterioration of performance significantly above that experienced on other types of missions of equal duration. As far as possible, pilots should avoid continuous turbulence even if minimal. Helicopter and crop-dusting pilots should plan on shorter flights with longer rest periods between them, if other fatigue-provoking factors are known to co-exist.

Aerial Equilibration

Aerial equilibration is defined as the flyer's sense of balance, that is, his awareness of the attitude of his aircraft with reference to the pull of gravity. Maintaining equilibrium in the air is much more difficult than on the ground. Whether in flight or on land, the sense of balance by which man is able to stand, walk, sit, swim, or fly is actually a combination of three balancing senses:

a. Visual sense—eyes.
b. Muscle sense—muscles and deep tendons.
c. Vestibular sense—inner ear.

These three senses work together to keep the body properly positioned relative to the earth and the immediate environment. In the healthy person, these senses are more than adequate to maintain balance on the earth's surface.

A person standing on the ground keeps his balance even with eyes closed because his equilibrium is maintained by the other two senses. In the air, certain imperfections of these balancing mechanisms are manifest. Even when all are functioning, they may not insure that the flyer will maintain his equilibrium under all conditions of flight. If the effect of one of the senses is lost (for example, vision may be of little use on a dark night), then equilibrium is seriously compromised. Man's balancing senses, then, are primarily designed to be used on the ground, to supplement each other, and to accommodate for only relatively gradual changes in position. In the air, not only may one or more of the triad lose its effectiveness, but man is subject to rapid and violent changes of direction in three dimensions.

THE VISUAL SENSE

On the ground or in flight, the eyes are the most accurate of the three means of maintaining equilibrium. In flight, however, even with good visibility, they are not as reliable as on the ground because they lack stable visual references. To the man on the ground, the horizon and earthly surroundings are readily visible and are valuable references, as they change only gradually if at all. While flying on a clear day the pilot may see the earth below, other aircraft in the formation, and most important, the distant horizon. Aerial equilibrium is easily maintained by watching the ground and the horizon as long as these can be seen. Under these conditions the eyes act as a check on the other two balance senses and may even make corrections for them.

Because of weather conditions or darkness, the horizon and the ground below may be lost to view for variable periods so that the visual sense is ineffective. Even if the horizon remains visible, it may change suddenly and radically due to the maneuvering of the aircraft. Visual reference either outside the aircraft (ground, horizon) or inside the cockpit (flight instruments) is absolutely necessary for aerial equilibration. Visual reference to the earth is most useful when there is a clearly defined horizon.

THE MUSCLE SENSE

The muscle sense of equilibrium comes from minute nerve endings in the muscles, tendons, ligaments, and joints. These are stimulated by pressure and tension in the feet, legs, or buttocks when man stands, walks, or sits. The muscle sense is effective enough that man is able to stand or walk with his eyes closed and still maintain balance. In certain diseases, in which these nerve endings are damaged, the patient must keep his eyes open or lose his balance. Muscle sense measures only the up and down components of movements and so is helpful chiefly when movement is in the vertical plane. Vision is required in order to perceive circular motion.

By means of his muscle sense the experienced flyer can identify many movements of the aircraft by the pressure of the seat and the cockpit floor. For example, this pressure increases when going into a climb and decreases as descent is begun. Thus, although the pilot can tell that he is in a turn, spiral, or zoom, he cannot differentiate between these maneuvers without visual reference to flight instruments or the horizon. To some extent, position is "felt" in this way and has given rise to the expression "flying by the seat of the pants." Besides its failure to record circular motion, the muscle sense has another weakness. During flight without benefit of visual references such as instruments, the tops of cloud layers, or the horizon, vision alone does not always differentiate between the normal effects of gravity and similar sensations which are produced by accelerative forces. In turbulent air or during aerobatics, many erroneous and conflicting impressions of equilibrium are thus sent to the brain.

THE VESTIBULAR SENSE

The vestibular apparatus is located in a small cavity in the temporal bone of the skull and is part of the inner ear. It consists of a system of three *semicircular canals* arranged at right angles to each other and ter-

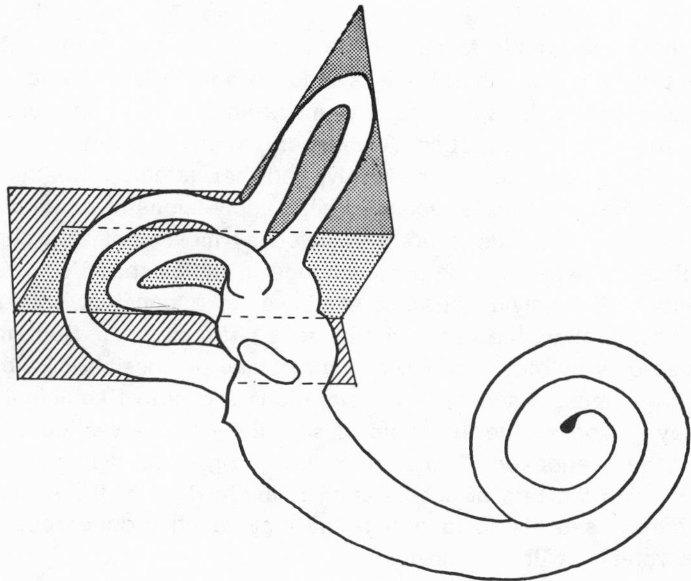

Figure 7.19 Diagram of the vestibular apparatus of the inner ear. The three semicircular canals are shown at right angles to each other. For each motion of the head there is a corresponding movement of fluid within the canals which stimulates the vestibular organs of equilibrium. *(Drawn by Charles J. Shaw, Chief of the Gunter Branch Graphics Section, Air University Library, Gunter Air Force Base, Alabama.)*

minating in sac-like enlargements (Figures 7.7 and 7.19). The canals and sacs contain fluid and sensory hairs which are delicate organs of balance.

One of these looped canals is in the vertical plane, one in the horizontal plane, and one in the transverse plane (Figure 7.19). When the head is moved, the fluid within the canals in each inner ear moves in the same direction. This stimulates the sensory hairs and gives them an appropriate impression of motion which is transmitted to the brain. Because of the special geometric arrangement of the canals in three different planes, there is a corresponding movement of fluid in at least one pair of canals each time the head is moved. Owing to the inertia of the fluid there is a brief pause before its rate of flow equals the motion of the head. Likewise, when the head motion is stopped, the fluid continues to flow for a short period. This continued motion of the fluid causes the same sensation as actually moving the head in the opposite direction so that the individual feels that he is turning in the opposite direction.

In prolonged turns the fluid movement catches up with the movement of the canal, and the hairs are no longer stimulated. This gives an erroneous impression to the brain that turning has stopped. Therefore, the semicircular canals are unable to perceive a turn after it has been continued for a few seconds, particularly if it is made gradually. If a rapid turn is abruptly stopped, the fluid continues to move and gives an impression of turning in the opposite direction. A common example of this is the child who spins rapidly about, stops suddenly, and then attempts to stand still. He falls because his brain is receiving false impressions of balance.

The vestibular apparatus is not stimulated by movement at a constant velocity, that is, there must be some change in either speed or direction (acceleration). Since flying straight and level at a constant speed produces no acceleration, the vestibular sense is not stimulated. Such motion is perceived only by means of visual impressions or possibly by vibration of the aircraft (muscle sense). If accelerations are not of sufficient magnitude, they are below the threshold of sensitivity of the vestibular sense and so will be overlooked. This occurs during a gradual maneuver of the aircraft in which the rate of acceleration is minimal. If, at the same time, the flyer cannot see his surroundings, he may reach a dangerously high degree of rotation without knowing it.

Having left the earth, the flyer loses much of the value of his muscle sense because it is no longer reliable. During blind flying conditions he also loses the advantage of his visual sense except by reference to instruments. In this situation, while relying on the vestibular sense he may be confused by it because:

a. it is excessively stimulated by the unusual accelerative forces experienced in flying, *or*
b. small, but significant, accelerations produced by aircraft maneuvers may not be perceived.

As long as all three of the balance senses are detecting and transmitting the same information to the brain, the flyer is fully aware of his true position in the air. If these sources are not coordinated and there is a conflict in the stimuli received, then equilibrium is lost.

Vertigo is the term loosely applied by flyers to loss of aerial equilibrium. As generally used, vertigo also refers to almost any state of confusion occurring in flight. Actually, true vertigo has a rather restricted medical meaning and is unusual in flight. The various phenomena causing loss of equilibrium are more properly called *sensory illusions.* These sensory illusions of flight may be classified as *visual, vestibular,* or *mixed.*

VISUAL ILLUSIONS

An illusion of *relative motion* occurs when the motion of one aircraft is falsely interpreted as motion of the adjacent aircraft in the formation. If the flight leader maintains a straight course and the rest of the flight veers to the left, the leader may appear to have turned to the right. A simple illustration of this illusion is seen in city traffic when stopping at a traffic signal. If the adjacent automobile moves slowly forward, there is a false impression that one's own automobile is coasting backward.

The visual sense becomes less accurate as distance from the earth is increased or as the horizon becomes less distinct. While flying at a few hundred feet off the ground, if one wing is low, it is immediately apparent. At 15,000 ft such an abnormal flight attitude may be unnoticed if the horizon is not readily available for reference. A *false horizon* illusion occurs when a pilot who cannot see the true horizon flies over an inclined cloud bank. If this takes place gradually, the pilot is misled and changes the flight attitude of the aircraft by aligning it with the cloud bank. Thus, although flying in a wing-low attitude, he believes his aircraft to be horizontal. One other visual illusion, autokinetic movement, was discussed in connection with night vision.

VESTIBULAR ILLUSIONS

Because the accelerations which they produce are below the threshold of sensitivity of the vestibular apparatus, certain motions of the aircraft are frequently overlooked. The confused state which results is a *vestibular illusion.*

"Leans" of the Same Direction If turbulence causes the aircraft to roll abruptly to the left and it then slowly resumes horizontal flight, the pilot may be aware of the tilt but not the recovery. He feels as though the plane is tipped to the left and corrects this sensation by leaning far to the right. He may persist in doing this for a short time even though his instruments are indicating horizontal flight.

"Leans" of the Opposite Direction If the aircraft is very slowly rolled to the left, the pilot is not aware of this and believes his aircraft to be horizontal. A rapid recovery of the aircraft to true horizontal is perceived as a tilt to the right. In this instance the flyer leans to the left in order to correct the sensation.

Illusions of Pitch The average person can be tilted upward 20° and downward 10° without being aware of it when this is done slowly and without visual reference. In turbulence, if the aircraft pitches upward less than 20° and then recovers slowly, the sensation of pitch will persist. The pilot feels as though the aircraft is climbing steeply, even though it is flying straight and level. If pitching is downward, a false sensation of diving will persist after a slow recovery to horizontal. The pilot may react to this sensation by pulling back on the stick and so go into a steep climb.

MIXED ILLUSIONS

When accelerative forces stimulate the muscle and vestibular senses, the resulting sensory illusions are called *oculogravic illusions.* Without visual references to clouds, terrain, horizon, or instruments, the type of aerial maneuver is rarely correctly identified. The *g* forces of one maneuver are falsely interpreted by the pilot as arising from a completely different maneuver.

Sensation of Climbing While Turning In a properly banked turn, acceleration tends to force the body firmly into the seat in the same manner as when the aircraft is entering a climb or pulling out of a dive. Without visual references, an aircraft making a banked turn may be interpreted as being in a climbing attitude, and the pilot may react inappropriately by pushing forward on the control column.

Sensation of Diving While Recovering from a Turn The positive *g* forces sustained in a banked turn are reduced as the turn is completed. This reduction in pressure gives the flyer the same sensation as going into a dive and may be interpreted in this way. He may overcorrect by pulling back on the control column and cause the aircraft to stall.

Sensation of Diving Following Pull-Out from a Dive The accelerative forces on the body during the pull-out from a dive are reduced after recovery is complete. This reduction in *g* force may be falsely identified as originating from another dive.

Sensation of Opposite Tilt While Skidding If skidding of the aircraft takes place during a turn, the body is pressed away from the direction of turning. This may be falsely perceived as a tilt in the opposite direction.

Illusions which are the result of stimulation of the visual and vestibular senses are called *oculogyral illusions.* These result when conflicting impulses from the eyes and the semicircular canals are transmitted to the brain.

The Coriolis Phenomenon This is a severe loss of equilibrium in which true vertigo results. When the pilot is rotating with the aircraft and then moves his head out of the plane of rotation, there is a differential stimulation of two sets of semicircular canals. For example, if during a spin the pilot moves his head forward or backward, an additional pair of semicircular canals is stimulated and extreme dizziness and nausea are suddenly produced. The consequence of such an unusual reaction in flight is apparent.

Sensation of Reversed Rotation If a rotary motion persists for a short period and is then discontinued, there is a sensation of rotation in the opposite direction. This occurs in a spinning aircraft when the pilot has poor visual reference to the earth. After recovery from a spin to the left, there is a sensation of turning to the right. In attempting to correct for this, the pilot puts the aircraft back into the spin to the left. Flyers have given this illusion the sinister name of "graveyard spin."

PREVENTION OF SENSORY ILLUSIONS

Although sensory illusions in flight occur infrequently, they are extremely important because each is a serious threat to the flyer's safety. They are most likely to occur when an inexperienced or overconfident pilot is flying under conditions of poor visibility, but may occur at any time. All pilots are susceptible, but those who have developed and who maintain proficiency in basic instrument flying are least vulnerable.

Because of this vulnerability, flight instruments, and particularly *attitude* instruments have been developed (Chapter 5). The more a pilot understands how sensory illusions are produced, the more he will come to rely on the visual presentation of flight instruments, and the less susceptible he will be.

There is a special type of vertigo which is limited to helicopter and reciprocating engine pilots. This is called "flicker vertigo" and is caused by the rotor or propeller interrupting light in a rhythmical manner between 10 and 20 cycles per second. Rarely, in particularly susceptible individuals, this repetitious interruption of light can produce convulsions. Severe disorientation has been reported by light-aircraft pilots flying into the setting sun with an idling or windmilling propeller, and by helicopter pilots whose rotors came between their eyes and the sun. It is not necessary to look directly at the light source to become disoriented, as reflected light from the periphery of the visual fields will also cause this phenomenon. The frequency of interruption that will produce disorientation varies from individual to individual. Flicker vertigo can be avoided by not allowing the propeller or rotor to come between the eyes and any strong light source.

Airsickness

Airsickness is nausea, vomiting, and a general feeling of discomfort caused by the motion of an aircraft in flight. It is essentially the same as other forms of motion sickness (car, swing, train, and seasickness) in its cause and manifestations. Its primary cause is recurrent disturbances of equilibrium through overstimulation of the vestibular sense. It appears to be produced in much the same way as sensory illusions, that is, by lack of coordination of the stimuli which are sent to the brain by the balance senses. The up and down components of motion appear to be most important in producing this condition. The vertical "bumping" motion of the aircraft in turbulent air rather than yawing or rolling is the usual cause of symptoms. In addition, psychological factors probably are important in some people. Apprehension and anxiety of any kind increase the tendency to become airsick.

OCCURRENCE

Nearly everyone is susceptible if turbulence is extreme and prolonged. Flyers rarely become airsick while they are actually operating the aircraft, but they may while riding as passengers. Among civilian airline passengers, only about 0.6% are affected. This low incidence is explained by the precautions taken by the airlines to make passengers comfortable, such as reclining seats and avoidance of turbulent air. In military flying, airsickness has been much more frequent. In one series of about 2000 airborne troops studied during routine training, 23% experienced some degree of airsickness. Another analysis of 2080 flying cadets showed that 5.7% were airsick on their first flight, but only 1.1% were affected after they had made ten flights. While up to 40% of students may become sick during training, less than 1% of Air Force students fail their training because of persistent airsickness.

PREVENTION

Airsickness is difficult to avoid completely in military operations because combat aircraft are not built for comfort, and missions must be flown regardless of turbulence. The following measures may be taken to prevent or control symptoms of airsickness:

a. A reasonably gradual introduction of the flying student to the motion of aircraft—particularly in aerobatics.
b. Selection of the most favorable flight route to avoid turbulence.
c. Avoidance of violent and unnecessary maneuvers.
d. If possible, choosing a position in the aircraft near its center of gravity where there is less motion.
e. In turbulence, lying down with eyes closed. Shifting visual references cause increased susceptibility.
f. Avoidance of strong odors or hot stuffy air in the aircraft.
g. Avoidance of overindulgence in food or alcohol prior to flight.
h. Fixing the gaze on a stable visual reference outside the aircraft, preferably the horizon.
i. The taking of antimotion-sickness drugs by susceptible passengers prior to flight.

It is possible, to some extent, for most persons to become accustomed to aircraft motion and so to develop some resistance to airsickness. This is commonly observed in flying cadets after they have made several flights. The use of preventive drugs by aircrews is not an acceptable practice because of certain secondary effects such as visual disturbances and drowsiness. In special instances drugs may be prescribed temporarily by a flight surgeon for relief of airsickness in a beginning student.

Noise in Flight

Noise is unpleasant sound due to acoustic waves of scattered frequencies and intensities. In aviation, noise is not as great a problem during flight as it is on the ground, since higher noise levels for longer periods of time are experienced by ground maintenance crews than by aircrews. Nevertheless, flyers are subjected to noise of sufficient intensity and duration to produce significant effects. The principal effects of noise in flight are interference with radio and voice communication, contribution to fatigue, and partial hearing loss after repeated exposure.

THE MECHANISM OF HEARING (FIGURE 7.6)

The outer ear collects sound waves from the air and conducts them inward to the middle ear, causing the eardrum to vibrate. This, in turn, sets up motion in the small bones of the middle ear by which vibrations are transmitted to the *cochlea* in the inner ear. From here, stimuli are sent through the auditory nerve to the brain where the vibration is perceived as sound. This is the perception of sound by air vibrations. Sound can also be perceived by vibrations being conducted through the bones of the skull to reach the *auditory nerve.*

MEASURING SOUND

Every sound has two measurable components, *pitch* (tone) and *intensity* (loudness). Two sounds may have the same pitch but different intensities, or vice versa. The human ear can hear sounds only within a certain range of intensity and a certain range of pitch. Since sound is a wave-like phenomenon, its pitch is measured in cycles per second or Hertz (Hz). Sound intensity is measured in units called *decibels* (dB). Audible tones for man vary from 20 Hz to 20,000 Hz. Human hearing is most acute for sounds between 500 Hz and 5000 Hz, which is the usual range of the human voice. Audible intensities range from 10 dB to 140 dB. There is no upper limit to audible sound intensity, but above 140 dB sound can actually be felt as a vibration in parts of the body other than the ears. The decibel values (intensity) of various sounds are shown in the following table:

Sound	*Decibels*
Human heartbeat	10
Whispered voice	20 to 30
Spoken voice	40
Vacuum cleaner	50
Loud shout	80
Aircraft maintenance hangar	100
T-29 aircraft, cruising	117
F-102 aircraft, cruising	125
Artillery fire	150
B-52 aircraft	156
F-100 aircraft, military power at ground level	172

CHARACTERISTICS OF AIRCRAFT NOISE

In-flight noise from propeller-driven aircraft is produced by the propeller, the engine and accessory power plants, engine exhaust, the ventilating system, and aerodynamic noises (slipstream). The propeller is the greatest contributor to the total noise intensity. Propeller noise is mostly in the lower frequencies below 300 Hz. Since this is the predominant component of propeller aircraft noise, the latter has its greatest intensity in the low frequencies. Propeller aircraft may seem louder than jets if this low-frequency noise is intense enough to be felt as vibrations, even though both aircraft are putting out identical sound intensities. Intensities of 90 dB to 130 dB are produced in propeller aircraft.

The two principal sources of noise from jet aircraft are the engines and the aerodynamic noise. Jet noise differs from that of propeller aircraft in that all the frequencies of the audible sound range are represented at equal levels of intensity. The proportion of the total jet noise from aerodynamic sources is much greater than that for propeller aircraft. This proportion becomes still higher with increasing speed but tends to diminish with altitude. Jet noise gives a sensation of smoothness and does not seem to be as loud, even though the total decibel values may be the same as for propeller aircraft. Since most noise originates outside the

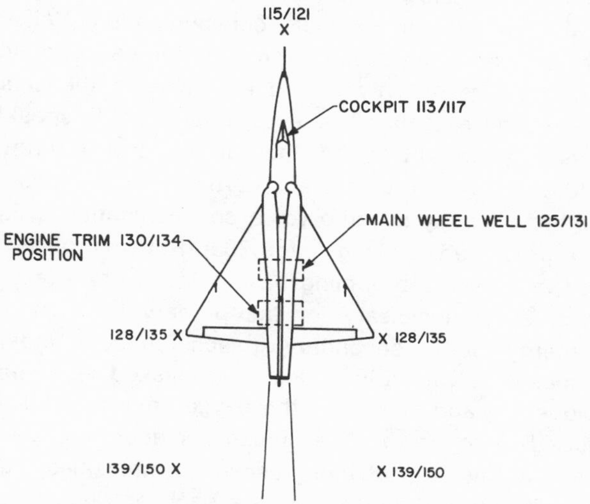

Figure 7.20 Sound intensities produced by jet aircraft. Noise levels are shown for various points around an F-106A aircraft. Highest intensities are found near the tail. *(Drawn by John Cole, Aerospace Medical Research Laboratories.)*

cockpit, its intensity within the cockpit is greatly reduced by the walls of the cabin. Pressurized aircraft are particularly well insulated in this respect because of the tightly enclosed cabin.

Flyers are constantly subjected to voice or radio signals. The amount of static accompanying these signals varies with conditions and may reach high levels at times. The intensity of radio noise (exclusive of static) is much lower than the general level of noise in the cockpit.

EFFECTS OF NOISE ON THE FLYER

Noise and In-Flight Communication Perception of voice and radio communication is made difficult in flight by interference of the aircraft noise. When subjected to two similar sounds the ear detects the louder sound more clearly and may overlook the lesser sound. When an undesirable sound thus interferes with the perception of a desired sound, the effect is called "masking." Jet noise has a greater masking effect on the sound of the human voice than propeller aircraft noise of equal intensity. This is because the greatest proportion is within the speech range, that is, at the same frequencies as the most common sounds of the human voice.

In addition to the masking effect of noise, the decreased barometric pressure at altitude adversely affects communication. With diminished air density, the spoken voice does not produce the same sound pressures as at sea level. The sensitivity of the ear remains the same, but the intensity of the sound reaching it is less. Equal effort in speaking gives a sound of lesser intensity at 30,000 ft than at sea level. Aircraft radios are built with additional power to correct partially for this loss in speech intensity. Another difficulty in radio voice communication at high altitude is the effect of pressure breathing (page 363). Reversal of the respiratory cycle required in pressure breathing has an inhibitory effect on speech. The amount of effort necessary for the primary function of breathing leaves little energy for the secondary speech function. Under these circumstances speech is very tiring. Also, it is masked, to some extent, by the frequent opening and closing of the oxygen mask valves.

Hearing Loss Due to Noise The human ear does not hear two simultaneous sounds as the sum of their respective intensities, but only as a small increase. If two aircraft engines are each producing sound at 130 dB, this will be heard as about 134 dB rather than 260 dB. Except for this fact, sound levels in or around multiengine aircraft would be too high for tolerance. Continuous or repeated noise of high intensity can produce temporary hearing loss. This depends upon several factors:

a. Duration of exposure to the noise.
b. Interval between exposures.
c. Noise intensity (number of decibels).
d. Pitch (number of cycles per second).

For example, 130 dB for 10 min will produce a transient hearing loss of about 20 dB. If there is sufficient interval before the next exposure, hearing will be fully regained. Thus temporary partial hearing loss is common after a flight and is no cause for concern. If exposure is frequent and prolonged, some permanent hearing loss may result. Temporary loss may follow exposures to 90 dB. Sounds of 140 db and above cause pain in the ears, and 160 dB may rupture the eardrum.

Hearing loss due to high noise levels follows a fairly typical pattern in that the individual first loses his ability to hear high-pitched tones at about 2048 Hz and 4096 Hz. Failure to hear shrill sounds that are at a higher pitch than the human voice is the first indication. Although there is general agreement that in-flight aircraft noise will produce some high-frequency hearing loss over a period of years, the exact degree of this is not established. A large percentage of nonflyers have hearing impairment above 2048 Hz. Also, hearing ability in these frequencies commonly diminishes with age. For these reasons the exact amount of hearing loss caused by flying is difficult to estimate. Because of its frequency range, jet noise is more likely to cause hearing loss. Currently, however, propeller aircraft are more damaging in flight because the crew is exposed for longer periods and the amount of sound penetrating to the cockpit is greater.

Fatigue Due to Noise Work done in the presence of noise is followed by a degree of fatigue which is out of proportion to the work itself. Since noise interferes with concentration, more energy is expended in performing work in a noisy environment than in a quiet one. Operating an aircraft is a work situation which demands sustained concentration in a noisy environment. Aircraft noise is an important factor contributing to the overall effect of flying fatigue.

NOISE PROTECTION IN FLIGHT

Aircrews may be protected against noise by the wearing of insert-type *ear defenders* or flight helmets. Insulation of the aircraft cabin will materially reduce the sound level but has limited application in military aircraft because of the extra weight involved.

Insert-Type Ear Defenders Ear plugs of synthetic rubber, plastic, cotton and cotton-wool which insert into the external ear canal are effective and practical. Impregnating cotton or wool with paraffin increases their ability to block sound. Plastic or rubber plugs are of most value when individually fitted to the ear canals. All types of ear defenders tend to protect against high-frequency noise more effectively than against noise of low frequency. Properly fitted soft plastic ear plugs may reduce noise intensity by 20 dB in the lower frequencies and 40 dB in the high frequencies. For this reason, plastic plugs are relatively more effective against jet noise because it has a higher frequency range. In high noise levels, ear defenders do not mask out speech and radio signals even though they do reduce the total noise. This is because only a small part of the sound frequency range is used for speech. This phenomenon is often not appreciated by aircrewmen who may be reluctant to use ear defenders in the mistaken belief that they will dangerously compromise their hearing of signals and speech.

Helmets for Noise Protection Because the ear is not the only route for the transmission of sound, the insert-type ear defender's effectiveness is limited. Some of the sound energy which reaches the auditory nerve is transmitted via the bones of the skull. Such bone-conducted sound does not add to the total loudness reaching the auditory nerve in the inner ear if the normal air-conduction channels are open. However, if the external ear canal is blocked (insert-type defender), then considerable sound is transmitted via the skull. The amount of sound energy absorbed and conducted by the bones of the skull depends upon the total area of the skull exposed. The wearing of a well-fitted flying helmet, which is padded with sponge rubber, eliminates almost all possibility of bone conduction of noise as well as much of the air-conducted noise (Figure 7.4). Helmets alone are not as effective as insert ear defenders and maximum protection is afforded by wearing ear defenders in combination with a helmet. Snugly fitted plastic or rubber insert-type ear defenders may so completely seal the external ear canal that a partial vacuum develops inside the canal during rapid descents. Because of the atmospheric pressure change, a relative negative pressure may develop in the external canal between the ear defender and the eardrum unless the seal is broken by manipulation of the ear defender. This is not possible if the flyer is wearing a helmet. For this reason, cotton ear defenders are preferred for use when a helmet is worn in flight.

Aviation Toxicology

It is accepted as only common prudence to guard against such hazards as carbon monoxide poisoning from fuel, heater, and exhaust system leaks and to protect crop-dusting pilots from their toxic cargo. But there are other toxic exposures which, being more insidious, can be even more dangerous. *Medications* are a far too common and serious hazard for the uninformed or careless flyer. Medications used to treat common respiratory or gastrointestinal illnesses may adversely affect the airman's visual acuity, depth perception, reaction time, and state of alertness. Many drugs which are in virtually everyday use for the common cold, allergy, gastrointestinal upset, and headache have side effects which can seriously compromise the flyer's effectiveness. Many anti-cough preparations contain narcotics which even in small doses can render a pilot unsafe in his aircraft. Weight-control pills and anti-smoking drugs are particularly hazardous.

In recent years as piloting of private aircraft has become more accessible to the general public, aviation accidents are being linked to misuse of *alcohol* with increasing frequency. The effects of alcohol are greatly intensified by even the small degree of hypoxia experienced at 5000 ft of altitude. Thus one or two cocktails can seriously impair judgment and coordination. *The combination of alcohol and flying in the same 24-hr period may be deadly.*

8

Basic Flight Techniques in Light Aircraft*

This chapter presents the maneuvers and techniques applicable to the piloting of light aircraft in visual flight conditions. It is based on the curriculum of the U.S. Air Force undergraduate pilot training schools, and much information on maneuvers is drawn from excellent Air Force training manuals.

The aircraft currently used for this chapter is a low-winged, all-metal type with a 225-hp engine, constant-speed propeller, retractable tricycle landing gear, and landing flaps. It is stressed and powered for normal aerobatic use. Most of the information in this chapter is based primarily on such an aircraft, it being illustrative of modern light aircraft, although other propeller-driven lightplane types are considered where appropriate.

Each aircraft has its own set of flight characteristics, and the underlying purpose of flight training must be to develop skills and safe habits that are transferrable to any aircraft. If the lightplane pilot flies with precision and with safe habits, he will find the transition to

*Revision by Major Glenn W. Young, United States Air Force, and the Editor.

heavier aircraft much easier than he probably expects. His time in the lightplane will be more safely spent, too, although the forgiving nature of the lightplane may conceal dangerous habits for many hours of flight.

Preparing the Aircraft for Flight

PREFLIGHT INSPECTION

Even for the "simple" lightplane, and even with good maintenance service, the wise pilot will form the habit of making a thorough preflight inspection with the aid of a printed check list.

Check the cockpit area first to insure that the master and ignition switches are off. At the same time, the landing gear handle can be checked for firm seating in the down position. Aircraft forms usually are kept in the cockpit and should be inspected at this time.

The flight handbook for each aircraft, published by the manufacturer or the military service, lists specific items to be examined during the exterior inspection. Make this check during a complete circuit about the aircraft (Figure 8.1). Some items of the check are common to all aircraft —security of control surface fittings and tire inflation, for example. Any aircraft, however, has at least one item or two on its recommended preflight inspection that is peculiar to that aircraft alone because of design or operational experience. The reward for meticulous inspection habits is safe, pleasant, and inexpensive flying; the penalty for carelessness is always too great.

COCKPIT PROCEDURES BEFORE ENGINE STARTING

Fire is a remote but constant possibility during any start, and a fire extinguisher should be positioned near the aircraft or installed in the cockpit. Set the seat and rudder pedals, if adjustable, so that full rudder and forward stick can be obtained, and so that all controls in the cockpit can be reached without strain. Adjust and fasten the shoulder harness and seat belt. The shoulder harness should be locked at this time if all controls can be reached after locking. If the harness is of the inertia reel type that locks automatically in case of impact, it can be left unlocked manually during all flight unless a crash landing appears likely.

The cockpit now can be readied for the start. By common practice, the readying process starts at the pilot's left side rear and proceeds around to his right side rear. Excluding the throttle, propeller, and mixture con-

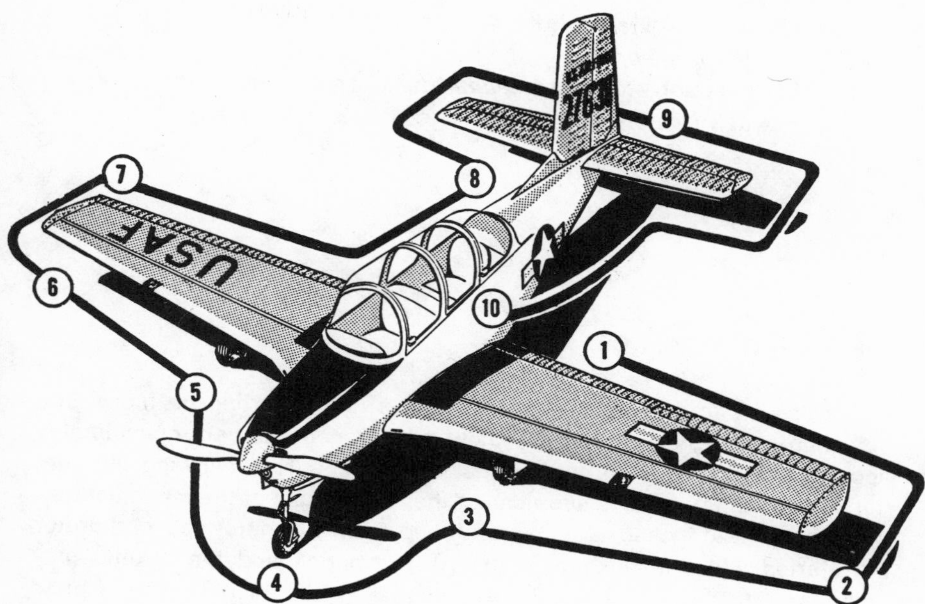

Figure 8.1 Exterior inspection of the T-34 Trainer. 1. *Left wing:* Visually inspect flap, aileron, trim tab; move surfaces to check for looseness. 2. *Left wing tip:* Condition of wing tip, navigation light. Remove pitot cover. Check condition of leading edge. 3. *Left main gear:* Condition of wheel, strut; wheel well free of obstructions. Tire pressure 35 psi, strut extension $3\frac{3}{32}$ in. Air intake clean, fuel access door secure. 4. *Nose:* Cowling secure, augmenter tubes unobstructed. Condition of passing light, propeller, nose gear, door, wheel well. Tire pressure, 30 psi, strut extension $3\frac{3}{16}$ in. Main gear fairing doors closed. 5. *Right main gear:* Perform the same checks as for left gear. 6. *Right wing tip:* Perform the applicable checks as for left wing tip. 7. *Right wing:* Perform the same checks as for left wing. 8. *Fuselage right side:* External canopy release handle undisturbed, antennas secure. Static air vent clean. 9. *Empennage:* Condition of control surfaces, trim tabs; move surfaces to check for looseness, check rudder trim tab for antiservo action. Condition of navigation light, underside of fuselage. 10. *Fuselage left side.* Static air vent clean, baggage compartment door secured closed. Check fire extinguisher pressure gage. *(Courtesy of U.S. Air Force.)*

trols, which are considered separately, set the controls affecting the engine start as follows during this check:

Parking brakes—*applied.*

Radios, lights, and other unnecessary electrical equipment switches—*off.*

Carburetor air control—*cold air* (or perhaps *filtered air*).

Oil cooler and engine cowl flaps—*open.*
Fuel shutoff valve—*open.*
Fuel tank selector—*to recommended tank* (or perhaps both).
Master switch (battery and generator switches if installed)—*on.*

Starting

STARTING SEQUENCE

Improvements in modern lightplane engines make starting no more difficult than starting an automobile; however, procedures vary considerably according to the type of engine and fuel system. The following information is general and should supplement the instructions of the manufacturer.

Horizontally opposed engines equipped with a venturi-type carburetor are started with the mixture in the RICH position and the throttle partially open. If the engine is cold, the manual primer should be used prior to start. Amount of priming varies from one to two strokes in cool temperatures to eight strokes when the temperature is well below freezing. During extreme conditions it may be necessary to have the primer pulled out so that, as the engine begins to fire, additional fuel can be supplied by slowly pushing in the primer knob. The starter-ignition switch operates exactly like that in an automobile. To crank the engine, turn the switch to the START position. As the engine fires it will automatically be carried away from the starter. At this time release the switch, which is spring-loaded to the BOTH position, and adjust the throttle to the desired rpm.

Horizontally opposed engines equipped with a fuel-injection system are started with the aid of an electrical boost pump, since the engine-driven fuel pump will not supply sufficient fuel until the engine is operating at approximately 500 rpm or above. The mixture is set at RICH and the throttle is partially opened. Use of the manual primer is necessary only in very cold weather. Actuate the boost pump just before cranking and check the fuel flow to be within limits. Do not delay cranking the engine or excess fuel will accumulate in the intake manifold which will cause flooding and a possible fire hazard. After the engine is running smoothly, turn the boost pump off and adjust the throttle to the desired rpm.

Larger engines of the radial or inverted inline-type are normally started by breaking down the start procedure into separate steps.

First Make sure the start will not damage the engine. Rotate the engine through one complete cycle (two or three revolutions) without introducing fuel. At the first evidence that the starter may stall, the engine should be checked for presence of oil or fuel in the inverted cylinders. A start with fluid in the cylinders may produce a condition known as hydraulic lock, which can bend or break a piston rod. Note: Horizontally opposed engines are not subject to hydraulic locks from oil, although a partial lock can occur from overpriming.

In addition to the check for hydraulic lock, turning the engine improves lubrication at the first of the start.

Second Provide a combustible fuel-air mixture to the cylinders. Since larger engines are usually started with the mixture control in the IDLE CUT-OFF position, all starting fuel initially must come from the primer. Unless aircraft design provides fuel by gravity flow, as in high-wing monoplanes, an electric fuel boost pump must be on to deliver priming fuel. The primer is operated either continuously or intermittently, depending on the rate of flow it delivers.

A proper air mixture must be provided for primer fuel; to do this, adjust the throttle to the position which would produce about 1000 or 1200 rpm. This position usually is about one inch forward on the throttle quadrant in the cockpit. A cold engine requires less throttle at the start than a hot engine, because the cold fuel does not vaporize as well.

As described above, light aircraft engines with fuel injection and no impellers are started with the mixture in RICH position, boost pump ON, and without the use of primer except in very cold weather. The larger engines also *can* be started in this manner, and there are certain advantages to the method. If the battery is weak, the current drain by the primer pump is eliminated. If the engine has a blower (single-stage supercharger), the fuel from the carburetor will be vaporized as it enters the cylinders more than will primer fuel put directly into cylinder or manifold. The danger of the latter method is that the possibility of induction systems fires is much greater.

Third Provide ignition for the combustible mixture. One does this by turning the ignition switch to BOTH. The engine should fire within one or two revolutions.

Fourth Adjust the engine to normal combustion. If the start is accomplished on an initial charge of manually introduced primer fuel only, move the mixture control to RICH position as soon as the engine definitely fires; otherwise, use more priming.

Most electric primers are capable of supporting combustion at 1000 to 1200 rpm. There is no reason for hurrying the transition to mixture control fuel, and the throttle may be adjusted slightly to provide smooth combustion before the transition. This procedure will generally prevent engine backfire, which can damage the induction system.

Check manual primers carefully after the start to ensure that they are locked closed, and check electric primer switches in the OFF position.

Otherwise, leaking primer fuel will be drawn into the engine, causing an excessively rich mixture.

The propeller control should be in full high rpm (low-pitch) position for all starts. Changing pitch angle too quickly after a cold start can deprive the engine of needed oil pressure.

Safety Precautions During Starting Before cranking the engine, clear the area 360° and call "clear." If a fire guard is standing by the aircraft, make sure he acknowledges. Have your feet on the brakes in the event the parking brake system is inoperative and keep one hand near the throttle-mixture controls ready for immediate adjustment.

Starting Difficulties and Malfunctions If the mixture is decidedly too lean or too rich, no start can be obtained. Raw fuel draining out of the exhaust or out of the impeller section drain valve under the engine indicates the rich condition. Discontinue priming. If the engine is of the horizontally opposed type, set the throttle FULL OPEN, the mixture at FULL LEAN, and continue cranking to clear the rich mixture from the cylinders. When the engine first fires, return the throttle and mixture to the starting position.

When the engine does not fire at all and no raw fuel appears, the probable difficulty is that the mixture is too lean. Additional prime and a check of fuel quantity and flow will usually solve the problem.

A mixture that is slightly too rich will permit the engine to fire weakly on one or two cylinders. Black exhaust smoke may be seen. With priming discontinued, the engine should "catch" after another revolution or two.

A mixture that is slightly too lean will permit the engine to fire intermittently, possibly with backfiring. Additional priming will help the engine to "catch." On large engines with injection-type carburetors and a continuous prime for the start, the difficulty probably is in the throttle being too far advanced. Since the priming is continuous already, the obvious correction is to retard the throttle slightly.

If no start is obtained after a reasonable interval (10 to 30 sec of operation, depending upon starter specification), discontinue the start by cutting off fuel and disengaging the starter. Turn the ignition switch off *after* the engine stops turning, so that no combustible fuel mixture can remain in the cylinder after the engine stops. Check for hydraulic lock before another starting attempt.

Engine fires during start usually result from overpriming and may occur in the intake or exhaust manifolds. The first corrective action is to set the mixture at FULL LEAN, boost pump OFF, discontinue priming, throttle FULL OPEN, and continue cranking. If the engine starts, an induction or exhaust fire will be blown out the exhaust. If the fire persists, discontinue cranking, turn the ignition and master switches OFF, and evacuate the aircraft. Fires not controlled by these methods usually are the result of leakage from fuel lines or accumulated fuel in the engine compartment.

PROPPING OFF

Some very light aircraft do not have electric starters. Larger aircraft sometimes must be started when the battery is very weak and no external power supply is available or when the electric starter is inoperative. In such cases the propeller can be swung by hand. Engines up to 500 hp have been started by this method.

To keep the job safe, strict adherence to procedures is required. On first approaching the aircraft, the prop man ascertains that the wheels are chocked and calls "Switch off." The pilot checks the master and ignition switches and replies "Switch off." The prop man calls "Gas off," and the pilot checks and replies. The fuel may be shut off either with a valve in the fuel line or with the full lean position of the mixture control if the carburetion system is so equipped. With the fuel off, the propeller is pulled through two or three revolutions to check for liquid in the cylinders.

The prop man then calls "Gas on and throttle cracked." The pilot assures that a supply of fuel will be available for the start. If a carburetor mixture control is used, it is set to RICH. Two or three strokes of the primer are normally used if the engine is cold. Priming may be unnecessary for a warm engine. The throttle is "cracked" from the idle position about ½ to 1 in. open—to the position normally producing about 1000 to 1200 rpm. The pilot then replies "Gas on and throttle cracked."

The prop man has positioned one of the propeller blades at a convenient height where stiffness of rotation indicates that a cylinder is just short of a compression stroke. He assumes the stance shown in Figure 8.2. He should stand just clear of the propeller arc, since standing too far clear will cause him to lean forward dangerously unbalanced. His fingers should rest across the top of the blade, but should not grip the blade. The prop man calls "Switch on," and the pilot replies *before* turning the ignition switch to BOTH position. He will usually turn the master switch on at this time also, although the master switch might be left off until after the start if the aircraft is normally started with the electric starter. This would prevent possible inadvertent operation of the starter while the prop man was handling the propeller.

The prop man calls "Brakes and contact." The pilot applies brakes before replying. The prop man spins the propeller with a hard, quick, snapping motion, stepping back with the foot that is raised for balance. If no start is obtained, the switches are turned off, the propeller is rotated to clear the cylinders of fuel from the starting attempt, and the

Figure 8.2 "Propping off."

starting procedure is repeated. Since engine rotation is limited to one or two compression strokes with this starting method, success depends upon introduction of a correct fuel-air mixture before the start. Take care not to overprime.

Minor deviations of the procedure given above may be necessary for certain types of carburetion systems. The important thing is to duplicate as closely as possible the ideal starting procedure for the engine with the electric starter, adding safety conditions for protection of the prop man.

ENGINE WARM-UP

After start, operate the engine at a setting between 1000 and 1200 rpm that produces smoothest operation. Watch oil pressure during warm-up, and if it does not register an increase within 30 sec after the start, shut down the engine for investigation. Since taxiing usually requires less than 1000 rpm, continue the warm-up in the parking position until temperatures approach operating limits. Use of idle rpm with a cold engine produces fouled spark plugs. During the warm-up, engine instruments and aircraft equipment can be checked. Save engine performance checks until just before takeoff. They are more valid then, and the propeller blast is less unpopular when created off the parking ramp.

Taxi Technique Taxiing is the movement of the aircraft on the ground under its own power. The objective at the moment is to get out to the takeoff position. At a tower-controlled airport, first obtain taxi clearance from the control tower. This is done by radio or, in the event of communications failure, by means of light signals from the tower (Figure 8.3).

In congested areas, ground crewmen should provide initial taxi guidance. If wing-tip clearance is doubtful, a "wing-walker" should accompany the aircraft.

Normal taxi speed is about that of a brisk walk—somewhat slower in congested areas and faster on open taxiways. The engine power required may vary from idle to 1500 rpm, depending on wind and the slope of the surface.

Movement of the rudder pedals turns the aircraft, acting through the aerodynamic force of the rudder surface and, on most present-day aircraft, through a steerable nose or tail wheel. The effectiveness of the rudder increases along with the airflow over its surface, whether that airflow comes from increased propeller rpm, increased taxi ground speed, or increased headwind. As the effectiveness of the rudder surface increases, that of the steerable tail wheel decreases. This occurs because the increased airspeed acts to lift the horizontal stabilizer, lessening the tail wheel traction. To keep as much pressure on the tail wheel as possible, hold the stick full back during taxi, especially when using engine power. The only exception to this is when taxiing with a tailwind that significantly exceeds taxi speed. Forward stick then will act to keep the tail down.

With the tricycle gear, elevator technique is less important during taxiing. Because the taxi attitude is approximately level with the ground, increased airflow tends to strike the top and bottom of the horizontal stabilizer almost evenly. Any tail-up tendency that does occur puts *more* pressure on the nose wheel, thus increasing its steering effectiveness. Leave the control stick in neutral during taxi in tricycle-geared aircraft, except with a strong tailwind. As with a tail-wheeled aircraft, hold the stick forward in this situation to keep the tail down and prevent the aircraft from tipping.

Steerable nose or tail wheels usually can be steered to about 15° to 20° of arc in either direction, after which point they are manually or automatically disengaged to permit tighter turns. With or without a steerable wheel, the brakes must be used for tight turns. The brake pedals usually are mounted on each rudder pedal, and they may be used selectively or in concert. Because braking for the turn slows the aircraft, anticipate the need for additional power and apply it before turn entry. Be careful to

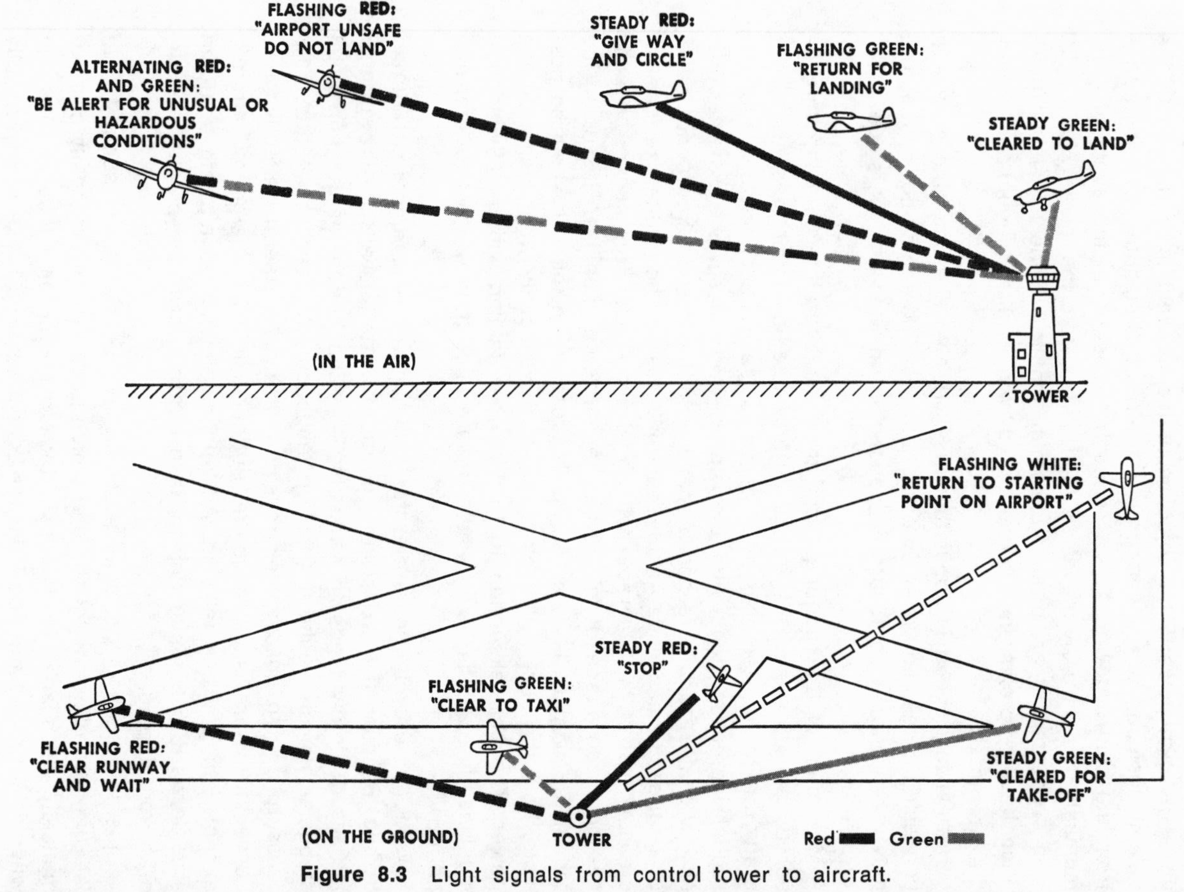
FLASHING RED: "AIRPORT UNSAFE DO NOT LAND"
ALTERNATING RED: AND GREEN: "BE ALERT FOR UNUSUAL OR HAZARDOUS CONDITIONS"
STEADY RED: "GIVE WAY AND CIRCLE"
FLASHING GREEN: "RETURN FOR LANDING"
STEADY GREEN: "CLEARED TO LAND"
(IN THE AIR)
TOWER
FLASHING WHITE: "RETURN TO STARTING POINT ON AIRPORT"
STEADY RED: "STOP"
FLASHING GREEN: "CLEAR TO TAXI"
FLASHING RED: "CLEAR RUNWAY AND WAIT"
STEADY GREEN: "CLEARED FOR TAKE-OFF"
(ON THE GROUND)
TOWER
Red
Green

Figure 8.3 Light signals from control tower to aircraft.

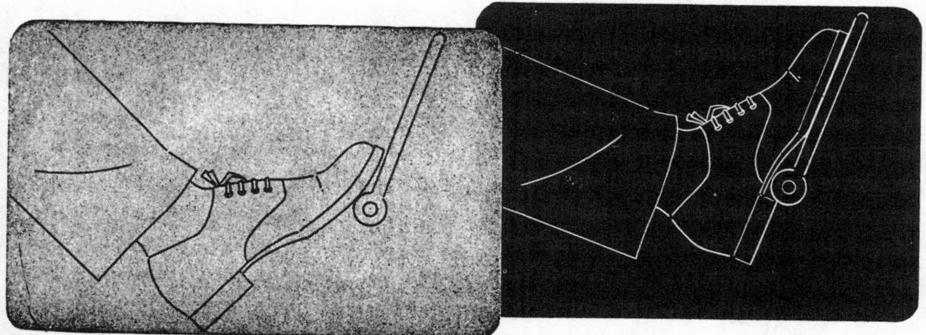

Figure 8.4 Normal position of pilot's foot. *Left:* on rudder. *Right:* on brake. *(Courtesy of U.S. Air Force.)*

coordinate brakes, nose wheel direction, and power to avoid nose wheel side loads.

At any time brakes are used to slow the aircraft, retard the throttle first. Modern aircraft brakes are so efficient that carelessness leads easily to abuse. The pilot's feet should rest with heels on the floor and toes only on the rudder pedals (Figure 8.4), unless the need for strenuous braking justifies sliding the balls of the feet up on the brake pedals. Use intermittent rather than continuous application for prolonged braking, so that the brakes may have a chance to cool.

The engine cowling obstructs straight-ahead visibility for taxiing in some tail-wheeled aircraft, and constant S-turning is necessary. Tricycle-geared aircraft, in which the pilot can easily see straight ahead over the nose, need not be S-turned.

A strong crosswind will try to lift the upwind wing during taxiing. Its effect will be greatest on very light aircraft with a high center of gravity, a large dihedral, and a narrow width of main landing gear. Holding aileron control into a quartering headwind and away from a quartering tailwind will help hold the wing down, for reasons substantially the same as those during flight. With a strong quartering tailwind, additional caution must be exercised to avoid sudden throttle bursts, hard breaking, and sharp turns. For some light aircraft, winds or gusts of 30 to 40 knots will require wing handlers to prevent tipping and weathervaning. Wing handlers and someone to hold the tail down are useful when taxiing tail-wheeled aircraft over rough or soggy terrain. This last requirement is not unique to lightplanes. The famed Royal Air Force Spitfire fighter of World War II was a bit light in the tail and had small wheels. The sight of several "Spits," each with an RAF aircraftsman draped over the tail, was not uncommon on the sod fields of Britain and France.

PRE-TAKEOFF CHECKS

Make final checks of the engine as close to the takeoff runway as practicable. Brake the aircraft to a halt directly into the wind with the nose wheel straight. By this time, the engine, if air-cooled, should be at normal operating cylinder head temperature. Complete the pre-takeoff check list, including controls free, fuel selector on proper tank, flaps and trim set for takeoff, and proper carburetor heat setting.

The test of a power plant prior to takeoff may include some or all of the following checks as recommended by the manufacturer.

Idle Speed With the throttle closed, the engine must operate smoothly at the idle rpm recommended for the engine.

Magneto Grounding Switch the ignition off momentarily while at idle rpm. If the engine does not stop firing while the switch is off, the following check of the ignition system cannot be valid. The aircraft should be returned for correction of the difficulty, and everyone near warned to keep clear of the propeller.

Propeller Governing At a specified rpm, usually about 1800, retard the propeller control to full low rpm position. The result must be the minimum rpm for which the propeller governor is set.

Power Check The power check on supercharged engines measures the ability of the engine to produce a specified rpm with the introduction of fuel-air mixture into the intake manifold at outside barometric pressure. The unsupercharged lightplane engine always will produce slightly less than outside barometric pressure in its intake manifold at full throttle, because, while at rest, air intake passages open to the atmosphere are at atmospheric pressure. The suction needed to deliver air to the cylinders fast enough lowers the pressure in these passages slightly at full throttle. Maximum allowable rpm should result from full throttle; additional rpm is evidence of faulty propeller governing. This check is not applicable to the lightplane without a controllable-pitch propeller; however, satisfactory rpm at full throttle should be checked during the initial part of the takeoff roll.

Ignition Check The ignition check, often called the "magneto" or "mag" check, tests the ability of each one of the two separate ignition systems to operate the engine at a power setting near normal cruise. The test usually is conducted at an engine rpm specified by the manufacturer, and this value may be as low as 1700 or as high as 2400. For supercharged engines with controllable-pitch propellers, the check should be made at the rpm achieved in the power check.

At the prescribed rpm, move the ignition switch to the R (right) position. Note the drop in rpm after the tachometer reading has stabilized. Return the switch to BOTH and again allow the rpm to stabilize. Repeat for the

L (left) position. The drop in rpm on either independent system should not exceed a specified value, usually 75 rpm. A drop of 25 rpm is considered "normal."

An excessive drop in rpm during the check may indicate magneto or plug troubles; or it may be evidence of carburetor, valve, or other malfunctions that are not apparent when both ignition systems operate. When reporting an excessive rpm drop in maintenance forms, mention whether it was slow or fast, and whether it was smooth or rough. This will assist maintenance diagnosis.

A marginal rpm drop may be caused by plugs fouled during extended idling. A fouled plug condition may be cleared by operating the engine at takeoff power for a few seconds. Avoid lengthy operation at high power and lean mixture to "clean" spark plugs. A satisfactory reading might be obtained because a faulty spark plug became sufficiently overheated to ignite fuel whether it was functioning properly or not. Such a "glow plug" might result in preignition detonation, and loss of power during takeoff.

Cruise Fuel-Air Mixture For aircraft equipped with a controllable-pitch propeller and a mixture control having RICH and NORMAL settings, adjust the throttle to a specified rpm (usually about 1700 rpm and not above that used for the ignition check in any case). As the mixture control is then moved from RICH to NORMAL, the engine speed should increase about 25 to 75 rpm, indicating a proper relationship between the two positions. This also provides a check against overrich idle mixture if the carburetor has an idle jet system that affects mixture in the cruising range.

Other Tests Scan the engine instruments continually during all performance checks. Other checks, such as of oxygen or hydraulic systems, may be required for particular aircraft or flights. Perform all engine checks as expeditiously as possible, because ground operation at high power settings produces uneven cylinder cooling and adds to engine wear.

The Elementary Skills of Flight

AIRCRAFT CONTROL

The aircraft can be considered controlled when the pilot is able to produce desired airspeed, altitude, and direction of flight. The pilot reads these three primary conditions of flight in the cockpit from the airspeed indicator, altimeter, and one form or another of the magnetic compass. Together these three most basic flight instruments can present to the pilot the results of lift, thrust, drag, angle of attack, and similar aerodynamic factors discussed in Chapter 2. Despite their theoretical adequacy, however, the instruments are not used for primary reference during flight under visual conditions. In fact, the object of considerable practice during early flight training is to learn to spend as little time looking at cockpit instruments as possible, except for quick glances to check aircraft performance. Pilots with their "heads in the cockpit" are a serious hazard in today's dense air traffic, and there are many maneuvers that require careful attention to the ground track of the aircraft or its attitude relative to the horizon.

FLIGHT BY ATTITUDE

The most important single reference that can be substituted for instrument watching is aircraft attitude, that is, visually establishing the aircraft's attitude with reference to the horizon. Attitude is the angular difference measured between an aircraft's axis and the line of the earth's horizon. Pitch attitude is the angle formed by the longitudinal axis, and bank attitude is the angle formed by the lateral axis (Figure 8.5). Since measurements from a line can be only two-dimensional, the vertical axis is pointedly ignored in relation to the horizon. Rotation about the vertical axis ("yaw" or "crab") is termed an attitude relative to the flight path of the aircraft, but not relative to the horizon.

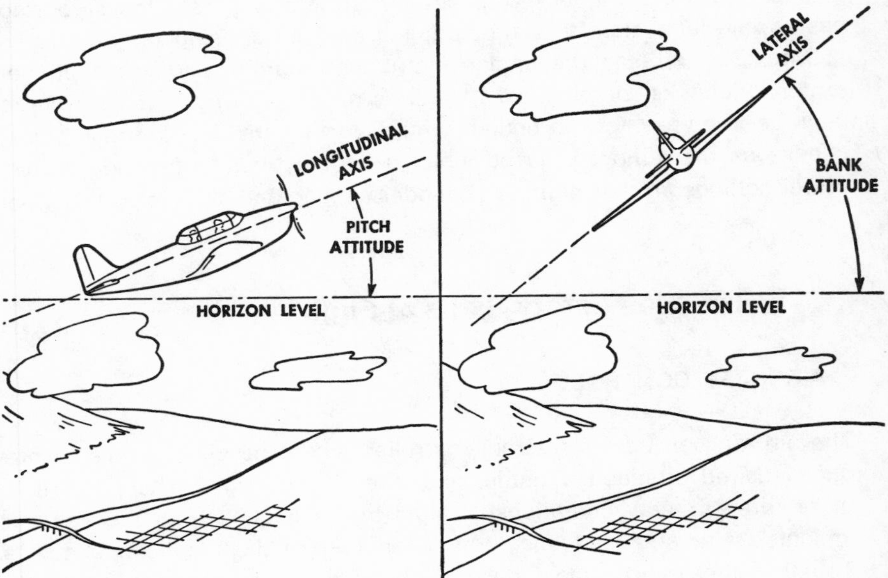

Figure 8.5 Aircraft attitude. Note that the angle of attitude is formed by the line of the axis and not in rotation about the axis.

COMPOSITE FLIGHT

Flying by aircraft attitude alone is obviously not the total answer when any degree of precision is required. The pilot must have available some means of determining aircraft performance. He does this by crosschecking the flight instruments to see if altitude, airspeed, bank, etc., are as desired. If a deviation is noted, the pilot then makes a pitch or bank change to correct the situation. This method of aircraft control is known as composite flight. More simply stated, it is the use of outside references supported by flight instruments to establish and maintain desired flight attitudes (Figure 9.1).

Although composite flight becomes second nature with experience, the beginner must make a determined effort to master the technique. The following fundamentals should be constantly applied:

First Establish and maintain attitude by positioning the aircraft in relation to the horizon. At least 90% of the pilot's attention should be devoted to this end, along with clearing the area to avoid other aircraft. If pitch or bank is ever rechecked and found to be other than desired, an immediate correction should be made to return the aircraft to the proper attitude. By making continuous checks and immediate attitude corrections, the aircraft will never have a chance to deviate from the intended heading, altitude, or flight path.

Second Monitor performance of the aircraft by making numerous quick glances at the flight instruments. It is important to remember that no more than 10% of the pilot's attention should be in the cockpit. Skill must be developed to bring one's eyes into the cockpit, instantly focus on the right instrument, and then immediately return outside to control the aircraft's attitude.

Third If the performance of the aircraft indicates a need for a correction, a specific amount of correction must first be determined, then applied with reference to the outside horizon, for example, by raising the nose ¼ in. farther above the horizon, or applying 5° left bank. The most common error made by the beginning student is to make a pitch correction while still looking inside the cockpit. Stick pressure is applied but the student does not know if the pitch changed two inches or two feet! As a result, level flight becomes a series of dives and zooms since pitch corrections made in this manner are invariably excessive.

Pitch versus Angle of Attack Pitch attitude is not the same as angle of attack (see Figure 5.26). Angle of attack is related incidentally to pitch attitude, because raising the nose leads to lowered airspeeds and a high angle of attack. Lowering the nose leads to higher airspeeds and a low angle of attack.

The pilot must understand angle of attack before he can understand why this wing works as it does—why it cruises most economically at a certain airspeed, climbs most rapidly at another airspeed, and "stalls" or refuses to fly at several different airspeeds, depending on other flight conditions. An angle-of-attack meter in the cockpit would be a valuable asset, and the stall warning device found in most modern aircraft is a step in that direction. If angle of attack were completely instrumented, however, the pilot still would use the pitch attitude of his aircraft to approximate the condition of climb, descent, or level flight that he wanted. Attitude is such a handy measuring device—immediate in its indications and presented many times larger than any instrument could be.

The difficulty with attitude is that it must be considered in relation to engine power, airspeed, drag condition, and aircraft weight (both static weight and *g* loading) before the pilot can use its indications. Certainly the largest part of learning to fly is in the acquisition of ability to calculate from the conditions mentioned just what is going to happen to the airspeed (or airfoil angle of attack) of an airplane at any selected pitch and bank attitude. The calculating job is not as difficult as it may appear. A motorist approaching a hill in an automobile solves the same sort of problem. He knows that in his new pitch attitude he must increase power or settle for less forward speed. As he climbs the hill, he keeps in mind the trend of his speed as well as the indication at any moment. If he is carrying several passengers, he may notice that the "old bus lacks its usual zip." His eye is not fixed on the speedometer, because he has learned to estimate his speed within reasonable limits by the sound of his engine and the airstream around the car.

An aircraft provides many ways, other than the airspeed indicator, by which the pilot can learn what is happening to his condition of flight. The lightplane is especially communicative in its reactions. The ability to sense flight condition is often called "feel of the aircraft," but senses in addition to "feel" are involved. The most important are the following.

Sounds The open-cockpit biplane is all but extinct, and with it have gone the wires and struts that would sing out the airspeeds as precisely as any visual indicator. The air that rushes past the modern canopy or cabin is often screened by careful soundproofing, but it still can be heard. When the level of that sound increases, the airplane is picking up airspeed, and for some reason.

The power plant may loaf in a glide, roar in a dive, hum contentedly in cruise, or labor in a climb; the amount of this noise that can be heard will depend upon how much the slipstream masks out. The relation between slipstream noise and power-plant noise helps the pilot estimate both his airspeed and the trend of his airspeed.

Sight Attitude has been touched upon so far as though it were a static thing. It is not always so. When the pilot changes his direction of flight, the rate of change provides one indication of what is happening to airspeed and some of the other aerodynamic essentials. The rate of change is especially meaningful in conjunction with sensations the pilot can *feel.*

Feel The term "feel" of the aircraft basically is correct. There are three sources of "feel," each highly important to visual flight.

One element of "feel" is in the pilot's own body as it responds to forces of acceleration. The *g* (gravity) loads imposed on the airframe are felt by the pilot with his famous vestibular organ, "the seat of his pants." Centripetal accelerations force him down into his seat or raise him against the seat belt. They affect his stomach in a manner familiar to any elevator passenger. Radial accelerations, as they produce slips or skids of the airframe, shift the pilot from side to side in the seat. These forces need not be strong to be useful. When the pilot can sense any change at all, he has an immediate index of control effectiveness.

A second element of "feel," and one that provides direct information concerning airspeed, is the response of the stick and rudder controls to the pilot's touch. The control surfaces move in the airstream, and there they meet resistance proportional to the speed of the airstream. When the airstream is fast, the controls are stiff and hard to move; but only slight movement is needed to obtain results. When the airstream is slow, the controls move easily; but they must be deflected a greater distance. Note the use of the word "air*stream*." Only the ailerons, outside the propeller arc, respond directly according to the speed of the aircraft through the air. The elevator and rudder are influenced also by the wash of air driven back by the propeller. Their response to pressures, then, must be considered cautiously—especially at slow speeds.

The third sort of "feel," in the literal sense, comes to the pilot through the airframe. It consists principally of vibration, either from the power plant or from airflow. An example is the buffeting and shaking that should precede a stall in a well-designed aircraft.

"Feel of the Aircraft"—A Restatement Perhaps now, in summary, it can be said how the pilot gets the heading, altitude, and airspeed he wants from his airplane. He does it by obtaining an attitude and power setting that his past experience tells him is about correct. First, of course, he has to judge whether his desired situation is a practical one. Here, again, he must base his judgment on past experience—on what he has learned about his airplane's capabilities and limits. It is this need of "experience" which makes the most competent veteran pilots seek a check flight in a strange aircraft with a pilot familiar with its characteristics. This is particularly true where stepping from a small to a large, or a fast to a slow aircraft, or vice versa.

The pilot's main concern is airspeed, not only in terms of knots but also in terms of how much reserve airspeed he must have to support his climb or the loads of accelerations. His air sense must be able to balance the trend of his airspeed against the requirements his maneuver creates for airspeed.

Each maneuver or operation in the air offers its own problems, and one maneuver may demand closer attention to stick and rudder coordination than it does to airspeed. The knowledge of this, too, is part of "air sense."

STRAIGHT AND LEVEL FLIGHT

Flight at a constant altitude and heading, with all aerodynamic forces in balance, is "straight and level" flight. All flight maneuvers basically are deviations from the central straight and level reference, and the pilot must become acquainted with the attitude of his aircraft at straight and level before he can do other maneuvers precisely.

Level Flight Proper pitch attitude for level flight comes after a sort of trial-and-error process. Level flight can be approximated by placing the top of the engine cowling down slightly below the horizon about where experience on other flights dictates (keeping in mind that the cowling slopes down to provide visibility over the nose, so that the aircraft in level flight always has a nose-low appearance). The wings can also be checked to see if their chord line is about level with the horizon on either side.

The altimeter will indicate whether altitude is being lost or gained. If that instrument is not resting comfortably on one indication, then the nose is going to have to go higher or lower. When the altimeter is stable, the beginner would do well to note carefully the point on his windscreen where the horizon appears to rest. If he adjusts his sitting height to the same position on the next flight, loads his aircraft with the same weight, and levels off with the same indicated airspeed, the horizon should be in the same spot.

Whenever the pilot changes power in level flight, the initial nose-up or nose-down reaction will be greater than the change in attitude that finally does result. This exaggerated initial effect occurs because the first reaction is produced by a changed force of downwash on the horizontal stabilizer, before the new airspeed stabilizes and a new condition of dynamic stability is reached.

All these complications emphasize the need for cross-checking the altimeter frequently during the first of the level-off. Except when near the ground, the pilot can determine gain or loss of altitude precisely only by checking his altimeter.

Straight Flight An aircraft is turned by banking and not by steering boat-like with the rudder. The best way for the pilot to keep his airplane headed straight, then, is to keep the wings level. Bank control in straight and level flight requires no trial-and-error process, but it does need some close watching. The surest way for the pilot to check that the wings are level is to look out at the wing tips and see that the horizon appears an equal distance above each tip (or below each tip for high-winged aircraft). The student pilot will have to check his wing tips frequently until he learns to detect small degrees of apparent tilt in the horizon ahead of him. Eventually one gets the idea that the aircraft must be in a bank if the horizon line appears 12 in. up from the right side of the cowl and 14 in. up from the left side.

When the wings are level, the pilot can expect his aircraft to fly something close to a constant heading. If it is to be truly constant, rudder control must be trimmed or held to correct for any yaw tendencies. As stated above, the rudder is not used to turn the aircraft, but at the low airspeeds of the lightplane it *can* be used for that purpose. Air-show stunt artists sometimes include tight wings-level turns in their repertoire. The feat should get more applause than it does, because to turn wings-level the aircraft must be *skidded* through the turn with opposite aileron applied. The rate of turn caused by wings-level yaw during normal flight usually is almost imperceptible, and that is the exasperating thing about it!

TRIM CONTROL

One of the duties of the aeronautical designer is to arrange his aircraft weight and structure so that the flight controls (rudder, aileron, and elevator) are streamlined when the aircraft is cruising straight and level at normal weight and loading. If the airplane is flying out of that basic condition, one or more of the controls is going to have to be held out of its streamlined position. The holding duties are too tiring for a busy aviator, and so small movable *trim tabs* have been provided at the trailing edge of each control surface. These tabs, deflected in one direction, hold the primary control in the opposite direction through aerodynamic force. Because of their low power and relatively small range of speeds, not all lightplanes have a complete set of trim tabs adjustable from the cockpit; some have only elevator trim, and the aileron trim quite frequently is adjustable only from the ground. If all three controls are present, a definite sequence of trim makes the job easier when trimming for a protracted condition of flight.

Elevators should be trimmed first, since any attempt to trim the rudders at varying airspeed is impractical in propeller-driven lightplanes because of the torque-correcting offset in the vertical fin. Once a constant airspeed has been established, hold the wings level with the control stick while rudder pressure is trimmed out. Finally, adjust aileron trim to relieve any stick pressure. To avoid overcontrolling with trim adjustments, hold the airplane in the desired attitude with primary controls. Then apply trim to relieve hand or foot pressure. Because proper trimming decreases the drag of control surfaces, airspeed will increase. As it does, repeat the trim cycle until the airspeed stabilizes.

No special sequence need be followed for occasional trim applied during maneuvers or power adjustments to relieve temporary pressures. The more experienced a pilot becomes, the more frequently will one hand be found among the trim tabs. There is, however, a trap in this for the beginner. As mentioned previously, he acquires a lot of his "feel" of the airplane out of control response; yet he is told to trim out all the pressure that tests control response, and especially on the all-important elevator during the all-important final approach!

There are two answers to the student's dilemma. One is that he should, in a general way, keep in mind the trim he has applied. The position of the stick will help him to do this. As long as the aircraft has any flying speed, the neutral point of "feel" for the stick will be in the center fore-and-aft position, provided that the stick is not trimmed out of neutral. Thus, when there are other evidences of slow airspeed, and the stick has its neutral "feel" some place back of the central position, trim is the cause. The second answer is that one should not trim out *all* the "feel" of the stick during any maneuver requiring close control. Some pilots prefer to leave the aircraft slightly nose-heavy. The untrimmed pressure that is left to hold will give the pilot evidence of any change in airspeed.

AIRCRAFT STABILITY

One of the customary early lectures from pilot instructor to pilot student runs like this: "You don't have to balance this machine in flight as though it were on the point of a pin. It *wants* to do the right thing! We will go up and I will trim for level flight. Then I will push into a dive or pull into a climb, and I will release the stick. The aircraft will do a few dives and climbs and gradually work its way back to level flight." He doesn't say much about directional stability. They go up, and they do the experiment, and it works out pretty much as the instructor said (Figure 8.6). He does have to help the wings back to level now and then, but "this aircraft is slightly out of trim, and the changing airspeed affects the torque rigging of the vertical stabilizer."

The instructor is taking the easy way out of a problem. Most present-day aircraft are extremely stable in respect to pitch. Generally speaking, for a given trim condition the aircraft tends to find and hold a constant airspeed. It will keep that airspeed in a climb, a dive, or in level flight, depending upon how much power is used. Aircraft are not so stable directionally. An aircraft disturbed into a slight bank by a gust will tend

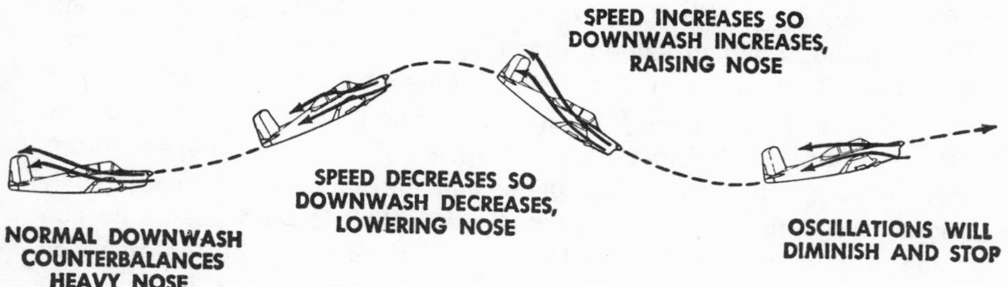

Figure 8.6 Stability in level flight.

to return to a wings-level position, *provided little or no turn develops first.* Once the aircraft has started turning, the turn will tend to increase. The outside wing in the turn will travel faster than the inside wing, will produce more lift, and will cause an overbanking tendency. At the same time, loss of vertical lift from the banked airfoil will cause the nose to drop, further increasing speed and tightening the turn. The end result, if allowed to ensue with disinterest by the pilot, is a tight spiral down.

The most important thing for the student pilot to learn about aircraft stability is that the airplane is not going to fall out of flight in any direction so rapidly that normal attention will not provide plenty of time to correct.

Climbing and Descending

One of the most perplexing discoveries to be made by a student pilot is that his plane appears to have two controls, the stick and the throttle, each of which regulates both airspeed and climb or descent. Unless his instructor has risked profound discussion on the matter, the problem will not present itself at once. The student probably brought with him a pretty good idea of what those two controls do. "The joystick," he remembers, "is what you push forward to go down and pull back on to go up. The throttle sets the speed, like in a car."

After the student has refined this theory to accommodate the effects of airspeed on trim and the effects of attitude on airspeed, it will work for him most of the time. It will work all the time when he wants to descend, but it fill work in respect to climb only if there is enough airspeed to make it work. When the aircraft approaches the stall condition, pulling further back on the stick is exactly the wrong way to maintain altitude or to gain any more.

The student's concept is deadly when he tries to extend his notion of "up" to include "farther" during a glide. The situation is a famous one. The airplane is gliding toward a landing point, but the glide is not going to reach quite far enough. The trouble, as the student sees it, is that he is going to reach the ground too quickly. Therefore he will pull back on the stick and go "up." Temporarily it works, but soon the airspeed drops well below the best speed for glide; and the temporary gain is quickly wiped out. If the student does not put that stick forward again and add some throttle, he will not only fail to make the runway, but he may stall and become another statistic in the column, "attempted to stretch glide while landing."

Now, every student with one hour of instruction should know that he cannot "stretch" a glide with back stick. That is one of the first pieces of flying lore his instructor should have given him. Why, then, do students and even old pilots sometimes try the impossible? Simply because every instinct that is natural, and most of the habit patterns developed in flight, do associate back stick with "up."

One school of thought on this matter reasons that what pilots must do is relabel stick and throttle controls. The student's first idea is wrong, they say. The throttle actually is the "up" and "down" control and the stick selects the airspeed. This manner of reasoning would eliminate quite a bit of faulty thinking, and it is quite close to describing what actually does happen; but, like virtue and prohibition, it is more easily understood than practiced. After being convinced that his stick is not an "up" and "down" control, a pilot is likely to spend an hour or so in flight watching the airplane go up and down when he moves the stick back and forth. The airspeed changes that occur at the same time just do not make such a direct impression. When that stick can, it will control altitude; and every time that it does, it leaves its impression on the pilot's memory.

"All this is very interesting," says the student, "but how do I climb or descend?" There is no simple and accurate answer to that question. One must understand the effects of both power and elevator control working together. The best that can be done for a formula is to go back to the concept of *aircraft attitude* and say:

At any pitch attitude, the amount of power used will determine rate of ascent or descent.

Through a wide range of nose-low attitudes, a descent is the only possible condition of flight. Additional power in those attitudes will make the aircraft descend at a faster rate and at a faster air speed.

Through a range of attitudes from very slightly nose-low to about 30° nose-high, the aircraft can be made to climb, descend, or maintain altitude, depending on the power used. In about the lower third of this range, the aircraft will descend at idle power without stalling. As pitch attitude is increased, engine power will be required to prevent a stall. More power will be required for level flight, and even more for a climb. Finally, at about 30° nose-high, full engine power will provide only enough thrust to keep level flight. A very slight increase in the steepness of climb or a very slight decrease in the power will produce a descent. From that point the least inducement will lead to a stall.

To select a desired condition of flight in the range of attitudes just discussed, the pilot must set both his pitch attitude and his power. He can make a shallow descent at high airspeed with nose slightly below the horizon and lots of power or he can produce the same shallow rate of descent at low airspeed with the nose slightly above the horizon and idle power. He can make a descent at fast airspeed with little power and the nose low or a descent at the same airspeed with lots of power and the nose slightly below the horizon.

If the climb or descent is to be at a certain airspeed, the pilot will set his engine power to the value that he has learned will give a satisfactory rate of climb or descent at that airspeed. He then has one control, the elevator, with which to adjust his pitch attitude until he has his desired airspeed. If he wants a climb or descent at a definite rate *and* a definite airspeed, he will begin by setting power and pitch attitude to the values which he has learned are about correct. For fine adjustments only, he will alter pitch attitude to adjust the rate and alter power to adjust the airspeed, if necessary.

When the pilot changes his power setting, he affects pitch attitude not not indirectly through the new airspeed that results, but also immediately through altered downwash over the horizontal stabilizer and possibly through the difference between the line of thrust of the power plant and the aircraft's vertical center of gravity. The result is that in most aircraft an increase in power tends to raise the nose immediately to an attitude higher than that at which it would stabilize. A decrease in power tends to lower the nose in the same manner. To keep his pitch attitude constant following a power change, the pilot must counteract the immediate trim change with stick pressure or elevator trim.

TECHNIQUE IN THE CLIMB

The mistakes of a new student pilot in learning to enter a climb usually do not stem from ignorance of his difficulties but rather from overconcern with them. If he would trust the pitch attitude and power setting demonstrated by his instructor, he probably would find them very close to correct. Instead, he manages a glance at his airspeed, finds it too high or too low, decides it is time *that* was settled, and tries a new pitch attitude. Had he noticed the *trend* of his airspeed, he might have seen that the needle was slowly working its way to the desired reading.

The attitude test selected usually will not be exactly correct because of variances caused by altitude, sitting height, individual aircraft performance, and the pilot's memory. Some minor corrections will therefore become necessary, but should be made only after the airspeed has stabilized or its trend carefully analyzed. At this time a small pitch correction, usually no more than ¼ in. to ½ in., may be made with reference to the outside horizon.

In a constant-airspeed climb, the student should not think of the necessary correction as an adjustment to his airspeed indicator, but rather as an adjustment to the pitch attitude. The difference is vital because the student can succeed in keeping attitude constant. It takes a lot more practice to master that airspeed indicator.

The problems of leveling off from a climb are similar to those encountered during the entry. As the desired altitude draws near, the pilot begins to lower the aircraft nose. In the lightplane, the level-off can be started about 25 to 50 ft below the desired altitude. When the level-off has begun, the pilot must cross-check the altimeter as his principal instrument. He uses the altimeter as he did the airspeed indicator during the climb, watching its trend but making his corrections through pitch attitude. If cruise airspeed is to be faster than climb airspeed, power should be left at the climb setting until a few knots short of cruise airspeed. Because the airspeed is increasing gradually, the aircraft has a persistent desire to climb. Forward stick pressure and trim must keep pace. Then, as the throttle is reduced to the cruise setting, a little back stick probably will be needed before retrimming.

SOME PRACTICAL CONDITIONS OF CLIMB

It is important to know the approximate power settings and pitch attitudes for at least the following conditions of climb.

Normal Climb Normal climb usually is 5 to 10 knots faster than the aircraft's best rate of climb. The additional airspeed provides better engine cooling and easier control. Normal rated power of the engine is commonly used. Turns while climbing should be shallow-banked to avoid an undue increase in drag and a corresponding decrease in rate of climb.

Best Rate of Climb The best rate of climb is obtained at approximately the same airspeed for any power setting. It is the airspeed where the most excess *power* is available over that required for level flight (Figure 2.35). This condition of climb, with full engine power, should be used when the pilot wants to gain the most altitude in the least amount of time.

Steepest Angle of Climb The airspeed for steepest angle of climb gives the most distance up for the least distance forward and is much lower than that giving the best rate of climb. It is the airspeed where the most excess *thrust* is available over that required for level flight. This airspeed should be found in the pilot's handbook for the aircraft or in the manufacturer's publications. The steepest angle of climb is of value in clearing obstacles after a minimum-run takeoff, but unless the pilot knows the correct speed for his aircraft weight and configuration, he should do his guessing on the high airspeed side and use the extra airspeed in a zoom before reaching the obstacle.

During protracted climbs at low airspeed and high power settings, the pilot must watch his engine instruments for evidence of overheating. Cylinder head temperature usually is the limiting factor, although design of cowling facilities may be such that excessive oil temperature is encountered first.

With lightplane engines—and with most of the larger reciprocating-type engines that are not equipped with barometric manifold pressure control devices—the pilot will have to advance his throttle during climbs and retard it during dives if he wants to keep a constant engine power setting. This becomes especially important during prolonged descents, when the increased power obtained at lower altitudes can cause excessive manifold pressures in engines with controllable-pitch propeller installations.

SOME PRACTICAL CONDITIONS OF DESCENT

The pilot should learn the approximate power settings and pitch attitudes for at least the following conditions of descent.

Descent at Minimum Safe Airspeed This nose-high, power-assisted descent condition is useful principally for skirting obstacles during a landing approach to a short runway. Considering a margin for pilot technique and the possibility of wind gusts, the minimum safe speed for approach to landing is a little closer to normal approach speed than to the power-on stall speed of the aircraft. Some margin must be left because of excessive power required to produce acceleration at low airspeeds. With a 10% reduction in airspeed at the critical point, a 100% increase in engine horsepower might be required to keep the rate of descent constant. If the engine already is being operated at 75% power, only the exchange of altitude for airspeed will restore the balance.

Partial-Power Descent The normal method of losing altitude is to descend with engine power slightly above idle, usually with 15 to 20 in. of manifold pressure for aircraft equipped with controllable-pitch propellers. Airspeed may vary from cruise to that used on downwind leg in the traffic pattern; however, do not interpret this wide range in airspeed to permit erratic pitch changes. Select the desired airspeed, pitch, and power combination and attempt to keep them constant. The moderate airspeed and the use of some engine power help to keep the engine from cooling excessively in the descent, reducing possibilities of plug fouling or carburetor icing.

Glides Gliding flight is flown with the throttle closed and at the airspeed giving the most favorable airfoil lift-drag (L/D) ratio (Figure 2.34). This results in traveling the most distance forward for the least altitude lost. Practicing glides at this airspeed improves the pilot's ability to cope with an engine-failure situation and benefits the traffic pattern since it is the same airspeed and pitch attitude used for the power-off landing approach. If a protracted glide is made without power, the engine must be "cleared" every minute or so by advancing power momentarily to at least the cruising setting. If a mixture control is provided for the carburetor, it should be set to the RICH position during the glide. This will help compensate for the "leaning" of the fuel-air mixture caused by unsatisfactory vaporization in the cold engine.

Dives There is no sharp dividing line between a glide and a dive. As a general rule, if a pilot's primary visual reference is below the horizon, the maneuver may be considered a dive. Some engine power is essential during a protracted dive, for the same reasons mentioned in connection with glides. The pilot should know the limiting airspeed permissible in dives with his aircraft and avoid that speed by a wide margin. If the engine rpm exceeds allowable limits in a dive, the proper corrective action is to place the throttle in "idle" position and raise the nose of the aircraft to place a load upon the propeller.

Level Turns

The turn is so fundamental a maneuver in all phases of flying that a clear understanding of what happens to an airplane in a turn is essential to the modern airman.

WHAT DO THE CONTROLS DO?

There are four controls, and this is what the pilot needs to know about each of them:

The ailerons bank the wings and so determine the rate of turn at any given airspeed.

The aerodynamicist says: "For a given airspeed and rate of turn, there is one correct angle of bank." This same principle is familiar to any motorist who has tried to negotiate a corner with greater speed than the road engineer had in mind. The pilot does not have to compute what his bank angle should be at his airspeed (except for the special conditions of instrument flying) because he does not have to make good a precise rate of turn. He banks slightly (about 10°) for a gentle turn, a little more (about 20°) for a moderate turn, and steeply (30° or more) for a tight turn. If he must arrive at a certain heading at a certain spot, he will watch his progress and increase or decrease the rate of turn as needed to correct his first judgment.

TABLE 8.1
Effect of Banking Angle

Angle of Bank (°)	*Load Factor ("g" Load)*	*Percent Increase in Stalling Speed*
0	1	0
20	1.065	3.0
40	1.31	14.4
60	2.00	41.4
80	5.76	140.0
90	Infinity	Infinity

If pilots kept all their turns gentle to moderate, accidents would be fewer. The indicated airspeed at which an aircraft will stall in the turn increases sharply after the bank angle exceeds 45° (Table 8.1). The bank angle is only an accessory to the crime, the direct cause being the elevator control; but bank angle provides the pilot with a measuring stick of what he is demanding from his aircraft. He should not try selecting steep angles of bank unless he has sufficient power or altitude to keep the required airspeed in the resulting turn.

The elevator moves the nose of the aircraft up or down; that is, "up or down" as the pilot sits, and perpendicular to the wings. Doing that, it both sets the pitch attitude in the turn and also "pulls" the nose of the aircraft around the turn.

When the wing of the aircraft is banked, any lift enjoyed at right angle to the plane of the wings will have a "vertical" component opposing gravity and a "horizontal" component parallel to the horizon (Figure 2.27). The further the wing is banked, the greater will be the percentage of total lift exerted horizontally and the less will be the percentage of total lift exerted vertically. If the aircraft is to maintain a constant altitude in the turn, total lift will have to be increased to provide enough for both jobs. Arranging for the needed extra lift is the job primarily of the elevator, although throttle can, of course, assist.

By increasing the back stick pressure in a bank, you increase the angle of attack, (Figure 5.26), thus increasing the total lifting ability of the wing. With exactly the right amount of back stick pressure, at any airspeed and bank attitude, the "vertical" component of lift will be just enough to keep the altitude constant. Any further back stick pressure will result in a climb; any less will result in a descent. To increase the rate of turn (usually expressed in degrees per second), the airplane must be banked steeper and more back pressure applied. To decrease the rate of turn, the bank must be shallowed and less back pressure applied.

When you succeed in reaching desired bank angle with correct back stick pressure for level flight, your altitude worries are not over. The airplane will continue to lose airspeed in a constant turn, just as it did in a constant climb, until the momentum of the entry airspeed dissipates. The steeper the bank, the lower the airspeed that eventually will result. As the airspeed drops off, you must increase the back stick pressure slightly, and thus the pitch attitude, to provide the required angle of attack. Unless you are quite familiar with the aircraft, you can do this only by continually checking the altimeter and the horizon ahead of the turn to see that the turn is level.

The throttle provides thrust which may be used for airspeed to tighten the turn or to provide climb.

If you leave the throttle constant during a turn, it can be dismissed as a control. Should you advance the throttle, you will notice the response almost immediately from lift, from both the vertical and the horizontal components of lift. This is due to the same effect considered in climbs and dives—the immediate increase in flow of downwashed air from the wing on the horizontal stabilizer and elevator. In a steep turn, when you first apply additional power, you may have to relax some of the back pressure to avoid stalling!

In any event, just as in climbing or diving, to get a change of airspeed from throttle adjustment you will have to hold or trim out the natural tendency of the aircraft to climb and tighten the turn with added power, or to descend and turn slower with reduced power.

The rudder offsets any yaw effects developed by the other controls.

And that is all it does. Except to apply rudder pressure when you add or subtract power, when losing or gaining airspeed, and when using the ailerons to bank the wings. In the last instance the rudder is counteracting yaw from *aileron drag.*

This is the only feature of rudder control that is exclusive to turns. In modern aircraft with their improved aileron design, and at higher speeds in any aircraft, the effects of aileron drag are reduced. However, in light aircraft rudder coordination is still a necessity and should be an item toward which the pilot constantly strives for perfection.

MAINTAINING THE TURN

Some major difficulties of the turn are overcome when you realize that creating a turn and keeping one constant are two individual problems.

Once the required angle of bank for the desired rate of turn is obtained, no more aileron is required in that direction. In fact, the aircraft has a tendency to keep increasing its own bank. The outside wing, traveling faster than the inside one, creates more lift. To keep the bank constant, you hold just a little top aileron—opposite to that used for the turn.

With the aileron almost streamlined, aileron drag disappears. The only requirement for rudder pressure, then, is that created by engine "torque effect" at the reduced airspeed. Only in steep or slow climbing turns does that become a problem. Generally speaking, a skid will result if uncoordinated rudder is held into a turn, and a slip will result if uncoordinated rudder is held away from a turn. Only by cross-checking the turn and slip indicator for a centered ball can coordinated flight be guaranteed.

Leaving the Turn To roll out level on a particular heading, begin the rollout in advance of that heading. Start the aileron pressure back in the direction of level flight. Reduce back stick pressure, which in a rapid rollout may have to be reversed to avoid climbing out of the turn.

Some Tips on Learning Turns No substitute has been invented for practice. Before a student pilot can practice turns intelligently he *must* know the functions of his controls in turn so well that action follows need, without cogitation interfering! To develop such response, try entering turns and then exaggerating the application of one of the controls. This should be practiced at a safe altitude with the instructor present, although it is not necessary to be roughshod or to continue the exaggeration too long.

Try turns, leaving out one or more of the essential controls, and note what happens to the aircraft. Instructors should allow the students to attempt some fairly tight turns in which they are permitted to push on the rudders alternately. The sensing of a slip or skid is one of the most difficult skills to acquire, but many hapless students never are allowed a full-fledged slip or skid with some *g* loads pushing them into the seat. They must learn slips and skids from light pressures on what doctors insist is one of the least sensitive parts of the anatomy!

COORDINATION MANEUVERS

There are many varieties of coordination maneuvers. All involve rolling into some sort of turn in one direction and then rolling into the same type of turn in the opposite direction. They all provide good practice in learning to handle any airplane and consist merely of applying coordinated rudder and aileron so as to roll from side to side, at the same time holding the nose on a point on the horizon. They are being properly performed when the nose stays on a point and when there is no sensation of roughness, slip, or skid.

This maneuver can be modified to allow the airplane to turn as much as 30° right or left, rolling back into a snake-like succession of coordinated turns in opposite directions about a line on the ground.

CLIMBING OR DESCENDING TURNS

The most difficult part of climbing and descending turns probably will be in use of the rudder. On entering a climbing left turn, for example, the turn entry will require left rudder; but the diminished airspeed at the climb power setting reduces the requirement for left rudder and eventually may require right rudder to counteract torque effect at low airspeed.

Takeoff Technique

If an aircraft is taxied fast enough to reach flying airspeed and is allowed to assume a shallow climb attitude, it will become airborne. The takeoff may be considered in three phases: *ground run, transition to flight,* and *climb-out.* These divisions are not exactly precise, because the effectiveness of certain controls changes with the progression of the takeoff. Since the takeoff involves both ground and flight operation of the controls, you must be able to make the transition from the ground functions of the controls to the flight functions with smoothness and coordination.

GROUND RUN

Tower clearance is necessary before the aircraft can occupy the runway, but such clearance does not relieve the pilot of responsibility to check the pattern visually. Landing aircraft always have priority.

The wise old pilot lines up on the very end of the runway for takeoff, and he does not use a taxiway intersection of a slightly downwind runway to save taxi distance. A trite aviation saying bears the point out: "Two things you can't use—the altitude above and the runway behind."

When the aircraft is aligned in takeoff position with nose or tail wheel straight, release the brakes and open the throttle smoothly to the recommended takeoff setting. Do not use reduced power settings for takeoff to "save" the engine. Occasional operation at full power helps to keep spark plugs clean and firing properly. Rated takeoff power will get the airplane to safe altitude and airspeed quickly; and if the engine is not functioning properly, the difficulty can be detected early enough to permit safe discontinuance of the takeoff. Smooth throttle advance is essential, not only to avoid engine wear and plug fouling, but also to avoid directional control problems during the first of the takeoff run. The takeoff setting of the rudder trim is the correct setting for the effects of airspeed and engine torque at approximately takeoff airspeed. If the throttle is advanced abruptly, the aircraft will tend to yaw excessively to the left because of uncompensated propeller torque. Some right rudder pressure will have to be held at the start of any takeoff run in single-engine, propeller-driven aircraft; but the more gently the throttle is advanced, the easier the rudder correction will be.

Hold the elevator in neutral on a smooth runway, so that pressures developing with increasing airspeed may be sensed naturally. During rough field operation some back stick pressure is needed to avoid nosing down as the result of shocks during the roll. If a crosswind exists, the upwind wing is held down with aileron by moving the stick against the wind.

TRANSITION TO FLIGHT

There are several ways of determining that the aircraft is nearing flying speed. Most of these were mentioned in the discussion of "air sense." Like a motorist, you can check the "speedometer" or airspeed indicator. The runway to each side becomes more blurred. Flight controls at the start of the run yielded to light pressure and required large movement to produce effect. Now the controls offer resistance, and only slight movement is required. On tail-wheeled aircraft, the tail has a tendency to rise of its own accord. Engine noise appears to lessen as the slipstream is heard rushing past fuselage, wings, and landing gear. Forward acceleration, felt conspicuously at the start of the run, decreases. Also there is the knowledge that the airplane has passed a reasonable time with the engine working at full power and should be about ready to fly. All this has happened within 7 to 10 sec, so that there is little wonder that the beginning student sometimes is overwhelmed by the barrage of changing sensations. After a few flights, the sensations become familiar; and their correlation informs him that takeoff speed is near.

As the aircraft accelerates, the elevator becomes able to hold the aircraft in the shallow climb attitude from which it will soon leave the runway. With tricycle gear, lift the nose wheel slightly from the runway as soon as moderate back stick will do the job. The aircraft then will be in takeoff attitude, and the nose gear will be relieved of high-speed runway shock.

Tail-wheeled aircraft rest on the ground in an attitude more nose-high than needed for climb. As speed increases, lift on the tail section causes it to rise. When this natural development places the nose of the aircraft in takeoff attitude, maintain that attitude with stick pressure as required. Once the correct attitude is found and maintained, there is no difference of technique between tricycle and tail-wheeled aircraft.

The lightplane can be made to leave the ground in a wide variety of pitch attitudes. The correct attitude is approximately that to be used during the normal climb; thus there are only slight pitch adjustments to be made between the later part of the ground run and climb to altitude. Make no effort to "pull" the aircraft into flight with increased back stick pressure, as it will fly off most safely without such assistance as soon as flying speed is reached.

If no crosswind exists, hold the wings level through the ground run and initial flight. Directional control is a function solely of the rudder until the wheels leave the runway.

CROSSWIND TRANSITION TO FLIGHT

Aileron pressure was applied into the wind at the start of the crosswind ground run. This initial correction was a mechanical one, because the ailerons lacked effectiveness at slow speed and the full weight of the aircraft on its tires gave sufficient traction to prevent drift effects from the crosswind. As the airspeed provides increased aileron effectiveness, so does the increasing wing lift act to relieve weight from the landing gear. By the time flying speed is near, use the now responsive ailerons to hold the wings level. If you maintain too much aileron, the aircraft will bank into the wind and may leave the ground hazardously wing-low. With too little aileron, the force of the wind will lift the upwind wing and will cause the aircraft to skip downwind across the runway as soon as traction of the tires becomes light enough to permit. Because the skipping is the more difficult of the two alternatives to control, most pilots prefer to keep extra aileron pressure into the wind during the latter part of the ground run. They accept a bank into the wind as the aircraft leaves the ground and level the wings when safely airborne. In a stiff crosswind, hold the aircraft on the runway with slight forward stick pressure until airspeed is slightly above normal takeoff speed. The aircraft then may be pulled cleanly into the air to avoid side skipping.

Directional control remains uncomplicated by problems of bank until the aircraft has left the ground. Firm and aggressive use of the rudders is the means to keep the aircraft headed straight down the runway.

CLIMB OUT

The third phase of the takeoff is that portion between the leaving of the runway and the exit from the traffic pattern. If the runway surface is rough, the aircraft may bounce a few times before definitely becoming airborne. Concentrate on keeping directional control and the takeoff pitch attitude.

After the wheels quit the ground, crosswind may induce a drift across the runway. This can be tolerated for a brief second until a few knots more of airspeed and a few feet more of altitude can be acquired. Then a shallow coordinated bank will turn the aircraft slightly into the wind. When the new heading has counteracted wind force, resulting in a ground track directly aligned with runway, level the wings and continue the climb. Because the force of a crosswind may vary markedly within a few hundred feet of the ground, check as the climb continues, in order to be sure that the ground track remains aligned.

Raise the retractable landing gear when you are certain of remaining airborne. The raising of the gear will produce only a slight trim change for most aircraft, but this change must be resisted with stick pressure to keep takeoff pitch attitude. If flaps are used for takeoff, they generally are retracted when airspeed is slightly less than that used for climb. Raising the flaps on most aircraft will affect trim more than retracting the landing gear, and definite back stick pressure usually is required to prevent settling from the climb path as the flaps come up.

At full power, the takeoff pitch attitude should tend to produce more than the desired climb airspeed. When that speed is reached, retard the throttle to the normal climb power setting, and adjust pitch attitude as necessary to hold constant the desired airspeed.

Always follow a definite sequence when adjusting power in aircraft equipped with controllable-pitch propeller and fuel-air mixture controls (Figure 8.7). To increase power, advance the mixture first, followed by propeller and then throttle. To decrease power, retard the throttle first, followed by propeller and then mixture. This sequence is necessary to provide adequate cooling in high power ranges and to prevent the introduction of excessive pressures into the cylinders at low rpm.

Exit the traffic pattern when past the end of the runway and at a safe altitude and airspeed. This is usually done by making one 90° turn fol-

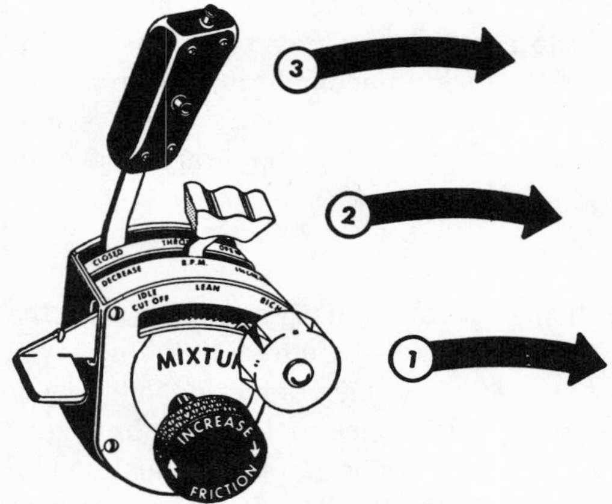

Figure 8.7 Sequence in power adjustment. 1. Mixture must always be prepared for rpm. 2. Rpm must always be prepared for throttle. 3. Do no exceed the recommended manifold pressure for rpm.

lowed by an immediate 45° turn in the opposite direction. The first of these turns is made in the same direction as the final turn for landing on the same runway, unless local procedures specify otherwise.

OTHER FACTORS AFFECTING TAKEOFF DISTANCE

Few lightplanes require more than 1500 ft of runway for takeoff under average conditions, so a short runway seldom is a deterrent to flight.

Table 8.2 illustrates the effect of five important variables upon takeoff distance. The table is based on data extracted from the USAF Flight Handbook for the T-34A trainer. Similar data, in one form or another, are available to the pilot of any civil or military aircraft.

The principal factors affecting the length of takeoff roll are altitude, temperature of the ambient air, aircraft weight, headwind, obstacles, and runway surface. Table 8.2 indicates that thin air experienced at high altitudes and high temperatures can multiply the required takeoff distance as much as three times. Although indicated takeoff speed will remain the same, the true airspeed, and hence the ground speed, will be increased. The time required to reach the necessary safe airspeed will also be increased because of decreased engine and propeller efficiency at the higher altitude.

Not considered in Table 8.2, but significant, are the runway surface

TABLE 8.2
Takeoff Distances in Feet

(10° Flaps, Hard Dry Runway Engine: Continental 0–470–13)

Gross Weight of Aircraft	Pressure Altitude	23°F (−5°C)				60°F (+15°C)				130°F (+55°C)			
		Zero Wind		30-Knot Wind		Zero Wind		30-Knot Wind		Zero Wind		30-Knot Wind	
		Ground Run	Clear 50 ft	Ground Run	Clear 50 ft	Ground Run	Clear 50 ft	Ground Run	Clear 50 ft	Ground Run	Clear 50 ft	Ground Run	Clear 50 ft
	S L	910	1310	300	510	1130	1610	390	660	1690	2360	630	1020
2900 lb	1000	1020	1460	340	580	1270	1800	450	750	1880	2620	720	1160
	3000	1270	1810	450	740	1580	2220	585	960	2360	3250	950	1500
	5000	1600	2230	590	960	1980	2730	770	1220	3040	4150	1280	1950

Source: USAF Technical Orders.

Hard surfaces: Concrete runway, highway landing strips, macadam and asphalt, packed snow or ice.

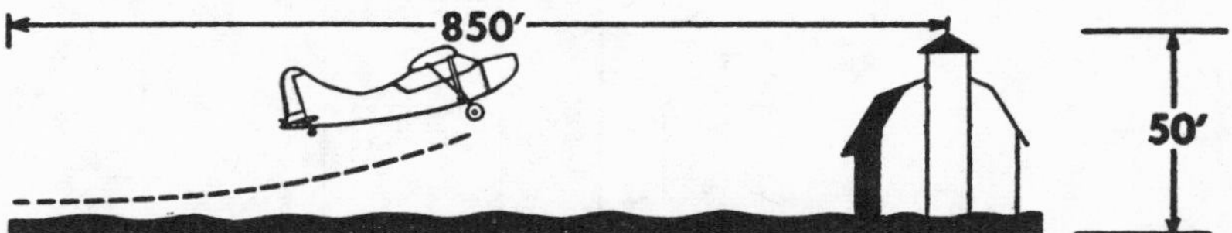

Medium surfaces: Sod turf, cinders, dry dirt runway, dry field roads, or cow pastures.

Soft surfaces: Muddy field, soggy turf, soft snow or sand, loose gravel.

Figure 8.8 Effect of runway conditions on the takeoff of a typical lightplane over a 50-ft obstacle. Takeoff flaps down 30°, no wind, G. W. 2050 lb at sea level. *(Courtesy of U.S. Air Force.)*

(Figure 8.8) and runway slope. Careless consideration of all of these factors has brought many a pilot to grief.

SHORT-FIELD TAKEOFF

If a short-field takeoff is necessary, revised technique will depend on how marginal the distance is. To go "all the way," drain fuel down to that actually needed, remove baggage and even radio equipment, consider pilot weight, and so on. If the wind is contrary to the otherwise best takeoff direction, it may be a good idea to wait for better winds. Partially deflating tires will assist if the surface to be used is soft. Use all possible runway, including over-run surface. (Old-time barnstormers literally "parked the tail on the fence," or tied it there with a rope to be cut by an axe after full engine power was obtained. These stratagems were useful before the development of the wheel brake for aircraft but are not of value today.)

The role of wing flaps in short-field operation has been subject of much hangar talk. Part of the answer lies in the type of flap employed. *Simple flaps* or *split flaps* increase both drag and lift throughout their travel—mostly drag after about 50% of travel. The lift is needed in order for the aircraft to leave the ground at slower speed; but the drag is an unwelcome obstacle to the obtaining of that speed.

The best answer to "How much flaps for short field?" is in the recommendations of the manufacturer or the military flight handbook for the particular type of aircraft. This figure, usually guaranteed by flight tests, is seldom more than 30° of flap travel for simple or split flaps. *Fowler* or other *lift-type flaps* reach their optimum at greater extension, but this type of flap is not often found on light aircraft.

Because the lift of the flaps is needed only at the moment of takeoff, it might seem advantageous to leave them retracted during the ground run until just before takeoff. The possibility of the mishandling of controls or flap actuator malfunction makes this a hazardous proceeding of questionable value.

When the aircraft is aligned for a short-field takeoff, be sure you have full power—with satisfactory instrument readings—before releasing brakes. It is important that the stick be held full back at this time if the aircraft is a tail-wheeled type. There is little danger of nosing over if the brakes are firmly held, and no forward motion allowed. Should the aircraft start to creep forward, or the tail start to rise, release the brakes entirely and begin the takeoff roll while applying the remainder of the power quickly but smoothly. The danger of nosing over on a full-power run-up occurs in tail-wheeled aircraft when the airplane is allowed to roll a few feet and *then* brakes are reapplied.

Leave the elevators approximately in neutral, and avoid imposing a takeoff attitude by back stick pressure until just before reaching flying speed or until the tail naturally arrives at the takeoff attitude. Attempts to raise the tail of tail-wheeled aircraft too early will only create extra drag through the deflected elevators. "Feel" of the aircraft is important in leaving the runway. Just under flying speed, move the stick back rapidly but smoothly. When clear of the runway, retract the gear and lower the nose slightly to pick up climbing airspeed. If the objective is to clear obstacles as well as to get airborne quickly, you must know the speed at which the aircraft will deliver its highest angle of climb. Note that here the speed for *steepest* climb, which may be 10 to 20 knots less than the speed for the best *rate* of climb, is the required speed. If the speed for the steepest climb is not available, however, it is safer to err on the high airspeed side. Altitude lost in mushing along too slow cannot be regained, whereas that lost by too much climb speed may be regained partially in a zoom over the obstacle (Figure 8.9). The takeoff flaps setting is never retracted until the plane is clear of all obstacles.

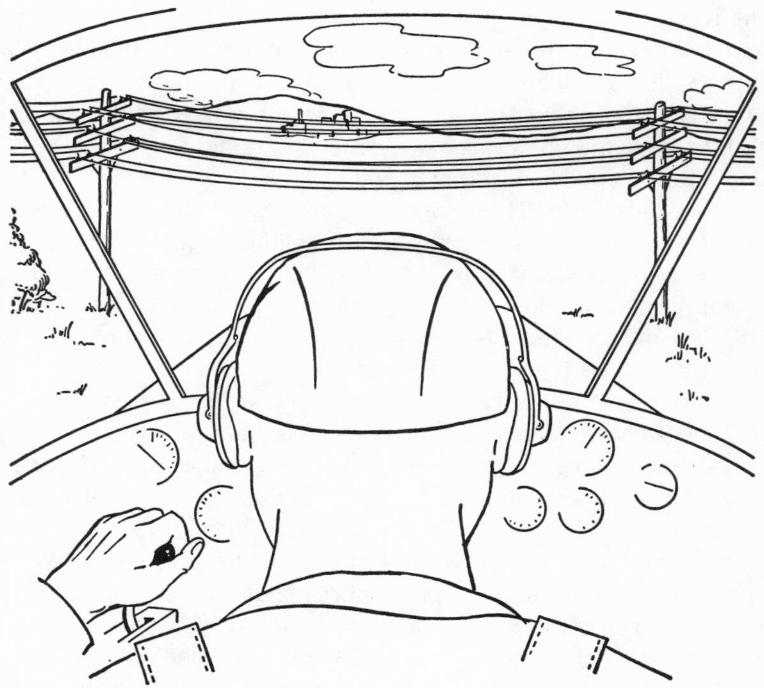

Figure 8.9 An old trick of the trade. If in doubt about getting over those wires, aim slightly under them at first. If you have enough speed when you get there, you can pull over. If you haven't the speed, YOU GO UNDER.

DON'T!

Three additional items are considered worth comment in a discussion of take-off distance. They are "killer" items that become a hazard only because of pilot contempt or neglect:

Don't attempt takeoff with ice or frost on the wings. Frost, particularly, has a spoiling effect on airflow far beyond its insignificant appearance. A layer of frost can add as much as 20 knots to the stalling speed of an aircraft.

Don't exceed center-of-gravity limitations in loading the airplane. Center of gravity ("c.g.") will be discussed in the next chapter, where it has particular application to larger aircraft. For the lightplane pilot's safety, he need only know and heed the placarded weight limits of the aircraft baggage compartment and fly in the recommended seat when solo.

Don't attempt takeoff with a malfunctioning engine. This would seem an impertinent piece of advice were it not violated consistently by aviators experienced and inexperienced. A pilot spends considerable effort and all of 15 min time inspecting a lightplane, entering it, starting it, and taxiing to run-up position. Returning to the parking line with an engine that does not quite check out is not an inviting idea, but it has been proven a safer one than "trying it out on takeoff."

Characteristic Maneuvers

The maneuvers about to be described are known collectively as characteristic maneuvers. They are designed to teach the limits of safe flight and to give the pilot the confidence and skill necessary to avoid abnormal flight attitudes or to recover from them; they are fundamental equipment for any airman.

CLEARING TURNS

Before considering several maneuvers that require a large block of unoccupied air space for their safe completion, the subject of clearing turns seems appropriate. Most pilot training programs have hard-and-fast rules about clearing turns—thus, two 90° turns in opposite directions before stalls, and acrobatics, and two 180° turns in opposite directions before spins. The essential idea of the clearing turn is to be certain that the next maneuver is not going to proceed into another aircraft's flight path. While complying with the letter of clearing-turn rules, the pilot should take special care to examine the area likely to be covered in the maneuver. He must be quite sure that the area will be clear when he gets there, regardless of the number of turns required to get that assurance. Clearing turns are good common sense in or out of a training program before any practice maneuver described hereafter, except for lazy-8's maximum-performance climbing turns, and chandelles, which are clearing maneuvers in their own right.

STALLS

When an experienced pilot flies an aircraft new to him, he invariably will try a few stalls or approaches to stalls before landing. He is going to be landing in a stall, or very close to one. The landing pattern and final approach will require positive control at speeds not far above stalling, and the pilot wants to know how the aircraft feels and reacts at those speeds.

He wants to know what kind of warning precedes the stall, whether the aircraft becomes unstable in a stall, and what kind of recovery techniques are most effective. All these objectives also apply to the practice of stalls by student pilots, who have assigned to them a practice routine of stalls covering several representative conditions of stall entry.

The Stall Curriculum The exact procedures for practice stalls vary, but each stall is designed to represent a condition that might arise from the pilot's failure to do some normal maneuver properly. *Power-on stalls,* straight ahead and turning, simulate stall out of climbing flight. Power is usually a little less than normal climb power, so that the pitch attitude need not be too great to induce the stall. *Power-off stalls,* straight ahead and turning, simulate stall out of gliding flight; and especially out of the turn to final approach. The *characteristic stall* is a final approach, round-out, and landing touchdown, all done at safe altitude to see how the airplane will react during landings. Landing gear and flaps are down, and the power is at idle, as they would be during actual landing. *High-speed stalls,* or *"accelerated" stalls,* will be discussed at more length later. When included in the student stall series, they simulate stalls out of tight turns or abrupt pull-ups such as might occur during acrobatic maneuvers. *Demonstration stalls,* as the name implies, usually are demonstrated by the instructor and offered for dual practice to show the result of grossly abusing aerodynamic principles. The student should leave them alone in solo practice until he is competent at acrobatics. Demonstration stalls are as varied as the possible insults to safe flight, but may include: *top and bottom rudder stalls,* with severe lack of rudder coordination during turns; *secondary stalls,* resulting from excessive back stick pressure immediately after stall recovery; *vertical stalls* (if the airplane is not restricted from them) such as might be encountered in aerobatics not properly performed; and *elevator trim stalls* to show the results of not controlling nose-up tendencies created by the elevator trim being set for glide during sudden application of power for go-arounds.

Together, the practice and demonstration stalls should establish that the airplane will stall at any airspeed, any attitude, any power setting, any configuration, and at any weight or *g* loading.

All that is necessary is that one of these factors be sufficiently on the debit side so that drag and effective weight will exceed the lift produced by the airfoil plus any component of lift derived from the propeller.

High-speed stalls (or *"accelerated stalls,"* as the aerodynamicist prefers to call them) are stalls incurred during centripetal accelerations, such as pull-ups or turns. More lift is required to sustain the acceleration than would be needed for stabilized flight, so stalling speed is proportionately higher. When increased angle of attack demands more lift for acceleration purposes than the airfoil can produce at the existent speed, the stall will occur.

Stall Warning Recognition of an approaching stall must become instinctive, because most accidental stalls occur while the pilot's attention is distracted from his primary task of aircraft control. If acceleration is not involved, airspeed is still the most reliable indication of what is about to happen to the aircraft. Stalling speeds for different weights and configurations, power-on and power-off, are published in the aircraft flight handbook. If the airplane will stall at 70 knots in a certain condition, and the airspeed indicator shows 75 knots in that condition, a stall can be anticipated from almost any new inducement. It is, of course, no more necessary to stare fixedly at the airspeed indicator at this time than at any other time. The sound of diminishing slipstream and laboring engine becomes especially noticeable just prior to stall, and controls become quite "sloppy" and lack effectiveness. These are the same customary signs of diminishing airspeed used in all visual flight.

Airspeed is a less reliable warning of high-speed stalls, which can happen at any airspeed if the turn or pull-up is tight enough. Here we must depend mostly upon the feel of control pressures, and upon the feel of *g* loads that are equal and opposite to the lift used in acceleration.

How the Aircraft Acts in the Stall When the stall actually occurs, there should be no mistaking the event. Airspeed and control effectiveness will drop sharply with the rapid drag rise. The nose will start to drop, and more back stick will serve only to aggravate that condition. Turbulent air from the stalled airfoil will buffet the airplane structure, causing a shaking vibration that can be felt through the airframe, seat, and pilot's controls. If the entire airfoil were to stall at the same airspeed, these sensations would be even more pronounced; but it then would be too late to take any action except a full stall recovery. By providing "washout" (in effect structurally decreasing the angle of attack at the outer portion of the wing), the designer has arranged for the airfoil to stall progressively. This provides *stall warning* (partial stall) about 5 to 10 knots before the full stall and permits some aileron control during the range between partial stall and full stall.

When fully stalled, the aircraft becomes a falling object with some residual forward velocity in addition to that provided by propeller thrust. It is a curiously shaped object, though, and is not by any means "uncontrollable." Control surfaces lose their effectiveness in a definite order: *ailerons, elevators,* and *rudder.* They regain effectiveness in just the reverse order. *rudder, elevators,* and *ailerons.*

Some aircraft have slots in the leading edge of the wing and restricted elevator travel, so that it is impossible to get a prolonged full stall of the airplane over the wing ahead of the ailerons. These aircraft give good aileron control in the "full" stall; but they are not often used as primary trainers, in which capacity they might engender bad habits.

The rudder control is the least affected in the stall and will assist in bank as well as directional control. The elevator remains effective to lower the nose, where it is only aiding gravity; it cannot raise the nose without the airfoil's lift.

The nose drops in a stall because the aircraft designer has located the center of gravity slightly ahead of the center of lift, this difference being compensated by airflow across the horizontal stabilizer during flight. If left to its own devices after a stall, the aircraft will accelerate like any falling body and the acceleration will be aided by any propeller thrust in the nose-down attitude. As soon as flying speed returns, the resulting lift and correct airflow over the tail will tend to raise the nose (Figure 2.29). If the stall-producing situation has been removed, the aircraft will have made its own recovery. If the stick is held back, however, as soon as the elevator becomes effective enough to impose too much load on airfoil lift, the stall will recur. That is what happens when a high-speed stall is not relieved by easing off the causative back stick pressure. The pronounced shuddering in continued high-speed stalls is the result of a continuing series of stalls, partial recoveries, and stalls again.

Stall Recovery Although the trainer will effect its own recovery, even from such aggravated stall conditions as a spin, too much altitude is lost in the process for the pilot to rely too heavily on automatic recovery. The *standard stall recovery* procedure is designed to restore controlled flight with the least possible sacrifice of altitude. It consists of a *positive forward movement of the control stick,* accompanied by smooth application of *maximum allowable engine power.* The wings, if banked, are leveled as soon as the ailerons recover effectiveness; and that will be almost immediately after the other recovery action, although some caution must be used as to rate of roll attempted at that point.

The phrase "positive forward movement of the control stick" needs some qualification. The object here is to get the nose in a shallow or moderate dive attitude as quickly as possible, *unless* flying speed returns before that attitude is reached. In a high-speed stall, of course, flying speed was there all the time; and as soon as some back pressure is released, the stall will cease. No throttle is needed for recovery from high-speed stalls, unless the airspeed at entry was only slightly above normal straight-ahead stalling speed. Some aircraft respond well to "popping" the stick briskly to just forward of neutral for stall recovery. In other aircraft, with quicker recovery characteristics, a few items might be lifted from the floor by negative *g* forces as the stick is "popped." The best all-around technique is a moderately rapid forward pressure, with its effectiveness judged by rate of nose travel and the degree with which positive elevator control returns. If excessive negative *g* forces develop from the stick movement, the pilot should reduce his amount of forward pressure. He is starting to fly again. The rate at which control returns will depend, to a large extent, on the pitch attitude at time of entry, and also on whether the stall was complete. If the exercise involved only an *approach to the stall,* a modified stall recovery will be made with full control of all flight surfaces available during the entire recovery. If the recovery is from a partial stall, control will return earlier than for a full stall.

During practice stalls, recovery is easier, and the airplane may be in a better position for the next stall of the series, if airspeed is built up in a moderate dive angle recovery. The student (and the instructor) should not forget that one of the objectives of the stall series is to learn to recover with minimum loss of altitude, and to become familiar with that type of recovery so that panic will not delay the pilot's reactions when the altitude actually is not there to spare. To recover with minimum altitude loss, the recovery dive angle should be as shallow as possible, the wings should be level as soon as possible, and the dive should be abandoned for level flight as soon as possible—all without incurring too much drag penalty due to acceleration loads.

The customary word of caution about engine torque seems necessary. Flight controls should be fairly well trimmed for the condition preceding a practical stall entry. A rapid application of throttle for recovery will produce yaw tendencies to the left. If yaw is allowed to develop at stall speeds, a rolling tendency will accompany. Rudder will be found the most effective control for both yaw and roll until the ailerons come into service.

SLOW FLIGHT

There are occasions other than a minimum-altitude stall recovery when the aircraft must be maneuvered at speeds just above stalling—late go-arounds, short-field landings, and maximum-performance aerobatics, for example. Practice of *slow flight* will ensure a good "feel" of the aircraft in this condition: the *minimum controllable airspeed.* The airplane is flying at the maximum angle of attack. To enter slow flight, ease the throttle back so that airspeed decreases to a point slightly above the stall. Maintain altitude by gradually increasing pitch as the airspeed decreases. When just above the stall, readvance the throttle to stabilize the airspeed. Experiment with gentle turns and variations of pitch and power, trying to keep just enough airspeed to avoid an actual stall.

Lower the nose only as far as necessary to recover at the first appearance of stall buffeting. Flying speed should return by the time the nose reaches the horizon. If a partial stall is not encountered occasionally during slow flight, the airspeed probably is being kept too high to get value out of the maneuver.

SPINS

The building of "spin-proof" airplanes has progressed to the point where applicants for private pilot licenses no longer are required to demonstrate their proficiency at spin recovery. The lightplane trainer must be forced into a spin; will recover unaided within a couple of turns if the controls are released; and will recover within one turn or less after the controls are neutralized. Most high-speed aircraft also have excellent spin recovery characteristics; and those that do not have good characteristics usually required a modified recovery technique. Yet, the teaching of spin recovery remains a firm part of any pilot training that is intended to do more than get the Sunday pilot around his county airport. In addition to the fact that the best-mannered lightplane can be brought out of its spin a little faster assisted than unassisted, the spin recovery is the best possible training for remaining oriented under stress and potential confusion.

Practice Spin Before entering an intentional practice spin, clear the area below carefully. To prevent overcooling and possible propeller overspeed during the spin and recovery, set the throttle slightly above idle. Use rich mixture, and possibly also carburetor preheat. Raise the nose slightly above normal climb attitude during the last of the clearing turns, and begin the "lead-in" with a small amount of rudder before the stall. As the first stall warning buffeting occurs, apply rudder briskly as far as the control will travel. When you feel a definite stall, bring the stick straight and fully back in a smooth manner. Hold both stick and rudder fully with the spin until ready to start recovery, because partial release of controls may permit a partial recovery and a secondary stall. Take care to avoid introducing aileron, which may increase rate of rotation in the spin or cause erratic rotation. Because of the large fore and aft movements required of the stick during entry and recovery, the student pilot is often guilty of inadvertent aileron movement. The best remedy is to use both hands on the stick. The left hand has no occupation at the throttle just then.

Some aircraft will oscillate during spins. The nose will rise during part of a revolution, and the rate of rotation will be slower at that time; then the nose will drop at an increased rate of rotation. Recovery can be started at any point of such oscillation, and the most effective point varies among different aircraft types. In most cases the oscillations will diminish after the first turn or two.

The standard method of recovery from spins (Figure 8.10) is:

First. Apply full rudder briskly against the direction of spin rotation.
Second. Move the control stick briskly straight forward of neutral.
Third. As the rotation stops and control feel returns, neutralize the rudder, correct the wings to level bank, and recover smoothly from the dive.

As in the case of stall recoveries, there are some finer points to spin recoveries. The most effective spin recovery for any aircraft is the one recommended in the appropriate flight handbook. Some aircraft respond best to rudder and elevator control applied almost simultaneously; in others, the rate of rotation should be perceptively slowed (or even halted!) by rudder action before forward stick is brought in. Normal control returns to most lightplanes almost immediately after the forward stick part of the recovery. The pilot must be alert for returning pressures on his controls, or else some uncomfortable negative *g* and yaw will result. But the part of the spin recovery requiring the most "feel" is the pull-up after flying speed returns. To recover from the dive with minimum loss of altitude, it is important that the airplane be kept just comfortably outside the high-speed stall condition through the entire pull-up. This is a bit of a touchy job when airspeed is low, but that is when the most good can be done. If the airspeed is allowed to build up, excessive *g* loads must be imposed later to save altitude. An occasional high-speed stall probably will be encountered during practice of minimum altitude recoveries; relax back stick pressure at the first stall indication, and no ill effects other than slightly increased altitude loss should occur. A normal spin in a typical lightplane trainer will cost about 500 ft of altitude for each turn, plus another 1000 ft for a smooth, rapid pull-up. Practice spins in light aircraft should be planned to leave at least 3000 ft of altitude available after recovery.

Inadvertent Spin and Recoveries If the spin was accidental, circumstances may be quite different from those in the typical practice spin. Because most modern aircraft do give ample stall warning and do not spin easily, an accidental spin most likely will start from an extremely nose-high attitude with engine power or misguided rudder pressure supplying uncorrected yaw. From unusual attitudes of entry, and especially if the entry stall was an accelerated one, the start of the spin may be a gyration that is difficult to follow or analyze. The first step in such an event should be movement of the throttle to idle. To avoid aggravating the stall, all flight controls can be held in neutral until some pattern of rotation is apparent. As a general rule, retract landing gear

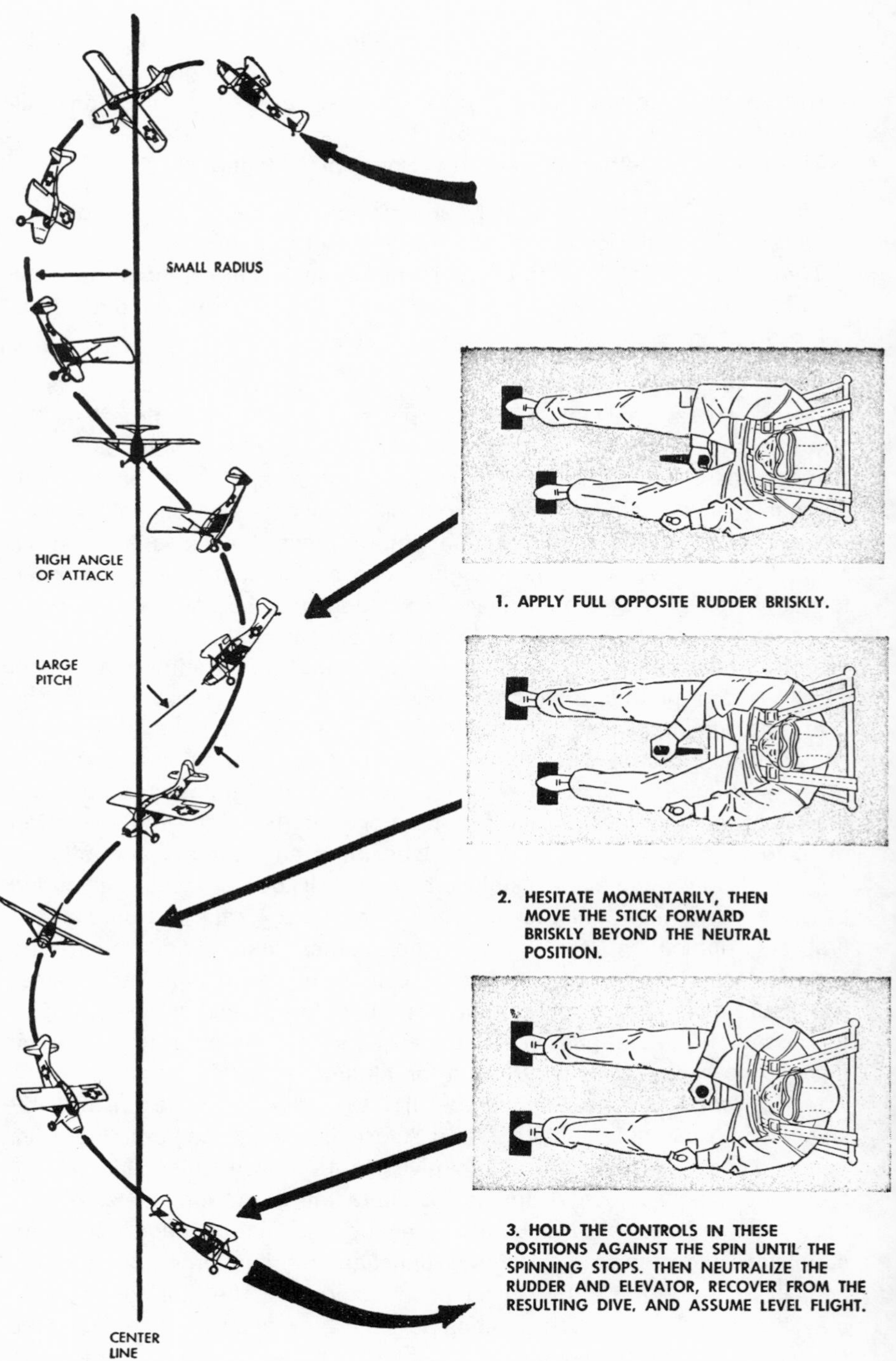

SMALL RADIUS
HIGH ANGLE
OF ATTACK
LARGE
PITCH
CENTER
LINE
1. APPLY FULL OPPOSITE RUDDER BRISKLY.
2. HESITATE MOMENTARILY, THEN MOVE THE STICK FORWARD BRISKLY BEYOND THE NEUTRAL POSITION.
3. HOLD THE CONTROLS IN THESE POSITIONS AGAINST THE SPIN UNTIL THE SPINNING STOPS. THEN NEUTRALIZE THE RUDDER AND ELEVATOR, RECOVER FROM THE RESULTING DIVE, AND ASSUME LEVEL FLIGHT.

Figure 8.10 Spin recovery procedure.

and flaps as soon as there is time. If altitude permits (and altitude *should* permit when one goes about courting accidental spins), the controls can be moved to the normal spin entry position, with rudder applied in the direction of existing rotation. The gyration should quickly become a normal spin, from which recovery will be routine. And if altitude does not permit? If skilled in recognizing stalls, you can prevent an accidental spin from materializing.

It seems quite possible that training programs develop a little too highly the "one turn or two turns and standard recovery" outlook of student pilots toward spins. The recovery method must be learned; but, as you gain experience at spins and various types of slow flight, you should acquire an ability to ease the aircraft out of an *incipient* accidental spin without going the whole route. During the first quarter turn or so, before the autorotation and the excessive angle of attack which characterize the spin are well developed, the stall probably can be broken by correcting yaw with opposite rudder and *easing* the stick toward a nose-down attitude. Rolling tendencies must not be resisted with ailerons. The roll usually helps to get the nose down for recovery. Throttle should not be advanced unless you know *exactly* what you are doing. In fact, the best thing to do with the control is to retard it to idle. The uncorrected yaw caused by a blast of throttle at this point may be all the help that the spin tendencies require to take over. The amount of airspeed that engine power can contribute during the recovery is negligible. The chances are that airspeed already is adequate; you probably had to "snap" your aircraft into the spin situation through accelerated and uncoordinated flight above the straight-ahead stalling speed. Under these conditions, there should be enough airspeed to enable you to regain control, although the aircraft may exhibit an apparent inclination to spin.

Inverted Spins These usually are not pleasant to perform and have been barred from most training curricula. Any modern trainer will have to be forced into the inverted spin by holding full forward stick and either rudder as the aircraft stalls, preferably in an inverted or very nose-high position. The stick must be held forward to maintain the spin, or it will degenerate into a normal spiral or normal spin. If there is any doubt, the inverted nature of the spin can be recognized by the pressure exerted against the seat belt by negative *g*. Two or more negative *g* may be experienced in the spin, and this may lead to headaches and bloodshot eyeballs for the daring aviator. Recovery usually will result when the forward stick is released, but keeping the rudder in with the spin and pulling the stick smoothly straight back should immediately convert the spin to the normal erect type, from which the usual recovery can be made.

RECOVERY FROM HIGH-SPEED DIVES

Thus far, several undesirable results of too little airspeed have been considered. The airplane also has certain limitations at the other end of its speed range. These limitations are structural and are reached with excessive airspeed or excessive *g* loads.

The maximum permissible diving speed of any aircraft is listed in the flight handbook, probably will be found on a placard on the instrument panel, and is represented on the airspeed indicator by a painted *red line* on the glass or a red needle on the instrument face. Beyond the listed airspeed, aerodynamic drag pulling at the flight surfaces creates dangerous loads on the aircraft structure. There is also a possibility that the propeller may overspeed because of the windmilling force of the airstream exceeding the engine load at the rpm setting.

Excessive *g* loads are caused by a too-rapid pull-up from a dive. The load of the airplane in acceleration must be borne by lift on the wing surface. Both wing and tail structure have certain carefully designed limits. The fully aerobatic military trainer is stressed to permit approximately 7.33 positive *g* at its maximum airspeed, with ultimate failure point at about 11*g*. This is more than adequate for any sensible maneuver, the average pilot being unable to withstand a sustained load of more than 4 to 4½*g* without impairment of faculties. The instrument in the cockpit that measures acceleration force (in centripetal acceleration only) is the *accelerometer,* or "*g* meter." The pilot also can learn to estimate *g* with fair accuracy by the pressure forcing him into the seat, and by an appreciation of his own tolerance for *g* loads. By any method of measurement, the maximum allowable *g* should be avoided by good margin during any flight in turbulent air. Sudden *gust loads* from turbulence will add sharp stresses up to 3 or 4 additional *g* without warning. Another limit, not appreciated by many experienced pilots, is imposed if the pull-up involves also a rolling maneuver. For rolling pull-ups the stress limits are reduced to approximately two thirds of their normal value, because the rising wing must bear the load imposed by the rotation as well as the pull-up.

The damage to the aircraft from excessive speed or excessive *g* load may not be immediately apparent if the wings and tail remain attached, but the damage may be found on post-flight inspection, in the form of wrinkled skin, "popped" rivets, and twisted structure.

To avoid excessive *g,* the dive recovery should be smooth. Roll the wings level as soon as possible and do not apply back pressure until the bank angle is 90° or less. Start the pull-out at least 10 to 20 knots before the limit airspeed is reached, depending upon dive angle, because the airplane will continue to accelerate in its nose-down attitude after pull-up is begun. The throttle should be idle if near limiting speed or if recovery in minimum altitude is the objective. The more airspeed the airplane has, the greater will be its centripetal acceleration during any degree of pitch change. Put even more simply, at higher airspeeds the pilot will have to "pull" more *g* to get out of the dive.

Ground Track Maneuvers

This group of maneuvers includes Eights On Pylons, S-Turns Across Road, Eights Along a Road, the Rectangular Course, and Forward Slips. They are important to give the airman a firm grasp of the effect of wind drift on his maneuvering judgment, particularly in maneuvering for landing.

WIND DRIFT

The airplane, moving through a mass of air, also shares the motion of the air relative to the earth below. Displacement of the aircraft's flight path due to its movement with the wind is known as *drift.*

Drift is not difficult to detect in level flight. In traffic pattern and ground track maneuvers, there is a runway or other line to be paralleled. If the aircraft heading is parallel, but the line moves closer or further, wind drift is the cause when the wings are level. To correct drift, make a coordinated turn of a few degrees into the wind. At the proper correction angle, the airplane will be pointing partially into the wind and away from the ground track. The point on the horizon toward which the aircraft is now traveling will appear off the centerline of the cowling ahead, as it would be in uncoordinated yaw. The airplane is not yawing, but is crabbing into the wind to produce its straight ground track (Figure 8.11).

Drift correction grows more complicated during a turn, while the aircraft constantly changes its direction in respect to the wind. If you have had an opportunity to check the drift or other evidence of wind direction and velocity during level flight, you will know what to expect in turn. That will help because there is no visible ground track to parallel while turning. You can visualize what that ground track ought to be, and can observe the ground speed by watching the rate of travel past objects underneath. If you are not correcting for drift, the ground track will be lengthened downwind and shortened upwind. The ground speed, if the wind is significant, will be appreciably faster downwind

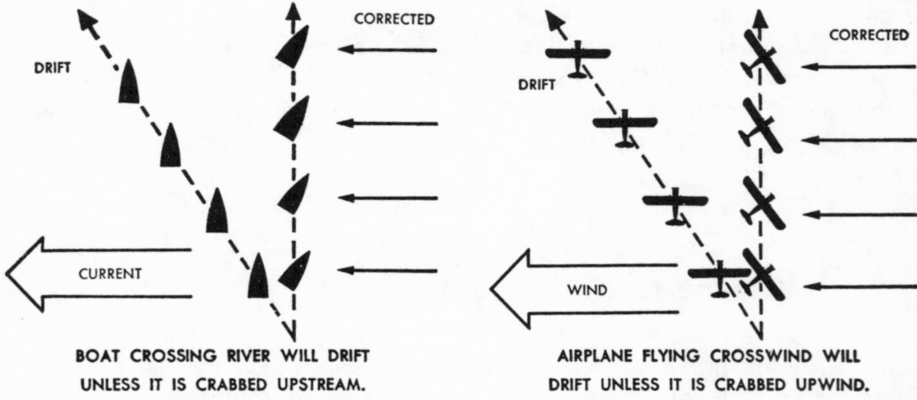
CORRECTED
DRIFT
CURRENT
BOAT CROSSING RIVER WILL DRIFT
UNLESS IT IS CRABBED UPSTREAM.
CORRECTED
DRIFT
WIND
AIRPLANE FLYING CROSSWIND WILL
DRIFT UNLESS IT IS CRABBED UPWIND.

Figure 8.11 Correcting for wind drift by crabbing.

and slower upwind. When you start a turn in the traffic pattern or a ground track maneuver, you have an objective—a place that you plan to reach with a particular heading on arrival. Through experience you know that a steep, a shallow, or a moderate turn should enable you to reach place and heading at approximately the same time. If it seems that this is not going to occur, wind drift is the probable cause.

This subject is vital because many a crash described in the newspaper as "the plane, turning onto its landing approach, was seen suddenly to dive into the ground out of control . . ." is simply the result of the pilot not appreciating the effect of wind to the extent that, preoccupied with making good a landing pattern with reference to the ground, he tightened the turn to the point where he simply stalled too close to the ground to recover.

SLIPS

The slip is included as a ground track maneuver because the principal use of the slip is to shorten the distance of a power-off glide on landing, final approach, or turn to final approach. The slip does this by the simple expedient of adding the drag of the aircraft side through a controlled yaw.

An intentional slip, just like those encountered accidentally in turns, results from an excess of bank (aileron) for coordinated flight. Opposite rudder may be used to keep the flight path of the aircraft aligned with the runway or other ground reference.

A *side slip* and a *forward slip* actually are the same maneuver from an aerodynamic point of view. The difference is in the position of the

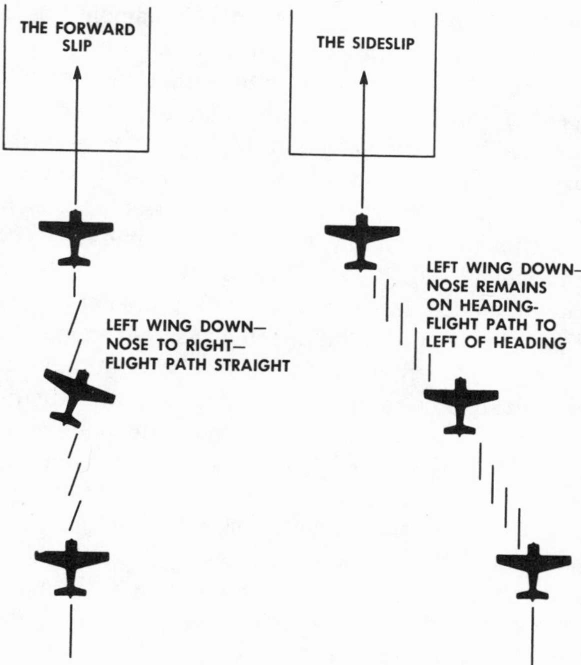

Figure 8.12 Forward slip and sideslip.

aircraft relative to features on the ground. When you slip so that the aircraft moves toward a desired point, you are *forward-slipping.* Should you add additional bank, the aircraft will begin to move laterally from a track toward the point; you are then *side-slipping* (Figure 8.12).

The aircraft can be slipped in a turn as well as in straight flight. Excess aileron should be toward the inside of the turn, and compensating rudder toward the outside of the turn. If an inadvertent stall should then occur, any "snap" tendencies will tend to be toward the outside, reducing rather than increasing the bank angle.

The Rectangular Landing Traffic Pattern

A traffic pattern is a rectilinear course flown above the ground at a prescribed safe altitude, so that a landing approach may be accomplished in a systematic sequence (Figure 8.13). It is also a means of controlling aircraft returning to or leaving a field. There are many varieties of landing pattern. At this time only that most commonly used in light aircraft, the rectangular traffic pattern with a 45° entry to the downwind leg, will be considered. This is the pattern that the lightplane pilot normally is expected to fly at a strange field, unless another type is announced to or requested by the control tower. It is a basic pattern, and the skill to fly it can be adapted readily to other types of patterns.

First to be discussed is the pattern with a power approach since it is the most widely used and offers the most advantages. By the single device of throttle manipulation, you can correct for overshooting or undershooting the intended landing point. For propeller-driven aircraft, the propeller slipstream improves the effectiveness of rudder and elevator control, and with any type engine, acceleration to go-around power can be made more quickly and safely. The use of power permits lower approach speeds, but most important, it allows the pilot to adjust the size and shape of his pattern when landing at airports with high-density traffic.

The power approach used consistently will reduce engine maintenance and extend engine life. The most excruciating punishment an aircraft engine takes in "normal" operation is a go-around from an idle-power glide. Temperatures over all the engine increase sharply and—what is worse—unevenly under such treatment.

In the event of power failure, the power approach does not guarantee a safe glide to the runway. More accidents, however, have resulted from misjudged approaches than from the unlikely chance of sudden power failure during the approach glide.

TRAFFIC INFORMATION

Before flying the pattern, the pilot must know which runway is in use, what the wind conditions are, and what altitude to use for entry. There are two ways to get this information, plus other data of interest. One way is to request landing information from the control tower. The control tower operator will respond with the runway direction, direction of pattern (right-hand or left-hand), wind direction and velocity, *altimeter setting,* and possibly other items of interest to the pilot.

Some aircraft have no communications radio, some airfields have no control tower, and radio calls from individual aircraft might not be practical during intensive student training. Under these conditions runway direction can be indicated by other aircraft already in the pattern, or by a "tee" located within the field boundaries. If neither "tee" nor aircraft can be seen and there is no radio contact, the runway that looks most suitable is selected. Traffic direction normally requires all turns to be

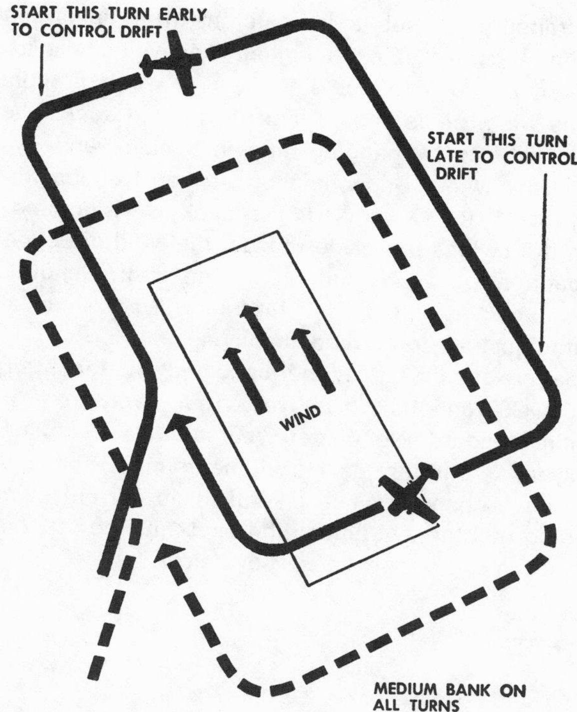

Figure 8.13 Rectangular course. Skill at the rectangular course results in skill and good judgment in the landing pattern. Safe, smooth landings, by which all pilots are inevitably judged, are made more in the pattern than in the final approach. Note that the method of correcting for drift is not the same here as that used in S turns or eights. The wind is allowed to affect the ground track, and the objective is reached by adjusting the place to start the turn. This makes possible flying a traffic pattern *without* steep turns. Practice on both left- and right-hand patterns is important.

made to the left. If right-hand traffic is in effect, the landing tee will so indicate or the airport control tower will advise by radio.

Wind direction can be obtained from a *tetrahedron,* the large three-dimensional "arrow" found on some military and significant civilian fields. These are illuminated at night. At lower wind velocities (under 10 to 15 knots) the tetrahedron is set to indicate the most favorable runway, if the tetrahedron is controllable. At higher wind velocities, a controllable tetrahedron is released to indicate the actual wind direction. To learn more about the wind, pilots should look for a *wind sock*. The wind sock indicates wind velocity by hanging limp in a calm, and by erecting to a cone in a strong wind. Depending on its construction, the sock may reach rigidity at 15 to 30 knots. If the sock is rising and falling, the wind is gusty. If it swings from side to side, the wind direction is variable.

Wind direction also can be judged by the aircraft's drift; and gusty winds can be expected if the air is turbulent. Smoke can also be used as an indicator, just as for forced landings.

A traffic pattern altitude may be specifled by local airport policy, usually between 800 and 1200 ft above terrain. Away from home, 1000 ft is the common standard. No matter what altitude the pilot selects, he can fly it only as accurately as his altimeter measures it. Atmospheric pressure may have changed since takeoff. If no current altimeter setting is available to correct the instrument, the pilot must be especially watchful for other aircraft in the pattern, above or below.

PATTERN ENTRY

Make your visual reconnaissance or "pass" over the traffic pattern to check landing information at least 1000 ft above pattern altitude, and make any let-down to pattern altitude well clear of the pattern and its entry point. During the let-down, check the cockpit and get as many chores done as practicable, so as to reduce the last part of the approach to as simple a process as possible. Make your descent in a constant series of turns to alternate directions, *watching* for aircraft ahead and below.

Make the entry to traffic on a course 45° to the downwind leg, just as in the rectangular pattern maneuver. Aim the entry leg so that there is room for a downwind leg of adequate length (Figure 8.14). Lower the landing gear and complete the prelanding check. Reduce airspeed to use the pattern speed recommended in the flight handbook for the aircraft. Determine drift and correct for it.

DOWNWIND LEG

The proper distance to place the downwind leg from the runway is best demonstrated in flight. From the cockpit of most low-winged aircraft, the runway should appear to rest just above on the wing tip. Here on the downwind leg is the place to determine the drift to expect on final turn and final approach. Note especially the correction required for any cross-wind that tends to blow you towards the runway. (As will be shown, that can be a hazard.) Adjust the start of the turn to base leg for wind conditions, just as done in the practice of the rectangular course.

BASE LEG

The start of the turn to base leg is one of the more important judgments to be made in the pattern. If headwind on landing is going to be strong, place the base leg close to the end of the runway. Then there will not have to be so much ground covered during the final approach at a low ground speed. If the wind is calm, place the base leg further from the runway end. If the turn to base leg is to be medium-banked, the place-

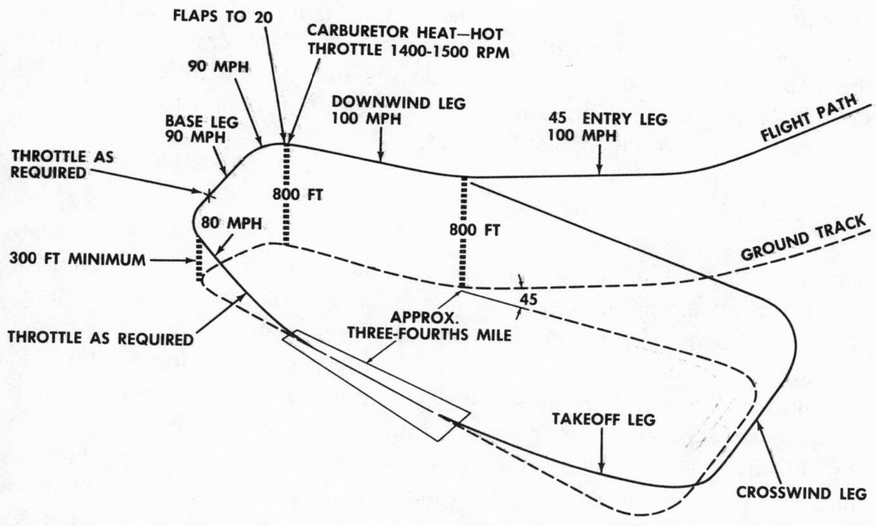

Figure 8.14 Rectangular traffic pattern, Cessna 172. *(Courtesy of U.S. Air Force.)*

ment of the base leg and the effect of wind during the turn both must be considered in choosing a place to start the turn.

As the turn is started, reduce the throttle to a point slightly above idle and lower half flaps if flaps are desired. Maintain altitude until base-leg airspeed is approached, then lower the nose and trim the aircraft for this airspeed. Usually, base-leg airspeed is approximately 10 knots higher than final approach due to the increased stalling speed encountered during the final turn. Complete the base turn with the necessary drift correction to maintain a ground track perpendicular to the runway.

After established on base leg, continue the descent and adjust the throttle as required. If it appears that you are high or that your present glide will take you too far down the runway, retard the throttle and lower the nose to keep your base-leg airspeed constant. This will result in a steeper descent and should correct the situation. Conversely, add power and raise the nose if you are low or your glide will take you to a point short of the runway. In all cases, plan the turn to final approach so that it will be completed at least 300 ft above the terrain.

Most pilots prefer partial flaps on base leg, reserving the rest for final approach. Wing flaps are not normally lowered during the final approach turn because (a) the change in trim as the flaps go down complicates control of the rate of turn and (b) mechanical failure of the flap-operating mechanism on some aircraft may cause a "split flap" condition in which the flap on one wing goes down while the flap on the other wing does not. The result is a rolling tendency which can be difficult to diagnose or correct in the already banked attitude.

THE FINAL APPROACH TURN

The turn to final approach should be not more than medium-banked, and base-leg airspeed should be maintained until wings level on final. If there is a crosswind on the final approach path, consider that fact carefully in planning the turn entry. A crosswind from inside the turn (tailwind on base leg) is potentially hazardous unless the turn is begun early to prevent an "overshoot." If the wind blows the aircraft toward the runway line faster than anticipated, the runway can then be "made" only by (a) steepening the bank to increase rate of turn, or (b) allowing the aircraft to drift past the runway line and then S-turning back to correct, or (c) keeping the turn medium-banked until almost aligned, and then rolling out abruptly. In actual practice, all of these three corrections are used occasionally by experienced pilots—and there are accident statistics to prove it. The student must remember that the airplane is about midway between its straight-ahead stalling speed and cruising speed. It is in a high-drag condition and power cannot be increased instantly from its low settings. Tightening the turn under these conditions is the way you produce your practice power-off turning stalls. As you tighten the turn, the speed at which the airfoil will stall is increased. To avoid the stall, speed must be acquired through engine power or diving in the turn; and the latter alternative inevitably seems the more attractive. The result is increased loss of altitude during the turn, and a dive attitude that makes recovery from any stall more difficult.

If you cannot reach the runway by a medium-banked turn, remember that millions of landings have proved that the pilot should *apply power, go-around,* and *try again.* S turns also are frowned upon. They lead easily to overcorrection. They may occupy air space needed by other aircraft using a parallel runway. They take time and attention that should be spent adjusting glide path, and they thus contribute to bad landings. The third-mentioned technique, delaying the roll-out of the turn, is a legitimate correction if not overdone. Its effectiveness is limited.

If the wind is from outside the turn, blowing the aircraft away from the runway line, you should correct by delaying the final turn. Shallowing the bank and rate of turn will also adjust for the wind. If you badly miscalculate the rate of turn, the glide path probably will not be right either. Because extra time will be spent in the turn against the wind, the final turn may end with too little altitude unless power is added.

FINAL APPROACH

The final approach begins when the flight path is aligned with the runway in preparation for straight-ahead descent and landing. As defined for air traffic control purposes, the final approach ends when the aircraft contacts the landing surface. Thus defined, final approach may be considered to have at least four, and possibly five, distinct phases:

1. Level approach.
2. Approach descent.
3. Roundout.
4. Float.
5. Touchdown.

The last three of these phases constitute the landing operation, which has its separate problems of technique. These will be discussed separately; but it is well to remember that final approach, to a control tower operator, extends all the way to touchdown (Figure 8.15).

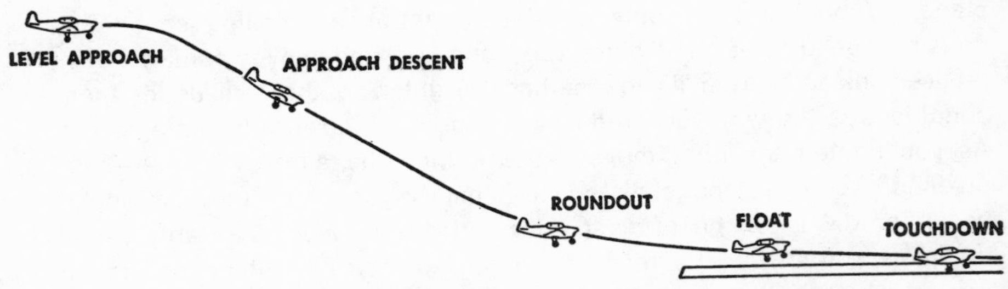

Figure 8.15 Final approach extends from line-up to touchdown.

Level Approach A rectangular traffic pattern does not normally involve a *level approach* portion, because the location of the base leg is planned to permit a continued descent to the landing spot after completion of the turn from base leg. The level approach is of most value in instrument approach procedures, where descent must be initiated at a precise point.

Approach Descent The approach descent (or "glide path") is designed to bring the aircraft forward to the landing area and down to an altitude at which conversion to landing attitude may begin. This is done by flying down a straight-line glide path from the point of rollout on final to a point near the end of the runway. Airspeed in the descent is usually slightly less than that speed giving the best glide ratio, so that the aircraft will not have to float so far down the runway before landing speed is reached.

The importance of a good glide path is not always evident to the beginner, but any experienced pilot knows that it is the first necessary step toward a good roundout and touchdown. If the glide path is a straight line and is flown at a constant airspeed, then pitch, power, and trim can be adjusted for "hands-off" flight. With this done, the pilot is free to devote the major part of his attention outside the cockpit to keep the aircraft lined up with the runway and to monitor altitude above the ground for the roundout. If the glide path is not held constant, then power and trim must be continually adjusted, and the pilot's attention will be taken away from outside references at a time when they are critically important.

The manner by which you establish and maintain a constant-angle glide path has long been considered one of those mysterious functions of "air sense" that make the aviator feel set apart from ordinary mortals. Yet, any judgment of movement in space and time depends on certain clues. When the clues are complex and varied, the reaching of conclusions from them does defy description. Some judgments of that type are mentioned in connection with the roundout for landing.

The judgments of the final approach basically are simple, provided that you maintain a constant final descent airspeed and configuration. Assuming a no-crosswind condition, there is only one significant question to be answered— "Am I staying on my glide path, or am I going high or low?" Sometimes there is a subquestion—"Will I clear the tree?" Both are answered from the same clues.

An aircraft descending at a constant rate and airspeed will be traveling in a straight line toward a spot on the ground ahead. This will not quite be the spot at which you will land because when you start the roundout you will float some distance before touching down. Neither will it be the spot toward which your nose points, because you are flying with a fairly high angle of attack, and the component of lift exerted parallel to the earth by your wings will tend to carry you forward horizontally.

The point toward which the aircraft is setting will be termed the "aiming point." To a pilot moving straight toward an object, it appears to be stationary. It does not "move." The aiming point is no exception. *But objects in front of and beyond the aiming point do appear to move as the distance is closed, and they appear to move in opposite directions.*

Because the entire picture is drawing closer, the changed angle at which you view distance past the aiming point is not too apparent until you are close to the ground. The further ahead that an object rests, the less apparent will be its relative motion to the aircraft. When you extend your glance to the horizon, the relative motion is so slight that the horizon remains in an apparent constant position during the glide. Now, if the horizon line and the aiming point both appear constant, it is evident that the distance between them also will appear constant!

For a constant-angle glide path, the distance between horizon and aiming point will appear constant (Figure 8.16). If a final approach descent has been established but the distance between the aiming point and the horizon appears to increase, then the glide will carry the aircraft farther than first thought, and the real aiming point is farther down the runway. Decreased distance below the horizon indicates an actual aiming point short of desired. This is one way you can determine whether your glide path is correct or not. Many pilots do not realize that they use the technique, but they do.

A second related cue as to correct height on final approach is in the apparent shape of the runway, shown also in Figure 8.16. The importance of runway shape becomes apparent when a pilot who is used to operating from a runway of normal dimensions encounters a grass field or runway that is very narrow or very wide. He will have trouble estimating altitude until he learns to accommodate to the new proportions.

In a project undertaken at the University of Illinois, students were briefed on use of the aiming point and runway shape cues. They were

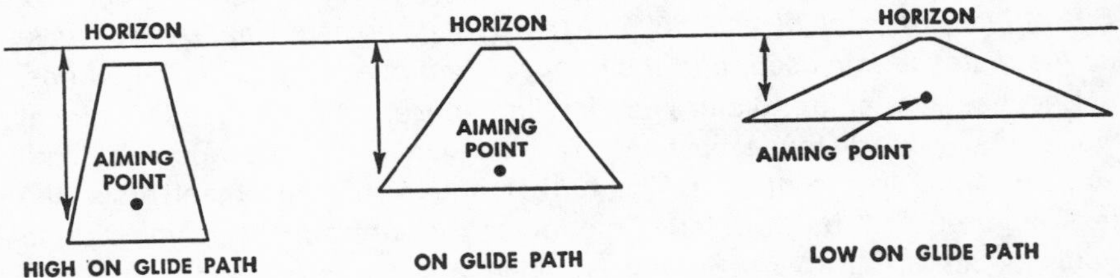

Figure 8.16 Runway appearance. *Upper:* For a constant-angle glide path, the aiming point and the horizon will appear a constant distance apart on the windshield. *Lower:* Distance between aiming point and horizon changes, as does the shape of the runway, for different approach angles.

introduced to use of these cues in a modified Link instrument trainer as a flight simulator. After practice in the simulator, the experimental group of students required 61% fewer practice approaches in actual flight practice of landing approaches; and they made 74% fewer errors during the flight phase of the operation.

What about poplar trees and power lines? Treat the obstacle as a possible "aiming point." If it does not move in one's angle of vision, that is what it is. (Some pilots call the "aiming" point the "crash" point; perhaps the latter term is more appropriate here.) If the obstacle moves up toward the desired aiming point, you will not get over it in your present descent (Figure 8.17). If it moves down away from the horizon and aiming point, even to a barely noticeable degree, you will get over it without changing the approach angle.

Figure 8.17 Obstacles in the glide path. If the trees appear to move up toward the aiming point, the airplane will not clear them.

Staying On The Glide Path Immediately after rolling out on final, adjust the pitch attitude so that the aircraft is descending directly toward the aiming point. Obtain the final flap setting, adjust the throttle to maintain the recommended airspeed, and trim for "hands-off" flight. As the airspeed is reduced from final turn speed to final approach speed, be prepared to increase pitch slightly so as to stay on the established glide path. Now that the approach is set up, you can devote almost all your attention toward outside references. Do not stare at any one place, but keep your eyes moving about from one point to another, such as from the aiming point to the horizon, to the trees and bushes along the runway, to an area well short of the runway, and back to the aiming point. Only in doing this will you be able to perceive a deviation from the desired glide path and whether or not you are going directly toward your aiming point.

If you notice yourself going slightly high or low, make a small pitch change to correct the glide path and adjust the throttle for airspeed. Large deviations may require two corrections—one to get back to the glide path and another to stay there. A double correction such as this is almost always necessary when excessively low and still at a great distance from the runway. Reestablishing a new glide path from low altitude to the end of the runway will only cause a low, dragged-in approach from a half-mile or so out. Of course, when it is too late to correct or when corrections must be excessive, the best action is to go around and try again. The best pilots never hesitate to go around if there is doubt.

Trimming for the Approach Adjust the trim controls during final approach up to the start of the roundout. In a glide, the counter-torque rigging of the vertical stabilizer will produce a need for left-rudder trim, and possibly for additional left rudder pressure beyond the trim-tab capabilities. Trim off all stick pressure so that you can sense changes in airspeed and control the aircraft more precisely.

Landing

To land an aircraft, bring it smoothly within a few feet above the runway, aligned with the runway, and in a semistalled condition. To describe such complexities of that act as space will allow, the discussion has been divided into three phases: *Roundout, float,* and *touchdown.* The description is confined to a power-on approach with the wind straight down the runway. Variations will be considered later.

ROUNDOUT

Without reservation, the roundout requires keener judgment and more practice than any other single part of basic flying. The objective is to reduce the airspeed and rate of descent obtained in the approach descent, so that the aircraft is near its stalling speed while barely descending as close to the runway as possible. In the power approach, accomplish the reduction in airspeed and descent by smoothly retarding the throttle to idle and by gradually increasing the pitch attitude. Raising the nose of the aircraft, without adding power, produces a higher angle of attack. This momentarily adds to lift, reducing the descent. It also adds to drag,

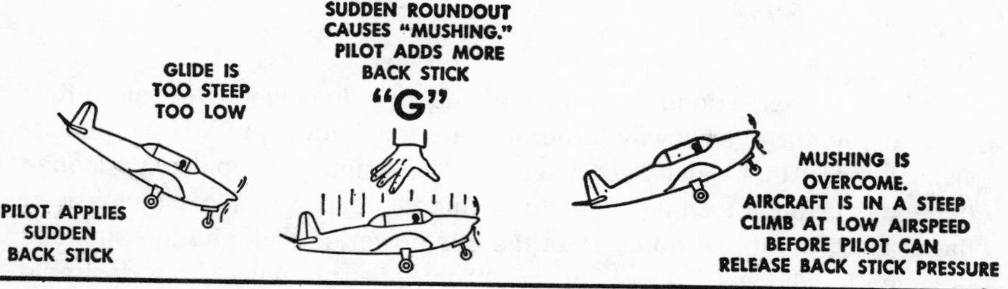
SUDDEN ROUNDOUT
CAUSES "MUSHING."
PILOT ADDS MORE
BACK STICK
"G"
GLIDE IS
TOO STEEP
TOO LOW
PILOT APPLIES
SUDDEN
BACK STICK
MUSHING IS
OVERCOME.
AIRCRAFT IS IN A STEEP
CLIMB AT LOW AIRSPEED
BEFORE PILOT CAN
RELEASE BACK STICK PRESSURE

Figure 8.18 The story of a "balloon."

reducing the airspeed. The reduced airspeed again decreases lift, so that further increase in pitch attitude becomes necessary. Note that, as speed diminishes, both the pitch attitude and the airfoil angle of attack are increased.

There can be considerable variation in the rate of which you accomplish the roundout, that is, the rate at which you bring the nose of the aircraft up to landing attitude. The runway and surrounding terrain will appear to "come up" to meet the aircraft. Back stick pressure can be regarded as a kind of a brake, serving to reduce the rate of closure between aircraft and runway. The "brake" must be applied to slow the rate of closure progressively. You can judge the amount of airspeed remaining, and thus the amount of "brake" you have left, by the pitch attitude of aircraft. Here the practice of power-off stalls pays off. If the aircraft approaches stall attitude well above the runway, then the roundout has proceeded too abruptly. Engine power must be added to cushion the descent or to go around. If the aircraft is near the runway, but pitch attitude is well below that for the stall, then hold the aircraft off from contact until further back stick pressure raises the nose and dissipates airspeed. The aircraft will stall, at idle power, in nearly the same pitch attitude (relative to the horizon) as it did at 4000 ft practicing power-off stalls.

A frequent error during the learning or roundout technique is "ballooning" (Figure 8.18). This occurs when you delay roundout too long. Suddenly realizing that you are too close to the runway for your condition of glide, you pull back sharply on the stick. If the airspeed is adequate to support the nose-up acceleration without a high-speed stall, the aircraft responds with a climb. By the time you level off from the climb, your airspeed is too low for the altitude at which you now find yourself. To correct, you can add a small amount of throttle to maintain safe speed in the descent or you can make a go-around. The choice of correction will depend on the height of the balloon and the airspeed lost in the process.

FLOAT

The float is that extended portion of the roundout when the aircraft is close enough to the runway to permit safe touchdown but still has excessive airspeed that must be dissipated. The amount of float experienced depends on pilot technique in the roundout, aerodynamic cleanness of the aircraft, the thrust obtained at the idle power setting, and the airspeed at which touchdown finally is made. A long float normally is not desirable because maintaining the correct attitude is difficult, the landing point is difficult to predict, and the aircraft is highly vulnerable to gusts of wind.

During the float, continue to apply back stick pressure. The aircraft is ready for landing when it reaches the correct pitch attitude in its descent. For tail-wheeled types, this pitch attitude can be learned on the ground. It is the "three-point" attitude, with the tail wheel on the runway. Tricycle-geared aircraft land in the same attitude as the tail-wheeled types, because that attitude is determined by wing angle of attack rather than landing gear placement, and it is important to avoid making first contact with the nose gear to avoid porpoising.

TOUCHDOWN AND LANDING ROLL

As the aircraft makes contact, the pilot of the tail-wheeled aircraft should continue back stick movement to the limit of travel—cautiously at first, to avoid pulling the aircraft into the air again. The force thus exerted on the tail wheel improves its steering effectiveness. With tricycle gear, the stick can be left as it was at touchdown until the nose begins to lower from reduced airspeed in the landing roll. For best aerodynamic braking, hold the nose wheel off the runway by continuing back stick pressure; but allow the nose wheel to descend gradually, or it may fall with considerable impact when elevator effectiveness finally is lost.

Be alert for directional control difficulties immediately after touchdown (Figure 8.19). This is especially true in tail-wheeled types. Because the longitudinal center of gravity is behind the main gear, any difference between the direction the aircraft is traveling and the direction it is pointed will be aggravated as the aircraft swerves about its main gear pivot point. Tricycle-geared aircraft make the task easier, because of gravity *ahead* of the main landing gear tends to right the aircraft in its path. Directional control is maintained by alert rudder action, aided by brake if necessary.

Ground Loops Loss of directional control may lead to a vicious, uncontrolled tight turn on the runway, known as a *ground loop.* Centrifugal force during the ground loop may cause the outside wing tip to contact the runway and may even collapse the landing gear. Tail-wheeled aircraft

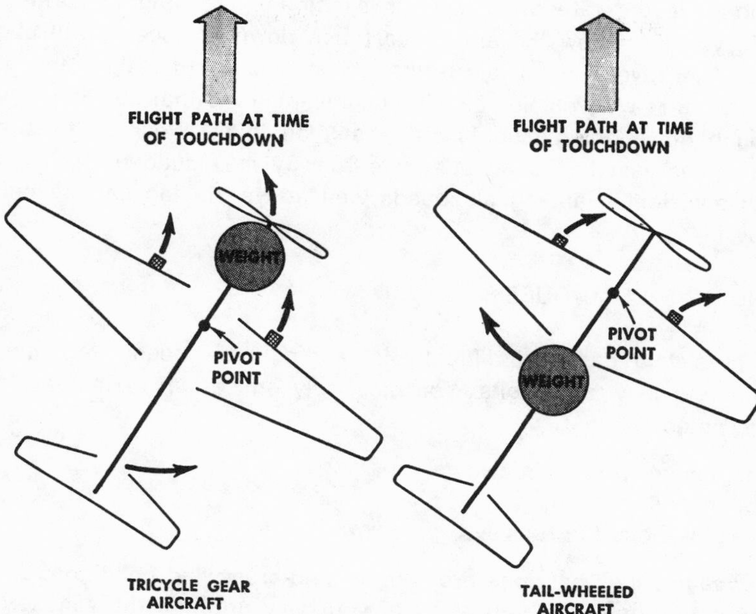

Figure 8.19 Why the tricycle gear is inherently stable at touchdown, touching down with a crab.

are most susceptible to ground loops, which usually occur late in the landing roll. Rudder effectiveness at the time of touchdown is high, but as the aircraft slows, the rudder loses effectiveness. Because the full weight of the tail still does not rest on the tail wheel, control at this point is only marginal. The moral: Hold the stick full back, and be ready with the brakes if they are needed. "Fly the airplane" until it stops. When using brakes to slow the aircraft, apply them intermittently for periods of one or two seconds. This permits necessary cooling between applications.

STALL IT IN?

Should the aircraft be landed in a stall? In tail-wheeled aircraft it is difficult to avoid a stall when landing three points power-off. Sometime before reaching the three-point attitude, the aircraft will begin to sink with increasing rapidity due to the rise in aerodynamic drag just before the stall. Interested in getting the tail wheel on the runway, you increase back pressure as the aircraft drops. Acceleration loads resulting from the change in pitch attitude practically insure the stall. (Done carefully, it is an excellent technique for short-field or rough-field landings, and avoids long bounces.)

As long as the rate of descent is slight and the landing surface is smooth, you can allow the aircraft to touch down at speeds well above stalling. The advantage of this is that the possibility of stalling too high above the runway is eliminated. The disadvantage is that sometimes you will touch down going much faster than you think. Wear on tires and brakes is increased, and an adequate runway may suddenly prove too short. Consistently landing at speeds well above stalling can be called "sloppy flying."

LANDING VISUAL CUES

Many persistent cases of difficulty in landing have been overcome by improvement in visual habits. You must rely on certain definable visual cues to detect:

a. alignment with the runway
b. pitch attitude
c. height above the runway.

Alignment brings only one problem in a no-crosswind condition: Divide your attention between both sides of your view through the windscreen. If you tend to concentrate toward one side you often unknowingly add opposite rudder and will destroy correct alignment.

Pitch attitude also has its familiar measuring device—the horizon line.

Height above the runway brings new visual elements. They are complicated. One source of visual cues is in details such as tufts of grass, texture of runway surface, and—at night—local illumination around runway lights. Another source is the overall perspective of the runway and surrounding terrain as it appears to flatten from the lower viewing angle. Though not of much use in detecting alignment, perspective is highly important for height. You are accustomed to viewing perspective from a height of 5 to 6 ft. Your height is the same or only slightly greater at the time of touchdown in the cockpit of a lightplane, so the correct perspective is easy to learn. Depth perception, the ability to separate near objects from far objects, is an important adjunct to perspective, although research has established that binocular or "stereo" depth perception is not as essential as once was thought. Most of our ability to perceive depth is based on known or assumed size of adjoining objects, viewing angle, obscurement of far objects by near objects, and differences in illumination.

Immediately ahead of the aircraft, as it nears the surface, objects lose their identity in the "speed blur." Far down the runway, the rate of changing relationship between objects is less apparent. Between these two extremes, you get most of your information. *As a general rule,* looking too far ahead will cause a high level-off; and looking too close will cause a late level-off. For the most effective canvass of visual requirements, sit with head slightly back. Sit centered and resist the temptation to peer around one side or the other of the aircraft nose, if the nose obstructs vision at touchdown. Eyes should be constantly scanning the horizon, the terrain, to each side, and the surface just ahead of the speed blur.

Planning the Touchdown Point Unless the runway is very short, you should plan to touch down about 500 to 1000 ft from the approach end. This is done by adjusting the aiming point for wind speed and direction. If the wind is calm, the aiming point must be placed short of the runway to allow for a longer float. Conversely, the aiming point must be farther ahead (toward the touchdown zone) for a strong headwind. However, it must be remembered that it is the headwind *component* that affects float distance, not the crosswind.

BOUNCES

When the rate of descent is too great at time of touchdown, the aircraft will bounce. The severity of impact depends entirely on rate of descent. The height to which the aircraft bounces depends on the severity of impact, airspeed, your control action, and type of aircraft. A high bounce most commonly occurs, like "ballooning," when you realize too late that the airspeed is too high and the pitch attitude too nose-low for the landing. At the instant of impact, then, you will be applying forceful back stick pressure.

The design of tail-wheeled aircraft is no help in a bounce. The weight of the tail section still descending at the moment of impact causes the tail to "pivot" down just as an upward force is being applied to the front (main gear) section. The result, after a hard bounce, is an abrupt increase in pitch attitude as the aircraft rises in the bounce.

The tricycle gear takes bounces better. The forward center of gravity provides nose-down tendencies when the shock of the bounce is put to the main gear, counteracting back stick that you may be holding. In a severe bounce, the nose-wheel tire and strut help to cushion the pitch change much more than does the relatively stiff tail-wheel assembly.

If the bounce is severe, or an excessively steep pitch attitude has resulted, the only proper action is an immediate go-around. Apply full power, keep the aircraft straight with rudder and aileron, and lower the nose as close to a shallow climb as time and control permit. The aircraft may contact the runway again before you regain controlled flight. If so, do not try to get the stick all the way back again before contact, nor try to "flatten out" a bounce with a lot of forward stick pressure. Such efforts are usually about a half-step behind their purpose, and can get one into serious porpoising difficulties. Engine power and a *constant,* moderate, back stick pressure eventually will get the aircraft back under full control.

A very shallow bounce, or "skip," requires little corrective action. Usually the pitch attitude can be raised slightly before the second touchdown. If the bounce is a little beyond the "skip" class, but no cause for alarm, use a little added engine power to cushion the rate of descent after the bounce. The dividing point between a "skip," a "bounce," and a "severe bounce" is one for you to determine from your intimate view of the situation.

POWER-OFF APPROACHES

Although the power-off approach does not offer as many advantages as the power-on approach it does have its value. For the beginner, when touchdown accuracy is not as important, airspeed control on base and final becomes a simple matter of adjusting pitch. Also, the power-off approach develops the necessary judgment to make an accurate forced landing.

In planning for a normal power-off approach, the base leg must be spaced closer to the runway; however, it must still be adjusted for wind as with the power approach. After established on base, reduce the airspeed a few knots to slow the aircraft closer to final approach speed and trim for hands-off flight. When the end of the runway is approximately 45° from the aircraft (that is, halfway between the nose and wing tip), you must be able to move the throttle to idle and glide the rest of the way to landing. As you approach this 45° key point you may decide that the base leg was placed in too close or out too far for the glide approach. The key point can be adjusted as a correction for the misplaced base leg. When practicing repeated accuracy landings, try to keep the 45° angle for the key point constant, adjusting the location of each succeeding base leg until the correct distance for wind conditions has been found.

As the throttle goes to idle, hold altitude constant until airspeed decreases to the final turn glide speed. Then lower and trim the nose for normal glide attitude and check the airspeed indicator to be sure of the result. Lower flaps on base if desired and determine the proper lead point to begin the final turn.

As soon as possible after rolling out on final, obtain the final flap setting, idle power, and glide airspeed. The resulting constant-angle glide will permit you to judge whether the descent is toward the correct spot, or whether you are aimed too short or too long. The techniques involved in this judgment are exactly the same as those used in the power approach.

Action When Glide is Insufficient Once the flaps have been extended, engine power is the best way to correct for an undershooting approach. The only other satisfactory method is to lower the nose slightly. This will extend the glide distance if gliding speed was slower than that giving the best glide, although it results in a flatter glide and may not help to clear obstacles short of the runway. To get better engine temperatures and to avoid a long float after rounding out, pilots usually make the final approach glide speed a few knots slower than the best glide for the aircraft. The all-too-human tendency to "stretch the glide" by raising the nose of the aircraft has been discussed sufficiently on previous pages so it needs no repetition here. The difficulty is not that pilots do not believe the best glide speed exists; the difficulty is that instinct short-circuits reason when panic enters the picture. It is unfortunate that each student cannot be given one premeditated shot at making a practice forced landing where some wires short of the field appear to be too high to get over. There surely are hundreds of crop dusters and ex-crop dusters alive in the land because they chose the route under the wires rather than over. None of those men will ever try stretching a glide.

Often discussed with serious intent is the idea of retracting the lowered wing flaps to extend the glide. The airplane would, indeed, glide farther if the flaps were up; but while the flaps are retracting, aircraft attitude must be changed, and airspeed must be increased to the value required for the no-flap condition. Both these actions consume altitude, and the apparent result to the pilot is the general impression that the "bottom has dropped out." There is a break-even point, in terms of altitude, where glide distance can be extended by retracting the flaps; but that altitude is above that normally employed on the last stages of the final approach.

When There Is Excessive Glide If the approach is overshooting the landing area, there are two means of correction that might be employed. The first of these is to lower full flaps if less had been selected for landing. The second is the slip. Almost all light aircraft have good slipping characteristics as long as the gliding speed is kept up to normal. Some training programs do not permit the use of slips as a normal adjustment, because larger and faster aircraft do not always have flight characteristics which permit slipping. The technique, however, may some day be handy to know in almost any aircraft.

There are other conceivable means by which excess altitude could be lost. One of these is the flying of S turns while on final approach. The S turns are undesirable in normal landing because they interfere with precise control of gliding speed and also create an air traffic hazard. Another means not approved is that of increasing or decreasing gliding speed from that giving best glide ratio. Increasing the speed is not very effective, because most of the altitude lost is converted to float distance after the roundout commences. Decreasing the glide speed can easily prove too effective and the practice is hazardous. It is mentioned here only because the young pilot will probably be exposed to hangar talk about "walking the wings down." When landing the aircraft, there must be a sufficient airspeed margin to support the acceleration loads induced by pitch changes in rounding out. Reducing the glide speed may leave a safe margin during descent, but the margin will be insufficient for roundout, and, instead of leveling off just above the runway surface when the nose comes up, the airplane will simply mush at the same rate of descent, "dropping" onto the runway with a severe and possibly dangerous jolt.

GO-AROUNDS (WAVE-OFFS)

The go-around got into this section by default. It is a takeoff, with special considerations. The term "go-around" ("wave-off" in the Navy) usually is applied to the discontinuance of the landing approach, just before touchdown. If you add power to regain flight after touchdown, the maneuver is termed a "follow-through" or a "running" takeoff, or possibly a "touch-and-go landing." All require the same basic technique. Advance the throttle smoothly to whatever the approach rpm permits, because the aircraft is not trimmed for takeoff. It is trimmed for a glide and must be retrimmed as soon as possible.

If the aircraft is about to land, it may touch down before regaining flying speed. If any yaw has been allowed to develop from uncorrected propeller torque, some quick rudder might be required to keep the aircraft straight. Otherwise the brief touchdown should present no problem.

When safely airborne with the landing gear retracted, a shallow turn to permit looking behind for other go-arounds is good practice. Retract the wing flaps only after the aircraft is retrimmed, the gear is up, and airspeed has reached approximately that to be used for the climb-out.

ADVERSE LANDING CONDITIONS

These can be covered only briefly.

Strong Gusty Winds Use a power approach. Add one-half the gust velocity to the minimum approach airspeed, for example, for a 20-knot wind gusting to 30, add 5 knots. Plan on a low roundout to keep the airspeed high until near the runway. Partial flaps, or no flaps at all, will reduce the ability of quartering gusts to raise the upwind wing. In extremely gusty winds, tail-wheeled aircraft should be literally flown onto the runway in approximately level flight attitude, using engine power until after touchdown. Just after touchdown In a wheel landing, slight forward pressure on the stick will hold the aircraft on the runway and prevent skipping. Raise flaps before lowering the tail and be ready for positive rudder action to retain control.

Wet or Icy Runways Expect poor braking and do not land long. Test the braking action by gradually increasing the strength of brake applications. On ice or snow, be alert for patches of dry runway. If one wheel is sliding when it reaches good braking surface, directional control suddenly will become difficult.

Soft Terrain Land with stick well back, in the "three-point" attitude. Be sure to keep the stick full back until slowed to safe speed. If a tail-wheeled aircraft starts to nose over, the application of engine power, *with the stick full back,* may hold the tail down.

Short-Field Landings When runway length is marginal, a power approach with full wing flaps is good policy. If at all possible, the new pilot should do some slow flight and power-on stalls before descending into the landing pattern. Technique on the approach depends, to a great extent, on the nature of obstacles in the approach zone. If the zone is clear, the approach descent can be made at normal or slightly less than normal airspeed—but aimed well short of intended landing. As the aircraft nears landing attitude and altitude short of the end of the runway, gradually increase engine power to forestall touchdown. Hold up the nose of the aircraft and add power. The airplane should cross the end of the runway with the nose slightly above normal landing attitude, and with at least ¾ normal rated engine power. The airplane should be just ready to stall at that point. Reduce power to idle just before crossing the end of the runway, and the aircraft will drop to the runway at once.

If obstacles must be cleared, reduce the airspeed on approach to the limit that runway length and pilot competence justify (as little as 5 knots above power-on stalling speed in the full-flap configuration). Then aim the approach just short of the intended landing point. Maintain a pitch attitude in the descent at almost that required for landing. Keep engine power until the aircraft is ready to land, because the aircraft will drop as soon as power is retarded. Because of the low airspeed, this type of power approach provides a steeper glide angle than does the power-off approach. The base leg will have to be placed proportionately closer.

If the aircraft floats after the throttle is cut, it is possible to reduce float distance and get the aircraft on the runway for braking action, by retracting the wing flaps when a foot or two above the runway. (Is it necessary to add that you must be quite *sure* you are only a foot or two high when you start the flaps on their way up?) Tricycle-geared aircraft with adequate wheel brakes can be stopped in the shortest distance with wing flaps retracted during the landing roll. This is because the lift provided when flaps are down decreases effective weight on the main wheels, and the resulting reduced traction permits the tires to skid during high-speed braking. Retracting flaps during the landing roll is less effective in tail-wheeled aircraft, because (1) braking capability is limited by nose-over tendencies and (2) location of the center of gravity behind the main gear produces weight on the tires in proportion to the braking action.

Exploit every possible drag device if runway length is critical. Curiously the feature of next effectiveness to braking is often overlooked—that is, shutting off the engine. Opening the cowl flaps (if possible) the canopy, will help.

Like takeoff distances, landing distances at various temperatures and altitudes, as well as landing roll and distances over a 50-ft obstacle, are available to you in either the manufacturer's handbook or from the handbook of flight operations for military aircraft.

No-Flap Landings Most light aircraft do not have radically different characteristics with or without landing flaps. The cleaner the design of the aircraft, the greater the difference will be. The flaps are quite important in light jets, as in their larger and faster kin. Technique for a no-flap landing is essentially the same as for a short-field landing. Use additional airspeed on final approach, because the stalling speed without flaps will be perhaps 5 to 10 knots faster. Pitch attitude for any airspeed will be higher without the flaps, and you must become accustomed to the no-flap approach attitude. Float distance after the roundout will be longer. It is safe to say that nine out of ten no-flap landings made without recent practice result in overshooting the touchdown point.

CROSSWIND LANDINGS

Most landings are made with some degree of crosswind. There are three parts to the problem: First, to compensate for drift so as to track directly along the runway heading during final approach. Second, to have the aircraft aligned with the runway at the time of touchdown—to avoid side

SLIPPING COUNTERACTS THE DRIFT THAT RESULTS FROM A CROSSWIND.

Figure 8.20 Wing-down crosswind correction. *(Courtesy of U.S. Air Force.)*

loads on the landing gear at touchdown. Third, to maintain control after touchdown.

Make the final approach longer than usual at the minimum approach speed plus the gust factor, remembering that most aircraft are more easily controlled in crosswind landings with a reduced flap setting. The long approach will permit establishing an accurate glide speed and the proper drift correction for tracking directly down the extended runway centerline. As the runway is approached, lower the upwind wing and apply opposite rudder to produce a slip into the wind. Use bank to control the lateral position of the aircraft (that is, to keep the aircraft on the centerline of the runway), and use rudder to keep the heading of the aircraft parallel to the runway. Be prepared to reduce bank and rudder during the float since wind speed normally decreases close to the ground. The upwind gear will touch first and will be followed shortly thereafter by the other gear without any action by the pilot. Continue to hold aileron into the wind to keep the upwind wing from rising, and use rudder for directional control.

A second technique often used with heavier aircraft is acceptable, but requires near-perfect timing. As you make your flare-out, level the wings, and with aggressive rudder action, eliminate crab. If you make the flare properly, without too much excess speed, the aircraft will not float long enough to gain momentum in a sideways direction, and will touch down with a minimum of side load on the gear. It is far better to land on the upwind gear, in an upwind wing-down attitude, than to land on both gear with sideways movement. *Do not attempt to land with a crosswind factor greater than the maximum allowable for your aircraft.*

Retaining control on the ground is the most critical problem, because the weather cocking effect of the wind on the aircraft, plus tire side load from runway contact while drifting, frequently generates ground loops in tail-wheeled and rollovers in tricycle-geared, aircraft. Because these are among the greatest causes of all accidents, understanding them is worthwhile.

The basic factors are *cornering angle* and *side load* (Figure 8.21). Cornering angle is defined as the angular difference between the heading of a tire and its path. Whenever a load-bearing tire's path and heading diverge, a side load (*s*) is created. It is accommodated by tire distortion. Although side load differs in varying tires and air pressures, it is completely independent of speed, and through a considerable range, is directly proportional to the cornering angle and the weight supported by the tire. As little as 10° of cornering angle will create a side load equal to half the supported weight; after 20° the side load does not increase with increasing cornering angle.

A 10° cornering angle corresponds to the drift of an airplane traveling

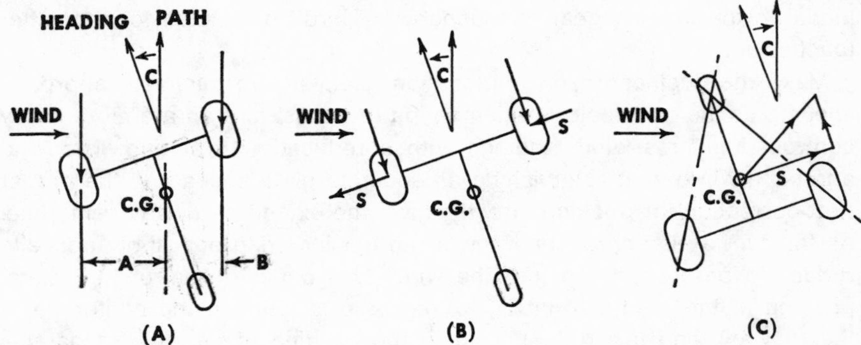

Figure 8.21 Ground-looping and roll-over forces. *(A)* If forces on tires paralleled plane's path (they don't), unequal moment arms about the *(A,B)* would cause ground loop. *(B)* Forces on tires are actually in plane of wheel and 90° thereto; tire side loads cause ground loop or roll-over. *(C)* Lines linking nose and main wheels are roll-over axes; roll-over force vectors from perpendicular to axis. *(Courtesy of John H. Geisse, AOPA pilot.)*

at 60 mph with a direct crosswind of just over 10 mph; at the same speed, a 5° drift would result from a direct crosswind of 5 mph. A cornering angle of 10° would be required at a taxi speed of just under 20 mph to make a turn of 50 ft radius. The same turn at just under 14 mph would require a 5° cornering angle.

In a test conducted in England on a representative group of tail-wheel airplanes with pilots of varying skills it was found that the most expert pilot, fully alert, could not prevent a ground loop following a touchdown with 10° of drift. An average pilot could cope with only a 5° drift at touchdown. While (Figure 8.19) tricycle gear are not vulnerable to ground loops, they are subject to roll-overs (Figure 8.21c). A cornering angle at 10° will cause roll-over in a typical high-wing aircraft. The force required for roll-over is proportional to the distance of the roll-over axis from the c.g., and the height of the latter.

While the weathercocking effect of crosswinds also affects loss of control of aircraft during landing, ground loops and roll-overs are primarily caused by wheel side loads resulting from excessive drift at touchdown and careless taxiing, either in crosswind or in turns. The hazard can be considerably lessened by using crosswind gear, but lacking that, by observing these warnings:

Tail-wheel gear: For each tail-wheel-geared aircraft there is a cornering angle beyond which the most expert pilot, fully alert, cannot stop a ground loop. At lower angles avoidance is dependent upon how quickly and how forcibly corrective action is taken. If too little or too late the ground-looping moment will increase faster than the antiground-looping moment the pilot is applying.

Tricycle gear: For each high-wing, tricycle-geared airplane there is a cornering angle at which roll-over is inevitable. At lesser angles the roll-over may be avoided by use of ailerons, rudder, or steerable nose wheel *but not brakes.*

After the Flight

AFTER LANDING

A cockpit "clean-up" is due after the landing roll is complete and the aircraft off the runway. If taxi distance to the parking area is short, the check might be delayed until then. The essential of the "after-landing check" usually are:

1. Cowl flaps—*open* (if adjustable).
2. Wing flaps—*up.*
3. Propeller and fuel-mixture controls—*full advanced and rich.*
4. Trim tabs—*reset.*
5. Fuel boost pump switch—*off* (if used for landing).

A post-flight check of engine condition should be conducted after the last flight of the day. This check parallels that given before takeoff and will save much in maintenance, ground running, and annoying delayed take-offs.

PARKING AND STOPPING

Signals used between pilot and ground crew are the same as used during taxi-out. If a visitor, the pilot may be conducted from first taxi-way to the parking area by tower instructions or by a "follow-me" vehicle. The "follow-me" usually is equipped with an illuminated sign and directional turn signals for night operation.

Before stopping, the cylinder-head temperature in air-cooled engines should be stabilized at a temperature conducive to good cooling. This temperature usually is specified at less than 200°C, the exact value depending on cowling and exhaust stack arrangement. If the temperature is too high, it can be reduced by facing squarely upwind and running at 1000 to 1200 rpm for a few minutes. In any case the last full minute of engine operation should be at 1000 to 1200 rpm, to provide most efficient scavenge of engine oil and to insure lubrication for the next start. During this time, radios can be turned off, and other final cockpit procedures completed.

Aircraft without mixture control are stopped by turning the ignition to OFF at idle or up to 1000 rpm, and then turning the fuel shutoff valve to OFF. If a mixture control is present, it must be moved to FULL LEAN position ot stop the engine. The master and ignition switches must be turned off *after* the propeller has stopped turning. The pilot calls "switches off" *after* they have been turned to OFF.

Advancing the throttle on aircraft with mixture-control carburetors after selecting FULL LEAN is *not* recommended procedure. "Cleaning the cylinders out" with a blast of cold air serves no important purpose, and the rapid interior cooling thereby obtained may warp intake valves or valve seats.

Release parking brakes as soon as chocks are provided under the wheels. Then fill out forms for the flight and trudge happily to the coffee bar—if you have someone to do the post-flight exterior inspection, refueling, and tie-down. The need for a post-flight exterior inspection is obvious. Refueling immediately on landing is a good practice to prevent condensation of moisture in empty or partly empty tanks and to have the airplane ready for use when next needed.

TIE-DOWN

Securing the aircraft for outside-the-hangar parking deserves a few comments, even for those pilots who normally can leave the chore to the mechanic. Parking brakes and chocks are the first necessities. The chocks should be placed fore and aft of each main wheel. Control surface locks are essential in high or gusty winds. These may be external and are slipped over the control surfaces and adjoining structure.

TABLE 8.3
Aircraft Tie-Down Guide

Type of Aircraft	*Maximum Wind Velocity (knots) for Parking Without Tie-Down*
Average lightplane (up to 2000 lb gross weight)	20
Four-passenger, single-engine civilian types and military primary trainer (up to 4000 lb gross weight)	35
C-46, C-47, DC-3, etc.	45
Modern tricycle-geared 2-engine	60

The wind velocity at which any aircraft requires tie-down in addition to parking brakes and wheel chocks is a function of both weight and shape, predominantly weight.

For aircraft with tail-wheel landing gear, spoilers (obstructions to normal airflow) may be placed on the wing top. These usually are small bags of sand or similar material. They should be about 4 in. in diameter. Wooden L-shaped rails may be used in place of the bags. The rails should be padded on the undersurface and tied to the wing. Whatever material is used should extend across three quarters of the wing span and should be located about midway between leading edge and the thickest portion of the wing (10° to 15° average chord).

Ropes used for tie-down should be at least ⅜-in. nylon. If the aircraft has rungs for tie-down, they will be located near the main wing spar, about two-thirds distance out from the fuselage. Some aircraft have sockets at that point, into which rungs may be screwed on occasion. External struts beneath the wing of lightplanes make the attachment problem simple. If no tie-down rungs can be located at all, the main landing gear must serve.

For the other end of the rope, parking ramps should have permanent tie-down stanchions. For dirt or sod parking, barbed stakes should be used. The most effective stake is a type that is driven into the ground with the barb recessed. A half turn of the head then cocks the barb, and a few additional blows extend the barb. Such stakes can be removed from the soil only by digging them out.

Tie-down ropes should be at a 45° angle from ground to aircraft. They should be tied either with a bowline or square knot. Some slack must be left in the rope to allow for tightening due to moisture.

Advanced Maneuvers

A concert artist spends countless hours practicing scales and exercises that audiences never hear. For a similar reason, the conscientious pilot devotes effort to master certain practice maneuvers. Ability to perform them properly is a matter of craftsman's pride, but the important benefits are in the sharpening of fundamental skill to the degree that the pilot can cope with unusual or unforeseen circumstances occasionally encountered in normal flight.

These maneuvers are termed "advanced" because they require a degree of skill for proper execution that a pilot normally does not acquire until he has soloed and has obtained a sense of orientation and control feel in "normal" maneuvers.

A first group of advanced maneuvers includes the *maximum-perform-*

ance climbing turn, the chandelle and the *lazy-8.* These are set apart, because, if done as presented here, they are not usually considered to be *acrobatic* maneuvers. The attitudes, airspeeds, and accelerations involved are well within the capabilities of any certificated aircraft; and the pilot has good visibility at all times.

The remainder of the maneuvers are acrobatic (or "aerobatic" as some purists will stoutly insist). The catalogue of acrobatic maneuvers is bounded principally by ingenuity and aircraft design limits. Stalls and spins, previously presented as "confidence maneuvers," fall within the definition of acrobatic flight. Acrobatic flight is defined by Federal Air Regulations, as "maneuvers intentionally performed by an aircraft involving an abrupt change in its attitude, an abnormal attitude, or an abnormal acceleration." Other maneuvers currently taught in the Air Force and Navy courses of instruction are the *loop, barrell roll, aileron roll, half roll* and *split S, Immelman, Cuban eight,* and *cloverleaf.* Also to be considered in less detail are the *slow roll, inverted flight, snap roll, vertical reversement, vertical stalls, English bunt, outside loop,* and *inverted loop.*

Acrobatics are an essential part of military flight training. Through acrobatics, the pilot learns to control his aircraft precisely through its entire range of airspeeds and attitudes. The sense of confidence thus acquired is fully as important as the stick and rudder skills. And, certainly not the least of benefits is that acrobatics add immeasurably to the joy of flying. The thrill of mastering movement and acceleration in flying is the same as that which sends people down ski slopes and sailing a skiff close to the wind. Mount Everest was climbed and pilots do acrobatics because of the challenge to man's skill and daring.

Acrobatic maneuvers should be attempted only in aircraft properly stressed for them. An aircraft with limit load factors of 6 positive and 3 negative *g* is considered stressed for acrobatics, but the real limiting factor is pilot technique. A loop can be done with less than three positive and with no negative *g.* Even helicopters and four-engined bombers have been looped without fatal results. It is also quite possible to impose sufficient *g* loads during loop recovery to deform or detach the wings of any "fully acrobatic" trainer. Certain maneuvers involving inverted flight can be accomplished only in specially stressed and modified aircraft; these maneuvers will be described only briefly.

The relationship between limiting speed and *g* loads will be explored at greater length in the next chapter. Here it shall be noted only that maximum obtainable or allowable *g* is dependent upon aircraft weight, center of gravity, speed, and configuration; and that published *g* limits are based on straight flight. For a rolling maneuver, the normal *g* limits should be lowered by approximately one third.

The reader who has yet to enjoy acrobatic flight should not infer that normal acrobatic maneuvers must be meticulously planned and executed to remain within a narrow safe operating range. No maneuver in the military acrobatic curricula requires special talent to complete with less than 4 positive or 1 negative *g*. Loads outside that range produce evident discomfort in blurred vision and pressures against the seat or seat belt. *The beginner should have dual instruction* on any maneuver to be attempted until he acquires a sense of control orientation and an appreciation of speed and load relationship, and until he can do fundamental acrobatics with reasonable precision and with confidence.

Because of the wide variation in performance of different aircraft, precise recommendations for airspeeds and power settings cannot be given. The best source for specific information is the manufacturer's or the military service's flight handbook for the aircraft. Lacking these, the capable pilot can find his own speeds and power settings by experiment, discontinuing any maneuver that threatens to lead to trouble. The range of satisfactory entry speeds for any maneuver except snap rolls is quite wide. The power setting used for normal climb will serve for most acrobatics involving vertical ascent.

Clearing Turns Make at least two steep 90° turns before each acrobatic maneuver to permit careful inspection of surrounding air space. Begin maneuvers as soon as possible after the turns. The lazy-8 and chandelle are in themselves clearing maneuvers. Fedearl Air Regulations prohibit acrobatics in control areas (federal airways), control zones (airport), over populated areas or open-air assemblies of persons, and at less than 1500 ft altitude above the ground. *Look around as much as possible during any of these maneuvers, especially watching behind during the starting turns.*

MAXIMUM-PERFORMANCE CLIMBING TURN

This maneuver does not require a specific amount of turn, but it does require some precision to execute it properly. Begin from straight and level flight, cruise airspeed, and cruise or normal climb power. Smoothly and simultaneously blend in aileron, elevator, and rudder pressure to start a coordinated climbing turn. Use enough back pressure to keep the nose rising and aileron pressure to roll at a constant rate. When the bank angle reaches its maximum (45° to 60°, depending on aircraft performance), immediately begin rolling the wings level at the same rate you rolled in. Keep the nose rising at a constant rate until the wings are level. As airspeed decreases in the climb, right rudder in increasing amount will be required to maintain coordination. Because of torque effect, rolling out of a left turn will require strong right rudder, but not much right aileron. Rolling out of a right turn can be accomplished mostly with aileron, relaxing the right rudder torque correction to obtain coordination. Your roll-out should bring the wings back to level just before reaching maximum altitude and at an airspeed just above a stall. Pause momentarily, then lower the nose to level flight attitude for that airspeed.

The maximum-performance climbing turn is often used to regain altitude lost in another maneuver.

THE CHANDELLE

The chandelle is a maximum-performance climbing turn, with precise entry speed and a precise 180° of turn (Figure 8.22). It is entered in a shallow dive about 20° to 30° below the horizon; select a road or other reference line on the ground, along which the maneuver may be oriented. Normal cruising power probably will suffice. Use an airspeed about 20% above normal cruising.

Begin a coordinated climbing turn from the entry point. The object from this point on is to trace with the nose of the aircraft a straight line diagonal to the horizon, the pitch attitude becoming steeper at a constant rate until the 180° of turn are complete. The climb should pass up through the horizon between 30° and 45° of turn at the same time the bank reaches its maximum of about 60°.

After 135° of turn, begin to roll out of the bank, but continue the con-

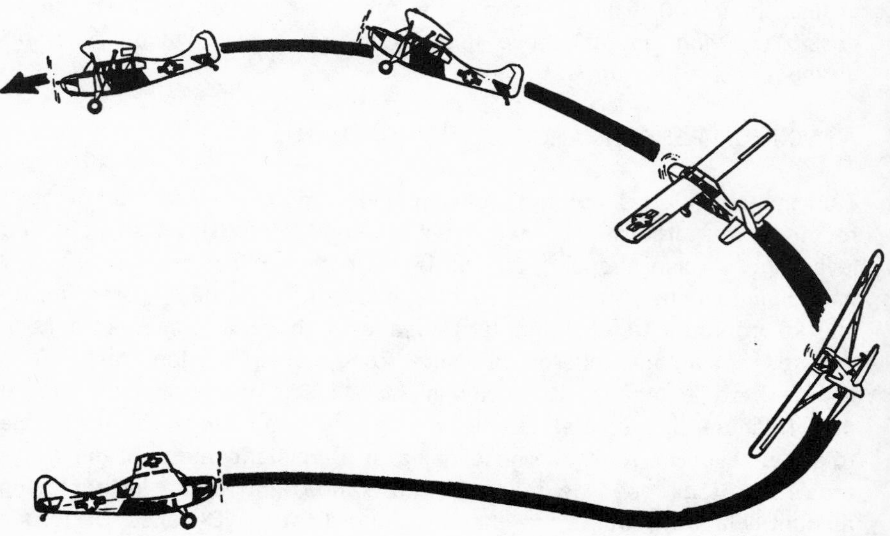

Figure 8.22 The chandelle.

stant rate of increasing pitch attitude. Some back stick pressure will have to be relaxed as the wings roll back toward level, because the wings now will produce a greater vertical component of lift. (This does not imply forward stick *movement,* as the decreasing airspeed will require the stick to be at least as far aft in order to maintain equivalent pressure.)

Time the roll-out so that the wings become level precisely as the 180° point is reached, and as the nose reaches the highest pitch attitude in the maneuver. The aircraft should be near the stall. This should all occur simultaneously. At this point, maximum torque correction should have been applied with right-rudder pressure. Hold the flight attitude constant momentarily, and then slowly lower the nose to level flight attitude.

The airspeed at entry, the power, and the rate of turn will determine how steep the climb path in the maneuver can be. If the rate of climb is fast, the rate of turn should be fast in order to reach the 180° point before stalling. If the rate of climb is slow, the turn must be slow so that the 180° point will not be reached with excess airspeed. Of course, the rate of turn depends on the amount of bank and the amount of bank will depend on the rate of roll-in. Hence, if you pull up fast, roll in fast. If you pull up slowly, roll in slowly. This relationship is responsible for the sage observation that there are just about as many types of chandelles as there are aviators. The "dive, bank, and yank" school is now in a minority, and a slow, smooth chandelle is preferred in most quarters.

The roll-out from the chandelle is the same as for the maximum-performance climbing turn.

LAZY-8

The lazy-8 (Figure 8.23) is a maneuver designed to develop the coordination of controls through a wide range of airspeeds and altitudes, so that certain accuracy points in the maneuver are reached with planned attitude and airspeed. It is a practice maneuver without peer and is one of the finest ways for a pilot to acquire the feel of an aircraft new to him. It consists of two 180° turns in opposite directions. During the first 90° arc of each turn, the nose of the aircraft describes a climbing and then descending path above the horizon. During the second 90° arc of each turn, the nose of the aircraft describes a descending and then a climbing path below the horizon. To an observer viewing the maneuver from the side and level, the total flight path traces a figure-8 lying on its side. The horizon bisects the 8 from one end to the other.

To execute the lazy-8, select a ground reference line with which to align the maneuver. If no ground reference is available below, it can be omitted, but you must align the entry so that a prominent feature on the horizon is at right angles to the aircraft heading. Normal cruise power

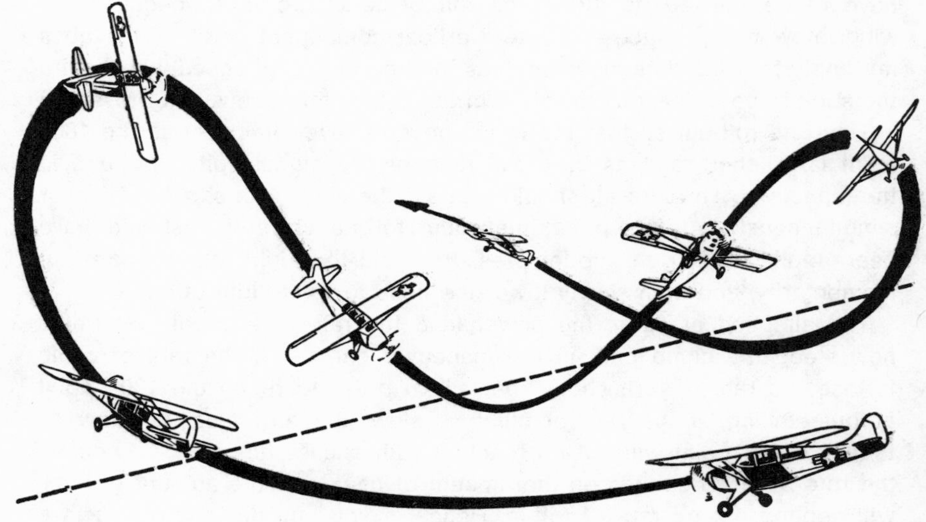

Figure 8.23 The lazy-8. *(Courtesy of U.S. Air Force.)*

is adequate for the lazy-8. Entry airspeed should be above normal cruising, about the same as used in the chandelle.

Obtain the entry speed in a shallow dive and then pull the nose *straight up* to the horizon. At the horizon, begin a gradual climbing turn toward the 90° reference point selected during entry. The initial degree of bank should be very shallow, because time must be allowed for climb and descent during the 90° of turn. The first part of the maneuver is mostly a climb, with rate of roll very slight. The maneuver should be "lazy," and *g* loads throughout should be negligible.

Make the climb and descent toward the first 90° point symmetrical in pattern, so that the steepest point of the climb will be after 45° of turn. As airspeed decreases in the climb, apply the usual correction for torque. If the turn is to the right, considerable practice probably will be required before adequate right-rudder pressure is maintained. Coordination may be checked by the rate of travel along the horizon as well as by sensing of slip or skid.

Bank angle at the 45° point should be about 45°. From that point continue to increase the bank angle and relax some of the back stick pressure to lower the nose toward the horizon exactly at the selected 90° point. Airspeed will continue to dissipate until just before the nose reaches the horizon.

Rate of roll and amount of back stick pressure together will determine where the nose of the aircraft crosses the horizon on its way down. Increasing the rate of roll or decreasing back stick pressure will bring the aircraft to the horizon earlier. Decreasing roll or increasing back pressure will carry the aircraft further along the horizon. Bank angle will be at its steepest on reaching the horizon. This bank will vary from 60° to 90°, depending on just how lazily the maneuver is flown and what airspeeds are selected. The bank angle should be predetermined as an accuracy condition for the maneuver. Airspeed as the nose passes through the horizon should be comfortably above stalling. It too may be an accuracy consideration, but too much attention should not be paid the airspeed until a good feel for the lazy-8 is developed and accuracy points can be made successfully.

As soon as the nose crosses the 90° reference point on the horizon in the descent, begin to roll slowly out of the turn. Again time back stick pressure and rate of roll so that the arc below the horizon traces a pattern like that just completed above the horizon. When the aircraft reaches the horizon at the 180° point, the wings should just be coming to level, and the airspeed should be the same used for entry.

Precisely upon reaching the horizon, and without hesitation, begin a climbing turn in the direction of the original 90° reference point. Complete a second 180° pattern, identical to the first except that the turn will be in the opposite direction.

During the entire lazy-8 maneuver, the pitch and bank angle should be constantly in change. If a protracted pitch or bank attitude must be held in order to reach an accuracy point or to stay within airspeed limits, the planning of the maneuver has gone astray.

THE LOOP

The loop (Figure 8.24) is a 360° turn in the vertical plane. It is the most easily performed of all aerobatic maneuvers, for it involves a change only in the pitch attitude of the aircraft. The elevators are the basic control, and the ailerons and rudder are used only for maintaining a straight heading in coordinated flight. The power setting used for normal climb probably will fit the loop well. To insure precise control of heading, start the loop in alignment with a road or other straight line on the ground below. On reaching the correct entry speed, start the stick straight back with gradually increasing pressure. The wings should be level as the nose passes up through the horizon.

With the proper rate of pull-up, you will feel a definite but not uncomfortable seat pressure that results from *g* loads. A lack of seat pressure indicates the maneuver is proceeding too slowly, and too much airspeed may be lost in the climb portion. Any blurring of vision or evidence of high-speed stalling indicates an excessive stick pressure.

The decreasing airspeed in the climb will create a need for gradually increased right-rudder pressure to counteract engine torque. When the horizon ahead has disappeared beneath the nose, look out at the wing tips and keep them equidistant from the horizon. When a little past vertical flight, tilt your head straight back to use the approaching horizon for directional control and the planning of back pressure. Use rudder to keep aligned, and the ailerons to keep wings level.

Maintain back stick pressure through the entire loop maneuver, and keep the rate of travel of the nose around its 360° fairly constant. Some of the back pressure exerted in the climb must be relaxed at the slow airspeed "over the top" of the maneuver. At any time that stall buffeting occurs, relax back stick pressure enough to stop the stall, but maintain positive seat pressure.

As the nose of the aircraft passes through the horizon from the inverted position, the airspeed will be increasing. Additional back stick pressure will have to be reapplied to keep the nose moving around its

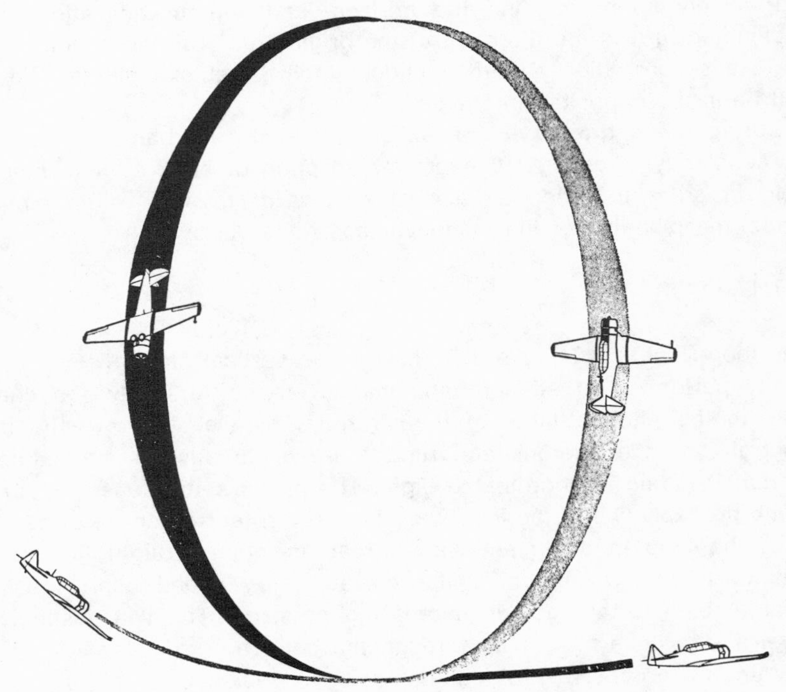

Figure 8.24 The loop. *(Courtesy of U.S. Air Force.)*

360° at a fairly constant rate. A little extra back stick pressure—just comfortably outside the stall region—while below cruising speed will prevent acquiring too much speed in the recovery dive. As the nose nears level-flight attitude, ease off back pressure and make a final check to insure that the wings are level. The loop should require 3 to 4 positive *g* and no negative *g*.

BARREL ROLL

The barrel roll (Figure 8.25) is a maneuver in which the aircraft rotates 360° around the longitudinal axis while the nose of the aircraft describes a circle about a real or imagined reference point on the horizon. It is a precision maneuver and should be smooth and coordinated. The circle described should be of constant radius around the reference point, and

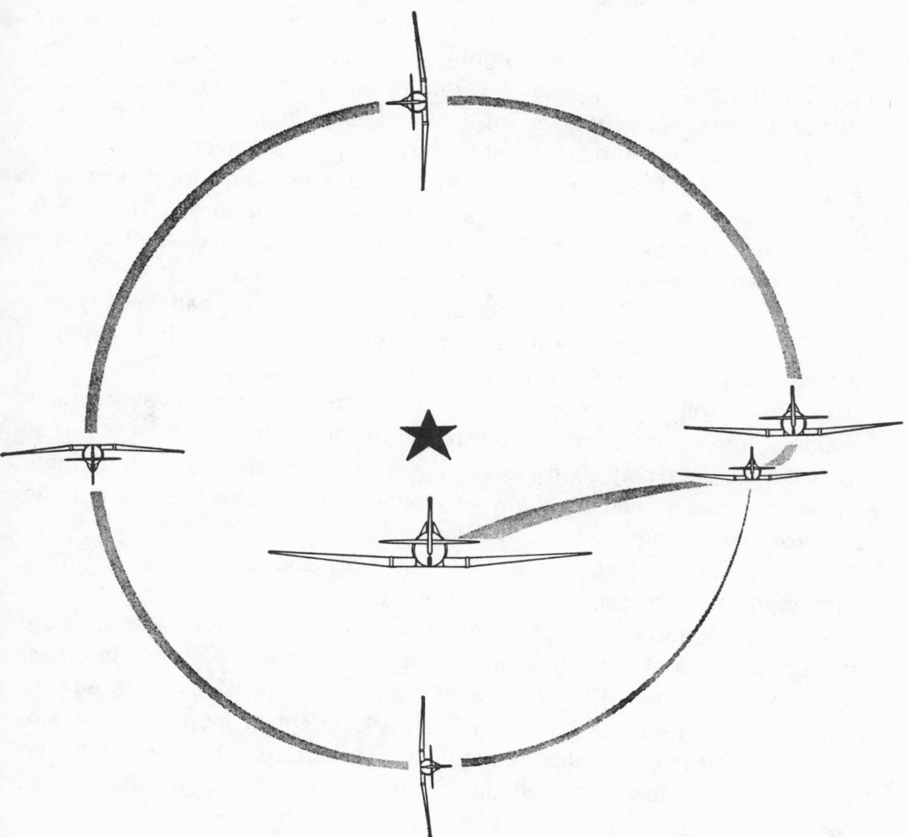

Figure 8.25 The barrel roll.

the aircraft should arrive with prescribed attitudes at accuracy points to the sides, top, and bottom of the center reference.

The barrel roll can be started from a wide range of speeds. The usual recommendation is slightly above normal cruising. Engine power should be at cruise or at normal climb setting.

Reach the entry airspeed in a shallow-dive attitude about 20° below the selected center reference point. Bend stick and rudder to produce a coordinated climbing turn toward the accuracy point about 20° to either side of the center reference. On the way up to the horizon, roll out of the original turn so that the side accuracy point is reached with wings level.

With no hesitation, continue the climb and the new direction of the roll-up through the horizon and around the circle to the top accuracy point, about 20° above the center reference. At the top point, the rate of roll should have carried the aircraft to a vertical bank.

From the vertical bank position, relax some of the back stick pressure and increase aileron pressure slightly. Time the rate of roll so that the aircraft will reach the horizon inverted, with wings level, at the same distance on the opposite side of the reference point as it was when passing through the horizon on the start of the maneuver.

As the roll continues down through the horizon, some increased top-rudder pressure and back stick pressure will be required. The wings should reach the vertical position with the nose pointed at the same distance below the horizon from which the maneuver was started. Difficulties with "dishing out" of the maneuver in the bottom half usually are due to insufficient rate of roll and to insufficient elevator force shortly after crossing down through the horizon.

The barrel roll is completed when the aircraft, wings level, reaches the side where it first crossed up through the horizon.

Use the rudders only as necessary to keep the maneuver coordinated. Positive g forces should be slight throughout the barrel roll, but a definite seat pressure should exist at all times.

To coordinate the rate of roll with arrival at accuracy points, you must understand the effect of each control in any attitude. At the position in vertical bank above the center reference point, excessive back pressure between the vertical bank and the next 45° of roll can result only in crossing the horizon wide of the next side accuracy point. But as the aircraft continues its roll 45° past vertical bank, the effect of increased elevator pressure is directed predominantly down toward the horizon, thus decreasing the distance traveled along the horizon. If you accelerate the rate of roll proportional to the elevator pressure, you can meet the horizon in correct attitude, but the net effect will be a maneuver executed in a tighter than normal circle.

Examining another aspect of the same problem, one will see that a rate of roll too fast for the elevator pressure used will result in each quarter of the circle being reached with the bank too far advanced, and the "circle" decreasing in radius as the maneuver progresses.

This matter has been gone into at some length, because the principles are very basic to any precision rolling maneuver. If the student of acrobatics has difficulty in timing rate of roll, he can probably work his problem out by interrupting the maneuver just where he first senses difficulty and there exaggerating or deliberately subordinating the use of the control that seems to be at fault.

AILERON ROLL

The aileron roll is similar to the barrel roll; but no effort is made to reach accuracy points, and the rate of roll is accelerated by increased aileron pressure throughout the maneuver. The aileron roll can be started at any airspeed and pitch attitude that will not lead to airspeed difficulties before completion of the maneuver.

Normal rudder pressure to coordinate must be used at the start of the roll, and rudder also will be required as the aileron returns to neutral at the completion of the maneuver. If the aircraft has a good rate of roll, elevator pressures will be negligible. A small amount of back stick will be required during entry and recovery, and this is relaxed while the aircraft is at or near inverted flight.

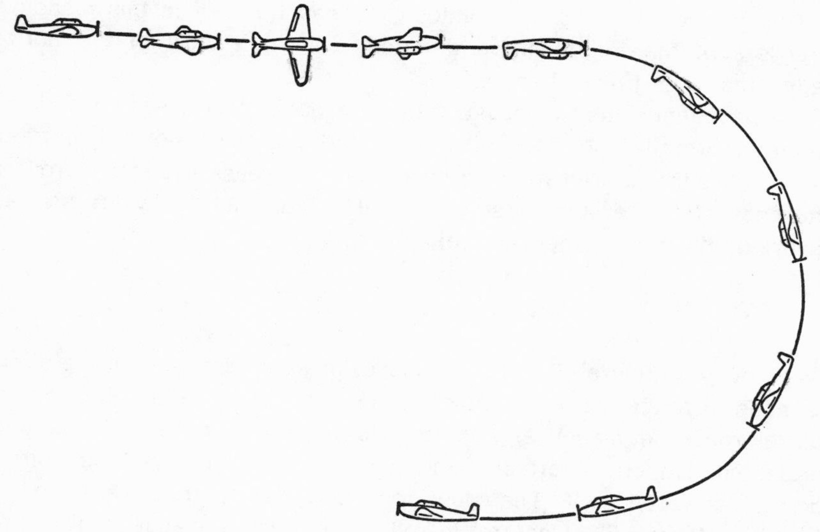

Figure 8.26 The half-roll and split-S.

HALF-ROLL AND SPLIT-S

The half-roll is just what the name implies. Neutralizing stick and rudder while inverted will halve any roll at the midpoint. A half-roll also can be executed from the inverted position to level flight.

The half aileron roll usually precedes the split-S (Figure 8.26). Start the aileron roll 10° to 20° nose-high and with 25% above stalling speed. As the rate of roll is reduced at midpoint, some forward stick may be necessary for a moment in order to prevent falling below the horizon before the wings are level inverted.

A split-S is exactly the second half of the loop. If you use throttle to enter the half-roll, retard it in the split-S to prevent accumulating too much airspeed. *Do not enter a split-S without plenty of altitude.*

VERTICAL ROLLS

One or more aileron rolls (Figure 8.27) can be executed in a vertical climb, provided the aircraft has a good rate or roll, low power loading, and an adequate maximum limiting airspeed. Entry speed should be at least above that used for the loop.

As soon as entry speed is reached in a dive, come back smoothly but rapidly with the stick to establish a vertical climb. When vertical, start the roll with rather drastic aileron pressures and accompanying rudder. Release almost all the rudder pressure after entry.

The ground will be a little difficult to keep track of in this maneuver. Progress of the roll must be determined from a view of the horizon rather than the ground beneath.

To discontinue the maneuver, introduce back stick pressure and slow the rate of roll. The back stick will start the nose down toward the horizon. As the aircraft reaches level flight, decrease the rate of roll and the back stick pressure or stop the roll as soon as the wings are level inverted; leave the maneuver with a split-S.

SLOW ROLL

The slow roll (Figure 8.28) is a maneuver in which the nose of the aircraft is made to rotate 360° *on* a point, rather than around the point as in the barrel roll. The maneuver has lost its popularity because it is uncoordinated and uncomfortable, and because modern high-speed aircraft do not slow-roll well. The slow roll does demonstrate very well the function of each flight control in rolling attitudes, because control pressures must be exagerated to meet the requirements of the maneuver.

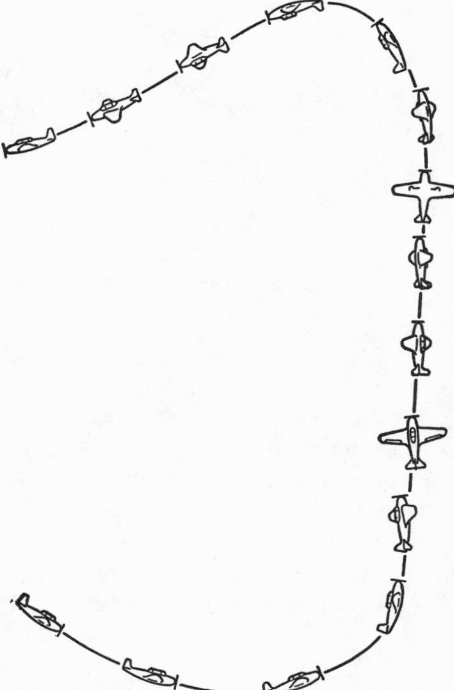

Figure 8.27 The vertical aileron roll.

Begin the slow roll at slightly above cruising speed, with the nose of the aircraft pointed about 10° to 20° above a prominent point on the horizon. Start it to either direction, using aileron and a touch of rudder for coordination. As soon as the roll has started, the nose will want to move off the point in the direction of roll. It must be held on the point by pressure on the "top" rudder, opposite to the aileron that continues the roll.

As the roll progresses toward the inverted attitude, release back stick pressure and introduce a definite *forward* pressure. The nose will drop below the point if this forward stick pressure is not maintained while inverted. After passing the inverted position, progressively relax forward stick and the top rudder again becomes the control that staves off gravity and holds the point. This bears repeating: The slow roll is *not* a coordinated maneuver. When the aircraft is at or near either vertical bank position, considerable top rudder will be needed to hold the point. You will definitely sense the skid that results. Complete the slow roll by neutralizing aileron and rudder as the aircraft again nears level flight.

Figure 8.28 The slow roll.

As long as turns are not being attempted while inverted, do not worry about the controls "exchanging their functions" as the nose of the aircraft rotates in the roll. The elevator does not act like the rudder at any time. It moves the nose of the aircraft toward the top or bottom of the aircraft as the pilot sees top and bottom from within the cockpit. The left or right rudder will always tend to move or hold the nose of the aircraft to the pilot's left or right, respectively. How these movements affect the aircraft's relation to outside references is a matter for separate judgment.

IMMELMAN

The Immelman turn is a combination maneuver, consisting of the first half of a loop followed by a half-roll to level flight. The maneuver is named after a German World War I ace, who first perfected the maneuver to gain altitude and reverse direction 180° simultaneously (Figure 8.29).

The Immelman requires a few knots more airspeed for entry than does the loop, but otherwise proceeds in the same manner—to within about 20° of inverted flight. Before the nose of the aircraft reaches the horizon, inverted, relax back stick pressure. At the same time move the stick well to either side to start the roll-out. The use of the word "move" in connection with aileron technique is significant. Because of the low speed and the fairly rapid rate of roll required, most aircraft require almost full aileron deflection for the Immelman roll-out.

The aileron executes the half-roll portion of the Immelman. Regard the rudder not as a coordinating control but as an independent control *to keep the aircraft headed straight* while the ailerons are rolling it to level. Rather extended rudder travel may be required near the completion of the maneuver.

The back stick pressure was relaxed when the roll-out started, to forestall pulling the nose down below the horizon. As the aircraft nears level flight, add back stick again. Complete the maneuver at slow air-

Figure 8.29 The Immelman.

speed, and keep the pitch attitude well above the horizon to maintain level flight at the high angle of attack.

The Immelman requires approximately 4 positive *g* to complete. There should be no negative *g*. A common error in learning the maneuver is the use of forward stick while inverted, to "hold the nose up." If the roll-out is commenced above the horizon and is fairly rapid, the nose will not have to be "held up."

CUBAN 8

The Cuban 8 (Figure 8.30) is another combination maneuver, combining in this case the loop and a diving aileron roll. Each half of the "eight" can be visualized as an Immelman turn, completed 45° below the horizon. Entry speed and power setting should be the same as used in the loop.

Start the maneuver like a loop, but relax all back stick pressure when the nose is about 45° below the horizon, in inverted flight after going over the top. Immediately perform a half-roll to place the aircraft in an upright 45° dive Continue the dive until entry airspeed is obtained, and then repeat the maneuver.

Do the half-roll "on a point," a reverse heading from that used for entry. The half-roll can be a slow roll or, more frequently, a rapid aileron roll with some added rudder to stay on the point.

The Cuban eight, as described here, is known in Britain and on the Continent as a variant of "the spectacles," a combination of an erect

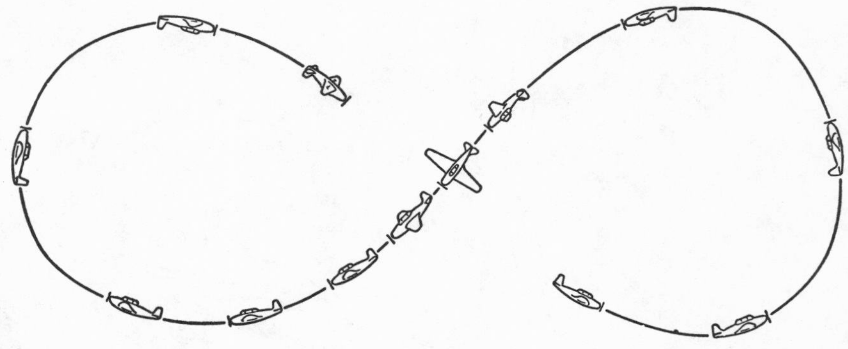

Figure 8.30 The Cuban 8.

and an inverted loop. Labels for various types of loop also are unstandardized.

THE CLOVERLEAF

The cloverleaf (Figure 8.31) has in it part of the loop and part of the lazy-8. It is composed of four very steep climbing turns, with a change of direction 270° in each turn.

Enter the cloverleaf from a speed a little less than that needed for a loop. From a dive, pull the nose of the aircraft straight up to about 70° nose-high pitch attitude. Then begin a roll in either direction, so timed that the horison is reached in inverted flight after rolling 90° from the entry heading. During the 90° change of direction, continue the climb with back stick pressure, so that the climb attitude becomes almost vertical before the bank angle reaches 90° and the nose starts down toward the horizon.

The wings must be precisely level as the horizon is reached in inverted flight, and the rate of roll may have to be modified during the maneuver so that this will happen at exactly 90° from the entry heading. Here are required the same skills in timing of back stick and aileron pressures that are exercised in the barrel roll and the lazy-8. The cloverleaf is perhaps the most exacting test of the three.

At the horizon inverted, add back stick pressure sufficient to keep the aircraft just comfortably outside the high-speed stall region as you pull the nose through a vertical dive and into a normal climb attitude for the next "leaf" of the clover. During the dive, increased speed will demand increasing back stick pressure, and you will feel additional *g* loads as the pull-out continues. If the pull-out is not kept tight immediately after crossing down through the horizon, the aircraft will pick up excessive

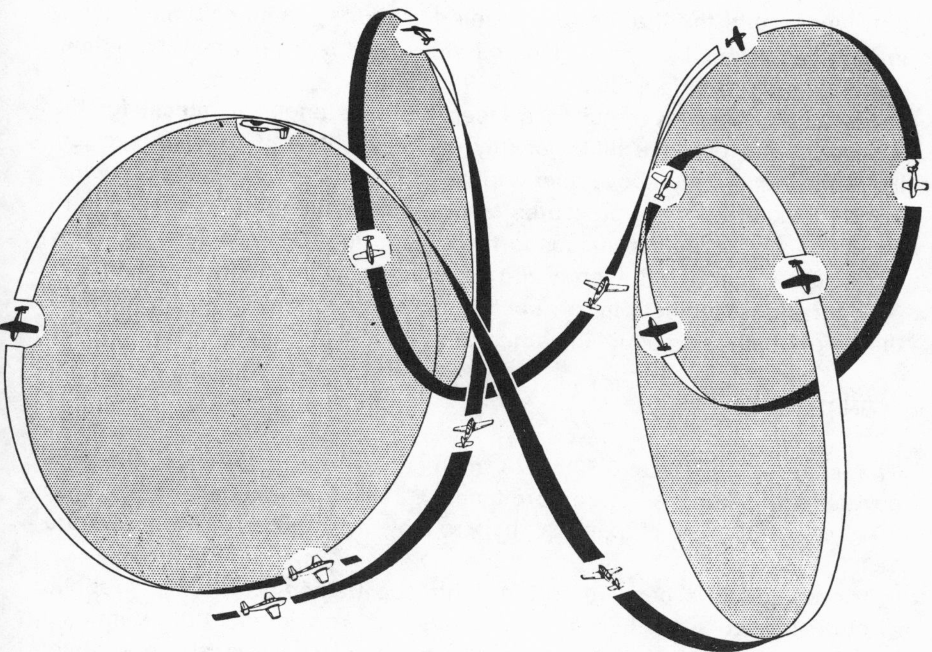

Figure 8.31 The cloverleaf. *(Courtesy of U.S. Air Force.)*

speed. You then must choose to accept the higher speed (and resulting loss of altitude) or incur additional *g* loads to complete the pull-out.

Enter the next leaf of the clover without pause after the dive recovery, with the roll to right or left as chosen for the first part of the maneuver.

The cloverleaf may be performed in any aircraft stressed for normal acrobatics. A dual introduction is especially advisable, because you can lose orientation easily during the climbing roll when learning the maneuver. An inadvertent vertical stall could be the result.

INVERTED FLIGHT

Inverted flight for more than about 10 sec requires a specially equipped aircraft. It must have an extra oil sump or hopper and an extra fuel tank or hopper to supply lubrication and fuel to the inverted engine. The carburetor must be the injection type if altitude is to be maintained.

Inverted flight can be maintained for brief periods in any acrobatic aircraft. Half-roll the aircraft to the inverted position, and apply forward stick to keep in level flight or a shallow glide. If the carburetor is a float type, retard the throttle to idle position. If the carburetor is an injection type, retard the throttle toward idle to reduce the lubrication requirement. Watch the oil pressure gage carefully, and recover when the indication drops below safe limits.

Maintaining altitude requires a steep negative angle of attack, for the wing does not produce lift efficiently off the camber of its undersurface. Hold the nose well above the horizon with forward stick. Turns while inverted require control pressures contrary to all habit, but a shallow turn produces no particular discomfort. To turn to the right (as you view the world) requires left aileron and right rudder with added forward stick.

Secure loose objects in the cockpit before inverted flying, and tighten the safety belt and shoulder harness.

SNAP ROLL

The snap roll (Figure 8.32) is a high-speed stall maneuver in which severe yaw from the rudder produces a roll. The roll can be held for 360° of rotation or stopped at half roll by neutralizing controls before 180°.

The snap roll is peculiar to the lightplane trainer or special acrobatic aircraft. Larger aircraft, such as fighters, are restricted from intentional snaps. Start the snap roll from a speed about 30 knots above stalling. There is one best entry speed for each aircraft at about that figure. A slower entry speed will not leave sufficient control to halt the maneuver precisely. A faster speed may result in a partial recovery while inverted.

To perform the full snap roll, bring the stick sharply back to its full rear limit of travel. As the stick comes back, introduce aileron in the desired direction of roll, and add full rudder travel briskly in the same direction. The result in some aircraft is quite breathtaking. The nose comes up sharply about 20° and the roll occurs quickly. Hold entry controls. The rate of roll will slow as the roll nears completion. Near 360° of rotation, neutralize rudder and aileron and retain only enough back stick pressure to keep level flight.

A half-snap can be done in many aircraft without using aileron. This makes the initial "snap" less violent, and aids precise recovery inverted. Some aircraft will do an excellent half-snap to erect flight if back stick

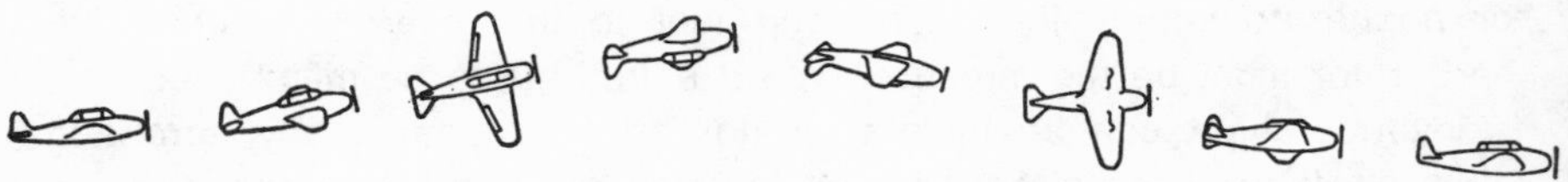

Figure 8.32 The snap roll.

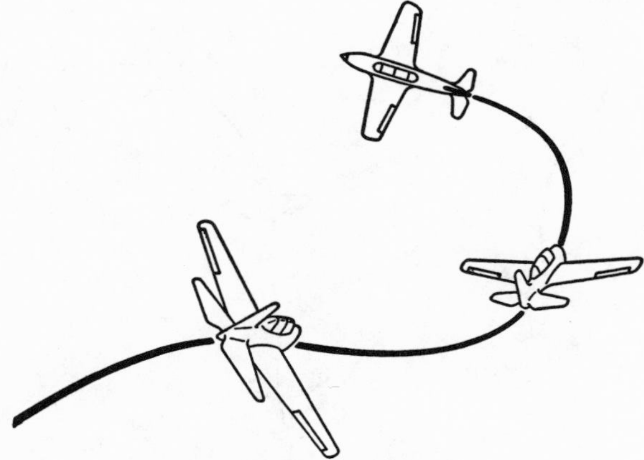

Figure 8.33 The vertical reversement.

is accelerated at the top of a loop. Propeller torque effect supplies the necessary yaw.

VERTICAL REVERSEMENT

The vertical reversement (Figure 8.33) is a snap maneuver executed from a tight, low-airspeed turn. Added back stick and top rudder cause the aircraft to snap "over the top" into a turn the opposite direction. Aileron only is needed to recover precisely in the new turn.

VERTICAL STALLS

Vertical stall maneuvers are of two types: the *whip stall* and the *hammerhead stall* (Figure 8.34).

The *whip stall* is not a recommended maneuver for any aircraft. It is sometimes encountered accidentally when the pilot exerts back stick pressure in a vertical or near-vertical climb near stalling speed for his aircraft. The aircraft slides tail-first momentarily, and then pitches violently forward and down. If you do not hold the stick firmly, reverse flow over the elevator may wrest the stick from your grasp and slam it forward. Should a whip stall be encountered, the best procedure is to do nothing except hold the stick firmly until the nose of the aircraft drops below the horizon. Then make a normal stall recovery.

The *hammerhead stall* also is entered from a vertical climb. It is not as violent as the whip stall and is a safe maneuver in an acrobatic aircraft if properly performed. If a whip stall appears imminent, it can be converted to a hammerhead. Near the stall, in vertical or near-vertical

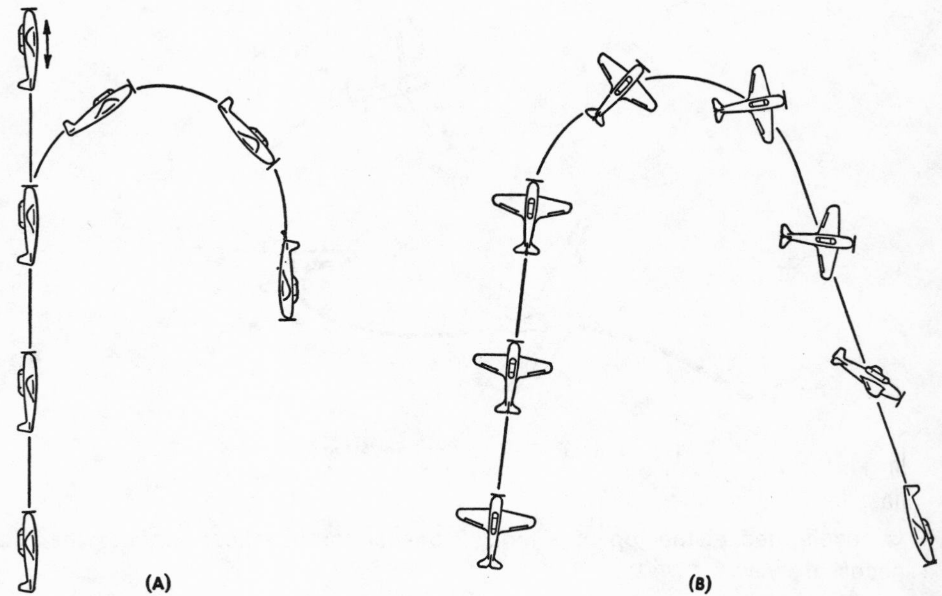

Figure 8.34 Vertical stalls. (A) A whip stall. (B) A hammerhead stall.

climb, apply almost full rudder travel in either direction. The rudder must be applied smoothly. As the nose drops toward the horizon, begin a quarter roll to level flight. Leave the stick about in neutral until sufficient air speed is regained for the normal, nose-down, stall recovery.

ENGLISH BUNT

The English Bunt (Figure 8.35) is a maneuver for special acrobatic aircraft. It is a sort of inverted Immelman. The maneuver is performed by applying full forward stick in level flight or a climb at near stalling speed. The forward stick is held until the aircraft is flying inverted on a heading 180° from entry. A half-roll is then made to level flight.

INVERTED AND OUTSIDE LOOPS

The normal loop starts with a climb from level and erect flight. As illustrated in Figure 8.36 the aircraft can be put through a "360° turn in the vertical plane" via three other routes.

The pilot can half-roll from level flight, *split-S,* and finish with an Immelman turn. This is an inverted loop. It is a practical maneuver for any acrobatic aircraft, the main precaution being not to develop too much speed in the *split-S* part of the maneuver.

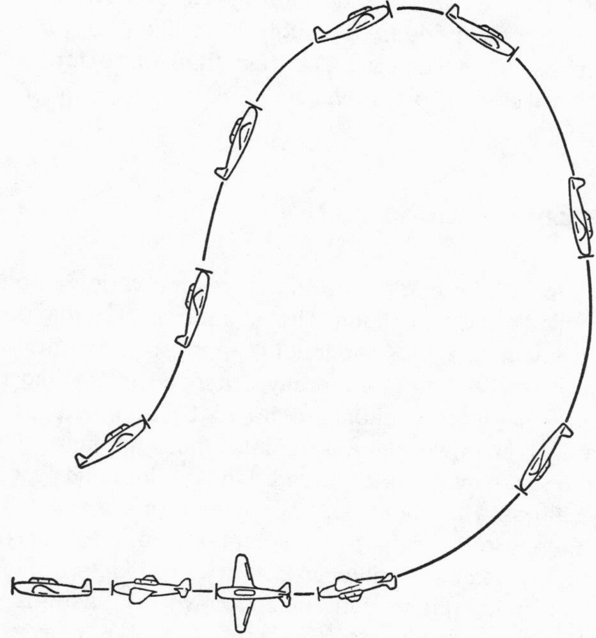

Figure 8.35 The English bunt.

The other two forms of the loop are strictly for the air-show artist and his specially constructed aircraft. That aircraft must be stressed for extra negative *g* loads, must get fuel and oil to the engine while it is inverted, must have large control surfaces, a low power loading, and good "lift" from the wing when inverted.

The *outside loop* begins from level flight, inverted. The pilot applies forward stick pressure all during the maneuver, until he half-rolls to level flight again at completion. The *inverted outside loop* begins with a push-over from level flight, as for a steep dive. Both these maneuvers

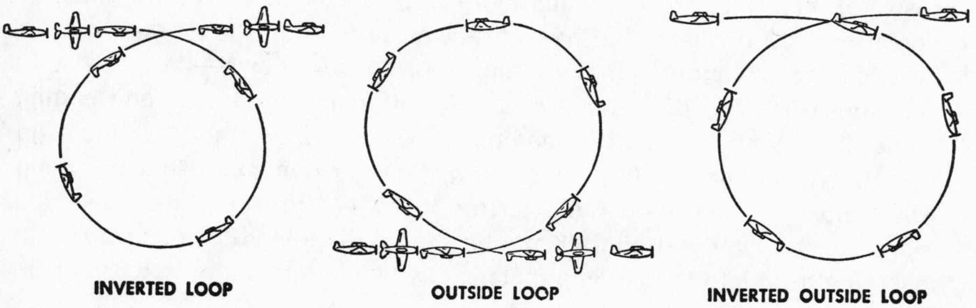

Figure 8.36 Loops.

put stress on the pilot as well as the aircraft. He can tolerate about 3.5 negative *g* for protracted periods, although he is likely to get headaches and bloodshot eyes. If he suffers more than that figure for longer than about 10 sec, he will begin to lose vision.

If the Engine Quits

No attempt will be made here to discuss the variety of emergency situations that might arise in flight. The situations and the procedures for coping with them are too dependent upon specific aircraft types. Only one emergency situation is generally practiced in training programs for light aircraft—the forced landing dictated by complete power loss.

Despite reliability of modern power plants, the lightplane pilot should always keep the possibility of a forced landing in mind. Most of his flight is at low altitude. He has no extra engines to carry along to replace one that fails. Except in the military services he usually has no parachute and would probably choose that way out of his troubles only on very rare occasions. The lightplane can be set down on pastures or roads that would not even be considered by the pilot of a heavier aircraft. His greatest assets are knowledge of his aircraft's glide capabilities and an attitude of relaxed alertness.

PRACTICE FORCED LANDINGS

The practice forced landing is like the emergency one, up to the point at which you must make a go-around, except for one rather important consideration—the aircraft does not glide the same in practice as it would with no engine power at all. There is no way that the lightplane can simulate precisely the complete loss of engine power. The engine thrust at idle rpm will provide more gliding distance from any altitude than would a windmilling propeller. A propeller that is "frozen" (as a result of engine seizure) creates more drag than one that is windmilling. For aircraft with retractable gear, a power setting can be worked out for practice forced landings that will equal—with gear down—the glide ratio and approximate glide attitude of an aircraft with the gear up and engine inoperative. When a suitable landing area is reached, the gear must go down anyway; and the best you can do then is remember that the glide would not be taking you quite so far if the emergency were real. This is the reason why you aim all practice forced landings to touch down at least one third into the landing distance available, no matter how successful you become at hitting that spot.

During extended glides for practice forced landings, "clear" the engine at least each minute by advancing throttle briefly to cruising power. Thus your familiarity with the glide capability of your aircraft is further increased.

With these qualifications noted, the principles following apply both to practice and to actual forced landings.

GLIDING DISTANCE

The first qualification of a landing area is that it be within the glide range of the aircraft.

During normal landing glides, the apparent distance between aiming point and the horizon was found earlier to remain the same at any altitude in the glide, as long as glide conditions remained constant. That same relationship exists during the forced landing glide—from any altitude. At the higher altitude you have difficulty detecting the aiming point by the apparent motion of near and far objects. You can, and should, learn the apparent distance beneath the horizon for your aiming point at the best glide speed in calm wind conditions. For a particular airplane, you can remember this as so many inches below the horizon line where that line appears across the windscreen.

Use the aiming point idea with caution when deciding whether you can reach a field without power. Modify the glide capability determined by experiment with idle engine power for engine failure conditions. Sometimes the wind is even more important. A tailwind will extend glide distance and a headwind will reduce it, and you cannot always know wind direction and velocity. Expect the wind observed on the ground to change direction and speed with altitude. There also are vertical currents to worry about, especially downdrafts over an area of water or heavy vegetation.

The sum of information on glide distance is that you should not try to gauge it too closely. You will do better to use your altitude to position yourself properly for a field at hand rather than try to reach a better-appearing one at marginal distance. If an airfield or other first-class surface is at marginal distance, it usually is not worth a try, provided other areas short of the airfield are usable.

CHOICE OF FIELD

Suitability of a forced-landing area depends on its size, type of terrain, surface, obstructions on the field, obstructions to the glide path, orientation to the wind, and distance from help (if injured or unable to leave the cockpit after landing). All these must be balanced, but the type of terrain and obstructions on the field easily can be called more important than the others. If you bring the lightplane down in landing attitude with landing gear retracted, it needs no more than 300 ft to stop on any surface except ice. If the wing tip digs into a boulder just after touchdown, the next 2000 ft of terrain may be of little interest.

A recent study by the USAF Flight Safety Research Branch indicates that forced landings with a tricycle-geared aircraft *in any sort of terrain*

TABLE 8.4
Forced Landing—Choice of Fields

Type of Field	*Appearance*	*Use It?*
Runway	Watch for small private dirt or sod strips in farm or desert land, usually near house or work buildings.	The best!
Roads and highways		Beware of dirt roads in isolated areas. They may be badly eroded.
Stubble field	Light straw color on visible ground. No motion in wind.	Usually good. Avoid fields with contours and unusual growth patterns.
Plowed fields	Dark brown or black. Large furrows.	Not good, especially with gear down. Land with the furrows if the wind allows.
Growing vegetation	Green. Casts shadows. Motion in wind.	Possibly workers in field. Thick growth may snag wheels of lightplane. Avoid extra dark or light spots or strips. They may conceal rocks or ditches. Land with furrows.
Pasture	Irregular light green and light brown. Contours usually visible. Animals. Usually has stock tank or pond.	If it were level and free of large stones, it would have been plowed. Avoid it.
Water		Last resort. Hard impact and plane sinks immediately.
Sand	Beach at water's edge, sandbars in river.	If the edge of the water is straight, the sand will be level. Pick dark (damp) sand if possible.
Dry lakes	White.	In desert country, very good. Behind a dam, may be filled with rocks and old stumps!

are less likely to result in injury or fatality if the landing gear is in the *down* position. The study was based on historical analysis of fighter aircraft accident reports.

In general, you will look for the longest and smoothest land area that can be approached into the wind (Table 8.4). Frequently, you will not see telephone or power lines on the approach until after you have chosen the field. In most cases, it will be best to continue the approach to the planned field.

Judging the Wind Wind direction and speed may be important in reaching the field, but always are important in touching down. The difference between landing into a 20-knot wind and landing out of a 20-knot wind totals 40 knots of ground speed. That means 40 knots faster into any obstacles on the ground, and touchdown 200 to 300 ft farther past a 30-ft-high telephone line.

At or near an airfield, there are the usual wind indicators and also the landing pattern to check if other aircraft are using it. Away from a field, smoke and dust are the best indicators of wind direction. Smoke rising straight up indicates calm wind. Smoke lying more or less flat to the earth may indicate high winds or it may indicate presence of a low inversion layer, especially on winter mornings.

Poplar or aspen trees are good wind indicators, exposing a dull silvery tone to moderate or stronger winds. Wavelets on water and clothes on clotheslines are two other usable wind indicators. The calm side of a pond is upwind. Generally, by the time you can see trees and bushes bending before a wind, you will have determined the direction by other means.

PLANNING THE APPROACH

When you have selected the best field, try to maneuver so as to arrive at a normal base leg by "key position" (Figure 8.37) about 500 ft above the ground. If you approach "key position" with too much altitude, you can lose it in a spiral, establish a downwind, or make S-turns approaching the key position. Try to avoid placing the base leg wide to compensate for extra altitude; the familiar pattern is easiest to fly.

At low altitude, it is too late to do much maneuvering. As a general rule, do not plan more than 90° of turn below 500 ft and try to complete all turns with at least 200 ft.

"Play" the turn to final approach with a wide or tight turn. You can also "play" the landing area in an open field by planning originally on the center and changing to either edge of the field during final turn or on approach.

Lower landing flaps either during the turn or just after the turn to final approach, unless it then appears that the glide to the field may be

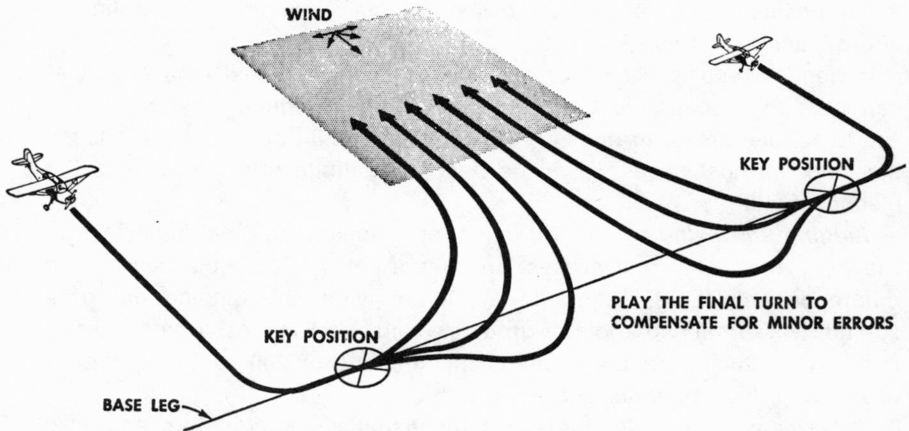

Figure 8.37 Play the turn to final approach.

short with the flaps down. The advantages of lowering them early are that they give a constant sink rate on final approach and indicate whether or not the flaps will operate in plenty of time to lose altitude by other means if necessary.

Pilots of fighter-type aircraft usually use a 360° overhead approach for forced landings. Their high sink rate makes it difficult to plan arrival at the "key point" by other means. The same pattern can be used in light aircraft, approaching the field in the direction of intended landing at an altitude 1200 to 1500 ft above the terrain. Alignment slightly to one side of the runway centerline will permit you to keep the end of the runway in sight, so that you can make the first turn at the proper point. Delay the start of the 360° pattern until the aircraft has passed over the first third of the landing area if there is a significant headwind. Many pilots prefer to lower wing flaps completely at the start of the 360° overhead forced landing approach. This makes the pattern a bit tighter, but it provides a constant sink rate during the entire pattern and makes judgment of glide distance easier.

SETTING IT DOWN

Turn off master and ignition switches before touchdown. Jettison or open the canopy. Make the roundout and touchdown just as you would for a normal landing. If a crash appears to be coming, occupants should lean against the shoulder harness to take up any slack, protecting the head with some type of padding if possible. If the surface is at all level, the deceleration will probably be surprisingly slight.

Flight at Night

EQUIPMENT REQUIRED

The military services require that aircraft used for night flying be equipped with the following:

1. All flight instruments and communication/navigation equipment required for flight under instrument flight rules.
2. Position, landing, instrument, and cockpit lights.
3. A dependable flashlight for each crew member.

Federal Aviation Regulations, for civil aircraft not to be used for hire, require the following for night visual flight rule operation:

1. Instruments and equipment only as required for daytime operation.
2. Approved position lights.
3. Adequate source of electrical energy for all installed electrical and radio equipment.
4. One set of spare fuses.

The military services plan that aircraft may be operated at night over unfavorable terrain and in marginal weather for visual flight. The civilian pilot is allowed more discretion in the equipment of his aircraft, but should use that discretion and conflne his night flying to local operations near well-lighted airfields and environs if the aircraft is equipped with the minimum list.

TECHNIQUE AT NIGHT

While many of your most delightful experiences in flying will come from flight at night, and while the ability to fly safely at night doubles the utility of your aircraft, there some differences in the demands made upon the pilot. None of these demands are unusual, and all are well within the capability of the all-round pilot who is flying a properly equipped aircraft in good condition, and who has prepared carefully in advance.

Night flying does pose these problems:

1. The horizon is not visible, or is very indistinct.
2. Obstructions, clouds, and other aircraft are harder to see.
3. It is easier to get lost.
4. Forced landings on dark, unprepared surfaces require more luck than you can properly count on.

These problems all stem from man's limited ability to see in darkness, discussed in Par. 7.22.

The Night Horizon Remember, *you cannot fly by feel alone.* At night, the horizon must be provided by some small amount of light, or by instruments within the aircraft. Usually, pilots can rely on both. Because of the lack of depth perception at night, a good altimeter, properly set, is a primary requirement. An accurate airspeed indicator and a gyro-compass (or at least a well-dampened magnetic compass), are also necessities. There is no greater asset in the cockpit at night than an attitude indicator. (See Chapter 9.)

During takeoff, the problem is to remain on a straight line during the ground run. Look well ahead of the aircraft to the end of the runway or to a light at the end of the flying field. Landing lights, though not essential for takeoff, can be helpful, and serve to identify your aircraft to others in the area. As the aircraft lifts off, airspeed, orientation, and direction are the vital concerns. Maintain a steady airspeed and a consistently steady rate of climb to insure clearing all obstructions and to prevent inadvertent flying back into the ground once the lighted airfield has passed behind. The horizon provided by a city's lights, by remnants of daylight, or by the night sky will not always be adequate. Inevitably at some time or other you will suffer disorientation or vertigo when there is no clear horizon in view. It need not be a problem with proper cockpit instruments and the ability to use them with confidence. Keeping cockpit lights low, using red lights for cockpit illumination and map reading, and careful adaptation of the eyes to darkness will all help.

Approaches and landings are much the same as in daytime, though you should avoid steep turns and make traffic patterns accurately and precisely. Some pilots prefer to land on lighted runways without using landing lights; when haze, smoke, rain, snow, or fog obstruct visibility, reflection renders landing lights more of a hindrance than a help. By maintaining a careful approach speed, and by looking well ahead of the aircraft to improve depth perception, round-out and landing will present no serious hazard. A little power carried through roundout and touchdown will insure more consistently smooth landings.

Obstructions, Weather, and Other Aircraft When flying cross-country, observe IFR minimum en-route altitudes. Then the altimeter and good navigation will remove the hazard of obstructions. Careful planning, alertness, and the ability to do a 180° turn on instruments is the solution to encountering weather when VFR at night. As for other aircraft, remember that green wing-tip lights are on the right, red on the left, and white on the tail—so that you can tell the direction in which the other aircraft is flying. As long as there is relative motion between you and the lights of the other aircraft, you are not on a collision course. If there is no apparent relative motion, take evasive action immediately.

Getting Lost Lighted roads, cities, and villages look more alike at night, though aeronautical charts depict the shape of larger cities quite accurately. Careful preflight planning, using the basic principles of dead reckoning described in Chapter 11, are by far the most reliable means of knowing where you are at all times. Without careful observation of your position and headings after takeoff, it is quite possible to get lost right over your own airport, particularly if it is near a large city with extensive suburban areas.

Forced Landings at Night Engine failure is an extremely unlikely occurrence these days, but when it comes at night the only safe place for a pilot to put down his aircraft is on a prepared and lighted runway. Over any except the best terrain, a parachute may be considered an absolute necessity during night flying. Federal Aviation Regulations require that a single-engine aircraft flown for hire at night carry parachute flares of specified candlepower, and the pilot who ventures away from his local airport would do well to provide the flares for his own safety. Experienced pilots usually study the terrain past the ends of the runway of any field from which they operate. Such reconnaissance could save lives should an engine quit shortly after takeoff, with no recourse but to make an immediate forced landing.

NIGHT LIGHTING OF AIRFIELDS AND TERRAIN

The following colors of lights are standard for airfield installations and surrounding obstructions.

Runway lateral limits	White (intensity usually is adjustable from the control tower)
Taxiways and ramp area	Blue
Threshold lights defining ends of usable landing area	Green
Obstructions	Red (High structures such as radio towers may have blinking lights that appear to climb and descend. Construction on ramp may be bordered with flare pots.)
High-intensity approach lights and lateral limits of runway overrun	Red
Tetrahedron	Green outline and red center stripe

Wind sock and landing tee	White floodlight
Beacon lights	
Attended land airfield	Rotating white and green
Landmarks	Rotating white and red
Attended water airport	Rotating white and yellow
Hazards (such as mountain tops)	Rotating red

Airfield beacon lights revolve at 6 rpm. They are located atop the control tower or separate structure near the tower. The white or yellow beam at civilian airflelds is a single beam. The white or yellow beam at military airflelds is split, giving the observer two successive flashes.

Flying the Light Twin Aircraft

Much has been made of the problems of "moving up to twins." With a hundred hours or so—or less with good basic flying training, the "problems" are not unduly complex.

There are only three basic differences for the relative novice: (1) an increase in weight, with greater weight variation; (2) an incrase in complexity with need to devote more effort to knowing the airplane and its systems, and (3) the management of unbalanced power, assuming engines are in wing nacelles.

WEIGHT VARIATION

With a gross weight of 5300 lb, the typical light twin is a light aircraft. Its maximum weight variation during flight due to fuel consumed with auxiliary tanks, allowing 10% for reserve, is about 14% of gross weight. There is also the problem of passenger and cargo weight location. With a roomier fuselage, it is critically important to be aware of the load distribution specified in the operators manual so as not to exceed the limits which can seriously affect controllability.

A greater weight problem, of course, is the difference between a light load in emergency, and a heavy one—as is true in any airplane. There is no unusual flying problem associated with a larger weight variation. The principal problem is to be aware of it, and to know how it affects performance.

COMPLEXITY

There are two engines, controls, and engine instruments, instead of one. However, the throttle and propeller controls, and the engine instruments are designed to simplify the pilot's handling the engines individually or together. For substantial power changes, as in takeoff, climb, descent, and landing, they are as one. The hydraulic, electrical, and fuel systems reflect dual or individual engine functions, (e.g., on which engine is the hydraulic pump?), but the problem is merely one of knowing the systems before flying the airplane.

UNBALANCED POWER

Airplanes have two engines more to provide greater power than to provide greater reliability. But occasionally, engines do get sick. Being able to shut down one, or ease its load, is of course a distinct advantage.

The requirements for safe flight under one-engine-out conditions are just the same as for single-engine airplane flying: Know what the airplane will do, and practice enough to be able to get the performance built into it.

EMERGENCIES IN THE LIGHT TWIN

An abnormal situation is not always an emergency, depending on when it occurs. Failure of one engine as a twin breaks ground on takeoff is an emergency, but if one fails in level flight it may mean only a decrease in cruise altitude and a little less fuel reserve on arrival at destination.

Engine Failure In flying twins, this likelihood probably causes more pilot concern than any other, though each of the engines is as any single engine. Particularly over water or rough terrain, engines seem to go into "automatic rough"! Often a pilot will, and should, shut down an engine that is still producing power simply to save it from possible damage from low oil pressure, fuel or oil leak, high temperatures, etc.

Loss of Thrust With its larger margin of power available, loss of thrust on one engine is critical to a twin only during and immediately after takeoff. Such a failure reduces obstacle-clearing ability, and increases time needed to accelerate to climb speed. Directional control is the principal problem, and the pilot must never allow the airplane to drop below the *minimum safe speed* while reaching minimum safe climb speed.

Drag A propeller being windmilled by the slipstream and thus turning a dead engine causes a very considerable drag. It is almost completely

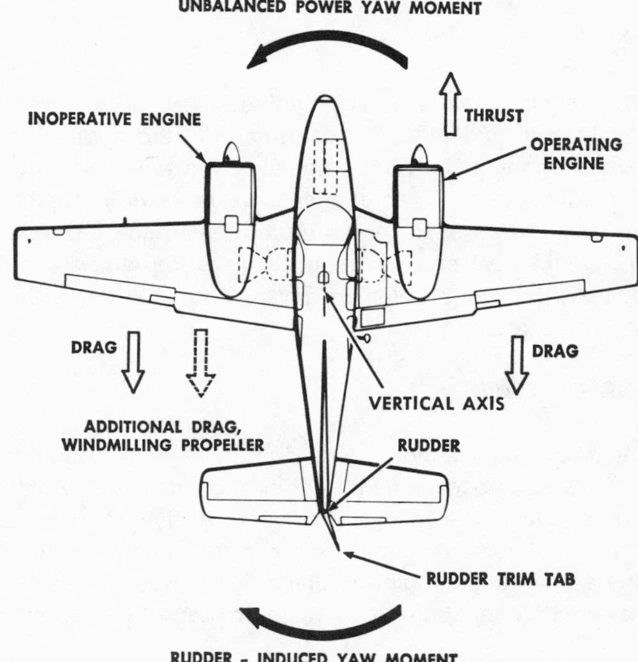

Figure 8.38 Forces and moments with engine failure.

eliminated by feathering the propeller. A propeller which goes out of control and "runs away" produces the greatest drag situation, because its engine is driven at very high speed; there is a possibility of destruction of the engine or dangerous loss of the propeller.

Effects of Unbalanced Thrust and Drag The principal result is a rotational moment about the vertical axis, Figure 8.38. The loss of power of the no. 1 engine causes an unbalanced moment acting counterclockwise around the vertical axis, assuming normal power from the no. 2 engine. The greater the power difference between the wings, the greater is the unbalanced moment.

The rudder counteracts the yaw moment. Right rudder in Figure 8.38 deflects it into the slipstream, which exerts a force that is translated into a clockwise moment to overcome the effect of unbalanced power. Trim reduces or eliminates the pilot's rudder effort needed. Placing the airplane in a slight bank toward the "good" engine also helps in maintaining directional control.

Minimum Control Airspeed The maximum moment the rudder can exert depends upon the airspeed, since the vertical stabilizer and rudder are merely a flap-equipped symmetrically cambered wing that stands on end. The MINIMUM CONTROL AIRSPEED for any unbalanced power condition is the minimum airspeed at which the rudder can exert enough yaw moment, without stalling, to overcome the unbalance caused by the "good" engine putting out full power.

A twin has only one possible minimum control airspeed; it is called *critical single-engine speed.* With adequate speed, a properly trimmed twin on one engine can turn safely in either direction.

Procedure with Engine Failure Should an engine failure occur on takeoff roll, abort the takeoff immediately if the decision point has not been passed and if it is possible to stop within the runway limits, or on the overrun. Experience and performance calculations before takeoff dictate whether a stop can be made. If the failure occurs after breaking ground, maintain full power on the good engine and fly the airplane level or with only enough climb to clear obstacles. Shut down and feather the faulty engine *as soon as it is positively identified,* in order to reduce drag and gain speed as rapidly as possible.

Minimum safe climb speed must be reached and maintained or the airplane cannot even safely climb over obstacles. During a go-around with one engine the exact procedure may vary for different aircraft depending upon the maximum power available, the drag or the extended gear, and the flap drag. Generally, minimum control speed is attained quickest by this sequence:

1. Maximum power.
2. Retract gear.
3. Retract or adjust flaps.

Until you have normal climb airspeed, limit the climb to that necessary to fly safely over obstacles. When you have safe altitude and airspeed, retract any remaining flaps slowly to avoid stall or excessive settling. Reduce power to normal rated or below if possible at the pattern altitude, establish a precise pattern if possible, and land—weather permitting.

Occasionally it happens that power loss occurs so late and is so extensive that the pilot can neither stop on the runway nor continue the climb-out. He then has no choice but to land, or continue to roll, straight ahead, using crash-landing procedures. At this point, any maneuver is better than a turn.

With engine failure in climb, cruise, or descent, the pilot first determines whether normal or nearly normal operation can be resumed by some simple measure such as changing fuel tanks, adjusting mixture, or reducing power. If power cannot be restored, or further operation will seriously damage the engine, or if there is danger of fire, it is shut down. Any necessary power adjustments are made on the other engine, and the aircraft is trimmed for the new power and airspeed configuration. Climb or descent rate and altitude are changed as necessary in conformance with the operator's manual.

A twin-engine airplane with an engine out should land at the nearest suitable airport.

Landing procedure after engine failure depends upon the amount of power available. If you can maintain level flight, fly a normal pattern, with adjustments in airspeed. When altitude cannot be maintained, a partial pattern is still desirable. Adjust the pattern so as to place the airplane at the proper position and altitude for as near normal a final approach as can be made. Use the flaps and lower the landing gear so that you will not have to use high power at slow speed to avoid undershooting, but with sufficient time remaining for the gear to extend, lock, and be checked. As you reduce power during final approach, take out rudder trim accordingly. Make the landing and roll normal, remembering that the failed engine is not available for steering or reversing, and its opposite should be reversed only in dire emergency. If you have to perform a go-around, do not hesitate. The earlier you decide the safer and easier it will be.

Systems Malfunction or Failure Airplane auxiliary equipment may not cause as immediately severe an emergency by failing as does an engine, but it can nevertheless lead to serious trouble or disaster. There are of course many other failure possibilities, including those to electrical systems, pressurization, heat, oxygen, and fuel systems. However, the most common are those pertaining to flaps, landing gear, and—above all—fire.

In any of these emergencies, it is generally better to declare an emergency and forget about embarrassment to others on the ground. In the long run this principle will pay off; if the emergency requires no aid, the ground services will at least have had a drill that may save someone else.

Low fuel pressure on one engine, with the engine still running, is a particularly critical problem. It may indicate a leak located so that any change in airflow in the nacelle may bathe the exhaust with fuel spray. With low fuel pressure, *never retard the throttle.* The best solution is to cut fuel off from the engine, then feather it. In any event, cut off fuel flow before landing. By retarding the throttle to land, explosion could easily result.

Flap Failure While most airplanes have emergency systems for extending flaps when they will not extend normally, an occasional landing without flaps is necessary. Fly a normal pattern but make the turn to final approach farther out to allow for a flatter glide angle. Approach speed will be higher, since the stalling speed is higher. It is important, too, not to overshoot. The nose will be higher than usual. On a big airplane, remember that as you pass over the end of the runway the main landing gear may be much closer to the ground than is apparent from your position in the nose. Expect a longer landing roll because of higher speed and the absence of flap drag.

Landing Gear Failure Landing with part of the landing gear extended is generally preferred to landing with all gear retracted. Less damage to the aircraft will result and there is less likelihood of injury to crew and passengers. Pattern, approach and flare-out are normal. Plan to touch down on the extended gear, and hold the nose or the affected side off as long as possible. Lower the nose to the runway before you lose elevator control. There is much less danger of fire if the airport fire department is able to lay down a strip of fire-extinguishing foam on the runway before the landing.

Brake failure is serious when it occurs on a short runway, or in conjunction with failure of drag devices during the landing roll. You may prepare to crash at the end of the runway, try to turn off on a taxiway or even try to ground loop to avoid going off the end, if brake failure becomes apparent during landing roll, and stopping appears critical. Some bigger aircraft have emergency brake systems which are independent of the normal systems. However, they have a limited number of applications only.

Landing with a known flat tire or blowing a tire during landing roll can complicate directional control. Ordinarily you can maintain control with steering and braking on the side with good tires.

Fire Aside from mid-air collision, fire is the most disastrous accident that can happen in the air. Every possible precaution is taken while building and maintaining airplanes to minimize danger of fire.

Engine Fires To control an engine fire in flight, shut down the engine immediately, feathering if it is a prop type, and cutting off all oil, fuel, and electrical power to it. With engine fire extinguishers, if the fire persists at all, discharge the extinguisher for the affected engine. After the fire is out, continue the flight but *never restart an engine in flight after it has been shut down because of fire.*

Engine fire on the ground is sometimes encountered during engine start. Keeping the engine turning over may draw the fire into the engine and thus eliminate it. If not, it must be controlled by use of installed engine fire extinguishers, or with the help of fire bottles in the parking area or the airport fire department. Avoid discharging extinguishing agents directly into the engine intake if possible, because severe damage to the engine is almost certain to result.

Fuselage Fire Hand-operated fire extinguishers are maintained in occupied portions of every aircraft fuselage. If oxygen is available, everyone in a compartment where a fire occurs should wear masks and breathe 100% oxygen, to avoid injury from smoke and fumes.

In fighting a cabin fire, first make sure everyone is breathing 100%

oxygen if possible, then determine the source of the fire. Cut off the source if possible, then try to extinguish the fire. Keep windows and hatches closed to reduce draft until the fire is out, then ventilate the cabin to remove smoke and fumes. Remember that pilot's side windows will draw air from the cabin outward. They are seldom usable for fume evacuation. Use some other hatch if possible.

Crash Landing and Ditching A crash landing may be necessary either because the airplane cannot reach a suitable landing area owing to lack of fuel or engine failure, or because the landing gear cannot be extended for landing. Ditching is a crash landing on a water surface. If there is any choice in the matter, crash landing should always be made while there is still some power available, because this gives the pilot a better choice of landing area and direction, and permits a slower descent. It also provides control of the aircraft up to the moment of landing. All engines that can be used should be operating.

Landing with Gear Up on an Airfield When it has been determined that part or all of the landing gear cannot be extended for landing, alert crash equipment and prepare the airplane, crew, and passengers for the crash landing. Give a report on fuel load and the location of crew and passengers by compartment to the tower for crash-crew use. If time permits and fire-extinguishing foam is available, the fire department may foam the runway to reduce fire danger during the landing.

Tie down or jettison all loose equipment in the airplane so that these items will not become projectiles to injure people on impact. Fasten all safety belts, and place any available padding material to reduce possibilities of injury. Facing aft, braced against a solid bulkhead is by far the safest position in which to survive the impact of a crash landing, if safety belts are available. Next best is an aft-facing seat with safety belt secured. Those in forward-facing seats should lean as far forward as their snugly fastened safety belts will permit. Those facing aft are instructed to lean back as far as possible, and place some kind of padding behind their heads. Crew members with shoulder harness should use it. Remember that a properly supported human body has withstood as much as 48 *g*'s of sudden deceleration. An improperly supported person cannot withstand even slight deceleration without injury.

When cleared by the tower, fly a normal landing pattern, except, of course, for the landing gear. Turn off all unessential electrical equipment.

Land on the runway, which has been covered with foam if possible, because experience has shown that less damage to the airplane and fewer injuries to personnel occur as compared with landing on an unprepared surface.

Landing on an Unprepared Area When you cannot reach a prepared landing field, select the best area available for the landing. Send distress radio messages, giving position, difficulties, and intentions, if possible. In addition to the criteria given on page 512 for picking a forced-landing field, give consideration also to landing near a town where fire-fighting equipment and some rescue help may be available. Choose the landing direction and prepare the airplane, passengers, and crew for the crash landing, using flares and landing lights, if possible, at night. Highways are notoriously attractive yet highly unsafe for forced landings because of poles, culverts, signs, ditches, and vehicles.

With some airplanes, landing on an unprepared surface with landing gear up will lessen the danger of rupturing a fuel tank and increasing fire hazard. With others it is better to land with gear down, since even if it is torn off it will absorb some of the impact and lessen personnel injuries. Whether to use the landing gear or not is largely a matter of judgment in a particular situation.

Final approach and landing are the same as for crash landing on an airport runway. As soon as the airplane stops, able-bodied crew members and passengers aid the injured, if any, in getting out. Lose no time in getting clear of the aircraft, because it may suddenly burst into flame, even after an apparently safe landing.

Ditching A water landing with a land-based airplane is a gear-up controlled crash landing with special problems. The preparation of the airplane, crew, and passengers includes making sure that everyone is wearing a life vest; placing first aid kits, food, water, blankets, and other usable equipment where it will be readily accessible after landing but will not tear loose on impact; and preparing the life rafts for launching. The life vests and rafts must not be inflated inside the cabin.

The landing direction for ditching must take into account not only the direction of the wind, but also the direction and size of any swells. The desired direction is upwind and downswell. Since this is usually not possible, a compromise choice is made, using the heading halfway between, but favoring the wind if it is strong. The best point to touch down is on the back slope of a swell just as it passes. This allows the aircraft to settle and decelerate before the next swell hits it. When two or more swell systems are present, the best touchdown point is in a fairly flat area where the systems cancel each other.

If at all possible, ditch near a surface vessel or a lee shore. Not only will the vessel be a valuable aid in rescue, but it also can give accurate wind and swell information. At night, a ship can lay down a row of flares to light up the surface and aid the pilot in lining up on the proper approach heading. The airplane may also carry flares which can be used to illuminate the surface.

An accurate position report transmitted as an emergency message is a vital element of success. Fly a descending pattern. During the first time over the prospective landing area, observe surface sea and wind conditions, dropping a flare if at night. On the second pass, get a better look and at night launch a second flare to light the area for final approach and landing.

Make the approach and landing with power on and at a slow rate of descent, because it is almost impossible to judge accurately the height of an aircraft above water. Expect two impacts on landing; the first light, the second severe. The nose will probably go under water, then re-emerge. After the airplane has stopped, the ditching exits are opened, and the life rafts are launched. All useful equipment is taken along, and those unhurt aid the injured. Never jump into a life raft, because the rubber floor may be easily punctured.

SUMMARY

The lore of multiengine flying, like flying in general, is vast. Competence requires an insatiable curiosity about the aircraft itself. Next comes drill in little-used procedures, and contemplation while things are going smoothly of what to do when they are not.

9

Instrument Flying*

Flying without easy and precise visual reference to the natural horizon is more and more the normal way. Modern cockpit design, which eliminates or reduces horizon reference points, aircraft having high rates of acceleration, of pitch, and of roll, the increased presence of smoke and haze, reliability in smaller aircraft which encourages flying at night and in marginal weather, and the economic need to use aircraft more and more regardless of weather restrictions, all these make the ability to fly by instruments to some degree an essential part of every pilot's equipment.

Instrument flying does require discipline, knowledge, and practice. It may thus be still considered an advanced flying skill.

Discipline

A strong self-discipline, acquired by knowledge and practice, is an abso-

*Revised by Lt. Col. Richard M. Dorsey, Instrument Pilot Instructor School, USAF, and the Editor.

lute essential. In Chapter 7, we saw the pilot's inability to sense correctly gradual aircraft accelerations, and his vulnerability to vertigo when denied visual reference to the horizon. Only a high degree of personal discipline even in experienced pilots can result in so complete a reliance upon instrument indications that all other sensations but those visually presented on the instrument panel are rejected automatically.

A high degree of discipline is also required to learn and use efficiently and easily the factors of time, communications, radio aids to navigation, and air traffic procedures needed to fit one's aircraft into today's dense air traffic flow. Fortunately this discipline can be acquired and improved under any flight conditions because the air traffic rules for instrument flying do not care whether the weather is clear or cloudy; an instrument flight plan can be filed and flown in any weather; and in clear weather the pilot can both initiate and cancel it at will.

Attitude Instrument Flying

The attitude of an aircraft is the relationship of its longitudinal axis (fuselage) and its lateral axis (wings) to the earth's surface or any plane parallel to the earth's surface. Attitude instrument flying means controlling the attitude of an aircraft by reference to flight instruments.

Both attitude instrument flying and visual flying use reference points to determine the attitude of the aircraft. While flying by visual reference to the earth's surface, the pilot determines the attitude of the aircraft by observing the relation between the aircraft's nose and wings and the natural horizon. While flying by reference to flight instruments, the pilot determines the attitude of the aircraft by observing indications on the instruments, which give him essentially the same information obtained by visual reference to the earth's surface. Because he uses exactly the same control techniques while flying by reference to instruments as he does in visual flying, the student of attitude instrument flying need not learn a different method of controlling the aircraft. Skill in basic instrument flying enables him to reduce the instrument flying problem to simple procedures in any aircraft. He is thus safely freed from concentration on the manipulation of controls to the point where he can navigate, communicate with traffic control agencies, and still remain relaxed and deliberate.

TRIM

Proper trim technique is essential to smooth and accurate instrument flying. An inexperienced instrument pilot may think that he is too busy

Figure 9.1 Instrument or contact—the basic reference is the same.

flying the aircraft by control pressure to devote time to manipulation of the trim controls; however, he cannot execute a maneuver precisely without trimming. *The degree of instrument flying skill which he ultimately will develop depends largely upon how well he learns to keep the aircraft trimmed.*

CONTROL AND PERFORMANCE INSTRUMENTS

As described in Chapter 5, flight instruments by usage fall into three groups: *control instruments, performance instruments,* and *navigation instruments.*

Attitude and *power* indicators are the control instruments. By proper use of the attitude indicator and power setting you can obtain the performance you need to maintain level flight, turn, climb or descend, accelerate or decelerate, and even takeoff and land.

ATTITUDE CONTROL

Proper aircraft attitude control is the result of maintaining a constant attitude, knowing when and how much to change it, and then changing the attitude smoothly a definite amount to obtain specific aircraft performance.

Figure 9.2 Functional grouping of the instruments. *(Courtesy of U.S. Air Force.)*

The attitude indicator provides an immediate and direct indication of any corresponding change in the aircraft's pitch or roll (bank) attitudes. Because small pitch or bank changes are easily seen and immediately evident, changes of any magnitude can be made smoothly and quickly.

Pitch Control For Level Flight The pitch attitude of an aircraft is the angular relation of the longitudinal axis of the aircraft to the true horizon (Figure 8.5). In level flight the pitch attitude varies with airspeed. A change of several degrees in the angle of attack is necessary to maintain constant lift with changing airspeeds. The aircraft flies relatively nose-high at low speeds and relatively nose-low at high speeds. The pitch attitude of the aircraft for level flight also changes with difference in load, the angle of attack of the wings having to be increased with increased load and decreased with a decrease in load.

To attain the proper pitch attitude in visual flight, you raise or lower the nose in relation to the horizon. In instrument flight you attain the proper pitch attitude by changing the "pitch picture" of the miniature aircraft or fuselage dot definite amounts in relation to the horizon bar of the attitude indicator. These changes are called "bar widths," or "half bar widths," or degrees, depending upon the type of attitude indicator. As described in Chapter 5 and shown in Figure 5.10, most modern attitude indicators have horizontal lines or dots (the pitch reference scale) in 5° increments.

Therefore, pitch changes of 5° or greater are called "degrees of pitch change," while pitch changes of less than 5° are normally called "bar widths" or "fractions of bar widths." Pitch adjustments can be refined in bar widths after establishing an initial pitch change in degrees. In attitude indicators such as the J-8, pitch changes are made with respect to "bar

Figure 9.3 Pitch attitude indications. Though these indications seem small, they are characteristic of the degree of pitch change required for effective attitude control.

widths." In instruments with clearly marked pitch reference scales (MM series), changes of any magnitude are made in terms of degrees.

PERFORMANCE INSTRUMENTS IN LEVEL FLIGHT

Before takeoff, if the "little airplane" is adjusted so as to be in line with the 90° indices at the sides of the instrument, it will usually be in the proper place for level flight. However, if it is not level with the horizon at normal cruising speeds in level flight, adjust it to show a level flight attitude at the preferred speed. Then leave it unchanged during varying airspeeds to provide a constant true picture of the attitude relative to a familiar flight condition.

The attitude indicator has virtually no lag; it gives an immediate picture of a change in pitch attitude. By remembering during rapid acceleration or deceleration that the indication will be nose-high or nose-low, you can avoid the effects of the small misrepresentation due to momentary gyro precession.

When using the attitude indicator to make pitch corrections, use extremely light but positive control pressures. Up to true airspeeds of 260 knots, the normal movement of the "little airplane" should not exceed one width of the horizon bar. In level flight, as the true airspeed increases, pitch corrections should be smaller to prevent overcontrolling; use the vertical velocity indicator to determine if you are overcontrolling. Any movement of more than 200 fpm from the desired rate indicates overcontrolling. Usually, to restore the aircraft to a desired altitude after a small (100-ft) deviation, a good pilot will use no more than 200 to 300 fpm. When it is obvious that this amount of correction is not enough, the best technique is to make a small correction on the attitude indicator and then observe performance instruments to determine if the correction is adequate. If not, make another correction of the same size immediately, and watch the result. Use prompt, light corrective pressures on the controls; this avoids later need for heavier corrective pressures. Although there is a small lag in the movement of the altimeter, for all practical purposes at lower altitude it may be considered as giving an immediate indication of a change or a need for a change in pitch attitude.

Altimeter The altimeter gives an indirect reading of the pitch attitude of an aircraft in level flight. The altitude should remain constant; any deviation shows a need for a change in pitch (and, possibly, power), and the rate of deviation shows the size of the pitch change needed. If gaining altitude, lower the "little airplane"; if losing altitude, raise it.

Vertical Speed Indicator Correct use of the VSI is essential for precise pitch attitude control. Although it gives an indirect indication of pitch attitude, it will, with smooth control technique, indicate by its initial movement the *trend* of vertical movement of the aircraft. Always use it in conjunction with the attitude indicator and the altimeter for any flight attitude. In level flight, if you detect the movement of the needle immediately and apply corrective pressure to return the needle to zero, the altimeter will usually indicate that there has been no change in altitude.

The amount that the altimeter is off governs the rate to use to return the aircraft to the desired altitude. After applying corrective pressure to change the attitude indicator, cross check the altimeter and VSI to see if further correction is needed. Whenever you apply pressure on the controls and the VSI shows a rate which exceeds the rate desired by more than 200 fpm, you are overcontrolling. For example, if attempting to gain lost altitude at the rate of 300 fpm, a reading of over 500 fpm would indicate overcontrolling.

While the initial movement of the needle is instantaneous and indicates the trend of the vertical movement of the aircraft, there is a lag. The lag is proportional to the speed and magnitude of the pitch change. Train yourself to apply smooth control technique by using light pressures for adjustments in pitch attitude; then the VSI is easy to interpret. Relaxation and cross-checking all the performance instruments to be always aware of the general pitch attitude will eliminate overcontrolling.

Airspeed Indicator The airspeed indicator gives an indirect reading of the pitch attitude of the aircraft. With a given power setting and the corresponding attitude, the aircraft flies level and the airspeed remains constant. If the airspeed increases, the nose is too low and should be raised. A rapid change in airspeed indicates a large change in pitch, and a slow change in airspeed indicates a small change in pitch. There is very little lag in the indications of the airspeed indicator. When pitch changes are made, they are reflected rapidly by a change of airspeed.

WHEN AND HOW MUCH TO CHANGE ATTITUDE AND POWER INDICATIONS

The basic concept of aircraft control requires you to adjust the aircraft attitude and power to achieve the desired aircraft performance. Therefore, you must be able to recognize *when* a change in attitude and/or power is required. It is equally important to know *what* and *how much* pitch, bank, or power change is required.

You will know *when* to change the attitude and/or power by observing the performance instruments. When you observe any indication other than the desired on the performance instruments, you must change the aircraft attitude or power.

You will know *what* to change by knowing which control instrument adjustment will achieve the desired indications on the performance instruments. Control the pitch attitude to maintain level flight or to maintain or change the rate of climb or descent; pitch attitude governs airspeed during maneuvers requiring a fixed power setting.

Conversely, the power setting determines whether the aircraft is in level flight, in a climb, or in a descent. For example, cruising airspeed, if maintained with cruising power, results in level flight. If you increase the power setting and adjust the pitch attitude to hold the airspeed constant, the aircraft will climb. If you decrease the power setting and adjust the attitude to hold constant airspeed, the aircraft will descend. Hold the *altitude* constant, and the desired airspeed will determine the pitch and power required. Any change in power at a constant altitude requires a change in pitch and gives a change in airspeed.

How much to change the attitude and/or power is, initially, an estimate based on familiarity with the aircraft and the amount you wish to change the indications on the performance instruments. After you make a change of attitude and/or power, observe the performance instruments to see if the desired change occurred. If not, make further adjustments of attitude and/or power. Instrument flight is a continuous and systematic process of monitoring the performance instruments and *adjusting* the control instruments. The systematic process used to monitor and adjust is termed *cross-checking.*

INSTRUMENT CROSS-CHECKING

During instrument flight, divide your attention between the control and performance instruments. Proper division of attention, and the *sequence* for checking the instruments vary among pilots and throughout various phases of flight. You should know the symptoms enabling you to recognize correct and incorrect cross-check technique.

One veteran flight instructor uses what he calls the "ATC Procedure" to make the process a routine which can be repeated almost subconsciously:

A Attitude and power
T Trim
C Cross-check

Remember that a knowledge of approximate power settings for various flight conditions will help avoid overcontrolling power.

Cross-check technique is influenced by the characteristic manner in which instruments respond to changes of attitude and/or power. While control instruments provide a direct and immediate indication of attitude and/or power changes, the responsive indications of the performance instruments will lag slightly. Inertia of the aircraft and imperfections in the capabilities of performance instruments cause this lag—it must be accepted as an inherent factor, though it need not appreciably affect the tolerances within which you can control the aircraft.

Lag in the performance instruments should not interfere with maintaining or smoothly changing the attitude and/or power indications. When you control the attitude and power properly, the lag factor is negligible and the indications on the performance instruments will stabilize or change smoothly. Do not be lured into making a flight control movement in direct response to the lag in indications on the performance instruments without first referring to the control instruments, because this invariably leads to erratic aircraft control and will cause additional fluctuations and lag in performance instruments. Always remember that the sooner you note a deviation and apply a correction, the smaller the required corrective adjustment of the control instrument will be.

The attitude indicator is the only instrument which you may observe continuously for any appreciable length of time. Approximately 10 seconds may be needed to accomplish an attitude change required for a normal turn. During this 10-second period, you may need to devote your attention almost exclusively to the attitude indicator to insure good attitude control. The attitude indicator is also the most frequently observed. For example, you may glance from the attitude indicator to the airspeed; back to attitude; then a glance at the altimeter; back to attitude, and so forth.

This example of a normal cross-check does not mean that it is the only method of cross-checking. It is often necessary to compare the indications of one performance instrument against another before knowing when or how much to change the attitude and/or power. An effective cross-check technique may require that you note the attitude indicator between glances at the performance instruments being compared.

Preponderance of attention to the attitude indicator is normal and desirable to keep the fluctuations and lag indications of the performance instruments to a minimum. This technique permits you to read any one performance instrument during a split-second glance and will result in smooth and precise aircraft control.

You must give a proper and relative amount of attention to each performance instrument. Pilots seldom fail to observe the one performance instrument whose indication is most informative in a particular maneuver, but they often devote so much attention to one performance instrument that they fail to cross-check the attitude indicator for proper aircraft control. Another error is to become so engrossed with one performance instrument that the others are omitted from the cross-check.

How can you recognize deficiencies in cross-checking?

Insufficient Reference to Control Instruments If you do not have in mind some definite attitude and power indication you want to establish or maintain, and the other instruments fluctuate erratically through the desired indications, you are not referring enough to the control instruments. Aircraft control will be imprecise, and you will feel ineffective and insecure.

Too Much Reference to Control Instruments This is rare indeed. It may be caused by your desire to maintain control indications within close tolerances. If you have smooth, positive, and continuous control over attitude and power indications, and are making small adjustments, but large deviations are occurring slowly in certain of the performance instruments, you need a closer cross-check on the latter.

Cross-checking incorrectly, you will omit some performance instruments from the cross-check, although you are observing other performance and control instruments properly. For example, during a climb or descent, you may become so engrossed with pitch attitude control that you fail to observe an error in the aircraft heading.

A 4° heading change is not as "eye-catching" as a 300- to 400-fpm change on the vertical speed indicator. Through deliberate effort and practice, you can insure that you include *all* the instruments in your cross-check. Do this, and you will observe performance instrument deviations in their early stages, when corrections are easiest to make.

The habit of analyzing your cross-check technique is very helpful in maintaining your skill. *Deterioration in effective cross-checking is the first evidence of lack of enough practice; it is always a danger signal and requires positive effort to correct.*

Figure 9.4 Throttle movement and power change indications are simultaneous.

POWER CONTROL

Proper power control results from knowing *when and how much* to change the power indications. These power changes are established by throttle adjustment and reference to the power indicators. Power indications are not affected by such factors as turbulence, improper trim, or inadvertent control pressures as are other flight instruments. Therefore, once established, little attention is required to insure that power remains constant.

Adjusting the power to a desired amount is an easy step of power control. For all practical purposes, power indicators change simultaneously with throttle movement, and the manner in which they are calibrated permits adjustments to be made with a minimum of attention to the power instruments.

BANK CONTROL

The banking attitude of an aircraft is the angular relation of the lateral axis of the aircraft to the true horizon. To maintain a straight course in visual flight, you must keep the wings of the aircraft level with the true horizon. If the aircraft is trimmed properly and in coordinated flight, any deviation from a wings-level attitude produces a turn. For instrument flight the "little airplane" and horizon of the attitude indicator are substituted for the real aircraft and the true horizon, as in Figure 9.1, and the banking attitude is indicated accurately.

Make changes by changing the "bank attitude," or bank pointers, definite amounts in relation to the bank scale. The bank scale is graduated at 0°, 10°, 20°, 30°, 60°, and 90°. Bank attitude control is used to maintain a heading or a desired attitude of bank during turns.

Basic Flight Maneuvers

For this portion of Chapter 9, the author is particularly indebted to the Air Force Instrument Pilot Instructor School which writes Air Force instrument flying manuals and develops a synthesis of the very best instrument flying techniques from Air Force and civil experience involving a wide variety of pilots, flight conditions, and aircraft. The author has not hesitated to use verbatim parts of the latest Air Force text, except for occasional adjustments to suit the needs of the civil aircraft pilot. The techniques, however, are generally applicable to all aircraft equipped with full instrument panels.

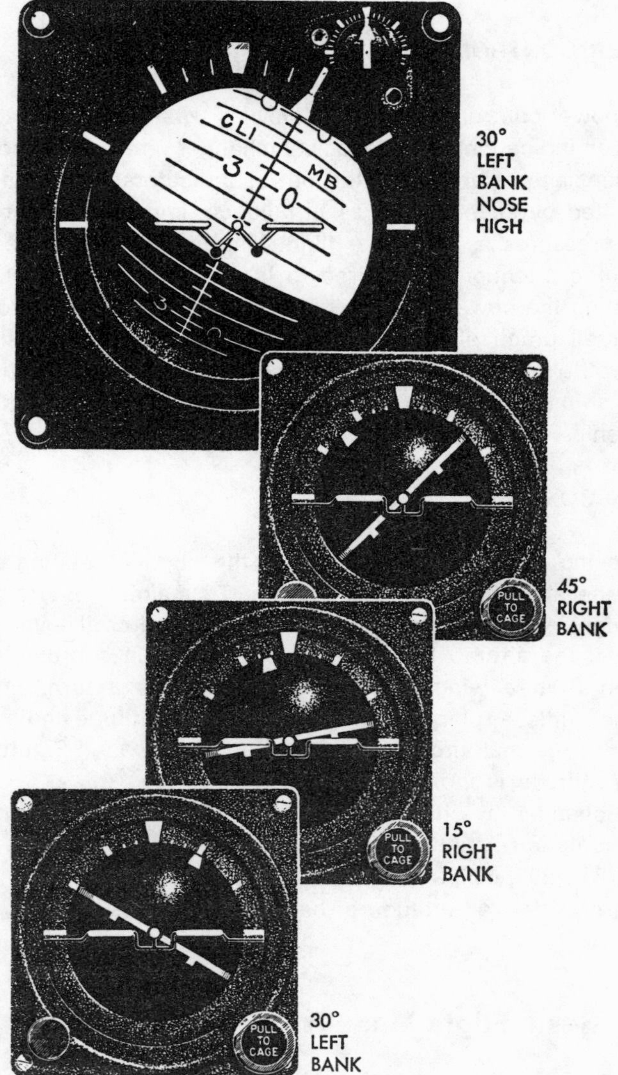

Figure 9.5 Bank attitude indications.

Because any instrument flight, regardless of how long or complex, is simply a series of connected basic maneuvers, these maneuvers can form the basis for both training and practice.

TRIM TECHNIQUE

Proper trimming is very important in any attitude. In fact, improper lateral trim usually results in an unconscious strain on the pilot which can be

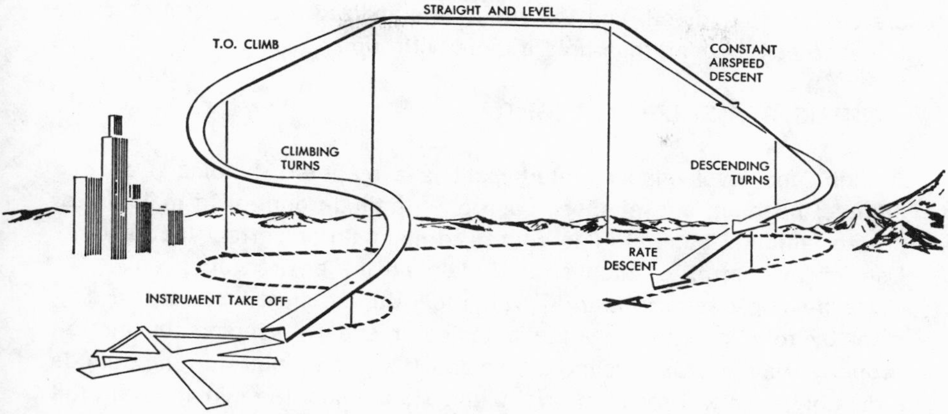

Figure 9.6 Typical instrument flight. Any instrument flight, regardless of how long or complex, is simply a series of connected basic flight maneuvers.

distracting and dangerous. And if the airplane is properly trimmed, momentary diversions for navigation or other needs are easy and safe.

An incorrect setting of the aileron trim tab will lower one wing and start a turn. Incorrect rudder trim causes a skid. Skids result in banks, and therefore turns, because they increase the speed and thus the lift of one wing. Improper opposite aileron and rudder trim together can stop the tendency to bank, but result in a constant-heading skid. This costs airspeed. When trimming, use all available bank instruments, but act on the principle that you are centering the ball with rudder trim and centering the needle with aileron trim. As trim is improved, speed will increase; small trim-tab deflections into the airstream will have greater effect. Continue the retrimming cycle, including elevators, until the needle and ball

Figure 9.7 Proper trimming. To trim properly, apply control pressure to maintain desired attitude. Then adjust trim until the control pressure is relieved.

are centered hands-off, and the speed is stabilized. Use control pressure to get what you want, then hold it there with trim.

STRAIGHT AND LEVEL FLIGHT

Straight and level unaccelerated flight is a matter of holding a desired altitude, heading, and airspeed. Use pitch attitude control to maintain or correct altitude; bank attitude control to maintain or correct the heading. Use power control to establish and maintain the desired airspeed.

Maintaining Desired Altitude The pitch attitude must first be held constant by reference to the attitude indicator and by keeping the aircraft properly trimmed. On leveling off, establish a pitch picture on the attitude indicator which will result in level flight. Then adjust the miniature aircraft reference of the attitude indicator to align it with the horizon bar. Readjust it as load and cruising airspeed change. This will simplify keeping a single cruise attitude picture, and will make pitch control much simpler.

When correcting back to the desired altitude, make pitch attitude changes of a definite amount, such as ½ or 1 bar width. With practice and observation, you will come to know approximately how much these pitch changes will affect the vertical speed. Know the vertical speed changes which result when these pitch changes are made at various airspeeds and configurations of gear and flaps used with your aircraft. Then, when you see the aircraft departing from the desired rate, you will know approximately what pitch attitude correction and power adjustment, if any, is required.

To avoid overcorrecting, change the pitch attitude just enough to give a vertical speed in fpm about double the altitude error in feet. For example, if 100 ft off altitude, use a pitch correction that will give you a rate of correction of about 200 fpm. Remember that your initial pitch change is only an estimated amount; you must note the resulting speed and refine the adjustment as necessary.

When correcting back to an altitude, begin the level-off before reaching the desired altitude, and with a lead about equal to 10% of the rate of climb; that is, if climbing at the rate of 200 fpm, start leveling off 20 ft below the desired altitude.

This technique will also help to compensate for the lag inherent in performance instruments. With experience you can judge from the initial indication of the VSI whether or not your initial pitch attitude change was too large or too small and can correct before the altimeter has had time to react. Do not be led into overcontrolling pitch attitude by the oscillation of the VSI in rough air. This is a common mistake which can be corrected by more reference to the attitude indicator.

Maintaining a Desired Heading If the wings are level, the aircraft

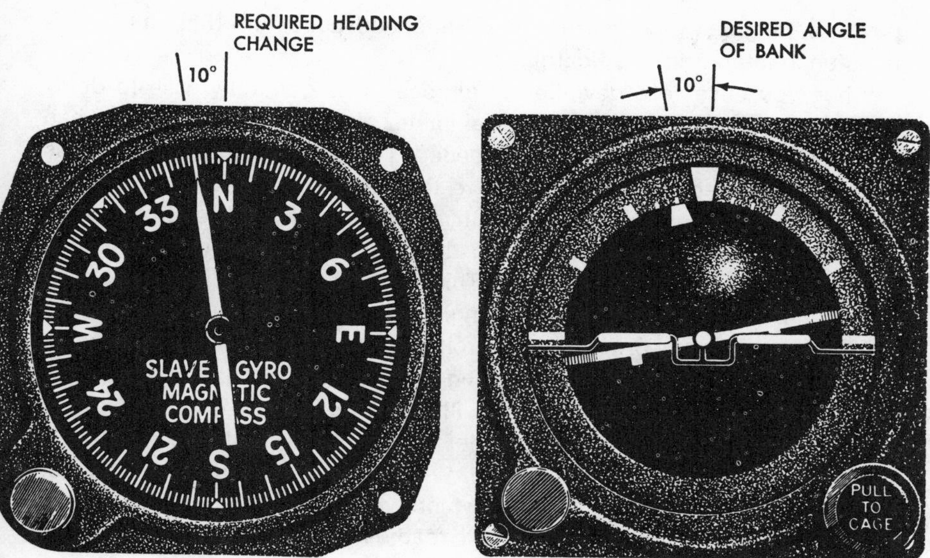

Figure 9.8 Limit the angle of bank to the number of degrees to be turned.

theoretically will not turn from the desired heading. Slight turbulence and slight banking will shift the heading, however, and the way to correct smoothly when the aircraft is properly trimmed is to refer to the attitude indicator and establish the amount of bank which will return the aircraft to the desired heading at a desirable rate. Most modern aircraft are designed with so little adverse aileron yaw that little rudder is needed, and correcting heading deviations with the rudder is a mistake, much less smooth than correcting by banking. By establishing an angle of bank on the attitude indicator equal to the number of degrees of heading correction needed, you will be able to make smooth, precise corrections with minimum control effort.

Slight movements of the heading indicator are not particularly eye-catching; only the habit of regular and frequent cross-checking of the bank attitude and the heading indicator will develop skill in maintaining a constant heading.

Establishing and Maintaining Airspeed To level off when the airspeed approaches that desired, it is helpful to know about what power will maintain that airspeed. Then you can set the approximate value, continue the cross-check of other instruments, and if the airspeed indicator and attitude indicator show that at the desired altitude the airspeed is high or low, make minor power adjustment, establishing the pitch attitude which will maintain constant altitude. Make it a point to know what approximate power setting will give you a desired airspeed under the different conditions encountered in a typical flight.

When you observe a deviation in airspeed it is generally wise to delay a power adjustment and check the altimeter and attitude indicator to see whether a pitch attitude change is needed. There are many times, such as below the desired airspeed but above the desired altitude, when the required pitch change will correct both airspeed and altitude. Conversely, remember that changing pitch when the airspeed is correct may induce the need for a power adjustment. This is most likely at low airspeeds, particularly in jet or in large multiengine piston aircraft.

Increasing Airspeed When controlling power to increase airspeed, advance the power beyond the setting required for the higher speed. As the airspeed increases, the aircraft will tend to climb. Cross-checking the altimeter and VSI with the attitude indicator will indicate the pitch change needed for the new airspeed. When the speed nears that desired, reduce the power setting to that which you estimate will support the new speed. Cross-check, retrim, and readjust pitch and power until the airspeed is stabilized.

Decreasing Airspeed When establishing a slower airspeed, reduce the power beyond that which you believe will support the slower speed. Cross-check pitch, altitude, and vertical speed with the airspeed. As it reaches the desired rate, bring up the power to support the slower speed. Cross-check, retrim and readjust pitch and power to stabilize the speed. If drag devices are used, it is good technique to reduce the power initially to that estimated for the new speed but not below it; as the speed slows to that desired, retract the drag devices, cross-check pitch attitude, altitude, and vertical speed with the airspeed. Adjust pitch and power as necessary, and retrim. Readjust pitch and power until the speed stabilizes. Retrim.

Extending or retracting drag devices on some aircraft will cause the aircraft to change pitch attitude. Be alert to this, and note the pitch attitude just prior to extending or retracting. Maintain this indication constant and trim out the control pressures needed. Then proceed as described above.

LEVEL TURNS

Two facets of turns give pilots trouble. The first is the effect of loss of vertical lift during a turn (Figure 2.27). Compensation for this factor requires changes in pitch attitude, power, and elevator trim during the turn.

The second factor is the tendency of most attitude indicators, and particularly air-driven attitude indicators, to precess slightly during and immediately after turns, or during acceleration or deceleration. For example: Following a turn, the aircraft may actually be in a slight bank and turn even though the attitude indicator shows wings level. Or the aircraft may be actually climbing or descending with a level-flight pitch attitude indication.

These errors will disappear as the attitude gyro corrects itself; in the meantime, careful cross-checking performance instruments and the awareness of these effects will permit using an attitude indication which will give the desired performance.

Establishing and Maintaining the Desired Bank Having determined what rate of turn you want, and what angle of bank is required at a particular aircraft speed and configuration to provide the rate of turn, enter the turn by reference to the attitude indicator. In normal instrument flying, and you will seldom exceed 30° of bank.

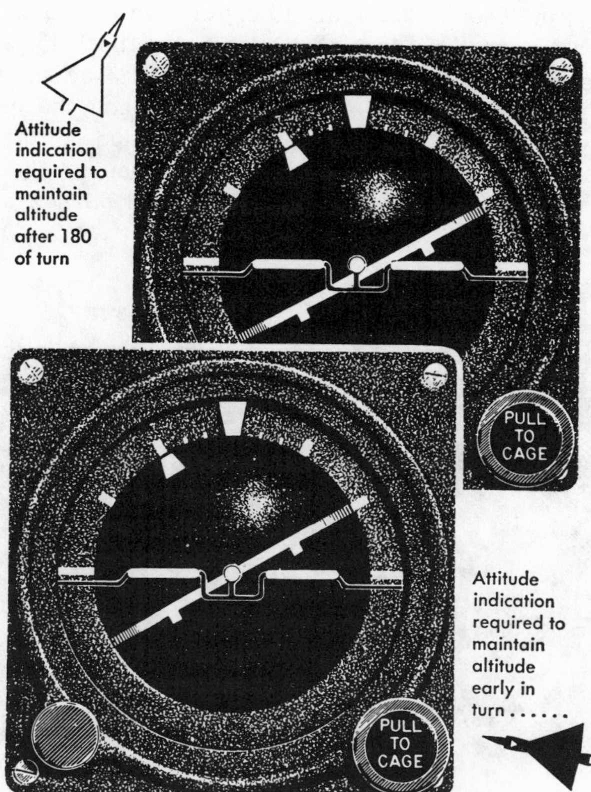

Figure 9.9 Effects of precession durıng turns.

Before entering a turn, make a definite decision on the angle of bank you require. You can then select a lead point in which to relax the control pressures to stop the roll-in smoothly. As the angle of bank increases, check the pitch attitude, changing it if necessary to prevent any change in performance instruments. Throughout the turn refer to the attitude indicator sufficiently to hold the bank indication constant, and use light pressures to readjust. It is important to use a precise, constant angle of bank.

To roll out of the turn on the desired heading, you must begin the roll-out before reaching the new heading. The amount of lead you use will depend on the amount of bank, the rate at which the aircraft is turning, and the rate of roll you use in rolling out. An average amount of lead in degrees is ⅓ the angle of bank. Once you have developed a consistent rate of roll-out, a little experimenting will tell you what your individual lead should be.

Maintaining Altitude in Turns Maintaining the altitude constant during a turn requires the same pitch attitude control used in straight and level flight. You will notice the effect of the loss of vertical lift, and should anticipate the tendency of the aircraft to lose altitude by cross-checking carefully the altimeter and VSI. As the need for a pitch change becomes evident, apply back pressure to adjust the pitch attitude of the "little airplane" or nose dot on the attitude indicator. As you roll into the turn, cross-checking the pitch attitude of level flight will provide a reference

Figure 9.10 Leading the roll out of a turn. A lead of a number of degrees about equal to 1/3 the angle of bank is a good average, though it is somewhat different for all pilots.

for a slight increase in pitch attitude in the turn. Your principal error will be insufficient reference to the attitude indicator for pitch control.

During the turn, the horizon bar may precess up or down, requiring a change in the pitch attitude necessary to maintain altitude. Proper cross-checking and trimming in the turn will, with practice, make this process almost unconscious.

While rolling out of the bank, do not allow the nose of the aircraft to rise as a result of the trim used to maintain the altitude in the turn. Apply forward pressure as you roll out to return the pitch attitude to that existing before the turn, remembering possible precession, and then trim out the forward pressure.

Maintaining Airspeed in Turns Power control is the same as in level flight, but the power also will have to be increased to maintain airspeed during turns. Compensating for the loss of vertical lift with a pitch attitude adjustment increases drag and reduces airspeed unless the power is increased. Anticipate this loss and be prepared to add the necessary power. At the higher airspeeds, the power needed may be negligible. At low airspeeds, particularly in jet aircraft and in larger piston aircraft in landing configuration, a considerable change in power may be required. If you are slow in applying the extra power as you roll into the turn, the airspeed may decrease rapidly to the point where changes in power require a substantial change in pitch attitude, and the turn can become difficult and unstable. To avoid this, at low airspeeds add an estimated amount of power as you roll into the bank rather than having to catch up later; don't wait for the first indication of a loss in airspeed.

STEEP TURNS

Steep turns are those requiring more bank than is normally used in instrument flying in a particular aircraft. The techniques for turning steeply in level flight are the same for standard turns. You use pitch attitude control to maintain or correct back to the altitude, power control to maintain airspeed, and bank attitude control to maintain the bank attitude constant. Steep turns are an excellent practice exercise for improving your cross-check in standard turns. In steep turns, hold the bank indication constant and make all corrections back to altitude by changing pitch attitude. If control of the pitch attitude and altitude becomes erratic, or if excessive elevator control forces are required, roll to wing-level and begin another turn. Perhaps you are using too much bank for your aircraft or your present cross-check ability, or you are delaying too long using back stick pressure on rolling in. Power control in steep turns is also magnified, and power increases must be started earlier. Steep turns are excellent practice if you make them precise. The three primary factors affecting aircraft control during steep turns are: (1) rate of roll-in and roll-out, (2) use of trim and power, (3) constant angle of bank.

TIMED TURNS AND USE OF THE MAGNETIC COMPASS

With modern directional gyros, failure is unlikely, but it could happen, and turns using the magnetic compass are the only alternative.

The magnetic compass gives reliable information only during straight, level, and unaccelerated flight. It fluctuates widely, rushing ahead on turns to southerly headings, holding back on turns to northerly headings, and swinging during acceleration as a result of the "dip effect" (page 236). For this reason it is best to make turns at a standard rate, timing them to reach approximate headings.

A timed turn is one in which the angle of bank is established to give the desired rate, shown by the needle of the turn and slip indicator, and this bank is held for a definite period before leveling out. By holding the desired rate of turn for the proper number of seconds, you can make a turn of the desired number of degrees. For example, with the 2 min needle (page 237), a full needle width turn at 3° per sec will turn the aircraft 90° if held for 30 sec.

Start timing as you apply control pressures to begin the turn. Start rolling out when the time has elapsed. If your rate of roll-in and roll-out are consistent, the timing will be accurate; if the angle of bank is held constant and correct, the number of degrees of turn will be accurate.

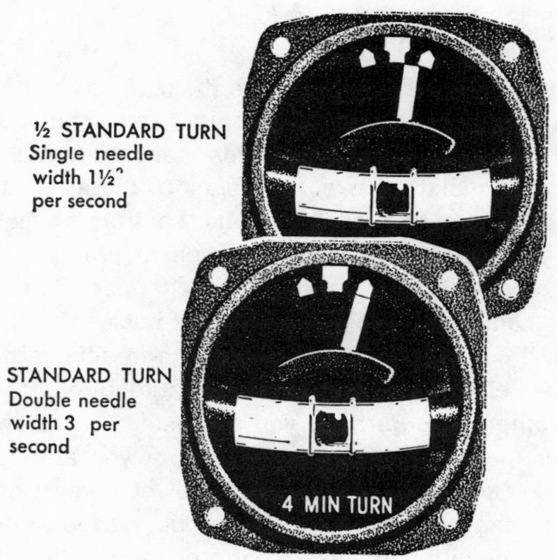

Figure 9.11 Turn indications.

As you practice holding definite amounts of bank by reference to the attitude indicator, note the turn needle to see what deflection is resulting. The rate of turn which results from any given amount of bank will vary with the true airspeed. By practicing turns at the various airspeeds normally used for your aircraft, you will soon become familiar with the angle of bank required for a desired rate of turn. Establish the initial bank, then cross-check, trim, and adjust the bank indication on the attitude indicator to produce the turn needle deflection desired.

As an alternate to timed turns, you may refer to the magnetic compass to determine the lead point at which to roll out. This method can be effective in smooth air if you use angles of bank less than 15° in order to minimize dip error.

Because of the dip error, you must allow, in addition to your lead, a number of degrees approximately equal to the latitude in which you are flying. When turning to south, turn past your normal lead point by this amount. Turning to north, turn short this number of degrees in addition to your normal lead.

Dip error is negligible when turning to east or west, and you can use your normal amount of lead if the turn is not too steep.

CLIMBS AND DESCENTS

In instrument flying, there are two general ways to climb or descend: constant *airspeed,* and constant *rate.* In the former you establish a desirable power indication to be held constant throughout the maneuver, and then control the pitch attitude to give the desired airspeed, accepting whatever vertical speed results.

In the *rate* climb or descent, you control the pitch attitude as required to provide some desired constant vertical speed, and control the power as required to maintain the desired airspeed.

In either type of climb or descent, the bank attitude control used in straight and level flight or in turning applies, and during the climb or descent, you can hold a constant heading, or can turn.

Constant-Airspeed Climbs and Descents Before entering the climb or descent, select the power setting you intend to establish, and estimate the amount the pitch attitude will have to change to maintain the airspeed you desire. Normally you make the pitch and power changes simultaneously.

If you are cruising at an airspeed appreciably different from that at which you want to climb or descend, it is generally best to establish first a pitch attitude which will change the airspeed at a desirable rate with the climb or descent power setting, and when the airspeed is reached, readjust the pitch attitude. In some cases you may wish to delay either the pitch or power change to make the airspeed change more rapidly.

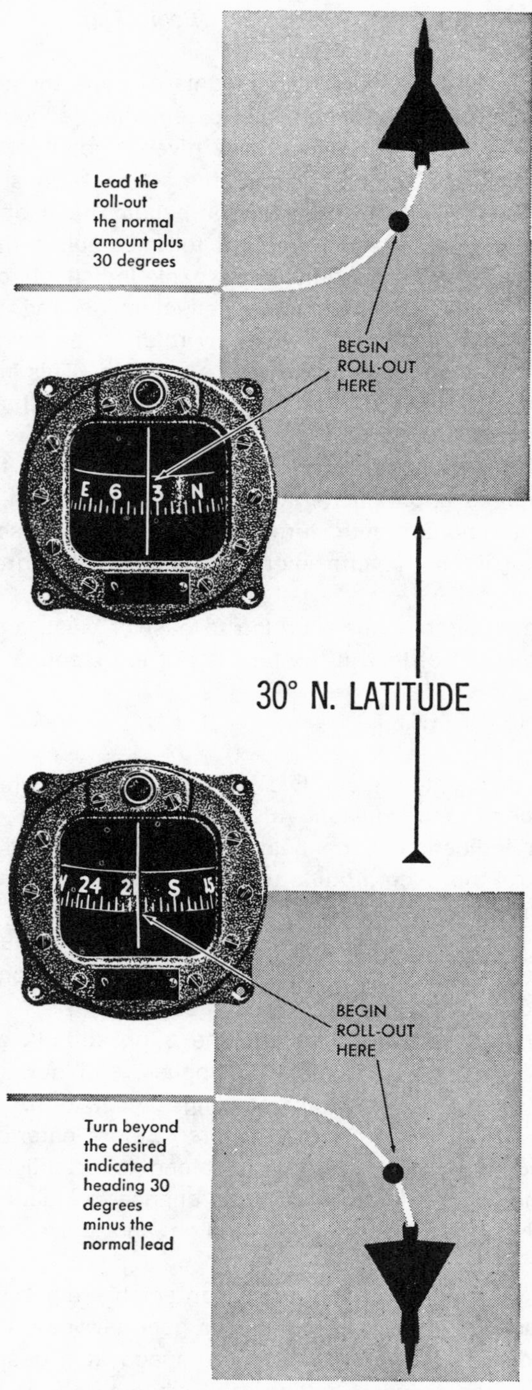
Lead the
roll-out
the normal
amount plus
30 degrees
BEGIN
ROLL-OUT
HERE
E 6 3 N
30° N. LATITUDE
W 24 21 S 15
BEGIN
ROLL-OUT
HERE
Turn beyond
the desired
indicated
heading 30
degrees
minus the
normal lead

Figure 9.12 Use of the magnetic compass during turns.

Figure 9.13 Pitch attitude determines airspeed.

The important thing is to control both pitch attitude and power smoothly and precisely, cross-checking to readjust pitch and power if necessary, and to see that the performance instruments are giving you the airspeed, vertical speed, heading or heading change, and altitude change you desire. Power changes should be smooth and uninterrupted, for good power control technique will simplify the coordination of pitch and power changes.

In some aircraft, particularly piston aircraft at lower altitudes, the change in air density will result in a change in manifold pressure unless the throttle is adjusted to hold the power constant. With a moderate amount of practice in power and pitch change coordination, and with orderly cross-checking, the airspeed will remain within close limits as you enter the climb or descent. The more familiar you are with the pitch-power relationship of your aircraft, the more precisely you will be able to make the initial pitch and power adjustment.

After you make a pitch adjustment, the airspeed indicator will soon show a change, but the VSI will often give a quicker indication of the results of the pitch change. For example, you note the airspeed slightly high and make a small adjustment of pitch. If there is a resulting small change in vertical speed, you know, even though the airspeed may not have changed, that the small pitch change was effective. It will soon be evident in the airspeed.

The VSI can also point out that you have made an inadvertent change in the pitch attitude. Suppose the desired airspeed and vertical velocity have been remaining constant, but the pitch attitude has changed unnoticed. The VSI will usually show this pitch change more quickly than the airspeed indicator, and you can correct the pitch attitude to return to the desired vertical speed. The effect of the correction will be that the pitch attitude will have been corrected before the airspeed has time to deviate from desired.

This process is not "chasing" the VSI because the changes *are made on the attitude indicator,* and these result in a precise, positive, immediate change in the aircraft attitude. As long as the attitude indicator is kept constantly in the circuit of cross-check, and in your consciousness, the rate of climb or descent will be stable in smooth air, and more stable in rough air.

Leveling Off from Constant-Airspeed Climbs and Descents As you approach your desired altitude, plan to lead the level-off by the number of feet on the altimeter about equal to 10% of the vertical speed. Adjust the power smoothly to that approximate setting required for level flight. Simultaneously change the pitch attitude of the miniature aircraft to the indication you believe will maintain the desired new altitude, and resume your normal level flight cross-check. Retrim. Reset the height of the "little airplane."

In piston aircraft where the climb speed is substantially lower than cruise, good technique requires that you set a level pitch attitude as required to hold the desired level-off altitude, and delay the change in power until the airspeed has increased to or slightly above that required. Retrimming is an important part of this process, and begins before the power change. In heavily loaded aircraft, it may even be necessary to climb above the desired altitude, level off initially with climb power, and drift down to the desired altitude to insure that the airspeed reaches the optimum for the cruise power desired or available.

Rate Climbs and Descents The requirement is to execute a constant airspeed and a constant vertical speed, both probably predetermined, as might be used during the final portion of an instrument approach to landing.

As a general aerodynamic principle, pitch attitude controls airspeed and power controls rate of descent or climb. Within the fine limits of adjustment made during a carefully controlled rate descent, we reverse the rule. Having established airspeed and rate of descent, we, *for all practical purposes, control the airspeed with power and the rate of descent with pitch attitude.*

The reason is that the changes in pitch attitude and power should be minute; in fact, they will have to be minute if the approach is to be smooth. Only if a large adjustment is required, as, for example, when the aircraft has gotten dangerously low too early in the descent, will power

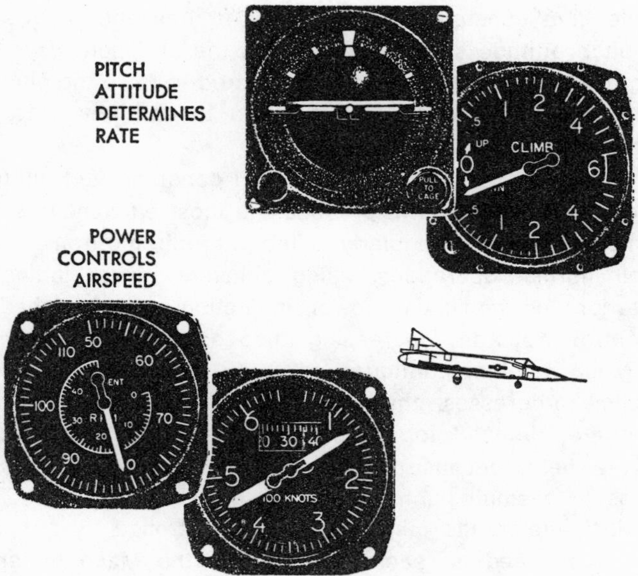

Figure 9.14 Rate climbs and descents.

govern descent. In this example, a substantial increase in power might be required to slow the rate of descent, or even climb.

Also, aircraft of the present day are so clean aerodynamically, and jet aircraft particularly carry so high a proportion of power during a descent with gear and flaps out, that a pitch change, directly affecting the angle of attack and lift, can correct small vertical speed error immediately without changing airspeed perceptibly. Similarly, the cleanness and high percentage of power held make the airspeed more responsive to small changes in thrust.

Just before initiating the climb or descent, estimate the pitch change you think will produce the desired vertical speed, and the power setting you think will maintain the desired constant airspeed. Smoothly, and as simultaneously as practicable, establish the new power and pitch indications. Retrim. Cross-checking, adjust the pitch attitude to correct the vertical speed and adjust the power to correct any deviation in airspeed. To level off, use the same procedure as for leveling off from constant-airspeed climbs or descents.

Bank Attitude Control During Climbs or Descents By using the same bank attitude control for straight flight or for turns described for straight and level flight, you can turn or hold constant headings precisely as in level flight (Figure 9.5).

Remember the loss of vertical lift which occurs with bank. If you enter a turn while in a constant-airspeed climb or descent, be prepared to lower the pitch attitude slightly to maintain the airspeed. If you enter a turn during a rate climb or descent, be prepared to raise the pitch attitude slightly to maintain the vertical speed, and to add power to maintain the airspeed.

Climb Schedules For any one given load condition and altitude there is only one airspeed which will produce the most efficient rate of climb. Because modern aircraft regularly climb through more than 40,000 ft during their normal operations, using constant power indications, or slowly deteriorating maximum power indications, climb schedules are used to control a steadily decreasing airspeed; and for jets a constant maximum Mach at higher altitudes.

As the climb progresses, change the pitch attitude so as to adhere to the appropriate airspeed for various altitudes. The vertical speed is here again a help, because it will be the quickest indicator of the effectiveness of a small pitch change.

With a Mach meter, the climb is usually controlled by airspeed until a certain Mach speed is reached; thereafter the Mach meter is held constant throughout the rest of the climb.

INSTRUMENT TAKEOFF AND INITIAL CLIMB

Many an accident otherwise unexplained, and many a scare, have occurred right after takeoff in reduced visibility and at night in aircraft of all sizes in good weather and foul. The ability to shift completely to instruments after the beginning of the takeoff roll, and until the climb and initial heading are well established, is an essential of safe flight at night and in reduced visibility. The rapid acceleration and rapid rates of roll of modern aircraft make this particularly true. Therefore, practice the instrument takeoff so that when the time comes, you can make the changeover successfully.

Preparation for Takeoff Make a complete cockpit check, as for visual flying. In addition, pay special attention to the gyro instruments and to trim tabs, because any irregularity could have a disastrous effect. Set altimeter setting in the Kollsman window. Check to see if it varies by more than ± 75 ft. If it does, have it changed, or don't take the aircraft into weather conditions.

After being cleared for takeoff, line up the aircraft with the centerline of the runway and allow it to roll straight ahead a short distance to be sure that the nose or tail wheel is properly aligned. Hold the brakes firmly to prevent creeping.

If you are using a vacuum-driven heading indicator, set it to the 10° mark nearest the published runway heading, and recheck it to be sure that it is uncaged. If using an electric heading indicator, set the heading needle and runway heading under the index at the top of the instrument.

Takeoff and Initial Climb Accomplish the takeoff roll and establish the takeoff attitude by combined visual and instrument reference. In the early part of your takeoff roll you can keep the aircraft properly aligned with the runway by observing the center line and runway lights. In extremely low visibility or hard rain this may become more difficult as the speed increases. Therefore, make it a point to include the directional indicator in your cross-check so you will know what heading will keep the aircraft on the runway. Remember that crosswind drift on the takeoff roll is recognizable only through outside visual reference.

In some cases, you must establish the takeoff attitude almost entirely by reference to the attitude indicator. Make it a definite point to know the takeoff pitch attitude required for your aircraft as indicated on the attitude indicator. Know also how much the attitude indicator can be expected to precess because of acceleration so that you can allow for the false nose-high attitude it will show. The important point to remember is that you include the instruments in your cross-check sufficiently so that a rapid or unexpected loss of outside reference will not cause difficulty.

Refer to the attitude indicator to hold the pitch-and-bank attitude constant as the aircraft leaves the ground. A small variation in pitch at this time may cause the aircraft to settle to the runway or stall. Wait for the altimeter to show an increase in altitude, and the vertical velocity indicator to show a definite climb before retracting the landing gear. Altimeters and vertical speed indicators sometimes indicate a descent during the takeoff roll and immediately after becoming airborne. Raise the wing flaps when appropriate for your aircraft, but after climb is established.

While the gear and flaps are being retracted, carefully maintain a climbing attitude on the attitude indicator. Refer to the VSI and altimeter to prevent leveling off, entering a descent, or allowing the vertical speed to increase or decrease excessively.

After the gear and flaps are retracted, control the pitch attitude to provide both a reasonable rate of increase of airspeed and a desirable rate of climb until you reach climbing airspeed. Control the bank attitude to maintain or correct back to the desired heading. Use trim as desired after takeoff, but avoid using trim to pull the aircraft off the ground. Doing so may result in an excessive nose-high attitude as gear and flaps are retracted and the airspeed increases.

EXERCISES IN BASIC INSTRUMENT FLYING

These maneuvers combine climbs and descents at a definite rate with precision turns and require maximum speed of cross-checking for precise execution. They are real tests of basic instrument flying skill when executed precisely and checked by timing; they also simulate many of the problems encountered during instrument approaches. They should be flown with errors not exceeding 50 ft altitude, 5 knots airspeed, and 10 sec per minute of time.

The Vertical "S" This is a continuing series of definite rate climbs and descents, made at constant airspeed and heading. Select a beginning altitude and heading, then climb or descend to another altitude, 500, 1000, or 2000 ft different, and reverse. As you become proficient at coordinating pitch attitude and power changes, the airspeed will remain within close limits during climb, descent, and reversal. You will soon be familiar with the lead points needed for your aircraft and control technique.

The Vertical "S" in Constant Turn Use a bank angle suitable for your aircraft. Enter the turn simultaneously with the initial climb or descent, and maintain the bank constant throughout the maneuver. Make several successive and precise climbs and descents with the same bank.

The Vertical "S," Reversing Turn At Descent Add to the foregoing maneuver a reverse in the direction of turn each time you begin a descent.

The Vertical "S," Double Reverse In this exercise, reverse the direction of turn with each change in vertical direction.

Recovery from Unusual Attitudes

Situations can occur when you may become confused regarding the attitude and performance of the aircraft. Regard any position, even in a mild deviation from the attitude desired, *in which you are confused,* as an unusual attitude. These situations may result from turbulence, vertigo, wingmen getting lost from leader, carelessness in cross-checking, *and failure to cross-check the instruments adequately when you suspect partial instrument failure.*

If the aircraft is in a moderate attitude, you can usually reorient yourself by establishing level flight and immediately resuming a normal cross-check.

RECOVERY PROCEDURES WITH NONTUMBLING ATTITUDE INDICATORS

The reliability of these instruments is well proved. Using them properly will permit rapid, positive recovery; even from extreme attitudes that can be entered easily in large and small high-performance aircraft.

Bank control will aggravate the attitude if misused, and will assist the recovery materially if properly used. Observe these principles:

In a DIVE, eliminating bank will aid pitch control.
In a CLIMB, using bank will aid pitch control.
Proper use of power and drag devices can aid airspeed control.

Recovery: First, verify attitude. Before taking any corrective action, verify the suspected unusual attitude by reference to the performance instruments and to the standby or copilot's attitude indicator, if available. Failure to take this step may create an unusual attitude where none previously existed, except in the indication of a faulty instrument.

Bank control by reference to the attitude indicator is of prime importance in recovery, and is simple and positive. *The bank index pointer is the key to this bank control.* Always consider it as pointing to "up"—a "sky pointer." To return to right-side-up, always roll toward the bank index pointer. Notice in Figure 9.15 that although the complete attitude may be difficult to determine immediately, you can tell quickly from the bank index pointer which way to roll to right-side-up. Many attitude indicators, in addition to the bank index pointer, have the background divided by the horizon bar into light and dark halves, representing sky and ground. This presentation will also assist in rolling right-side-up.

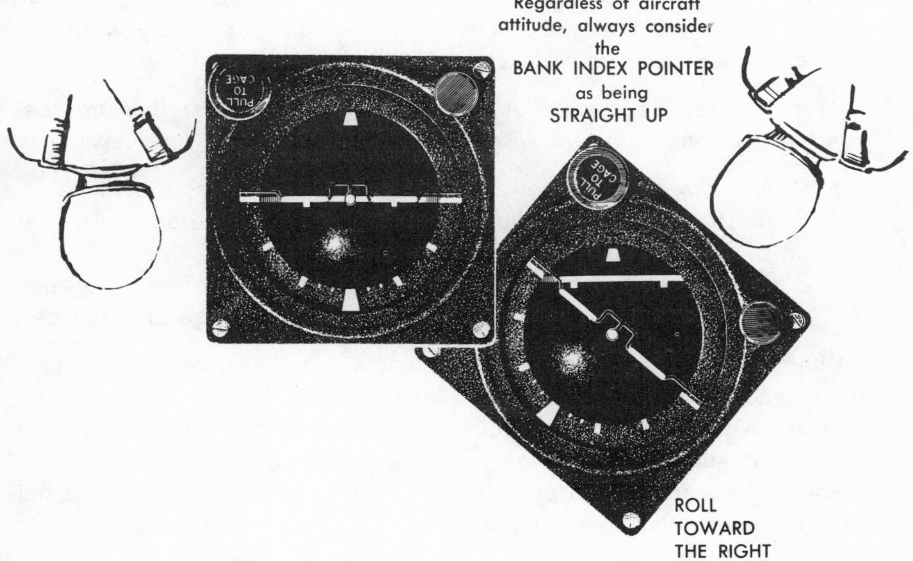

Figure 9.15 Inverted attitude recovery. At left, the aircraft is fully inverted, in level flight. At right, it is inverted, diving steeply to the left.

When you have the bank index pointer in, or moving toward, the upper half of the instrument face, decide whether you are in a climb or a dive. The airspeed indicator is usually the best indicator, but cross-check of the altimeter, vertical speed indicator, and attitude indicator will help to make this decision. Having made it, return to level flight by reference to the attitude indicator.

If you are diving, reduce power and roll level and upright. Use drag devices if appropriate for your aircraft. When at a level flight indication on the attitude indicator, resume a normal cross-check.

If you are climbing, add full power and roll, or continue your roll, until the bank index pointer *in the upper half of the case* approaches the 90° bank index mark. This will establish a banked recovery attitude which will allow you to bring the nose down to the horizon smoothly. Maintain the bank and just enough back pressure to keep seated comfortably. As the horizon and fuselage dot of the "little airplane" come together, roll the wings level, slightly nose-low, referring to the attitude indicator, and resume normal cross-check and power. In some larger aircraft, to avoid undue horizontal stabilizer side loads, level the wings first, then bring the nose down to the horizon smoothly.

RECOVERY PROCEDURES WITH PARTIAL PANEL

In the rare event an attitude indicator fails, or in aircraft equipped with attitude indicators that will tumble, a partial panel recovery with performance instruments is necessary. There are two cases:

High-Airspeed Recoveries: Airspeed indication is higher than that desired, or its trend is toward an indication which is higher than desired:

1. *Reduce power* to prevent excessive airspeed and loss of altitude.
2. *Center the turn needle and ball* with coordinated aileron and rudder pressures, in order to level the wings.
3. *Stop the descending indication* of the altimeter and the increasing airspeed by back pressure on the stick. If in a jet, use drag devices.

Change all components of control almost simultaneously with only a slight lead of one over the other, however, this lead is essential and *must* be in the above order. Suppose you start a turn and suddenly the airspeed is increasing, the turn needle is way to one side, and the altimeter is "unwinding." To apply back pressure to raise the nose would simply tighten the spiral. At this point, you would lose control, *unless you reduced power and centered the turn needle first.*

Use smooth control pressures. You are in level-flight pitch attitude when the movements on the airspeed indicator and altimeter stop before reversing their directions. Watch these instruments closely to avoid going into an uncontrolled climb. As their movements stop, observe the attitude indicator and VSI as a cross-check, and as the airspeed indicator comes back to the desired airspeed, support that airspeed with the necessary power.

Low-Airspeed Recoveries: If the airspeed indication is lower than that desired, or is decreasing rapidly toward an indication lower than that desired, this is the procedure:

1. *Apply power.*
2. *Center the turn needle and ball* to level the wings by coordinated rudder and aileron pressure.
3. *Apply forward stick pressure* to increase the airspeed and prevent stalling.

Here, again, while the actions are almost simultaneous, they must be done in the above order. With a rapidly decreasing or low airspeed, a stall may be imminent. The first thing needed is airspeed; without it, a worse condition from which lack of altitude may prevent recovery, may result. Use the same primary instruments as for high-speed recoveries. Make a smooth but large power adjustment. If in a jet, use 100% power because of the slow acceleration characteristic. In multiengined aircraft, be sure that power is balanced between wings. Better no power than high power on one wing and none on the other if near or below the critical single-engine speed.

Use caution when applying the forward pressure. Avoid an excessive and prolonged amount of forward pressure which in certain jets could result in a flame-out and, in any aircraft, could result in an unusually steep dive attitude which might require a subsequent high-speed recovery. Allow the airspeed to increase to a safe value before you apply back pressure to level out. Make this back pressure smooth to avoid a secondary stalled condition. Pitch attitude is level when the altimeter stops. When the airspeed builds up to the desired value, reduce the power to that needed to support it.

Because of the very nature of the occurrence of an unusual attitude, make the recovery prompt. Excessive loss of altitude is undesirable and may be dangerous. Begin a climb or descent back to the original altitude and heading as soon as you have regained full control of the aircraft and a safe airspeed.

If your recovery from an unusual attitude occurs while making a low approach, consider going to the emergency altitude at once to collect your wits and make sure of your position before trying again.

RELAXATION

Instrument flying requires a state of mind and body best described as alert detachment. One is detached from natural references and stimuli and is virtually suspended solidly in another world in harmony with the stable, familiar references of known attitude and power. In this state of detachment, the mind is occupied with direction, speed, time, and useful radio voices. It can respond clearly and accurately without laboring unduly with the body over control manipulations, which most of the time require only fingertip pressures anyhow. Without relaxation, this state can be neither acquired nor maintained.

Instrument Flying Procedures

As shown in Figure 9.6, an instrument flight consists of a series of connected basic maneuvers. Instrument flying procedures connect these maneuvers using the navigation instruments. Precise execution of these procedures is the means by which single aircraft use the system of airways and air traffic control facilities safely in marginal or adverse weather; precise execution also permits the orderly flow of the large volume of air traffic, particularly in congested areas.

Instrument navigation is essentially dead-reckoning navigation using radio aids; the technique is discussed in Chapter 11, and brings us to the point of the approach and landing at destination.

There are various types of approaches, as shown in Figure 9.21. Air Traffic Control (ATC), in giving the approach clearance, will usually specify the type of approach. Pilots should indicate the type of approach desired on their initial radio contact with approach control.

HOLDING

When traffic is heavy, it is occasionally necessary to wait for other traffic. This is *holding.* It is done over a radio fix specified by air traffic control. The fix may be the intersection of bearings from two stations, a DME distance and bearing from a station, or a station itself. While holding, the aircraft flies an elliptical pattern designed and oriented to facilitate the subsequent descent, the final approach, and the landing.

The pattern flown during holding receives airspace protection when entered and flown as prescribed in the Airman's Information Manual. The standard no-wind length of the *inbound* legs of the holding pattern

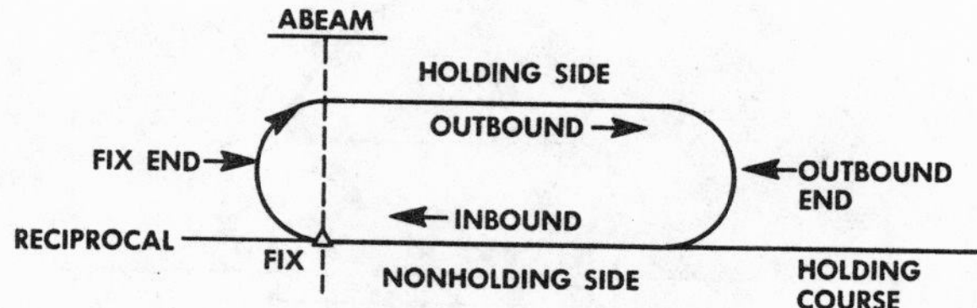

Figure 9.16 Holding pattern basic terminology. A standard pattern with right turns is illustrated. Nonstandard pattern is made with left turns. Check AIM for required airspeeds for specific aircraft. Generally, speeds are (IAS maximum) propeller, 175 knots; civil turbojet up to 6000 ft, 200 knots; 6000 to 14,000 ft, 210 knots; above 14,000 ft, 230 knots. Turboprop aircraft may climb in holding pattern at normal climb speed; turbojet aircraft may climb at 310 knots or less. *(Redrawn from Airman's Information Manual.)*

is one minute when holding at or below 14,000 ft and 1½ min when holding above that altitude. With DME, the maximum *outbound* leg is specified in miles.

Pattern Entry Enter the holding pattern at not more than the maximum airspeed, slowing down when three minutes from the holding fix. When entering, use the pattern shown in Figure 9.17.

Timing The *initial* outbound leg should not exceed the appropriate time depending on altitude, though aircraft holding at 100 KIAS or less may fly 2 min on the initial outbound leg. The inbound timing of subsequent legs is maintained by adjusting outbound legs. Start the outbound timing when the aircraft is abeam the holding fix or wings-level, whichever occurs *last.* Start inbound timing whenever the aircraft crosses the inbound holding course or wings-level, whichever occurs *first.*

Wind-Drift Correction Corrections are made on the outbound leg so that the aircraft will track the inbound holding course when inbound. The rate of turn can be adjusted between 15° of bank and approximately 30° of bank to lengthen or shorten the radius of turn. Less than 15° bank in high-speed aircraft risks going outside the holding airspace.

An understanding of wind-drift effect at various airspeeds is very helpful in maintaining courses in holding patterns. Table 9.1 is a helpful guide.

Meeting Expected Approach Time The holding pattern may be shortened but never lengthened to meet approach times; plan to leave the holding fix to arrive over the Initial Approach Fix (IAF) at an "expect

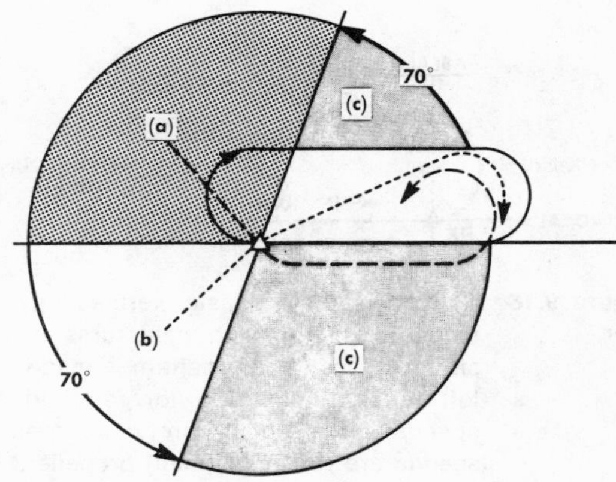

Figure 9.17 Entering the holding pattern. (a) Parallel procedure: Parallel holding course, turn left, and return to holding fix or intercept holding course. (b) Teardrop procedure: Proceed on outbound track of 30° or less to holding course, turn right to intercept holding course. (c) Direct entry procedure: Turn right and fly the pattern. *(Redrawn from Airman's Information Manual.)*

TABLE 9.1
90° Crosswind Effect

TAS	*30° Drift Correction Will Correct for a Wind of:*	*15° Drift Correction Will Correct for a Wind of:*	*10° Drift Correction Will Correct for a Wind of:*
150	75 knots	37 knots	25 knots
200	100	50	33
300	150	75	50
400	200	100	67
500	250	125	83
600	300	150	100

approach time." To make the adjustment, consider rates of turn and length of outbound and inbound legs.

EN-ROUTE DESCENT

When cruising at higher altitudes, you may request an en-route descent for approach, either to the IAF or the FAF, or to some other point from which you can conveniently continue. You may request vectors en route. This manner of descent is customary and greatly expedites the flow of air traffic. The traffic at the time will govern. A transponder-equipped aircraft has a great advantage during this maneuver because it is always clearly identified and does not need to make identifying turns. These and other time-consuming maneuvers may be necessary to insure positive identification and separation from other aircraft.

The controller and the pilot must both understand the type of approach to be made on reaching the IAF. Range, weather, desired descent rate, and low-altitude fuel consumption are factors to be considered before requesting an en-route descent.

INSTRUMENT APPROACH CRITERIA

Approach procedures are designed according to the FAA manual, *United States Standard for Terminal Instrument Approaches (TERPS).* These procedures are designed to provide a safe, orderly method for proceeding from the en-route structure to the point at which a visual approach to the runway may be made.

Because of differing performance, approach plates for each airfield define minima or limits for each category of aircraft. The categories are based upon maximum gross landing weight and the appropriate approach speed for that weight and aircraft. Speeds are computed at 1.3 of stall speed for the aircraft in approach configuration.

Category A Speed 50 to 90 knots, weight 30,000 lb or less
Category B Speed 91 to 120 knots, weight 30,001 to 60,000 lb.
Category C Speed 121 to 140 knots, weight 60,001 to 150,000 lb
Category D Speed 141 to 165 knots, weight over 150,000 lb
Category E Speed over 165 knots, weight not considered

An instrument approach usually consists of four segments: initial, intermediate, final, and missed approach. The Initial Approach Fix (IAF), Procedure Turn (PT), the Final Approach Fix (FAF), and the missed approach itself, or transition to landing are key points. Other terminology used in deciding whether to land or execute a missed approach are:

MDA "Minimum Descent Altitude" is the lowest altitude in feet MSL to which one may descend on final approach, or during circling to land maneuvering, when no electronic glide slope is provided.

DH "Decision Height" is the aircraft altitude MSL at which a decision must be made during a precision approach, ILS or precision approach radar (PAR), either to continue the approach or to execute a missed approach.

HAA "Height Above Touchdown" is the height of the DH or MDA above the highest elevation in the touchdown zone, published in conjunction with straight-in minimums.

The four above are published in the Airman's Information Manual with details of their use. Procedures using these criteria are designed to provide adequate maneuvering area and obstacle clearance altitude, proper runway alignment and descent gradients for each category of aircraft.

Nonprecision Instrument Approaches

The instrument approach, whether by VOR, VORTAC, or ADF is a simple blending of two skills: basic instrument flying and precise navigation. Both must be done regardless of the effect of wind or weather. A third vital element essential to any instrument flying, and particularly to approaches, is the judgment and personal discipline required to decide to go to the alternate destination when appropriate.

PRECAUTIONS

Planning The best approaches are made when the pilot has studied the approach plate and possible traffic, radio, terrain, airborne equipment, or other pertinent factors before taking off. At that time he will fix in his mind the circumstances under which he will proceed to the alternate destination. This is particularly true if the approach is to be made at night.

Radio Tuning and Checking Flying on the wrong radio signal has brought more than one pilot to grief, but certain habits will prevent it.

ALWAYS check the identification of any navigational aid station and monitor it during flight.

ALWAYS utilize *all* suitable navigation equipment aboard the aircraft and cross-check heading and bearing information.

ALWAYS carefully cross-check navigational aids and ground check points if possible before overflying an ETA. (Chapter 11.)

ALWAYS check NOTAMS and Flight Information Publications (FLIP) documents before flight for possible malfunctions or limitations on navigational aids to be used. Be sure the field and the approach runway you plan to use are available.

ALWAYS discontinue use of any suspected navigational aid and if necessary, confirm aircraft position with radar or other equipment.

TACAN AND VOR/DME (VORTAC) HOLDING

Distance-measuring equipment provides virtually an unlimited number of holding fixes and enables you to fly the holding pattern measured by actual distances rather than time. FAA Air Traffic Control maintains responsibility for defining holding patterns which provide vertical and horizontal separation and terrain clearance. With DME, patterns are different for various altitudes, speeds, and areas. The standard right-hand pattern is usually used.

In ATC parlance, holding fixes are called *feeder points.* From these points aircraft are told to hold or approach. The fix is defined in holding instructions in these terms: "Hold southwest of the 30 nautical mile fix on the 045 degree radial, 8 mile legs, left turns."

Because it is not necessary to pass over an intersection or station before entering a holding pattern, entry is simply a matter of maintaining course, either inbound or outbound, on the specified radial. Then at the proper distance indicated on the DME odometer, turn in the proper direction to enter a normal elliptical holding pattern, remembering that the nonstandard pattern has left turns. If a nonstandard pattern is desired,

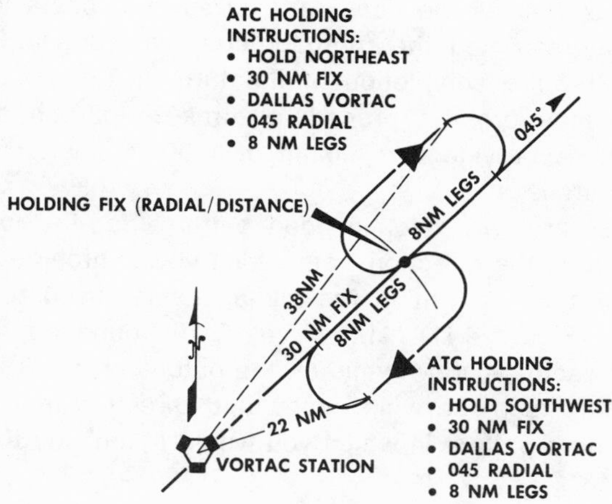

Figure 9.18 Holding on a VORTAC or TACAN fix. The direction of holding is relative to the holding fix—*not* the station. Note these are standard patterns, with right-hand turns. If ATC desires non-standard pattern, the controller will direct "Left turns" in holding instructions.

the controller will direct "left turns" in holding instructions. The length of both outbound and inbound legs is the direct DME distance.

Procedure Turns A procedure turn is a maneuver used to reverse course after passing a fix to save time, restrict the maneuvering area, and insure return to the fix along a specified inbound course. It is primarily used at low altitude to place the aircraft on the final approach course. While the procedure turn is depicted on some approach charts by a specific pattern, the actual pattern to be used is at the pilot's discretion. It must, however, remain within a definite airspace called the procedure turn maneuvering area, and must observe the minimum maneuvering altitudes published on the current approach plate, as in Figures 9.19 through 9.24.

The procedure turn pattern shown in Figure 9.19 is a holdover from low-frequency radio range (beam) procedures. They are excellent in slow aircraft because they provide a more precise orientation in any wind conditions which could give large drift angles. They have the disadvantage that with the precision of VOR bearing indications they are unduly cumbersome and require much more time to complete. The normal indication of a procedure turn is the barbed arrow (⟶) located on the "depicted side" of the final approach course.

The procedure turn maneuvering area provides safe separation from other aircraft, as well as the necessary terrain and obstacle clearance. If it is in any way restricted, the approach chart will show it. For example, the chart may require completion of the turn in 7 nm instead of the normal 10, or may prohibit procedure turns in certain sectors. The published altitudes provide a minimum of 1000 ft clearance within the procedure turn area.

In Figure 9.25 are two recommended patterns for the turn. The one used depends upon the direction from which you approach the fix. Enter the teardrop or parallel turn in the same manner used for entering a holding pattern (Figure 9.17). Always set the inbound approach course in the course selector window while on the outbound leg. It is, of course, very important to keep the wind speed and direction in mind in order to avoid selecting a pattern in which you would fly outside the maneuvering area.

If you fly inbound with the outbound course set in the course selector window, FROM will, of course, appear in the TO-FROM window, *and you will have to fly away from, rather than toward, the CDI to center it.*

Flying the Teardrop Procedure Turn As you approach the station, select an outbound course which is on the side indicated for maneuvering on the approach chart: the "depicted side." Turn immediately after station passage to intercept the outbound course, level the wings, set the outbound course in the course window, and note the time. Complete the

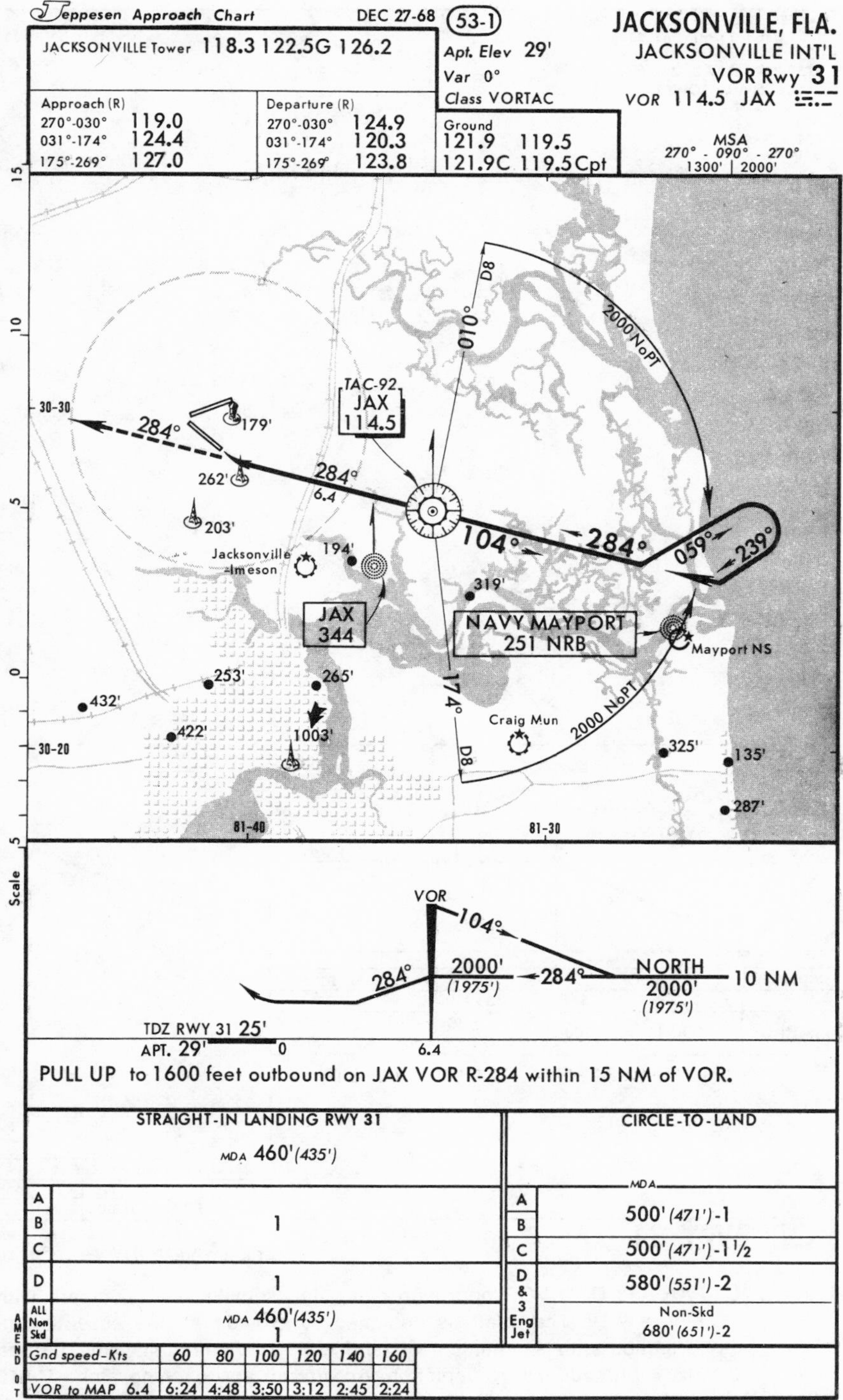

Figure 9.19 Jeppesen VOR approach plate, Jacksonville, Fla. Commercially designed and published. Extensively used by general aviation aircraft. Note depiction of obstructions. Procedure turn depiction is not mandatory; teardrop or parallel pattern, or the one depicted, may be flown. *(Courtesy of Jeppesen & Co.)*

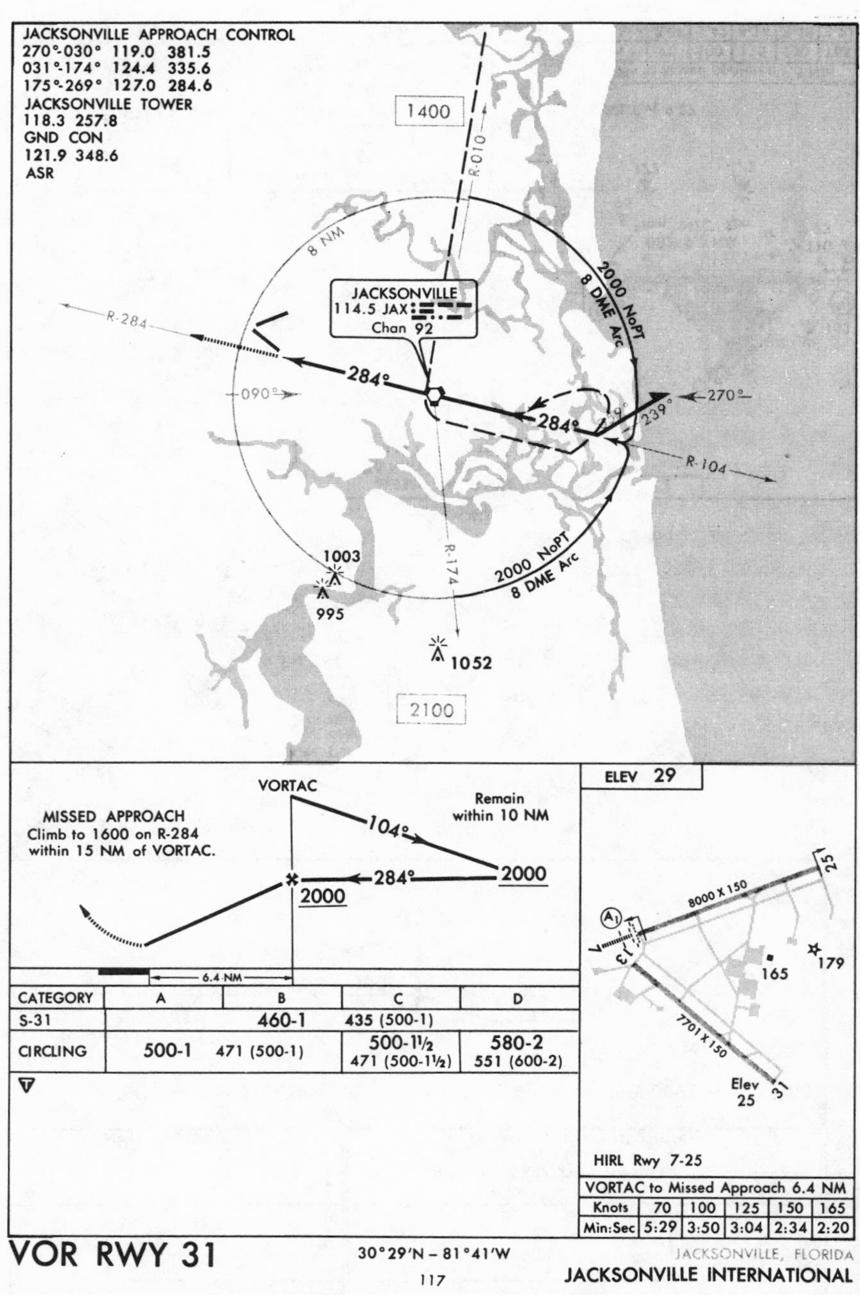

Figure 9.20 FAA and DOD VOR approach plate, Jacksonville, Fla. Compare with Figure 9.19. This plate is designed to provide all the essential information with a minimum of confusion or distraction. Note barbed arrow procedure turn depiction. An aircraft approaching along R-010 might make the parallel pattern shown in the broken line. Note that no procedure turn is required if final approach course is entered from the 8 DME arc.

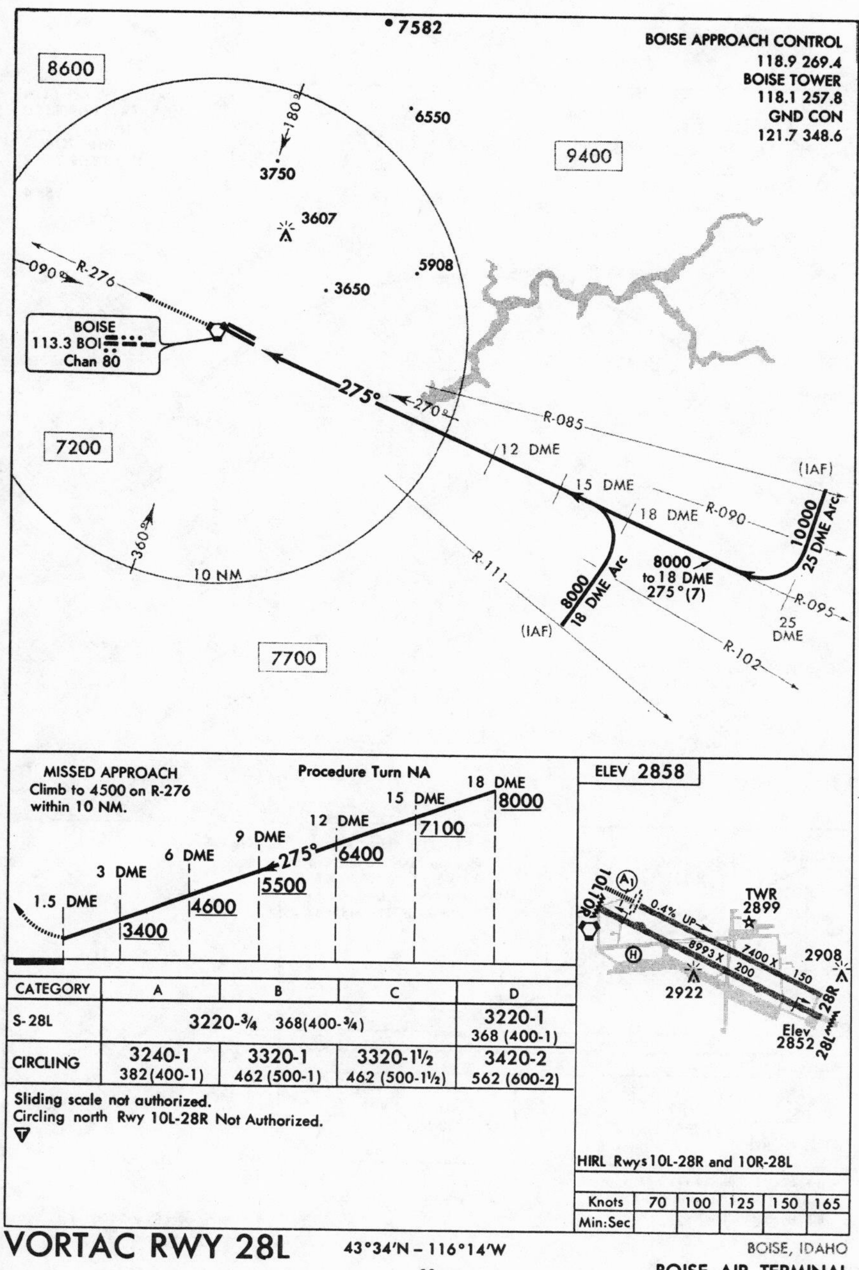

CATEGORY	A	B	C	D
S-28L	3220-¾ 368(400-¾)			3220-1 368 (400-1)
CIRCLING	3240-1 382(400-1)	3320-1 462 (500-1)	3320-1½ 462 (500-1½)	3420-2 562 (600-2)

Sliding scale not authorized.
Circling north Rwy 10L-28R Not Authorized.

Figure 9.21 VORTAC approach plate, Boise, Idaho. Note rate of descent indicated by DME distance and altitude, and runway lighting class. See Figure 9.37.

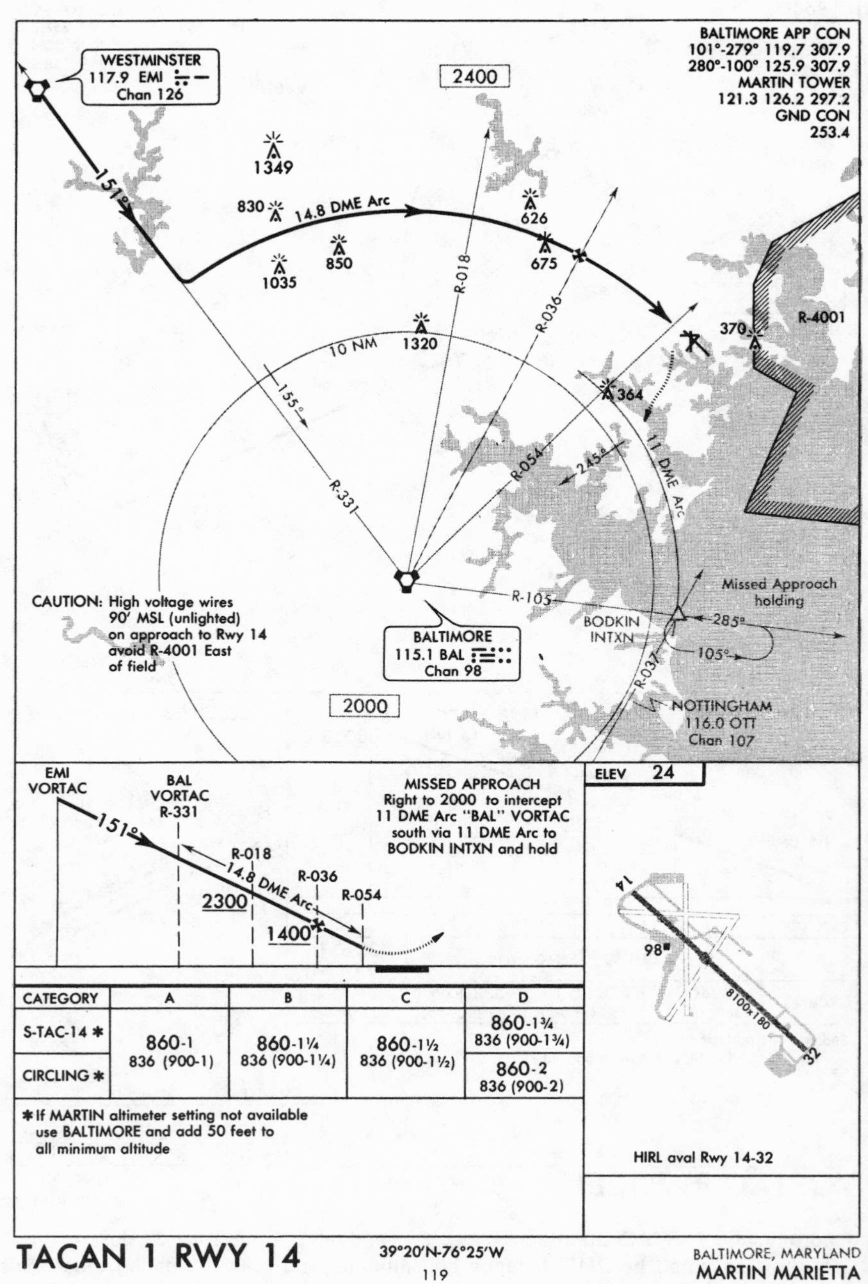
BALTIMORE APP CON
101°-279° 119.7 307.9
280°-100° 125.9 307.9
MARTIN TOWER
121.3 126.2 297.2
GND CON
253.4
WESTMINSTER
117.9 EMI
Chan 126
2400
1349
830
14.8 DME Arc
626
850
675
1035
151°
R-018
R-036
1320
10 NM
370
R-4001
155°
364
R-054
245°
11 DME Arc
R-331
CAUTION: High voltage wires 90′ MSL (unlighted) on approach to Rwy 14 avoid R-4001 East of field
R-105
Missed Approach holding
BODKIN INTXN
285°
105°
BALTIMORE
115.1 BAL
Chan 98
R-037
2000
NOTTINGHAM
116.0 OTT
Chan 107
EMI VORTAC
BAL VORTAC R-331
MISSED APPROACH
Right to 2000 to intercept 11 DME Arc "BAL" VORTAC south via 11 DME Arc to BODKIN INTXN and hold
ELEV 24
R-018
R-036
R-054
2300
1400
14
98
8100x180
32
CATEGORY | A | B | C | D
S-TAC-14 ✱ | 860-1 836 (900-1) | 860-1¼ 836 (900-1¼) | 860-1½ 836 (900-1½) | 860-1¾ 836 (900-1¾)
CIRCLING ✱ | | | | 860-2 836 (900-2)
✱ If MARTIN altimeter setting not available use BALTIMORE and add 50 feet to all minimum altitude
HIRL aval Rwy 14-32
TACAN 1 RWY 14
39°20′N-76°25′W
119
BALTIMORE, MARYLAND
MARTIN MARIETTA

Figure 9.22 TACAN arc approach, Martin Marietta, Baltimore, Md.

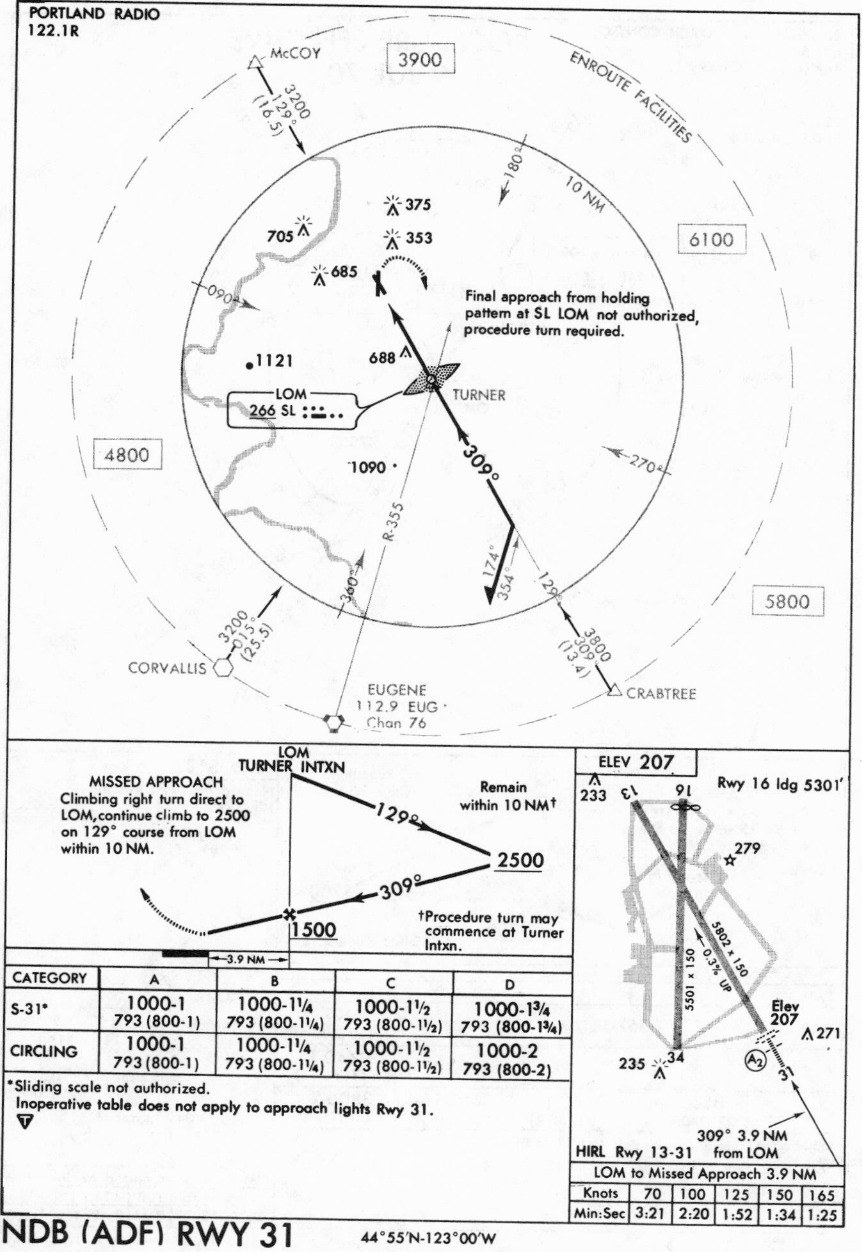

CATEGORY	A	B	C	D
S-31*	1000-1 793 (800-1)	1000-1¼ 793 (800-1¼)	1000-1½ 793 (800-1½)	1000-1¾ 793 (800-1¾)
CIRCLING	1000-1 793 (800-1)	1000-1¼ 793 (800-1¼)	1000-1½ 793 (800-1½)	1000-2 793 (800-2)

*Sliding scale not authorized.
Inoperative table does not apply to approach lights Rwy 31.

LOM to Missed Approach 3.9 NM					
Knots	70	100	125	150	165
Min:Sec	3:21	2:20	1:52	1:34	1:25

Figure 9.23 Nondirectional beacon ADF approach, Salem, Ore. Note that in this approach, an outer marker beacon is colocated with the radio beacon. This greatly facilitates station passage identification, though many ADF approaches are designed without the marker.

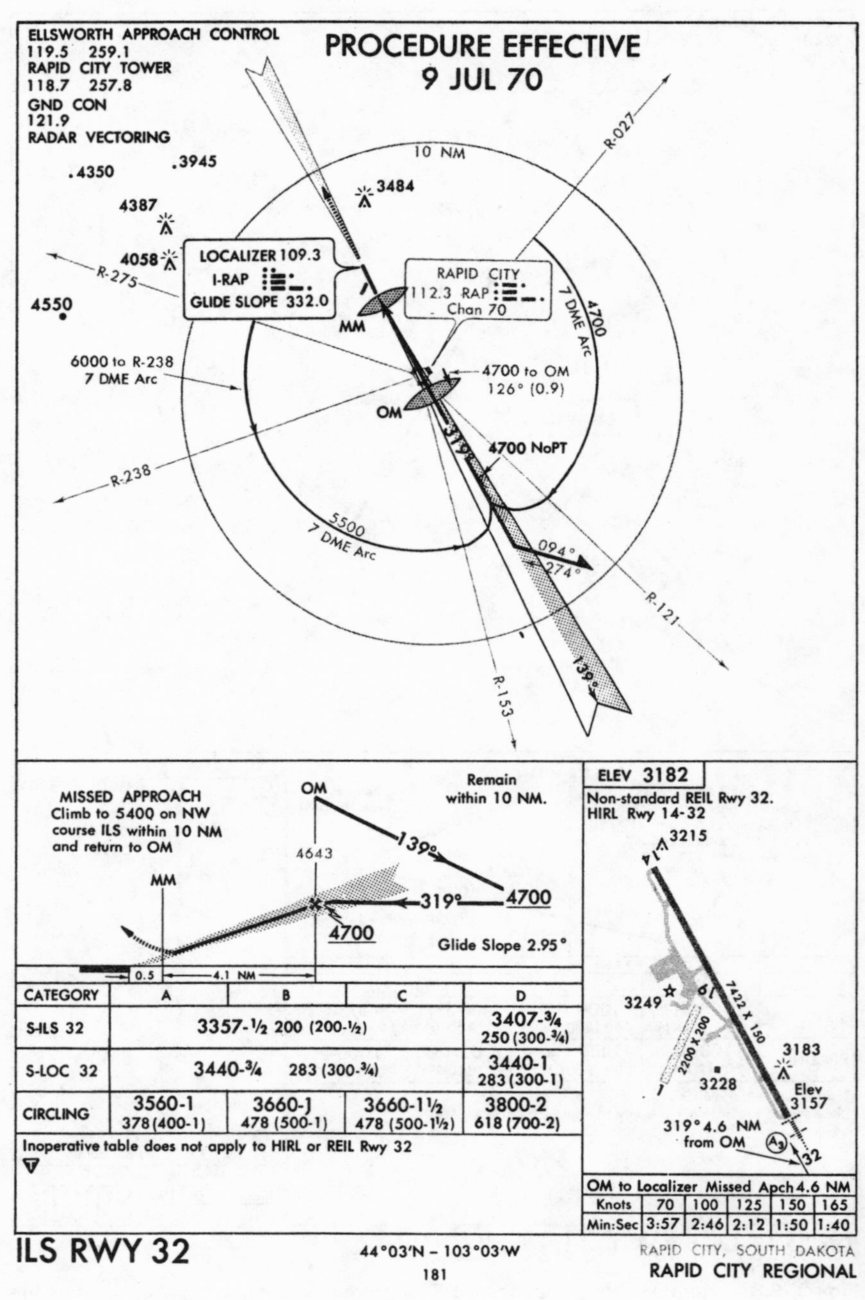

Figure 9.24 ILS approach plate, Rapid City, S.D.

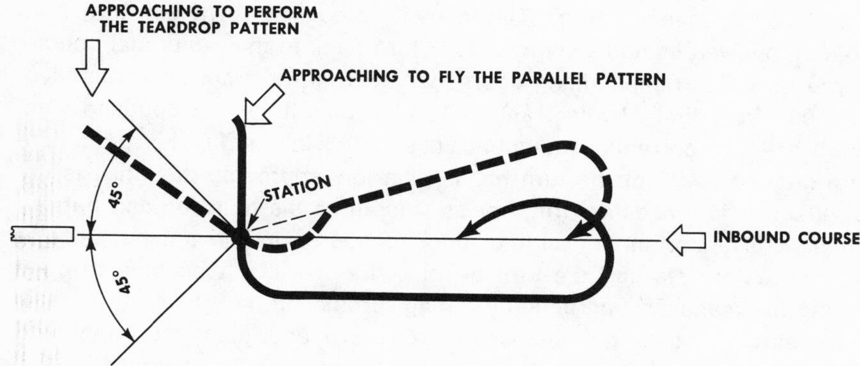

Figure 9.25 Standard flight patterns for performing the procedure turn. The 45° arcs are a general guide; to enter the teardrop from outside this arc is likely to use too much maneuvering space. *(Courtesy of U.S. Air Force.)*

interception and maintain the outbound course, applying an appropriate drift correction and descending to the procedure turn altitude. The teardrop is flown as in the holding pattern.

Set the inbound course in the course window before turning inbound. When the time outbound has elapsed, begin the turn to the inbound course. During the latter part of this turn adjust the rate of turn, if necessary, to roll out with the CDI centered. If the CDI is still fully deflected during the latter part of this turn, roll out 45° short and proceed with a normal course interception. If you fly through the course before completing the turn, continue turning and roll out to intercept from the other side. Remember that the procedure turn must be completed within the maneuvering area, above the minimum altitude. You may begin your descent to the FAF altitude when the aircraft is inbound and within 20° of the published inbound course.

Flying the Parallel Procedure Turn If you approach the VOR station on a heading that is not within less than 45° of the reciprocal of the inbound course, plan to fly the parallel pattern entering as shown in Figure 9.25. Immediately after station passage, turn to the reciprocal of the inbound course. When the wings are level, note the time, and begin your descent to the procedure turn altitude. The length of the outbound leg depends on your ground speed. If TAS exceeds 180 knots while on the reciprocal of the inbound course heading on a parallel pattern, turn at least 20° toward the reciprocal of the inbound course to avoid getting outside the maneuvering area. Turn inbound, and intercept and maintain the inbound course just as for the teardrop turn.

The 90° Procedure Turn This maneuver consists of a 90° turn from course followed immediately by a 270° turn back to the reciprocal course. If you have been maintaining course with a wind-drift correction applied, turn 90° from that heading, and roll out with drift of the opposite sign. (With a $-10°$ correction outbound, use $+10°$ inbound.) This procedure turn may be used for the turn phase of a low approach, though it is not as effective for checking drift, nor as smooth as the teardrop and parallel turns. It is important to set the inbound course in the course selector window before starting the turn because there will not be time to do it during the maneuver, particularly during turbulence.

Be sure to study the published procedure and plan your approach *through the missed approach procedure* before you reach the IAF.

Obtain your clearance from Approach Control. At the IAF, turn immediately to the outbound course of the procedure turn you have selected. Note the time, set the desired outbound course in the course-selector window, and report your position, time, and altitude to Approach Control. The flight manual for your aircraft will specify when to accomplish the prelanding check; usually it is done on this leg. Complete the procedure turn and establish your drift carefully on the final approach course.

On arrival at FAF, note the time carefully and report. If the station-to-field heading is different from the final approach course, turn to the former and reset the course selector. Maintain this course with the CDI centered. Station-to-field clearance permits you to descend immediately to the Minimum Descent Altitude. By doing this before the station-to-point-of-missed-approach time has elapsed, you place yourself in position

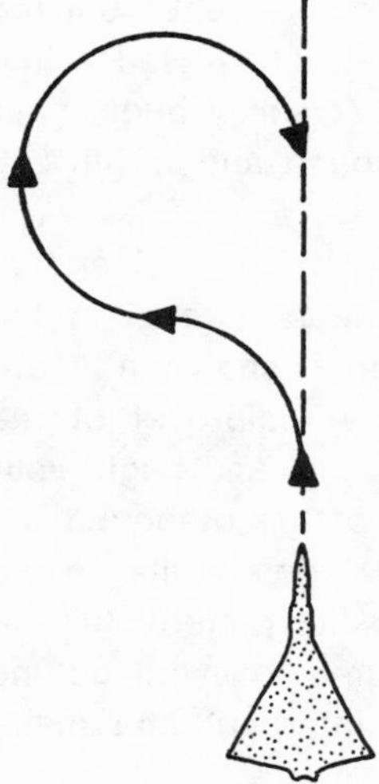

Figure 9.26 Ninety-degree procedure turn.

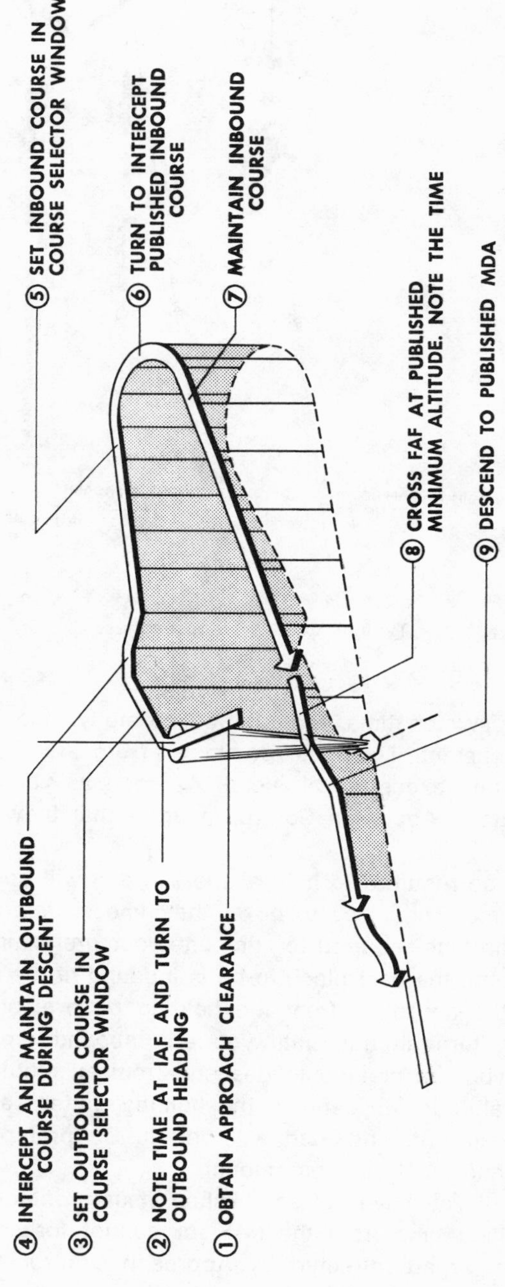

① OBTAIN APPROACH CLEARANCE
② NOTE TIME AT IAF AND TURN TO OUTBOUND HEADING
③ SET OUTBOUND COURSE IN COURSE SELECTOR WINDOW
④ INTERCEPT AND MAINTAIN OUTBOUND COURSE DURING DESCENT
⑤ SET INBOUND COURSE IN COURSE SELECTOR WINDOW
⑥ TURN TO INTERCEPT PUBLISHED INBOUND COURSE
⑦ MAINTAIN INBOUND COURSE
⑧ CROSS FAF AT PUBLISHED MINIMUM ALTITUDE. NOTE THE TIME
⑨ DESCEND TO PUBLISHED MDA

Figure 9.27 Typical VOR low-altitude approach. The key points of a low-altitude approach are the Initial Approach Fix (IAF) passage, and final approach. *(Courtesy of U.S. Air Force.)*

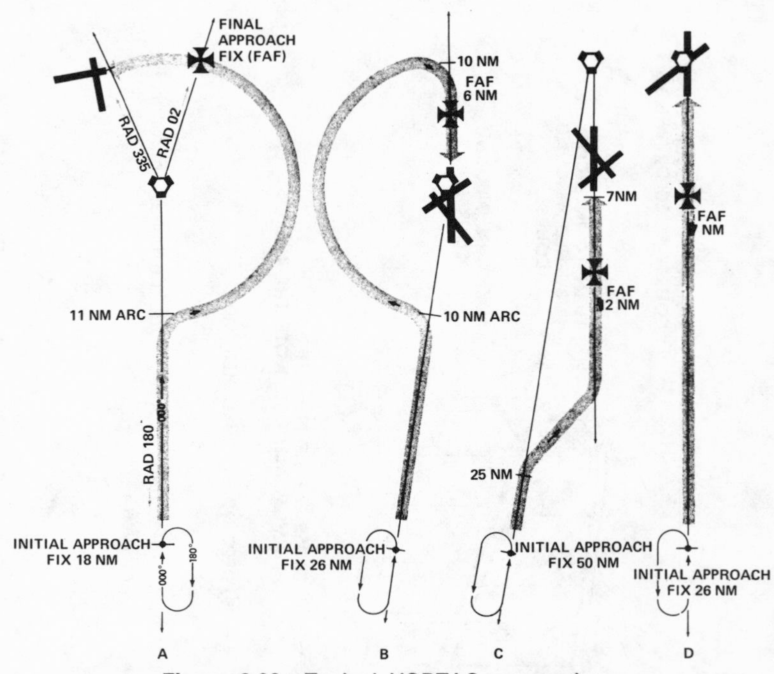

Figure 9.28 Typical VORTAC approaches.

to land more quickly. Watch time and altitude carefully, and keep the approach airspeed constant. The most common errors are to descend too late and to maintain excessive airspeed. As soon as you have the runway in sight, report to Approach Control in order that they clear the next aircraft.

You will frequently be required to hold at the IAF and will be given an expected approach time. The place to be at that time is determined by the type of aircraft, the time required to complete your prelanding check, and your proficiency, but the best place to be is inbound at the approach fix. You may make the approach from the holding pattern, but remain above the procedure turn altitude until you are inbound on the final approach course. If you are cleared to descend from an altitude above the initial approach altitude, descend in the holding pattern as quickly as your proficiency, aircraft, and load will permit. Be prompt, but be unhurried. Precision and safety are paramount.

Missed Approach If you have not established visual contact with the runway by the specified time from the FAF, or cannot for any reason make a safe landing, or are directed by Approach Control, you must execute the specified missed approach procedure.

The time-distance tables published on Approach and Landing Charts are based on zero wind. Therefore, you *must* consider the existing wind to determine the proper FAF-to-point-of-missed-approach time. Be prepared to execute a missed approach from every letdown; after you have started a missed approach and established your climb, call Approach Control and state your intentions, or request instructions.

TACAN and VORTAC Approaches Because TACAN and VORTAC have range information as well as bearing information, procedures using this greater flexibility have been provided. There is one primary difference: The FAF or the IAF or both may be designated along a radial at certain distances. A procedure turn is usually unnecessary to execute a VORTAC approach. Because they are the same from this viewpoint, VORTAC is used to mean VORTAC, TACAN, or VOR/DME in further discussion.

During precision approaches, when shifting to the ILS frequency, distance information will not be available unless the DME tuner is separate or there is a dual installation.

The Arc Approach This approach requires that you fly the aircraft along an arc around the VORTAC station a specified distance out (Figure 9.29). The more smoothly one can turn from an inbound course to an arc, or leave an arc on a final approach course, the more precise arc approaches can be. To estimate the lead needed to begin a turn to or from an arc, remember this general relationship: At 10 nm, 1 nm equals 6° of arc. At 200 knots and with a 3° per sec turn, one mile (or six degrees) lead will be required.

In theory it is a simple matter to remain on a particular arc, because maintaining the RMI bearing indicator at a relative bearing of 90° or 270° (wing-tip position) at all times would take you around the station in an exact circle. However, in practice, it is difficult to keep the station exactly off the wing tip, and wind effect further complicates the problem.

The arc is actually a series of straight lines. Maintaining the arc is illustrated in Figure 9.30. If in this example, you find that you will go inside the 10-nm arc to 9 nm, simply stop or reverse your turn to place the bearing indicator behind the wing tip. Make a correction appropriate to the amount you are off, but keep it less than 30° to avoid overshooting in the other direction. If, on rolling out of your initial turn, you appear to be intercepting the 11-nm arc, roll out with an angle of interception remaining, with the bearing indicator ahead of the wing tip. This will decrease your distance from the station. Remember that most arc approaches guarantee obstruction clearance for only 2 nm either side of the arc. Do not become so engrossed with maintaining the arc that you miss crossing key radials related to altitude changes or missed approaches.

Under zero wind conditions, as the bearing indicator approaches the

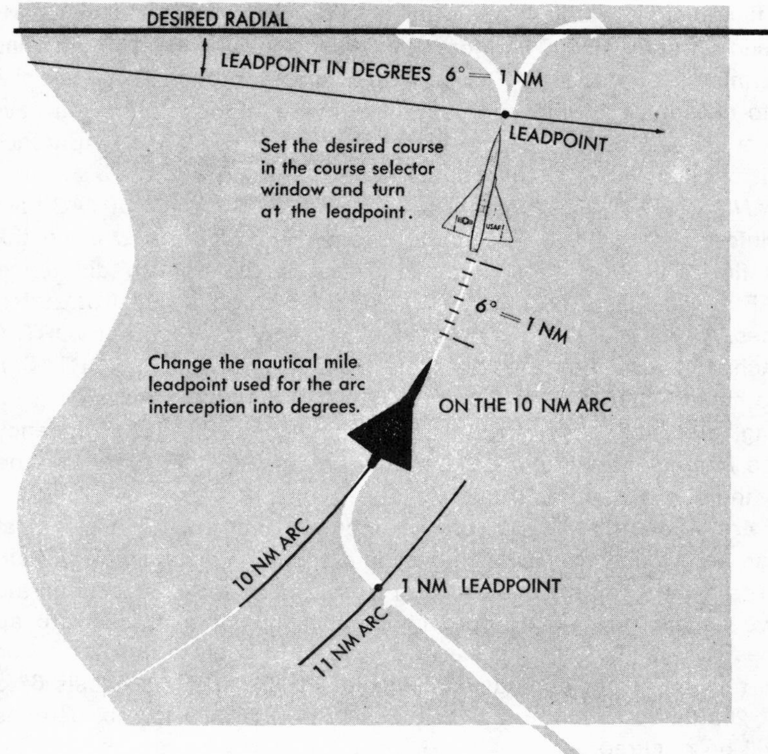

Figure 9.29 Intercepting an arc or a radial.

wing-tip position, you are as close to the station as you are going to get on that particular heading. The best technique to use to remain near the desired arc is to fly a series of short legs. If you drift off the arc, make as small a correction as is practicable to return to it. *The size of your correction is continually reflected in the relationship of the bearing indicator to the wing tip.* In a crosswind you may find it is necessary to keep the bearing indicator ahead of or behind the wing tip to remain on the arc. Because the graphic presentation of your position provided by the bearing indicator is so important, the bearing indicator is practically an essential instrument for this maneuver.

ADF HOLDING, PENETRATION, AND LOW APPROACHES

ADF procedures for holding are the same as for VOR, with the exception that the CDI is not available.

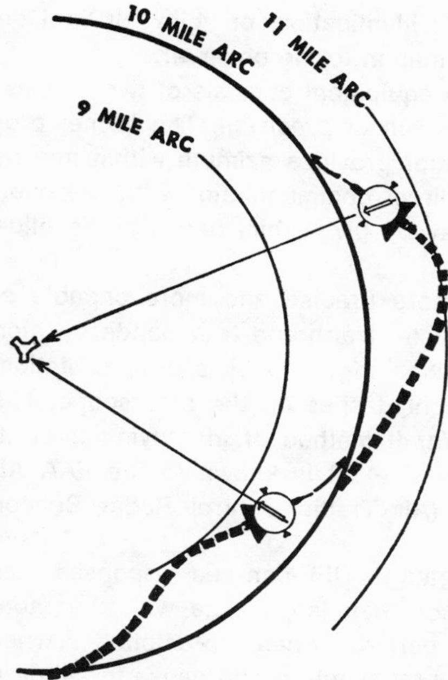

Figure 9.30 Correcting to maintain the arc.

Low approach procedures, too, are the same as with the VOR. When using ADF, measure your relative position only when the wings are level. In turns the ADF will give an erroneous indication. This is caused by the dip error in the ADF, in which the bearing indicator points directly to the station; when the aircraft is in a turn or descent close to the station, the direct line to the station may not be the actual bearing. Therefore, make precision turns to predetermined magnetic headings, and if in doubt, level the wings before reading the final approach course; then intercept the final approach course and proceed.

As in VOR approaches, planning before the approach is a prime ingredient of a safe and efficient approach.

Radar Approaches

*Ra*dio *d*etection *a*nd *r*anging (radar) equipment is based on the time differential between transmission of a radio signal and its reflection of an object, and on the ability of a reflected object to illuminate the face of a calibrated cathode ray tube, referred to as a "scope." The time lag provides distance information, and the illumination, or "blip" of light on the scope face provides position information to the observer.

Ground Controlled Approach (GCA) equipment consists of two scopes: *search* or *surveillance,* and *final approach* or *precision.* The former provides position information, and the latter provides azimuth within narrow limits and elevation. The GCA is in direct communication with the pilot, and directs him to the landing runway by giving him heading and glide slope information.

GCA equipment has been made more precise and more capable of identifying individual aircraft by the use of airborne transponders which operate by transmitting a response when triggered by a ground station. The station appears as a series of light dashes on the radarscope. The equipment, adapted from a World War II method of identifying aircraft, is called IFF (Identification Friend or Foe). It is known to the FAA Air Traffic Control System as ATCRBS (Air Traffic Control Radar Beacon System).

Ground radars equipped to interrogate the IFF can see responses from the beacon at much greater distances than is possible with the radar alone. This is particularly true during periods of heavy precipitation when the IFF return will supplement the raw radar return and cause the aircraft to show more clearly on the scope.

GCA SCOPE CHARACTERISTICS

Small aircraft will appear on the search scope up to 20 mi. Large transports will appear up to 30 mi. The search radars that have an elevation angle from —.5° to 45° above the surface can locate aircraft up to 8000 ft.

Aircraft will appear on the precision scope (PAR) when they are within 10 mi slant range from the runway. The system scans horizontally through an arc of 20° and vertically through an arc of 7°. The precision system, sometimes called AZEL (azimuth and elevation) uses a divided scope. The elevation presentation appears on the upper portion, and the azimuth or heading information appears on the lower portion. Both have the desired final approach course and glide path etched on the face of the scope.

PROCEDURE

Precision Approach (PAR) Your approach pattern may be either straight in from a fix, or rectangular as in a normal traffic pattern. The published approach chart will tell you whether radar approaches are available at your destination, and will give the frequencies needed. As soon as you have made radio contact with the approach controller, it is

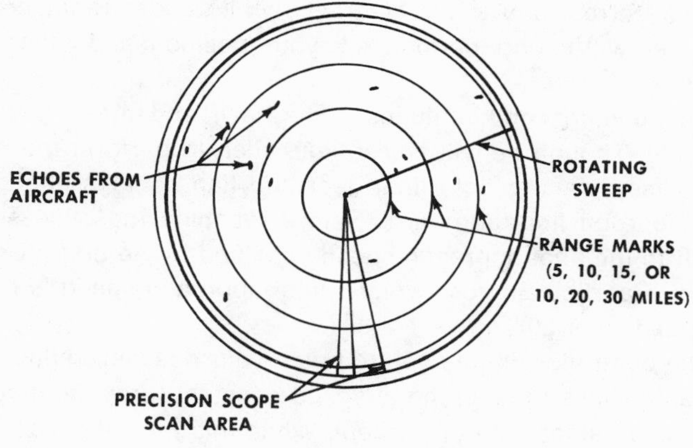

SURVEILLANCE SCOPE (ASR)

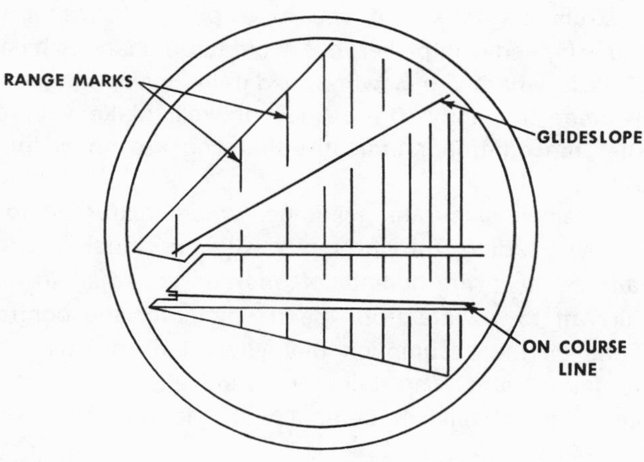

PRECISION APPROACH RADAR SCOPE (PAR)

Figure 9.31 Ground-controlled approach radar scopes.

important that you follow his instructions precisely. He will first give you any significant changes in current weather, direction of landing, runway information, missed approach instructions, and lost communications instructions.

The controller will direct you by stating headings and altitudes. His reference is the track you make after receiving initial heading instructions, so do not change the setting of your gyro-stabilized heading indicator once set. Descend promptly to the altitudes he gives. You are assured safe terrain and traffic clearance while under radar control, and the controller will report periodically your position and other traffic as appropriate.

Maintain headings and altitudes accurately, and make your turns at standard rate. Though he will advise you when to perform the prelanding check, you may elect to hold final gear and flap settings until you reach the glide slope on final approach. Before reaching the glide slope, slow the aircraft to the final approach speed specified in the aircraft operations manual; for a particular gross weight, final approach speed is roughly the stalling speed plus 30%.

When the controller directs you to begin your descent, reduce power or extend drag devices to keep the airspeed constant throughout your transition to the glide slope rate of descent. While this rate of descent is different for different ground speeds and airport glide slope angles, it will be near 500 fpm.

Establish pitch changes on the attitude indicator and cross-check performance instruments to see if you are getting desired performance. Maintain your airspeed with power, but avoid large changes by anticipating the need. This is where the power-speed relationship of your particular aircraft will come in handy if you know it well. Make your corrections promptly after the controller indicates that you are above or below the glide slope.

Maintain extremely accurate headings. When instructed to turn right or left to a new heading, turn promptly with coordinated turns. *Use an angle of bank equal to the number of degrees you wish to turn.* Do not allow the aircraft to deviate from the heading, for the controller bases his corrections on the assumption that you are flying his last assigned heading. He cannot otherwise determine wind effect.

If you have not established contact with the runway environment at

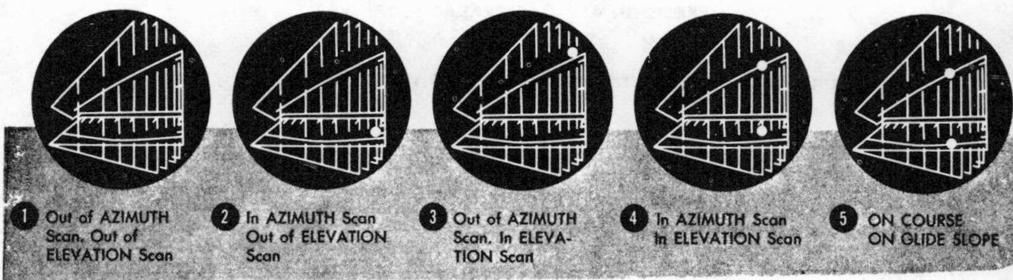

Figure 9.32 How aircraft look to the PAR controller. In normal use, scopes are more cluttered with ground reflections and other interference; however, if the controller cannot see you clearly, he will advise you of this fact, and direct you to execute a missed approach.

DH on a precision approach (PAR), or missed approach point on a surveillance approach (ASR), execute the missed approach procedure.

During the entire approach, be particularly aware of the continuity of the controller's voice. *If you suspect that you have lost contact, query the controller, and act immediately to discontinue the approach.*

The Surveillance Approach The surveillance (ASR) radar is not as precise as the PAR and cannot provide height information. It is used when precision approach radar is not available for the landing runway.

The traffic pattern and procedures are the same, except that instead of controlling your descent with reference to a precision glide slope, the controller will advise you when you are at the proper distance out on final to start your descent, and then will advise you to descend to MDA or minimum altitude.

Surveillance approach minima are higher than those for precision approaches because of the decreased accuracy of the ASR scope and the lack of altitude information.

Gyro-Out Approach If your directional indicator has failed, or if you are flying an aircraft without a stabilized direction indicator, you may make a gyro-out approach, using either precision or surveillance radars. In this approach, the only difference is that the controller will advise you to make standard rate turns during the traffic pattern phase and half standard rate turns during the approach phase. Execute turns immediately on hearing the words "Turn right" or "Turn left." Stop the turn immediately on hearing "Stop turn."

VOICE PROCEDURES

Because the radar approach system is based entirely upon voice contact, you must use precise, crisp voice procedures. After the initial contact, identify your aircraft by the last three numbers of the serial number or the name and two numbers—"Smokey 26." During the approach repeat all headings, altitudes, and altimeter settings, and acknowledge all other instructions.

Instrument Landing Systems (ILS)

The ILS is a precision approach system designed to permit landings under lower ceiling and visibility conditions than is possible with other radio aids. To do this, ILS provides extremely accurate course alignment and glide-slope descent information during the approach to the runway.

GROUND EQUIPMENT

Localizer transmitters are installed approximately 1000 ft beyond and 300 ft to the side of the far end of the ILS runway with the antenna in line with the runway centerline. The localizer transmits 90-Hz and 150-Hz signals on opposite sides of the centerline to provide course information. The 150-Hz signal is always on the right as you approach from the outer marker to the runway, and forms the "blue" sector. The 90-Hz signal is always on the left and forms the "yellow" sector. The signals overlap along the runway centerline extended. The resulting overlap area forms a course line of equal signal strength.

The course through the outer marker is called the *front course.* Most localizers have a second transmitter which provides also a *back course* extending in the opposite direction. While some airfields have published approaches which use the back course, glide slope information is usually not available.

A reliable localizer will provide a usable signal for a distance of at least 25 mi in a sector 10° either side of the course line at an altitude of 1000 ft above the terrain. You could expect to receive the localizer a distance of 40 mi at 5000 ft, or 80 mi at 10,000 ft.

Localizers use only odd decimal frequencies between 108.0 and 111.9 mHz (for example, 109.9). They broadcast a continuous three-letter coded station identification which will always be preceded by the coded letter "I" for ILS, and which may use the same letters as the local LF or VOR facility.

Glide-slope transmitters, usually installed between 750 and 1250 ft from the approach end of the runway, send 90-Hz and 150-Hz signals which overlap to form a glide slope for guidance in a vertical plane. The 150-Hz signal forms the lower portion of the glide slope, and the 90-Hz signal, the upper. The transmitter produces a signal which is normally usable at 10 to 15 mi in an 8° sector either side of the localizer course line.

The glide-slope beam width is approximately 1°, half above and half below the glide-slope line. The glide-slope line elevation varies, depending upon local terrain features. While 2.5° is desired, the angle may vary from a maximum of 4.0° to a minimum of 2.0°.

There are several glide-slope frequencies, between 331.0 and 335.0. Most control boxes automatically crystal tune the glide slope when its companion localizer frequency is selected.

Marker beacons, used in conjunction with ILS systems, provide definite fixes along the approach. These markers transmit vertically on a frequency of 75 mHz. They appear on the ILS approach chart the same as any fan marker, but are identified by the letters OM or MM for the *outer marker* or the *middle marker.* The outer marker transmits an audible

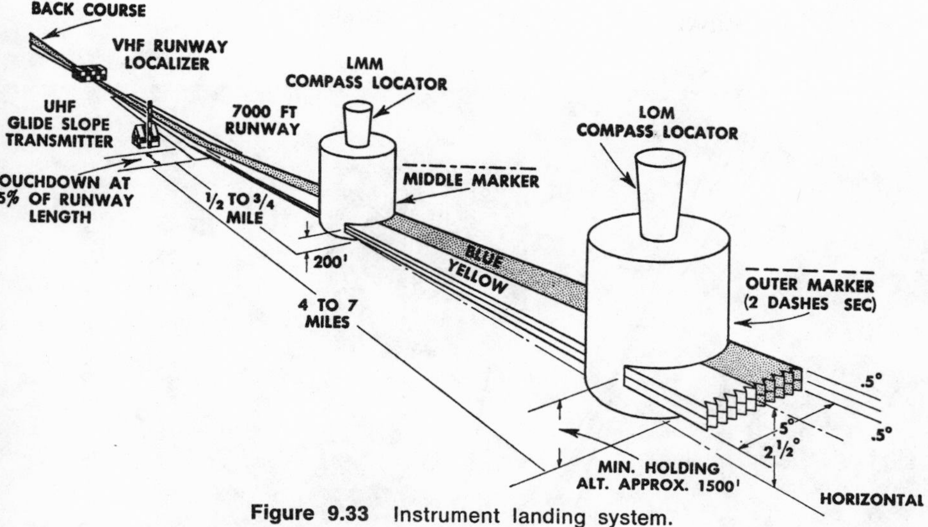

Figure 9.33 Instrument landing system.

series of dashes at 2 per sec. It is usually located so as to intercept the glide slope within ±50 ft of the procedure turn altitude, and is usually 4 to 7 mi from the end of the runway. The middle marker is identified by continuous alternating dots and dashes. It will normally be from ½ to ¾ mi from the end of the runway, and intersects the glide slope 200 ft above the terrain.

Radio compass locators, if installed, are located with the marker beacons, but use separate transmitters. Nondirectional beacons, they operate between 200 and 410 kHz, and transmit a continuous carrier wave and a keyed identifier. They are usually 25-watt facilities, and appear on the ILS terminal chart in the same manner as any other radio beacons, except that the line forming a square around the radio information is broken by the letter L. Locations are identified by only two letters. At the outer marker, these are the first two letters of the three-letter ILS localizer identification. At the middle marker, they are the last two letters.

AIRBORNE EQUIPMENT

While separate ILS receivers were widely used, and are installed in many modern aircraft, the principal receiver used now is the VOR receiver, tuned to the ILS frequency. When a glide slope receiver is installed, it is tuned automatically to the proper glide slope frequency when the VOR receiver is tuned to ILS. Localizer and glide slope indications are shown on the course indicator. The CDI indicates localizer course, and the horizontal GSI indicates glide slope. The warning flags appear whenever the localizer

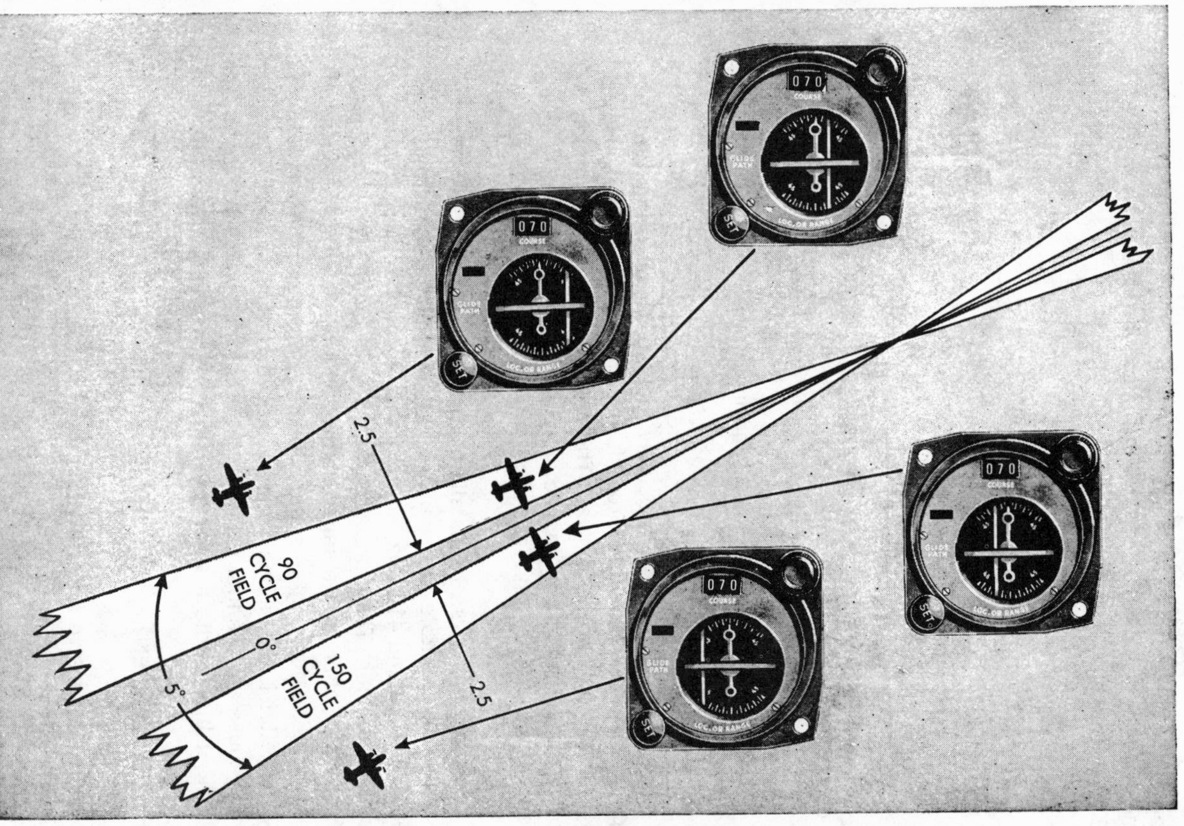

Figure 9.34A Relation of the localizer beam to CDI indications. Note that To-From indicator is blank, front course is set in course selector window, and CDI is directional.

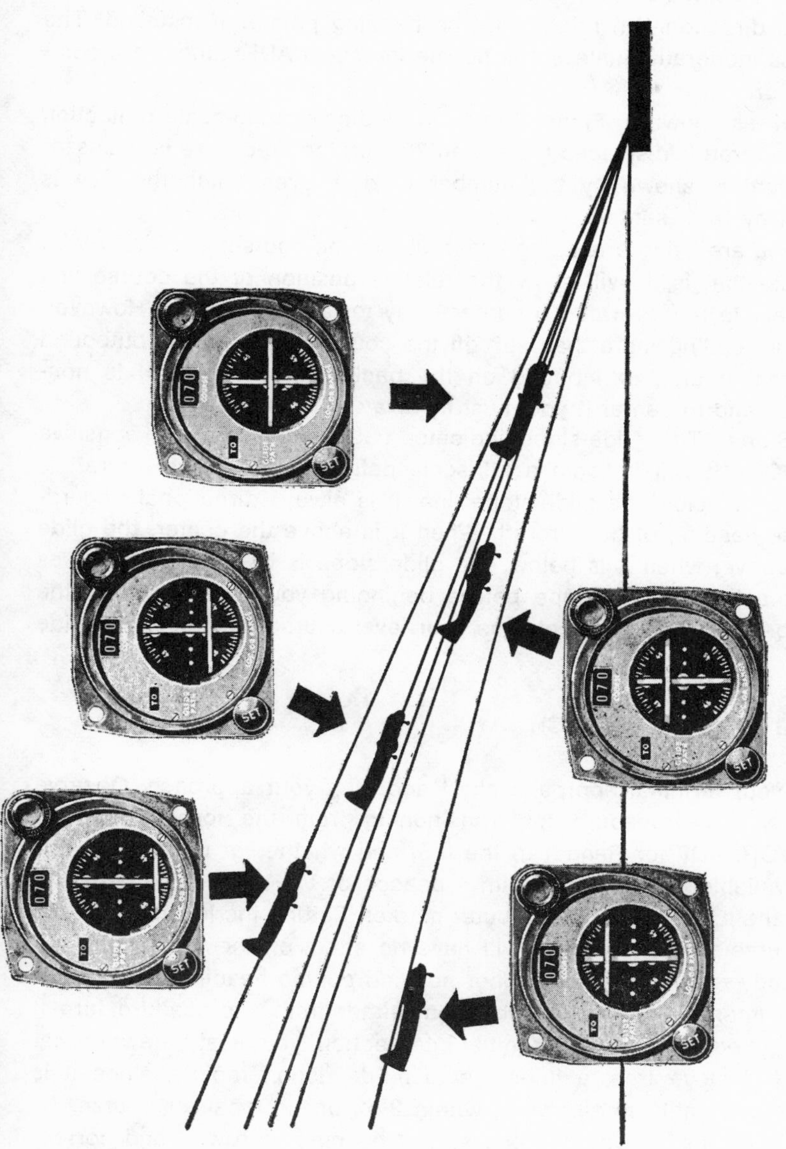

Figure 9.34B Relation of the glide path to the glideslope indicator.

or glide slope is not being received. When tuned to an ILS frequency, the TO-FROM indicator and the course selector are inoperative. The heading shown in the course selector window is important: Set at the front course; the CDI is directional in relation to the heading pointer if installed. The RMI is also inoperative unless one needle indicates ADF, tuned to a compass locator.

The CDI, as shown in Figure 9.34A, will indicate a full-scale deflection when the aircraft is displaced more than 2½° off the on-course line. Lesser displacement is shown by the number of dots over which the CDI is located away from center.

When you are flying a heading within 90° of the course, the CDI will be directional—that is, it will show the relative position of the course line with respect to the aircraft. To center it, fly toward the needle. However, when on a heading more than 90° off the course line—that is, outbound on the front course or inbound on the back course—the CDI is nondirectional, and to center it you must fly *away* from the needle.

Glide Slope The glide-slope indicator (GSI) is much more sensitive than the CDI. It will indicate a full-scale deflection when the aircraft is 0.5° above or below the glide-slope line. It is always directional, regardless of the heading of the aircraft. When it is above the center, the glide slope is above; when it is below, the glide slope is below. Therefore, as you approach the glide slope before beginning your final descent, the GSI will be high, and will center as your level course intersects the glide slope.

FLYING AN ILS APPROACH

Refer to your terminal approach chart and plan your approach. Observe particularly the procedure for transitioning from the local navigation facility (VOR, ADF, or Range) to the ILS, and whether or not the ADF or RMI, if available, can be used with a beacon or VOR station to help you intersect the ILS localizer at the outer marker. Setting the localizer course in the course selector window will have no effect on the instrument, but it is a handy reminder of the proper no-wind course heading.

As you intercept the course inbound, either from a procedure turn if one is required, or during your initial interception, you must be aware that the CDI will move from a full-scale to no-deflection rapidly, since it is fully deflected until the aircraft is within 2½° of the localizer course. As you approach the runway, the course will become narrower, and corrections will have to be smaller and more promptly executed. Make all corrections by reference to the control and performance instruments, cross-checking the CDI; a common error is to attempt to "fly" the CDI. Establish your landing configuration according to the operating instructions for your aircraft, usually before reaching the outer marker.

Maintain the glide slope intercept altitude while reducing the airspeed to the final descent speed. At most installations, the GSI starts downward from full-scale upward reflection in the vicinity of the outer marker or the compass locator. When the GSI starts to move, prepare to begin your rate of descent.

The rate of descent required with no wind is published on the ILS approach chart. Fly the descent just as though you were flying at GCA, but with reference to the GSI. Hold your rate of descent constant until the GSI indicates a deviation; then correct by a change in pitch. Maintain airspeed with careful throttle control. During the final approach descent, you will have to scan and cross-check your instruments with increasing speed. As you approach the runway, indications of deviation from the course and glide slope will occur more rapidly. You must make small prompt corrections to stay on course and on glide slope.

Be ready, as with other approaches, to go to the missed approach procedure immediately when you reach the DH unless you have established visual contact with the runway environment.

Many approach charts will show an approved approach for the back course. During the final approach on the back course, the CDI will be nondirectional and there will be no glide slope information. At most installations the ILS glide slope will be identical to the PAR glide path. The PAR controller can monitor your approach, or you can make a PAR approach and monitor it with ILS course and glide slope.

RADAR HAND-OFFS AND COMBINED APPROACHES

The present capability of ATC radar is such that when traffic permits or is helped by the process, the ATC approach controller can greatly simplify approaches. Having identified you by use of your transponder, or by a positive identifying turn, he can direct you to the final approach fix with an en-route descent, and can clear you for the final approach. Or, he can direct you to a fix for pick-up by the final PAR controller for an approach. Another popular method is to have the Approach Controller direct you to the ILS outer marker or similar fix and monitor your ILS approach as a safety measure. These procedures are very helpful to both pilot and controller, for they serve to expedite traffic and increase safety.

Landing from Instrument Approaches

The most critical part of your approach, assuming you have made it accurately, is the moment of transition from your instrument panel to the runway ahead. Your glimpse of it may be fleeting, and transition to ground contact under minimum conditions demands careful planning beforehand, as well as established cockpit procedures. *The principles you find here for low ceiling and visibility approaches are also applicable to approach and landing at night.*

PLANNING

The best time for planning is before takeoff. Study the weather and airfield conditions which will govern the type of approach you will be making —straight-in or circling. Know what unusual conditions you will encounter by checking NOTAMS. A careful study of the terminal-approach chart for the airfield of intended landing will show the airfield and runway layout, approach lighting, obstructions, and type of approach lighting. It will give you a very important mental picture of the location of prominent landmarks at and near the airfield, the minimum altitudes and the direction of traffic for circling approaches. With this information, and above all a clear orientation of direction, you will know what to expect during the transition from instrument to visual flight.

When you check the weather, or when you hear it in flight, remember that when the ceiling is reported as "obscured," "indefinite," or "precipitation," your visibility will probably be much less than reported. You are interested in the slant range from your eye to the nearest point of contact on the ground. This distance is a combination of many factors, such as approach and runway lighting, the shape, size, and slope of your windshield, its condition, your own adaptation to darkness, your fatigue, and the effects of rain or snow on the windshield or between you and the runway.

TRANSITIONING FROM INSTRUMENTS TO CONTACT

You may have been on instruments for some time. You will be tired and inclined to rush the final part of the flight. Coupled with darkness and low ceilings and poor visibility, the brief time available for changing your complete frame of reference may make the required transition from instruments to contact very difficult, particularly if you are flying a high-performance aircraft.

Cloud bases may be ragged. As you near the end of the approach, you will get occasional glimpses of the ground or the runway ahead. The problem is solved by using your occasional ground reference as simply another factor to be cross-checked in an organized manner. Ground reference is no more important than your other control, performance, or navigation instruments. Approach lights, with which you are familiar as a result of prior planning, are a most important aid, but *continue to fly instruments.* If you have a copilot, have him watch for the runway and report when it is in sight.

You will have a pronounced tendency to reduce power sharply and dive for the runway before you are entirely clear. To make such an extreme change in attitude or power at this time is hazardous. You have been maintaining a shallow approach with higher-than-normal power to hold the airspeed at the desired indications. It may be that you have the air-

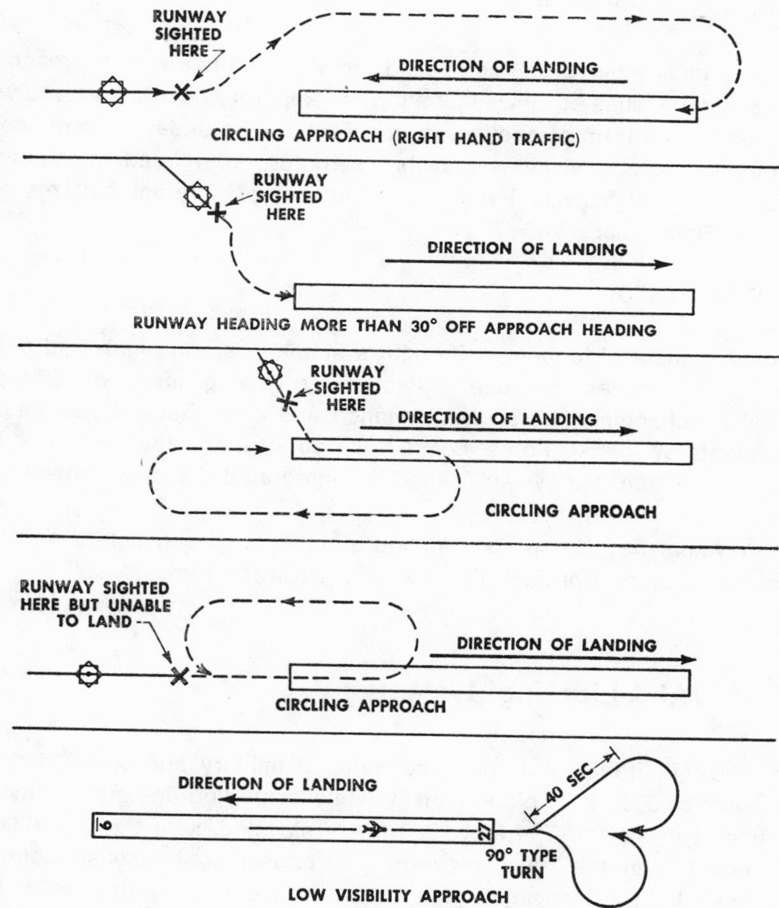

Figure 9.35 Circling and low-visibility approaches. Plan type to use well in advance, depending upon local obstructions and weather. Precision in altitude, airspeed, and heading is essential. These will usually be flown at the published circling approach minimum and below local VFR traffic pattern altitude.

craft in such a configuration that very little change in attitude is necessary to land, particularly if on a straight-in approach. Therefore, as you reach the point where you have no further obstructions to visibility, or where you have them under control (as when you have the runway well in sight and windshield wipers operating and lights adjusted), make a gradual flare-out with carefully controlled airspeed. Avoid any abrupt changes in attitude or power.

CIRCLING APPROACHES

When you must reverse course to land, or when a straight-in approach is not possible because of runway location or temporary obstruction, you will be making some form of circling approach. It will be under marginal contact conditions, and visibility may be restricted; your heading, altitude, and airspeed will be very important. A number of different patterns are shown in Figure 9.35.

APPROACH LIGHTING

The development of high-intensity light systems to aid in night- and poor-visibility approaches has been affected by varying ideas of different authorities, changing aircraft performance and cost. Recently, extensive experiments by the Air Force, commercial airlines, and the FAA have resulted in one standard system, called the Integrated Visual Approach and Landing Aids (IVALA) system.

This system has two parts: Configuration A approach lights, and the narrow-gage system of flush lights imbedded in the runway itself.

IVALA Lighting Systems

Configuration A is now the national military and civil standard. It consists of 3000 ft of high-intensity white centerline lighting leading to the runway threshold. The first 2000 ft are elevated, with the last 1000 ft flush-mounted in the runway overrun. Stroboscopic beacons, mounted with these lights, flash in sequence toward the runway threshold, and greatly increase the distance at which the pilot can identify the runway. A horizontal decision bar and runway-threshold lights complete the system.

The stroboscopic, or "strobe" lights are a key feature of this system, and are used for other purposes as well. Although they are of 30 million candlepower or higher, there is practically no blinding effect because of

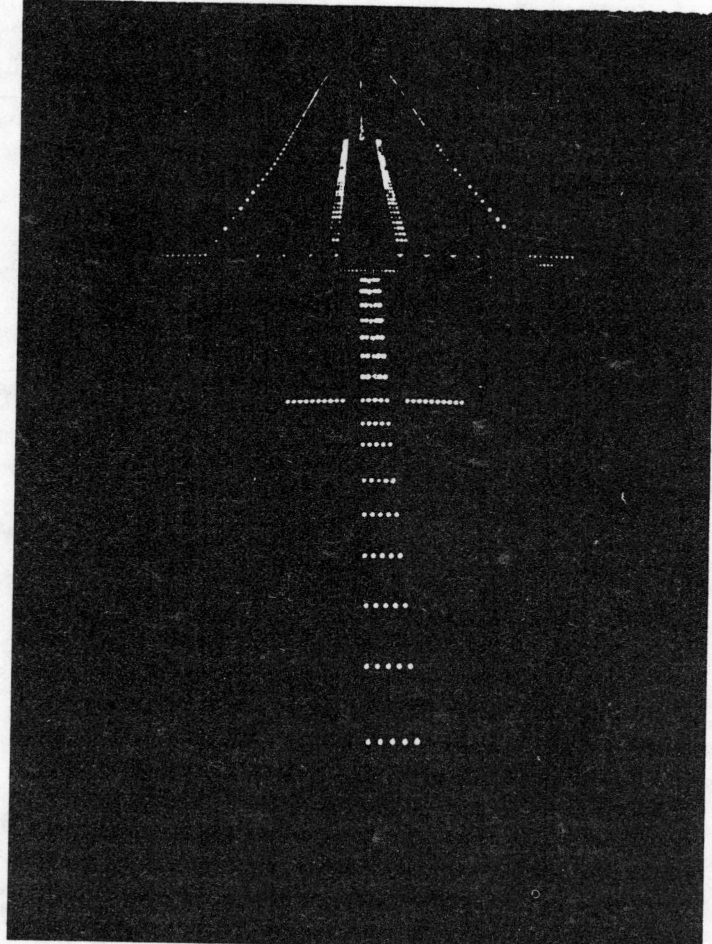

Figure 9.36 IVALA approach lighting system and narrow gage system.

the short duration of light emission. In the IVALA system, they flash swiftly toward the runway, cycling twice per second. The effect is that of a tracer bullet fired along the approach to the runway threshold. Strobe lights also are used to identify the active runway, since their brightness and characteristic flash make them easy to pick out from among all the other confusing lights a pilot sees near the larger airfields at night.

The narrow-gage system is designed to provide depth information for touchdown and directional information during the runout. They are needed because on wide runways the side runway lights do not provide

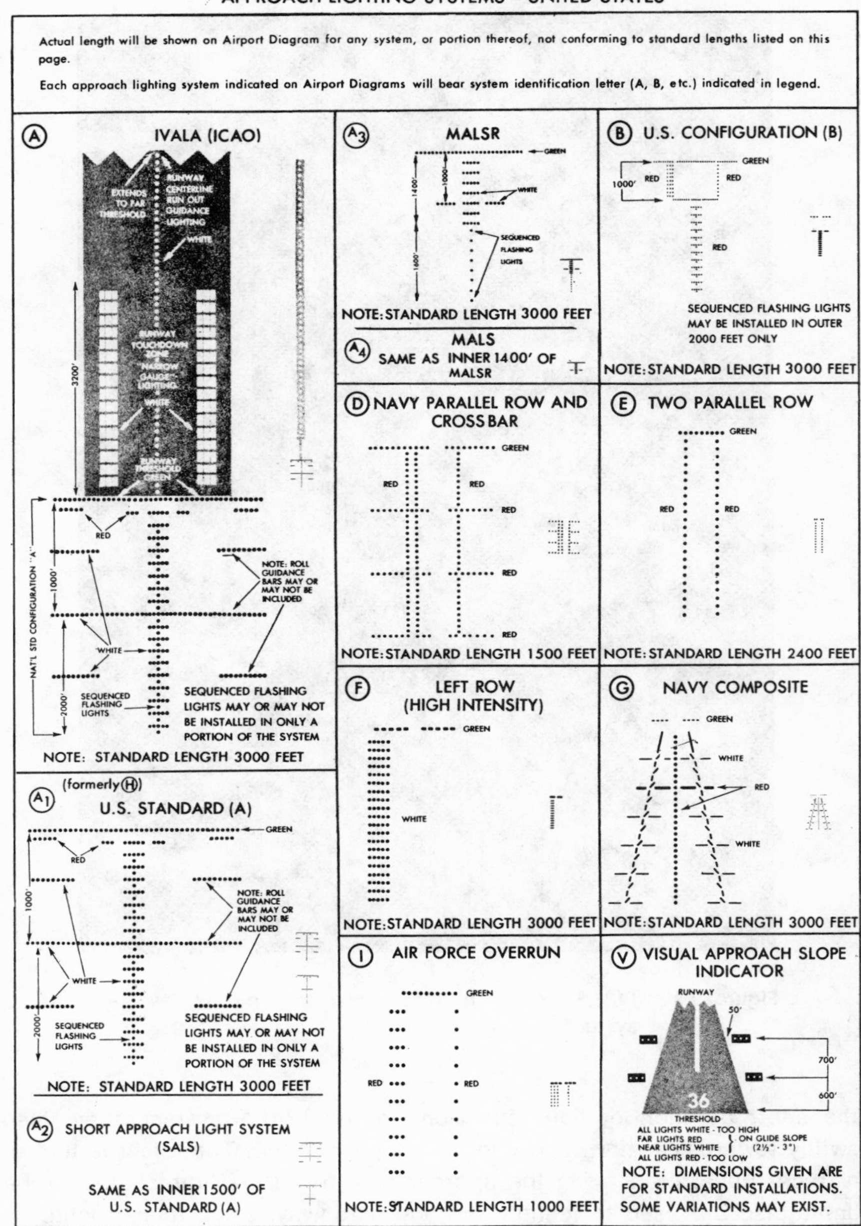

Figure 9.37 Approach lighting systems—United States. Note that each system is provided with a code for identifying with the appropriate approach plate. For example, in Figure 9.24, Rapid City Regional Airport has MALSR "Medium-Intensity Approach Light System with Runway Alignment Indicator Lights" (A_3).

sufficient reference. They are shown in Figure 9.36. Because each light fixture is covered by a steel grid capable of supporting aircraft weight, the light is not blinding. Heating elements in each light aid in ice and snow removal.

PRESENT APPROACH LIGHTING SYSTEMS

Because of the high cost of lighting systems, the existing systems are likely to be in use for some time to come. They are indicated on the approach charts by a small diagram at the end of the instrument runway. While there are several varieties, the principal ones are shown in Figure 9.37.

The Pilot's Burble Point

When a wing has too heavy a load, it stalls; the airflow departs from its smooth course at what may be called its "burble point."

Pilots also have a "burble point." Given a properly equipped and properly maintained aircraft, proper ground facilities, and weather within his competence, the pilot's thorough and careful planning is the factor that makes instrument flying, and particularly instrument approaches, routine and safe.

When a pilot overestimates his instrument-flying ability, or when the unforeseen happens at the critical point of an approach, or when fatigue and poor planning result in his having too much to do too fast, he has reached his "burble point." The result is disaster. The air, even more than the sea, is unforgiving of carelessness or incompetence.

10

Flying Higher-Performance Aircraft*

The turbine engine in high-powered aircraft eliminated the complications and vibration of the Otto cycle. Except for short haul and military transports designed to operate from marginal airfields, propellers have disappeared with their inherent limitations on speed and on high altitude efficiency.

JET AIRCRAFT CHARACTERISTICS

Jets differ from prop aircraft in takeoff, climb, speed, and handling qualities; in the increased importance of the environmental factors discussed in Chapter 7; in the increased preflight planning needed; and in the fact that though most jet flying is above the weather, it is, even in aerobatics, largely attitude instrument flying.

It is important to realize that most light aircraft and heavy multiengine prop aircraft, having straight wings and operating at lower speeds, are basically stable longitudinally and directionally. These aircraft move about their axes in a way

*Revised by Col. Deane G. Curry, USAF (Ret.) and Lt. Col. Patrick J. Halloran, USAF.

that can be considered almost mutually independent. That is, they move in uncoupled modes of motion. Transonic and supersonic aircraft, on the other hand, can move in modes that result from coupling of longitudinal and lateral directional response. This coupling is caused by increased dominance of inertial and gyroscopic forces at high rolling rates over stabilizing aerodynamic forces, and while it becomes more and more pronounced as speed increases, it is more a function of configuration than speed. While relatively "stable" aircraft can be trimmed to fly "hands-off," this is almost impossible to achieve in swept or delta wing jets. Stability augmenting systems are essential in most swept or delta wing jets to aid the pilot in his control responses. The Lear Jet is an exception. It is quite stable and can be flown "hands-off" at all altitudes including its maximum of 41,000 ft.

It is important to understand other characteristics in which prop and jet aircraft differ. In jet aircraft, level-flight and dive speeds are higher, climb speeds are greater, but takeoff performance is generally inferior; engine controls, however, are simplified and torque is eliminated. The jet's outstanding performance characteristics are not achieved automatically. In order to get the best results, the pilot must be willing to apply techniques different from those he would use under similar circumstances in prop aircraft. Further, he will be greatly helped by more training, particularly in theory, and he must "think ahead" of the aircraft he is flying.

Thrust characteristics of the turbojet engine are responsible for these airplane characteristics. Since power is the product of thrust and speed, the power available is directly proportional to the speed: low at low speed, high at high speed. This dependence of power on speed explains the inferior takeoff characteristics of some jet aircraft as compared to their superior performance characteristics after accelerating.

The relationship of speed and power also explain the high climb speed of jets. Maximum rate of climb occurs at the speed of maximum excess power, as shown in Figure 10.1.

Note that maximum excess power for the propeller-driven aircraft is shown at "A." The corresponding speed is the best climb speed for the propeller-driven aircraft. The situation in the jet aircraft is different. "B" indicates that the speed for maximum excess power is relatively high. Therefore, the best climb speed for jet aircraft is correspondingly high, and produces much higher rates of climb. One can readily see how important it is to maintain proper climb speed in order to obtain optimum power. This higher jet climb speed and rate should not be confused with the very high angle of climb observed, for example, as a Boeing 727 takes off. This high angle of climb at the relatively low speed after takeoff is largely the result of the high thrust-to-weight ratio of its three engines and takeoff weight.

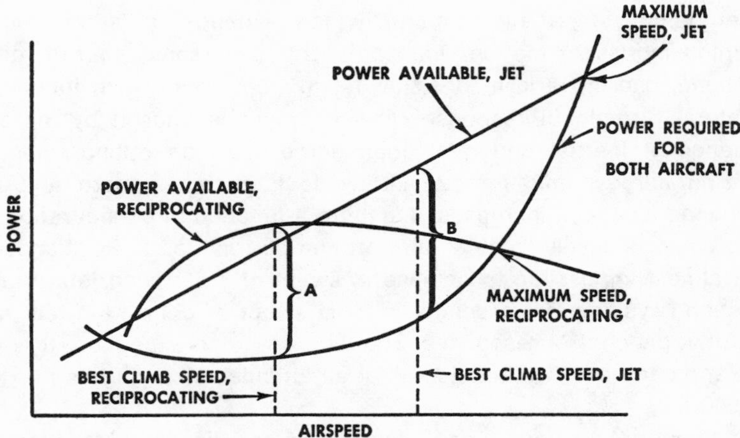

Figure 10.1 Approximate relationship, best climb speeds, reciprocating and jet engines.

Another jet aircraft characteristic associated with the speed-power relationship is the jet's ability to obtain a variation of airspeed in level flight without any change in throttle setting. At certain cruise conditions (particularly at speed ranges just below optimum cruise), as the speed increases—with no change in throttle—the power available also increases just enough to equal the power required. This characteristic makes it necessary for the pilot to accelerate *above* his cruise setting and then *reduce* power to recommended cruise settings. Theoretically, there is a proper power setting for every airspeed. At high altitude, only a slight increase in power is required to obtain a significant increase in speed.

Flying on the low-speed side of the speed-power curve (also called "area of reversed command") is most likely to occur when the airspeed is low, as in the traffic pattern or during a go-around, and under high-attitude, high gross-weight conditions, regardless of the type of aircraft (Figure 2.35). This is not an ideal situation, and may be very dangerous, because the angle of attack is high, approaching stall conditions. Full power may be inadequate to maintain level flight. The best, and often the only, solution for recovery is to put the nose down and sacrifice altitude, if available, to regain speed.

FLIGHT PLANNING

Most smaller jet aircraft have small cockpits. The extensive planning necessary if the flight is to be efficient and safe cannot be accomplished after the plane is airborne because of limited time and space. Therefore, preflight planning can and must be precise. The pilot, who usually does the high-speed navigation as well, must do it rapidly and accurately.

Weather Considerations In planning your jet flight, you should not be much concerned with en-route surface weather, except as it affects your choice of emergency en-route landing fields. The wind, however, is very important, because of the rate of fuel consumption, particularly if a jet stream should lie along the route. If it is blowing in your direction, plan to fly in it. If it is against you, plan to fly above it, below it, or to one side. Whichever choice you make is determined by the altitude of the core of the jet stream, the velocities of the surrounding winds, and the aircraft performance at that altitude. Because of high cruise speed, wind has less overall net effect on range of jets than on range of conventional aircraft, since the jet is exposed to a particular wind a shorter period of time.

Fuel Planning The available fuel for a flight includes, except in rare instances, the full capacity of the tanks. For planning purposes it is divided into three portions. These are the requirements for climb, cruise, and reserve at destination or alternate. The fuel for start, taxi, and takeoff is included in the requirements for climb. For this phase of planning, use the cruise control data from charts in your Operations Handbook. Cruise fuel is that projected for use from the end of a climb to arrival over destination at cruise altitude. Reserve includes the fuel needed for descent, approach, and landing, as well as a safe margin to allow for adverse winds, landing delays, and flight to an alternate airfield if required.

TAKEOFF PERFORMANCE CALCULATIONS

The takeoff performance of jet aircraft is highly sensitive to temperature and pressure changes. The effect is illustrated by this tabulation from the Lear Jet Takeoff Performance Charts using takeoff weight of 12,500 lb.

TABLE 10.1
Takeoff Performance Chart

Pressure Altitude	*Temperature*	*Takeoff Roll (ft) (no wind)*
Sea level	59°F	3150
Sea level	95°F	4150
5000 ft	41°F	4500
5000 ft	95°F	6500

For every take-off it is necessary that you not only compute take-off roll, but also the acceleration check speed and time, go-no-go speed, refusal speed, and decision speed. The commonly used terms are:

Takeoff Ground Roll The distance required with existing conditions for the airplane to accelerate to takeoff speed with all engines operating normally.

Rotation Speed (V_R) The indicated airspeed at which the nose wheel should be lifted from the runway to obtain the desired performance.

Takeoff Speed (V_2) The indicated airspeed at which the airplane can be safely flown off the runway. This is also the minimum speed for directional control in the air in the event of engine failure—usually about 5 knots above rotation speed.

Critical Field Length The length of runway needed under existing conditions for the airplane to accelerate to critical engine-failure speed, lose all power from one engine, then either continue to accelerate with the reduced power available to safe takeoff speed, or stop, using brakes, drag devices, and reverse thrust if available, within the remaining distance.

If critical field length is less than the runway length available, a safe takeoff can be made allowing for the loss of one engine at or beyond critical engine-failure speed. If critical field length is greater than runway length available, the airplane cannot either stop or become safely airborne within the remaining runway, should an engine be lost at critical engine-failure speed. While marginal conditions may tempt one to take a chance, the solution, except in an emergency, is to off-load enough weight to make critical field length equal to or less than runway length.

Single-Engine Go-No-Go Speed The minimum speed from which single-engine takeoff should be attempted.

Critical Engine Failure Speed (V_1) The speed at which under existing conditions, should one engine fail, the distance required to complete the takeoff exactly equals the distance required to stop.

Acceleration Check The time required to accelerate between two preselected speeds. Usually 80 to 120 knots (or V_1, whichever is lower). If at the expiration of the precomputed time the 120 knots (or V_1) has not been reached, the takeoff should be discontinued.

Due to many variables, including wind, that enter into checking acceleration against a point along the runway, most acceleration checks in aircraft with more than one crew member are made using the time and speed method. This time may be quite short. For example in a Boeing 707 weighing 240,000 lb on an 80° day at 1000 ft pressure altitude and a flat runway the time between 80 and 120 knots would be 10.4 sec.

STARTING YOUR AIRCRAFT

Starting usually requires a ground crewman. Observe the normal safety precautions, particularly the distance from intakes to ground crewmen and tailpipe distances to other aircraft or persons. Safe distances are shown in the applicable Handbook listed under ground operation. Chocks and a suitable fire extinguisher are considered essential.

There is a certain sequence of events that occurs in the starting of jet engines. While the starting sequence may be manual or automatic and vary with the aircraft, the fundamentals are the same.

First: The engine must reach a high enough rpm to obtain a steady flow of air through it. Most jet aircraft will require auxiliary power units to obtain the proper start rpm. Most jets start using one of three types of systems, the explosive cartridge-operated starter, compressed air, or electric starter. Electric starters are most common for the smaller jets. Commercial-type business jets do not require the auxiliary ground equipment used and required for military and airline jets, because they require less energy to accelerate the compressor and turbine.

Second: An ignition spark must be introduced into the sequence in the burner cans, to ignite the fuel when it is injected.

Third: Fuel is sprayed into the burner cans through the fuel manifold and controlled through the fuel nozzles by use of the throttle. The proper sequence is absolutely necessary to prevent a fire on start. If the raw fuel were to enter the fire cans first, the introduction of the spark would result in a mild explosion and fire. Most jet starting systems are automatic and sequenced through the electronic fuel control. The primary instruments to watch during start are the exhaust gas temperature (EGT) gage and fuel flow meter.

Each jet engine has a maximum allowable temperature limit for starting. Temperatures increase very rapidly, and must be monitored closely to avoid exceeding the limit. You should have your hand on the throttle ready to shut off the engine if the EGT should approach or exceed the start limits. The EGT gage is usually calibrated in 50°C increments from 0°C to 1000°C. Normal start range would be 500° to 700°C with an allowable instantaneous 800°C reading. If the temperature should exceed 800°C for two seconds or longer, it would be a *hot start.* With a hot start, shut down immediately. Allow a few minutes for fuel drainage, then attempt another start. Should the temperature exceed 900°C even momentarily, make no attempt to restart the engine because it will have to be removed for disassembly and detailed "teardown" inspection without further operation. After completing the start use your check list for all systems operation. The ground crewman will assist by visually checking that hydraulic-controlled rudder and elevator slab are in proper takeoff position and that flap-to-stabilizer or similar control interconnect is correctly set for takeoff. Turn on your radio, call the tower for clearance, and proceed with your taxi.

TAXI AND TAKEOFF

The same taxi precautions applicable to prop aircraft apply to jet aircraft. In order to leave the parking area it is necessary to increase power to approximately 60% to 70%, start rolling, check your brakes and engage nose-wheel steering. Taxi out of the area to the taxi lane, complete pre-takeoff checks as required, and obtain clearance to take the runway and line up. When cleared to take off, advance to 100% rpm or to limiting exhaust pressure (no warm-up is required), release brakes, and you're on your way.

You will notice that there is no torque produced yawing in a jet as there is in a propeller-driven aircraft. The takeoff distance and acceleration will probably be the first noticeable difference. You will feel you are not going to become airborne as the runway is rapidly used up. However, the aircraft accelerates slowly at first, then rapidly until you reach your precomputed rotation and lift-off speeds. This is where you must remember your takeoff performance calculations and use them. Upon reaching rotation speed, ease the nose up and the aircraft will fly off the ground. Do not attempt to pull the aircraft into the air because it may mush back into the ground. It cannot "hang on the props." The takeoff angles will be rather shallow initially. Crosswind effect on jet aircraft is not of much consequence, but during flight planning you should check the crosswind component chart for your aircraft because in severe crosswind the nose wheel must be held on the ground longer than normal, and the aircraft crabbed into the wind immediately after lift-off to remain over the runway.

CLIMB

In the T-38, the initial climb is the same pitch attitude as takeoff (about 5° to 7° nose up) until reaching 300 knots. At 300 knots the throttle is retarded to shut off afterburners for a military power climb unless a continuous maximum power climb is desired. The aircraft is allowed to accelerate to the prescribed climb speed schedule, which is about 400 knots up to 10,000 ft, then to .78M to 15,000 ft, .81 to 20,000 ft, .86 to 25,000 ft, .90 to 30,000 ft, .92 to above 40,000 ft. If a maximum power climb is to be maintained from takeoff then the pitch angle is approximately 25°. The aircraft is allowed to accelerate to .92M and holds this throughout the climb. This rate of climb will be in excess of 12,000 fpm.

Aircraft capable of high-performance and high pitch-angle climbs, such as the T-38 and Lear Jet, have visibility restrictions over the nose in this attitude. Therefore, it is highly desirable that in areas of air traffic concentrations, the climb be conducted under radar control or in assigned climb corridors.

Air Traffic Control centers are familiar with jet aircraft and the excessive fuel consumption they experience at low altitude. They will clear you to climb to altitude as rapidly as possible, and try to avoid giving you involved low-altitude departure procedures.

During the acceleration after takeoff and during climb-out, the aircraft will feel stable and solid. The electric elevator trim control, usually under the thumb on the pilot's stick or yoke, permits continuous trim adjustments as the aircraft accelerates. Large changes in pitch and roll can occur fast and easily, however, unless one pays close attention to the pitch and roll attitude, to the airspeed, and to trim, during the climb-out.

CRUISE

Fuel consumption is the primary problem in jet cruising. It is only the high speed obtainable that makes jet flying practicable and economical in cost despite the fuel needed for acceptable ranges. The ideal flight profile in a jet aircraft is a climb to the most efficient initial altitude for the weight, followed by a slow climbing cruise as the weight is lowered by fuel consumption. In practical application, however, both from the standpoint of pilot technique and air traffic control, jets, like other aircraft, fly at assigned altitudes, which, if changed, are changed in steps.

In order to cruise efficiently, jets must cruise at a high percentage of maximum power. The thrust of a jet engine varies directly with power, roughly as follows:

100% rpm = 100% thrust
90% rpm = 75% thrust
80% rpm = 50% thrust

During cruise at altitude, a combination of fuel flow in pounds per hour, percent of maximum rpm, exhaust gas temperature (EGT), and engine pressure ratio (EPR), in some aircraft, are used to obtain optimum cruise. With proper preflight planning, it is seldom necessary to make corrections to power to maintain the flight plan and its schedule of fuel consumption. In large airline transports fuel is limited and carefully computed even over short routes because of the cost of carrying unneeded thousands of pounds of fuel. In the T-38 and Lear Jet, fuel is limited because the size of the aircraft limits the amount available. For this reason, some sort of meticulously prepared and meticulously kept fuel log is essential. While there are many types of logs designed to suit many different needs, one which has served well in the Air Force is shown in Figure 10.2.

PILOT'S FLIGHT PLAN AND FLIGHT LOG

ARTC FREQ				
	HOU 335.6	FT. W 307.9	MEM 286.5	430 TAS	FL 330
	" 290.5	MEM 336.5	IND 290.3	Winds 260/50 MEM	300/40 FFO
	" 269.0	" 322.3	" 322.5		

AIRCRAFT IDENT	TAKE-OFF TIME	TOTAL DISTANCE	TOTAL ETE	TOTAL AMT FUEL
62-4467 UTAH 32	ETD 1300Z ATD 1256	983	2 + 15	6864

FIX	ROUTE	IDENT VOR / FREQ	IDENT TACAN / FREQ	MAG CRS	DISTANCE / REMAIN	GROUND SPEED	ETE / REMAIN	ETA / ATA	LEG / REMAIN	ACTUAL FUEL REMAIN
	Seguin 3	SAT		080	72	310	+14	1310	↓	
Weimar ▲		116.8	115		911		2 + 01	:11		
	DCT	LFK		045	14	380	+02	:13	1230	-84
L.O		112.1	58		897		1 + 59	:13	5634	5550
	DCT	↓	↓	045	136	470	+17	:30	545	-39
Lufkin					761		1 + 42	:29	5089	5050
	J-29	SHV		017	107		+14	43	450	-39
Shreveport		117.4	121	019	654	450	1 + 28	43	4639	4600
	J-29	MEM		048	232	470	+30	1413	960	+21
Memphis		115.5	102	051	422		+58	12	3679	3700
	J-29	EVV		025	208	425	+29	41	895	+16
Evansville		113.3	80	028	214		+29	41	2784	2800
	DCT	CVG		064	158	450	+21		650	
Cincinnati		117.3	120		56		+08		2134	
	DCT	FFO		032	56	430	+08		246	
Patterson		111.6	99		0		0		1888	
	Dayton App Con 327.1									
FFO Tower 289.6 Gnd. Cont. 335.8										
	Tie in FFS - Dayton 255.4									
	Stopover Flight (Est. 1 Hr. Ground Time)									
RETURN FLIGHT ON BACK										

AF FORM MAY 66 70 REPLACES AF FORM 21A, JAN 63, WHICH WILL BE USED UNTIL STOCK IS EXHAUSTED.

Figure 10.2 Pilot's flight plan and flight log. This standard USAF form is used on most flights and on all AFR flights. The plain-language clearance from Randolph AFB, Texas, to Wright Patterson AFB, Ohio, is: "Utah 32 cleared as filed; maintain flight level 230. Departure Control will be on 381.4 squawking Mode 3 code 1100." For the return,

ATD 1615

TOTALS				966		2 + 28		6864	
ROUTE / FIX	IDENT VOR / FREQ	IDENT TACAN / FREQ	MAG CRS	DISTANCE / REMAIN	GROUND SPEED	ETE / REMAIN	ETA / ATA	LEG / REMAIN	ACTUAL FUEL REMAIN
Radar	CVG		212	56	305	+11	1626		
Cincinnati	117.3	120		910		2 + 17	25		
DCT	EVV		244	42	360	+07	32	1290	-24
L.O.	113.3	80		868		2 + 10	33	5574	5550
DCT	↓	↓	244	116	410	+17	50	540	+16
Evansville				752		1 + 53	49	5034	5050
J-29	MEM		208	208	430	+29	1718	920	+36
Memphis	115.5	102	205	544		1 + 24	19	4114	4150
J-29	SHV		232	232	385	+36		1090	
Shreveport	117.4	121	228	312		+48		3024	
DCT	AUS		225	246	390	+38		1150	
Austin	112.5	72		66		+10		1874	
DCT	LVR		190	66	415	+10		305	
Lavernia	112.0	None		0		0		1569	

MISCELLANEOUS DATA

Return Flt FL 350 TAS 430

Winds remain same

VOR Penetration to RND

Randolph Tower 349.0
Randolph Gnd 275.8
Pilot to Disp. 372.2

C UTAH 32 AS FILED → FL 230
DC 381.4 SQ. M 3-1100

C UTAH 32 RND APT VIA VALLEY 2
DEP. → CVG → EVV FPR → 8,000
< TKOF EXP FL 230 10 MIN < TKOF

★ U.S. GOVERNMENT PRINTING OFFICE : 1966 O—215-842

clearance was: "Utah 32 cleared to the Randolph Airport via Valley 2 departure, direct Cincinnati, direct Evansville, flight planned route. Maintain 8000 after takeoff. Expect flight level 230 ten minutes after takeoff."

While the difference likely to appear between forecast and actual winds may cause the computations to be off, the chances of their being either favorable or unfavorable are about equal; an appropriate adjustment can be made at the first check point, and the cumulative effect can be detected early enough to alter the flight plan if necessary, insuring always the reserve needed to meet the unforeseen and land. The T-38 normal fuel flow at 40,000 ft is 1400 lb/hr; if, for example, you reached the cruise altitude with 2800 lb of fuel remaining, you would have enough for only about an hour and thirty minutes of flight with an 800 lb reserve. Here again, Air Traffic Control is cognizant of this problem, and will usually expedite your descent with minimum holding time at lower altitude, or provide you an en-route descent under radar control.

MANEUVERING

While some jet aircraft, like the Lear Jet, have mechanical linkage controls, fighter types and large transports have hydraulically operated controls. Without this augmentation, it would be impossible to maneuver them easily and efficiently at high speeds. With augmented controls, fighters are highly maneuverable at both supersonic and subsonic speeds. Augmented controls are provided with an artificial feel system to indicate changes in pilot's control pressure.

The development of high-performance jets has been marked by problems in stability, and in the past most high-performance aircraft were very unstable. Either through design improvements in newer models, or modification of older ones, jet fighters and transports are now quite stable in the entire speed range.

These early stability problems were generated by lack of pilot understanding of dihedral effect and inadequate design compensation for it. Dihedral effect is manifest in two distinct flight characteristics. They are *Dutch roll,* or roll due to yaw, and *adverse yaw,* which is yaw due to roll. Both are primarily encountered while maneuvering at high angle of attack or in turbulence. Yaw dampers and stability augmentation systems of varying design are incorporated in most high-speed aircraft to minimize the effect. (See Figure 2.41.)

If an aircraft is caused to yaw by rudder mismanagement, turbulence, or in multiengine aircraft, unbalanced power, the wing away from the direction of yaw will swing forward, generating more lift and thus rise, causing a roll in the same direction as the yaw. When this occurs it is relatively easy for the pilot to get out of phase with the oscillations and accentuate rather than dampen out the roll. In some aircraft it is possible to have the aircraft on its back in about five oscillations if yaw dampers and stability augmentation are not present or proper recovery technique is not applied.

With most aircraft, proper recovery technique is to neutralize rudder and level the wings with ailerons. In the Boeing 707 the period of oscillation is relatively long (4 to 7 sec) and, as in all aircraft, can be controlled by stopping either roll or yaw. Dutch roll cannot exist without both roll and yaw.

Adverse yaw, or yaw due to roll occurs at high angle of attack when an attempt is made to roll the aircraft with aileron. The yaw is produced by the drag of the down aileron; the dihedral effect, in turn, inhibits the roll. The yaw in this case is away from the intended direction of roll and the aircraft will in fact turn opposite to that intended. At very high angles of attack, that is, at or near stall, aileron inputs may cause rapid spin entry. Adverse yaw is predominantly a problem in fighter-type aircraft.

STALLS

The McDonnell Phantom II is typical in its stall characteristics of swept-wing supersonic fighters. 1*g* stalls are preceded by a wide band of buffet warnings. Onset of buffet normally occurs approximately 40 knots indicated airspeed above stall. A rudder shaker is activated by the angle of attack indicator. *Wing rock* is generally unpredictable but starts about 10 KIAS prior to stall and can progress to as much as 40° bank at stall. If there are no rudder or aileron inputs wing rock may be delayed or absent. The stall is characterized by a yawing motion in either direction. The yawing is caused by a loss of directional control.

Stall recovery is effected by positioning the stick forward of neutral, while holding aileron and rudder neutral. Accelerated stalls are preceded by a moderate buffet increasing progressively to heavy buffet just prior to stall. Prompt neutralization of controls will quickly effect recovery from accelerated stalls.

Clean configuration stalls are practiced only up to heavy wing rock or nose slicing (yawing). In the landing configuration the Phantom II has substantially the same characteristics as in the clean configuration. Wing rock is somewhat reduced and a nose rise accompanied by lightening of aft stick forces is noted just prior to the stall. Even with maximum power a sacrifice of up to 3000 ft of altitude may be required to recover from the landing configuration stall.

The Boeing 707 is typical of large high-performance jet transports in its stall characteristics. As the stall is approached in the clean configuration a very gentle buffet may be felt in smooth air. Fifteen to twenty knots slower another buffet is felt but is still not strong and may be masked by turbulence or by the flaps and/or landing gear, if extended. Just prior to stall an airframe buffet is felt. This is a much stronger buffet and much less likely to be masked or confused with anything else. The buffet continues and just at the stall a mild nose rise occurs. Following the stall the nose pitches down and normal recovery procedures are easily executed. Due to the wide range of weights and configurations, altitude loss during recovery will vary considerably but 1500 ft loss of altitude is about average.

Stalls in the Lear Jet are not normally practiced in checking out the airplane because its stall warning devices make approaches to stalls an adequate preparation. From a moderately nose-high attitude, the Lear Jet will stall and recover smoothly. In a straight-ahead landing attitude stall, the nose will fall through with little or no roll. With power increased, the aircraft returns to straight and level flight.

The Lear Jet Model 23 has a *stick shaker* which provides a stall warning when the airspeed is 5% to 7% above stall speed. To assist in stall recoveries, and to inhibit further the possibility of an inadvertent stall, a *stick pusher* is installed.

It is characteristic of T-tail airplanes to pitch up viciously when stalled in extreme nose-high attitudes, making recovery difficult or violent. The stick pusher inhibits this type of stall. About one knot above stall speed, an 80-lb force automatically moves the stick forward, preventing the stall from developing. A "*g*" limiter is incorporated in the system. This prevents the pitch down generated by the stick pusher from imposing excessive loads on the aircraft. In addition, an angle of attack indicator is installed on the instrument panel, both to warn of near-stall attitudes, and to serve as a checking reference for the stick shaker and stick pusher.

From a normal stall, no forward pressure is required for recovery; rather a release of the back pressure that was needed for the entry will suffice. The stall speed in the landing configuration at 12,500 lb gross weight is 98 KIAS. The angle of bank increases the stall speed proportionately, as in any airplane. With the landing configuration and the bank indicated, the stall speeds are: 20°—102 KIAS; 40°—113 KIAS; and 60°—143 KIAS. A turning stall in the Lear Jet is accompanied by slight buffet; sufficient warning is given to the pilot during stall approach. At 12,500 lb in a 1.5 *g* maneuver, a low-speed buffet will occur at 145 knots. High-speed buffet at 1.5 *g* does not occur until the speed is in excess of the maximum allowable Mach.

As in the straight-ahead stall, a turning stall recovery is made by releasing the back pressure, increasing power, and leveling the wings. The recovery is very smooth. A cross-check of the vertical speed indicator is necessary to determine sink rate associated with the complete stall.

Due to the extreme aerodynamically clean design and the great mass of jet aircraft, very rapid speed build-up can be anticipated in the nose-down attitude. In view of this mass and rapidly building speed, a high sink rate should be anticipated during and immediately after rotation out of a stall recovery dive. A pilot's overreaction to this high sink rate can cause him to place the aircraft in a high angle of attack again and risk an accelerated secondary stall.

While all high-performance aircraft will spin and will recover from spins, they are not practiced. Very great altitude losses are required in recovery. High-performance aircraft are also subject to another post-stall maneuver beside the conventional spin. This is simply called the *post-stall gyration* and is described as a departure from controlled flight with random rotations about any or all axes. If the angle of attack is not reduced these can be expected to develop into a spin. Spin recoveries are generally effected by neutralizing rudder and aileron and use of pitch control to reduce angle of attack. Drag chutes may also be used in this effort. In flat spins, if the drag chute is deployed early in the spin, recovery may be possible. Unfortunately, in fully developed flat spins there is no known recovery technique for swept-wing aircraft.

Aerobatics and High-Speed, High Angle of Attack Maneuvering Modern jets, like the advanced trainers and jet fighters can perform the full range of aerobatic maneuvers easily and precisely. The lack of propeller torque makes only little rudder control necessary, even in "over-the-top" maneuvers such as loops and Immelmans. There is, however, considerable altitude variation and lateral space required if these are performed at high speed. An F-4, with its wide range of speed and weight, may require from 3000 to 10,000 ft or more altitude to execute a loop. Speed build-up in vertical descent is very rapid.

The use of speed brakes is one of several pilot techniques used in controlling acceleration in descending maneuvers. Speed brakes may be used at any airspeed, and though they produce some buffeting and vibration at higher speed, they affect trim and control characteristics very little.

The ability of the fighter pilot to maneuver his aircraft for long periods of time at high speed and at very high angles of attack are his stock in trade. It is immaterial whether he maneuvers his aircraft into an attacking position on an opponent or forces his opponent into uncontrolled flight. The end result is the same. In other fields of flying, except perhaps for crop dusting, high angle of attack maneuvering is generally confined to takeoff, approach, and landing, and during conditions of reduced thrust.

Because of the great amount of vertical and horizontal space required to maneuver, and the rapid, positive control response of high-performance aircraft, a full understanding of high angle of attack maneuvering is essential.

The term "high angle of attack" is frequently confused with two other terms. They are "pitch angle" and "flight path angle." Pitch angle is the angle formed by the longitudinal axis and the true horizon. Flight path angle is the actual flight of the aircraft through space relative to the true horizon. Angle of attack is the difference between the two (see Figure 5.26). Angle of attack for all practical purposes is a function of gross weight, indicated airspeed, and *g loading.* Altitude is not a factor since we are concerned with indicated, not true, airspeed.

Of importance to the high-performance aircraft pilot is the effect *g* loading has on his aircraft. There is no difference from the effect on light aircraft, but the greater potential for high values of speed, weight, and control response make *g* loading and unloading of the aircraft a prime control technique.

g loading is equal to the product of weight and the cosine of bank angle, provided the aircraft is being maintained in a constant plane such as a constant altitude. *g* loading is always controlled by the longitudinal control (elevator or its equivalent). *g* loading and unloading can be used to accelerate or decelerate the aircraft as well as to increase or decrease its stall speed.

To illustrate, assume a 50,000-lb aircraft in 1 *g* flight. Fifty thousand pounds of lift are required to sustain it. If the aircraft is placed in a 60° banked turn, 2 *g*'s will be generated to hold altitude in this turn and now 100,000 lb of lift are required, and are acquired by increasing angle of attack. The stall speed has now also been increased. Conversely, if the same aircraft is maneuvered into less than 1 *g* flight, such as .5 *g,* only 25,000 lb of lift are required and the stall speed has decreased.

Theoretically an aircraft maneuvered into zero *g* flight requires zero lift and thus will not stall at zero IAS. The only problem here is that with aerodynamic controls there would be no way to maintain the zero *g.* As long as control can be maintained, *g* loading and unloading an aircraft is a highly effective control technique. For slowing down aircraft, a high-*g* turn or roll will rapidly bleed off airspeed. For getting out of a high angle of attack condition, reducing *g* to as much as zero *g* will prevent a stall. A technique used by fighter pilots to accelerate rapidly is to use full thrust and then maneuver to near zero *g.* When this is done from a high-*g* (4 *g* or 5 *g*) maneuver it produces spectacular acceleration.

The Angle of Attack (AOA) Indicator This is a relatively recent development in aircraft instrumentation. The need for this instrument was recognized by Wilbur Wright as early as June 1907, but the production of an economic, reliable system was long in coming. Most modern fighter aircraft are now equipped with these instruments and large jet transports are rapidly being equipped. Currently, standardization of presentation has not been achieved. Most indications are indexed in arbitrary "units" rather than specific angles and some have only warning lights indicating "*slow*,"

INDICATOR	INDEXER	ANGLE OF ATTACK UNIT	AIRSPEED	ATTITUDE
		20.3-30	VERY SLOW	
	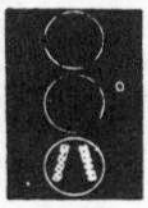	19.7-20.2	SLIGHTLY SLOW	
	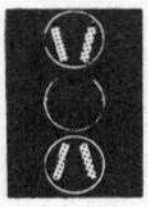	18.7-19.6	ON SPEED	
		18.1-18.6	SLIGHTLY FAST	
		0-18.0	VERY FAST	

Figure 10.3 Angle of attack conversion and displays. *(Courtesy of U.S. Air Force.)*

"*on speed*," or "*fast*" for final approach to landing. The required angle of attack will change with flap setting and not all systems now in use compensate for this. Some systems are affected by airflow distortions caused by landing gear position and are inaccurate with gear either up or down, though in other installations the AOA indicator system compensates for change gear and flap position. These installations usually consist of an indicator on the instrument panel, indexer lights on the wind screen, and a headset tone that increases in pitch as angle of attack is increased. A rudder or stick shaker or pusher may also be incorporated. As presently designed and used, the AOA indicator system is predominantly a stall warning system. With increased use, and since an aircraft wing has a desired angle of attack for any particular maneuver, that is, final approach, climb, maximum endurance, and maximum range, the AOA is rapidly relegating the airspeed indicator to a purely navigational instrument.

JET FIGHTER-TRAINER TRAFFIC PATTERN

Dear to the heart of the pilot of jet fighters and trainers is the "tactical approach" pattern shown in Figure 10.4. Originally designed to keep high-

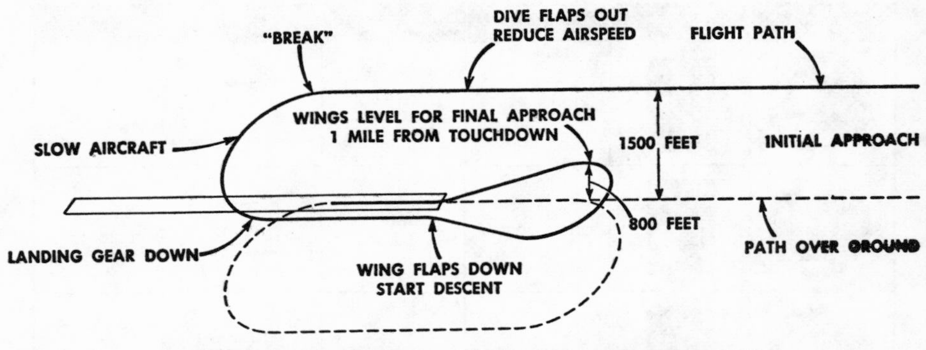

Figure 10.4 Typical jet fighter landing pattern.

performance fighters within gliding distance of the field once the landing approach was started, it found use in early and present small jets because it does permit the rapid landing of many aircraft, as from a formation, usually all low on fuel. It is seldom used by other jets because of passenger discomfort and because jet transports and bombers are usually making some form of instrument approach.

The aircraft enters an initial approach about 3 mi out from the end of the runway at 1500 ft above the terrain. Airspeed on initial approach varies with the airplane, and is about 280 knots for the T-38. On the initial approach, the pilot lines up with the runway or slightly to the traffic side. The *pitch* or *break* point is approximately halfway down the runway. Retarding power slightly, the pilot makes a constant 60° bank to the downwind leg, reaching the gear-lowering speed by exerting *g* forces, and the airspeed decreases proportionately to the *g* forces used in the turn.

APPROACH AND LANDING

From a tactical pattern the normal approach to the runway is from a point ¾ to 1 mi out from its end. At this point, the proper final approach speed, approach angle, and landing attitude are attained. The altitude is normally 400 ft above the terrain. Now only minor throttle corrections are needed because with power well above idle, the newer jet aircraft have excellent acceleration characteristics and minor throttle corrections can change airspeed rapidly. The approach in the T-38 is flat with almost a level flight attitude even though the rate of descent is 500 to 750 fpm. Final approach speed depends on gross weight of the aircraft computed from a standard minimum speed for normal landing weight. For instance, in the T-38 approach speed is 155 knots for aircraft with 1000 lb of fuel or less. One knot is added for every hundred pounds over the thousand.

Extra airspeed on final approach requires more runway for the landing roll. A rule of thumb is: 1% additional airspeed on final approach requires 2% additional roll out on landing. Thus, the *proper* airspeed is important, especially when landing at an airfield with a relatively short runway. Too little airspeed results in getting behind the power curve, and a dangerously high sink rate from which recovery is not possible with the remaining altitude.

Airspeed on touchdown in the T-38 will be approximately 140 knots. As airspeed decreases, the pilot brings the stick back, holding the nose at a 10° to 12° attitude for aerodynamic braking after touchdown. Touchdown occurs on the main gear, and after the nose lowers to the runway at about 100 knots, the pilot begins wheel braking. It is important that the nose wheel not touch down before the main gear, because a porpoising motion, usually curable only by going around, will result.

Landings in the smaller passenger jets are quite similar to the above, except that the nose-high attitude is not so pronounced. Lear Jet approach speeds vary depending on the gross weight of the aircraft. The final approach speed for a Lear Jet weighing 10,900 lb would be 122 knots, while one weighing 10,000 lb should be flown at 117 knots. Passenger comfort being paramount, landings are usually in a flat attitude with the nose gear touching down shortly after the main gear. Their deceleration characteristics do not normally require aerodynamic braking, and the sooner all wheels are on the ground, the sooner wheel braking is effective.

Ground effect must be considered when operating jet aircraft. There is no more effect on jet aircraft than on any lightplane but size, speed and mass make it more obvious to the pilot. Ground effect tends to reduce the angle of downwash and diminishes the effect of wing-tip vortices. The result is a reduction of the aircraft's induced drag when near the ground. Generally ground effect is not a problem during takeoff in jet aircraft since takeoff speed, distance, and acceleration are checked during the takeoff roll, and the rate of acceleration is so rapid as the jet aircraft approaches its takeoff speed and immediately after takeoff that it passes through ground effect quickly.

During landing the effect is more noticeable. Many jet aircraft do not change attitude (pitch angle) for landing. In the F-4 the same pitch angle as was used on approach is used during landing. Increased back stick is required to maintain the attitude constant since ground effect tends to force the nose down and angle of attack is rapidly increasing. In the Boeing 707 a reasonably good landing can be made out of a normal approach without changing attitude. In any aircraft if an excessive speed is maintained during approach the aircraft will appear to, and may in fact, accelerate, if power is not reduced, as it comes into ground effect.

OTHER BUSINESS JET CHARACTERISTICS

The Lear Jet has certain interesting and informative flight characteristics somewhat different from the T-38.

It is usually taxied on one engine to conserve fuel and brakes. The location of the engines close to the fuselage centerline as opposed to being mounted in the wings facilitates single-engine taxiing, and greatly reduces the problem of yaw during single-engine flight. In fact, this yaw is very easily compensated for by rudder and trim.

Like the T-38, the Lear Jet accelerates spectacularly during takeoff, despite the fact that it has no afterburners. During the takeoff roll, the nose-wheel steering is disengaged at about 45 knots, when rudder control becomes effective. The aircraft rotation and lift-off speeds, precomputed, are precisely met, and gear and flaps must be retracted quickly to avoid acceleration beyond the limit speeds.

The Lear Jet accelerates to 300 knots for best climb, then climbs at 300 knots to .7 Mach; from that point it continues to climb at .7 Mach. It requires only 13 min to reach 41,000 ft. However, the takeoff rpm and EGT limit is 5 min, so a power reduction is required during climb to remain within maximum continuous engine limits, which are 100% rpm and about 675° EGT.

Jet executive aircraft such as the Lear Jet are perhaps the most efficient form of high-speed, highly reliable transportation for small groups whose time and flexibility is valuable enough to warrant the expense of operation. As the high-performance aircraft they are, they require meticulous maintenance and professional operation within the performance limits which the designer intended. To a competent and proficient pilot, flying them is sheer delight.

FORCED LANDINGS

The original jet trainers and fighters required pilot techniques for forced landings. As performance advanced to that of modern fighters with performance comparable to and exceeding that of the T-38, forced landing became impracticable and ejection is now the rule. With the advent of business jets without ejection equipment, the requirement again exists, though forced landings are extremely unlikely because all are multiengined aircraft and air start procedures have been made much more reliable.

It is generally recommended that a crash landing with a smaller aircraft be made with the landing gear extended. The gear will most likely tear off on rough terrain, but the process of tearing it off absorbs a great deal of the shock of deceleration, resulting in less serious injury to the occupants. This does not apply to ditching.

The crew of a jet fighter or trainer carries all emergency equipment attached to parachute harness. Ejection is therefore preferred to ditching except at extremely low altitudes.

EJECTION AND BAIL-OUT

Military jet aircraft, particularly trainers and fighters, are equipped with ejection seats. They are necessary because of the impossibility of climbing safely into the high-speed slipstream, and the probability of being unable to clear the empennage. Ejection seats are propelled by an explosive cartridge or by rockets. They are actuated by a trigger in the seat. While the dangers of high-altitude bail-out or ejection—low temperatures, lack of oxygen, and parachute-opening shock—can be minimized by descending to lower altitudes if possible, or by the automatic features of modern parachutes which provide for automatic free fall, opening at below 14,000 ft, the greatest danger is from waiting too long and ejecting from too low an altitude.

With the advent of the rocket seats, the chance of survival from low-altitude and low-airspeed ejection has been greatly increased. Present seats can eject a man at zero altitude and zero airspeed to sufficient height for automatic parachute deployment if the pilot is using the seat properly. The absolute minimum *reliable* altitude for a controlled ejection is 2000 ft. Below that altitude, fatalities increase rapidly. The decision on when to eject must be firmly established in the pilot's mind before the emergency occurs.

The most advantageous aircraft attitude for ejection is a climb. When the aircraft is descending, the sink rate can be so great, and the direction of ejection so far from the actual vertical, that the capabilities of the ejection seat and parachute are greatly compromised. Successful ejections from modern high-speed aircraft require forethought and thorough training.

Supersonic Flight

FLYING THROUGH MACH 1

Since October 14, 1947, when Capt. Charles E. Yeager, USAF, flew the X-1 faster than the speed of sound, supersonic flight has become com-

Figure 10.5 The Bell X-1. Flying high over the Mojave Desert, the Bell X-1 made history as the first aircraft to fly faster than the speed of sound. Now in the Smithsonian Museum. *(U.S. Air Force photograph.)*

monplace. In that flight, the conventional and unpowered controls of the X-1 provided positive stability up to Mach .70. From there to Mach .87 the elevator lost 50% of its effectiveness due to movement of the shock wave across the stabilizer, and Capt. Yeager regained full effectiveness only by readjusting the horizontal stabilizer. This experience, however, resulted in the development of the "flying tail" found on many of today's aircraft.

Light buffeting occurred when entering the transonic speed range, and the right wing became increasingly heavier by Mach .92. In fact, one-third opposite aileron deflection was necessary to hold the airplane level. Once past Mach 1.05, these conditions gradually cleared, though constant nose-up trim was necessary as airspeed increased to Mach 1.25.

Pilots flying modern supersonic aircraft find the experience of supersonic flight unnoteworthy. Control and engine designs have so greatly improved that a pilot's first indication of having gone supersonic may be a glance at his Mach meter. Each aircraft has its own individuality in the transonic and supersonic regions but the early experiences of control reversal, instability, and compressor stalls are largely history. Thermal limitations are and will be the limiting factors for atmospheric high-speed flight in the foreseeable future.

For many pilots, breaking the sound barrier in level flight also breaks a mythical bubble associated with this maneuver. The pilot can trim his aircraft for level flight, advance the throttle to the military power setting and start the afterburner by moving the throttle outboard. Acceleration to

Mach .95 is good. After this speed, acceleration is slower due to high drag rise. Then the pilot detects a hesitancy in his airspeed indicator for a second or two, followed by a more rapid movement of the indicator through Mach 1. Associated with this is a rapid change in altimeter reading, sometimes from 500 to 800 ft, as the shock wave passes over the static ports. Then all settles down again at Mach 1.05 and acceleration continues.

Meanwhile, controlling the airplane is quite normal. A slight increase in nose-down trim is necessary for level flight, indicating positive stability in this range. Lateral control remains as good as ever. The airplane can be turned and rolled, flying as if below the speed of sound. It must be remembered, supersonic flight is not without cost—in pounds of fuel consumed.

HIGH-SPEED STABILITY AND CONTROL

As noted earlier, most high-performance aircraft lack inherent stability. The amount or intensity varies with the aircraft and the particular flight condition, in any case, it makes the pilot's job more difficult.

Dynamic longitudinal damping is one instability characteristic. Longitudinal oscillations occurring from normal acceleration ideally damp to one-tenth amplitude in one cycle only at 10,000 ft in the power-approach configuration, gear and flaps down, and below Mach .89 at 25,000 ft in the cruise configuration. Since good damping throughout the speed range of the aircraft is also necessary for ease of control, pitch dampers are designed and made part of the longitudinal control system, thereby artificially providing the desired stability.

The *dynamic lateral-directional characteristics* of most high-performance aircraft are a headache to the military pilot when maneuvering his airplane as a gun platform. When stability is good (positive), the aircraft resists change caused by rough air and maintains a steady desired path, without rolling and yawing objectionably. Transonic aircraft are equipped with a yaw damper to improve the characteristic tendency. With the yaw damper operating, lateral-directional oscillations dampen almost immediately.

The F-4 provides an example of adequate *static directional stability* since rudder deflection produces a sideslip angle in the proper direction without lightening or reversal of rudder forces. Static lateral-directional stability is positive, with left aileron required to hold a straight path while in a steady left sideslip. From a pilot's viewpoint, the most important aspect is that there is no reversal of rudder or aileron controls throughout the speed range of the aircraft.

OTHER HIGH-PERFORMANCE CHARACTERISTICS

As a Mach 2.0 airplane, the F-4 is an excellent example of other high-performance phenomena.

Thermal Limitations Engine air-inlet temperatures are a recognized limitation of Mach 2.0 aircraft. In channeling the air into the compressor section, the inner chambers must dissipate large amounts of heat generated by the compressing function of the inlet and ducts. Many theories exist on how to cool this air, such as spraying water into the flow, improved duct design, etc.

Duct Problem Supersonic speeds require efficient engine operation and subsonic airflow to the engine. One of the problems is converting supersonic outside air to subsonic speeds and distributing it uniformly around the compressor section of the engine. In the F-4, automatically controlled variable inlet ramps and variable bypass bellmouths in the engine bay control the air volume and velocity delivered to the engine compressor face.

Negative-Dihedral Wings When an aircraft is sideslipped, a rolling moment (dihedral effect) is induced. When left sideslip produces a right rolling moment, the aircraft possesses positive dihedral effect. Considering low-tail and high-tail configured airplanes coupled with any sideslip, the restoring force developed by the induced roll acts through the aerodynamic center of pressure (c.p.) of the aircraft. The high tail raises the c.p., increases the restoring capability of the tail, and in essence increases the positive dihedral effect. Too much positive dihedral introduces objectionable lateral-directional oscillations (Dutch roll). Therefore, wings are given negative dihedral to reduce the overall dihedral effect of the wing and tail combination.

Wing Fuselage Effects Aerodynamic studies and flight-test results indictate that lift, in some cases, continues to increase above the wing stall, indicating that the fuselage itself provides lift. This characteristic can carry the aircraft into an extreme angle-of-attack condition where the horizontal stabilizer is acted upon by disturbed airflow from forward parts of the aircraft and wing downwash. The restoring moments of a high-mounted tail are negated under these conditions and the aircraft will pitch up instead of down when the full stall condition is reached. Clearly this is not a desirable characteristic, since the aircraft usually enters a spin at that point. To prevent the condition from occurring, supersonic aircraft so affected have an automatic pitch-control system that senses pitch rate and angle of attack, warning the pilot of the condition and causing automatic control movement to keep the aircraft from entering the extreme attitude.

Ventral Fin Supersonic aircraft often tend to lose directional stability above Mach 1.0 due to characteristics of supersonic airflow. To counter this effect, such aircraft require increased vertical fin area to restore directional stability. Some have a ventral fin below the fuselage for this purpose which is always in the free-air stream; in contrast, the vertical fin is partially blanked out due to the downward circular airflow from the forward fuselage and wings.

Thrust and Drag Some of today's supersonic aircraft can exceed Mach 2.0 and altitudes above 100,000 ft because their thrust-drag characteristics greatly vary with change in altitude. Figure 10.1 typifies the thrust-drag relationship at low altitude since the "power required" curve may also represent a "drag curve." The excess thrust available for developing rate of climb and accelerating to higher speeds is the important point. Where the thrust and drag curves cross, thrust and drag are equal; here speed and altitude stabilize. At low altitude and in the transonic speed range, drag rises steeply and requires a relatively high level of thrust to attain supersonic speeds. At altitudes around 35,000 ft, thrust exceeds drag over the complete speed range for a typical Mach 2.0 temperature-limited aircraft. The excess thrust over drag at this altitude results in higher rates of climb and aircraft ceiling. As altitude increases, the thrust-drag relationship changes and there is a new point where the thrust-drag curves meet. This is the supersonic ceiling of the aircraft, and its location depends on the particular aircraft configuration. Although today's supersonic aircraft have a supersonic ceiling, their speeds at this ceiling are well above their stall speeds. Consequently, this speed or energy can be exchanged at any time for altitude. This fact introduces the so-called *energy-transfer climb* or *zoom climb* technique. The amount of zoom capability available can provide a one-shot tactical advantage when additional altitude is needed.

COMPRESSOR STALLS

At some time during the jet pilot's career, he may encounter engine stalls. This will most likely occur when he initially advances the throttle, rather rapidly, while taxiing away from the line. It could also happen under low-airspeed maneuvering conditions at high altitude and high angle of attack, during rapid throttle movement, or under any conditions that will create an instability of the airflow over the blades of the engine compressor section. Stalls are characteristic of the twin-spool engine as well as other engine types. At times the stall is a very dramatic condition. It is variously referred to as a "pulsation," "chugging," "choo-choo," or "explosion"—and at times it certainly does sound like an explosion. Engine stall or breakdown of airflow over the compressor blades is sometimes compared to breakdown of airflow over a stalling wing. Stalls vary in severity and stem from marginally overrated engines and faulty duct design. Probably the worst type encountered are the "machine gun" variety. When this occurs, usually at high altitude, the engine cannot recover unless the throttle is retarded and the aircraft pitch attitude lowered to increase speed. If this is not done, rapid overheating of the engine occurs and engine failure follows.

SPECIAL DEVICES

The nature and complexity of high-performance aircraft demand special devices to provide satisfactory inherent stability for all flight conditions. For example, a vertical tail that gives satisfactory directional stability in the landing pattern and at high subsonic speeds may be entirely inadequate at supersonic speeds; damping in pitch may be satisfactory subsonically but intolerable supersonically. Considering these facts, it has been necessary to design stability devices that change or augment the inherent characteristics of the aircraft.

Yaw dampers on modern high-performance aircraft sense yaw and dampen reactions as a function of altitude and Mach number. They also keep the airplane in directional trim and give turn coordination automatically without the reactions being apparent at the pilot's controls. Yaw dampers are also designed to correct for either adverse or favorable yaw that develops when an aircraft is initially rolled. The yaw damper, based on a lateral accelerometer which senses the slip or skid of the aircraft, induces correction of infinitesimal yaw variations from the desired flight path. The end result is a better gun platform for military aircraft and a better ride for commercial aircraft.

Pitch Dampers The pitch damper is similar in principle to a yaw damper. However, unlike the yaw damper—which operates on a control that is rarely used except for trim by the pilots of modern fighters—the pitch damper operates on a control which is continuously in use, frequently at maximum rates of displacement. As a consequence, the pitch damper is designed to eliminate residual pitch deviations without interfering with the pitch changes made by the pilot to maneuver his aircraft. The pitch damper is primarily needed for supersonic flight at high altitudes, where the air is thinner, and the characteristic restoring qualities of the aircraft to external or pilot-induced motion is less, despite supersonic speeds.

Roll Dampers Although, academically speaking, aircraft do not inherently produce roll oscillations directly related to the lateral axis of the aircraft, there is a need for roll stability devices in high-performance aircraft to assist the pilot in maintaining roll attitude during climbs and cruise, and to improve the spiral divergent qualities of some aircraft. (An aircraft with poor spiral tendencies tends to steepen rapidly in a descending turn.) These dampers sense roll rate from the roll-rate gyro of the autopilot, inducing small aileron deflections to compensate for this condition.

Mach Box High-performance aircraft require pitch trim changes throughout the wide range of their speeds, especially through the transonic speed range. The Mach box has been devised to reposition the horizontal stabilizer continuously as a function of Mach number, so that undesirable trim changes are minimized and necessary ones are in the proper direction. When speed is increased the nose of the aircraft is trimmed down to maintain level flight, and vice versa.

Pitch "g" Limiter The possible malfunction of automatic pilot systems can create control movements that will induce flight outside the structural limits of the aircraft. This is possible because these aircraft are equipped with irreversible hydraulic control systems. The pitch *"g"* limiter is a typical "black box" which senses a malfunction in an automatic control system and in microseconds disengages the system before structural damage can occur. To be effective, the device must be electronic (because of the time element) and reliable (to prevent false alarms). The *g* limiter utilizes pitch-rate gyro information, which, when added to the output of a linear accelerometer, is amplified and used to trip a sensitive relay placed in the automatic flight system. Here then is an electronic device that prevents damage to an aircraft in a manner that could not normally be accomplished by the pilot.

Stick Shaker and Automatic Pitch-Control Systems The stall in any aircraft is a precarious maneuver. While in some high-performance aircraft the nose drops in a stall, in others the aircraft pitches up with subsequent loss of control. Some aircraft that lack proper stall-warning characteristics need stall-warning devices. The warning takes the form of a shaking control column, audible buzzer, or visual warning light. These devices are actuated prior to the stall, normally by sensing units that detect either angle of attack or a breakdown of the airflow pattern over the aircraft wing.

In aircraft that develop pitch-up, a more complex system is involved. When the aircraft enters the pitch-up region, a push force of between 25 and 30 lb is automatically applied to the control stick to return the aircraft to a normal flight attitude. The stick-pusher mechanism is actuated by angle-of-attack probes on the fuselage and a pitch-rate gyro which detects accelerated maneuvers that will result in pitch-up. While the pilot can overpower the stick pusher, it is in some aircraft deenergized when the wing flaps are in the takeoff or land position to prevent a hard nose-down movement at low altitude during takeoff or landing.

Unconventional Aircraft

Today's high-performance tactical aircraft are the direct result of aerodynamic testing of the "X-Series" or experimental aircraft. In the short span of ten years these aircraft were used to penetrate the sound barrier at Mach 1.0 and to help solve the complex problems of stability, control, and aerodynamic heating associated with speeds of 2100 mph and altitudes up to 126,000 ft. The requirement for "X-Series" aircraft was visualized by Mr. John Stack of the Langley Aeronautical Laboratory, NASA, and made a reality by the military and industry. The combined efforts of many individuals—some of whom gave their lives—translated the idiosyncrasies of research aircraft into practical applications, resulting in the increased performance and improved stability of our present-day service aircraft. The Bell X-2 and the North American X-15 are two outstanding examples.

BELL X-2 RESEARCH AIRCRAFT

A low-wing, single-seat, rocket-propelled, supersonic aircraft; stainless steel, K-Monel metal (alloy of copper and nickel) construction; landing gear, single center-fuselage skid, two inboard wing skids and nose wheel; 40° swept-back wings, 10% thick circular arc airfoils.

Performance Maximum speed Mach 3.20 at 67,000 ft; maximum altitude, 126,200 ft; thrust, between 2500 and 15,000 lb.

Dimensions Wing span, 32.3 ft; fuselage, 37.8 ft; height of tail from centerline, 9.1 ft.

Weight Launch, 24,910 lb; landing 12,375 lb.

The X-2 was a small airplane. Close inspection of this sleek, white rocket plane hunched slightly nose-down on her main skid and nose wheel revealed her true size. You could rest your arm on the canopy sill when standing alongside. The pressurized cockpit had barely enough room for a pilot, but everything was there—control stick, throttle, a small panel of instruments, and about 4 ft of nose up front. The fuselage tapered aft, somewhat resembling the X-1. The wings were swept back, evenly cambered on both surfaces; leading edges were sharp, a 10% thickness-ratio wing. There were leading and trailing edge flaps and a boundary-layer fence located on the upper surface of each wing to improve the low-speed pitching characteristics. Ailerons were outboard with blunt trailing edges to improve lateral control at transonic speeds. The flying tail sat just above the fuselage. The high vertical stabilizer was squared off and somehow dwarfed the rest of the aircraft; its size was intended to maximize directional control throughout the speed and altitude range of the aircraft. Two funnel-like nozzles of the rocket engine protruded from the fuselage end.

The X-2's control system was completely hydraulic, irreversible, and powered by storage battery. Pilot escape was provided by a detachable nose section which was separated just aft of the cockpit by a powder charge. After separation, a ribbon-type parachute would be released to decelerate and stabilize the capsule during its descent. Then at the proper time, the pilot could kick clear of the capsule and use his personal parachute for landing.

The X-2 had to be taken aloft by a mother ship and launched. Precious fuel replaced the extra weight of a landing gear and its space requirements.

Once aloft, the pilot entered from the mother plane below 10,000 ft, because of oxygen requirements above that altitude. Release of the X-2 was usually at 30,000 ft, depending upon atmospheric conditions. In order to familiarize pilots with the dead-stick handling qualities of the aircraft, initial checkout flights involved empty weight releases. Top speed under these conditions was kept to approximately 220 knots.

Full of fuel, the X-2 would "drop out" around 225 knots. At this heavy gross-weight condition, a mild airframe buffet was associated with initial flight and acceleration. Once safely clear of the mother aircraft (generally 6 sec after drop), the pilot started the engine, and the aircraft was rotated into an optimum low-drag flight path of approximately 30° while the elevator still provided maximum effectiveness. The pilot aimed for an indicated airspeed of 350 knots.

Two particularly outstanding flights made on the X-2 determined peaks of the flight envelope. One flight was flown by Capt. Iven C. Kinchloe, USAF, who later lost his life during a test flight. He reached an altitude of 126,200 ft. The drop and initial flight path followed the standard low-drag profile. Acceleration was normal. The X-2 was well stabilized prior to reaching Mach 1.0 at 50 sec after drop. The indicated airspeed was stabilized on 350 knots, and the altimeter read 41,000 ft. Then a slight lateral directional oscillation developed and a faint low-frequency longitudinal pitching movement was evident. At this time Capt. Kinchloe pulled the X-2 up into its optimum climb attitude. At about 75 sec he applied full-up stabilizer. The altitude was 56,000 ft at Mach 1.25. The indicated airspeed decreased slightly and the maximum climb angle reached 38°. In the next 20 sec the X-2 climbed 16,000 ft and held Mach 1.3. The normal acceleration was 1.2*g*.

"Burnout" came at 104,000 ft about 2 min and 20 sec after drop. The aircraft yawed nose-left and developed a left roll. At the same time it entered a ballistic flight path. Normal acceleration approached 0*g* and held below 0.2*g* for about 40 sec. The pilot finally stopped the left roll by judicious use of right aileron; however, he made no attempt to level the aircraft. *At the peak of 126,000 ft, Mach number was about 1.65 and indicated airspeed 110 knots.*

The pilot applied nose-down stick, which instigated a slow-motion longitudinal pitching oscillation. Still holding a climb attitude of 20°, prohibiting visual reference to the horizon, the X-2 fell back to the earth's atmosphere, one wing low, maintaining a constant-angle-of-attack descent. The pilot held full-aft stick until speed increased and normal acceleration rose to about 3*g*. He completed the pull-out at 40,000 ft, near Mach 1.0. The altitude reached during this flight was the highest flown by man at the time.

The last flight of the X-2 ended in tragedy. It was flown by the late Capt. Milburn G. Apt, USAF. The mission was planned to obtain maximum Mach-number performance. The drop was normal, and initial climb followed a low-drag profile. Fifteen seconds after drop, indicated airspeed reached 300 knots, altitude held at 30,000 ft. Slight airframe buffet and faintly noticeable lateral directional oscillations were prevalent. Acceleration increased and the X-2 attained the aim speed of 320 knots in 45 sec, holding stead on a maximum climb angle of 33.6°. Altitude gradually reached 35,000 ft and steadily increased. At 55 sec the X-2 had passed Mach 1.0, holding the aim airspeed and passing 39,000 ft. Flight was stable, no buffet, no oscillations. At 90 sec Capt. Apt started a gradual pushover to hold the climb schedule. The aircraft continued climbing to 60,000 ft, at Mach 1.40. Mach held steady while the X-2 pushed through the transonic drag rise. Then airspeed leaped ahead and the plane reached a peak altitude of approximately 72,000 ft, 2 min after drop. Indicated airspeed at this point was 400 knots, Mach number 2.20 and increasing.

Captain Apt continued the pushover into a slight dive and the engine continued to burn an additional 5.2 sec, longer than had been attained on any previous flight. At burnout the X-2 was 67,000 ft and Mach 3.20 (2094 ground-speed mph). Immediately after burnout, a pitching oscillation developed from the loss in thrust and induced stability. It damped in 10 sec. In the meantime, Capt. Apt elected to turn for home.

As speed decreased below Mach 3.18, the aircraft angle of attack was increased to maintain altitude. When Capt. Apt started the left turn, the angle of attack further increased and directional stability lowered to a near critical condition. He applied corrective aileron to stop the increasing left bank caused by dihedral effect. Yaw resulted from this action and exceeded the restoring action of the tail caused by sideslip. Also at this point the ailerons lost their effectiveness to control roll velocity. Finally critical roll velocity for inertial coupling was reached; the X-2 became uncontrollable about all three axes and the airplane crashed, killing the

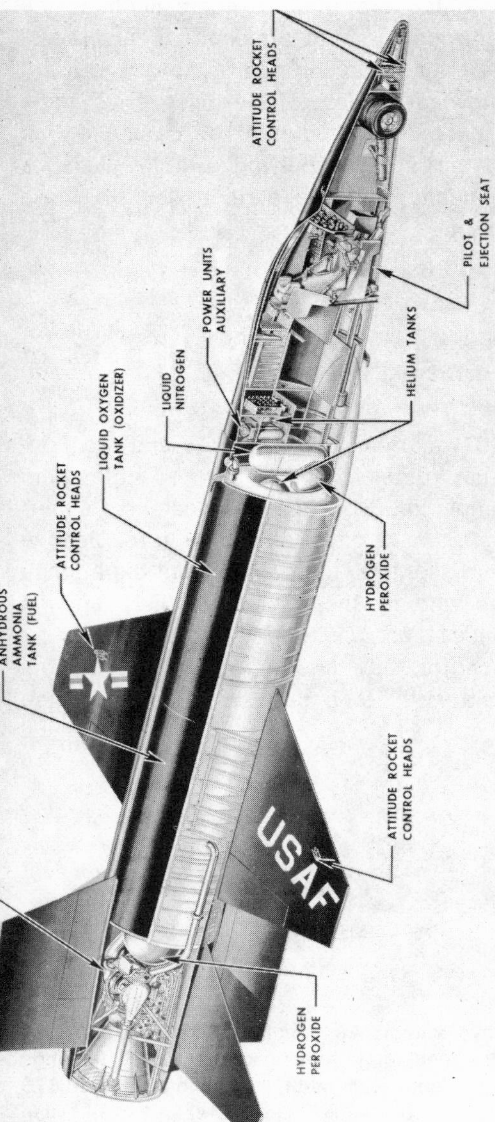

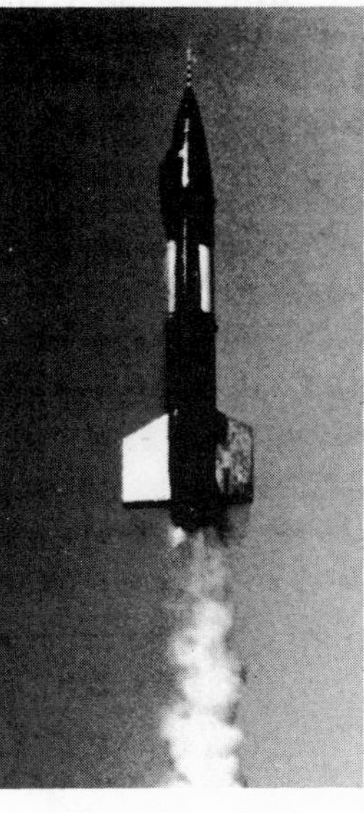

Figure 10.6 The North American X-15, flown by North American, NASA, and Air Force pilots, has already surpassed all speed and altitude records. Length 50 ft, span 22 ft, height 13 ft, wing area 200 sq ft, launch wt 31,275 lb. *(Courtesy of North American Aviation, Inc.)*

pilot. The speed attained during this flight is the fastest flown by man at the time.

There were a number of experimental aircraft to follow the X-1 and X-2. Some are modified tactical fighter aircraft, but others such as the X-15 were designed for no other function than atmospheric and aeronautical research. All of these aircraft have contributed to our present advanced state of aeronautical knowledge. More of the discoveries made by these research aircraft have been translated into the design of the SR-71 and YF-12 than any single airframe now flying. But for decades to come the entire aviation community will owe a deep debt to these experimental aircraft and their pilots.

Sustained Supersonic Flight

Supersonic transports (SST) such as the Concorde and the Boeing SST will soon be flying regular routes. The Air Force's supersonic B-1 bomber is apparently near completion. Experience in sustained supersonic flight as the most economical speed of an aircraft is rare. Despite the short supersonic dashes of many fighters, the only current experience is that of the Air Force aircrews who fly the Lockheed YF-12 and its counterpart in long-range reconnaissance, the SR-71.

The YF-12 is still a test interceptor, but the SR-71, as used by the Strategic Air Command in unit strength, is a peerless reconnaissance aircraft.

Figure 10.7 Lockheed SR-71. Used by Strategic Air Command, USAF, in strategic reconnaissance. Mach 3 speed range, ceiling above 80,000 ft, range more than 2000 nm, and global with mid-air refueling. Two J-58TB engines rated at 30,000 lb thrust each. "Double delta" wing, span 55 ft. Overall length, 107 ft, height of tail, 18 1/2 ft. The YF-12, an experimental long-range interceptor, is one version of this aircraft, and is used largely for experimental purposes. *(U.S. Air Force photograph.)*

DESCRIPTION

The airframe design, called a "double delta," offers an airfoil of remarkable lifting characteristics over its entire area. Though the "wing" shape is located rearward, the entire thin fuselage, throughout its length, generates lift. The lift developed by the forebody in particular is essential to the excellent stability characteristics shown in the entire speed range of the aircraft.

While many supersonic flight characteristics described earlier apply equally to the SR-71, its capability for economic cruise at supersonic speed is unique.

SR-71 limit speed is above Mach 3.0, and it becomes more efficient as Mach number increases. In fact, it is above Mach 2.0 that range factors are superior to those of subsonic flight.

Efficiency for any supersonic aircraft, whether flown in a dash profile or a cruise condition, is dependent a great deal upon drag reduction. The dominant controllable source of drag in supersonic cruise is the trim condition of the elevons, a control surface peculiar to delta-type aircraft.

As the aircraft moves into the supersonic ranges the center of lift moves aft, and to avoid the use of excessive trim to counter this condition, the center of gravity must move aft also. This is accomplished by automatic control and distribution of aircraft fuel so as to complement the center of lift. Since the SR-71 is a military aircraft, designed primarily for a standard, one-profile mission, c.g. control can be automatically programmed with little or no attention required from the flight crew.

Any time the standard profile is changed, such as for extensive subsonic cruise, the pilot must control his fuel distribution manually to provide optimum c.g. for the existing speed and center of lift location.

The pilot can use rule-of-thumb c.g. limits as a guide for varying speed ranges. A c.g. location indicator in the cockpit gives an easy reference for fuel transfer requirements. A pitch trim indicator permits monitoring the trimmed position of the elevon.

Center of gravity trimmed too far forward during any portion of flight is at best uneconomical. Trimmed too far aft, it can cause a dangerous condition of instability.

Speeds of Mach 3.0 and above create many departures from conventional flying procedures. Autopilot control is for the most part essential during supersonic flight. Although it would be perfectly safe for a pilot to hand-fly an entire mission above Mach 3.0, precision would suffer and errors would be magnified.

A very sophisticated navigational system employing inertial guidance with star-tracking updating is utilized to provide the accuracy and timeliness needed for inputs to the autopilot. Deviations from programmed track are absolutely minimal throughout global operations using this combination. Displays from the navigational system are also presented to the flight crew and, in the event of an autopilot malfunction, the pilot can fly the aircraft manually along the same course, though some degradation in track maintenance results.

Because of the automated navigation capability, the flight crew need not prepare a conventional type of flight plan. The entire mission is prepared and "canned" by a staff of technicians. The result is a computer tape which is fed into the astro-inertial navigation platform, and 35 mm film strips installed in projectors in the crew compartments. The projectors automatically display a map presentation of the aircraft position at all times, regardless of speeds flown. They also show pertinent flight data such as fuel, times, heading, climbs, and descents. Mission planning for the supersonic flight crew then consists of studying the mission from back-up maps and cruise cards which are prepared for crew use in the event of display failure in flight.

PILOT AND RECONNAISSANCE SYSTEMS OFFICER (RSO)

These constitute the basic aircrew. They fly in tandem, in separate, isolated cockpits, dependent on interphone for communications. They both wear the full-pressure suit, (Figure 7.12) on all flights. Though these suits are encumbering and detract from flight comfort, they are considered economical and safe in comparison with the much heavier "capsule" which would provide "shirt-sleeve" flying. The military concessions to battle damage and crew ejection would of course not be present in the pressurized civilian SST environment.

Crews have ejected safely, using the installed ejection seats, from ground level to the limit speed and altitude of the aircraft.

The bulk of pressure-suit equipment makes cockpit layout very important, because it is very difficult to see or reach anything not in view with the head positioned forward. For this reason the forward part of cockpits are extremely "busy." There are conventional stick and rudders, twin throttles, and familiar high-performance cockpit instruments, modified as supersonic flight requires.

The RSO, a rated navigator, actually performs many duties that would fall to a copilot in a plane with a bigger crew. He has duplicate flight instruments (and must be proficient in interpreting them), fuel monitor systems, his reconnaissance system controls, and the astro-inertial navigation computer controls and displays. Crew coordination and standardization are extremely critical. There is no room for mistakes or confusion at Mach 3.0.

When aviation vaulted from propellers to jets the compression of time was considered to be a near insurmountable obstacle for all but the most adept of crew members. It has proven not so. SR-71 crews feel they are now sampling another such quantum compression, and that only time will tell the ability of the average crew member to adapt successfully. The RSO reads all checklists for both cockpits so as to free the pilot from distractions. The aircraft and crew are carefully monitored by a host of support technicians, including crew physical examinations prior to every flight. Ground crew checks continue right up to takeoff time.

TAKEOFF AND CLIMB

The aircraft uses afterburners during takeoff, allowing operation from conventional runways. Liftoff occurs slightly over 200 knots. The best subsonic climb speed is 400 knots to Mach .90. Conventional FAA instrument departures are made after takeoff. Since the most damaging and annoying sonic booms, the nemesis of supersonic flight, occur at lower altitudes, the flight path is planned carefully over unpopulated areas for beginning initial acceleration to supersonic speeds.

When supersonic, the crew transitions to a "triple display indicator" (TDI) which presents a computerized, digital readout of equivalent airspeed (KEAS), Mach number, and altitude. Although conventional pilot static instruments are also in the cockpit, the TDI presentation is used for supersonic accuracy since it is corrected for temperatures, compressibility, and altitude.

Programmed turns during the acceleration phase are avoided because they seriously degrade climb and acceleration performance due to the increased angle of attack. Acceleration is also a time of very high fuel consumption because of power requirements and relatively low altitudes. Corridor-type departures are very desirable after going supersonic. Because of the high fuel consumption, it is very critical to the success of the mission that, once begun, the acceleration to cruise speed and altitude not be interrupted. This proves unwieldy for traffic controllers but will be an essential factor in SST planning.

SUPERSONIC EQUIPMENT AND TECHNIQUE AT CRUISE

The SR-71 has flight control damper systems in all three axes, a Mach trim system that automatically generates pitch trim during acceleration and deceleration, and a "stick shaker" system to warn of approach to limiting angles of attack.

High-Mach cruise requires that external rotating beacons retract flush with the skin to avoid burning off. There is a tiny periscope mounted in the pilot's canopy to let him view the top of the fuselage and engines in flight. The blinding glare of high-altitude sunlight is muted by multi-positioned sunshades.

The extreme temperatures of high-Mach cruise require special precautions. Titanium is used extensively, since it is both light and can retain its shape despite the severely high temperatures experienced.

Yet there are limiting temperatures, most critical at the face of the engines, which the pilot must watch and control. On leading edges, temperatures of over 1000°F are sustained. To touch the cockpit windshield, even with an air-conditioned pressure-suit glove, is like touching a hot stove barehanded.

On reaching cruise altitude and Mach, the pilot throttles back to about one third of the fuel flow needed during the early stages of supersonic acceleration. The resulting range factors are most impressive and confirm the vital need for uninterrupted climb from low altitude.

Now the flight crew is primarily concerned with monitoring the aircraft condition, with navigation, and with the operation of required military equipment. The autopilot, placed in "Mach hold," or "KEAS hold" function, controls pitch to give smooth speed performance. In "Auto-Nav" (automatic navigation) position, the roll and yaw axes are controlled so that the aircraft follows precisely the computer-fed flight plan. The pilot must be alert to increase power manually to hold speed in programmed turns. A Mach 3 turn of 360° requires a radius of about 90 mi, depending on the angle of bank required and the angle of attack allowed.

The engine air inlet system works continuously to provide optimum control of inlet pressure, and makes constant, minute adjustments in air bypass doors and spike location. This compensates for altitude changes, speed deviations, turns, and out-of-trim conditions which might exist in yaw.

At high altitudes, though always in VFR cruising conditions, the pilot flies almost entirely on instruments.

External visual references are not only limited but can be misleading when maneuvers are being performed, such as turns or angle of attack changes with airspeed alterations. There is simply no time for sight-seeing, although the view is breathtaking. The conventional pilot static instruments are of very limited value during supersonic cruise. Inherent lag, reversals, and inaccuracies make them useful only as a backup or emergency reference. Instrumentation for supersonic cruise is still in the infant stage of development and a variety of approaches are being tried.

The basic flight director system presents a reasonable navigation picture, but newer director models are in development which display dual DME's and backup TACAN information for simultaneous selection and instantaneous presentations.

Flight reference platforms need major engineering improvements in their design to reduce inherent errors in heading, pitch, and roll axis during the vastly extended periods of acceleration, deceleration, and turns. The primary reference source for accurate attitude and heading displays falls on the astro-inertial navigation platform with the standard Flight Reference System serving as a poor backup.

Angle of attack information is one of the most critical displays available to the pilot. It is very conveniently displayed by a modified glide slope indicator or "bug" on the left of the attitude director indicator (Figure 5.42). This "bug" shows angle of attack information except when the pilot switches to ILS mode, when it reverts to its normal purpose, showing degrees above or below glide slope.

The angle of attack indicator is backed up by "shakers" and audio warnings as angle of attack limits and limit rates of approach to critical angles of attack are approached.

Pitch corrections require habitual precision and rapid cross-check because a ¼ bar width attitude indicator correction can result in pitch excursions that have devastating effect on speed and altitude. The "instantaneous" vertical speed indicator is a great help in resolving angle of attack, pitch, and attitude corrections.

CRUISING While cruising, SR-71 pilots usually maintain Mach constant on the TDI, and allow airspeed to decrease slowly as altitude increases with fuel burn-off. Reversing this procedure, or establishing a different constant requires considerable practice in both the aircraft and the flight simulator. A momentary excursion beyond the target or limit of one parameter is usually a "wipeout," or near loss of control, on the other two. From this it is evident that continuing research and development in high-speed instrumentation is vital.

The YF-12 uses vertical tapes (Figure 5.42), while the SR-71 uses round dials. Both aircraft have the supersonic TDI supplementing the flight director system. Pilots who fly both aircraft express preference for the tape display as easier to interpret.

Monitoring the condition of the aircraft systems and engines fully occupies the remainder of the pilot's time. Many of the aircraft systems, such as the engine air inlets, must be operating at optimum at all times and demand immediate attention from the pilot if malfunctions occur. He must also show immediate response to a c.g. which moves 1° beyond desired, an inlet temperature which reaches the limit, a bank angle which may be a few degrees in error or a simple FAA advisory of conflicting traffic.

The lack of timely response to the development of such conditions can result in exposure to conditions of instability, equipment damage, violent inlet shock wave expulsions, and gross course deviations. All of these conditions can develop rapidly from an otherwise serene and uneventful flight if crew attention wanders. Recovery from such conditions can be time-consuming and operationally degrading at best. Communications, which are frequently an untimely distraction, are handled by the RSO, whose duties are usually (though not always) less critical than the pilot's.

Clear air turbulence is occasionally encountered at high altitudes and can be very disconcerting due to the sharp, sudden impact associated with high speeds. This is essentially a matter of education, however, since the *g* forces exerted on the aircraft at such a high altitude are acceptable, despite the high Mach condition. They are usually minimal in duration because of the speed.

Present weather forecasting is rapidly becoming quite accurate in determining the location and severity of CAT. Large air mass temperature changes are also quite noticeable in supersonic cruise. They are detected by rather subtle but sudden changes in the indications of Mach, altitude, and KEAS. These temperature deviations are also passed quite rapidly and usually constitute more of a nuisance than a discomfort or hazard.

A similar, subtle excursion is frequently encountered when cruising the aircraft at its ceiling altitude. A long period oscillation, known as a "phugoid," develops around the pitch axis. It is a common characteristic of longitudinal stability and constitutes a very gradual interchange of potential and kinetic energies about some target or equilibrium speed and altitude. It is usually handled adequately by the autopilot and creates only a minor physical sense of altitude and speed change that would hardly be discernible to a non-crew member.

Collision Avoidance Generally it is considered a "see and be seen" environment for the few military aircraft that operate above Flight Level 600, but the traffic is a little more dense than one might suspect. B-57's and U-2's have been there for years. FAA has become increasingly concerned over traffic separation above FL 600 and have put into effect a modified control system that places all traffic on a common, discrete UHF voice frequency and employs a common SIF code. Flight crews must give their altitudes in code to each new controller as they enter his area of responsibility.

Reporting altitudes in the clear will be a necessary change in the future. Controllers provide such traffic advisories as possible to minimize conflicting tracks and provide a 5000-ft altitude separation. With a head-on closure rate of over 4000 mph, it is easy to see why controllers are concerned about how to evaluate control problems and issue instructions to two SR-71's. Of course the capability for a Mach 3.0 aircraft to accomplish meaningful maneuvers is severely limited. For this reason slower high-altitude aircraft, such as the U-2, are asked to do most of the maneuvering involved. Pilots have also discovered that momentary use of the aircraft fuel jettison system will create an immediate "contrail" of many miles which substantially aids in mutual visual detection. In the future, hard altitude assignments for SST aircraft, in lieu of the cruise climb profiles now used by the military, will probably be necessary for safe traffic separation.

SONIC BOOM

One of the most controversial aspects of supersonic flying is, and will continue to be, the sonic boom. As mentioned before, the most damaging boom effects occur when the aircraft is at medium altitudes during the acceleration and deceleration phases. The overpressures at these times can be quite severe and great care must be exercised in selecting routes of flight. Since pressures from supersonic shock waves vary with the speed, altitude, and size of the aircraft, a comparison of the SR-71 with future SST's would be theoretical. The SR is relatively small (approximately 107 ft long) and the overpressures that result from its sonic booms are reasonably light because of the altitudes involved. Even so, it can constitute a large nuisance factor as was proven during an extended supersonic boom test program initiated several years ago.

Although the total test is still not completed and the final results will not be published until some time in the future, it is known that literally thousands of alarmed victims lodged complaints when the SR was purposely and repeatedly flown directly over many of the biggest cities in the United States. It is clear that an SST program will have many problems to overcome in the area of sonic booms due to its larger size and resulting higher overpressures. Daily training flights in the SR now cross the country from coast to coast but purposely and painstakingly avoid all metropolitan areas. They are flown within a timetable that prevents too frequent a repetition of specific tracks. In this manner pilots have survived over four years of continual training with relatively few complaints and even fewer damage claims.

DECELERATION

Deceleration from high Mach is generally a reverse of the crew procedures employed during the acceleration. The most critical phase of planning a deceleration is the accurate initiation of descent procedures a set distance from projected subsonic level-off point. All understandings and clearances with traffic controllers have to be confirmed prior to initiation descent since, for all practical purposes, it is on irrevocable decision. Since altitude and equivalent airspeed (KEAS) are usually undergoing a constant change, descent timing must be continually updated. It will usually require in excess of 300 mi to descend and decelerate from above Mach 3.0 to an altitude from which a conventional instrument approach can be initiated, or to an altitude for air refueling. A delay of several seconds can result in missing the target by miles, just as in a space reentry and splashdown. Although some latitude for adjustment of the descent profile is available to the pilot it is still rather limited because of the established inlet configuration, engine temperatures, and fuel consumption. Communications become extremely critical and crew actions must be paced well ahead of the aircraft throughout the entire flight.

LANDING

Upon reentering the subsonic speed regime, and the altitudes of conventional aircraft, the SR fits beautifully into normal traffic molds. The maneuverability of the vehicle, wide selection of compatible speeds, and adaptability to standard instrument approach procedures all tend to minimize the dramatic differences that existed only moments before. The SR pilot does have the difficulty of limited visibility in subsonic traffic. He is not only encumbered by the restrictions of the full-pressure suit but has rather small windows out the sides of his canopy. Forward visibility is quite good.

Conventional TACAN/ILS and radar instrument approaches are suitable for the SR. An exception is the use of a "modified precision approach" at bases where the SR's are stationed. This provides for a glide slope which is flatter by ½° and has a glide path ground intercept point short of the runway. These approaches are restricted for use by the SR's and are a concession to their float characteristics when entering into ground effect. Conventional radar approaches are considered acceptable at alternate fields, if required.

Ground effect during landing is very noticeable and speeds must be accurately controlled or excessive float can result before touchdown. There are no landing flaps or speed brake features on the aircraft. As soon as the aircraft touches down a large landing parachute is deployed which results in a very dramatic deceleration. Differential braking is quite touchy, despite a good anti-skid system, and care must be exercised to avoid excessive tire wear. The feel of the brake system is quite diluted because of the heavy pressure suit footgear, and a degree of trial and error exists in developing a good braking technique. Nose-wheel steering visibility from the cockpit is adequate for conventional taxiing. The aircraft retains a very high residual heat from its exposure to the high-Mach cruise and ground personnel must use care handling it immediately after completing a sustained high-Mach cruise leg.

Several turns in a holding pattern or low-altitude air work before landing will result in adequate cooling.

Flying Large Multiengine Aircraft

The complexity and cost of flying multiengine aircraft are such that their crews are professionals, especially in attitude and outlook. The professional multiengine pilot, who loves the beauty and dignity of the "magnesium monsters," is invariably a man with a passion for precision and a deeply developed sympathy for things mechanical and aeronautical. "Straight and level" flight—scorned by the single-engine fighter or sport-plane pilot—is to him an absorbing succession of familiar, always changing events. With 200 hr in an airplane, he begins to feel that he knows it well; he can place it precisely where he wants it with an exact combination of flight and power control. Yet, in emergency, when faced with the loss of part of the airplane's capabilities, his flying skill is such that, coupled with intimate knowledge of the airplane's every flight characteristic, he can reduce the aircraft to the simple proportions of a trainer plane.

What is different about multiengine flying? First, in all except the light twins, the plane demands a crew. One man cannot handle it alone. The crew members are specialists in engineering, navigation, radio, and in caring for passengers or cargo. The pilot is their captain. It is up to him to develop the closely integrated teamwork essential for efficient flying—efficient enough to provide either a profit (in commercial flying) or a measure of superiority against an enemy in wartime.

Second, there are from two to several engines. They eliminate the problem of the single-engine pilot—constant consciousness of a place to set down—but they introduce complexities in control.

Third, multiengine planes are heavy, and their load can change by 60 tons or more in a single flight. With their enormous momentum is a degree of complexity and calls for a high order of planning and control.

FLIGHT PLANNING

In a commercial airline, a large business fleet, or a military organization, much of the burden of planning may be taken over from the flight crew by the operations section. Nevertheless, a flight plan must be prepared, and the crew must know the plan before takeoff. Even a flight over a route that the crew flies regularly requires detailed new-flight planning to accommodate load, weather, wind, and runway limitations. While nowadays this process is usually a computer process, the steps are the same.

As the first step in flight planning, the crew or operations section assembles the known information concerning the flight to be made. This will include load to be carried, destination, route to be flown, en-route stops, and time schedule to be followed—perhaps half around the world. They agree on a tentative general plan.

The pilots plan the takeoff and departure, fitting it into traffic control procedures of the departure airfield. They study the weather forecast for the route and the destination, and the location of possible alternate landing fields. They plan for approach and landing at destination under any weather conditions. They may draw up a detailed communications plan for position reporting, and also do the specialized planning for any function or position not covered by the crew.

If the crew includes a navigator, he assembles his materials and plans the flight in as great detail as necessary, generally following the procedures outlined in Chapter 12.

The flight engineer (or one of the pilots if the crew does not have one) obtains a loading list or manifest, to give him the approximate load so that he can estimate the weight and center of gravity. Using performance charts for the airplane, he determines the optimum altitudes and recommends them to the pilot. If these altitudes cannot be flown for reasons of traffic, wind, or weather, the best possible compromises are made. With altitudes selected he can make final determination of the best long-range airspeeds. This information he gives to the navigator, who develops a no-wind flight plan, or a metro wind flight plan based on forecast winds. Fuel requirements are then computed, and the plan is complete.

Takeoff Computations While the light-twin pilot need only glance at the wind sock or call the tower for his takeoff data while taxiing out, the multiengine-plane pilot has a complex problem. He must consider airplane gross weight, engine thrust available, temperature at the runway, pressure altitude, wind direction and velocity, runway surface, and runway grade. The computations are made by the crew from charts showing takeoff performance in the aircraft operating manual. The primary results of these computations are the Critical Engine Failure Speed (V_1), Takeoff Ground Roll, Rotation Speed (V_R), Takeoff Speed (V_2), Critical Field Length, and Acceleration Check Time, as discussed earlier in this chapter.

AIRCRAFT PREPARATION AND LOADING

Size makes this a tedious task. Necessary maintenance, inspections, loading, and servicing may be the responsibility of maintenance sections, but the pilot must make sure that they have been accomplished.

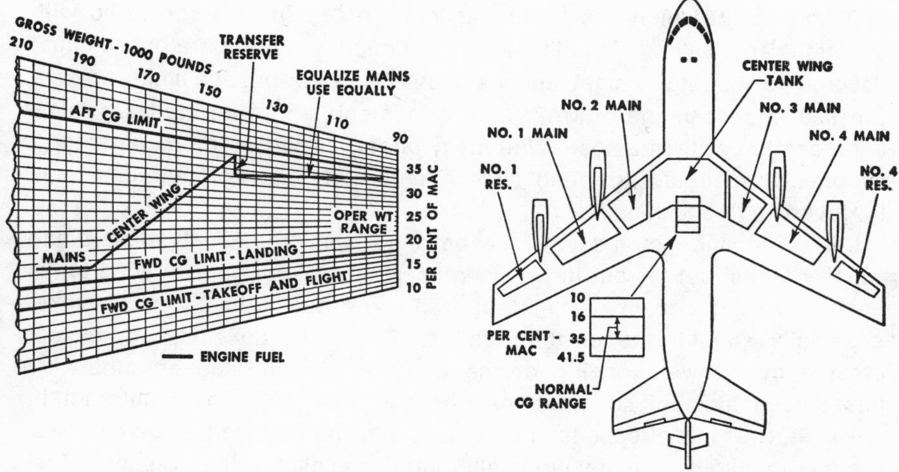

Figure 10.8 Center of gravity shift in flight. This schematic of the KC-135 shows the distribution of fuel, indicating its effect on lateral and longitudinal stability. Note that any load in addition to fuel would have to be placed so that fuel consumption did not exceed C.G. limits, and that uneven use of fuel in the wings would disrupt lateral trim.

During flight planning, loading is itself a major problem. The load must be within the capacity of the airplane, must be so placed as to locate the c.g. within limits, and must be tied down so that it cannot shift or bounce around in flight, changing the c.g. or damaging the aircraft. The preflight loading plan must provide also for a suitable landing condition.

The c.g. condition for landing is specially important. Figure 10.8 shows the takeoff c.g. load distribution in a KC-135. A safe takeoff can be made because the load is within limits. Assume that fuel is used only from forward of the center of lift, so that the c.g. travels aft. This is possible in many aircraft, and particularly in large aircraft with swept-back wings. The airplane remains controllable (although considerable nose-down trim is required) until it slows down for landing. At that time the nose-up moment, only partly compensated for by reduced downwash on the tail, becomes greater than the elevator can counteract at the reduced airspeed and power setting. The results are stall and disaster unless the pilot recognizes his problem in time and makes a highspeed landing. The same condition will exist in turbulence, and may result in loss of control.

Correct c.g. location also avoids drag due to poor trim. Whenever a trim tab must be deflected into the slipstream, drag is added, slowing the airplane or requiring an increase of power. The most economical operation is obtained when the location of the c.g. is so established and maintained in flight that cruising speed trim requirements are zero.

Each aircraft which can be loaded outside c.g. limits is provided with a Weight and Balance Handbook, or a section in the Operator's Manual devoted to loading, weight and balance. Center-of-gravity limits are expressed in percentage of MAC, and in moments about an arbitrary reference point, usually the nose. With many larger airplanes, the manufacturer supplies a specially designed slide rule for this c.g. computation, used to govern airplane loading.

Lateral location of the c.g. can be a serious problem in an airplane which carries fuel far out in the wing or in tip tanks; opposite wing tanks must be loaded equally. In flight, uneven use of fuel from outboard tanks, especially should one of them fail to feed, can develop into a real emergency. Uneven loading of the wings could produce an otherwise unbalanced moment so great that the ailerons could not counteract it, particularly at low airspeeds. If an outboard or tip tank cannot be emptied, the fuel manifold system will usually permit transfer of the remaining fuel sufficiently to get lateral c.g. within aileron control limits.

The wing-bending moment is a special consideration in the loading of fuel on a multiengine airplane with a wide wingspan and tanks far out in the wings. The lift of a wing is distributed along its span. To avoid excessive spanwise bending moments, it is desirable to distribute as much weight as possible along the span also. If the fuselage is carrying a heavy load, fuel *must* be placed as far out in the wings as possible, and *must* be used first from the tanks nearest the center of the airplane. Doing so appreciably increases the positive-*g* acceleration safety margin.

GETTING AIRBORNE

The vast lore of flying is available to the pilot of any large airplane who will follow the prescribed procedures for that aircraft. Preflight inspection —a job in which all crew members participate with particular reference to their own specialties—follows careful checklists; a haphazard approach always causes trouble sooner or later.

Actually, the procedures of starting multiengine planes and getting to the end of the runway are little different from those for any other airplane; however, the increased size and complexity again requires a passion for orderliness. Planning will avoid starting engines too soon and wasting fuel; it will also prevent a late start which results in rushing to make good a tight schedule. Whether the aircraft carries a load of revenue-producing passengers who can choose another airline if you're not careful of their comfort and thrifty with their time, or whether it carries a huge and lethal bomb load, smoothness in engine starting, taxiing, stopping, braking, and turning is the true measure of piloting skill. The light twins are not too small to be flown under the same principles.

TAKEOFF

As is landing, takeoff is one of the two most hazardous parts of flying. Every takeoff must be made as carefully and skillfully as the experience of the crew and the quality of the airplane permit.

Runway acquisition rates are such at most large airports that the pilot will not be allowed the luxury of applying full power and checking his instruments before brake release. In fact some jet aircraft now have enough power available that full power with brakes locked will cause tires to skid, or worse, to rotate on the rims. For these reasons a running takeoff is usually made. This means that preparations for the takeoff must be completed in advance of the anticipated runway clearance. These preparations must include review of the planned departure route, re-briefing of emergency procedures and takeoff performance data.

When the pilot is cleared on the runway, if he is also cleared for takeoff, he will advance power to 80% to 85% and roll out to the runway. He will advance throttles to takeoff thrust as he acquires the runway centerline. Care must be exercised to prevent excessive side loading of the landing gear assembly during this turn onto the runway. There is no time for fumbling or misunderstanding on this type of takeoff roll. The crew briefing must have been explicit prior to the runway clearance and each crew member must know his exact duties. The takeoff roll may last 40 sec or less. Precise terms are used. A classic example of the failure to do this concerns a pilot who decided he could not land and would execute a go-around. He commanded "Takeoff power." The copilot complied by retarding power to idle! What the pilot wanted was "maximum power."

Takeoff Roll When brakes are released and the roll begins, the first concern is directional control, which is maintained with nose-wheel steering or differential use of throttles until the rudder is effective. Torque is less noticeable in multiengine aircraft, and of course not present in jets. The pilot avoids using brakes to maintain direction, except in emergency.

The copilot calls out the decision speed and acceleration check time as it is passed. Usually the pilot reserves to himself the job of flying, and copilot and engineer observe engine performance. Close coordination is vital.

If the airspeed is low at the check speed or time, the pilot aborts the takeoff by using brakes, reverse thrust, and drag devices as necessary to stop safely on the runway. If the decision point is passed with airspeed equal to or better than that computed, the takeoff is continued despite the failure of a single engine.

The problem is somewhat different in light twins. No decision point is used on a long runway. Instead, *the minimum safe single-engine speed* for climb is the objective. With this speed, takeoff can be continued with maximum power on one engine, with one engine out. If this speed has not been reached when an engine quits, the pilot must either abort the takeoff or, if runway length does not permit, crash land *straight ahead,* power off. Any attempt to turn here means loss of control and disaster.

CLIMB-OUT

As the airplane approaches V_2, the rotation or takeoff speed, the pilot exerts back pressure on the yoke, and the aircraft smoothly leaves the ground. Rotating too soon causes the aircraft to leave the ground in too high an angle of attack; the increased drag delays reaching climb speed. Rotating too late wastes runway and may not permit safe obstacle clearance. Limit tire speed may also be exceeded.

The climb-out attitude then depends on acceleration characteristics. With rapid acceleration, the pilot keeps the nose high to avoid passing the maximum gear-retraction speed; with slow acceleration, the nose stays low, but in a definite climb attitude, to accelerate to safe single-engine climb speed as soon as possible. When the gear is up, flap retraction is next. At this time the power is set for the climb to cruising altitude. Particularly at night and in weather, it is very important to perform each of these operations in an orderly and smooth manner to avoid unusual deviations in rate of climb and possible disorientation.

If an obstacle has to be cleared immediately after takeoff, the pilot lets the speed build up after takeoff only to a value that will give the maximum angle of climb until the obstacle is passed.

Flying the heavier multiengine aircraft requires use of the flight instruments for every takeoff—not just those under instrument conditions. A night takeoff is almost the same as an actual weather takeoff. The cockpit lights are turned up high because of the usually bright field lights outside at night. They are dimmed after the bright outside lights have fallen behind.

CLIMB AND LEVEL-OFF

After the flaps are fully retracted, climb power is set and normal climb speed is reached.

For a climb of several thousand feet, pilots use the airspeed that will give the best rate of climb because it is most economical to establish cruise conditions in the shortest practical time.

Level-off from climb should be a smoothly coordinated maneuver. The technique is approximately the same in all aircraft. By delaying climb-power reduction until a small excess over cruising speed is attained, the job of trimming at cruise speed is made easier.

Because of very high climb rates in jet transports and the lag of pressure-operated vertical speed indicators and altimeters, level-off must be anticipated and initiated with a 400- to 800-ft lead on the altimeter. Initial cruise speed is quite close to climb speed in most jets, so establishing airspeed is easy.

CRUISE

Obtaining the most economical and dependable operation in a multiengine airplane is both a science and an art. The fact that it requires a great amount of attention in flight is the chief reason for having flight engineers on the larger airplanes.

Trim The pilot's ability to refine control-surface trim so that there is no lost speed due to trim-tab drag is most important here. The secret is simply to maintain a constant altitude, then repeat the cycle of elevator, rudder, and aileron trim adjustment until the speed is stable. He centers the ball with rudder trim, the needle with aileron trim, obtaining the desired condition with hand or foot pressure, then fixing it by relieving the pressure with trim-tab adjustments. A careful and skilled pilot can always get more speed out of a big airplane simply by precise trimming and retrimming as the fuel load diminishes.

Most sophisticated autopilots work on the aircraft trim control system, and engaging it will automatically trim the aircraft. Many pilots use the autopilot to trim the aircraft even if they plan to fly the aircraft manually.

ECONOMICAL ENGINE OPERATION

Maximum output, high altitude, and relatively high airspeed all improve turbojet economy. Airspeed increases the efficiency of the turbojet because the load of the compressors is reduced by the ram air effect.

With increasing altitude, fuel flow decreases while engine rpm and EGT are maintained, thus maintaining maximum efficiency while reducing thrust.

Reducing thrust without climbing reduces efficiency because the throttle must be retarded to reduce thrust at a constant altitude, thus reducing EGT and rpm; the most economical jet-engine operation is therefore obtained at high altitude.

MOST ECONOMICAL ALTITUDE

In Chapter 3 we saw that drag at a constant true airspeed decreases with reduced density at altitude. The power and therefore the fuel required to overcome drag is correspondingly less, and the airplane can fly the same true airspeed with less power, or a higher true airspeed with the same power.

Jets are equipped with Machmeters in addition to more or less conventional airspeed indicators. A Machmeter is a much more useful, quick reference for speed at high altitude, because the speed of sound varies only with absolute temperature. Experience has shown that best jet airplane economy is obtained at high altitude, flying a constant Mach number and a given power setting, and letting the airplane climb gradually as weight decreases with use of fuel. Fuel flow rate continues to decrease with the climb. This most economical operation occurs in most subsonic designs in the vicinity of Mach .75. Increasing to Mach .80, however, decreases range by only about 1%.

No attempt should be made to exceed the recommended altitude for a given weight for any jet aircraft. While the aircraft may be climbed above the recommended altitude for a particular weight, excessive fuel will be required in the climb and cruise, and the airspeed margin for maneuvering and penetrating turbulence will be greatly reduced.

CRUISE CONTROL

The performance section of the Operator's Manual for each airplane contains charts describing the performance under all conditions of range, altitude, airspeed, power setting and gross weight. These charts are based on data obtained from test flying the airplane.

It is rarely if ever possible to make a flight under maximum economy conditions, because of weather, other traffic, or operational requirements. Further, since the great advantage of air travel is speed, it is generally desirable to cruise faster than the most economical airspeed, accepting a penalty of somewhat greater fuel cost but reducing indirect costs per mile.

The problem of *cruise control,* then, is to obtain the maximum economy of operation under the existing conditions and requirements. There are three types of cruise:

Long-range cruise consists of operating constantly at power settings and airspeeds, within engine limitations, which will approach most economical, no-wind, miles-per-pound performance. This results in a gradual reduction of power settings, gradually increasing altitude as the flight progresses.

Constant-airspeed cruise requires adjusting of power as necessary to maintain a standard indicated airspeed once it is attained. Using this procedure a specific power is used until airspeed gradually builds up to specified value, and then power is gradually reduced as necessary to maintain the desired airspeed for the remainder of the flight.

Standard cruise consists of establishing a specified power after level-off and maintaining it while allowing airspeed to increase gradually as weight decreases.

DESCENT

Approaching destination, the crew can effect a substantial saving of both fuel and time by intelligent planning and skilled use of the airplane's capabilities, taking other traffic, weather, and Air Traffic Control clearance into account.

Because a jet airplane gets its best economy and minimum fuel consumption rate at high altitude, a long-range descent, with throttles in idle and the airplane "clean" is advantageous only when the descent can be timed so as to arrive at the final approach fix or the landing pattern entry point at the end of descent. Under VFR or radar control this is now usually done.

Under IFR without an ATC radar-controlled en-route descent, it is usually more efficient to remain at high altitude until over the destination fix, then to make a steep "penetration" pattern to the IAF (Chapter 9).

LANDING PATTERN

Before entering the landing pattern, one of the pilots or the flight engineer determines the gross weight and recommended pattern speeds. Standard cruise consists of establishing a specified power after level-off speeds. Because the gross weight of large airplanes may vary 100,000 lb or more between takeoff and landing, this step is vital. Pattern entry is as shown in Figure 10.9, or as the tower directs. The professional pilot flies a precise pattern: he usually establishes pattern headings by directional gyro rather than visually. When using a gyro with a rotating card, he sets the runway heading under the index at the top of the instrument. Both pilots must keep alert for other traffic throughout the letdown, approach and landing pattern.

Normal Pattern Every step of landing preparation should be planned by the crew for a certain point in the pattern. This eliminates variables that could adversely affect the pattern, and presents the pilot with the simplest possible problem on the final approach.

For example, enter the downwind leg at a point even with the upwind end of the runway, call the tower, and reduce airspeed to safe landing-gear extension speed. Opposite the midpoint of the runway, lower the

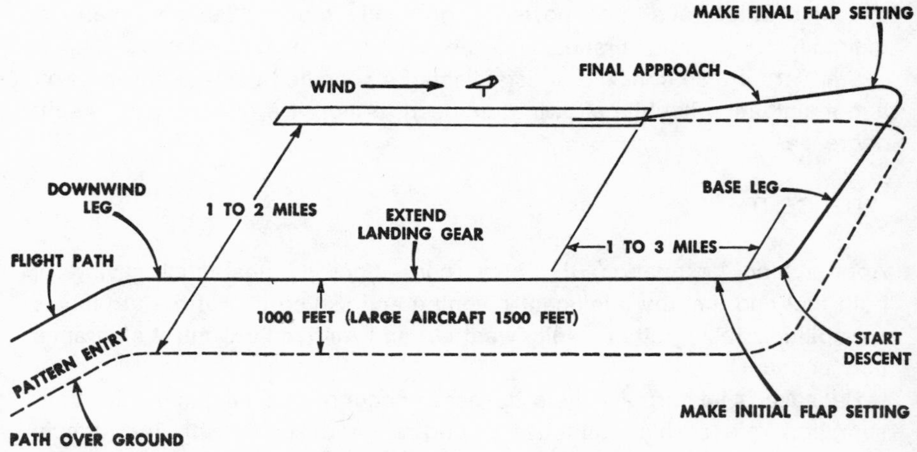

Figure 10.9 Multiengine landing pattern. Size of the pattern depends on the size and speed of the aircraft. Large aircraft fly the pattern 500 ft higher to allow more time to establish a good final approach, lose 500 ft on the base leg, use standard rate turns.

landing gear and adjust the power to traffic-pattern requirements. Opposite the landing end of the runway, lower the first quarter of flaps, then start descent and turn to the base leg when the end of the runway passes a certain reference point in relation to the airplane. Complete the landing check list before turning to base leg, except for final flap settings and landing lights. Lower the next quarter of flaps as soon as the plane rolls out on the base leg, and start the turn to final at a definite angle from the runway. Throughout the maneuver, altitude and airspeed should be changing to conform to values predetermined by calculations and experience.

Admittedly, this is a mechanical approach to the landing problem. The key to a good landing in a multiengine aircraft is a good pattern and approach. They can be made consistently smooth and safe only by an orderly, standard procedure.

Straight-In Approach This is a traffic pattern without any turns. It is frequently used with an instrument approach, and almost always used in scheduled airline flying. All the normal traffic-pattern checks must be made, and final approach must be established at the same point as in a rectangular pattern. A common mistake is failure to reduce airspeed, and to establish the correct attitude and airspeed for final approach before beginning the final descent. When VFR, some pilots prefer to establish the final approach configuration (except for power setting) somewhat early, then fly up to final approach at 500 ft above the runway, or at whatever altitude is normally used for turning on final. When they reach the correct approach angle with the runway they simply reduce power to obtain the necessary rate of descent; much as is done during an ILS approach.

Final Approach Under visual conditions, the final approach descent begins as soon as the aircraft has rolled out on the runway heading. Pilots make the final flap setting, and adjust attitude to obtain an airspeed about 30% above stall. The correct speed varies with flap setting and gross weight and has been precomputed. From this point, except for the effects of sheer weight, the procedure is the same as described in Chapter 8.

Avoid long flat approaches. The pilot who enters final approach too far out or at too low an altitude will do best to set power for level flight and delay the final flap setting until he attains the correct final approach angle with the runway. If he finds himself too far out at too low an altitude, he must maintain airspeed and level off by adding power. Raising the nose to level flight without adding power will almost certainly result in getting on the back side of the power curve (Figure 2.35). This can be dangerous when the airplane is heavy and has the high drag induced by gear and flaps. In this condition, the more the pilot raises the nose, the more power will be required to maintain level flight. Then the only solutions are either to lower the nose with added power and sacrifice some altitude to regain operation on the front side of the power curve, or to raise the gear, add power for go-around, then raise the flaps cautiously as speed permits.

Should a go-around be necessary, the throttles are immediately advanced to climb power, the aircraft is rotated to climb attitude, and the flaps, if full down, are partially retracted. As soon as the pilot is certain that the aircraft will not touch down, he retracts the landing gear for the climb-out.

LANDING

Here again, inertia is an important factor. The maneuver may be divided into two phases: before, and after touchdown.

Before Touchdown Adjustment for crosswind is discussed in Chapter 8. However, inertia makes it essential that final corrections be made as early as possible, two to five miles out from the runway end.

A few aircraft have crosswind landing gear. With them, the best technique is to hold the crab right through the landing. At touchdown the wheels swivel enough to allow the airplane to roll straight down the runway while still in a crab. An interesting variation of crosswind landing gear is found on the Boeing B-52. Through hydraulic steering cylinders the pilot sets all four of its main gear at an angle, equal to and away from the angle of crosswind. He lands the airplane in a crab, and reduces the setting to zero during the ground roll.

A properly executed approach has the airplane approaching the end of the runway, aimed at a point on the end or just short of it. Power, speed, and rate of descent are constant, and the pilot is ready to break the glide. At from 20 to 60 ft above the runway, depending on the type of airplane and the angle of approach, he eases back on the control column, rounding out the glide with the main wheels a foot or two above the runway surface. Power is reduced to idle and the aircraft settles to the runway. A stall landing is not recommended, because experience has shown that control is better and landing shock is less if the airplane is flown on to the runway, generally using a little power when landing distance is not critical. This is particularly true with large aircraft which vary greatly in landing weight. The main gear must touch down ahead of the nose gear, and definite stick pressure is necessary, once the main gear is on the ground, to lower the nose gear smoothly.

The Boeing 707 has excellent flight characteristics in the landing configuration and is typical of large jet transports. Approach speeds vary greatly due to the wide weight range possible. Full flaps (50°) are always used unless minimum in-flight control speed, crosswind, or other condition dictates the use of the 40° flap setting. Full flaps are not set until landing is assured. Approach speed for a 150,000-lb aircraft would be 141 knots. This would be bled off to 131 knots over the approach end of the runway for a touchdown of 121 knots. On an 80° F day, landing under these conditions at sea level would produce a 4550-ft ground roll without reverse thrust, if full-speed brakes were used just after touchdown. The approach itself is quite flat and the rotation for landing is minimal. In fact, a fairly smooth landing is possible out of a normal approach without changing attitude due to the cushioning of ground effect. If, however, a high rate of descent is acquired during final approach as the aircraft is rotated to break the descent, a high sink rate may develop. Pilots must understand the inertia of large, fast aircraft.

After Touchdown The pilot maintains directional control immediately after touchdown by use of the rudder. He changes to nose steering and differential braking as the rudder becomes ineffective.

If maximum braking is necessary, it is well to relieve the pressure partially at intervals to detect a skidding wheel. When a wheel skids, the rubber melts on the tread of the tire, and it provides less braking than if it continued to turn. If the airplane is equipped with antiskid devices, the pilot may apply full brakes. The antiskid system will detect the beginning of a skid by any wheel and release pressure on that brake just sufficiently to allow the wheel to return to speed.

If the pilot uses reverse thrust he applies it as soon as all the wheels are on the ground, removing it when the airplane has slowed to 50 or 60 mph. A four-engine airplane can reverse the inboards and outboards separately; the pilot may use only one pair if he desires.

The drag of the airplane is very effective in slowing it down. Landing gear, flaps, and spoilers all contribute to drag.

Jet bombers are fitted with drag chutes stowed in the tail section. After the aircraft touches down, the pilot or copilot releases the chute by a cockpit lever. The pilot chute pops out and pulls the drag chute out. It blossoms and acts as a very effective brake. While very high landing speeds may cause it to fail, it must be used early in the landing roll to be effective. So, the chute it deployed as soon after touchdown as chute speed limitations permit.

EMERGENCY OPERATION

All emergencies discussed in Chapter 8 are applicable to multiengine jets with the obvious exception of those peculiar to reciprocating engines and props. Certain others merit discussion here.

Modern technology, manufacturing specifications, maintenance and inspection procedures have progressed to the point that abnormalities of operation are rather rare in multiengine jets. In reciprocating-engine aircraft such as the older four-engine transports and bombers, loss of one engine was not at all unusual and loss of two engines not uncommon. Today's jet engines make it highly probable that a pilot will fly many thousand multiengine hours without experiencing an engine failure. Strut-mounted engines, either from the wing or fuselage, make engine fire a much less feared emergency than with the imbedded reciprocating engines. The lack of torque and prop drag makes the loss of a jet engine much less critical. Only loss of an engine at takeoff point, or after decision speed is passed, is likely to cause great concern. Even then, as long as minimum control speed can be maintained, while clearing obstacles, loss of one engine is not likely to be the calamity it was at one time.

Flame-out may occur in a jet engine anytime a fuel or air interruption occurs. Relight can usually be immediately effected by simply pushing the ignition button. If at high altitude an appreciable decrease in engine rpm has occurred before detection, descent to a lower altitude and an increase in indicated airspeed may be required to start the engine. If a relight does not occur, a check of the fuel system is made to insure that fuel is available to the engine. If the engine restarts and instrument indications are normal it can be operated normally for the remainder of the flight. Engines are never restarted in flight if the cause of failure was fire or overheating.

Shutting down a jet engine is simply a matter of putting the throttle in idle cutoff, and if fire is indiciated, cutting fuel and oil to the nacelle. This is usually accomplished with a single switch and need not distract the crew from flying the aircraft. Most large transports have a rapid fuel-dump capability so that weight may be reduced to cope with a power-loss emergency.

All jet aircraft have air-conditioning and pressurization systems. These give many false alarms about fuselage fires. This is caused by water separators being unable to cope with a high-humidity condition or due to a malfunction of the air-conditioning system. Increasing temperature will usually clear up the vapor and relieve the crew and passengers of the anxiety of having seen "smoke." In the event of actual fire or heavy fumes the air-conditioning system must be shut down and all persons on board must go to 100% oxygen. Once the source of the fire or fumes is located and eliminated, the air conditioner, or other faulty system, may be restarted.

11

Air Navigation*

". . . the winds and the waves are on the side of the ablest navigators."

EDWARD GIBBON

Flying and navigation are inseparable whether in the traffic pattern or crossing the arctic plain. Continuous movement, high speeds, limitations to visibility, and limited endurance all impose the need to begin navigating when the wheels leave the runway, and to plan for navigation before entering the aircraft.

This chapter, written by both pilots and navigators, is designed to instruct in the tested principles, and to describe the standards of performance met by airmen in most navigation problems. Like other topics in *Modern Airmanship,* it is highly condensed; yet the essential principles and details are here.

The Earth's Surface and Mapping

A map of the earth's surface is our primary instrument. Although maps designed for navigation are known as charts, the terms *map* and *chart* may be

*Major James E. Fischer and Captain James E. Rice, United States Air Force, revised by the Editor.

used synonymously. Any flat map is a compromise among the features to be portrayed, for obviously no completely accurate map of a round object can be made on a flat surface.

THE SHAPE OF THE EARTH

We think of the earth as round. Actually it is an oblate spheroid—a body that only approximates a true sphere. The centrifugal force of rotation has expanded the earth at the equator, causing a flattening at the poles. If the earth were represented by a ball 25 ft in diameter at the equator, the polar diameter would be approximately 24 ft, 11 in. Though small, this ellipticity must be taken into consideration by the map maker. For most navigation purposes, however, the earth may be considered as a perfect sphere.

CIRCLES ON A SPHERE

If a sphere is cut by a plane, the resulting intersection is a circle. If the plane passes through the center of the sphere, the circle formed is a *great circle* and is the largest circle that can be drawn on the given sphere. Any circle formed by a plane which does not pass through the center of the sphere is a *small circle.* Segments of a circle, called *arcs,* are measured in degrees, minutes, and seconds. If the circumference of any circle is divided into 360 equal parts, each curved arc would be 1° in length. The number 360 is not a particularly convenient one to work with in our decimal civilization, but it is historic, well-established, and probably beyond change. A degree further divided into 60 equal parts forms arcs of 1 minute each, and one sixtieth of a minute is a second. For very fine measurement beyond a second, decimal parts are used. Thus 8 degrees, 40 minutes, and 7.18 seconds would be written: 8° 40′ 7.18″. Measurements finer than minutes are rarely used in navigation, though the map maker must on occasion reckon with angles that are fractional parts of a second.

LATITUDE AND LONGITUDE

Determination of position requires a point of reference. It is sometimes satisfactory to pinpoint an aircraft as simply 8 mi south of Flemington or over Darby at 12,000 ft. Generally this is not sufficient, and over water not even possible. There is, moreover, the problem of locating the towns of Flemington and Darby themselves in relation to some other fixed point. On the earth's surface a universal positional reference system has been established by arbitrarily drawn lines of latitude and longitude.

On any sphere, circles make the best lines of reference. The only prob-

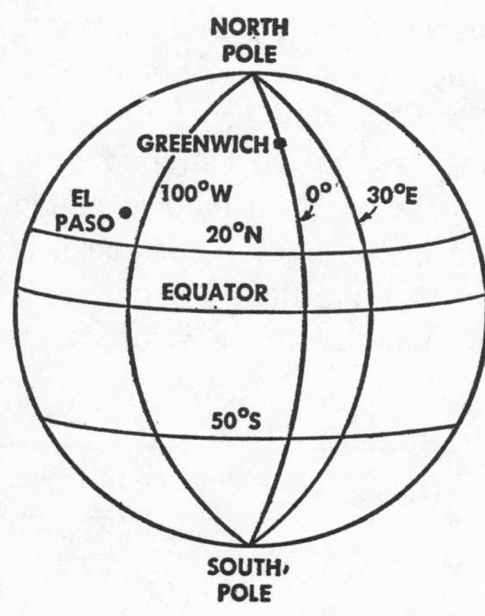

Figure 11.1 Designation of latitude and longitude. Representative parallels of latitude (20°N and 50°S), meridians of longitude (100°W and 30°E), and the points of numbering origin (equator and Greenwich meridian) are shown.

lem is where to draw the circles. On an ordinary ball, any orderly system of lines would do. Since the earth is a spinning ball, the axis of spin itself forms the most logical and convenient starting place. The ends of the axis are called the North Pole and the South Pole. Midway between them lies the great circle known as the equator. Latitude ranges from 0° at the equator to 90° north and 90° south at the poles. Any line of latitude other than the equator is a small circle parallel to it and is therefore known as a *parallel of latitude,* or more simply a *parallel.*

Half of a great circle passing through the poles is a *meridian of longitude,* or simply a *meridian.* All meridians intersect at right angles with parallels of latitude. Any number of meridians can be drawn, and each is exactly like the others. To be useful as reference lines, therefore, one specific meridian, a *prime meridian,* must be chosen as a starting line. Many such lines have been used in the past, and several are in use even now. The most commonly accepted prime meridian throughout the English-speaking world is the great circle passing through the observatory at Greenwich, near London, England. Longitude is measured around the earth both eastward and westward from this Greenwich meridian, through 180°.

Any point on earth can now be fixed by reference to the unique intersection of its parallel of latitude and its meridian of longitude. These lines are the coordinates of the point. By custom, when coordinates are given, latitude is named first, then longitude. Thus the coordinates of El Paso are 31° 47′ N, 106° 27′ W (Figure 11.1).

MAP PROJECTIONS

There are all sorts of maps, but most fall into one of several generic types called projections. Each has certain advantages and disadvantages which may either permit or limit its use for a given purpose. To understand each, it would be helpful to consider the cartographer's basic problem. For convenience, the user wants a flat map. Yet one has only to try to flatten an orange peel to realize that a rounded surface cannot be flattened without some stretching, wrinkling, or tearing. The result on a map is called distortion. In making a flat map of any portion of the earth's surface it is impossible for the cartographer to eliminate all distortion. He can only control or systematize it in such a way as to minimize those errors most detrimental to the purpose of the map.

CHARACTERISTIC	MERCATOR	LAMBERT CONFORMAL	POLAR STEREOGRAPHIC	MODIFIED LAMBERT
PARALLELS	PARALLEL STRAIGHT LINES UNEQUALLY SPACED	ARCS OF CONCENTRIC CIRCLES NEARLY EQUALLY SPACED	CONCENTRIC CIRCLES UNEQUALLY SPACED	ARCS OF CONCENTRIC CIRCLES NEARLY EQUALLY SPACED
MERIDIANS	PARALLEL STRAIGHT LINES EQUALLY SPACED	STRAIGHT LINES CONVERGING ABOVE THE POLE	STRAIGHT LINES RADIATING FROM THE POLE	STRAIGHT LINES CONVERGING AT THE POLE
APPEARANCE OF GRID				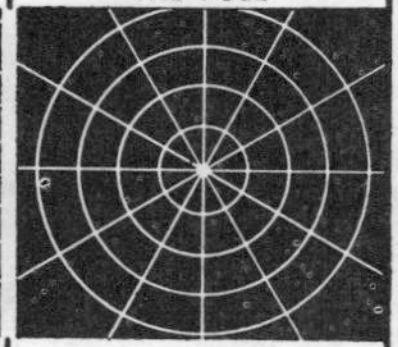
ANGLE BETWEEN PARALLELS & MERIDIANS	90°	90°	90°	90°
STRAIGHT LINE CROSSES MERIDIANS	CONSTANT ANGLE (RHUMB LINE)	VARIABLE ANGLE (APPROXIMATES GREAT CIRCLE)	VARIABLE ANGLE (APPROXIMATES GREAT CIRCLE)	VARIABLE ANGLE (APPROXIMATES GREAT CIRCLE)
GREAT CIRCLE	CURVED LINE (EXCEPT EQUATOR AND MERIDIANS)	APPROXIMATED BY STRAIGHT LINE	APPROXIMATED BY STRAIGHT LINE	APPROXIMATED BY STRAIGHT LINE
RHUMB LINE	STRAIGHT LINE	CURVED LINE	CURVED LINE	CURVED LINE
DISTANCE SCALE	MID-LATITUDE	NEARLY CONSTANT	NEARLY CONSTANT EXCEPT ON SMALL CHARTS	NEARLY CONSTANT
GRAPHIC ILLUSTRATION	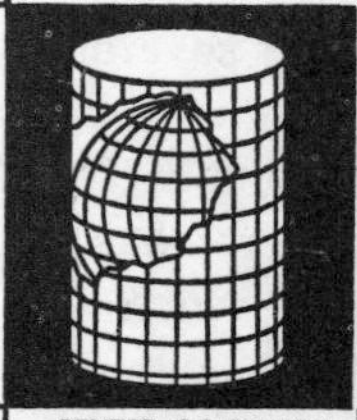			
ORIGIN OF PROJECTORS	CENTER OF SPHERE (FOR ILLUSTRATION ONLY)	CENTER OF SPHERE	OPPOSITE POLE	CENTER OF SPHERE
DISTORTION OF SHAPES & AREAS	INCREASES AWAY FROM EQUATOR	VERY LITTLE	INCREASES AWAY FROM POLE	INCREASES AWAY FROM STANDARD PARALLELS
METHOD OF PRODUCTION	MATHEMATICAL	GRAPHIC OR MATHEMATICAL	GRAPHIC OR MATHEMATICAL	MATHEMATICAL
NAVIGATIONAL USES	DEAD RECKONING AND CELESTIAL (SUITABLE FOR ALL TYPES)	PILOTAGE AND RADIO (SUITABLE FOR ALL TYPES)	POLAR NAVIGATION, ALL TYPES	POLAR NAVIGATION
CONFORMALITY	CONFORMAL	CONFORMAL	CONFORMAL	CONFORMAL

Figure 11.2 Characteristics of common charts used in navigation.

The framework of meridians and parallels on any map is called the *graticule.* Since the configuration of the graticule determines the general characteristics and appearance of the map, proper selection of the graticule is the primary and most critical job the cartographer must face. In practice, the graticule is drawn mathematically by formula. For some maps, however, it can readily be shown visually by actually projecting a picture on a screen—hence the name projection. Consider a translucent globe, marked with opaque lines of latitude and longitude, with a small, bright light inside. If a piece of paper is held anywhere near the globe, an image of the lines will be formed. The pattern of this projected graticule will be determined by the position of the light, the position of the paper, and the shape into which the paper is formed. For some maps, the paper is kept flat and held tangent to the surface of the globe, but for the most commonly used maps it is rolled into a cone or cylinder. Various positions and results achieved are illustrated in Figure 11.2.

DEFINITION OF COMMON MAP TERMS

An understanding of the following map terms will aid in understanding the discussion of map projections by type.

Statute Mile (SM) A distance established by law in English-speaking countries as 5,280 ft.

Nautical Mile (NM) A distance of approximately 6,080 ft, or 1.15 statute miles. It is the length of a minute of arc on the equator and varies slightly from country to country, depending on the accepted circumference of the earth. It is a convenient measure for navigators; since the equator is a great circle, one minute of arc will be a nautical mile on any great circle, and hence distance can be measured along any meridian. Some inaccuracy results from the slightly elliptical shape of the meridians, but it is less than human error in most nagivational practice. Any automatic computing device like the navigational system for missiles must take this error into account.

Map Scale Map scale is a ratio of length on a map to true distance represented. To express relationship of scale between maps the terms *small scale* and *large scale* are used. These terms can be confusing. A map showing much detail, and therefore a small area, is a large-scale map; a map including a large area on the same size of paper in comparison must be small-scale. Scale may be shown in several ways. On a road map it is most often given as "1 in. equals 10 miles." On aeronautical charts it is shown as a ratio, called a representative fraction, as 1:500,000, or 1/500,000. In this system one unit on the map equals 500,000 of the same unit on the surface of the earth.

Great-Circle Distance The shortest distance between two points on the curved surface of the earth lies along the great circle passing through these points. The shorter arc of this great circle is the great-circle distance.

Rhumb Line A rhumb line is a line crossing all meridians at a constant angle. This is the line which an aircraft tends to follow when steered by a compass. It is easier to fly because the true course remains constant, though it is a greater distance than the great-circle route between the same two points. Under certain conditions it is advantageous to fly a rhumb line course instead of a great circle, because (1) in low latitudes, a rhumb line closely approximates a great circle; (2) over short distances, a rhumb line and great circle nearly coincide; and (3) a rhumb line between points on or near the same meridian of longitude approximates a great circle.

Conformality (correct representation of angles) To be conformal, a chart must have uniform scale around any point, though not necessarily a uniform scale over the entire map. Meridians and parallels must intersect at right angles. The two most useful navigational charts, the Mercator and the Lambert, are both conformal.

COMMON CHARTS USED IN NAVIGATION

In navigation, charts are used principally for two purposes, (1) map reading and (2) plotting and measuring course directions and distances. Some maps serve several purposes quite well. Other maps, such as loran charts or those used for flights in polar regions, are designed for one specific purpose. A summary of the various types follows, indicating appearance, characteristics, and principal uses.

Mercator Projection The Mercator chart, one of the oldest precision charts ever devised, still serves an important navigational need. A Mercator chart is actually constructed mathematically, but an approximation of its graticule can readily be imagined by visualizing a cylinder tangent at the equator to a translucent globe with a light source at the center. All parallels and meridians on the globe will be projected on the cylinder as straight lines crossing at right angles. Meridians will be evenly spaced, whereas distance between parallels will increase rapidly with latitude. If the cylinder is then opened and laid flat, the graticule will appear as a series of rectangles, almost square at the equator and becoming increasingly elongated at higher latitudes.

Scale on a Mercator is true only along the equator. Elsewhere it expands as the secant of the latitude, so that at 60° N or S, scale is twice that at the equator. When expressed as a representative fraction, scale can apply to only one latitude, and a variable scale is required to measure distances. This is a disadvantage for the navigator, but it is readily over-

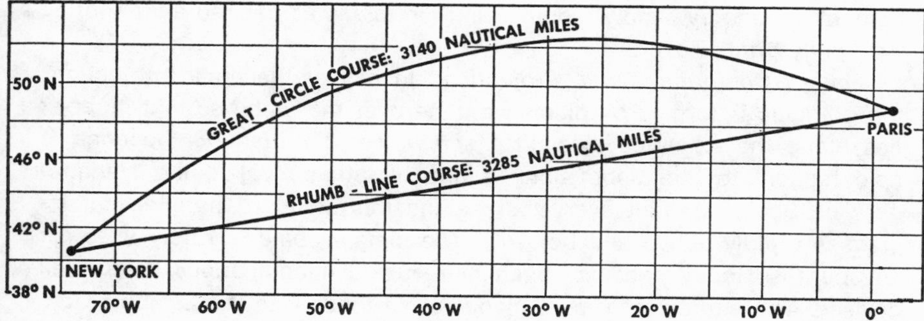

Figure 11.3 Rhumb line and great circle routes on a Mercator chart. Distance saved by flying a great circle instead of a rhumb line between New York and Paris would be 145 mi. At their maximum divergence, the great-circle route is 400 mi north of the rhumb line. If other considerations such as weather or favorable winds were of little consequence, most navigators would elect to fly the great-circle route by marking off rhumb-line segments at intervals of 5° of longitude.

come by measuring along a mid-latitude scale. This will be more fully explained in the section on dead reckoning.

The tremendous scale expansion in high latitudes restricts the use of the Mercator above approximately 70°. It is actually best suited for use within 25° to 30° of the equator. In this band of equatorial and temperate latitudes the Mercator will remain a most useful and popular projection so long as magnetic reference is used for steering, for its outstanding advantage is the fact that on it a rhumb-line course is a straight line. A line drawn between two points anywhere on the chart will thus have the same direction from true north at any point of measurement, an advantageous characteristic unique among all projections.

Except for the equator and any meridian, great-circle routes on a Mercator are curved lines, lying between the rhumb-line course and the closer pole. In low latitudes, rhumb line and great circle will be close together; at middle and upper latitudes the amount of divergence becomes quite marked (Figure 11.3). The great-circle route will always be shorter, and it is part of the navigator's duty to determine whether the bother of plotting and the increased risk of error in flying a series of changing headings is justified by the saving in distance. Ultimate choice of route will depend on many other factors as well, all of which will be summarized later in the paragraph on Flight Planning.

For some areas, Mercators with a light geographical overlay are available. On these, longitude is labeled to conform with features shown. In an emergency such a chart can still be used for other regions in the same bank of latitude by simply renumbering meridians as desired and ignoring the lightly printed overlay.

Lambert Conformal Conic Projection In any of the conic projections the graticule is formed by placing a cone over the globe so that its apex lies along the extended axis. In a *simple conic projection* the cone is held tangent to the globe along a line of latitude called the *standard parallel.* Scale is exact everywhere along this standard parallel, but increases rapidly above and below it. The simple conic is rarely used for any purpose today because much more useful modifications have been devised. The earliest and most ingenious of these was the Lambert Conformal Conic Projection, more generally known as a Lambert Conformal or simply a Lambert. Instead of holding the cone tangent to the globe, Lambert visualized the cone as making a secantal cut, thus giving two standard parallels. Scale along both is exact. Between them, scale is too small, and beyond them too large. The advantages over the simple conic are a reduction of total range of scale error and a more nearly homogeneous scale over the entire map.

Selection of the standard parallels to be used depends on the accuracy requirements for a given area of the entire chart. In general, for equal distribution of scale error, standard parallels are chosen at one-sixth and five-sixths of the total spread of latitude to be represented. By bringing them closer together, greater accuracy is obtained in central portions of the map, but at the expense of the upper and lower border areas. To map the United States, whose latitude is from 25° to 49°, standard parallels of 29° and 45° (one-sixth and five-sixths of the spread) would produce an equal distribution of scale error. But only a very small portion of the country lies between 25° and 30°. To provide more accurate portrayal of the vast central region over which most of the flying is done, aeronautical charts of the United States are generally drawn with latitudes 33° and 45° selected as standard.

On the Lambert, all meridians are straight lines that meet in a common point beyond the limits of the map, and parallels are concentric circles whose center is at the point of intersection of the meridians. Meridians and parallels intersect at right angles, and since scale is very nearly uniform around any point on a given chart, it is considered a conformal projection.

Any straight line on a Lambert chart very closely approximates a great circle, and the shortest distance between two points can therefore be drawn with a straight-edge. The actual difference between a straight line on a Lambert and the true great-circle course over small distances is negligible. Even between San Francisco and New York, a distance of 2570 mi, the two vary at mid-longitude by less than 10 mi. A rhumb line on a Lambert curves toward the equator, and is difficult to plot. For map reading and radio navigation the projection is unequaled, and most areas of the world through 80° latitude are covered by aeronautical charts with a scale of 1:500,000 and 1:1,000,000. Above 80°, scale on a standard Lambert is too inaccurate for navigational use.

Polar Stereographic Projection Mercator and Lambert charts complement each other for all usual navigational needs except flights in the polar area. For this specialized need two aeronautical charts are now in common use, the Polar Stereo and the Modified Lambert. The older of these is the Polar Stereo, a true perspective projection made on a plane tangent to the earth at the pole, with point of projection at the opposite pole. The graticule is easily visualized: pole in the center, meridians radiating outward like spokes of a wheel, and parallels as concentric circles with the pole as the center. A stereographic chart may be drawn to include an entire hemisphere, but for navigational purposes it does not generally extend beyond 15° to 20° from the pole.

Such a chart has several useful properties for navigational needs. Since the scale is uniform in all directions around a point, and since angles are correctly shown, the chart is conformal. For all practical purposes, great circles are straight lines. All meridians, which are true great circles, are precisely straight lines. Other great-circle routes close to the pole will be slightly curved, but not detectably so. If use of the chart is confined to those polar areas above 70° to 80° latitude, any straight line on the chart may be considered a great-circle route. A straight line crossing any fair number of meridians will obviously change true direction from the pole quite rapidly. This is objectionable for magnetic steering of an aircraft. However, this type of chart is used with a grid overlay for Polar Navigation (Figure 11.54). The map still has considerable value, however, since most polar steering is by gyroscope. This point is elaborated upon in the section on Polar Navigation.

Modified Lambert Conformal Conic Projection A true Lambert chart could not accurately show polar regions, because the apex of the cone cutting the earth at two standard parallels would always lie some finite distance above the pole. When projected on a map, therefore, the pole itself, a point on the earth's surface, would be expanded into a complete circle. For this reason, a Lambert Conformal chart is not used above 80°. Formerly only the Polar Stereographic was used north of 80°, but a more recent chart, better suited for aerial navigation over the North Pole, is now available in the Modified Lambert Conformal Conic Projection.

The Modified Lambert utilizes a very shallow secant cone with the upper standard parallel cutting the earth very close to the pole. The lower standard parallel is chosen arbitrarily, depending upon the area to be charted. When any very shallow cone is unrolled, the gap between the cone and a complete circle is quite small. If the gap is closed by distributing the space equally around the entire circle, error in bearings or area at any one place on the chart becomes negligible. It is so insignificant on the Modified Lambert that for navigational purposes the chart is considered completely conformal.

In appearance the Modified Lambert closely resembles the Polar Stereographic described above. On both, straight lines are approximately great circles. The Modified Lambert, however, is now used for polar navigation more than the stereographic because area of accurate portrayal can be extended farther from the pole. Whereas stereographic charts are not generally used below 75°, special charts for long-range arctic navigation are now available on Modified Lambert projections giving full coverage from 64° N with an overlap of 60 nm over the pole itself.

Dead Reckoning

The basis of all navigation is *dead reckoning* (DR). This method of finding one's way over land or sea is used in varying degrees depending on the situation. A pilot flying along airways over or within sight of land with radio positioning uses dead reckoning to find the *estimated time of arrival,* commonly called ETA, to the next check point or destination. Over water, dead reckoning is supplemented with some method of checking or fixing the aircraft's position such as celestial or loran.

Dead reckoning is the method of determining where the aircraft should be, or will be, based on the wind applied to its true heading and true airspeed from the last known position. The accuracy of DR is dependent upon how closely the wind used in planning approximates the actual wind encountered. Headings and ETAs to reach check points or destination must be determined by DR because *there is no practical method of fixing ahead of the aircraft.* DR encompasses many things such as: (1) plotting and measuring, (2) reading flight instruments to determine the aircraft's airspeed, heading, and altitudes, (3) flight planning with the forecast winds, (4) calculating the winds encountered during the flight, and (5) altering heading and changing the ETA as new fixes and changing performance data reveal unpredicted changes in speed and path of flight. Whatever the fixing technique, DR is always the foundation, and an understanding of DR is therefore the most logical starting point in learning the art of navigation.

The four basic elements of DR are *known position, predetermined direction, distance,* and *time.* Over Dallas, Texas, 070 degrees, 300 miles to Kansas City, 2 hours en route, is a specific reference to those elements.

TOOLS OF DR

Known position, direction, and distance are established by plotting and measuring on a chart. The tools required are pencil, eraser, dividers, and plotter—and, of course, the chart.

Little need be said about *pencil* and *eraser* except that the pencil should have a medium lead and the eraser should be soft. A hard pencil cuts into a chart, leaving a mark that is both hard to see and hard to eradicate, while too soft a pencil tends to smear on the chart making it messy and leading to error.

Dividers, too, need scant mention. Their principal use in navigation is for the measurement of distances. Along a desired scale the dividers are spread to span a desired distance; this distance can then be transferred to another part of the chart. Or conversely, an unknown distance on the chart can be spanned and the distance found by comparison with the distance scale. Remember that when dealing with nautical miles, one minute of latitude, measured along a meridian, is a nautical mile. The line to be measured very often exceeds the maximum convenient spread of the dividers. In this event, set the dividers to a convenient distance along the scale, perhaps 60 to 90 mi, and then simply "walk" them along the line and reset for the shorter last step. Take care then that the total distance is correctly computed; using the correct number of steps plus the shorter last step.

The *plotter* is a device for drawing and measuring courses and distances. It is nothing more than a transparent straightedge and protractor combined, but it is one of the most indispensable of the navigator's tools. Several brands of plotters are made, but world-wide the most famous is the Weems Aircraft Plotter Mark II. The use of nautical miles in all air traffic control and in radio facility charts confuses those American airmen who still think in terms of automobile odometers; to solve this problem, many current plotters have both statute and nautical mile scales.

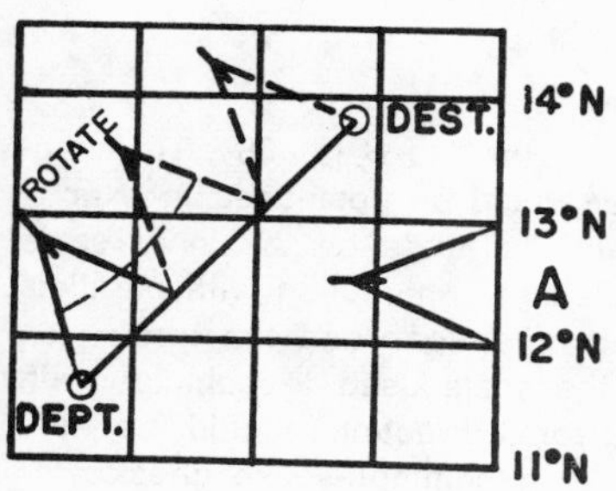

Figure 11.4 Using dividers. Friction of the divider joint is adjustable and should be tight enough to prevent slipping. Note that the measurement is made on a meridian.

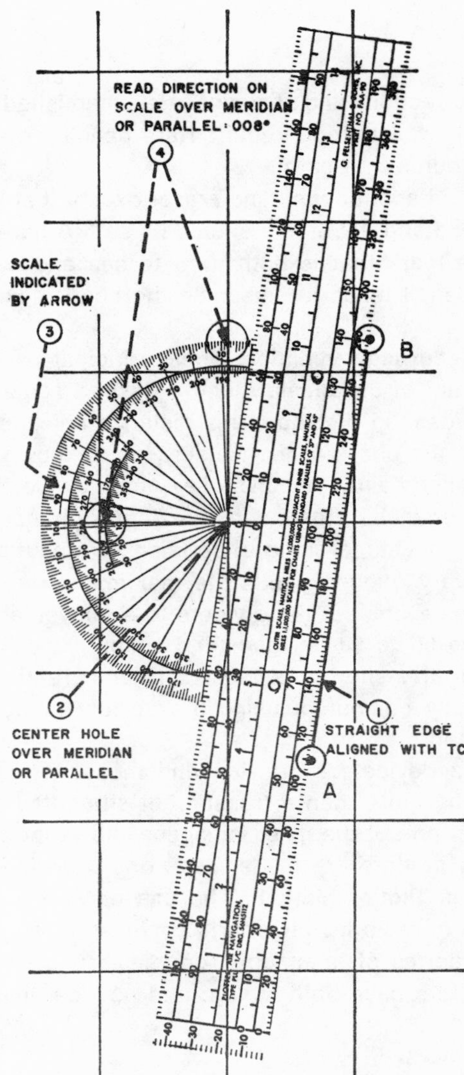

Figure 11.5 Using an aircraft plotter. The course from *A* to *B* is 008°. To measure direction from *B* to *A*, the plotter would be positioned in exactly the same way, but the reading would be made on the inner scale (188°). NOTE: The small scale is used in conjunction with parallels of latitude for measuring north-south directions and the arrows on the large angular scale indicating the scale used to coincide with the direction of flight. To avoid errors, direction should be estimated prior to exact measurement as a common-sense check.

The principal use of a plotter is the measurement of *true course,* which is the line on a chart representing the path over which the aircraft is to travel. True course direction is determined by the angle it makes with the meridians, which run north and south. Direction in aerial navigation is always expressed as an angle measured clockwise through 360° from North, or 0°. Due East is thus 90°, due South 180°, and due West 270°. With a plotter, any intermediate course may be accurately measured. It is possible, with sharp, carefully drawn lines, to read a plotter to ½°. Since the manufacturer's tolerance of the plotter itself is ½°, however, it is meaningless to read direction finer than the nearest whole degree. Even then, the inaccuracies of other variables, such as instrument error, map errors, and the pilot's ability to fly closer than an integral heading, make more precise measurement unnecessary.

To measure the direction of any line on a chart, lay the plotter lengthwise with the outer edge or one of the black inscribed lines coincident with the line to be measured, and the hole at the center of the plotter directly over a meridian (Figure 11.5). A course between 0° and 180° is measured along the outer scale; between 180° and 360° on the inner scale. In working rapidly, it is easy to make an erroneous reading by using the wrong scale. It is therefore wise to estimate the direction roughly prior to exact measurement as a common-sense check, and note the arrows at the 90° to 270° point indicating the proper scale for each direction.

PLOTTING AND MEASURING ON A LAMBERT CHART

The method of measuring course lines described above will give the direction from true north at any meridian chosen for the measurement. Because the graticule of a Lambert chart is characterized by converging meridians. A large deviation in measurement could exist, over any extended course, depending on location of the meridian selected for reference. This error will be at a maximum for east-west courses and at a minimum for north-south courses. You have two choices when the true-course measurements at departure and destination are at variance. For distances of 200 to 300 mi, it is generally advantageous to make one course measurement for the entire route at mid-longitude; for longer runs it is wiser to break the course into segments, changing to new course with each new segment encountered (Figure 11.6). In either case, the path of the aircraft over the earth will be a rhumb line which is always slightly bowed toward the equator from the nearly-great-circle route made by a straight line on the Lambert.

On Lambert charts, the plotter may be more convenient than dividers as a means of measuring distance. Because one of the chief advantages

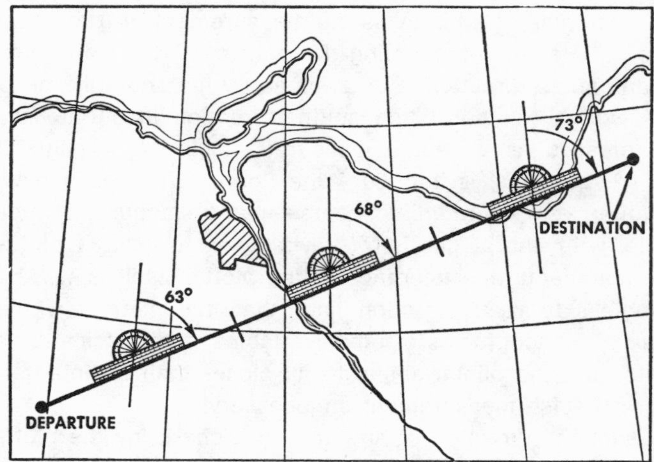

Figure 11.6 Measurement of courses on a Lambert chart. Flights over 300 mi are generally broken into legs, and course measurement of each leg is made at its mid-meridian.

of the Lambert is its uniformity of scale over rather large areas, dividers spanned to 100 mi on one Lambert would measure 100 mi on any part of any Lambert of the same scale. As mentioned earlier, the Weems II plotter is calibrated in statute miles; the II N and the new PLU-1/c and PN-1 (Jeppesen) plotters are in nautical miles, or in both.

PLOTTING AND MEASURING ON A MERCATOR

This is unusual, but worth knowing. In the discussion of maps, the Mercator was shown to be the antithesis of the Lambert in almost every respect. It is only logical, therefore, that methods of measuring distance and direction on a Lambert will not apply to a Mercator as well. On a Mercator, meradians are parallel lines. Any straight line cutting them will cut across each at the same angle. Direction from true north may therefore be measured accurately at any meridian and not only at mid-longitude as on a Lambert.

Distance on a Mercator is measured in nautical miles along a graduated meridian. Measurements cannot be made with a fixed scale, as on a Lambert, because the scale of a Mercator is constantly changing. The scale along any Mercator course is relatively contracted on the portion nearest the equator, and relatively expanded toward the pole. The true Mercator distance of the entire course can therefore be measured only against a scale chosen along a portion of the course where an average

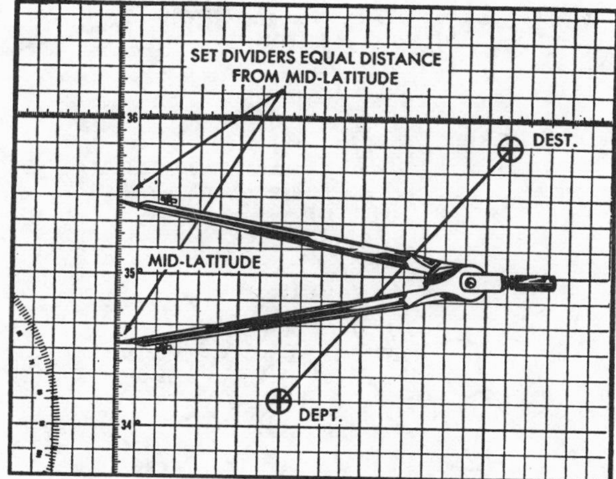

Figure 11.7 Measuring distance on a Mercator chart. Scale on a Mercator changes so rapidly in a north-south direction that distances must be measured against a scale representative of the average scale for the area of flight. Scale along a meridian at mid-latitude approximates such an average. *(Courtesy of U.S. Air Force.)*

scale exists. For ordinary navigational purposes this average is assumed to be a section of the graduated meridian whose mid-latitude is the same as the mid-latitude of the course (Figure 11.7). This mid-latitude scale is not precisely equal to the average scale, but for dead reckoning use the difference is undetectable.

DETERMINATION OF DIRECTION

To find direction, the navigator uses a compass. Two possible sources of large error must always be considered. In all navigation, whether land, sea, or air, these are known as *variation* and *deviation.*

Variation Most measurement of direction is expressed as an angular distance from the North Pole. Any *true direction,* as true course or true heading, refers to angular measurement in relation to the true pole. Compasses, unfortunately, point toward the North Magnetic Pole, a gradually shifting area at present located in northern Canada more than 1100 nm from the true pole. The difference in angular measurement between true north and magnetic north is known as *variation* and is expressed as an angle east or west of true north. When the compass needle points

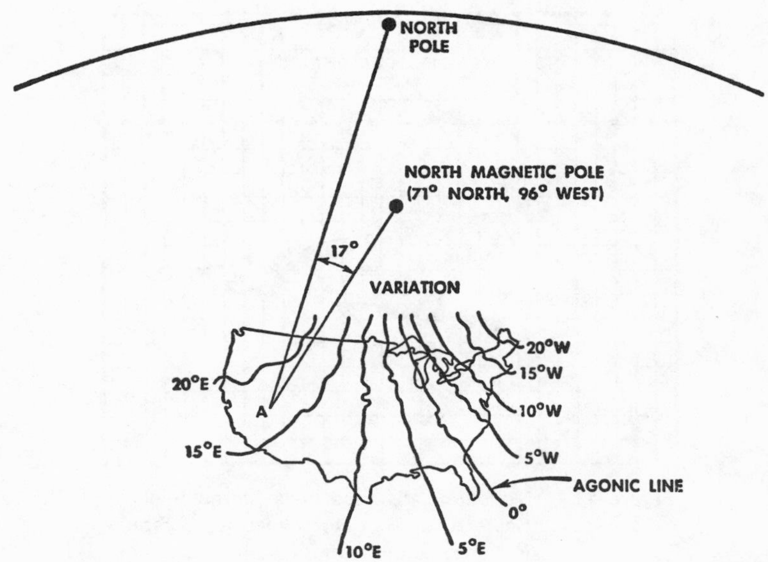

Figure 11.8 Variation chart of the United States. The variation at point *A* is 17° E, because the compass needle is deflected 17° E of the true North Pole at that point. Irregularities in the isogonic lines are caused by the attraction of local magnetic deposits. The agonic line is the line of no variation.

east of true north, the variation is said to be *east;* when the needle points west of true north, the variation is called *west.* The extent of this difference for the United States alone is at present over 45° (Figure 11.8).

Finding the value of local variation for navigational purposes presents no problem. All aeronautical charts show these data by dotted lines called *isogonals* or *isogonic lines.* The variation at any one point changes somewhat rhythmically from year to year, the extremes of this change sometimes exceeding 50° over a long period. The year for which the isogonic lines are drawn is therefore indicated on aeronautical charts. On some charts the annual change is also given. Usually, however, the chart is obsolete for other reasons long before the change in variation is great enough to cause any navigational difficulty.

On flights of some distance, variation may change only slightly or may change by many degrees. If the change is small, an average value is generally used for the entire flight. For large changes the flight is divided into legs, and an average value used for each leg. No arbitrary rule can be made fixing a value at which one method or the other should be used. The decision is a matter of individual practice, depending on the nature of the flight.

Deviation In common with all instruments, compasses have both inherent and induced errors. The sum total of these errors is called compass deviation.

The process of finding deviation and recording it for future use is known as "swinging the compass." An airplane can be either ground-swung or air-swung, but neither is completely satisfactory. In ground swinging, the engines and electrical equipment are operated to simulate flight conditions, and compass readings are compared with the true heading of the aircraft as measured by transit.

After variation is taken into account, the remaining difference between readings is assumed to be the deviation. These readings are recorded on a card and mounted near the compass for flight use (Figure 11.9). One method of air-swinging is to obtain a reference reading by flying along a landmark of known bearing, such as a runway, and then flying headings on which deviation is to be determined by using the gyrocompass, which is assumed to precess uniformly while the compass is being checked. Ground-swinging has the advantage of steady platforms for both compass and reference readings, but it is difficult to find an area entirely free from extraneous magnetic disturbance. Air-swinging, on the other hand, can be done under actual conditions of operational flight, but accurate readings are more difficult to obtain, even in smooth air, than they are on the ground.

Long-range aircraft which carry a navigator are fortunately no longer

NAVIGATOR'S COMPASS
SWUNG: 29 JUNE 55 BY: H.C.N.

TO FLY	STEER	TO FLY	STEER
N	000	180	177
15	016	195	192
30	031	210	208
45	047	225	223
60	062	240	238
75	078	255	254
90	092	270	270
105	106	285	285
120	120	300	301
135	134	315	316
150	149	330	331
165	163	345	345

Figure 11.9 Compass deviation card. Magnetic heading is listed on the left under TO FLY; compass heading is listed under STEER. Thus, to fly a magnetic heading of 215°, the aircraft compass should read 213°, or a correction of —2° is applied to the magnetic heading.

harassed by vagaries of deviation. Their compasses are still swung for emergency use, but little trust is placed in the deviation card as a precision navigational aid. By use of the periscopic sextant, the heading of the aircraft, and hence compass deviation, can be found quickly whenever a celestial body is in view.

USING VARIATION AND DEVIATION

Variation is a plus or minus quantity, depending on location of the compass in relation to the magnetic pole. Use the jingle "East is least and West is best" to describe the algebraic sign to be used. A chart variation reading of 17° E becomes − 17°; 8° W becomes + 8°. Compass deviation may also be plus or minus, as shown on the compass card in Figure 11.9. To use this apparently confusing data, there is a very simple formula:

TRUE HEADING − E or + W VARIATION = MAGNETIC HEADING
+ DEVIATION = COMPASS HEADING

While considering deviation is important, modern compass systems are sufficiently accurate that for pilot navigation, deviation is usually neglected; *magnetic and compass headings are considered similar.* In the discussion of navigation techniques following in this book, unless there is specific reference to the importance of pilots' considering deviation (as the navigator, in his role, must always do) it may be neglected, and it may be assumed that

TRUE HEADING −E or + W VARIATION = COMPASS HEADING

TIME

Local time varies all over the world; in the United States it is further complicated by the use of Daylight Saving Time. To standardize navigation across these time zones, and to facilitate position reporting, local time is corrected to Greenwich Mean Time (GMT). It is the time on the 0° or Prime Meridian at Greenwich, England; in the Z zone of the world time. It is therefore written as 0900Z or 1400Z, using four digits and the 24 hour clock.

Conversion factors for time zones in the U.S. are:

Local Zone	*Abbreviation*	*Conversion Factor to Z*
Eastern Standard Time (EST)	E	Plus 5
Central Standard Time (CST)	C	Plus 6
Mountain Standard Time (MST)	M	Plus 7
Pacific Standard Time (PST)	P	Plus 8

Note: When going from local to Z time, "East is least and West is best" applies.

WIND AND WIND EFFECT

The basic formula for all DR is

$$\text{SPEED} \times \text{TIME} = \text{DISTANCE}$$

The art and complexity in navigation comes from the fact that this formula is true only in still air, since the pilot's indication of speed is *airspeed.* Any other speed involves a computation.

If air were absolutely motionless, aerial navigation would be simple. A pilot could easily set his aircraft on any desired course by merely correcting his compass for variation and deviation. He could determine his position at any time and compute arrival time at destination by using true airspeed. His only errors would arise from unknown instrument errors, unsteady flying, and poor arithmetic. Such a condition, of course, rarely exists. The air mass through which man flies is also moving—a motion known simply as wind. It is wind that makes navigation with its costly equipment and detailed procedures necessary. To say the art of navigation is *wind finding* is almost true.

Wind has both direction and speed. Like other directions in navigation, it is expressed in degrees from 0° to 360°. Thus a wind blowing from the west is a west wind with a direction of 270° true. Wind direction differs from other directions used in navigation in that it is the direction *from* rather than direction *toward.* This seemingly reverse labeling of wind direction is a traditional practice and it actually causes little problem to the airman.

To understand dead reckoning, it is absolutely essential to understand that wind effect on any untethered object is completely independent of other motion. A toy balloon released into a steady 20-knot wind will in one hour be 20 nm downwind from the release point. An aircraft flying in the same wind for one hour will also be displaced 20 mi regardless of its own airspeed. Flying directly into the wind at 200 knots, it will in one hour be only 180 nm from departure point; flying with the wind, it will be 220 mi away; flying at right angles to the wind, it will be 20 mi right or left of its intended path, and ground speed will be the same on the northern course as on the southern course (Figure 11.10). The lateral displacement in this last instance is *drift,* and the angle between intended and actual track is *drift angle.*

Knowing that the aircraft is drifting to the right or left is not in itself enough to get to a desired destination. A correction must be made in the aircraft's heading in order to compensate for the wind. The number of

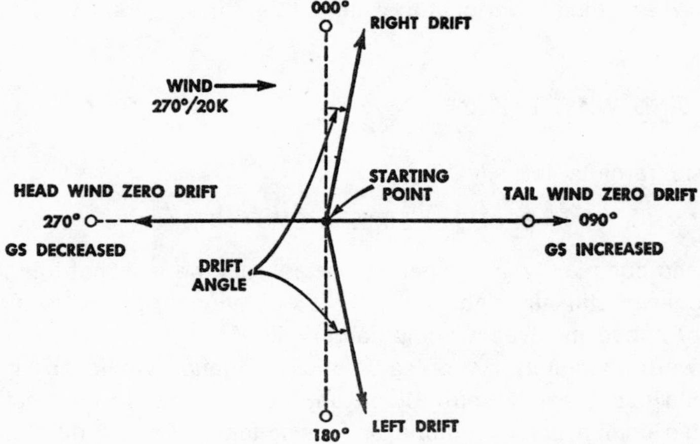

Figure 11.10 Wind effect on Aircraft heading due north, south, east, and west. Circles represent what the position of the aircraft would be if there were no wind; arrowheads indicate the actual position if wind is blowing from the west at 20 knots (270/20).

degrees that an aircraft is turned into the wind in order to fly a desired path over the ground is called the *drift-correction angle,* or *crab angle.* Drift-correction angle is the same quantity as drift angle but is applied in the direction opposite to that of drift. When the drift angle is 10° left on a desired course, the drift correction is 10° right (the aircraft is steered 10° right of the original desired course) in order to compensate for the wind. In making a drift correction, the pilot has not prevented drift but corrected for it. All he has done is to head off-course enough so that the wind will cause the aircraft to drift along the intended course to its destination.

VECTORS AND THE WIND TRIANGLE

In dead reckoning there are six basic measures with which the navigator is continually concerned:

TRUE AIRSPEED: Speed of an aircraft through a mass of air (TAS).
TRUE HEADING: The direction from true north in which the aircraft is pointed (TH).
WIND DIRECTION/VELOCITY (W/V): Wind direction is always reported as true, not magnetic; speed is always reported in knots.
GROUND SPEED: Speed in relation to a fixed point on the earth (GS).

TRUE COURSE: The intended or actual path over the ground measured from true north (TC). Actual path is also called TRACK (TR).

The navigator's job is to give value to these quantities by measuring, computing, and sometimes by little more than guessing. He does this by pairing the six quantities into vectors (Figure 11.11). Although there are many others, the vector quantity of most importance in navigation is speed and direction—speed having only magnitude. To the navigator, the six measures listed above always pair together as the following vectors:

Wind direction—Wind Speed
True heading—True airspeed
True course—Ground speed

Wind direction and wind speed together form the vector known as wind velocity. The other pairings have no such specific names, though True heading—True airspeed could be considered *indicated velocity,* or *air vector,* and True course—Ground speed thought of as *actual velocity,* or *ground vector.* In any vector problem, take care to use compatible units of measurement. *The inadvertent use of statute miles for airspeed and nautical miles for wind ranks next to mistakes in addition and subtraction as the most common cause of error in dead reckoning navigation.*

These three vectors form the *wind triangle.* It is the very heart of dead reckoning. You can obtain True Heading from your compass corrected for variation and deviation; True Airspeed from your airspeed indicator corrected for altitude and temperature.

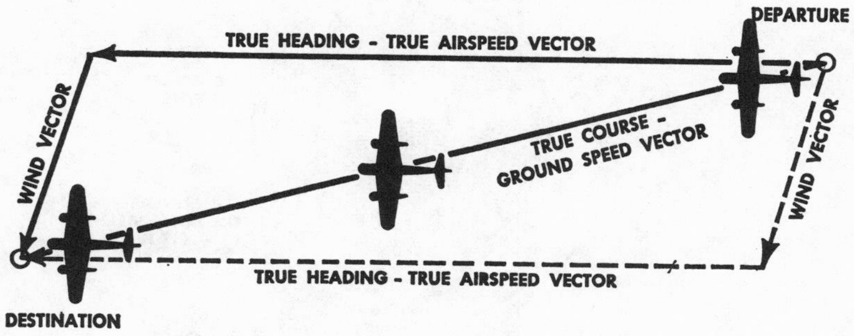

Figure 11.11 The wind triangle. The aircraft travels along the true course line at a ground speed dependent on true airspeed and wind. Note that the aircraft is never on the true heading line, but its longitudinal axis is always parallel to it. Note also that if the wind vector were drawn in at departure, and the true heading line joined head to tail, the same true course line would result.

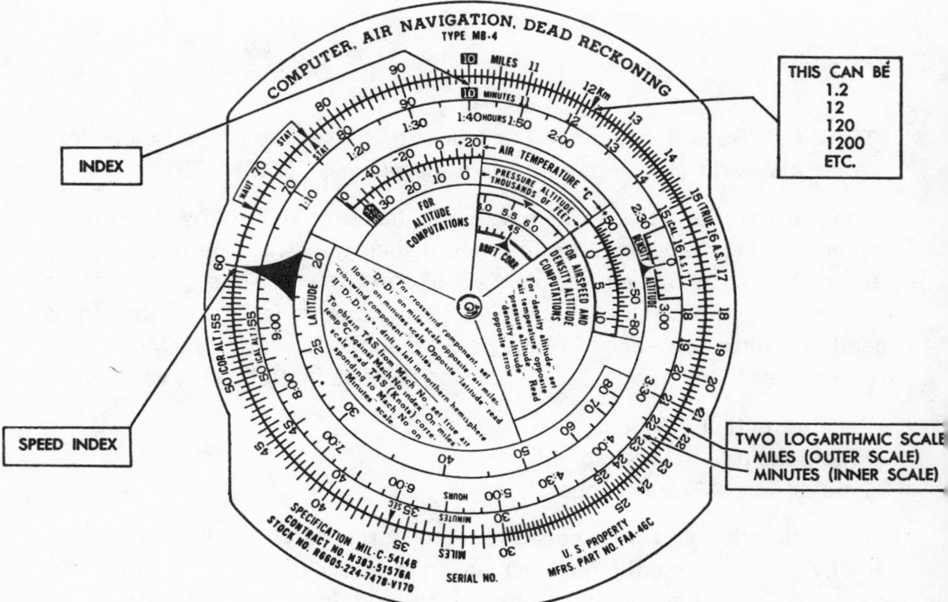

Figure 11.12 The MB-4 computer. The MB-4 is the high-speed version of the famou Dalton E-6B. The slide rule face above is used for basic mathematical con putations of distance, rate, and time and also for correction of altitude ar airspeed meter readings. *(Courtesy of U.S. Air Force.)*

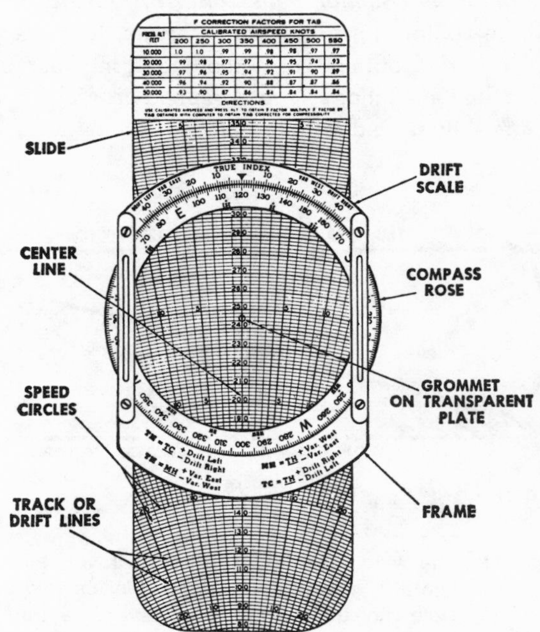

PRESS ALT FEET	CALIBRATED AIRSPEED KNOTS							
	200	250	300	350	400	450	500	550
10 000	1.0	1.0	.99	.99	.98	.98	.97	.97
20 000	.99	.98	.97	.97	.96	.95	.94	.93
30 000	.97	.96	.95	.94	.92	.91	.90	.89
40 000	.96	.94	.92	.90	.88	.87	.87	.86
50 000	.93	.90	.87	.86	.84	.84	.84	.84

Figure 11.13 The wind face of the MB-4 computer is used for solving wind-triangle problems. The sliding insert can be turned over to provide a speed range from 70 to 800 knots. *(Courtesy of U.S. Air Force.)*

If you know either of the other sides of the triangle you can find the remaining one by simply completing the triangle. In planning a flight you will use the forecast wind from the weather office; in actual flight you will compute wind or estimate it from your observed ground speed between check points (fixes), and the heading correction (crab) needed to offset the drift angle and stay on course.

You could determine this vector by actually drawing a wind triangle to scale on your chart. In practice, when determining the wind vector or another vector, you will use the computer as a quicker, less cumbersome method.

DEAD RECKONING COMPUTER

There are many types of aircraft computers, but they all serve the same fundamental purpose: rapid solution of dead reckoning mathematics. The arithmetic of navigation is not difficult; it is just endless. How far? How fast? How many minutes? What direction? What is the wind? In a single 4-hr flight as many as 150 individual computations might be made. A speedy mathematician might get the arithmetic done, but he might get hopelessly lost, too. Any airman given the responsibility for safe guidance of a high-speed aircraft finds some sort of mechanical computer indispensable.

The most famous and popular of all computers is the Dalton E-6B. A newer version, the MB-4, is a modification for high-altitude, high-speed jet navigation (Figures 11.12 and 11.13). They both work essentially the same way. The front face is essentially a circular slide rule with several auxiliary scales specifically designed for navigation; the reverse is a rotating compass rose used in conjunction with the sliding insert for solving wind and other vector problems. Representative dead reckoning problems solved on the slide rule face are shown in Figure 11.14. Wind vector problems will be discussed later. Consult the detailed instruction booklet accompanying the computer for more information on the wide variety of problems that can be solved.

CALCULATION OF AIRSPEED

The computer also serves as a rapid means of calculating true airspeed. One of the problems in navigation of any sort is a precise determination of speed. On land this presents little problem; but in the air it is more difficult because all mechanical connection with the earth is broken, except, of course, where distance measuring equipment (DME) is available. The airman must therefore rely on the air itself for his speed data. The basic reference value is indicated airspeed. (Figure 5.14).

Only rarely is the speed indicated on the meter the true airspeed of the aircraft. The difference exists because the meter can give proper readings only at sea level with barometric pressure reading 29.92 in., and the temperature 15°C. True airspeed at altitude is therefore generally higher by about 2% per thousand feet of altitude. The correction is very easily found by use of the computer, as shown in Figure 11.14D. The data needed are

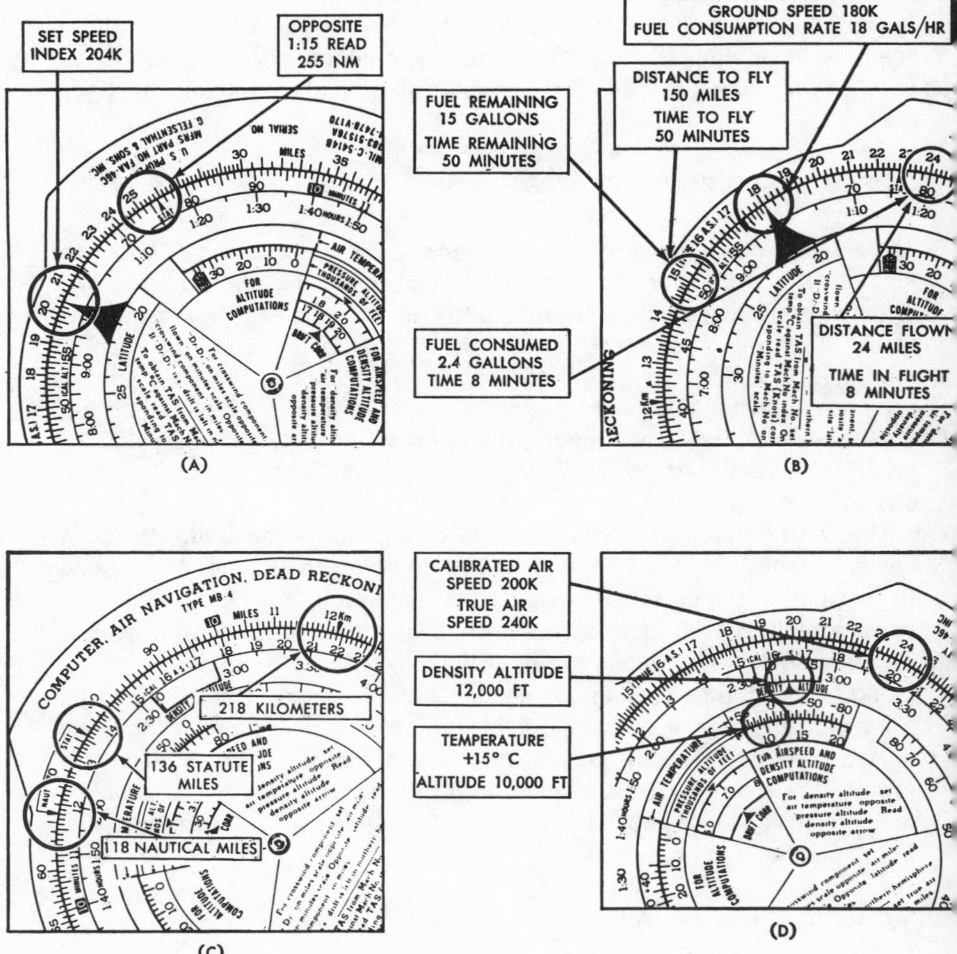

Figure 11.14 Representative problems solved on the slide rule face of the MB-4 computer (A) Ground speed is known to be 204 km. Find the distance traveled in 1:15 (B) The aircraft has traveled 24 mi in 8 min. Find the ground speed and time required to fly another 150 mi. Fuel consumed is 2.4 gal in 8 min. Find the time remaining if you have 15 gal left. (C) Distance is known to be 136 statute miles. Find the equivalent distance in nautical miles and kilometers (D) The aircraft is flying at 10,000 ft at a calibrated airspeed of 200 km The temperature is +15°C. Find the true airspeed and density altitude *(Courtesy of U.S. Air Force.)*

calibrated airspeed (page 224), pressure altitude and outside air temperature.

FINDING UNKNOWN VECTORS IN THE WIND TRIANGLE

In this, the wind face of the computer is invaluable. Recall that in the wind triangle, there were six factors, two associated with each side: wind direction and wind speed, true course (track) and ground speed, true heading and true airspeed. These sides were referred to as the wind vector, the ground vector, and the air vector.

The slide in the wind face of the computer, shown in Figure 11.13 is developed as shown in Figure 11.15. There are many problems which can be solved concerning the six variables, and there are several ways to do each one.* Some ways are preferred by navigators whose methods

*These and other solutions are found in Air Force Manual 51-12, *Dead Reckoning Computers,* for sale by the U.S. Government Printing Office.

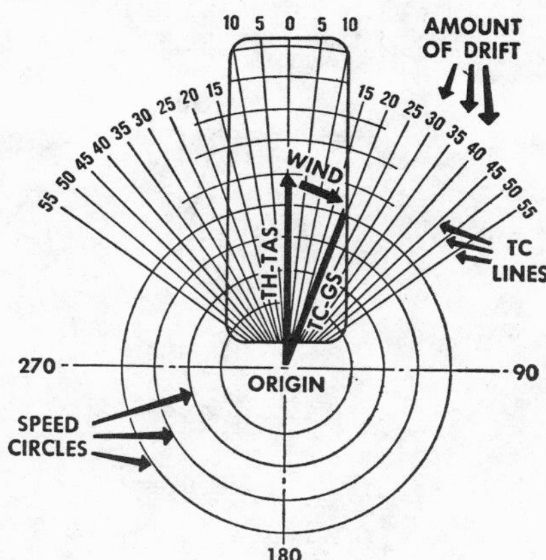

Figure 11.15 The wind triangle on the computer slide. Point of origin is omitted so that a higher range of speeds can be placed on the slide. The tip of the true heading arrow is positioned by setting the speed circle representing true airspeed under the center of the plastic window on the frame of the computer. The wind arrow is drawn from this same point.

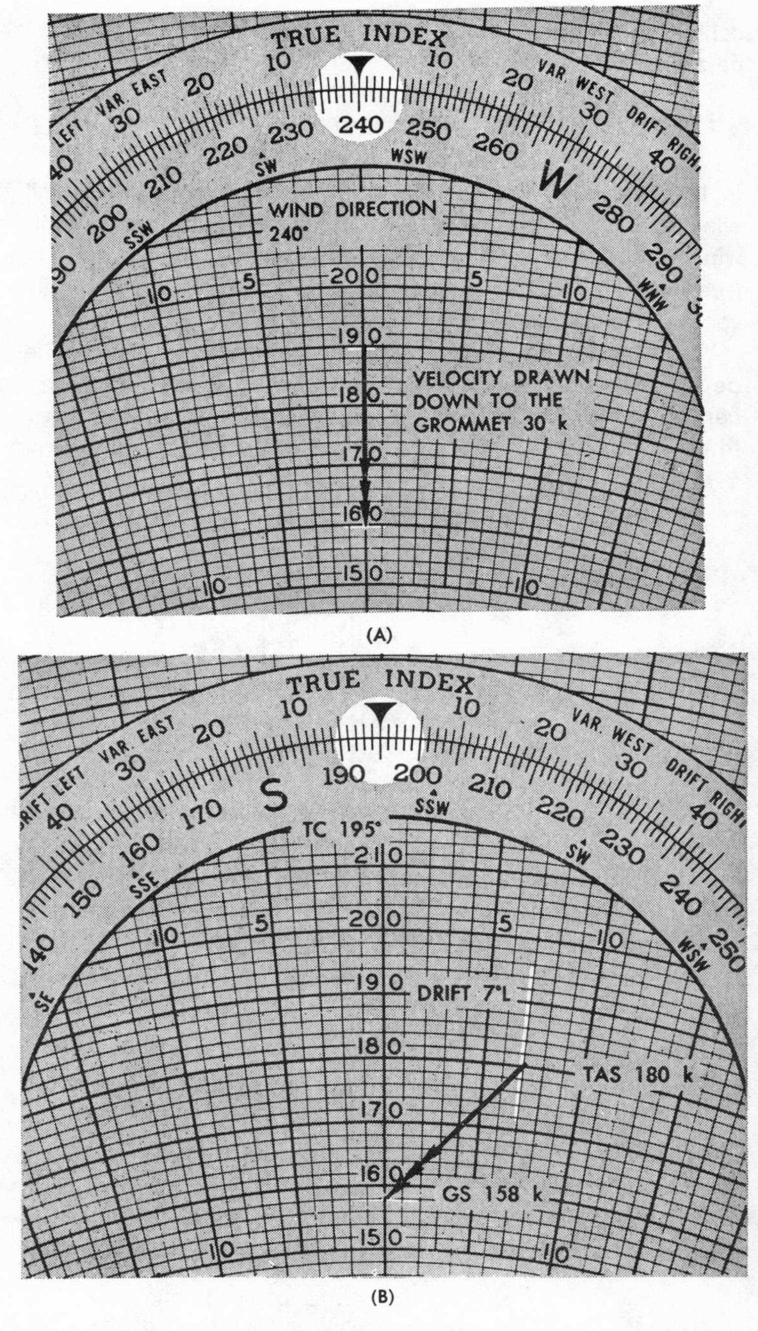

Figure 11.16 Finding true heading and ground speed. *(Courtesy of U.S. Air Force.)*

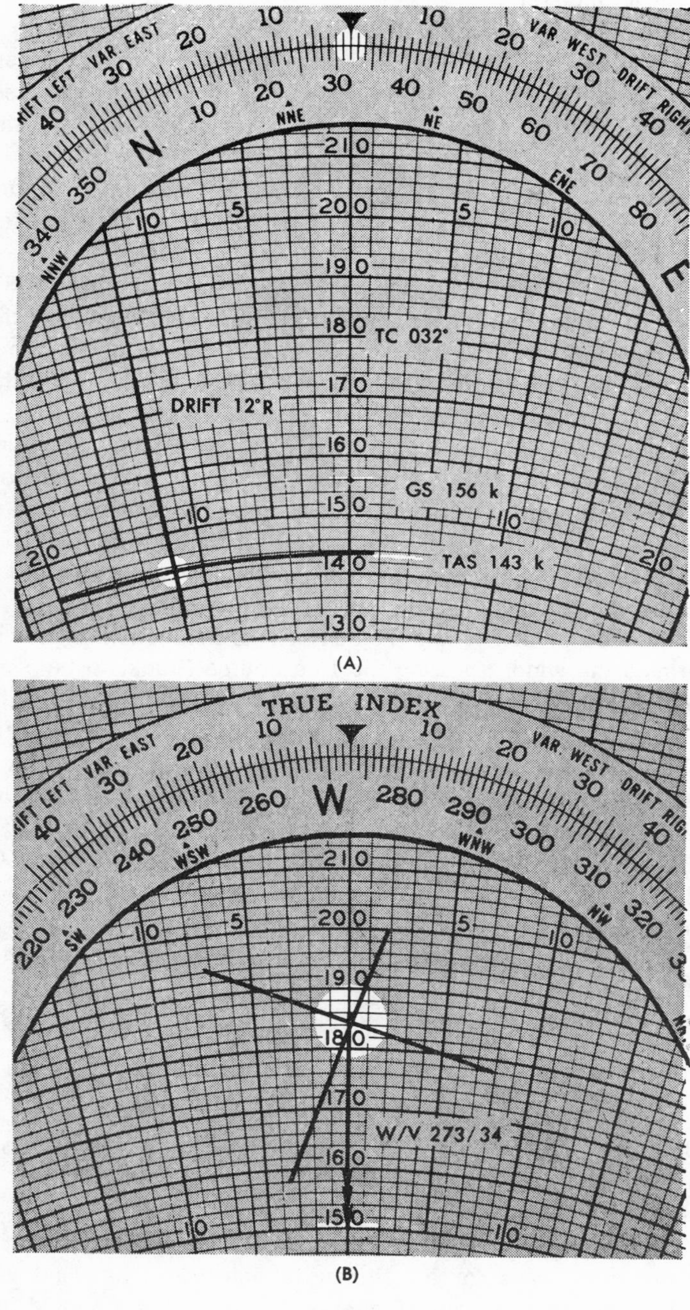

Figure 11.17 Finding wind direction and velocity. *(Courtesy of U.S. Air Force.)*

require more precision and whose workroom is larger; others are preferred by pilots. Two solutions of great use to pilots are described here. In these solutions, disregard "Drift Left" and "Drift Right" on the True Index Scale.

To Find True Heading and Ground Speed This solution is useful in flight planning, or in using a wind value which has just been determined in the air. We are given:

Wind direction, 240°. Wind speed, 30 knots. True course, 195°. True airspeed, 180 knots. Referring to Figures 11.16 A and B, set wind direction (240°) under TRUE INDEX. Draw the wind vector down along the centerline to the center of the disc, to the proper length for 30 knots; the head of the vector is on the grommet.

Set the true course (195°) under the true index. Move the slide until the tail of the wind vector is on the speed circle for the true airspeed (180°). Read the drift (7°). Since the heading line is now to the right of the track line, the drift is left and the drift correction is + 7°. The true heading is therefore 195° + 7° = 202°. Read the ground speed (158 k) under the grommet.

To Find Wind Direction and Velocity This solution is useful in flight to determine the wind. Knowing the true course (track) to be 32° with a true heading of 20°, the wind is obviously from the left. With a true airspeed of 143 knots and a ground speed of 156 knots, it is also from the rear.

Place the true course (32°) on the circular scale opposite the true index. Move the slide to set ground speed (156 k) under the grommet. Take the difference between true course and true heading to determine the drift correction angle. A minus drift correction angle is plotted to the left of the centerline, and a plus drift correction angle to the right. Mark the intersection of the wind correction angle and the true airspeed on the transparent disc.

Rotate the transparent disk until this cross is at the top of the computer directly over the centerline of the computer. Read the wind direction on the rotating scale opposite the true index (273°), and the wind velocity (34 k) on the slide from the marked cross to the grommet. Note, to avoid error, that our original estimate of a wind from the left rear is confirmed.

WIND DETERMINATION

There are many ways for an airman to determine the wind vector so essential to aerial navigation. Whenever possible, wind should be cross-checked by use of several methods. Wind finding is at the same time so important and so subject to error that only when necessary should you trust completely a wind determined by only one means.

Forcast Winds Any weather office can give an approximation of winds at flying altitudes for use in planning a flight. Once airborne, every possible wind-finding technique should be tried before further reliance is placed on such forecasts. Winds change with altitude and with the nature of the terrain over which they pass. It is unrealistic to expect that forecasts made many hours ahead of time for an area hundreds of miles away will be accurate enough for precision navigation, though they are remarkably accurate at high altitudes.

Direct Observation At altitudes of only a few thousand feet above the ground, wind direction can sometimes be checked by watching smoke plumes; over water, by the washback of foam from whitecaps. The number of whitecaps is also an indication of wind speed. These are, of course, only indications and not accurate measures. Winds change in both speed and direction with altitude, so that surface phenomena are not necessarily applicable at flight altitude. The passage of cloud shadows across the ground is also usable at times as a check on wind direction. If the clouds are close to flight altitude, the same wind is acting on both clouds and airplane and direction can be more closely estimated. In fast, high-flying aircraft none of these devices is of much value even if the ground can be seen.

Winds Between Positions When a wind is determined from departure to a known position or between two known positions, it is the average wind between the positions. A wind of "light and variable" (L/V) could be a composite of two winds of 090°/10K and 270°/10K and possibly many more.

Aids to Dead Reckoning

The importance of sound dead reckoning procedures in navigation cannot be overemphasized. In large or small measure it is always used, and it is difficult to imagine any system of navigation without it. For dead reckoning has one advantage which overrides any limitation or failing which is leveled against it: it can always be used. No matter what the condition of visibility outside an aircraft or of electronic aids within, so long as an airplane can fly, its position can be roughly estimated by the simple mathematics of distance, direction, and time.

DR LIMITATIONS

Though basic to all navigation, dead reckoning is not a self-sufficient system. Two limitations restrict its sole use. First, the errors of dead reckoning are cumulative. The farther an aircraft flies, the greater is the likelihood that a plotted position is in error. Errors may be small and undetectable, arising from instrument inaccuracies, unknown magnetic disturbances, poor plotting technique, and so forth. Or they may be gross human errors in computing, measuring, plotting, and instrument reading which are detectable only by constant check and double check of every step of the work.

Second, once an erroneous position has been plotted, there is no way to reestablish a true position through dead reckoning means alone; the aircraft must be positioned by a DR aid.

The navigator must therefore have some reliable method of providing a continuing check on the accuracy of his dead reckoning. In the early days of flying the problem of dead reckoning error was solved simply by watching for, and correcting back to ground landmarks, a method of navigation known as *pilotage* or *map reading.* As man's flying capabilities increased, however, it became necessary to have dependable systems that would work at night as well as day, over water as well as land, and under all conditions of visibility.

Civil and military aviation has gone to considerable trouble and expense to provide aids to dead reckoning that would be reliable enough to permit safe navigation under such conditions, and the end is not yet in sight. The art of navigation is part of the art of flying: As man flies higher, faster and farther, navigational techniques that were once satisfactory must be improved or become outmoded. Map reading, for example, is already impossible for the navigator of a jet transport. Jet aircraft fly so high and so fast that direct observation of the earth provides little navigational aid even under clear weather conditions.

TERMS USED IN AIRCRAFT POSITIONING

Bearing The direction of an object *from* an airplane is called the bearing of the object. Bearings are angular measurements from 0° through 360°. They may be true bearings or relative bearings, depending on reference point. A *true bearing* is measured clockwise from true north; a *relative bearing* is measured clockwise from the heading of the airplane. To be useful in position finding, the navigator needs true bearings, but most of his measuring devices give him relative bearings. He must therefore convert to true bearing by combining the relative bearing with the true heading of the aircraft:

$$TH + RB = TB \qquad \text{(see Figure 11.18).}$$

A rough example: "Our heading is 315°" (TH). "That isle is off our right wing" (+ RB of 90°). "Its true bearing is 045°." Note that when the sum of true heading and relative bearings exceeds 360°, the true bearing is found by subtracting 360° from the total. In celestial navigation, the true bearing of any heavenly body is called its *azimuth.*

Line of Position A line of position, generally referred to by the initials LOP, is a line connecting all possible geographic positions of an aircraft at a given instant. The line can be straight or curved, depending on the source of information: a true bearing from a mountain peak will be a straight line of position; distance from an object will be a circle of radius equal to the distance.

LOP's determined by bearings, as in map reading or radio, cannot be plotted directly. A reverse bearing, or reciprocal, must be plotted from the known point to the aircraft. A reciprocal bearing is found by adding or subtracting 180° from the true bearing (our LOP from the isle mentioned above is 225°) (Figure 11.18).

Fix A fix is an established geographic position of an aircraft for a given instant of time. It is a point, not a line. It is sometimes possible to establish a fix directly, as in flying over a landmark the exact location of

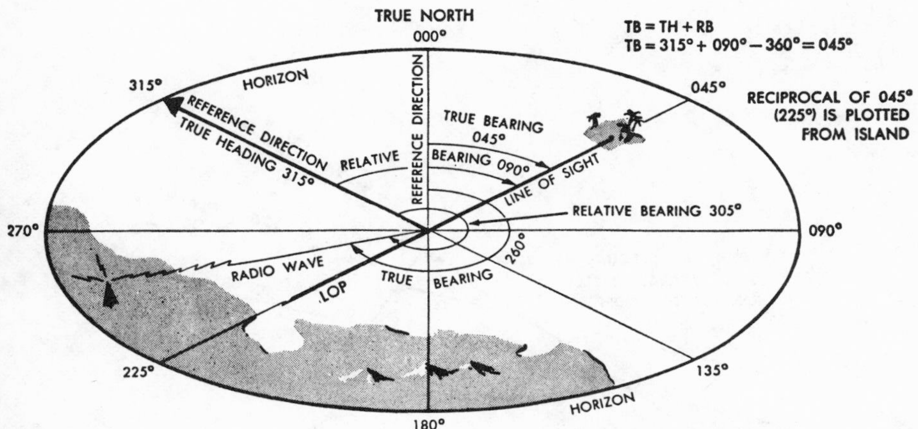

Figure 11.18 Lines of position. A relative bearing is obtained on the island. It is converted into a true bearing by adding it to the aircraft heading. Since the exact position of the aircraft is unknown, no origin for plotting this true bearing exists. A reciprocal bearing must therefore be computed by adding or subtracting 180°, and the LOP plotted from the known island. From any point along this line the island bears 045° from true north. Bearings obtained from radios or radar must also be converted to true bearings and the reciprocals plotted from them. The exception is the OMNI bearings which are always magnetic bearings.

which is known. Often, however, a fix can be found only by crossing two or more LOP's independently determined (like being over a known highway intersection). Though any two LOP's intersecting at an angle greater than 30° will normally provide reliable fixing, the best results are obtained when they cross at right angles. Whenever possible, a third LOP is used as a check on the point where the other two LOP's cross. The symbol Δ used in log keeping to indicate a fix evolved from the hopeful anticipation that three well-chosen LOP's would actually cross as a small triangle.

Two LOP's can rarely be obtained at the same instant of time. It is therefore necessary to rectify the time difference by advancing or retarding LOP's. When an LOP is advanced or retarded, it is along the best-known track at the best-known ground speed. This provides a line which is assumed to fall where a true LOP would have been plotted if taken at the same time as the other LOP (Figure 11.19). Some slight error is introduced since DR track and ground speed are probably somewhat in error. To minimize the error, it is wise to move the LOP more nearly paralleling the course line, since this line will require less linear displacement. If no such advantage is offered by either LOP, the first-found is advanced to the time of the second in order to provide the more recent fix.

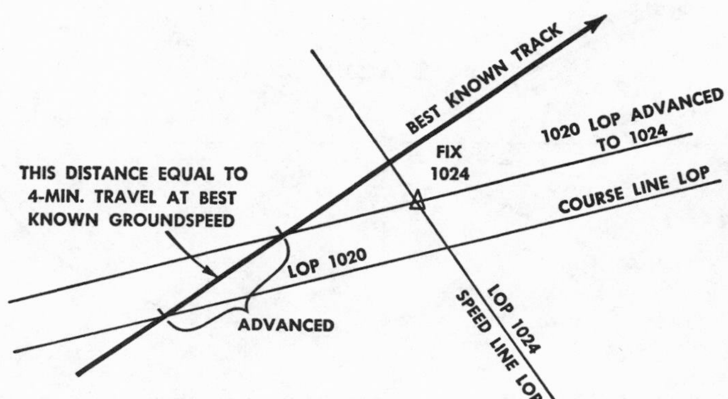

Figure 11.19 Advancing a line of position. At 1020 an LOP is obtained as shown. A second LOP is plotted at 1024. To rectify the time difference, the first LOP is adjusted to the time of the second by moving it up along the best known track a distance equal to 4 min × best known ground speed. The adjusted LOP is always drawn parallel to its reference LOP.

Map Reading Aids to DR

Many pilots regard map reading as visual cross-country flying. Actually it is the identification of landmarks from their representation on a chart and the utilization of this information to fix the position of the aircraft or to establish lines of position.

ADVANTAGES AND LIMITATIONS OF MAP READING

Under ideal conditions, map reading is the best means of checking dead reckoning. No fix is more precise than a positive identification of an accurately mapped landmark. If conditions were always ideal, there would be no need for any other aid to dead reckoning. But sometimes map reading is difficult or even impossible. It cannot be used when the ground is obscured by clouds or when flying over water. Even when the ground is visible, landmarks cannot always be readily identified on a chart. This is especially true at night and over uninhabited regions where the terrain is relatively uniform. It may also be true if the chart is incomplete or inaccurate. A chart may even be too complete. Among the world's most surprised people were navigators trained during World War II over the broad reaches of Texas who were suddenly required to map-read their way over England. Towns were so closely spaced, railroads and rivers so numerous, major highways so insignificantly different from country lanes, and everything so uniformly green, that English navigators, to whom it all seemed so simple, were accorded a substantial respect.

MAP FEATURES USED IN MAP READING

Map reading is not always an easy job. No map can look precisely like the earth itself. The cartographer uses symbols to represent ground features, and the selection of symbols and features to show is not simple. Effort is made to represent those characteristics which have the most distinctive appearance when seen from the air and to avoid those which would make the map a hopeless clutter. Successful map reading depends on correct interpretation of the symbols and, as in all navigation, success comes through practice.

Three general types of information appear on charts designed for pilotage purposes: (a) navigational reference data, (b) cultural features, and (c) terrain features. The symbols for all of these appear on the aeronautical chart "Legend" printed on the chart border.

Navigational Reference Data Every aeronautical chart contains a larger amount of data which can never be seen from the air. Meridians, parallels, isogonic lines, VOR's, tower frequencies, airways, and Air Defense Identification Zone boundaries fall into this category. Caution areas and danger zones are also marked, though these sometimes can be seen. All are necessary to safe, legal flight, but they may be confusing to anyone trying to follow on a map the path of an aircraft over the ground. Airways and radio aid data especially seem to clutter a map in metropolitan areas where the clearest presentation of the ground is generally wanted. The cartographer shows these data in light overprint colors through which other features can be read, but only with practice can they be disregarded until needed.

Incidentally, in the United States, the Coast and Geodetic Survey continuously revises aeronautical charts. Be sure to check the date on your chart.

Cultural Features These are man-made features: cities and towns, roads and railroads, bridges, dams, racetracks, and so on. They are not always the best navigational check points, but they are generally the easiest for the beginner to use. Once properly identified, a cultural feature provides a pinpoint fix more readily than does any other map feature. In populated areas, only a few outsanding cultural features are shown—large towns, the most prominent highways, and individual buildings only when they stand out clearly in contrast to surrounding terrain. In sparsely populated areas the reverse is true: every cultural feature possible is shown—small buildings, ranches, even roads that are little more than wagon paths.

Terrain Features Rivers, mountain peaks, coast lines, lakes, and islands provide excellent check points and are therefore prominently featured on aeronautical charts. Other topographic characteristics are also shown, but greater skill is required to use most of this information. Colored shading is used for terrain height, and contour lines are shown. These features are needed for safety, but only an experienced navigator can get usable navigational aid from them. Wooded areas are sometimes marked, but are mostly difficult to distinguish from the air. Dry river beds and dry lakes frequently blend into surrounding land areas, and marshy areas may look more or less wet with seasonal change.

MAP-READING TECHNIQUES

Do not use map reading as the only means of navigation. It is merely an aid to dead reckoning and should always be employed in conjunction with it. Even in clear weather it is possible to become hopelessly confused in map reading without the supporting mathematics of dead reckoning. The small amount of actual calculation that must be made is tremendously outweighed by the gains of safety, efficiency, and assurance.

It is not necessary, and in fact it is inadvisable, to try to find every available check point. So much time is consumed that long-range planning is impossible. Without long-range planning, a flight can quickly become hazardous if bad weather or aircraft emergencies are suddenly encountered. Good navigational practice consists of definitely locating the aircraft at a given instant, and then preparing to establish another definite fix at some instant of time later. This may vary from 5 to 30 min later, depending on many other factors. In good weather, where visibility is expected to remain clear and where wind patterns are expected to remain constant, and at higher altitudes where an emergency is not so apt to require instant action, fixing every 20 to 30 min is usually adequate. When approaching destination under poor visibility conditions, more frequent fixing is advisable.

A navigator prepares for his next fix by three easy steps: (1) he selects a good check point some distance ahead of his present position; (2) he measures the exact distance and computes on the basis of his best known ground speed an estimated time of arrival (ETA) at the check point; and (3) a minute or so before this ETA is up, he watches for the check point and notes the exact time of passage. Using this time, he can update his groundspeed.

Visual Cross-Country Flying As a solo pilot you probably use the same procedure in a simplified form. With practice, it becomes more and more mental, but a good pilot navigator follows the process meticulously and unconsciously. With your chart prepared before takeoff with a heavily marked course line, subdivided into legs of convenient length between clearly defined check points and with compass headings indicated, you are ready. The chances are that you ignored deviation (page 664), but that you arrived at compass headings by application of the rule, *"East is least and West is best,"* to account for variation. It means "Subtract east variation and add west variation, to obtain magnetic heading from true course."

You will be much better prepared if you have checked the probable wind direction and velocity, have estimated drift, have computed the ETA's for each check point, and have predicted your fuel consumption and reserve. *This is particularly important at night, and nothing helps find a check point like knowing in advance when you ought to see it.* During flight, you may only mark down the time of each fix on the chart. You are less likely to get lost or run out of fuel if you compute an ETA to the next check point, and compare the predicted to the actual elapsed time and ground speed. It can be done by taking notes on a chart, but a log of some type is much more accurate because it permits comparing proposed and actual performance. To avoid confusion in identifying landmarks, the best procedure in map reading is to orient your map with the direction you are traveling. On an easterly heading, the East-West axis of your chart would be lined up with East at the top. As an aid in estimating correctly your distance from passing landmarks, observe the distance between any two terrain features near your DR position. Then compare the two.

MAP READING LINES OF POSITION

In map reading, fixes are generally obtained directly by either flying over a check point or by estimating distance and direction from a check point close by. Occasionally, however, it is necessary to use lines of position because the only available reference is too remote for accurate estimate of distance. Over water, such reference points might be islands, lighthouses, or prominent spits of land. When flying over clouds, mountain peaks projecting through the cloud layer can be used. A rough bearing can sometimes be obtained by aligning a plotter with the longtitudinal axis of the airplane and sighting along the protractor markings. Making a few practice sightings when the position of the aircraft is known is good preparation for later emergency. Bearings are converted to lines of position and plotted on the map by methods shown in Figure 11.20.

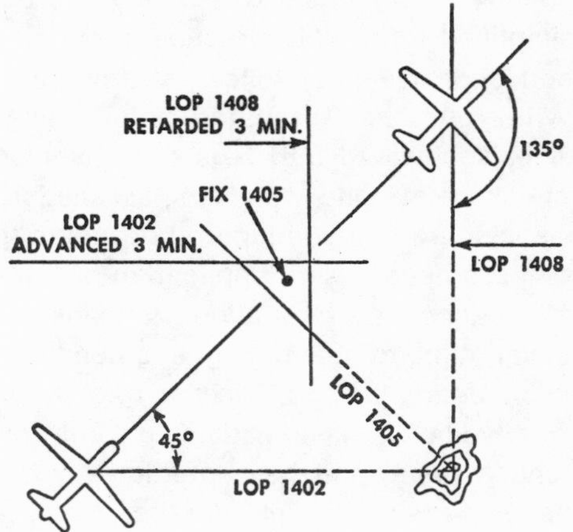

Figure 11.20 Running fix. The first LOP is taken at 1402 when the peak bears 45° from the aircraft. The second LOP is taken when the bearing is 90°, and the third at 135°. The first and last LOPs are adjusted to the time of the middle LOP, providing a fix for 1405.

FIX FROM ONE ORIGIN

Three different bearings on one subject can be used to establish a fix, generally referred to as a *running fix.* Bearings are taken when the object —mountain peak, island, radio station—bears 45°, 90°, and 135° relative to the right of the aircraft heading or the reciprocal relative bearings on the left side of the aircraft headings. The first and last bearings are then adjusted, at the best known ground speed, to the time of the 90° bearing in order to minimize errors caused by moving LOP's. Procedure for plotting a running fix is shown in Figure 11.20. A running fix is reasonably accurate, and is far better than most estimates of bearing and distance from remote objects.

NIGHT MAP READING

Map reading by night is more difficult than by day, but as an aid to DR, it may be easier because there is less confusing detail. Even on moonless nights some ground features such as rivers can occasionally be seen. During the Korean War much of the navigation in light B-26 bombers was done by night map reading. So skilled did the navigators become that they were able to fly by night at over 200 knots along valleys below the level of surrounding mountain ranges, with only the barest hints at check points as a guide. Night navigation is normally not nearly so hazardous, but it should be attempted only after most careful planning. Reliable radio aids should also be available for auxiliary use. In clear weather, lights from towns and cities can be relied on as check points even in the very early morning hours. Highways can be spotted by automobile headlights, and even railroads can be found by the characteristic swinging headlight of locomotives. Terrain features should not be counted on unless they are very prominent or marked by some man-made feature, such as the lights of a dam or bridge across a river, or a beacon on top of a prominent peak (Figure 11.21). Terrain features stand out more clearly if the eyes are accustomed to darkness. The best way to insure this is to use a light with a red lens, which will not destroy night vision. If a red light is not available, inside work on maps and log should be done with a low-intensity light. One cautionary note must be considered if a red lens is to be used, however: it will cause map markings or course lines in red pencil to become almost invisible. Map features in red to be used as check points should therefore be circled or underscored before takeoff.

Usually at night, the haze that limits visibility during the day appears to dissipate, thus increasing visibility. Lights from large cities can be seen from over 100 mi away when at only 8000 ft. The principal error in

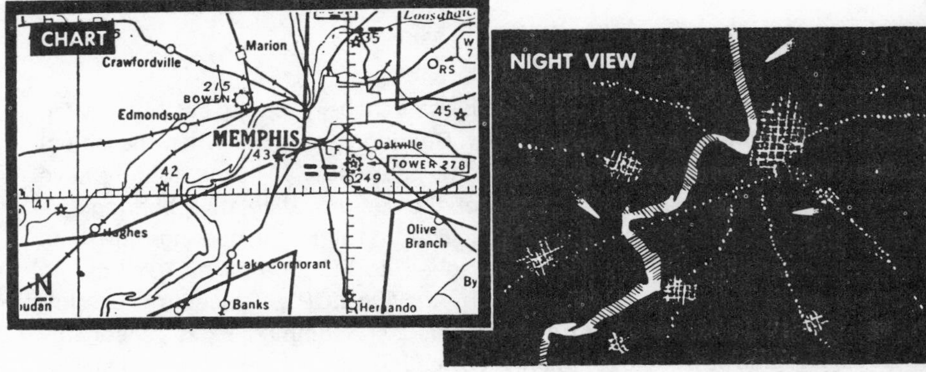

Figure 11.21 Night map reading. All features are not distinguishable at night such as the small streams, small towns, and country lanes. However, beacon lights (comet appearing in the figure) can be seen for considerable distances. Note the highways by the headlights of cars and the checkerboard pattern in the cities formed by street lights. On nights when the moon is bright, rivers and lakes will stand out clearly. *(Courtesy of U.S. Air Force.)*

night map reading is underestimating distance. A good rule of thumb, until you are confident of your accuracy, is to double your estimate of distance. If radar or radio aids are available, cross-check your estimate with them.

MAP READING ERRORS

There are two basic errors against which the inexperienced navigator should be cautioned. The first is a human failing that sometimes plagues even skilled navigators; the error of wishful thinking. It is easy under the pressure of rapid air work for a navigator to mis-identify a check point by fitting what he sees into what he wants to see. Since all features in any area are not always shown, he can readily convince himself that the map is in error. At any time of doubt, it is necessary to check back and forth from chart to ground, comparing every possible feature, before positive identification is assumed. *It is usually best to select a feature on the map and then try to find it on the ground, rather than to work from ground to chart.* A ground feature may be newer than the map or simply not have been selected for presentation.

The other error arises after the navigator becomes lost, or after a period of flying over an undercast which has obscured the ground. In either case, a check point suddenly appears. The inexperienced navigator will search all over the map in a frantic effort to identify the check point

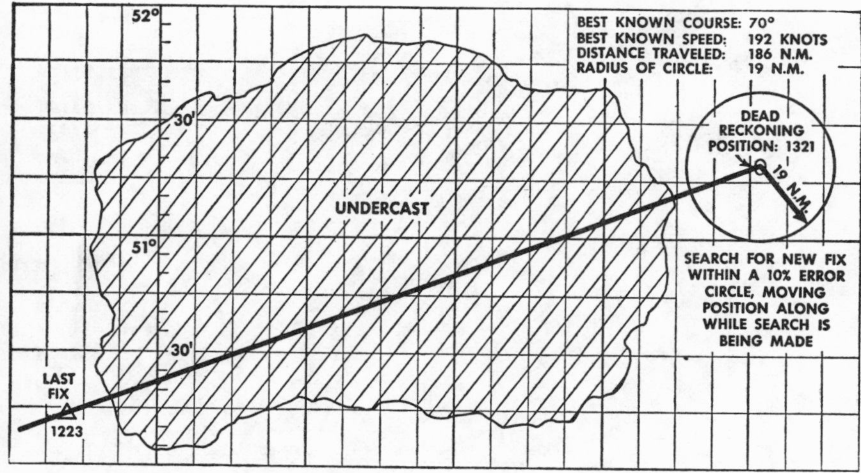

Figure 11.22 Establishing a position after being lost. While the aircraft is over the undercast the best known course and distance traveled are continuously plotted. When the ground can again be seen, search is made within a 10%-error circle. Precise measurement is not needed. Approximate mathematics and a freehand circle are generally adequate.

and reestablish his position. With a little experience, he soon learns to systematize his efforts and to search only in that portion of the map where he could possibly be. *This area is roughly a circle with a radius in miles equal to about 10% of the distance traveled since the last fix.* It is drawn around the dead reckoning position plotted from the best known ground speed and heading information (Figure 11.22). This is a good reason for flying steady, rather than wandering, headings.

If it appears that only a quick glimpse of the check point is to be afforded before it is passed or before clouds again obscure it, make a quick sketch of the most prominent features: rivers, major roads, railroads, bridges, airfields, prominent outlying buildings, and so forth, oriented with respect to each other and to aircraft heading. Record your time over the point. You can then make a more leisurely search for a similar pattern on the map after the area has again become obscured.

EXAMPLE OF A VFR MAP READING FLIGHT

Figure 11.23 depicts a flight from Scottsbluff, Nebraska, to Rapid City, South Dakota. It is planned direct, largely ignoring radio facilities plotted on the chart, in order to illustrate map reading principles.

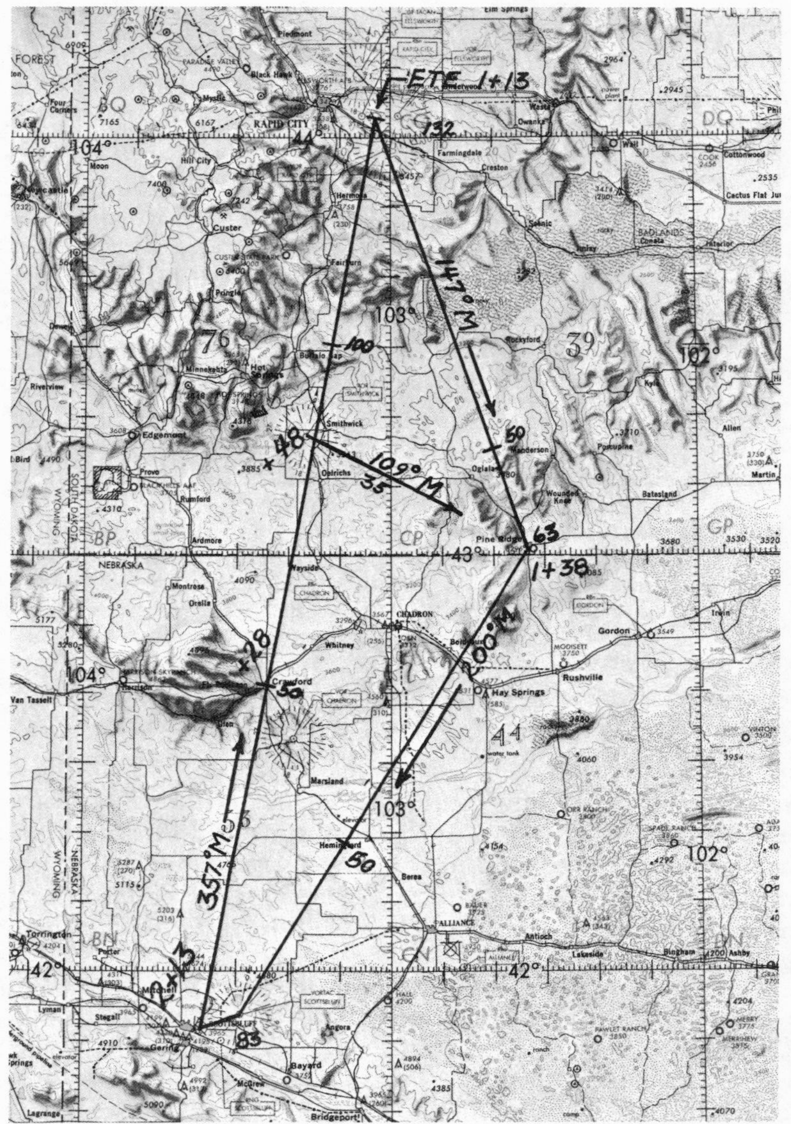

Figure 11.23 Example of a map reading flight.

Flight Planning Select the charts you wish to use, either Sectional or a World Aeronautical Chart (WAC) as used in the illustration. With an idea of where you are going, call the weather office or better, visit it, to determine what the weather will be en route and at destination at the time you expect to arrive. Having determined that the weather will permit you to fly VFR, determine the wind along the route at the altitude you intend to fly. This will be determined by the aircraft you are flying, the heading, and the terrain. In the Cessna Skylane used for this example, 8500 ft was chosen. The wind at 8500 ft was forecast to remain constant from 300° at 25 knots.

If you have not done so before, spend some time with Section III, Flight Data and Special Operations, and III A, NOTAMS, of your FAA Airman's Information Manual, and observe the following:

Are your charts current? Are there any restricted areas in your way? If you are concerned with radio facilities, are they operational? What altitude should you fly on each leg? Study the "Aeronautical Symbols" tabulation printed on the chart.

Check Section IV A, Airport/Facility Directory to obtain tower and Flight Service Station frequencies you may want, and write them down. Note any construction or other peculiarities at airfields along the route which you may wish to use as an emergency alternate.

Draw your true course from Scottsbluff to Rapid City, to Pine Ridge, and to Scottsbluff VOR (which we will use to illustrate homing) with you, and measure the mileage, dividing it conveniently into 50-mi segments.

Measure the true courses of each leg and subtract the 13° Easterly variation taken from the isogonic lines on the chart. Write in the magnetic headings thus determined along each leg, with an arrow indicating direction. Notice that at Chadron VOR the heading of 357° approximately parallels the 0° radial; this is because OMNI roses are oriented to magnetic direction, with variation accounted for. Notice the good check points along the route: Crawford, Nebraska, with the high ground to the west, Angostura Reservoir, about five miles west of course at Smithwick, and the road network en route and near Rapid City. Coming back to Pine Ridge, not the Oglala Reservoir and the stream leading into Pine Ridge. Notice also that Pine Ridge bears 109° from the Smithwick VOR; if you were using your radio, this would be a helpful additional check. Notice the Rock Butte Reservoir, the road and railroad pattern at Hemingford and the water and road pattern back at Scottsbluff. While during this flight you might not need to know these checkpoints, having noticed them could be very helpful in the event of decreased visibility due to a sudden shower, snow, or evening darkness.

Assuming that you will indicate about 130 mph, a normal day this time of year would give you a temperature of about 0°C at 8500 ft; from the slide rule face of the computer you determine that your TAS will be 146 mph. Change this into knots: 127 knots. Now with the procedure on page 674, determine your ground speed for each leg and your probable drift correction required. Then determine the time it will take to fly to each checkpoint and note it on the chart. A log is generally better for this because it is more orderly and saves your charts; but doing it on the chart gives you one less piece of paper to worry about, a permanent record of your flight, and helps visualize the problem. The data come out like this:

Checkpoint	*Magnetic Heading*	*Distance*	*Ground Speed*	*Elapsed Time*	*Total Time*	*Drift Corr.*
Crawford	357	50	109	:28	:28	8°L
Reservoir	357	36	109	:20	:48	8°L
Rapid City	357	46	109	:25	1:13	8°L
Pine Ridge	147	63	150	:25	1:38	3°R
Hemingford	200	49	133	:22	2:00	11°R
Scottsbluff VOR	200	29	133	:13	2:13	11°R
Airport	240	5	115	:03	2:11	11°R

It is true that for this short flight this seems like a lot of trouble. There are many shortcuts you can take, up to the point of gross carelessness. But the process illustrates how it is done professionally, even though a large part of it may be mental. It will be very difficult to fly the magnetic headings corrected for drift to compass headings to 1° in the Cessna 182; however, if the speed and headings *are* held with care, the habit of holding careful headings will grow; you will always have a better check on your winds and will develop a good deal more confidence in your basic DR.

Flying the Plan File your flight plan with FAA. Take off and climb directly on course, with a compass heading of 349° (drift correction is 357–8). Traffic pattern turns and the climb will slow your TAS somewhat on this leg, but not more than two or three minutes. By turning directly to a compass heading and holding it, the nature of the first checkpoint is such that it is not easy to miss, and you will have a good check on both your compass and the wind. Right after takeoff, note the time of takeoff on the chart or log. You may either hold the compass heading until the time has elapsed to Crawford to see just where you do come out, or you may "home" visually on Crawford, not trying to check the drift. But when you cross Crawford or a point near it, and know your position, make a small triangle Δ around the point, denoting the fix, and record the time. Then make whatever corrections appear appropriate and continue on course. By the time you reach the Reservoir, your next check point, you will have a good check on your ground speed and drift, and can make an accurate ETA to Rapid City. By always making an ETA whenever you pass a check point, you will always know when you SHOULD be over the check point. This is a great help in finding one, particularly in congested areas. It is also vital in determining your fuel consumption. It is wise to note the fuel remaining each time you obtain a fix, and record it.

Though you can continue your map reading flying after leaving Rapid City, note also that by passing directly over the Rapid City VOR you can track outbound on the 147° radial, thus determining accurately your proper compass heading to get to Pine Ridge. Also, if you were in doubt about Pine Ridge, you could check it by intercepting the 109° radial from Smithwick VOR, establishing a VOR LOP which would be over Pine Ridge. Also note that on passing Pine Ridge you are more than 4000 ft above the ground and according to your Airman's Information Manual, you should be on a quadrantal VFR heading of 8500 ft unless you elect to descend.

In the vicinity of Hemingford, you can continue your map reading direct to Scottsbluff, or you can home on Scottsbluff VOR if your equipment permits. If you have ADF, you can home also on Scottsbluff Radio Beacon. Remember, though, that the flight is not over until the wheels are chocked, the ignition switches are off, and you have closed your flight plan!

Radio Aids to DR

Unquestionably today most airplanes—private, commercial, military—rely more heavily on electronic aids to dead reckoning than on any other. An order of their importance based on frequency of use would place the VOR DME in the United States well out in front because of the U.S. airways structure. The radio compass (automatic direction finder, or ADF) would be next. ADF is also used worldwide and for long-range navigation. These are complemented by systems based on simple radio receivers, loran, airborne radar including Doppler radar beacons, and inertial systems.

AIRWAYS FLYING

The Federal Airways depicted on Radio Facilities Charts (page 759) greatly simplify flight planning because checkpoints, headings, and distances are already laid out. Despite the apparent simplicity of following airways, radio aids are still an aid to dead reckoning navigation, and the principles apply with equal force.

Airways flying is best done with a log, as shown in Figure 11.24.

In the columns from left to right are (1) radio facilities or checkpoints and the airways followed; (2) radio facility call letters and DME or TACAN channel and the VOR frequencies; (3) the magnetic no wind headings between the check points; (4) the nautical miles between check points

PILOT'S PREFLIGHT CHECK LIST					DATE 12/2/65
X	WEATHER ADVISORIES	X	ALTERNATE WEATHER	X	NOTAMS
X	EN ROUTE WEATHER	X	FORECASTS	X	AIRSPACE RESTRICTIONS
X	DESTINATION WEATHER	X	WINDS ALOFT	X	MAPS

FLIGHT LOG

DEPARTURE POINT	VOR IDENT. / FREQ.	RADIAL TO / FROM	DISTANCE LEG / REMAINING	TIME PT-TO-PT. / CUMULATIVE	TAKEOFF / ETA / ATA	GROUND SPEED
LAX (INTL)					0710 TAKEOFF 1510Z	9,500 TAS 90
CHECK POINTS					ETA / ATA	
LONG BEACH	LGB C-104 115.7	100 / 080	20 / 310	13 / 13	1523 / 23	200/15 95
THERMAL V-64	TRM C-109 116.2	081 / 076	96 / 214	45 (47) / 58	08 / 10	137
BLYTHE V-64	BLH C-121 117.4	077 / 079	70 / 144	28 (27) / 1+26	38 / 37	230/25 151 (155)
BUCKEYE V-16	BXK 110.6	062 / 077	97 / 47	37 / 2+03		153
DESTINATION PHOENIX V-16	PHX C-103 115.6		47 / TOTAL 330	18 / 2+21		

POSITION REPORT: FVFR report hourly, IFR as required by ATC

ACFT. IDENT.	POSITION	TIME	ALT.	IFR/VFR	EST. NEXT FIX	NAME OF SUCCEEDING FIX	PIREPS

REPORT CONDITIONS ALOFT—CLOUD TOPS, BASES, LAYERS, VISIBILITY, TURBULENCE, HAZE, ICE, THUNDERSTORMS

PHX-SKY HARBOR 258 deg. - 6 N.M.
FREQ: EN ROUTE RADIO 126.7, 135.9
SKY HARBOR TOWER 118.7, 120.9
" " GROUND 121.9

CLOSE FLIGHT PLAN UPON ARRIVAL

Figure 11.24 FAA pilot's flight log. This log is printed on the back of the FAA Flight Plan Form (Figure 12.2). In the illustration, flight planning entries are typewritten, en-route entries are handwritten. A similar form used for Air Force piston and jet flying appears in Figure 10.2.

and the cumulative distance remaining; (5) above the slash, the number of minutes between check points using the forecast winds for elapsed time for each leg, and speed adjustment for climb; below the slash is the cumulative time. In the last column is the ground speed determined from the forecast wind, and revised en route from the elapsed time between stations. The next to the last column indicates flight progress. Takeoff was at 0710 (1410Z), and the progress of the flight indicates each successive estimated time of arrival and actual time of arrival over the check points. Actual times and speeds are in parentheses.

The paragraphs following describe how the radio facilities themselves are used as aids to DR.

USING THE VOR—TUNING AND ORIENTATION

To tune the VOR equipment, turn on the power switch, select the desired frequency, and adjust the volume until the station is positively identified by the call letters. *Identification is very important* because you may not have read or set the frequency correctly, or the receiver, if crystal controlled, may not have channeled to the correct frequency (Figure 5.31).

VOR Bearings When the station is identified, the Radio Magnetic Indicator (RMI) will be giving the magnetic bearing to the station under the head of the needle. The Omni Radial on which the aircraft is located is the magnetic bearing from the station, and will be shown under the tail of the needle. VOR magnetic bearings may be plotted directly on Radio Facilities Charts and on maps as magnetic rather than true bearings because the OMNI compass roses around each station symbol are oriented with magnetic North; that is, variation is already accounted for.

If you have no RMI (Figure 5.29), determine the bearing to the station by turning the course selector knob until the CDI is centered and TO appears in the TO-FROM window. The course then appearing in the window is your magnetic bearing to the station; neglecting deviation, it is your no-wind compass heading to the station (Figure 11.25).

HOMING

With RMI After the VOR station is tuned and identified, turn the aircraft until the head of the bearing indicator is directly under the top index. If you keep the indicator under the index, the station will always be directly ahead of you. Any crosswind during homing will cause the aircraft to follow a curved path to the station. Neglect crosswind only when you are close to the station and the bearing on which you approach is unimportant.

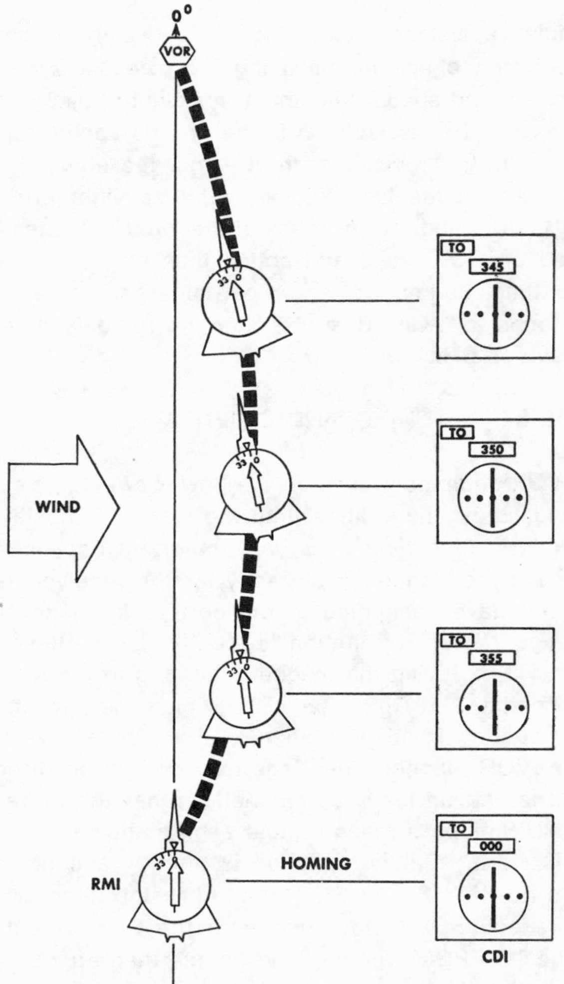

Figure 11.25 Curved flight path resulting from cross-wind homing. The stronger the wind, and the greater the distance to the station, the greater the distance off course. The triangular index on the aircraft symbol indicates the compass heading. The double-barred arrow indicates relative bearing to the station which, if read on the RMI compass card, is also a magnetic bearing.

Without RMI Turn the course selector knob of the course indicator until the CDI is centered and TO appears in the TO-FROM window. Turn the aircraft to the compass heading indicated in the window and adjust the knob to recenter the CDI. Repeat this process until over the station. Additional course knob changes will be necessary if you do not correct for crosswind or hold an accurate heading.

Station Passage Upon reaching the VOR station, you will encounter the cone of confusion over the station. Since the width of the cone varies with altitude, the time spent in the cone will vary from a few seconds at low altitude to as much as 2 min at 40,000 ft. As you enter the cone, the bearing indicator will begin to rotate aimlessly, the TO-FROM indicator may fluctuate between TO and FROM, and the CDI will move from side to side. The alarm flag may also appear.

After you have flown through the cone, the bearing indicator will stabilize near the bottom index of the RMI, the CDI will resume its normal indications, and the TO-FROM indicator will settle on FROM. The latter is the most precise indication of station passage. If you intend to maintain the same course from the station, no change is necessary. When you desire a different course from the station, turn immediately to that heading and set this new course in the course-selector window. Then intercept and maintain the new course (Figure 11.27).

COURSE INTERCEPTION INBOUND

To intercept a predetermined magnetic course to the station, such as a VOR airway, set the desired course in the course selector window and insure that TO appears. If FROM appears, you have either set the wrong course, or have passed the station.

Note the position of the CDI and the RMI bearing indicator. Turn toward them until you reach a heading 30° beyond the desired course. This is your interception heading. While any heading beyond the desired heading is an interception heading, the effects of unknown drift, and the desirability of intercepting the desired course promptly make a 30° interception angle generally desirable. A greater angle may be better during a high crosswind, but otherwise too great an angle results in overshooting the desired course. A number of factors can affect your selection of an interception angle.

For example, suppose you have the following situation: a high true airspeed, the desired course is downwind, you are fairly close to the station, and the bearing indicator is 15° from your desired course. Since you are close to the station and only 15° from the desired course, the lateral distance between you and the course is quite small. In addition, both your high true airspeed and effective wind will cause you to intercept

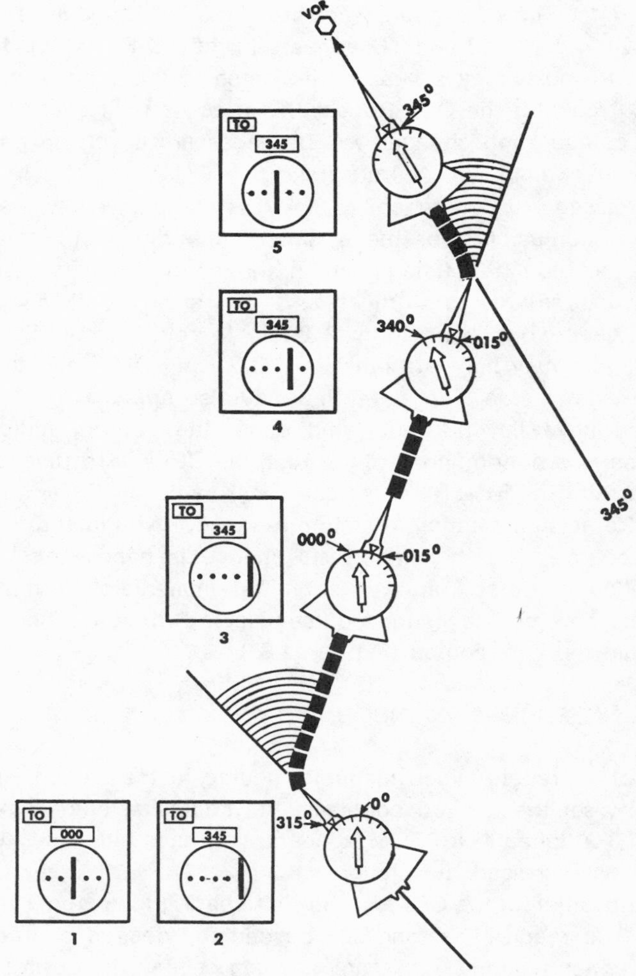

Figure 11.26 VOR course interception inbound, showing successive steps and action of CDI and RMI.

at a rapid rate. Under these conditions, and to prevent overshooting the desired course, you should use a small interception angle. A satisfactory one would be formed by turning to a heading about 10° beyond the bearing indicator. Remember that an interception angle is the angle between the desired course and the intercept heading. In this case, even though you had turned only 10° beyond the bearing indicator, your interception angle is 15 plus 10, or 25°.

If you assume an opposite case, in which you have a low true airspeed, the desired course upwind, a long distance from the station, and the bearing indicator 40° from the desired course, a much greater interception angle would be required. By turning to a heading 50° beyond the bearing indicator, an interception angle of 90° would be formed. Never exceed an interception angle of 90°, since this would take you away from the station.

Interception with Course Indicator Only If the RMI is not available, make the interception with the course indicator. First turn the course set knob until the CDI is centered, and TO is in the TO-FROM window. The resulting heading in the course window is, of course, the direct bearing to the station. Now set the course you wish to intercept in the course selector window. If the CDI is to the right, turn the aircraft right to the selected course *plus* 30°; if the CDI is left, turn the aircraft left to the selected course *minus* 30°. The result will be the intercept heading. It may be varied according to the examples shown above for the RMI interception. Fly on the intercept heading until the CDI is centered, when you will be on the desired course. Turn then to the heading inbound to the station.

COURSE INTERCEPTION OUTBOUND

To intercept a predetermined course *from* the station, set the desired course in the course-selector window and insure that FROM is in the TO-FROM window. If TO appears, you have set the course incorrectly, or have not passed the station. Note the bearing under the tail of the RMI bearing indicator, and turn the aircraft until the heading at the top index of the RMI, the aircraft heading, is on the opposite side of the desired course from the tail of the bearing indicator. Any heading beyond the desired course will be an intercept heading under zero wind conditions, though 30° is a desirable minimum for most intercepts.

Outbound Interception with Course Indicator Only The outbound procedure differs from the inbound procedure only in that FROM rather than TO should appear in the TO-FROM window.

Course Interception Immediately after Station Passage Because the aircraft is close to the station, the displacement from the desired course is exaggerated. Therefore, use an angle of intercption which does not exceed the number of degrees off the course indicated by the tail of the bearing indicator, or by the desired course set in the course selector window.

COMPLETING THE INTERCEPT AND MAINTAINING COURSE

Because the CDI is sensitive to small changes, it is the most useful indicator for turning onto the desired course as the aircraft approaches it.

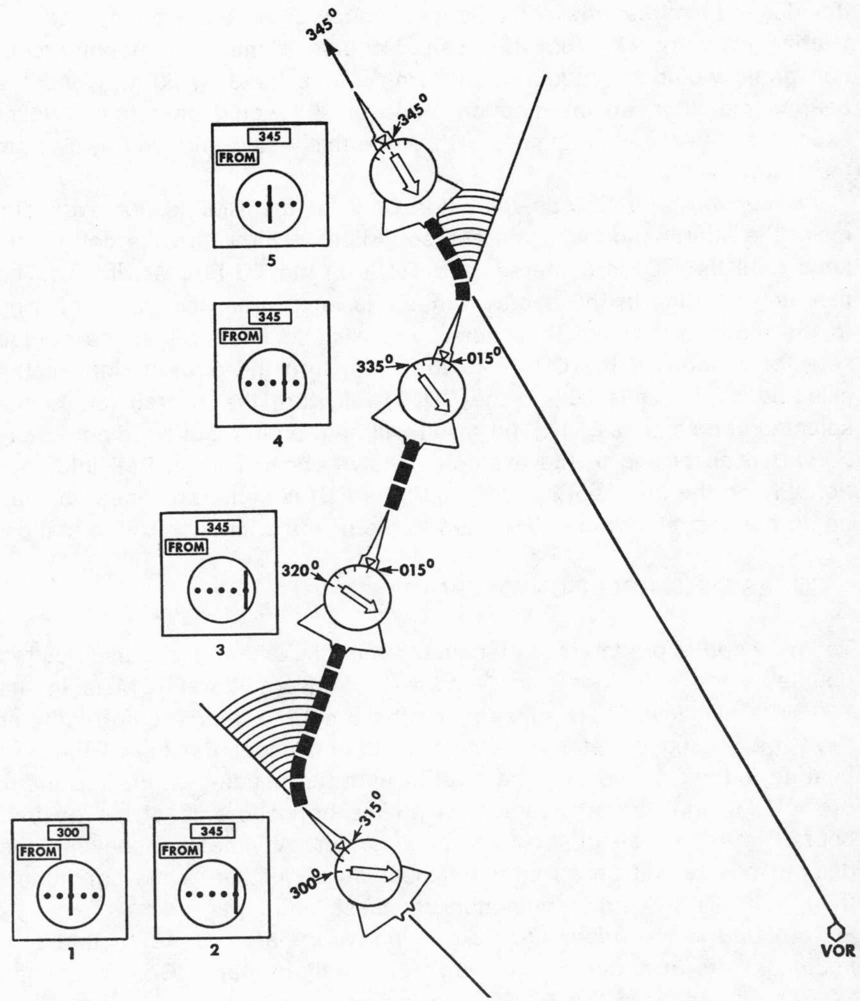

Figure 11.27 VOR course interception outbound.

Hold the intercept heading constant with the desired course set in the course-selector window. The CDI will begin to center as you approach within 10° off course. By watching its rate of movement, you can regulate the steepness of bank needed to turn onto the desired course without over- or undershooting. This rate of movement is governed by the angle of interception, distance from the station, true airspeed, existing wind, and the rate at which you intend to turn on course. The angle of bank can be regulated during the turn so that you are directly on course when the wings are level.

Once on course, maintain a heading the same as that shown in the course selector window. If the CDI begins to move from center, it indicates that you are drifting away from course, or that you are not holding an accurate magnetic heading. As soon as you determine that you are drifting, turn toward the CDI, usually an amount double the number of degrees off course. Make a firm and precise correction in order to return to course as soon as possible. Returning to course quickly will be helpful in establishing your correct drift correction promptly. This is particularly important in instrument approaches.

As soon as you have returned to course, establish an estimated drift correction. Any further corrections are made to this new heading as a base. *Remember that a 30° correction is sufficient to counteract a direct crosswind of one-half the true airspeed of the aircraft.*

Maintaining Course with RMI Only If the RMI only is available, level off after interception so that the head of the bearing indicator is over the desired course and under the top index. If, while holding the desired heading, you note that the bearing indicator drifts off this position, you are drifting opposite the direction of movement of the head of the bearing indicator. Turn toward it an amount equal to double the amount of the deviation, exercising the same judgment as used to determine the drift correction for the CDI. Fly this heading until the head of the bearing indicator is over the desired course. You will be back on course. Establish a drift correction. The head of the bearing indicator and the desired course will be together, but will not be under the top index. The difference is the drift correction. If the indicator moves toward the top index, the correction is too small; if away, the correction is too large. With no RMI, the drift correction will equal the difference between the course selector setting and the aircraft compass heading.

Maintaining Course Outbound This procedure is the same as the inbound procedure, but uses the tail of the bearing indicator in relation to the outbound course. After applying the drift correction, if the tail of the bearing indicator moves toward the top index, the drift correction is too large; if away, it is too small.

TIME-DISTANCE CHECK

To compute your time and distance from an omnirange station, turn the aircraft until the RMI bearing indicator points to either wingtip index. Then set that wingtip bearing into the course-selector window, and adjust it until the CDI centers. Note the time. While holding the heading accurately, set a 10° bearing in the course-selector window. (If the station is on your left, subtract 10°; if on your right, add 10°.) When the CDI centers again, note the time, and use these formulas:

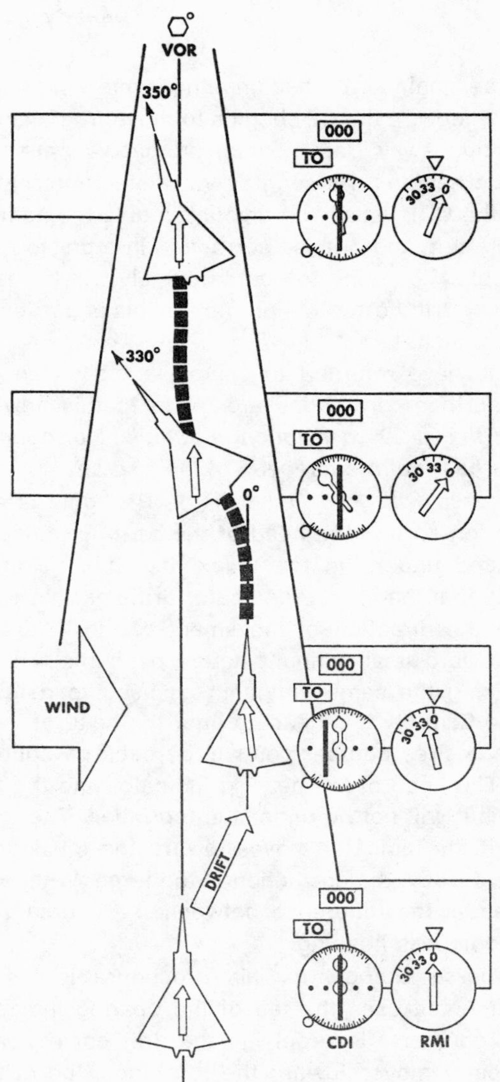

Figure 11.28 Maintaining course. Relative RMI bearing indicator position is shown on both RMI and aircraft symbol. Note action of the Course Director heading pointer, which indicates aircraft heading relative to course. Heading pointers are used on most high-performance aircraft installations.

$$\frac{\text{time in seconds between bearings}}{\text{degrees of bearing change}} = \text{minutes to the station}$$

or

$$\frac{\text{TAS* } \times \text{ time in minutes between bearings}}{\text{degrees of bearing change}} = \text{miles to the station}$$

For example, if it requires 2 min to fly a 10° bearing change at a TAS of 400 knots, you are:

$$\frac{120}{10} = 12 \text{ min from station; or, } \frac{400 \times 2}{10} = 80 \text{ nm from station}$$

While the results is an approximation, it is fairly accurate. Limiting the bearing change to 10° not only simplifies calculations, it increases accuracy. Other factors affecting accuracy are the existing wind and the accuracy of timing.

To make a time-distance check without the RMI, first rotate the course knob until the CDI centers. Turn the aircraft to a heading 90° from that in the course-selector window. Recenter the CDI and note the time. Holding the heading carefully, set in a 10° bearing change as described above. When the CDI centers again, note the time and compute the time or distance.

TACAN AND VORTAC AS AN AID TO DR

Because bearing information is presented to you on the RMI and CDI as with VOR, the only difference is the addition of distance information from the same station. This simplifies VOR procedures by helping you to decide upon the best angle to intercept a course, the number of degrees of correction required to return to course, and to determine ground speed more accurately. You also have an infinite number of distance and bearing fixes available when within reception range of a station.

Ground Speed Check Because DME measures slant range, ground speed checks between DME fixes made close to the station from high altitude may be inaccurate. Checks made 30 nm from the station will be accurate up to 40,000 ft. At 5000 ft, they will be accurate any distance from the station. Determining the ground speed is a simple matter of measuring the distance flown over a carefully checked period of time, then solving a time-distance problem to find ground speed.

Station Passage The cone of confusion over a TACAN or VORTAC station is larger than that over a VOR station, approaching 15 mi at 40,000

*Use ground speed, if known.

ft. In the cone of confusion, the RMI, CDI, and TO-FROM indicator act the same as VOR.

The range indicator will continue to show that you are approaching the station until you are directly above it. Next it will stop momentarily, then begin to increase. The minimum range indication is station passage. The minimum indication will equal your altitude above the station in miles.

USING THE RADIO COMPASS

The radio compass, or Automatic Direction Finder (ADF), is the most versatile low-frequency radio navigation aid in use today (Figure 5.38). While it does not have the short-range flexibility or precision of the VOR, it may be used over much longer distances. It is so advanced that many recent long-range flights by small aircraft have used ADF as their sole aid to dead reckoning; they have crossed the Atlantic and Pacific in both directions and continued on around the world with no other DR aid. The navigator uses the radio compass to obtain bearings which he can plot as LOP's.

Radio Compass Bearings When the radio compass needle points to a station either as an ADF or an RDF (page 256) the indication is a radio bearing. If the instrument face is an RMI, the needle points to a *magnetic bearing;* if the card is fixed or manually adjusted with 0° at the top, it is a *relative bearing.* To be plotted as an LOP, either must be converted into a true bearing. With the RMI, the true bearing can be read directly by applying variation and deviation. With the fixed or manually rotated compass face, you obtain the true bearing by adding the aircraft's true heading to the relative bearing:

$$\text{TRUE BEARING} = \text{TRUE HEADING} + \text{RELATIVE BEARING}$$

With a rotatable radio compass face, you can do this mechanically simply by setting in variation and deviation and rotating the compass face until the true heading is under the top index. Then the true bearing *to* the station lies under the head of the needle, and the true bearing *from* the station lies under the tail of the needle. Because bearings are always plotted *from* the station *to* the aircraft position, read the bearing under the tail of the needle, or add 180° to the reading under the head of the needle.

Plotting Radio Compass Bearings To obtain an LOP, plot the true bearing like any other bearing by simply drawing a straight line from the station in the direction of the bearing. Unless the station lies dead ahead, behind, or is nearly off one wing-tip the LOP to be useful must be combined with some other bearing—visual, or radio, and all LOP's must be advanced or retarded to a common time to obtain a fix.

Bearings over 150 mi long plotted on Mercator charts must be corrected because all radio bearings are great circles and all straight lines on a Mercator chart are rhumb lines. The rhumb-line correction is obtained from navigator's flight-planning documents. Usually it can be ignored safely, particularly near the equator. It increases with latitude and with the number of degrees of longitude between the aircraft and the station. However, up to 50° latitude, the error in a 500-mi bearing would not exceed 4°.

Radio Bearing Inaccuracies While radio bearings over 150 mi long are not fully reliable, knowledge of the sources of error will help to use them intelligently. *Night effect,* indicated by a fluctuating radio-compass needle, is caused by unpredictable sky-wave reflections. Commercial broadcast stations over 1000 kHz and the now obsolete loop radio ranges are the most vulnerable, and particularly at sunrise and sunset.

Thunderstorms also will deflect the needle in the direction of the storm. Shorelines bend the radio waves seaward when the bearing crosses the shore at angles less than 30°. Mountains also reflect radio waves. Quadrantal error results from deflection of the waves when they must strike portions of the aircraft such as tail or engines, before striking the loop antenna. This makes location of the loop antenna important.

RADIO DIRECTION FINDING (RDF) PROCEDURES

RDF, or more commonly, *aural null* procedures are used in emergency when ADF operation is not possible. The aural null is the absence of audible sound, or at times the area of minimum reception. RDF procedures are valuable when the COMP and ANT positions of the ADF are unreliable in an area of thunderstorms, and frequently in ice crystal static or precipitation static. Under these conditions, the bearing indicator may fluctuate excessively or give erroneous indications when you use the COMP position. Loss or malfunction of the sensing antenna renders both the COMP and ANT positions inoperative. In LOOP position, reception under these conditions will be best because the loop is a shielded antenna.

The aural null results when the plane of the loop antenna, indicated by the direction of the bearing indicator, is perpendicular to a line to the station. In practice, the minimum signal can be obtained within a few degrees by loop rotation. The width of the null (the number of degrees through which the loop may be rotated and still give no signal) may be varied by the volume control. Decreasing the volume widens the null; increasing it sharpens or narrows the null. At a considerable distance from the station with full volume, the null may still be quite wide. The minimum width is determined by the power of the station, the aircraft's distance from it, and the volume-control setting (Figure 5.39).

The center of the null, and the direction to the station, is taken as the center of the arc which the bearing indicator can describe with no signal. For example, if no signal is received between 40° and 60°, the relative bearing would be 50°. Navigational procedures for course interception, maintaining course, and even making approaches are substantially the same for RDF and for ADF, except that the bearing indicator must be positioned to determine the center of the null, and station passage is not as easy to identify.

TUNING

More than one airman has followed his ADF to disaster by tuning inadequately or carelessly. The set must be tuned accurately to obtain the performance that is built into it. Because there are different procedures for ADF and RDF tuning, both are shown.

ADF Tuning:

Function Switch—ANT
ON-BFO Switch—ON
Select the proper frequency band
Volume at an intermediate position
Tune to the desired frequency for the best audible signal
Identify the station

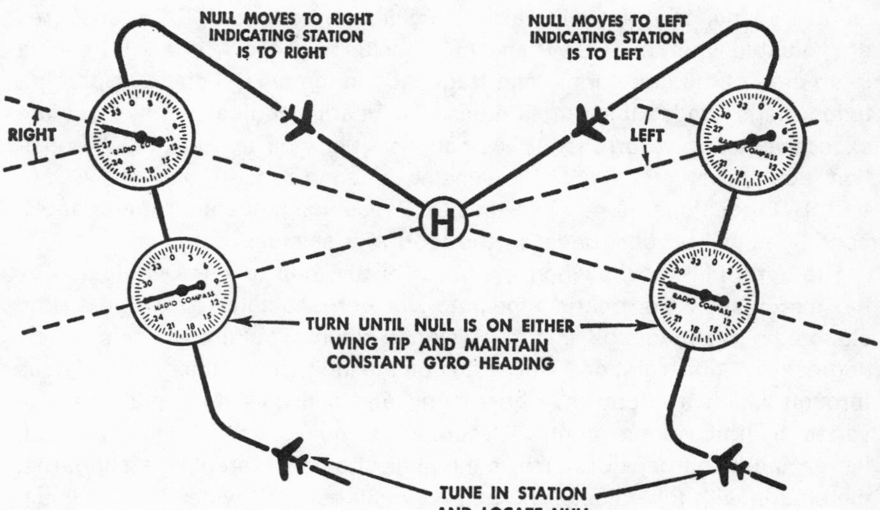

Figure 11.29 Orientation aural-null. *(Courtesy of U.S. Air Force.)*

Function Switch—COMP
Retune for maximum tuning meter needle deflection

RDF Tuning:

Function Switch—ANT
ON-BFO Switch—ON
Select the proper frequency band
Volume at an intermediate position
Tune to the desired frequency for the best audible signal
Identify the station
Function Switch—LOOP
ON-BFO Switch—BFO
Rotate the loop for maximum reception
Retune for high pitch (solid tone)
Rotate the loop to locate the null
Adjust the volume for a 5° to 8° null width.

Be careful to hold a precise heading during RDF tuning. Even a slight heading deviation will result in other than the desired null width. For all RDF navigation, maintain a 5° to 8° null width, if at all possible.

HOMING

ADF Homing Observe the position of the ADF bearing indicator and turn in the nearest direction to place the head of the bearing indicator under the top index. Maintain this indication while proceeding to the station. The principles are the same as described on page 691 for VOR homing with RMI.

RDF Homing First solve the 180° ambiguity. To do this, maintain a constant heading and rotate the loop to locate the null. Observe the direction and amount of turn needed to place the null off the nearest wing tip. If the null appears between 0° and 90°, or 180° and 270°, turn left; if it appears in either of the other quadrants of the bearing indicator dial, turn right. After completing the turn, set the bearing indicator to the 90° or 270° position. Adjust the heading until the null is exactly off the wing tip, and maintain that heading. If the null bearing increases, the station is to the right; if it decreases, the station is to the left.

Now note the relative bearing of the station, and turn right or left toward it that number of degrees. Place the bearing indicator at 0°. On leveling out, the null will be directly ahead. As you proceed inbound, you must keep the volume at a constant level to assure a 5° to 8° null width By holding the heading necessary to keep the null on the nose of the aircraft, you will home to the station. Drift has the same effect as for the ADF.

COURSE INTERCEPTION

Inbound First turn the aircraft to the magnetic heading of the desired course and check the bearing indicator to determine the position of the aircraft in relation to the desired course. Unless you are exactly on the desired course, the bearing indicator will be deflected to the left or right. Turn toward the head of the indicator the number of degrees of deflection plus 30°. The number of degrees turned is the angle of interception. Proceed on this heading; when the bearing indicator is deflected the same

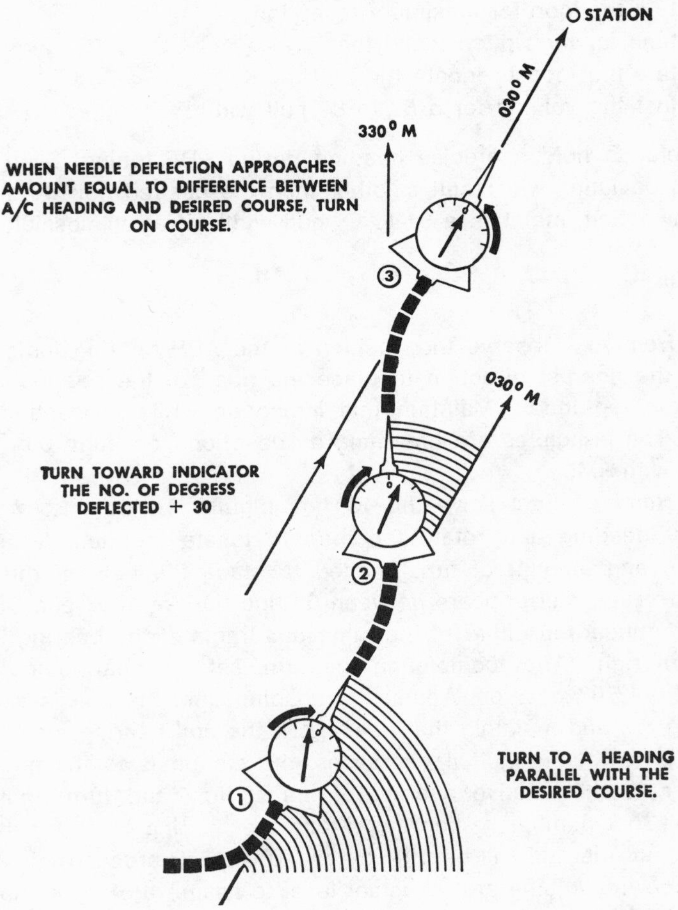

Figure 11.30 ADF inbound course interception. *(Courtesy of U.S. Air Force.)*

number of degrees as the angle of interception, make the turn on course with an appropriate lead to avoid overshooting.

Outbound Turn the aircraft to the magnetic heading of the desired course and note the position of the tail of the bearing indicator in relation to the top index. If the tail of the bearing indicator is deflected to either side of the top index, turn away from the tail of the indicator a sufficient number of degrees to insure course interception at a moderate rate. Maintain this intercept heading. When the bearing indicator is deflected the same number of degrees from the top index as the angle of interception, the aircraft is on course. As the tail of the bearing indicator

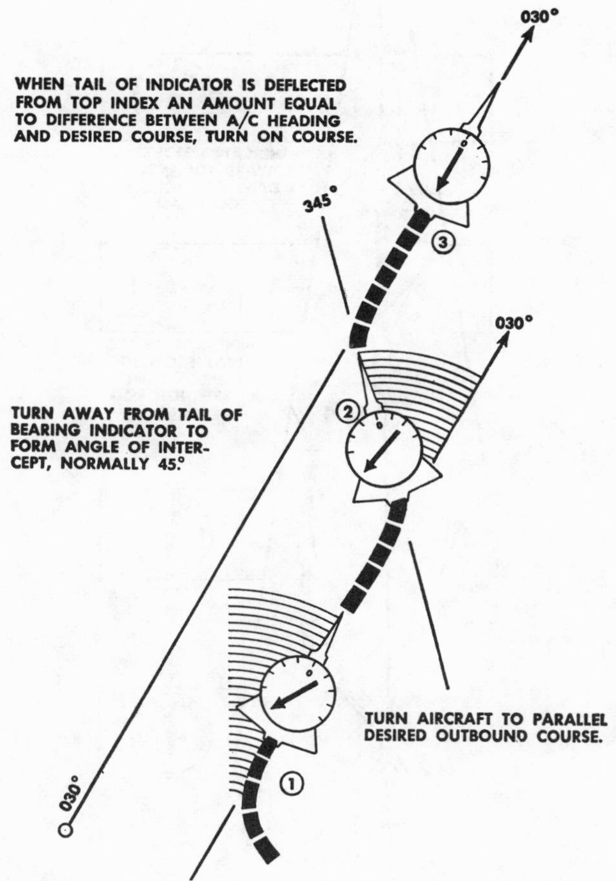
030°
WHEN TAIL OF INDICATOR IS DEFLECTED FROM TOP INDEX AN AMOUNT EQUAL TO DIFFERENCE BETWEEN A/C HEADING AND DESIRED COURSE, TURN ON COURSE.
345°
3
030°
TURN AWAY FROM TAIL OF BEARING INDICATOR TO FORM ANGLE OF INTERCEPT, NORMALLY 45°
2
TURN AIRCRAFT TO PARALLEL DESIRED OUTBOUND COURSE.
1
030°

Figure 11.31 ADF outbound interception. *(Courtesy of U.S. Air Force.)*

approaches the desired course, lead the turn to roll out on the desired outbound course.

Immediately after Station Passage Because you are quite close to the station, the angular amount you are off your new course is exaggerated, and you may use a simpler method. After definite station passage, immediately turn the aircraft to the magnetic heading of the desired course. Maintain this heading until the bearing indicator has stabilized. Then turn toward the desired course the same number of degrees the tail of

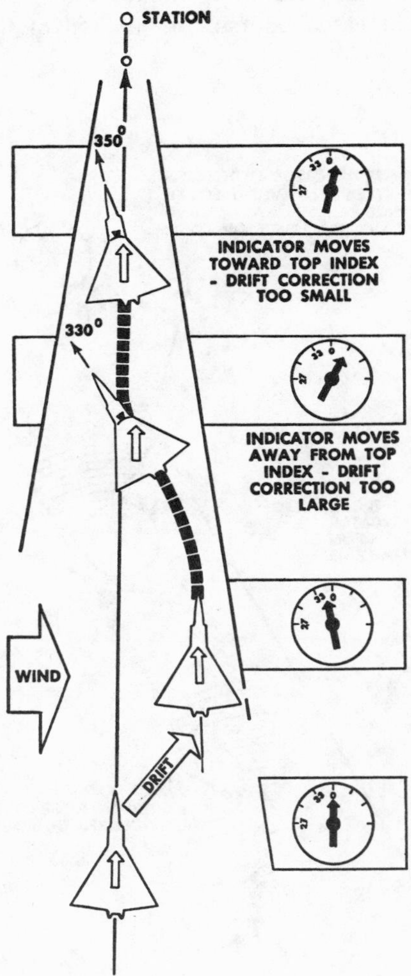

Figure 11.32 Maintaining course inbound with ADF. *(Courtesy of U.S. Air Force.)*

the bearing indicator is deflected from the top index, not exceeding 45°. Turn to the desired heading as soon as you are on course.

MAINTAINING COURSE

Inbound After turning onto a desired course which you desire to maintain to the station, hold the magnetic heading until the bearing indicator shows a deflection. Make a turn of sufficient magnitude to return to course. The size of this turn will depend upon how fast you drifted off course, your distance from the station, and how far you have allowed the aircraft to drift off. When back on course, resume the course heading with a wind correction applied. The bearing indicator will continue to point to the station, though it will be deflected from the top index the amount of your drift correction. If the bearing indicator moves toward the top index, the drift correction is too small. If it moves away, the drift correction is too large.

Outbound This procedure is similar to the inbound procedure, but utilizes the tail of the bearing indicator in relation to the outbound course. After applying a wind-drift correction outbound, if the tail of the indicator moves toward the top index, the drift correction is too large, and if it moves away from the index, the drift correction is too small.

RDF Procedure While aural null procedures are the same as ADF procedures, be sure to insure that you are flying a constant heading before adjusting the null. Approaching the station, the null width will decrease or sharpen unless you regulate the volume control to keep it at 5° to 8°. With too much volume, it may disappear entirely. While maintaining course outbound, the null will widen unless regulated with the volume control.

TIME-DISTANCE CHECK

ADF Procedure Turn the aircraft until the bearing indicator is exactly at the nearest wing-tip position and level out. Maintain that heading, and note the exact time you complete the turn. If the indicator is not at the exact 90° or 270° position when you complete the turn, adjust your heading until it is. Then take new note of the exact time. Hold this heading until you observe a 5° to 20° bearing change. When a convenient bearing change has occurred, note the time and turn immediately to a direct course to the station. Using the elapsed time and the number of degrees of bearing change in the formulas on page 699, determine your time or distance from the station.

RDF Procedure The only difference between this and the ADF procedure is in handling the null. After you have located the station, turn to a heading which places the station on a wing tip, and turn the bearing indicator to that wing tip. Maintain heading carefully. Set the bearing indicator so that the CW tone on the forward side of the null is barely audible. Note the time. Holding the same heading carefully, move the head of the bearing indicator forward through a 10° bearing change. Note the time again when the tone on the forward side of the null is again audible. If the null is less than 10° wide, as it should be, you will hear the null appear and then begin to disappear as the tone again becomes audible.

It is very important to RDF procedures to keep the bearing indicator always pointed toward the station to help in remaining oriented.

STATION PASSAGE

ADF Procedure With a constant reading on the bearing indicator, lateral displacement from course varies directly with the distance from the station. Consequently, a slight change of aircraft heading close to the station will result in a relatively large deviation of the bearing indicator. As you approach the station, do not attempt to "chase" the bearing indicator. Maintain a constant heading with the established drift correction.

Particularly at high altitude, the aircraft enters a cone of confusion which will cause the indicator to swing as much as 30° in either direction immediately before you reach the station. Consider that you have reached the station, and begin timing as soon as the indicator passes either wing-tip point on the dial. From one to three minutes may elapse at high altitude before the indicator stabilizes at the bottom index. At low altitude these effects are less noticeable, and while the indicator may fluctuate, it will swing promptly to the tail position.

RDF Procedure As you approach the station, you will have to adjust the null width more frequently to keep the desired width. If you are using a commercial broadcast station or radio beacon, you may be able to hear the voice or station identification above the carrier wave.

Constant narrowing and then widening of the null indicates that you have passed directly over the station.

Rapid movement of the null from the nose position is the most positive indication of station passage. It will occur when you pass slightly to one side. By keeping the head of the bearing indicator pointing at the station with the left-right switch, you will not lose track of the null as it swings to the tail position.

Apparent shift of the null from one side of the nose position to the other is another indication, when the aircraft passes close to but not directly over the station. The null will shift to one side, disappear, then quickly reappear on the other side of the top index (Figure 11.33).

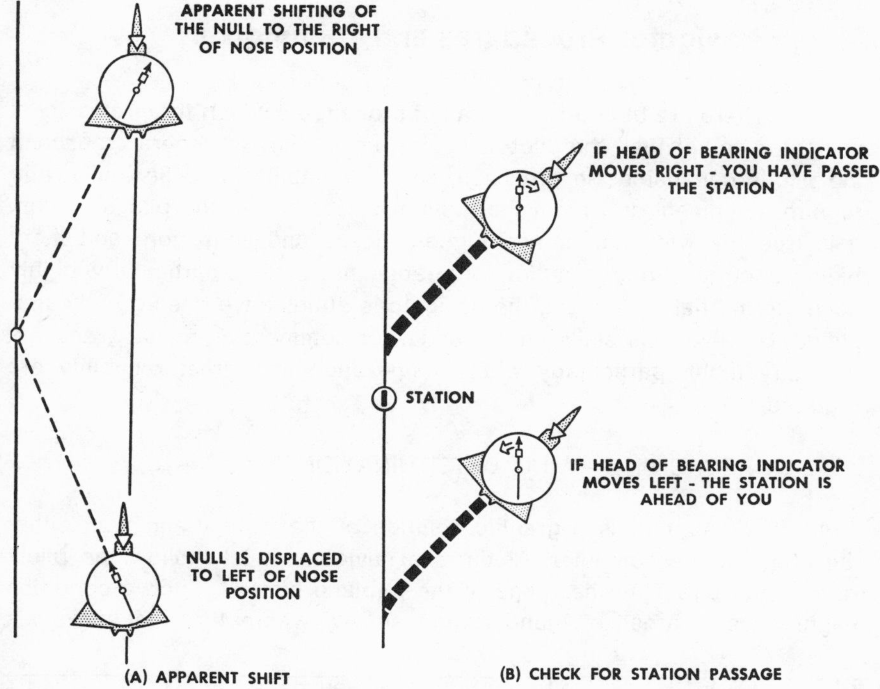

Figure 11.33 Aural-null methods of determining station passage.

Wing-tip null station passage can be determined when you know you are close to the station, and on course. Move the indicator to either wing tip when about 1 min out. Adjust the volume to a normal level and maintain this level. As you approach the station, the volume will tend to increase until it suddenly decreases to a definite null; it will then increase suddenly again and decrease rapidly as the station falls behind.

During any RDF navigation, particularly near the station, it is imperative that you hold constant headings, for a change in heading also changes the relative position of the null. To insure that you detect station passage when directly on course, turn 10° off course when about 2 min out (Figure 11.33B). Keep the indicator displaced to keep track of the null; when it begins to move rapidly, you are passing the station. If you are not sure whether you have passed the station, turn 45° right or left of course and position the bearing indicator directly over the null. If the null moves toward the nose position, you have passed the station; if it moves toward the tail, the station is still ahead.

Navigator Procedures and Techniques

There are of course navigation procedures which the professional navigator, rather than the pilot-navigator, uses. They in general transcend the pilot's capabilities in precision, safety, reliability, and flexibility, and require equipment and room that cannot be located in the pilot's station. It is true that with higher and higher speeds and with more and more highly accurate equipment for long-range navigation, particularly highly accurate inertial equipment, the navigator's duties have been greatly simplified. However, his skills are essential for commercial, military, and exploratory flight, particularly where long range and great reliability are required.

DEAD RECKONING—WIND DETERMINATION

Air Plot Air plot is a graphic solution of the wind triangle on either the chart or the computer. At times a navigator must "follow the pilot" rather than direct the headings of the airplane himself. Such a condition might arise in areas of thunderstorm activity where the pilot picks his

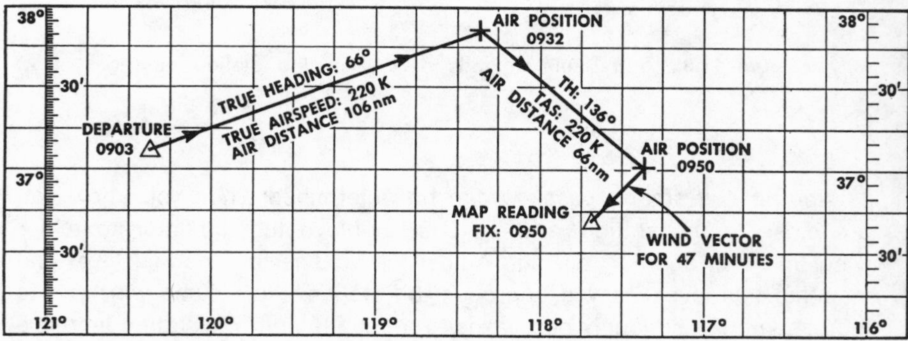

Figure 11.34 Determination of wind by air plot. After departing at 0903, a navigator plots his air position at 0932, when he alters heading. At 0950 he fixes the aircraft by pilotage pinpoint. Assuming his instruments to be correct and his work to be accurate, he attributes the difference between air position at 0950 and actual position at 0950 to wind effect. By measurement he finds the wind vector to be 038° and 29 nautical miles. Since this is for only 47 min, he converts to an hourly rate by proportion on his computer and finds wind velocity to be 038°/37 knots. (29nm/47 min = 37nm/60 min.) The DR position is plotted in the same manner as the air position except TC or TR and ground distance is used in lieu of TH and air distance. The symbol for a DR position is ⊙, a fix is △ and an air-plot position is +.

own headings to avoid the most dangerous weather. In order to keep up with the numerous turns which might be made, the navigator forgets momentarily about ground position and concentrates solely on air position. On his chart he plots true headings as they are flown, computing distance on each heading by multiplying true airspeed by time. All this information comes from the instruments within the airplane itself. At the end of the period of following the pilot, the final point will represent the air distance flown (Figure 11.34). If it were not for wind effect, this would also be the ground position. Excluding errors, any distance between the ground position and the air position must therefore represent wind effect. An arrow drawn from air position to ground position will be a wind vector for the period or time elapsed from the start of the air-plot work. Conversion to knots for the wind speed is a matter of simple proportion solved on the slide rule face of the computer.

Air plot is not restricted to use under adverse weather conditions. It is a very convenient method under any conditions where a reliable fix is available. Means of obtaining fixes will be considered in the next section.

The accuracy of an air plot wind is limited only by instrument reliability and the certainty of locating the aircraft at a given ground position. Instruments and position-fixing aids are rarely reliable enough to permit accurate air plot work over a period of flying less than 20 min long. By finding several such winds, an average picture of wind trends can be obtained. When coupled with meteorological data obtained from the weather office prior to flight, an experienced navigator is able to predict winds over the next hour or so of flight accurately enough for navigational purposes.

Driftmeter Several transport-type airplanes are equipped with a driftmeter, a relatively simple device for measuring drift and ground speed.

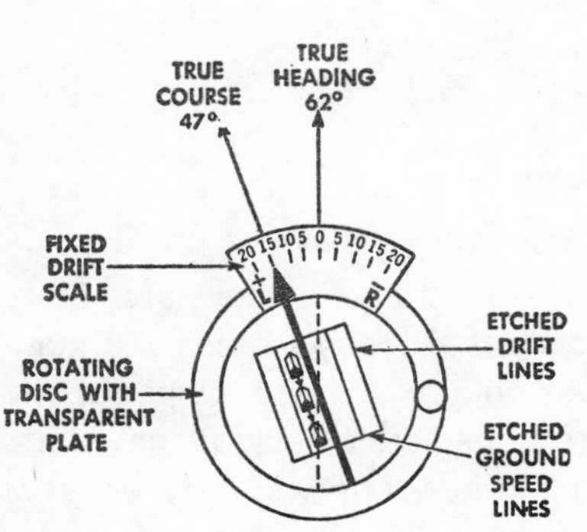

Figure 11.35 Typical transparent plate of a driftmeter. Etched drift lines are aligned with the angle of passage of any object on the ground. The angle of drift is measured on the reference plate. The letters *L* and *R* indicated the direction of drift left or right of aircraft heading. The + and — indicated the sign to be applied for drift correction. In the case above: TC = 47°; drift = 15°L; drift correction = +15°; TH = 62°.

The driftmeter provides accurate drift readings with a minimum of operator practice or effort. Comparison of true course and true heading is made by rotating a transparent plate until lines etched on its surface match the track of objects passing on the ground below. The angle of rotation of the plate is measured from a reference line along the longitudinal axis of the ship. Drift is indicated as "Left" or "Right," or by the letters L or R. For convenience, the sign of the angle to be used as *drift correction is* also indicated by plus or minus (Figure 11.35). Drift taken on two or more headings 45° apart and plotted on the wind face of the computer, provides a wind. Readings should be taken within several minutes of each other. This process is called a "double drift." Driftmeters vary in complexity from little more than the simple plate described above to the complex B-3 meter made by Eclipse Pioneer. The transparent grid of the B-3 is gyroscopically stabilized for more reliable use in rough air, and its optical system is not restricted to the vertical but can be rotated forward and back of the aircraft to provide a means of taking bearings.

The driftmeter is also used to measure ground speed. Lines are etched on the grid at right angles to the drift lines (Figure 11.35). By timing the passage of an object from one line to the other and adjusting for the height of the aircraft over the ground, ground speed can be quickly determined on the computer. For greater accuracy, several readings are made and averaged. From the drift and ground speed data thus obtained, combined with TH and TAS, the wind vector can be readily computed by solution of the wind triangle.

Driftmeters provide a very accurate source of drift and ground speed information, but their use is restricted to those periods when objects on the ground are visible. Over water, they can be used only when the sea is rough enough to provide distinguishing patterns visible through the meter. At night, lighted objects from which drift might be read are often impossible to find. From very high altitudes, drift is difficult to read at any time.

Celestial Navigation

For thousands of years man has been studying the stars. Stars move in relation to each other, but so slowly that today we see the stars in almost the same positions as studied in ancient Greece. Of the many thousands of stars in the sky, only 57 are considered navigational stars.

The main purpose of celestial navigation is to provide a means of positioning the aircraft and checking the aircraft's heading. The computations required for celestial LOP's have been made relatively easy through the use of the *Air Almanac and Sight Reduction Tables* (H. O. 249 Tables). The computations are to give the navigator the altitude and true bearing of a celestial body from an assumed position. This altitude and the altitude obtained from a sextant are compared to determine the LOP.

BASIC PRINCIPLES OF CELESTIAL NAVIGATION

The stars and planets are at such great distances from the earth that they are assumed, for the purpose of navigation, to be on the inner surface of an infinitely large stationary sphere, called the *celestial sphere,* whose center coincides with the earth's. Thus the earth's rotation causes the celestial sphere to appear to rotate from east to west about the extension of the earth's polar axis (Figure 11.36).

Bodies are positioned on the celestial sphere by *declination* (DEC) and *sidereal hour angle* (SHA) which correspond to *latitude* and *longitude* on earth. The *equator* and prime *meridian* on earth are similar to the *equinoctial* and the *first point of Aries* (♈) on the celestial sphere. Aries is the point at which the sun crosses the equinoctial on its way from southern to northern declination; the first day of spring (Figure 11.36).

The geographical position of a body projected from the celestial sphere to the earth is known as the *subpoint* of the body. A part of celestial computations is positioning a body's subpoint. DEC will give the latitude of the subpoint and the *GHA* of the body will give its longitude. *GHA* of the body is determined by adding the SHA to the GHA♈. GHA♈ is measured from Greenwich, England (0° to 360°), in a westerly direction to the subpoint of Aries.

The next step is to find the distance and direction of the observer from the subpoint. This is done by constructing a spherical triangle, called *astronomical triangle,* at the DR position. If the latitude of the DR position and the DEC of the body are known then the *co-latitude* and *co-declination* can be obtained by subtracting the latitude and DEC from 90°. Co-LAT and Co-DEC form two sides of the astronomical triangle. The angle between the longitude of the DR position and the longitude of the subpoint is called the *local hour angle* (LHA). LHA is also measured (0° to 360°) in a westerly direction from the DR position and is determined by subtracting the DR longitude from the GHA when in west longitudes or adding the DR longitude to the GHA of the body when in east longitudes. By trigonometry, the third side, called *co-altitude or zenith distance,* and the other interior angles can be determined. This information will give the distance and direction of the observer from the subpoint (Figure 11.36).

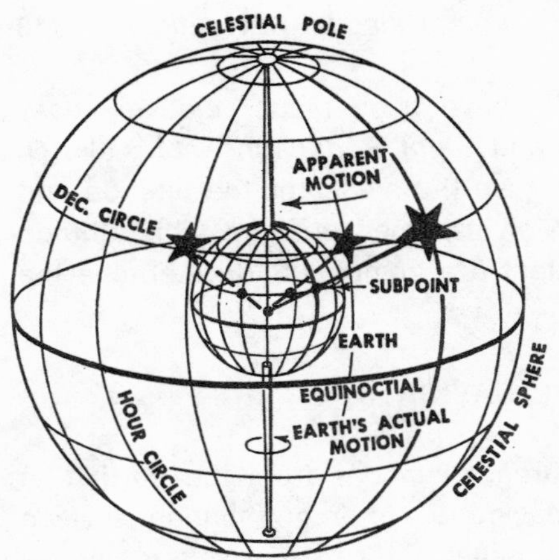

Figure 11.36A Hour circles and declination circles. Hour circles and declination circles correspond to longitude and latitude. The rotation of the earth from west to east causes the celestial sphere to appear to move from east to west and the subpoint of the body also to move from east to west on the surface of the earth.

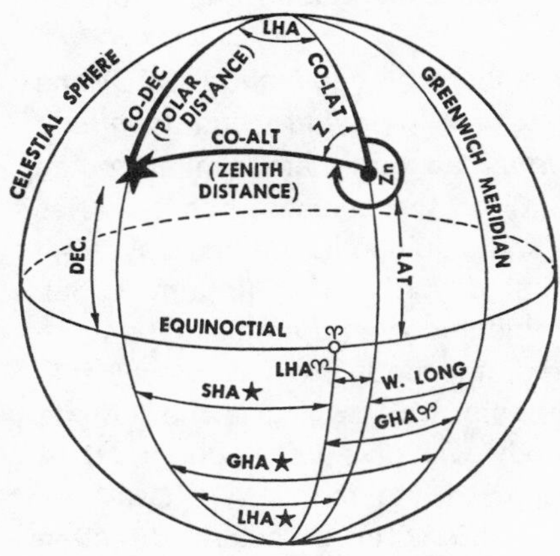

Figure 11.36B The astronomical triangle. The astronomical triangle is actually a spherical triangle that can be drawn on the celestial sphere as pictured or drawn on the earth using the subpoint of the body. The assumed position of the observer is in northern latitudes and the LHA of the body is less than 180° making the formula for true bearing of the body (Zn) to be 360° — Z = Zn.

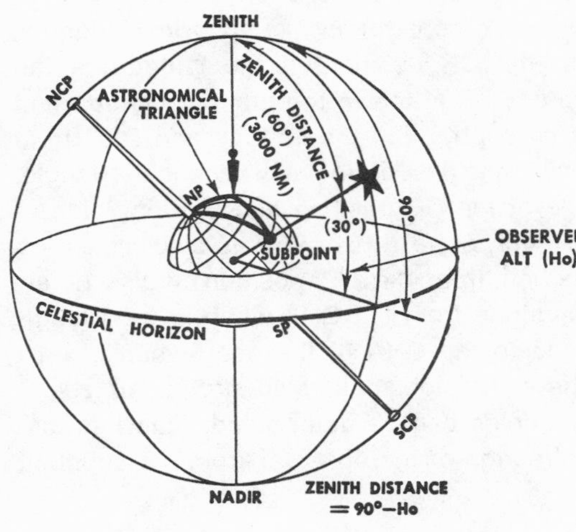

Figure 11.36C The celestial horizon and the astronomical triangle. Distance of the observer from the body's subpoint as observed with the sextant is computed by the formula: 90° − 30° (Height Observed) = 60° = 3600 n.m.

In place of the DR position used above, an *assumed position* is used to make the computations simpler by using whole degrees of LHA and latitude. The assumed position is usually near the DR position to reduce plotting errors.

THE AIR ALMANAC

This is an absolutely indispensable manual for celestial work. From it the navigator gets the basic data on which his determination of computed altitude of body is based. The arduous mathematics involved in celestial computations is made simple and purely mechanical by tables, but it would still be possible by pure mathematics to work out solutions without them. It would not be possible even to start the calculations without *Almanac* data. Yet the information the navigator does get from the *Almanac* is surprisingly simple. To find the computed altitude of any of the bodies in our immediate solar system—the sun, moon, or planets—he extracts two values from the *Almanac:* (1) GHA for the time of his

GREENWICH A. M. 1955 JANUARY 1 (SATURDAY)

GMT	☉ SUN GHA	SUN Dec.	ARIES GHA ♈	VENUS —4.3 GHA	VENUS Dec.	MARS 0.8 GHA	MARS Dec.	JUPITER —2.2 GHA	JUPITER Dec.	◐ MOON GHA	MOON Dec.
h m	° ′	° ′	° ′	° ′	° ′	° ′	° ′	° ′	° ′	° ′	° ′
00 00	179 13	S23 05	99 52	225 24	S15 25	109 00	S 4 36	340 54	N21 10	102 59	N 4 24
10	181 43		102 23	227 54		111 30		343 25		105 24	27
20	184 13		104 53	230 24		114 00		345 55		107 49	29
30	186 43	·	107 24	232 54	· ·	116 30	· ·	348 26	· ·	110 14	· 31
40	189 13		109 54	235 25		119 00		350 56		112 40	34
50	191 43		112 24	237 55		121 30		353 27		115 05	36
01 00	194 13	S23 05	114 55	240 25	S15 25	124 01	S 4 35	355 57	N21 10	117 30	N 4 38
10	196 43		117 25	242 55		126 31		358 27		119 55	40
20	199 13		119 56	245 25		129 01		0 58		122 20	43
30	201 43	· ·	122 26	247 55	· ·	131 31	· ·	3 28	· ·	124 46	· 45
40	204 13		124 56	250 25		134 01		5 59		127 11	47
50	206 42		127 27	252 55		136 31		8 29		129 36	50
02 00	209 12	S23 05	129 57	255 25	S15 25	139 01	S 4 34	11 00	N21 10	132 01	N 4 52
10	211 42		132 28	257 55		141 31		13 30	·	134 27	54
20	214 12		134 58	260 25		144 02		16 01		136 52	57
30	216 42	· ·	137 29	262 56	· ·	146 32	· ·	18 31	· ·	139 17	4 59
40	219 12		139 59	265 26		149 02		21 02		141 42	5 01
50	221 42		142 29	267 56		151 32		23 32		144 07	04
03 00	224 12	S23 04	145 00	270 26	S15 26	154 02	S 4 33	26 03	N21 10	146 33	N 5 06
10	226 42		147 30	272 56		156 32		28 33		148 58	08
20	229 12		150 01	275 26		159 02		31 04		[illegible]	11
30	231 42	· ·	152 31	[illegible]		[illegible]	· ·	[illegible]			
40											

Moon's P. in A. Alt. °	Corr. + ′
0	58
10	57
14	56
18	55
21	54
23	53
26	52
28	51
30	50
32	49
33	48
35	47

Figure 11.37 The *Air Almanac.* Part of a page from the *Air Almanac,* a.m. side. On January 1, 1955, at 0200 Greenwich Mean Time, the Greenwich hour angle of the sun was 209°12′, and its declination was 23°05′ south. At the same time the Greenwich hour angle of Aries was 129°57′. "Moon's P. in A." means "Moon's parallax in altitude." An observation of the moon at 27° altitude required on this date a parallax correction of +52 min of arc to be added to it.

sighting, and (2) DEC for the same instant of time. For a star, only one value is extracted from the *Almanac*—the GHA♈. The use to which these extracted values are put will be explained in the next paragraph. Part of a page from the *Air Almanac* is shown in Figure 11.37.

The *Almanac* also contains a considerable amount of other information useful in other areas of navigational practice. Time of sunrise and sunset for any place in the world can be readily computed from *Almanac* data. Duration of twilight, essential to the polar navigator and to the military planner, can also be found. Moon risings and settings and moon phases are given. A star chart and sky diagrams showing the appearance of the sky and location of important navigational stars for various latitudes at different times of the night also provide helpful aids to the celestial navigator. The *Almanac* is published in three volumes every year, each volume spanning a period of four months, by the Nautical Almanac Office of the Naval Observatory. Copies are obtainable at $3.75 per volume from the Superintendent of Documents, Washington, D.C. 20402.

NAVIGATIONAL TABLES

The second item of specialized celestial equipment needed by the navigator is a set of tables for rapid solution of the spherical trigonometry involved in finding the computed altitude of a body. Such tables are referred to a *sight-reduction tables* and are almost as indispensable as an *Almanac.* Without tables for rapid mechanical solutions a fast worker might get a single line of position occasionally, but a three-star fix would be out of the question.

Sight-reduction tables are entered with a combination of DR and *Almanac* data and provide the navigator with two items of information: the computed altitude of a body (H_C) from a given position on earth at a given instant of time; and the azimuth of the body, that is, its bearing from true north (Zn). Computed altitude and azimuth, properly combined with observed altitude, provide the necessary information for plotting a line of position.

For air use *Sight-Reduction Tables for Air Navigation,* published by the Navy Hydrographic Office, are the best and most convenient. They are more familiarly known as H.O. 249 tables. With the three volumes it is possible to find the computed altitude and azimuth of the sun, moon, planets, and principal navigational stars at any time from any place on earth. Volume I, *Selected Stars,* is especially convenient. If clouds should obscure the best stars, one of the other two volumes can be used to make necessary computations for any star whose declination (DEC) is between 30° N and 30° S. The procedure involved, however, is slightly more complex and time-consuming than use of the table of selected stars.

NAVIGATION WATCHES

Accurate time is essential to the celestial navigator. To an observer on the equator, a body appears to make one complete revolution around the earth every 24 hr. This is an angular rotation of 15° longitude every hour. Further reducing the units of both arc and time, the body passes through 1 min of longitude every 4 sec of time. Since 1 min of longitude at the equator is exactly equal to 1 nm, the need for accuracy in time becomes readily apparent. An error of a full minute in reading a watch translates at the equator to a 15-mi error in position. At latitudes closer to the pole, the error is not so great, but it is still sufficient that much effort has been expended to make watches for use in aircraft both reliable and convenient.

Watches made specifically for celestial navigation are called "hack" watches, or second-setting watches. This means merely that when the winding stem is pulled out to reset the hands, the watch automatically stops until the stem is again pushed in. This permits the navigator to "hack" his watch by reference to a chronometer of known accuracy or to a radio time signal. (Voice announcement of Greenwich Mean Time is made over radio station WWV every 5 min. Broadcast is on 2.5, 5, 10, 15, 20, and 25 mHz.)

The watch itself does not have to keep accurate time, but its rate of gain or loss should be constant and known. If a watch that loses, say, 12 sec a day is used 8 hr from its last setting, 4 sec should be added to the indicated time to give the best available time information.

SEXTANTS

A sextant is an instrument for measuring the altitude of a celestial body, that is, the observed altitude. Two general types are now in use—marine sextants and bubble sextants. A marine sextant measures altitude above the visible sea horizon. It cannot generally be used in the air because under conditions of cloud, haze, or darkness the actual horizon cannot be seen. The search for an artificial horizon for air use has led along several channels, but the most satisfactory air sextants in use today are of the bubble type. The body is sighted through a translucent bubble chamber, the bubble serving, as in a carpenter's level, to keep the sextant properly aligned. Bubble size is adjustable. For most celestial work a bubble 1½ to 2 times the diameter of the sun as viewed through the sextant gives the best results.

Every modern aircraft sextant has some provision for taking many shots of the same body to be averaged out for the period of time over

(A) Pioneer A-14. A heavy, rugged sextant. The averaging mechanism is key-wound, the battery pack providing only illumination for the various dials. The veeder counter does not indicate altitude directly, as does that on the A-10A. Coarse measurement is provided by the main scale, and the counter dial is combined with this reading for fine measurement. A hook is provided to hang the sextant by in the astrodome. This centers the instrument in the dome so that refraction error can be accurately determined, and also eases the burden of holding this heavy instrument during three 2-min sightings.

(B) Kollsman periscopic. This instrument was designed for use in high-speed aircraft on which an astrodome is undesirable. The sextant is positioned in a special mount built into the aircraft. When it is to be used, it is pushed out directly into the airstream. Dome refraction error is thus of no concern. The average altitude of any sighting from 30 sec to 2 min duration is continuously integrated by the averaging mechanism, and final reading is made directly on the counter dial. The averager is lever-wound. Aircraft power is supplied to the mount for illumination purposes only.

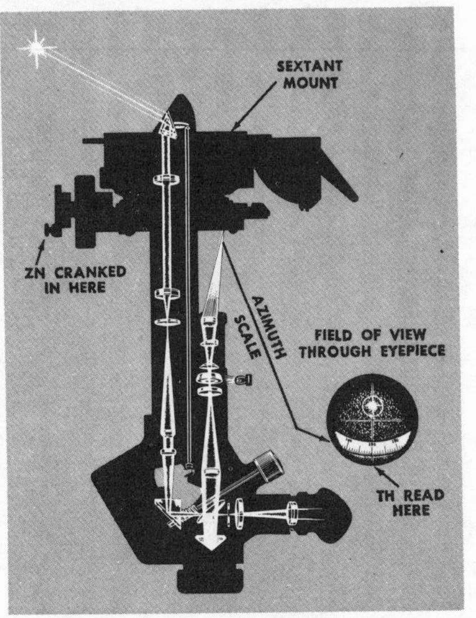

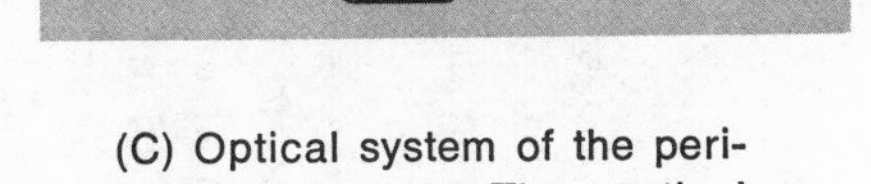

(C) Optical system of the periscopic sextant. The optical system shows the many lenses in the sextant and illustrates the necessity of careful sextant handling. The view through the eyepiece TH is read when sighting on a body for a compass check.

which they were taken. This is necessary because the unsteady motion of an aircraft, even in smooth air, causes *bubble acceleration error.* Random pitching, rolling, and yawing motions of the airplane act on the bubble chamber, giving a false reading, even though the navigator believes he is holding the sextant exactly level. Nothing can be done to prevent extraneous motions of this sort, but their effect can be minimized. In most aircraft the errors induced by random motion tend to cancel during a 2-min period. A navigator should therefore generally shoot a body for 2 min, using the mid-time of the shot for his celestial computations.

The two sextants most used in the United States today have averaging devices. The Pioneer A-14 contains a clockwork mechanism which runs for 2 min and a counting device which automatically averages the altitude of the shots taken. The Pioneer must be run for the full 2-min period for accurate results. The Kollsman periscopic sextant uses a cylinder-disk mechanical integrator which gives a continuous moving average for any period of time longer than 30 sec up to 2 min. This is an advantage under conditions of partial overcast, when a full 2-min view of any one star is not afforded. Figure 11.38 shows the two sextants mentioned and gives additional data on their various features.

In flight a means of checking the true heading and thus the compass heading of the aircraft is needed. This is accomplished by using an Astrocompass in dome-type aircraft and a periscopic sextant and mount in nondome-type aircraft. To do this, place the computed Zn on the *true bearing scale* of the Astrocompass, or in the *azimuth counter window* of the periscopic sextant mount, and sight on the body. True heading is obtained from the instrument's appropriate scale.

Sextants must be handled with considerable care, since they are made to, and must maintain, a high order of accuracy. With a good sextant it is possible to measure any angle from 0° to 90° within 3 or 4 min of arc.

ERRORS OF SEXTANT OBSERVATIONS

It is not enough simply to take a sighting on a body and use the altitude reading as observed altitude. The possibility for errors of several different types always exists, and the sextant reading must be adjusted accord-

---

Figure 11.38 Bubble sextants (see facing page). The two sextants at left are at present the most widely used celestial instruments in the United States. Another type of sextant, the Pioneer A-15, is similar to the A-14 except that it incorporates a continuously integrating average instead of a 2-min averager, thus permitting accurate observations for any desired length of time up to 2 min.

ingly. Accuracy in celestial navigation depends not only on shooting technique, but on the understanding of and proper correction for the following errors.

Sextant Error It is almost impossible to remove all error from a sextant, but the amount of error can be determined and added or subtracted as required from the sextant reading. The most accurate way to determine error in the sextant itself is by use of a *collimator,* a device designed for the sole purpose of checking sextants. If a collimator is not available, check can be made by viewing a distant horizon over water or by comparing readings of a distant object (at least a mile away) made with the sextant and with a transit of known accuracy. Once the sextant error is known, the instrument should be handled with care to prevent the optics from being jarred out of position.

If a sextant of unknown error must be used, it is possible on a three-

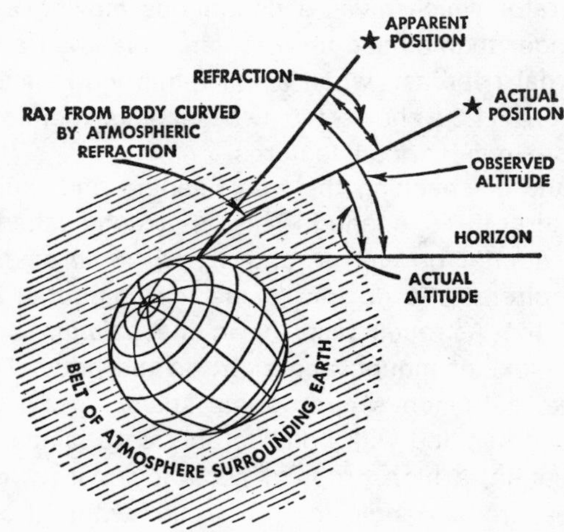

Figure 11.39 Refraction error. Sextant observations must be corrected for refraction caused by the bending of light rays passing through the earth's atmosphere. The amount of refraction is grossly exaggerated in the sketch. At 5000 ft, for example, an observation of a body 15° above the horizon requires a correction of only 3 min of arc, or 3 nm in distance. Errors as high as 60 m can result when bodies very low on the horizon are shot.

star fix to eliminate the sextant as a source of error by using stars differing in azimuth 120° from each other. The effect of sextant error will be to increase the size of the fix triangle, but since the center is taken as best known position anyway, error cancels out.

Atmospheric Refraction Light rays passing from a medium of one density to a medium of differing density bend in accordance with optical rules of refraction. A ray of light from a star, passing from the vacuum of space through successively denser layers of air, is refracted so that it appears higher than it actually is (Figure 11.39). The amount of refraction is dependent on the height of the star above the horizon and on the altitude of the aircraft. The higher the body above the horizon, the more nearly perpendicular the ray enters the atmosphere and the smaller the amount of refraction. The higher the aircraft, the less dense the layer of atmosphere between the star and the observer and the less the refraction. Tables of refraction using aircraft altitude and altitude of the observed body as entering arguments are found in the *Air Almanac* and in the back of the H.O. 249 sight reduction tables. Refraction error, like sextant error, can be ignored when taking a three-star fix if stars approximately 120° apart and approximately the same in altitude are used.

Dome Refraction The plastic astrodomes used in some aircraft refract light rays just as the atmosphere does. Domes are not uniformly manufactured, and each one is therefore individually calibrated and posted with a correction card. Consequently, the "Standard" table of dome refraction in the *Air Almanac* should be used with caution. Corrections apply to shots taken from the center of the dome, and for this reason the sextant hook built into the top of the dome should be used whenever possible. Shots made through an open window or with a periscopic sextant which projects outside the aircraft need no correction for dome refraction. Shots taken through the windshield or Plexiglas canopies are generally too unreliable for use because of unpredictable refraction.

Coriolis Error The rotation of the earth causes an aircraft flying a straight line on the earth's surface to fly a curved path in space, to the left in the Northern Hemisphere and to the right in the Southern Hemisphere. The change in direction is Coriolis acceleration, and the resulting error is Coriolis error. The liquid in the bubble chamber is deflected to the right when the aircraft curves left, and the bubble is therefore displaced to the left. The effect can be easily duplicated with a cerpenter's level or with a bubble trapped in a bottle of water. In attempting to hold the bubble in the center of the chamber, the navigator inadvertently tips the sextant off-center, and a false reading is made. Since the amount of Coriolis acceleration depends on latitude and ground speed, the effect can be approximated and correction for the error made. At speeds below 200 knots and latitudes below 40°, Coriolis error is quite small, amount-

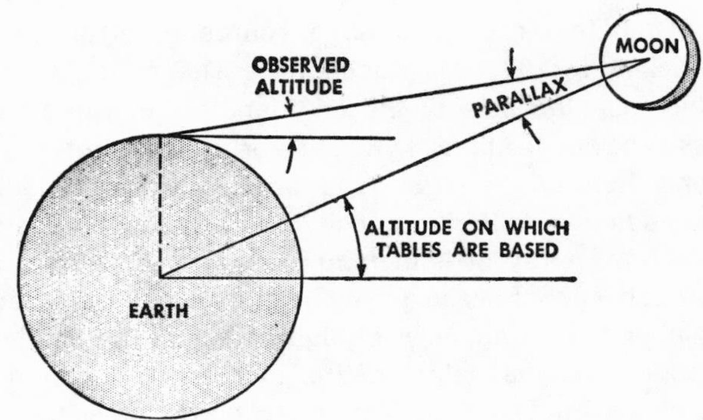

Figure 11.40 Parallax error. Observations of the moon must always be corrected for parallax error.

ing to about 2 nm in an LOP. At the higher speeds of today's aircraft, Coriolis error must be reckoned with at any latitude above 20°. Tables for determining the amount of Coriolis error, using latitude and ground speed as entering arguments, are found in H.O. 249 tables and the *Air Almanac.*

Parallax Parallax error exists only for observations taken of the moon. Sight reduction tables give computed altitudes as though observations were taken from the center of the earth. The sun, planets, and stars are so remote that no detectable error exists even though our position is actually 4000 mi removed from this point. The moon, however, is less than 240,000 mi away, and failure to take parallax into account may cause almost a full degree, or 60 nm, of error (Figure 11.40). Parallax varies from a maximum when the moon is on the horizon to zero when it is directly overhead. It also varies with the exact distance of the moon from the earth. Since this distance changes from day to day, exact values for various observed altitudes are given on the daily pages in the *Air Almanac* (Figure 11.37).

PLOTTING A CELESTIAL LINE OF POSITION

There are two ways of plotting a line of position from a celestial body, the *subpoint method* and the *intercept method.* Every body at a given instant of time lies directly over some spot on the earth, called the subpoint of the body. In the subpoint method, this point is plotted on the chart, and an arc is drawn in the vicinity of the dead reckoning position using the subpoint as a center and the complement of the observed altitude converted to nautical miles as a radius. For aerial navigation this method is impractical because the charts used must be either too large to handle or else of such small scale that accurate measurement would be impossible. The intercept method was therefore devised, and although rather roundabout, it provides a quick, simple solution of good accuracy if the assumed position is within about 100 mi of actual position.

To understand the intercept method, one more term must be defined. A *circle of equal altitude* is a circle from every point on which a body has the same altitude. An observer viewing the top of a flagpole at an angle of 40° from the ground could move around the pole along a circular path and maintain an angle of view of 40°. By observing the angle of elevation of the flagpole from any position, he could tell at once whether he was on the 40° circle of equal altitude, closer to the pole, or farther away. If his second measured altitude was greater than 40°, he would necessarily be closer to the pole; if it was less, he would be farther away. The same principle is used in plotting celestial LOP's by the intercept method. The computed altitude (H_C) determined by the sight reduction tables for an assumed position gives the circle of equal altitude passing through that position. If the observed altitude (H_O) is greater than the computed altitude, actual position is closer to the subpoint of the body; if less, actual position is farther away. The angular difference between H_O and H_C, converted to nautical miles, provides the distance from the assumed position to be plotted.

Only one problem yet remains: how to plot the circle of equal altitude given by the tables. If an actual circle had to be plotted, or even the arc of a circle, no advantage over the subpoint method would be afforded. The solution is simple. The circle from any body less than 73° in altitude has a radius greater than 1000 mi. Any small segment of arc appears to be, and for practical purposes can be considered, a straight line. The line of position given by the computed altitude can therefore be drawn through the assumed position as a straight line which is actually a tangent to the true circle of equal altitude at that point. The direction of the LOP is determined by the azimuth (Zn) of the body as read from the tables. The intercept, plotted along the Zn toward or away from the assumed position, may be regarded as a portion of the radius of a circle of equal altitude. Any tangent to a circle is perpendicular to the radius of the circle, and the LOP is therefore constructed perpendicular to the Zn. The method is graphically shown in Figure 11.41.

The use of a straight line instead of the actual arc of a circle makes speedy celestial work possible, but error is obviously introduced unless the assumed position is fairly close to the actual position. The amount of error will depend on the actual altitude of the body observed, error increasing as altitude increases. If choice is possible, stars less than 70° in altitude are chosen for navigation use. As an example of the

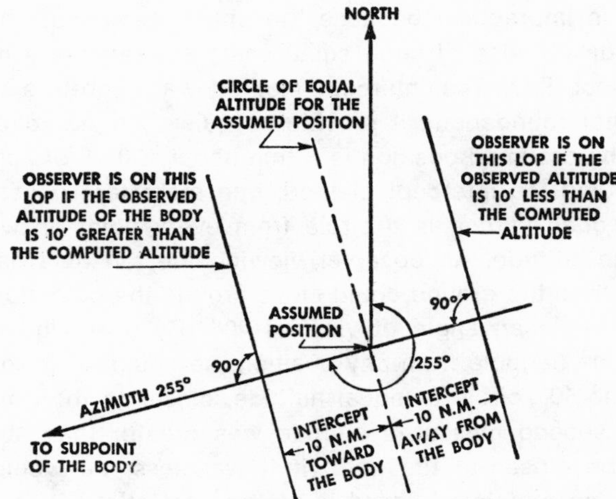

Figure 11.41 Plotting a celestial lop by the intercept method. LOPs are tangent to circles of equal altitude having the subpoint of body as a center. The LOPs are therefore drawn perpendicular to the azimuth.

amount of error involved: if the assumed position is 100 mi from actual position, and a star of 70° altitude is used for the LOP, maximum error could be just over 4 nm. Though not great (considering that it is rarely necessary either to shoot a body this high in the sky or to assume a position 100 mi from actual position), necessity for accurate dead reckoning is clearly indicated.

CELESTIAL PROCEDURE

As an aid to DR, the best celestial procedures are those which fit into the rest of the navigator's work in an orderly manner. From his celestial observations, the navigator seeks to get an LOP which will show him his deviation from the planned course (a course line), an LOP which will, when related to a previous similar line or a fix, show him his speed (a speed line), or a combination of three LOP's, preferably, which will give him a fix. He can also combine celestial with other LOP's such as loran or radio, to obtain a fix.

There are two general methods. One is to observe the altitude of a body and record it with the exact time, then perform the computations and plot the LOP. The other is to perform the computations first, then use the sextant. The latter is usually preferred because the fix can be plotted much quicker after the fix time, because knowing the approximate altitude and azimuth of a star aids in star finding, and because on many flights, much of the computation can be done even before takeoff. This procedure is known as *precomputation.*

Precomputation Many navigators use a "precomputation form," which may be separate or a part of the log, to guide computations and avoid error. While not necessary, it is handy, particularly when several fixes are precomputed prior to takeoff. Using precomputation, there are essentially six steps to obtaining a fix: (1) Determine by DR what your position should be for the time of the fix. (2) From the *Almanac,* select the GHA♈ and the bodies which will be most useful for your purpose; let us assume the object is a three-star fix. (3) From the Sight Reduction Tables, determine the probable computed altitude (H_C), and the Zn, for the three stars at the time of the fix, including adjustments for the various sextant and motion errors. (4) "Shoot" the stars with the sextant, and record the observed altitude (H_O) and the time for each shot. (5) Compare the H_O and H_C for each star to determine the length of the intercept, and whether it should be plotted along or 180° away from the direction of Zn. (6) Plot the lines of position to obtain a fix.

Electronic Aids to Dead Reckoning

LORAN

An abbreviation of *long-range navigation,* loran is the principal electronic navigation aid over the world's most heavily traveled ocean routes. It has a range varying from about 700 mi in the daytime to 1500 mi at night, and operates at slightly above the commercial broadcast band (1750, 1850, 1900, and 1950kH).

Loran requires two ground stations to furnish data for one LOP. The navigator has a loran receiver and a special loran chart.

The ground stations are called *master* and *slave* stations. The navigator, from his DR position, selects the most desirable pairs of stations. He tunes the receiver to one pair of stations. The first signal is received from the master station and is displayed as a pulse line on the scope face. The same signal, also received at the slave station, triggers the slave station, which, after a set time delay, transmits a signal on the same frequency. The slave signal is received, and the time difference between the two determines a line of position. There are many points where the time difference could be the same. The locus of these points is a hyperbolic curve. Loran charts are therefore printed with a series of hyperbolic curves giving microseconds of difference for each pair of stations.

A station pair is identified by two numbers and one letter—that is, ILO. The first number indicates the channel and the operating frequency. (Channel 1, 1950 kHz) The letter L denotes the basic *pulse recurrence rate* (PRR). It could be *Slow* (20 pulses per sec), *Low* (25 pulses per sec), or *High* ($33\frac{1}{3}$ pulses per sec). The last number indicates the individual station pair or specific PRR which changes the number of pulses per sec by $\frac{1}{25}$ for each Slow station, $\frac{1}{16}$ for each Low station, $\frac{1}{9}$ for each High station.

Theoretically, loran is set up to have eight stations (0 to 7) for any combination of the four channels (1 to 4) and three basic PRR's (Slow, Low, and High)—that is, 1LO, 3LO, 2H6, etc. However, seldom are there more than four station pairs in proximity to each other. The receiver will display the pulses for all the station pairs having the same channel number and basic PRR in the immediate area. Only the pulses from the station pair selected will be stationary; the others will be moving.

Loran signals, being radio signals, are reflected from the ionosphere resulting in *sky waves* which account for the increased range at night. With experience and procedures based on the operating instructions for the type of receiver being used, the navigator can determine which of the received signals are ground waves and which are sky waves.

The navigator tries first to match ground waves. If either of the ground

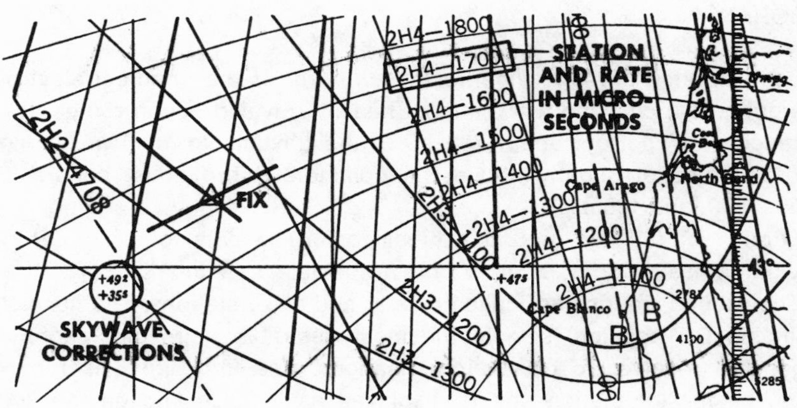

Figure 11.42 Fixing by loran. Section of a loran chart showing time-difference hyperbolas from four sets of loran stations. On the original chart the lines from each station pair are in a distinct color to minimize confusion. The fix shown above represents the crossing of an LOP of 1620 from station 2H4 and an LOP of 1250 from 2H3.

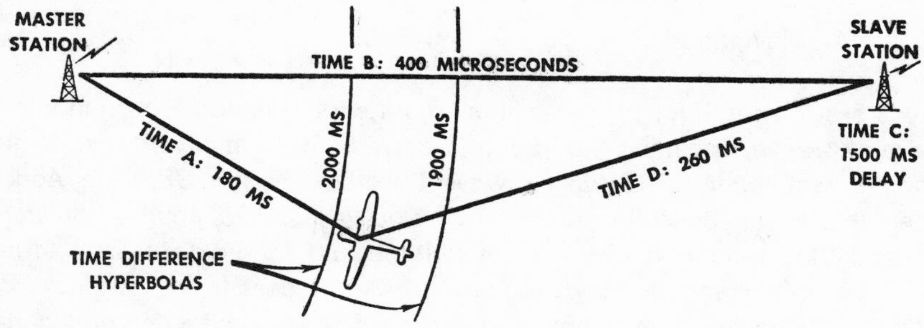

Figure 11.43 Measurement of loran rates. The loran set in the aircraft receives the master signal 180 microseconds (μsec) after transmission and starts with this signal as a reference. This same signal takes 400 μsec to travel to the slave station, which does not transmit until a controlled delay of 1500 μsec has been added. The slave signal reaches the aircraft 260 μsec after transmission. The loran set performs the following computation:

$$\text{Time B} + \text{Time C} + \text{Time D} - \text{Time A}$$
$$400 + 1500 + 260 - 180 = 1980\ \mu\text{sec}$$

The aircraft is therefore known to be on the 1980 μsec hyperbola.

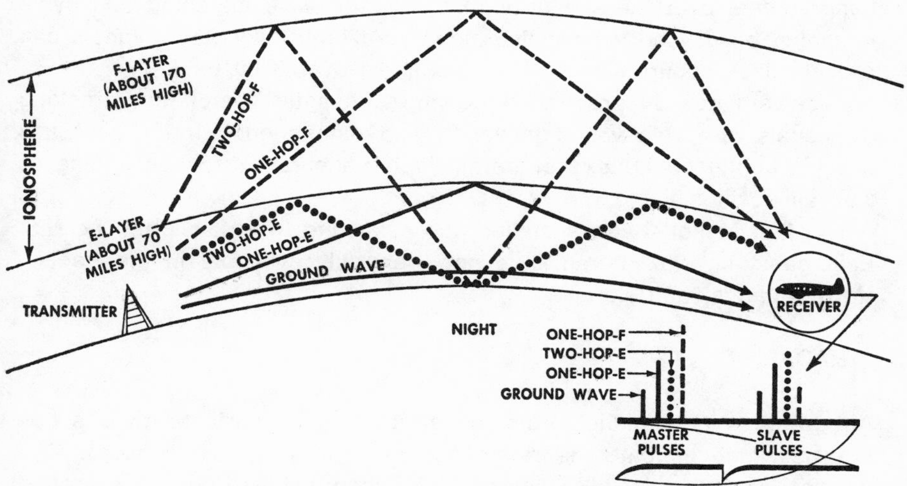

Figure 11.44 Sky wave reception. Sky waves are generally received only at night when the underside of the ionosphere is smooth enough to reflect energy striking it. Some energy may pass through the E-layer and still be reflected by the F-layer, so that at times four or five signals are received simultaneously. The sketch of the cathode-ray tube at the right shows the order in which signals are received. It is absolutely essential to know whether signals being matched are sky waves or ground waves. At times it may be necessary to use a sky wave from the master station and a ground wave from its slave. Unless this is recognized and proper correction made for it, serious error may result. For this reason, identification of sky waves is the most important single skill of a loran operator.

waves are too weak for proper matching, he should match a ground wave and a sky wave, but must then apply a correction, normally 70 ms, to his reading, remembering "*S*lave *S*kywave *S*ubtract, *M*aster *S*kywave *A*dd." When this is not possible, he matches sky waves, and applies the corrections that appear at every 5° of latitude and longitude on the loran chart. These corrections may be interpolated if necessary.

Once the navigator has obtained the readings for an LOP or fix, he plots them on the loran chart (Figure 11.42). This is done by interpolating for the value of the readings and drawing a line parallel to the printed hyperbolic curves on the chart near the DR position. With experience a navigator can obtain three LOP's and plot them in three minutes, giving an accurate and reliable fix.

Loran C is loran which operates in the 90 to 110 kHz band. It was developed by the Air Force Cambridge Research Laboratory and the Sperry Gyroscope Co. to provide a system that would have long range and a high order of accuracy over both land and sea.

Loran C provides ranges beyond 1000 mi with a fix accuracy of several hundred feet over the sea through automatic pulse matching and cycle matching on ground wave pulse signals. At night, sky wave signals can provide fixes accurate to 5 mi at distances over 3400 mi.

Receivers now in production provide automatic search and tracking of signals, are relatively lightweight and simple enough for pilot use even in fighter cockpits; they permit highly accurate direction finding as well as position fixing.

The first stations were installed, a master and two slaves, on the U.S. East coast in 1957. Loran C is now generally available in the Pacific, North Atlantic, and Europe.

RADAR

Airborne radar, "looking" from the aircraft to the surface, gives scope returns which indicate the range and bearing of terrain features. This information can be used to determine an accurate position, track, ground speed and wind under any condition of visibility. In addition to its use as an aid to dead reckoning, it is valuable for finding the best air path through weather (page 331), and for blind bombing. Radar operates on superhigh-frequency radio energy and reacts in much the same way as a beam of light, in that the angle of reflection is equal to the angle of incidence. A radar set transmits energy, picks up the reflected energy, and displays the returns as luminous spots or blips in patterns on a scope not unlike TV. The basic problem in using radar for navigation is proper scope interpretation.

BASIC PRINCIPLES OF SCOPE INTERPRETATION

The amount of energy returned to the radar antenna is dependent upon the reflectivity of the objects that the radar energy encounters. Reflectivity, in turn, depends on the material of which the object is made and the angle at which the energy strikes it. A large city, containing many surfaces perpendicular to the path of the radar energy, reflects much of this energy toward the receiving antenna, causing a considerable brightening of the scope trace. A smooth body of water, on the other hand, reflects all of the energy away from the antenna, and the scope is dark. The reflectivity of most cultural and terrain features is somewhere between these extremes of very light and very dark. Hilly or mountainous country gives brighter returns than flat plains or plateaus, and large industrial areas give a brighter return than outlying suburban areas. DR is used to determine an approximate position. Radar is then employed to position the aircraft accurately. Only with practice can a navigator become skillful at correct interpretation of the light and dark patches which to the novice appear to be a hopeless clutter.

DETERMINING RADAR RANGE

The basic fundamental in determining range is the timing of a specific burst of energy from the time it leaves the antenna, travels to some object, is reflected by that object, and returns to the antenna of the radar set. In order to time a specific burst of energy out and back, it is necessary to emit the energy in individual pulses, usually of about 0.5 ms duration. Enough time between successive pulses must be allowed for a pulse to be transmitted into space, reflected, and picked up by the receiving antenna before the next pulse is transmitted. If this were not done, the relatively weak returning signal would be lost within the next strong blast of transmitted energy. A timing device in the radar set determines the interval at which these pulses will be released, and measures the time required to receive the reflected impulses. A line called the *trace* or *sweep,* formed by the movement of a fluorescent spot on the scope of the tube, is used as the time base.

The trace appears on the scope at a rate and distance proportional to the rate and distance traveled by the pulse from the aircraft to the reflecting object. Thus, if the radius of the scope represents a range of 20 mi, and the radar pulse transmitted by an aircraft is reflected from an object 10 mi away, a brightening of the scope, called a *blip,* appears halfway along the trace. If the object were only 5 mi away instead of 10,

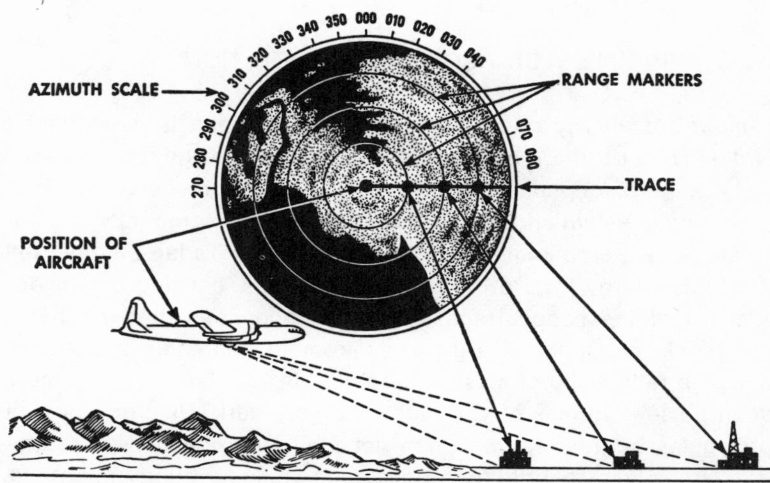

Figure 11.45 Navigation by radar. The trace moves in a clockwise direction around the scope face, painting blips every time the antenna receives a return from energy it has sent out. The navigator identifies the blip by reference to his maps. He then determines the distance the aircraft is from the object by reference to the range markers, and the bearing of the object by reference to the azimuth scale. This bearing and distance plotted from the object locate the aircraft in relation to it.

the blip would appear one-fourth of the way out on the trace. With the trace calibrated in miles, it is possible to determine from the position of the blip on the trace the distance in miles of any object from which the reflection of energy is strong enough to be picked up by the radar set. On most present-day radar sets, this calibration is accomplished by the use of equally spaced electronically generated markers, called range markers, superimposed on the face of the scope (Figure 11.45).

DETERMINING BEARING

To identify reflecting objects for either range or bearing measurement, the antenna rotates to cover either a wide sector or the full circle around the aircraft. This rotation of the antenna is known as *scanning.* Through electrical gearing the trace follows the rotation of the antenna, so that at any given instant the position of the trace on the azimuth scale represents the direction toward which the antenna is pointing. Thus if the radar beam is reflected from an object at an angle of 90° from the aircraft's line of flight, the blip appears when the trace is 90° from the

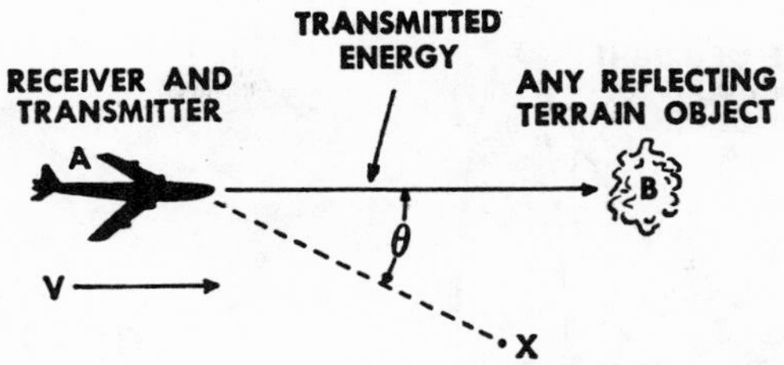

Figure 11.46 Measurement of velocity, Doppler principle.

aircraft's heading, indicating the relative bearing of the object from the aircraft. By placing an azimuth ring calibrated in degrees around the face of the scope, relative bearing in degrees can be read directly. By employing both pulsing and scanning techniques simultaneously, both range and azimuth of an object can be determined.

DOPPLER RADAR

The famous Doppler effect has resulted in the development of radar systems based on that principle. Doppler effect is usually illustrated by the change in pitch of a train whistle, increasing in pitch (frequency) as it approaches, and decreasing as it departs.

Doppler radar navigation equipment utilizes the difference between the frequencies of radar beams directed at approaching and departing targets, and the return frequency as reflected from points on the surface.

In Figure 11.45, an airplane, moving at V cm per sec, transmits a radar signal and receives its reflection from B. If the transmitting frequency is F_t, and the reflected returning frequency is F_r, it can be shown that the relationship will be

$$F_r = F_t + F_t \frac{2V}{C},$$

where C is the speed of light. If the reflection is from any other point, such as X, which is not directly in the aircraft's path, the values become a function of cosine θ, or

$$F_r = F_t \frac{2V \cos \theta}{C}$$

Therefore, the difference between the transmitted and received frequencies, calld the *Doppler shift, D,* is $F_r - F_t$, and

$$D = F_t \frac{2V \cos \theta}{C}.$$

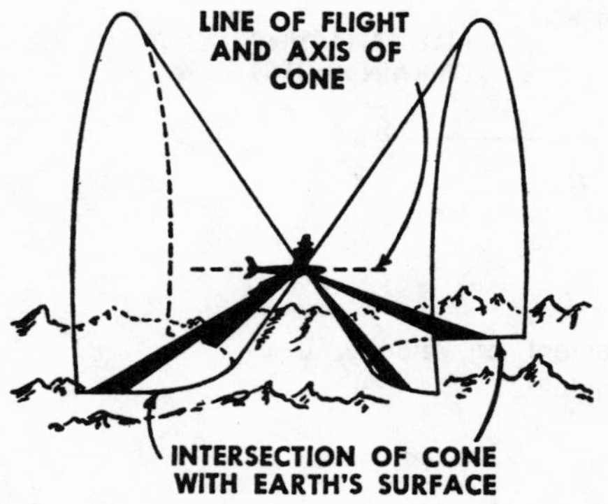

Figure 11.47 Diagram showing radar beams as a segment of an imaginary cone.

Thus, the Doppler frequency is directly proportional to the aircraft's invelocity and cosine θ. Obviously, when θ equals 90°, $D = 0$.

A Doppler radar navigation system, in order to measure D and at the same average terrain effects from an irregular surface, transmits signals in forward and rear conical patterns, as shown in Figure 11.47.

If the axis of the cones is the longitudinal axis of the aircraft, and the aircraft is flying with no crosswind, that is, aligned with its ground track, the radar beams will intersect the surface at four points as shown in Figure 11.48A.

The Doppler shift in this illustration is the same for all four beams, except that the sign of the aft beams is negative, since the received frequency is less than the transmitted frequency. Thus the sum of the Doppler shift for each AB pair equals $2D$, and is proportional to the aircraft's velocity along the track. The hyperbolic curves, called *isodops,* are the locus of all points at which the Doppler shift is equal, for each AB pair.

When the antenna is not aligned with the track, as would be the case with a crosswind, the antenna structure is rotated so that the A pairs of Figure 11.48B more toward the zero shift line and the B pairs move away from it. Because these pairs are pulsed alternately, the receiver can sense the magnitude and direction of the Doppler shift difference between pairs. This signal is used to drive a servo which rotates the antennas until they are again aligned; the angle of deviation from the aircraft's axis is the drift angle.

The antenna pattern described here has certain advantages over a simpler pattern. It is insensitive to changes in vertical velocity because an increase or decrease in vertical velocity changes the frequency shift of each pair by the same amount. Changes in pitch or roll angles also do not affect the system because as one beam is increased, the other is decreased by the same amount, thus the Doppler shift is due to horizontal velocity alone.

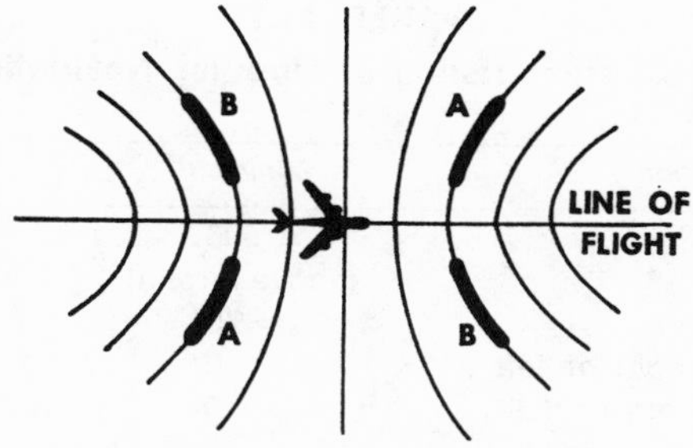

Figure 11.48A Illumination pattern, antenna aligned with ground track.

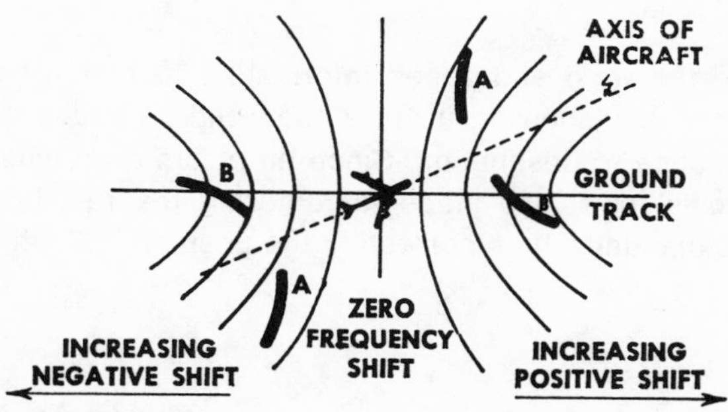

Figure 11.48B Illumination pattern, antenna not aligned with ground track.

Wind Computer The Doppler ground speed and drift information, and heading information from the aircraft's compass system, are fed into a computer that determines the speed and direction of the wind. As long as the radar reflections are of the required strength, this computer remains in the active mode. When the radar is momentarily turned off, as when radar silence is necessary, when the aircraft rolls or pitches beyond the limits of the antenna's pitch or roll limit stops, or when the surface does not reflect a sufficient signal (as when over a glassy sea) the computer is automatically switched into a memory mode. In this mode, the computer uses previously computed wind and drift information. It automatically returns to the active mode when the conditions which caused it to switch into the memory mode are corrected.

Operational Characteristics While different sets vary, a typical set has these characteristics:

TABLE 11.1
Operational Characteristics of Doppler Navigation System

Limits of Operation	*Minimum*	*Maximum*
Altitude, ft	500 (above terrain)	70,000
Ground speed, knots	70	700
Drift angle, degrees right or left	0	49
Wind speed, knots, from any direction, R or L	0	240
Aircraft roll R or L without loss of signal	0	15
Aircraft pitch rate, degrees per sec	0	18
Radiation frequency, MHz	8700	8900

Some sets use the wind and speed information to monitor the aircraft's position continuously, showing it on latitude and longitude counters, and in terms of distance to destination. Since all errors are cumulative over a long flight, provision is also made for entering the results of fixes into these counters manually, thus correcting the position indication during the flight.

Figure 11.49A Doppler navigation equipment components. Major components of basic equipment are: antenna (upper left), frequency tracker (center), and transmitter-receiver (right). Indicator and control panel are shown below. This equipment provides a constant reading of drift and ground speed. Weight: 68 lb.

Figure 11.49B Doppler navigation equipment components. Track navigation computer control panel. (The computer-amplifier which accompanies this equipment is not shown.) When used in conjunction with the basic Doppler equipment, it provides continuous reading of actual versus desired track, distance to go, and distance off desired track.

RADIO DIRECTION FINDERS

MF-, HF-, VHF-, and UHF-DF stations are located primarily in airport control towers, almost world-wide. United States stations, operated either by the military services or FAA, are principally for emergency homing and are a simple and readily available aid to any pilot who needs navigation assistance and has only a radio transmitter and receiver. Overseas, particularly in Europe, they are considered routine navigational aids.

A DF station is simply a ground based radio compass which on request of the aircraft can receive a transmitted steady signal, and using it, can report to the aircraft the heading it should fly to reach the station. Where DF stations operate in groups of three, it is possible to ask for a fix; one of the stations will act as a master station and will correlate the bearings of the other two, and will report a fix to the aircraft in latitude and longitude.

MF- and HF-stations can provide bearings up to 500 mi. They are plotted in the same way as radio compass bearings. The VHF and UHF stations are limited to line of sight distances.

DF stations are listed in flight planning documents. DF bearings or steers may be requested either by simply asking for a steer to base, or by using the international "Q" signal code, for example, "QUX" is a request for a steer to the station, while "QTE" is a request for a bearing from the station. The procedure for obtaining DF bearings or steers is quite standard:

(1) The aircrew calls the station on the assigned frequency, "HONOLULU DF, THIS IS AIR FORCE EIGHT SIX THREE ZERO, REQUEST A STEER TO HONOLULU, OVER."

(2) The DF station responds and asks the aircraft to transmit.

(3) The aircraft transmits its current course, altitude, and true airspeed, followed by a sustained signal on which the station takes its bearing. If using voice radio, the pilot transmits by simply holding down the microphone key or saying a prolonged "Ahhhhhh," for 10 sec. If using CW, the radio operator simply holds down the key for 20 sec.

(4) When the DF station has obtained a bearing, it reports the heading to steer to the station or the bearing from the station, and the time of the bearing. It will also classify the accuracy of the bearing, as follows: (1) as "reliable" or "doubtful," (2) as Class A (less than 2° error), Class B (less than 5° error), or Class C (more than 5° error). It may also be classified as "good" (within an area of 20 mi or less), "fair," meaning within an area of 40 mi or less, or "poor," within an area of 60 mi or less.

Because the receiving equipment is more stably mounted on the ground, DF bearings are generally more reliable than radio compass bearings.

CONSOLAN

The Consolan system is found primarily along the west European seaboard extending from Spain to Norway. There are two station in the United States, one in Nantucket and one in San Francisco.

A station system of three low-frequency antennas, set in line, transmits a station identification signal followed by a series of combinations of dots and dashes and an equisignal. These are transmitted in continuous 75-sec cycles, and emanate alternately around 360° of the station. Sectors 20° wide centered on each end of the base line are inaccurate. By tuning any LF receiver on CW or BFO the operator can identify the station, can count the dots and dashes in any cycle, and by application of his result to a special Consolan chart, can determine his bearing from the station. Under adverse conditions of static, a good operator can obtain a bearing when voice communications would be unintelligible at ranges of from 500 mi at low frequency in daylight to 1400 mi in higher frequencies in darkness. Consolan stations, which operate generally in the 190 to 516 kHz band, are located so that an operator can combine LOP's to obtain Consolan fixes.

Pressure-Pattern Flying

Pressure-pattern flying is a general term including three distinct air navigation techniques: (1) pressure lines of position, (2) single heading flight, and (3) minimal flight path. The first of these is an in-flight procedure, while the last two are based on forecast data and are used in preflight planning. All three, however, are based on the direct relationship between pressure systems of the atmosphere and wind.

THE GEOSTROPHIC WIND

It is rare for winds near the earth's surface to have the same velocity as winds in the upper atmosphere, a fact which may be readily verified simply by comparing cloud paths overhead with local surface winds. The principal causes of the difference between surface and upper-air winds are friction on the earth's surface, which reduces wind speed, and geographical and cultural obstructions, which deflect wind in direction. At approximately 2000 ft above local terrain the wind is generally free of extrinsic disturbance and has a velocity which is the resultant of two forces—pressure gradient force and Coriolis force. The movement of air which we call wind is caused by pressure differentials existing over various parts of the earth. As a freely moving fluid, air tends to flow from areas of high pressure to areas of lower pressure. The greater the difference between the pressures, the faster the air will travel. This is the pressure gradient force, upon which wind speed is largely dependent.

Wind is given direction by the initial location of the areas of pressure differential and by the action of Coriolis force. Coriolis force results from the rotation of the earth on its axis and acts on every particle of matter at motion on or near the earth with a magnitude proportional to the speed of motion. In the Northern Hemisphere it acts perpendicular to the direction of motion and to the right; in the Southern Hemisphere it acts perpendicular to the direction of motion and to the left. It is thus Coriolis force which gives wind a counterclockwise motion around a low pressure area in the Northern Hemisphere.

On the basis of pressure information gathered from actual soundings, and on the known Coriolis effect at a given latitude, it is possible to make a mathematical computation of wind direction and velocity called the *geostrophic wind.* The geostrophic wind is assumed to blow parallel to the isobars, lines of equal barometric pressure shown on a weather map. When these lines are fairly straight, wind does, in fact, blow parallel to them. Mostly, however, isobars are curved, and the wind in attempting to travel a curved path is subjected to centrifugal force as well as pressure gradient and Coriolis forces. Except in areas of very steep pressure slope, where isobars are close together and decidedly curved, no error of consequence to navigation is introduced by the assumption. For purposes of pressure pattern flying the geostrophic wind is a close enough approximation to the true wind in all latitudes above 20° N and below 20° S. In the region of the equator, the decreased Coriolis effect causes inaccuracies in the calculation of the geostrophic wind, and pressure pattern techniques are not considered accurate enough for use between 20° N and 20° S.

PRESSURE-PATTERN TERMS

"D" The difference in ft between *absolute altitude* (actual altitude above the surface of the earth) and the *pressure altitude* (altitude above the standard datum plane). In flight, "D" is determined by subtracting the pressure altitude from the absolute altitude, that is, absolute altitude 8500 ft, pressure altitude 8000 ft, "D" = +500 ft. Absolute altitude is measured by a radio or radar altimeter while pressure altitude is measured by a pressure altimeter with 29.92 in. Hg or 1013 mb set in the window. A radio altimeter operates on the same principle as radar. However, instead of showing range in miles to a target, it indicates altitude in feet above the surface.

Pressure Line of Position (PLOP) A computed LOP based on the slope of the pressure surface, effective true airspeed and Coriolis force for the period of time between "D" readings, drawn parallel to the effective air path of the aircraft.

Effective Air Path The *direct* air path between "D" reading regardless of heading changes.

Effective True Airspeed The effective air path miles converted to airspeed using the time between "D" readings.

Bellamy Drift (BD) The drift angle corresponding to the perpendicular displacement (Zn) from the effective airpath vector and ground distance flown for the period between "D" readings. Ground distance is normally estimated unless Bellamy drift is computed when fixes are taken as a cross check of the drift angle. It can be computed by formula or drawn graphically.

COMPUTING A PLOP AND BD

As an aircraft maintaining a constant-pressure altimeter setting and altitude flies through a pressure system, its true altitude will be constant as long as it flies along the contour lines of constant pressure. However, when it crosses the lines, flying either toward higher or lower pressure, the true altitude will change, increasing if it flies toward higher pressure, and decreasing as it flies toward lower pressure. The more nearly the aircraft flies directly across the contour lines, the greater the drift, since it is flying directly crosswind. The problem of finding the aircraft's true altitude was solved by the radio altimeter.

John C. Bellamy, a Chicago scientist, developed the formula for the use of upper-wind relationships to determine the effect of the geostrophic wind which has become:

$$Zn = \frac{K(D_2 - D_1)}{ETAS} \text{ or, computer use, } \frac{Zn}{K} = \frac{D_2 - D_1}{ETAS}$$

Zn = Distance blown perpendicular to effective air path
K = Coriolis factor for midlatitude between D_1 and D_2 and can be obtained from either tables or on the Minutes scales opposite latitude on an E-10 or MB-4 computer
D_1 = Height difference at first comparison
D_2 = Height difference at next comparison
$ETAS$ = Average effective TAS for the period between D_1 and D_2.

A PLOP must be plotted to be of practical value. However, BD is a rapid means of checking the aircraft's drift. Since Zn is already on the outer scale of the computer (needed for a PLOP), it is only necessary to place

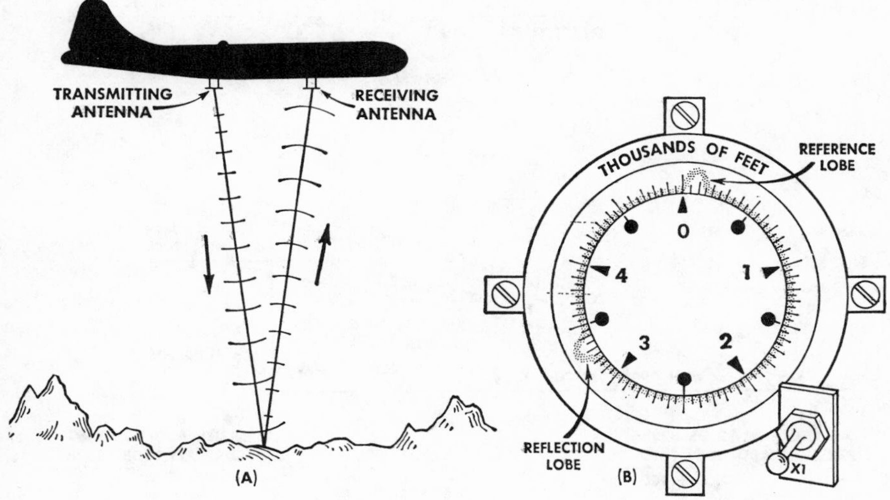

Figure 11.50 Determining altitude by radio altimeter. (A) The radio altimeter transmits a pulse of radio energy which travels from the aircraft to the ground and back to the receiver. (B) Face of the radio altimeter, showing the reference lobe produced by the transmitted pulse of energy, and the reflection lobe produced by the returning wave. Facility for accurate measurement of a wide range of altitudes is provided in the "times one-times ten" (×1-×10) switch. When the switch is in the ×1 position, the face of the tube measures multiples of 5000 ft; in the ×10 position, it measures up to 50,000 ft. In this illustration, with the switch at ×1, the reflected lobe indicates an absolute altitude of 3200 ft, 8200 ft, 13,200 ft, etc. (*Courtesy of U.S. Air Force.*)

ground distance flown between readings under it to determine BD. The formula for BD is

$$BD = \frac{Zn \times 57.3}{\text{ground distance}}$$

or, for computer use

$$\frac{BD}{57.3} = \frac{Zn}{\text{ground distance}}$$

Instructions on the face of many computers state that "air miles flown" should be used rather than TAS. If air miles flown is used, the Zn value obtained is lateral displacement per hour and must be converted for the length of time between D readings before plotting as a PLOP. To compute BD, Zn may be used as a rate per hour if GS is used instead of GD. The formulas would then appear as:

$$\frac{Zn\text{ (per hour)}}{K} = \frac{D_2 - D_1}{\text{air miles flown}} \quad \text{and} \quad \frac{BD}{57.3} = \frac{Zn\text{ (per hour)}}{GS}$$

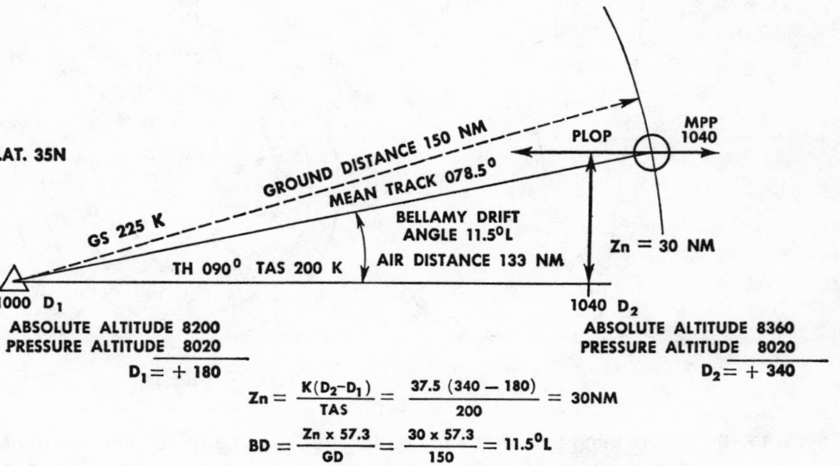

Figure 11.51 Plotting a pressure line of position. The PLOP is drawn parallel and at a distance, Zn, away from the True Heading/True Airspeed vector. The True Heading/True Airspeed vector is used in lieu of the Effective Air Path/Effective True Airspeed vector when there have been no heading changes between "D" readings. In the Northern Hemisphere when D_2-D_1 is a positive value the aircraft is entering a high-pressure area and would be displaced to the left; if D_2-D_1 were a negative value, the aircraft would be entering a lower-pressure area and drift would be right.

Whenever heading changes are made between D readings, BD cannot be correctly computed and is therefore of no practical value.

MINIMAL FLIGHT

Sometimes called Optimum Flight, this is the path between two points that can be flown in the shortest time. Under zero wind conditions, the great-circle route is the shortest route in both distance and time. In many cases a deviation from a great-circle route while longer in distance would result in a lesser time through minimal flight. Minimal flight planning involves considerable computations and is based on going around pressure systems on the side that gives tail-wind components or least head-wind components. With the sky becoming more crowded, ATC has established certain tracks on over-water routes for more positive control of aircraft. The flight planner works out a minimal flight path and picks the established track closest to the minimal track. Although this is a compromise, the established track selected is shorter in time than a great circle track.

SINGLE-HEADING FLIGHT

As the name implies, single-heading flight is a method of applying a single average drift-angle correction for an entire flight. Because of the difficulty of measuring true altitude over land, the procedure can only be approximated except over water. The drift angle is computed in the same manner in which en-route drift angle is computed, except that instead of the D difference between readings, the height of the pressure surface, at flight level above departure point (H_1) and destination (H_2) are used for D_1 and D_2. The resultant Zn is then used to determine the average drift. Single-heading flights are seldom used, except in training, because the uncertainty of the actual track prevents positive monitoring by Air Traffic Control.

Flight Planning

IMPORTANCE OF PREFLIGHT PLANNING

Planning is essential to safe flight. The longer the proposed flight, the more involved the planning, but no flight is short enough to permit complete elimination of preflight activity. The principal reasons for flight planning are to anticipate problems, and to reduce to a minimum the tasks to be done in the air. Not only must decisions be made more rapidly than time for proper consideration of all factors permits, but the thinking process itself is less efficient in the air than on the ground because of the added disturbances of nervous tension, noise, vibration and bulky flying equipment. By preparing for what might happen before it does happen, errors arising from snap decisions can be held to a minimum.

FACTORS TO BE CONSIDERED IN FLIGHT PLANNING

Federal Aviation Administration requirements such as altitudes, fuel requirements, pilot's qualifications, etc., change from time to time. Therefore, these items should be obtained from current flight planning documents, considered, and kept in the back of the flight planner's mind prior to any flight planning. The items listed below are roughly in the order to be considered in most flight planning:

Aircraft Characteristics (a) Maximum cruising altitude of the aircraft in order to avoid terrain features and clouds. (b) Oxygen availability to crew and passengers if aircraft is unpressurized and altitude is above 10,000 ft. (c) Maximum range for no wind conditions at various altitudes to plan en-route stops. (d) Navigation equipment carried aboard the aircraft and on the ground or sea (ocean vessels) for position determination.

Weather Weather along the possible routes that might require deviation from a particular route, close a terminal or alternate, limit celestial observation, or interfere with radio aids such as ADF and Loran.

Route For short flights of several hundred miles or less a straight line can be drawn on an appropriate aeronautical chart from departure to destination. This line may have to be altered some to avoid thunderstorms, obstructions, danger and prohibited areas, and locally controlled areas. For longer flights, particularly those over water, additional factors must be considered. The minimal flight path might be used, a single-heading path might be feasible, or a great-circle course or rhumb line might be the best. Many items must be considered in determining the route of a long flight. Experience will almost automatically condition the navigator to eliminate certain routes. Then the factors of aircraft limitation, navigation equipment and skill in its use, weather along the route and local restrictions will have to be weighed to select the best route. The important thing is to study the route carefully before takeoff.

Fuel Requirements Approximate fuel flow per hour for any aircraft can be found from operating manuals, and the amount of fuel needed between departure and destination can therefore be readily determined. Always carry extra fuel beyond this basic need. This reserve will take care of takeoff and climb requirements, navigation error, and continuing the flight to an alternate base in the event the destination is closed due to weather or an accident.

Civil and military safety regulations differ with regard to surplus fuel requirements to meet these contingencies. The current Air Force requirement, for example, for IFR flight is 10% fuel reserve when the weather is forecast to be VFR. When forecast to be IFR, fuel to destination, then to alternate, plus 10% of the total is required. No less than 20 min spare fuel can ever be carried, and no more than 2 hr extra is ever required.

Always check the amount of fuel actually on board to see that it agrees with the amount in flight planning. It is easier to get more before takeoff than after you are airborne!

FLIGHT PLANS

The documents used for flight planning vary from those used by the pilot in Figure 11.24, consisting of a small card carried on the knee pad, to the product of electronic data processing which produces the flight plans for transoceanic jet airline transports. The important part of any plan is the completeness and ease of use of information prepared before flight to insure that the flight is conducted safely, completing the mission. The private pilot is interested in pleasant, efficient, safe use of his aircraft. The airline pilot is interested in safe, efficient flight, conducted on schedule at minimum cost. The military pilot is interested in the precise positioning of his aircraft, usually at some predetermined time, to carry out a mission which may call for close coordination with other air, sea, or land forces.

In-flight Procedures The flight plan, whether it is an annotated line on a map or an electronic print-out, serves for the basis of comparison, determining just where the aircraft is and how it is progressing. Progress can be noted in pencil on the chart, by either the navigator or pilot, or it can be maintained in a formal log form. The primary requirement is neatness and orderliness to help reduce confusion and error. During instrument flight, regard for the requirements of air traffic controlling agencies makes it essential you have the information on your progress readily available and correct.

Specialized Problems in Navigation

A navigator is sometimes faced with special navigation problems. Among these are search procedures and controlled time of arrival.

SEARCH

Any navigator may be called upon at any time to participate in a search for downed aircraft, drifting vessels, lifeboats—even herds of livestock trapped by blizzard or flood. A military navigator must also know scouting procedures in order to detect enemy warships and submarines. And finally, any navigator must know how to search for destination, with the least waste of fuel, if it is not in sight or radio contact when estimated time of arrival is up.

Search is strictly a navigational problem. An area to be searched is generally fairly large, and the number of searching aircraft generally limited. Haphazard searching techniques, duplicating search over some areas and missing others, are unproductive. Since the success of any search mission depends on complete coverage of a given area, accurate navigation is essential. For this reason searches are more exacting navigationally than missions on which slight course errors can be tolerated and then corrected on the final leg into destination.

To find an objective in the least possible time, an orderly search pattern, precisely flown, is therefore mandatory and many patterns have been devised to meet special needs. Selection of the specific technique to be employed depends on the size and shape of the area to be searched, the number of aircraft to be used, and the range of visibility.

Typical search patterns are shown in Figure 11.52. In all cases, the *scouting distance,* the distance between aircraft or between successive lines of search by a single aircraft, is determined by estimated visibility. If navigation were perfect, the scouting distance could be twice the

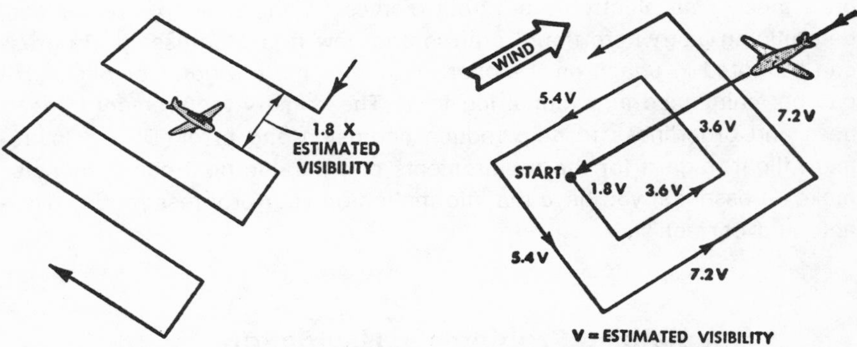

Figure 11.52 Typical search patterns for single aircraft. The parallel search on the left is used principally to cover an assigned area of rectangular shape. The expanding square search on the right is generally used to search for destination at the expiration of estimated time of arrival. In parallel search the area to be searched is assigned, and wind effect must therefore be computed on each heading. The expanding square is laid out at the navigator's discretion, and the first heading can therefore be plotted parallel or perpendicular to the wind to facilitate computation of drift and ground speed.

amount of the visibility. To allow for some error, in navigation as well as estimate of visibility, the range of visibility is usually multiplied by 1.8 instead of 2.

The *expanding square search* is the method most frequently employed to find an objective which is not in view on expiration of estimated time of arrival. Its simplicity makes it possible to plan the pattern in flight prior to arrival at destination in the event homing facilities are for any reason unavailable. Navigational calculations while search is in progress can be held to a minimum if each leg is flown directly upwind, downwind, or crosswind. If this is done, upwind and downwind legs will have no drift, and ground speed will be true airspeed minus or plus wind speed. On crosswind legs both upwind and downwind ground speed will be the same, and drift will be the same amount with opposite signs.

The altitude at which a search is flown depends largely on weather and the size of the objective being sought. Visibility increases with altitude in clear weather, but clouds frequently place an arbitrary top limit lower than optimal altitude. When searching for an island or a large vessel, an altitude of as much as 10,000 ft may be maintained by day in clear skies. At night, 1000 ft is more adequate for sea searches. To locate small objects such as a life raft, air-sea rescue missions are usually flown as low as 300 to 500 ft over rough seas, and rarely higher than 1000 ft over smooth water. Even though the visibility from 1000 ft in clear weather is over 25 mi, scouting distance when seeking a life raft is between 2 or 3 mi in areas where location of the raft is most probable.

CONTROLLED TIME OF ARRIVAL

Time of arrival depends on three factors: time of departure, ground speed, and distance to fly. By varying one or more of these factors, time of arrival can be controlled.

The most obvious way to control time of arrival is to control time of departure. It is not always possible to take off exactly as planned, and since ground speed en route almost invariably differs from preflight estimates, it is necessary to have some means for controlling time of arrival during the flight itself. Since it is easier to lose extra time than to gain time, departure should if possible be a little early rather than late.

Small amounts of time may be gained or lost in flight by varying airspeed, thus increasing or decreasing ground speed. It is not possible to gain or lose large amounts of time by airspeed control because of the operating limitations of the aircraft itself.

For gaining or losing more than just a few minutes it is necessary to vary the distance being flown. If the route plotted is a straight-line course, no time can be gained by this method. As a matter of practical tactics, there-

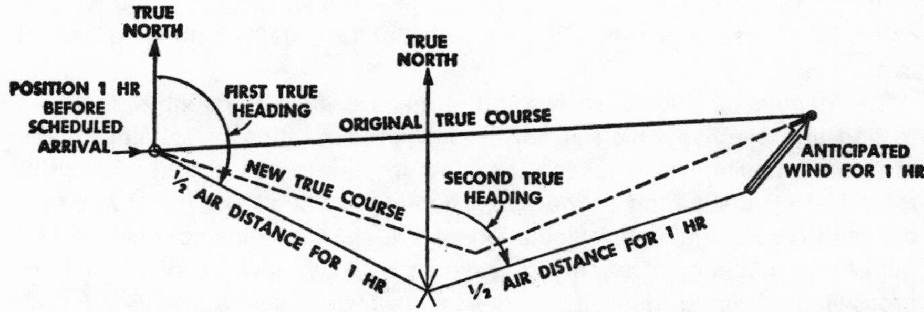

Figure 11.53 Controlling time of arrival by adding distance. One hour prior to scheduled arrival, a navigator, realizing that he will arrive too early, plots a fix. Using destination as an origin, he plots in the anticipated wind vector for the next hour. Using the end of the wind arrow and his fix position as centers and one-half his true airspeed as a radius, he swings equal arcs to one side of his true course line. The angle at his fix position is now flown as a true heading for 30 min. If wind and work are accurate, the aircraft will arrive over destination. The track made good by the aircraft is shown by the dotted line between original course and true heading lines.

fore, routes are generally set up as dog-legs which permit time to be gained simply by straightening the route as needed. Even large amounts of time are easily lost. Simple S-turns will consume some, and full 360° procedure turns even more. If it is absolutely necessary to lose more than a few minutes, it is best to fly an angular course, adding as much extra distance as needed to lose the required amount of time.

Polar Navigation

The areas north of the Arctic Circle (66°-30′ N) and south of the Antarctic Circle (66°-30′ S) are generally considered the polar regions. These areas have certain inherent problems, due to their geographical location, that a navigator must be aware of in order to fly over them safely. The most important problems are direction and steering, maps, and fixing. To solve these problems, special procedures are required. Because special training and preparations are required to fly the polar areas safely and space is too limited to cover them adequately, this section will cover only the major problems and briefly discuss some of the polar-navigation procedures used to solve them. A navigation manual should be consulted for detailed polar procedures.

PROBLEMS OF POLAR NAVIGATION

The problem of direction, steering, and maps becomes complicated in the polar regions due to the rapid convergence of meridians and the proximity of the magnetic pole. To overcome these problems, a grid overlay system has been devised. Because of the grid overlay, polar navigation is often referred to as *grid navigation.* The polar grid overlay is constructed on a transverse Mercator or other polar-projection chart as a series of straight lines parallel with the 0° to 180° meridian. The parallel lines portray Grid North, with Grid North in the direction of the 180° meridian (Figure 11.54). With the 180° meridian as 000° grid and the Greenwich meridian as 180° grid, the other directions are easily recognized—that is, 000° is at the top of the chart, 090° is at the right of the chart, etc.

All courses, headings, winds, and azimuths should be converted to grid directions when using polar procedures. With these directions expressed

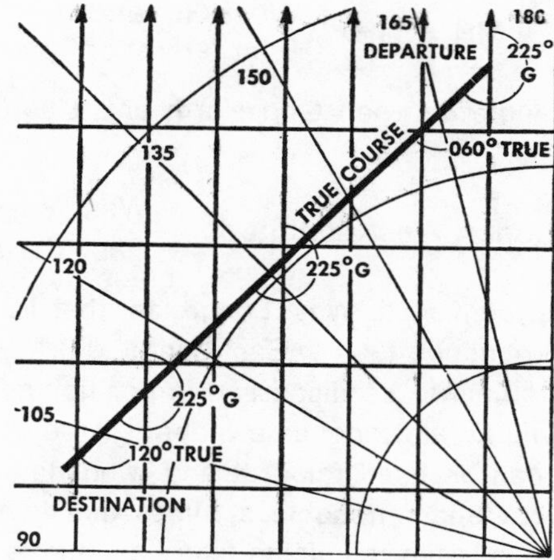

Figure 11.54 The grid system. The grid is drawn parallel to the 180° meridian. The grid system enables the polar navigator to fly a constant heading from departure to destination. As shown here, the true course measured at the local meridian changes from 60° at departure to 120° at destination, whereas grid course is a constant 225°.

in grid, DR procedures remain basically the same. Normal directions are converted to grid directions by:

$$\text{Grid direction} = \text{True direction} \begin{array}{l} + \text{West Longitude} \\ - \text{East Longitude} \end{array}$$

Steering in the polar regions is done by gyros, since magnetic compasses become unreliable. Because gyros precess, it is necessary to rate them to determine the proper average heading between two points. This is done graphically by comparing the gyro heading to the heading determined by celestial means. As the aircraft is steered by the gyro and the gyro precesses the aircraft will follow a curved path. By knowing the rate of precession, you can correct the heading of the aircraft for precession and determine an average heading from the curved air path. This is considered as the actual air path for computations.

In certain areas of the polar region, the horizontal component of the earth's magnetic field is such that a magnetic compass can be used. In such cases the compass can be checked by:

$$\text{MH} = \text{GH} \begin{array}{l} + \text{West Grivation} \\ - \text{East Grivation} \end{array}$$

Grivation is the angle between Grid North and Magnetic North and is determined by:

$$\text{Grivation} = \text{West Longitude} \begin{array}{l} - \text{West Variation} \\ + \text{East Variation} \end{array}$$

If in East Longitude, convert to West Longitude, that is, 155° East Longitude = 205° West Longitude (360 − East Longitude).

The last major problem to be discussed is positioning the aircraft. Due to the lack of landmarks and adequate mapping, radar and map reading are limited. Radar can be used for drift and wind determination. Radios are limited in number and unreliable at times due to magnetic disturbances. Celestial means is the remaining fixing aid and is used extensively.

The polar regions have long periods of continuous daylight, total darkness and twilight. During the season of constant daylight the sun is used and is supplemented by the moon and Venus (when visible). During the total-darkness season the stars are available. It is the twilight period that is of chief concern in polar areas. Although the twilight period has proved ot be a far less serious problem than originally expected, it is still a prime consideration when planning a flight.

To aid the navigator, several special devices have been developed to speed up and reduce the calculations necessary for celestial observations. The Twilight Computer rapidly computes the time of entering and duration of twilight. A second computer, the LHA Computer, provides the LHA of a celestial body for any given instant of time at a given longitude that is accurate to within one degree. This accuracy is sufficient for the purpose of setting up the astrocompass for heading checks. The Modified Astrocompass indicates grid heading directly without computations.

Jet Stream Flying

The jet stream, discussed on page 283, is a vitally important factor in high-altitude commercial and military flying in the temperate zones. Being able to locate and use (or avoid) the jet stream is an essential part of pilot's and navigator's knowledge. In fact, one airline flies routes direct from Tokyo to Honolulu, depending upon the jet stream to shorten the route to the point where stops are unnecessary. The substantial saving in time and money is obvious.

LOCATING THE JET STREAM

Jet stream are associated with frontal systems. The direction of the core is roughly parallel to the frontal surface and in front of it. The general area of the frontal surface, and thus the jet stream, can be found from the weather cross section. In flight, the frontal surface can be located by:

Temperature Change Observing a temperature change of 4° or more in a zone approximately four miles wide is a good indication of the presence of a frontal surface. If you are climbing through a frontal surface, the temperature will either remain constant or increase slightly.

Clear Air Turbulence This is caused by winds of different velocities rubbing together, creating eddies of turbulence. This type of turbulence is characterized by short, fast changes rather than prolonged updrafts and downdrafts.

FLYING THE JET STREAM

Once in the air you should locate the frontal surface defined in your upper-air forecast and stay above the slope until you reach your cruising altitude. Fly in the warmer smoother air 1000 ft on top of the slope and stay out of the cold air and turbulence. If you are climbing behind the front and have not reached the warmer air by the time you reach your cruising altitude, turn toward the direction of the front, usually to the south, until you pass the frontal surface and enter the warmer air. If you have passed through the frontal surface and are ahead of it—and can climb higher—also turn toward the front, usually to the north, and stay on the slope in the warmer air. These procedures help to take advantage of the high-velocity winds of the jet stream. If you encounter the jet stream when going in a direction contrary to its flow, turn to the north and descend to avoid the high headwinds. See Figure 6.9.

Area Navigation

The high cost of operating modern high-speed transports over both domestic and overseas routes, and the need for varied and precise entry into congested traffic control areas to facilitate expeditious landing have made navigation based on flying over land fixes (VOR/DME/TACAN) relatively cumbersome. *Area navigation* (RNAV) is an FAA term meaning a method of navigation which provides accuracy comparable to domestic airline flying without necessarily flying from radio fix to radio fix. There are three generally accepted modes:

Mark I. A *course line computer,* which converts bearings and distances from VOR and DME fixes into the heading required to maintain a course and a knowledge of current position, even though the aircraft does not fly over the fixes.

Mark II. Doppler systems which provide a heading reference, track, and current position. May be augmented by VOR/DME, loran, and Decca systems.

Mark III. Based on inertial navigation systems, with updating inputs from VOR, DME, TACAN, airborne radar, etc.

INERTIAL NAVIGATION SYSTEMS

Used for several years for overocean air transport and military navigation, and designed for the mid-course portion of long-range missile guidance

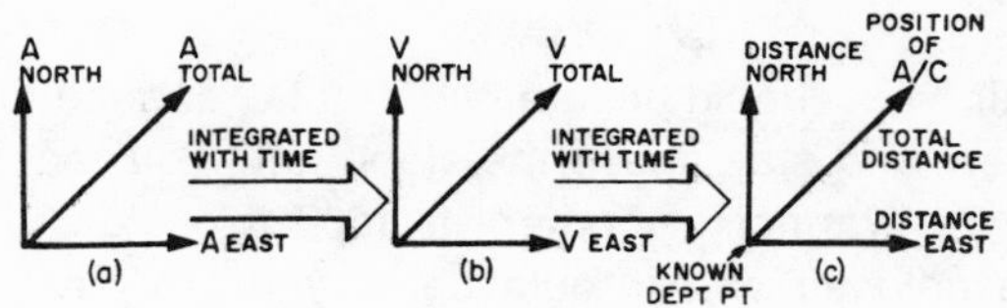

Figure 11.55 Vector solution to internal navigation. Accelerations *A,* when integrated with time, become velocity *V,* which integrated with time becomes distance and position.

systems, these systems are now used for domestic area navigation. Inertial navigation systems determine track, ground speed, and position accurately by measuring aircraft acceleration with reference to north-south and east-west axes. The accelerations are integrated with time, giving velocity and position (Figure 11.55).

A typical system consists of four components:

(1) *Accelerometers* to measure specific components of acceleration. These are pendulous devices. When the aircraft accelerates, the pendulum swings off its zero position. The amount of electric force needed to restore its position is the source of signals to the integrator.

(2) *Stable Platforms.* By using the gyroscopic property of rigidity in space, maintains the N-S and E-W accelerometers horizontal to the earth's surface, and stabilized in azimuth (direction). This position is maintained regardless of precession, earth rotation, and aircraft movement. This gyroscopic platform, when installed, is usually used also as the aircraft's primary gyroscopic flight instrument reference.

(3) *Integrators* combine acceleration with time to produce velocity, and velocity with time to produce distance.

(4) *Computers* receive signals from integrators and translate them into position (lat.-long.) and ground speed. They also produce signals to correct precession and keep the stable platform level and properly oriented in azimuth.

Inertial navigation systems are expected to solve area navigation problems both en route and in terminal areas.

12

Flight Control Agencies and Rules of the Air

Organizations Controlling Air Traffic

When you call or visit the airport FAA Flight Service Station office to file your flight plan, when you tune your "omni" to a range station, or when you ask for taxi clearance or weather information—you make partial use of the vast resources of Air Traffic Control. But when you file to fly under Instrument Flight Rules (IFR), in poor weather or in sunny skies, you really bring into full operation this huge system that is devoted to your safety and to the greater utility of your aircraft. Air Traffic Control cannot function without your intelligent help.

The system is huge because of the number of aircraft that use it and the wide difference in their individual performances. This fact was fully apparent in 1926, when the first U.S. legislation for aviation, the Air Commerce Act, was passed. This Act formed the Bureau of Air Commerce, as part of the Department of Commerce, to license pilots, make flying safe, develop new air navigation facilities, map the airways, and to furnish flight information.

This bureau, small at first, evolved through development and Congressional action into two separate agencies, the Civil Aeronautics Board (CAB), and the Civil Aeronautics Administration (CAA). These agencies served the nation's airmen until 1958, when the spectacular increase in numbers and the widely varied performance of modern aircraft required something better to protect the users of our national airspace from the rapidly increasing hazards resulting from this growth.

The Federal Aviation Act of 1958 repealed all previous acts, continued the CAB as an independent agency, and established the Federal Aviation Agency (FAA).

FEDERAL AVIATION ADMINISTRATION

This, however, was relatively short lived. In 1966 the President requested the establishment of a Department of Transportation with its Secretary of cabinet rank. A Congressional Act in 1967 established the Department of Transportation under which the Federal Aviation Administration (FAA) functions. All of the old functions of the Agency were transferred to the DOT. The Civil Aeronautics Board, which governed civil aviation for nearly 40 years, now regulates the commercial aspects of Air Carrier operations.

The National Transportation Safety Board, under the DOT and separate from FAA, is now responsible for accident investigation and safety programs.

The FAA has its headquarters in Washington, D.C. In addition to its globe-circling responsibilities for traffic control, facilities inspection, and maintenance, it is charged with the responsibility for operation of the National Capital Airports, notably Dulles and Washington National.

The FAA is a vast organization as can be seen in Figure 12.1. In addition to the direct functioning along the lines of responsibility shown, extensive liaison is required with such other organizations as the Departments of Defense, Interior, and Agriculture as well as with foreign countries. The latter is done primarily through the International Civil Aviation Organization (ICAO).

Military aviation is controlled by FAA except in specified training areas and certain emergencies. Equipment owned and operated by the military for Air Traffic Control is inspected and checked by FAA for compliance with FAA standards. FAA personnel in fact work in many military air traffic control facilities and completely man some of them. In particular, Radar Approach Controls (RAPCONS) maintained on a military installation will be manned by FAA personnel. Next to them and using the same equipment

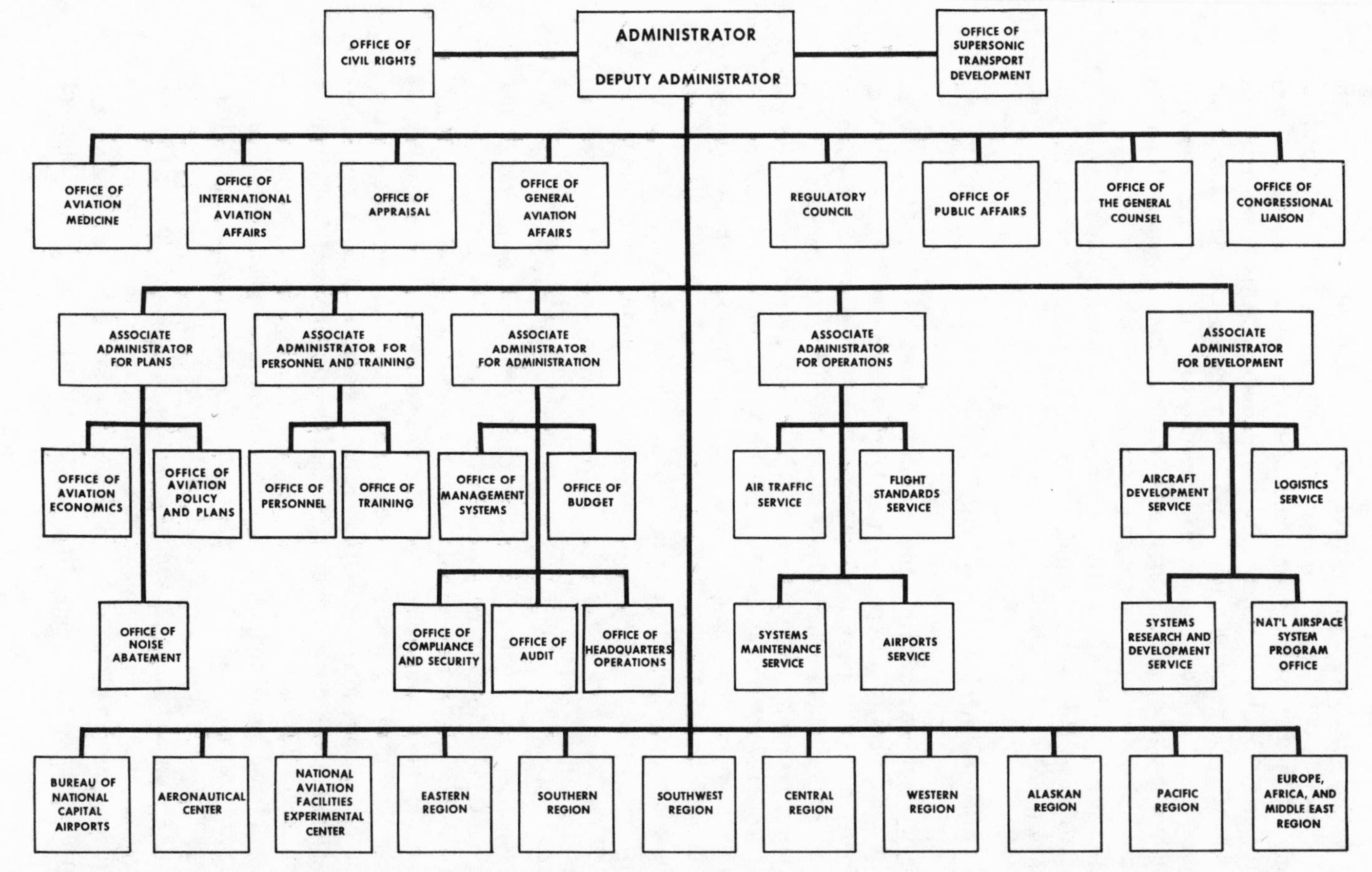

Figure 12.1 Department of Transportation, Federal Aviation Administration. *(Courtesy of Federal Aviation Administration.)*

may be a military man working a military aircraft on a ground-controlled approach.

The primary responsibilities of FAA are executed through field regions. Regional offices are located in New York, Atlanta, Fort Worth, Kansas City, Los Angeles, Anchorage, and Honolulu. One is also located in Europe. These regions supervise the Air Route Traffic Control Centers, over 300 Airport Traffic Control Towers, and over 300 Flight Service Stations. The one in Europe is primarily concerned with our forces assigned to NATO and with international liaison.

The principal functions of FAA which directly affect the airman are directed by major subdivisions of the Washington headquarters, called Services.

The Flight Standards Service establishes safe standards for manufacturers' use in the design and production of new aircraft. It prescribes standards of maintenance for all civil aircraft. It tests and certifies the competence of pilots and other aircrew members, and guards the quality of schools for aviation mechanics and technicians.

This Service formulates, administers, and enforces nearly all of the aviation regulations needed to enhance the safe operation of civil aircraft. It investigates and analyzes causes of civil accidents.

Safety inspectors observe continuously the actual operation of commercial aircraft on scheduled flights. The Service also flight-checks the hundreds of navigation and landing aids, radars, and communications systems of the Federal Airways System.

It serves the flying public through several Flight Standards Service General District Offices in each region, organized for both general aviation and air carrier support.

The Air Traffic Service is responsible for air traffic control, airspace allocation, the integration of different civil and military air operations, and the development of air traffic rules. Authority is decentralized as much as possible to the various Regions.

The *Airports Service* develops and publishes engineering and planning standards for airports and maintains an advisory service. It also administers the Federal Airports Act, maintains a National Airport Plan, and insures that airport sponsors comply with airport standards.

The Systems Maintenance Service has the task of maintaining equipment, facilities, communications, radars, and other electronic systems used in airways and in air traffic control.

In addition to the Services, the *Office of Aviation Medicine* sets medical standards and provides medical certification of airmen. It conducts aeromedical research and studies aviation environmental health. The *Office of General Aviation Affairs* effects liaison with Congress and with federal, state, and local government and aviation organizations. The *Office of In-*

ternational Affairs handles international problems and exchanges information with foreign countries. The *Office of Information Services* is the source of public information on FAA services and activity, and maintains liaison between the public aviation community and FAA employees.

The Aeronautical Center at Oklahoma City is one of the most complete civil aviation training facilities in the world. Hundreds of FAA personnel and students from nearly every country in the non-communist world receive training and up-to-date knowledge in almost every phase of aeronautics here each year.

INTERNATIONAL CIVIL AVIATION ORGANIZATION (ICAO)

The aims of ICAO are to promote the orderly growth of international civil aviation throughout the world to meet the needs of people for safe, regular, efficient, and economic air transport; to prevent the economic waste caused by unreasonable competition; and to promote safety in flight. Its headquarters offices are in Montreal, Canada.

Sixty nations are members at this time. All are sovereign and equal in the governing Assembly in which each state has one vote. As the organization's legislative body, the Assembly meets annually. It elects a council of 21 members to serve as an executive body. The Council has advisory and technical functions and remains in session about eight months of the year. It creates standards for international air navigation, an important feature of ICAO's work. Administrative functions are performed by the Secretariat, third principal organ of ICAO. Technical and administrative personnel are recruited on a broad international basis, and are selected for particular technical competence. Subdivisions of the Secretariat are located in key air traffic centers throughout the world.

ICAO work falls into four general categories: air navigation, safety and regularity of international flights, economic aspects of transportation, and international law. By a "joint support" plan, it aids in the financing of essential air navigation aids, such as weather ships and radio facilities, which an individual nation might not be able to establish alone. This program of ICAO is one of the most valuable contributions of the organization to international civil aviation.

Aviation Radio Publications

The FAA issues publications and charts containing data for use of airmen, including the Airman's Information Manual and its amendments, "Bi-weekly Notices to Airmen."

THE AIRMAN'S INFORMATION MANUAL (AIM)

Developed from the *Airman's Guide* and the *Flight Information Manual* and first published in January 1965, this is the most important basic information document for flight planning in the United States. A looseleaf book, it comes in four separate parts each of which is kept up to date by periodic amendments published by FAA. The various sections of AIM and the revision plan of each, which results in a completely new manual each six months are:

PART 1 Basic Flight Manual and ATC Procedures (quarterly, $4.00).
PART 2 Airport Directory (semiannual, $4.00).
PARTS 3 Operational Data (every 28 days), and Notices to Airmen,
and 3A (every 14 days, $20.00).
PART 4 Graphic Notices and Supplemental Data (semiannual, $1.50).

While there are many commercial and governmental publications available to pilots, designed to provide up-to-date information on the proper and safe flight planning and en-route procedures both VFR and IFR, none can match the FAA *Airman's Information Manual.* It is authentic, authoritative, well organized, and written in clear, simple English. It is the basic reference for commercial publications on the subject. Individual pilots and aero clubs who do not have access to an environment of information such as is provided by the operations staffs of military and air carrier organizations should consider a subscription to *The Airman's Information Manual* a necessity. Knowledge of its contents can prevent accidents, unnecessary expense, and embarrassment. It is the primary information source for the peace of mind that comes from a professional approach to flying in the National Airspace System.

While the "AIM" is available in all Flight Service Stations, copies may be obtained, with automatic amendment services, from the Superintendent of Documents, Government Printing Office, Washington, D.C. 20402.

Part 1, Basic Flight Manual and ATC Procedures, is a gold mine of educational, instructional, and training information. Both the professional and the inexperienced pilot can find information of interest and value. It even has something for the ornithologist: a section on bird hazards covering seasonal migrations by type, location, and time.

It contains the basic fundamentals required to fly in the National Airspace System and those items adversely affecting safety of flight.

Most pilots not affiliated with an air carrier or a military organization do not have ready access to health and medical facts relating to their physical, mental, and emotional airworthiness. AIM Part 1 has a section devoted to this vital subject. It also has sections devoted to altimetry, radio and lighting, navigational aids, and airport lighting and markings. It defines *controlled, uncontrolled,* and *special use* airspace.

A very important part of this manual details the services available to pilots including the invitation to visit FAA facilities. It is very important for pilots to know the services available to them particularly in an emergency or when some difficulty arises.

Air Traffic Control procedures are expertly covered in this manual, including instrument procedures for departure, en-route, and arrival. National Security procedures are outlined and there is an excellent section on weather. The section "Good Operating Practices" will save some embarrassment and expedite the pilot's handling by control personnel.

Part 2, Airport Directory, contains a directory of all airports, seaplane bases, and heliports in the conterminous United States, Puerto Rico, and the Virgin Islands which are available for transient civil use. It includes all of their facilities and services except communications. Each airport is listed alphabetically by state and the information is presented in easily readable abbreviated codified form. The up-dating of Part 2 is accomplished by a listing in Part 3 of all new and permanently closed airports. Included also is a list of selected commercial broadcast stations of 100 watts or more power.

United States Entry and Departure procedures including Airport of Entry and Landing Rights airports are listed in Part 2. Also telephone numbers for all Flight Service Stations and Weather Bureau Stations are included.

Part 3, Operational Data and Notices to Airmen, is in fact two parts. The Operational Data is a listing of all major airports with communications. It lists Air Navigation Radio aids and their frequencies; preferred routes, Standard Instruments Departures (SID's) and substitute route structure. A sectional chart bulletin which updates Sectional Charts, cumulatively, is included.

Part 3A, Notices to Airmen, contains the most current data available and may alter or amend any of Part 3 or 4. These notices are limited to those items deemed essential to safety of flight.

Part 4, Graphic Notices and Supplemental Data, contains more permanent-type information including the abbreviations used in all the other parts. It also contains descriptions of and graphics of special military activity such as high-speed, low-level navigation routes and parachute jump areas. It gives special ground and air VOR receiver check points. Navigational references are given in both geographic coordinates and VOR/DME radials and distances.

RADIO FACILITY CHARTS

Civil Charts The FAA, with the cooperation of the USAF, USN, and the Coast and Geodetic Survey, publishes radio facility charts. Each series consists of 10 charts. On the charts are shown the radio facilities (i.e., ranges, fan markers, H-facilities, etc.) in their exact locations, properly labeled by name and including their transmitting frequency and identification. The Federal Airways boundaries are also outlined as are all of the essential data pertaining to them. Each airway is identified by a statement as to its color and number, for example, Green 5, Amber 2, Red 49; and by number only for VOR airways, for example, 12, 15, 42. Fixes over which IFR position reports are mandatory or optional are shown and named. The mileage between fixes in nautical miles and the minimum en-route altitudes between fixes are also included. All ranges and associated airports are depicted and identified. Control zones, air traffic control area boundaries, and extensions are also included.

On each chart is a table of facilities shown on the chart with additional information similar to the tabulation of Air Navigation Radio Aids in *The Airman's Information Manual.* Included also are the bearing and distance from facility to the field.

Large-scale maps of selected congested areas are contained in the Terminal Area Chart series and the most used departure routes are depicted on the reverse side. These charts are issued as frequently as the changes warrant a reprint. The changes are indicated by an arrow alongside the name to indicate where the data differ from those of the previous issue. L/MF and VOR systems are portrayed on the same chart in the latest issue. Fourteen sheets cover the continental United States.

Because VOR and L/MF charts are printed back-to-back, reference should be made to individual charts by a double number, that is, RF 117/118, RF 119/120, etc.

Military Charts The USAF Aeronautical Chart and Information Center, St. Louis, Missouri, publishes radio facilities charts for Air Force and Navy use. They are generally comparable to civil charts except that they emphasize military air bases and facilities.

Jeppesen Charts Unquestionably the most convenient commercial source of up-to-date, complete airways, airfield, and traffic control information for the civil pilot is the various series published by Jeppesen & Co., Stapleton Field, Denver, Colorado. These charts are used extensively by airline, executive, and private pilots. They were standard also for U.S. Army aviation, and widely used by the other services. This service is complete, including distress and emergency procedures.

United States Federal Air Regulations and ICAO Rules of the Air

Federal Air Regulations are published by the Federal Aviation Administration. They are the traffic rules of the air in the United States. A knowledge of these regulations is a vital part of every competent airman's equipment, and adherence to them is mandatory for safe flying whether by private, commercial, or military aircraft. The following title outline of Part 91.0 illustrates the parts most valuable to the airman. Military aircrews are required by service regulations to follow the flight rules except during specific special training or combat operations.

FEDERAL AIR REGULATIONS PART 91.0—GENERAL OPERATING AND FLIGHT RULES (OUTLINE)

CONTENTS

Subpart A—General (Extracted)

91.1 Applicability
91.3 Responsibility and authority of the pilot in command
91.9 Careless or reckless operation
91.11 Liquor and drugs
91.13 Dropping objects
91.15 Parachutes and parachuting
91.17 Towing
91.19 Portable electronic devices
91.21 Flight instruction, and simulated instrument flight, and certain flight tests
91.23 Fuel requirements for flight in IFR conditions
91.25 VOR equipment check for IFR operations
91.27 Civil aircraft certificates required
91.29 Civil aircraft airworthiness
91.31 Civil aircraft operating limitations and marking requirements
91.33 Powered civil aircraft with standard category U.S. airworthiness certificates; instrument and equipment requirements
91.35 Flight recorders and cockpit voice recorders
91.37 Transport category civil airplane weight limitations
91.39 Restricted category civil aircraft; operating limitations
91.40 Limited category civil aircraft; operating limitations
91.41 Provisionally certificated civil aircraft; operating limitations

91.43 Special rules for foreign civil aircraft
91.47 Emergency exits for airplanes carrying passengers for hire

Subpart B—Flight Rules

GENERAL

91.61 Applicability
91.63 Waivers
91.65 Operating near other aircraft
91.67 Right-of-way rules; except water operations
91.69 Right-of-way rules; water operations
91.70 Aircraft speed
91.71 Acrobatic flight
91.73 Aircraft lights
91.75 Compliance with ATC clearances and instructions
91.77 ATC light signals
91.79 Minimum safe altitude; general
91.81 Altimeter settings
91.83 Flight plan; information required
91.85 Operating on or in the vicinity of an airport; general rules
91.87 Operation at airports with operating control towers
91.89 Operation at airports without control towers
91.91 Avoidance of disaster areas
91.93 Flight test areas
91.95 Restricted and prohibited areas
91.97 Positive control areas and route segments
91.99 Jet advisory areas
91.101 Operations to, or over, Cuba
91.102 Flight limitations in proximity of space recovery operations
91.103 Operation of civil aircraft of Cuban registry

VISUAL FLIGHT RULES

91.105 Basic VFR weather minimums
91.107 Special VFR weather minimums in a control zone
91.109 VFR cruising altitude or flight level

INSTRUMENT FLIGHT RULES

91.115 ATC clearance and flight plan required
91.116 Takeoff and landing under IFR
91.119 Minimum altitudes for IFR operations

Subpart C—Maintenance

INTERNATIONAL (ICAO) RULES OF THE AIR

These are the basic rules of the air, which are refined by each country for its own peculiar purposes. *By international agreement, they are designed so that pilots of any member nation who follow their own country's rules will be in compliance with these.*

ICAO RULES OF THE AIR

2.1. APPLICATION—The rules of the air shall apply to aircraft bearing the nationality and registration marks of a contracting state wherever they may be, to the extent that they do not conflict with the rules published by the state having jurisdiction over the territory flown.

2.2. COMPLIANCE—The operation of an aircraft either in flight or on the maneuvering area of an aerodrome shall be in compliance with general rules and, in addition, when in flight, either with:

(a) The visual flight rules; or
(b) The instrument flight rules.

A pilot may elect to fly in accordance with instrument flight rules in visual meteorological conditions, or he may be required to do so by the appropriate authority. During the hours of darkness the choice of rules is limited wherever the appropriate authority has prescribed flight in accordance with the instrument flight rules or such modification of the instrument flight rules as may be specified.

2.3. RESPONSIBILITY

2.3.1. *Responsibility of pilot-in-command*—the pilot in command of an aircraft shall, whether manipulating the controls or not, be responsible for the operation of the aircraft in accordance with the rules of the air, except that he may depart from these rules in circumstances that render such departure absolutely necessary in the interests of safety.

2.3.2. *Preflight action*—Before beginning a flight, the pilot in command of an aircraft shall familiarize himself with all available information appropriate to the intended operation. Preflight action for flights away from the vicinity of an aerodrome, and for all IFR flights, shall include a careful study of available current radio reports and forecasts, taking into consideration field requirements and an alternative course of action if the flight cannot be completed as planned.

2.4. AUTHORITY—The pilot in command of an aircraft shall have final authority as to disposition of the aircraft while he is in command.

2.5. USE OF INTOXICATING LIQUOR, NARCOTICS OR DRUGS—No person shall pilot an aircraft, or act as a flight crew member of an aircraft, while under the influence of intoxicating liquor or any narcotic drug, by reason of which his capacity so to act is impaired.

3.1. PROTECTION OF PERSONS AND PROPERTY

3.1.1. *Negligent or reckless operation of aircraft*—An aircraft shall not be operated in a negligent or reckless manner so as to endanger life or property of others.

3.1.2. *Minimum safe height*—Except when necessary for taking off or landing or except by permission from the appropriate authority, aircraft shall not be flown:

(a) Over the congested areas of cities, towns, or settlements or over an open-air assembly of persons, unless at such a height as will permit, in the event of an emergency arising, a landing to be made without undue hazard to persons or property on the surface; this height shall not be less than 1000 ft above the highest obstacle within a radius of 2000 ft from the aircraft;
(b) Elsewhere when as specified in 3.1.2 (a), at a height less than 500 ft above the ground or water.

3.1.3. *Dropping objects*—Nothing shall be dropped from an aircraft in flight that might create a hazard to persons or property.

3.1.4. *Parachute descents*—Parachute descents other than emergency descents shall not be made unless authorized by the appropriate authority.

3.1.5. ACROBATIC FLIGHT

3.1.5.1. No aircraft shall be flown acrobatically so as to constitute a hazard to air traffic.

3.1.5.2. Unless authorized by the appropriate authority, no aircraft shall be flown acrobatically over congested areas of cities, towns, or settlements or over an open-air assembly of persons.

3.1.6. *Airspace restrictions*—Aircraft will not be flown over areas where there are flight restrictions, the particulars of which have been duly published, except in accordance with the conditions of the restriction or by permission of the appropriate authority of the state imposing the restriction.

3.2. AVOIDANCE OF COLLISIONS

3.2.1. PROXIMITY

3.2.1.1. An aircraft shall not be operated in such proximity to other aircraft as to create a collision hazard.

3.2.1.2. Aircraft shall not be flown in formation except by prearrangement.

3.2.2. *Right of way*—The aircraft that has the right of way shall maintain its heading and speed but nothing in these rules shall relieve the pilot in command of an aircraft from the responsibility of taking such action as will best avert collision. An aircraft that is obliged by the following rules to keep out of the way of another shall avoid passing over or under the other, or crossing head of it, unless passing well clear.

3.2.2.1. *Approaching head-on*—When two aircraft are approaching head on or approximately so, when there is danger of collision, each shall alter its heading to the right.

3.2.2.2. *Converging*—When two aircraft are converging at approximately the same altitude, the aircraft that has the other on its right shall give way, except as follows:

(a) Power-driven heavier-than-air aircraft shall give way to airships, gliders, and balloons;
(b) Airships shall give way to gliders and balloons;
(c) Gliders shall give way to balloons;
(d) Power driven aircraft shall give way to aircraft which are seen to be towing other aircraft or objects.

3.2.2.3. *Overtaking*—An overtaking aircraft is an aircraft that approaches another from the rear on a line forming an angle of less than 70° with the plane of symmetry of the latter; i.e., is in such a position with reference to the other aircraft that at night it should be unable to see either of the aircraft's navigation lights. An aircraft that is being overtaken has the right of way, and the overtaking aircraft, whether climbing, descending, or in horizontal flight, shall keep out of the way of the other aircraft by altering its heading to the right, and no subsequent change in the relative positions of the two aircraft shall absolve the overtaking aircraft from this obligation until it is entirely passed and clear.

3.2.2.4. LANDING

3.2.2.4.1. An aircraft in flight, or operating on the ground or water, shall give way to other aircraft landing or on final approach to land.

3.2.2.4.2. When two or more heavier-than-air aircraft are approaching an aerodrome for the purpose of landing, aircraft at the higher altitude shall give way to aircraft at the lower altitude, but the latter shall not take advantage of this rule to cut in front of another which is on final approach to land, or to overtake that aircraft. Nevertheless, power-driven, heavier-than-air aircraft shall give way to gliders.

3.2.2.4.3. *Emergency landing*—An aircraft that is aware that another is compelled to land shall give way to that aircraft.

3.2.2.5. *Taking off*—An aircraft about to take off shall not attempt to do so until there is no apparent risk of collision with another aircraft.

3.2.3. *Towing objects*—No object shall be towed by an aircraft, except in accordance with requirements prescribed by the appropriate authority.

3.2.4. *Lights to be displayed by aircraft*—Between sunset and sunrise, or such other period between sunset and sunrise as may be prescribed by the appropriate authority, all aircraft in flight or operating on the maneuvering area of an aerodrome shall display lights as defined by the appropriate authority.

3.2.5. *Simulated instrument flights*—An aircraft shall not be flown under simulated instrument flight conditions unless:

(a) Fully functioning dual controls are installed in the aircraft; and
(b) A competent pilot occupies a control seat to act as safety pilot for the person who is flying under simulated instrument condi-

tions. The safety pilot shall have adequate vision forward and to each side of the aircraft, or a competent observer in communication with the safety pilot shall occupy a position in the aircraft from which his field of vision adequately supplements that of the safety pilot.

3.2.6. OPERATION ON, AND IN THE VICINITY OF AN AERODROME

3.2.6.1. An aircraft operated on, or in the vicinity of an aerodrome shall:

(a) Observe other aerodrome traffic for the purpose of avoiding collisions:
(b) Conform with or avoid the pattern of traffic formed by other aircraft in operation;
(c) Make all turns to the left, when approaching for a landing and after taking off, unless otherwise instructed;
(d) Land and take off into the wind unless safety or air traffic considerations determine that a different direction is preferable.

3.2.7. WATER OPERATIONS

3.2.7.1. When two aircraft, or an aircraft and a vessel, are approaching one another and there is a risk of collision, the aircraft shall proceed with careful regard to existing circumstances and conditions, including the limitations of the respective craft.

3.2.7.1.1. *Converging*—An aircraft which has another aircraft or vessel on its right shall give way so as to keep well clear.

3.2.7.1.2. *Approaching head-on*—An aircraft approaching another aircraft or vessel head on, or approximately so, shall alter its heading to the right to keep well clear.

3.2.7.1.3. *Overtaking*—The aircraft or vessel which is being overtaken has the right of way, and the one overtaking shall alter its heading to keep well clear.

3.2.7.1.4. *Landing and takeoff*—Aircraft landing on, or taking off from the water shall, insofar as practicable, keep well clear of all vessels and avoid impeding their navigation.

3.2.7.2. *Lights to be displayed by aircraft on the water*—Between sunset and sunrise, or such other period between sunset and sunrise as may be prescribed by the appropriate authority, all aircraft on the water shall display lights as defined by the authority, unless within an especially exempted area. No other lights shall be displayed by such aircraft if they are likely to be mistaken for these lights.

3.2.7.3. In areas in which the International Regulations for Preventing Collisions at Sea are in force, aircraft on the water shall, in addition to those covered by 3.2.7.1. and 3.2.7.2., comply with such other of the regulations as are pertinent.

3.3. INFORMATION ON FLIGHTS

3.3.1. *Flight Plans* (This section describes when flight plans are required, their contents, filing, deviations, and closing.)

Federal Airways and Air Traffic Control

THE FEDERAL AIRWAYS

The federal airways of the United States consist of a well-defined network of aerial highways on which the FAA has been given authority to control air traffic.

The airways system is designed in two levels. *VOR and L/MF* (low and medium frequency) *Airways,* called the "Low-Altitude Structure," extend from 1200 ft above terrain (or in some cases higher) up to but not including 18,000 ft MSL and is designed to serve aircraft which operate at these altitudes. These airways are depicted on Sectional Route Low-Altitude Charts U.S. series L-1 through L-28.

While this system is still referred to as L/M frequency airways system, low-frequency facilities are rapidly being decommissioned. They are now virtually replaced by the VOR airways which are predicated solely on VOR/VORTAC navigational aids. These airways are numbered similarly to U.S. highways. As in the highway numbering system a segment of an airway which is common to two or more routes carries the number of all airways which coincide for that segment. When such is the case a pilot in filing a flight plan need indicate only that airway number of the route which he is using.

The VOR airways system is composed of "main" airways and "alternate" airways, 10 mi in width. Main airways are normally designated on a straight line between successive omnidirectional (omnirange) stations. Alternate airways usually depart from the main airway at an omnirange station at an angle of at least 15° and return at an angle of at least 15° at the next omnirange station. Alternate airways are designated primarily for the purpose of establishing lateral separation between aircraft operating on IFR flight plans, when traffic conditions on the particular airways segment necessitate such action by Air Traffic Control. Lateral separation of this type is not used within 15 mi of an omnirange station, however. Within a radius of 15 mi from the station where courses converge, ATC employs altitude or time separation.

Alternate airways are identified by their location with respect to their associated main airway. Victor 9 West indicates an alternate airway associated with and lying to the west of Victor 9.

A pilot who intends to make an airways flight using VOR facilities will simply specify the appropriate Victor airway or airways in his flight plan. For example if a flight is being made from Chicago to New Orleans at 8,000 ft using omni ranges only, the route may be indicated as "Departing Chicago Midway cruising 8000 ft via Victor 9 to Moisant International."

TABLE 12.1
Alternate Victor Airway Mileages (3.527% Greater)

Primary Victor Airway Mileage	*To Obtain Alternate Airway Mileage*
40 to 70 mi	Add 2 mi
70 to 100 mi	Add 3 mi
100 to 130 mi	Add 4 mi
130 to 160 mi	Add 5 mi
160 to 185 mi	Add 6 mi
185 to 215 mi	Add 7 mi

Jet Routes The high-altitude structure consists of the *Jet Routes,* and extends from 18,000 ft to 45,000 ft. There altitudes are called *Flight Levels;* 21,000 ft is "FL 210." Standard-day sea-level altimeter settings, 29.92, are used exclusively at flight levels instead of the en-route current altimeter settings used below 18,000 ft.

Above 45,000 ft flights may be conducted on a point-to-point basis. Navigational guidance is provided on an area basis utilizing the facilities depicted on the En-Route High-Altitude Charts.

These airways are all depicted on Coast & Geodetic Survey Flight Information Publications, En-Route Low-(High) Altitude Charts, U.S. Series L-1 through L-28, and U.S. Series H-1 through H-4.

Flight Service Stations are the Air Traffic service facilities within the National Airspace system which have prime responsibility for pre-flight pilot briefing, en-route communications with VFR flights, assisting lost VFR aircraft, originating NOTAMS, broadcasting aviation weather information, accepting and closing flight plans, monitoring radio Nav-aids and operating the national weather teletype system. In addition, in selected locations FSS's take weather observations, issue airport advisories, administer airmen written examinations and advise customs and immigrations personnel of transborder flights.

Obviously these Flight Service Stations can be pretty busy places. However, pilots are encouraged to visit the stations, where group tours are conducted. All of the material required for flight planning is available in these facilities and the people manning them are highly qualified to assist the pilot in finding the information he needs to plan a safe flight.

OPERATING PROCEDURES OF ATC

The significant feature of ATC traffic control is aircraft separation. ATC separates aircraft vertically by assigning different altitudes; longitudinally by time when aircraft are on the same course; and laterally by different flight paths between the same destinations. ATC establishes standards of separation for different conditions and provides this separation between all aircraft operating on IFR flight plans except when ATC has approved flight in VFR conditions.

A substantial part of present air traffic separation in the low-altitude structure is by radar control, and all separation above Flight Level 240 is by radar. (In a large northeastern sector of the country this is now down to 18,000 ft.)

Limitations on ATC ATC jurisdiction contains several limitations with which the pilot should be familiar. ATC does not maintain control of IFR traffic that does not involve flight in controlled areas. Therefore it maintains no separation or control for any aircraft operating in instrument weather conditions if the flight is conducted entirely off airways and out of controlled areas. Without air-ground communications, traffic control is impossible, because the basis for traffic control is communications between the aircraft and the ground. The controller cannot control traffic expeditiously without frequent and accurate position reports from the pilot except when under radar control. The pilot should keep these limitations in mind, in order to promote safety and efficiency in the coordination between his flight and the control center.

The instructions a pilot receives from ATC are vital to his own safety, as well as that of other pilots who may be flying at that time. Each pilot should be familiar with ATC and its operational procedures, so as to realize the need for overall cooperation. A visit to an ATC center will be most illuminating to any pilot who has not done so. ATC personnel will welcome him and his interest.

FLIGHT CLEARANCES

Flights under the cognizance and protection of the National Airspace System of FAA receive ATC services only when the pilot files a flight plan before takeoff.

The Airman's Information Manual describes specifically how flight plans are filed for both VFR and IFR flights. But airmen should understand the importance and meaning of flight plans. A flight plan simply puts ATC on notice that you are going to make a certain flight, in a particular aircraft, during a certain time. It is not a request for permission to make the flight, but is a notice that you would like the service you have paid for, and which the people in ATC are eager to give. It is always to your advantage to file a flight plan, then to fly according to it or advise ATC that you are going to deviate, and finally to close or cancel it so as to relieve ATC of the responsibilities they have for handling an open clearance.

When you file IFR, there is an element of request. But it is not a request for permission; it is a request for certain routing, altitude, and ATC services. Granting approval is simply ATC's way of saying, "The route and facilities you requested are clear of other traffic—go ahead." Observing the obligations to the system you accept when receiving ATC approval "clearance" of your IFR flight plan request is essential if others are to receive the same service and protection you have requested and expect to get.

FEDERAL AVIATION AGENCY

FLIGHT PLAN

Form Approved.
Budget Bureau No. 04-R072.3

1. TYPE OF FLIGHT PLAN		2. AIRCRAFT IDENTIFICATION
FVFR	VFR	N1234T
X IFR	DVFR	

3. AIRCRAFT TYPE/SPECIAL EQUIPMENT 1/	4. TRUE AIRSPEED	5. POINT OF DEPARTURE	6. DEPARTURE TIME PROPOSED (Z)	6. DEPARTURE TIME ACTUAL (Z)	7. INITIAL CRUISING ALTITUDE
CESSNA 182	130 KNOTS	LAX	1500	1510	9500

8. ROUTE OF FLIGHT

LGB V-64 V-16 PHX

9. DESTINATION (Name of airport and city)	10. REMARKS
TUCSON INTL	VFR CONDITIONS ON TOP

11. ESTIMATED TIME EN ROUTE HOURS	MINUTES	12. FUEL ON BOARD HOURS	MINUTES	13. ALTERNATE AIRPORT(S)	14. PILOT'S NAME
2	21	4	30	N/R	VAN SICKLE

15. PILOT'S ADDRESS AND TELEPHONE NO. OR AIRCRAFT HOME BASE	16. NO. OF PERSONS ABOARD	17. COLOR OF AIRCRAFT	18. FLIGHT WATCH STATIONS
FLAGSTAFF, ARIZ.	3	WHITE AND BLUE	

CLOSE FLIGHT PLAN UPON ARRIVAL

1/ SPECIAL EQUIPMENT SUFFIX
A — DME & 4096 Code transponder
B — DME & 64 Code transponder
D — DME
L — DME & transponder—no code
T — 64 Code transponder
U — 4096 Code transponder
X — Transponder—no code

FAA Form 7233—1 (4-66) FORMERLY FAA 398 0052-027-8000

Figure 12.2 Flight plan. The pilot, Van Sickle, of Flagstaff, plans to fly his Cessna 182 from Los Angeles to Phoenix Sky Harbor, via Long Beach, airways V-64 and V-16. He is filing IFR, and flying VFR conditions on top, expects to cruise initially at 9500 ft. He expects to be 2 hr and 20 min en route.

You can file an IFR flight plan in any weather. While the ATC controller may know that in a particular position you are flying in clear air, he must assume that you are in clouds and cannot yourself maintain safe separation from other aircraft and terrain obstacles. So in clear air, when IFR, you get the same protection and service you would get on instruments. And in VFR conditions you can cancel your IFR flight plan at will, proceeding VFR.

EMERGENCIES

One of the great advantages on filing flight plans is that competent help can be directed to you if you need it. The services available to you are described in *The Airman's Information Manual.* However, a good deal depends on what you yourself do. The United States Coast Guard has developed a list of responsibilities which they call "The 5 C's—Your Key to Self Help." The 5 C's are:

CONFESS
COMMUNICATE
CLIMB
COMPLY
CONSERVE

CONFESS. Announce your predicament at the earliest possible moment to alert the Search and Rescue organization. It is far better to start the distress procedure than to delay until it is too late for assistance to reach you.

COMMUNICATE.

(A) Transmit "MAYDAY, MAYDAY, MAYDAY" (if threatened with grave or imminent danger) or "PAN, PAN, PAN" (if your situation requires urgent action, but is not an actual distress) followed by two ten-second periods humming with your microphone depressed and the call sign of your aircraft.

(B) Transmit the following to any ground station:

1. Radio call.
2. Type aircraft.
3. Position and time.
4. Heading.
5. True airspeed.
6. Altitude.
7. Fuel remaining.
8. Nature of emergency.
9. Pilot's intentions (crash landing, ditching, etc.).
10. Assistance desired (steer, escort, etc.).

(C) Use any available frequency:

1. The air/ground frequency you are working.
2. The VHF Emergency Frequency 121.5 MC.
3. FAA stations on 3023.5 KC/OMNI.
4. Any Coast Guard Radio Station on the MF Emergency Frequency 2182 KC.

Once you have firm radio contact, do not shift frequencies except for a very compelling reason.

CLIMB.

(A) If practicable, climb to a higher altitude for better communications, radar detection, and direction finding.

(B) If lost or unable to communicate, fly the following pattern twice. Make right-hand turns with receiver only. Make left-hand turns if both transmitter and receiver are inoperative.

Resume base course and repeat triangles at 20-min intervals until intercept by SAR or Air Defense aircraft. Listen for instructions 121.5 MCS.

COMPLY. Comply with instructions from your ground radio station or interceptor.

(A) If intercepted:

1. Attempt radio contact 121.5 MC.
2. Get in trail position and follow escort.
3. Attempt to fly 160 knots if practicable when interceptor is fighter type.

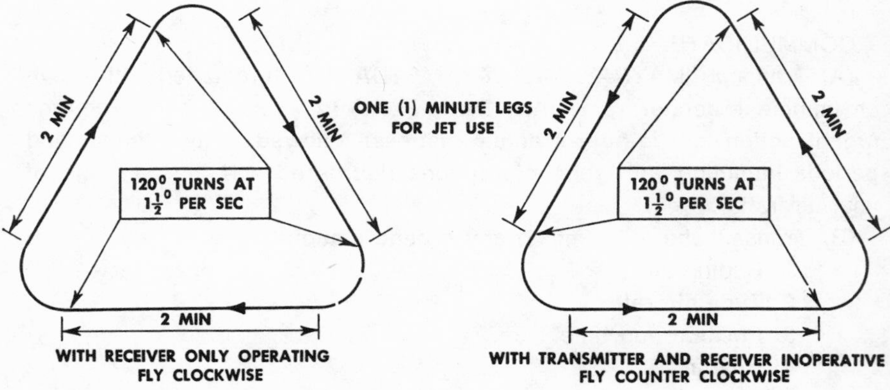

Figure 12.3 Lost or distress procedure for radar assistance. For radar direction or interception, these patterns will attract attention. Complete minimum of two patterns, resume original course, repeat at 20-min intervals until interception by SAR or Air Defense aircraft. Listen on 121.5 MHz or Guard channel.

(B) Actions by interceptor:

1. Interceptor will place running lights on steady and reduce speed.
2. Will inform ground controller of contact and follow instructions.
3. If escort turns lights to blink (night) or rocks wings (day) and breaks formation, continue on course. Escort must leave.
4. If escort turns light to blink for 30 sec then steady and breaks formation with lights steady (night) or fishtails (day), resume distress orbit.

CONSERVE. Whenever practicable, slow down, set up maximum endurance power.

Adhere to these five principles and you will obtain maximum assistance from your Search and Rescue organization.

AIRPORT TRAFFIC CONTROL

An airport traffic-control tower is responsible for controlling the movement of all airplanes on the ground or in flight in the vicinity of the airport. To accomplish this, controllers are required to keep a continuous watch on all visible flight operations in the control zone, including aircraft, vehicles, and personnel on the landing area; to issue all necessary instructions by radio or by visual means to pilots or other personnel; and to forward control messages and maintain records of traffic activities at the airport. Obviously, there must be standard methods and procedures for handling the many routine but complex problems that arise.

When operating to an airport where traffic control is exercised by a control tower, pilots are required to maintain two-way radio contact with the tower while operating within the airport traffic area unless the tower authorizes otherwise. Initial call-up should be made about 15 mi from the airport. Large, high traffic density airports usually will not give authority for non-radio equipped aircraft to operate in their traffic area. Most smaller airports will, at least during low-activity periods. Pilots must exercise extreme care when not in radio contact with the tower. Light signals and other "radio out" procedures, as outlined later in this chapter, must be fully understood and obeyed immediately.

Although the FAR's govern flight in the vicinity of airports, pilots should bear in mind that they have the authority to ask for a change in clearance if they believe another course of action will be safer than that used by an airport traffic-control tower. The clearance issued is not authority for a pilot to deviate from any rule or regulation nor to conduct unsafe operation of his aircraft.

When flying in VFR weather conditions (regardless of the type of flight plan or air-traffic clearance), it is the pilot's direct responsibility to avoid collision with other aircraft. The information and clearances issued by the control tower are intended to aid pilots to the fullest extent in avoiding collisions. A clearance issued by a tower (such as "cleared to land") either by radio or visual signal is permissive in nature and does not relieve the pilot from exercising a reasonable degree of caution in executing the provisions of the clearance.

Taxiing No person should taxi an aircraft until he has ascertained through information furnished by airport attendants, by the tower, or otherwise that there will be no danger of collision with any person or object in the immediate area.

Aircraft that do not have adequate brakes should not be taxied near buildings or parked aircraft unless an attendant is in a position near the aircraft to assist the pilot.

At airports where a control tower is in operation, it is the pilot's duty to obtain a clearance from the tower before taxiing onto the landing area, across active runways or into takeoff position.

No person should taxi an aircraft closer than 100 ft to an active runway for warm-up purposes unless authorized by an airport traffic-control tower or permitted by the airport management and depicted on local taxi pattern charts.

Landing and Takeoff Pilots of aircraft should not land or take off at a landing area, where an airport traffic-control tower is in operation, contrary to directions received by radio or visual signal from the tower. Arriving aircraft not radio-equipped should make at least one complete circle of the airport, conforming to the traffic pattern. The pilot should maintain a watch for other aircraft and be on the alert for a signal from the tower. Normally, this signal can be expected to be received from the tower when the aircraft is turning from the downwind leg into the base leg preparatory to landing.

Aircraft approaching for a landing should, unless impracticable, maintain a straight approach course for the last 1000 ft before crossing the airport boundary.

Pilots should land and take off on the runway specified by the tower. Pilots of aircraft not radio-equipped should observe the flow of traffic to determine the runway in use, or in the absence of such traffic, use the runway most nearly aligned with the wind.

Runways are numbered to correspond to their magnetic heading. Runway 27, for example, has a magnetic heading of 270°. Wind directions issued by control towers are also magnetic.

No turn should be made after takeoff until the airport boundary has been reached and the pilot has attained an altitude of at least 500 ft, and has ascertained that there will be no danger in turning into the path of a following aircraft, unless exceptions are authorized by an airport traffic-control tower.

With the present mixture of small light planes and huge high-speed transports, *every* pilot must always be keenly alert for the effects of prop- and jet-blast and trailing vortices, which are destructively turbulent.

TRAFFIC AND TAXI PATTERNS

Traffic and taxi patterns are prepared by the airport operator in collaboration with the FAA and aircraft operators. The tower controller bases his clearances on these patterns to obtain the desired flow of traffic in the vicinity of the airport.

Itinerant pilots are not expected to be familiar with all the details of the traffic patterns at each individual airport, and every effort is made to eliminate clearances to aircraft which would require unusual procedures. If a pilot does not know the traffic pattern, he should follow other aircraft unless otherwise instructed.

The following FAA terminology for the various portions of an approach to a landing has been adopted as standard for use by control towers and pilots:

Upwind leg—A flight path parallel to the landing runway in the direction of landing.

Crosswind leg—A flight path at right angles to the landing runway off its takeoff end.

Downwind leg—A flight path parallel to the landing runway in the direction opposite to landing.

Base leg—A flight path at right angles to the landing runway off its approach end and extending from the downwind leg to the intersection of the extended runway center line.

Final approach—A flight path in the direction of landing along the extended runway center line from the base leg to the runway.

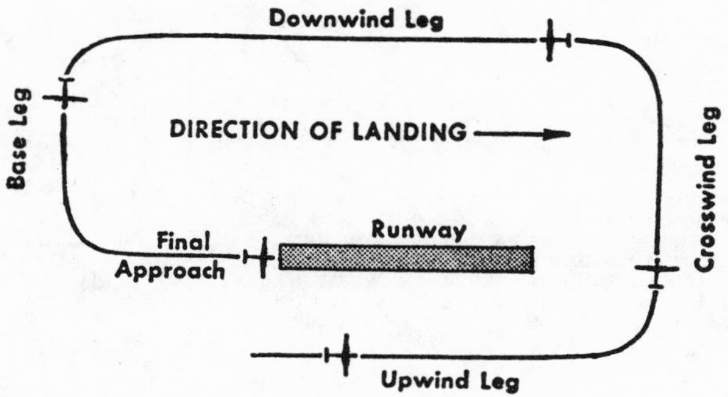

Figure 12.4 Standard traffic pattern terminology. *(From FAA Airman's Information Manual.)*

LIGHT-SIGNAL PROCEDURES FOR AIRPORT TRAFFIC CONTROL

Airport tower controllers use specific procedures to control aircraft not equipped with radio, or with radio inoperative. (See Figure 8.4.)

Light signals are given by a traffic signal-light "biscuit gun" which emits an intense narrow beam of either red, white, or green. Although the traffic signal-light provides some control over nonradio-equipped aircraft, it is obvious that: (1) The pilot may not be looking at the control tower at the time a signal is directed toward him, and (2) the directions transmitted by a light signal are very limited since only approval or disapproval of a pilot's anticipated actions may be transmitted.

The meaning of "Biscuit Gun" signals are given below.

Aircraft Inbound Between sunset and sunrise, a pilot wishing to land should turn on a landing light as he approaches the airport unless he has already been given a green light.

A series of flashes of a landing light by a pilot intending to land means:

1. If the floodlight is on, the pilot wants it turned off.
2. If the floodlight is off, the pilot wants it turned on.

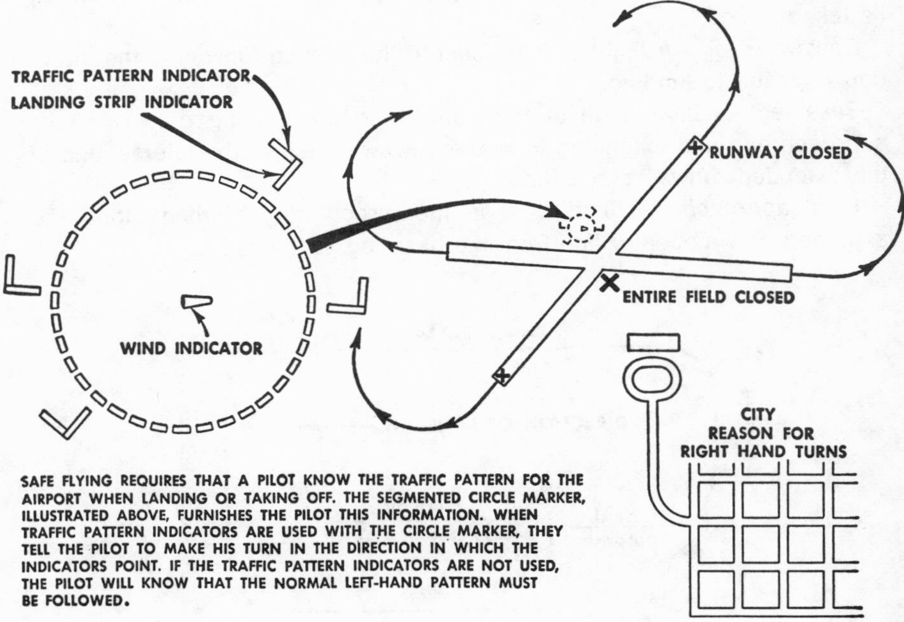

TRAFFIC PATTERN INDICATOR
LANDING STRIP INDICATOR
RUNWAY CLOSED
WIND INDICATOR
ENTIRE FIELD CLOSED
CITY
REASON FOR
RIGHT HAND TURNS
SAFE FLYING REQUIRES THAT A PILOT KNOW THE TRAFFIC PATTERN FOR THE AIRPORT WHEN LANDING OR TAKING OFF. THE SEGMENTED CIRCLE MARKER, ILLUSTRATED ABOVE, FURNISHES THE PILOT THIS INFORMATION. WHEN TRAFFIC PATTERN INDICATORS ARE USED WITH THE CIRCLE MARKER, THEY TELL THE PILOT TO MAKE HIS TURN IN THE DIRECTION IN WHICH THE INDICATORS POINT. IF THE TRAFFIC PATTERN INDICATORS ARE NOT USED, THE PILOT WILL KNOW THAT THE NORMAL LEFT-HAND PATTERN MUST BE FOLLOWED.

Figure 12.5 Traffic pattern indicated by segmented circle.

Pilots should acknowledge light signals by rocking their wings during hours of daylight or by blinking their landing lights during hours of darkness. Pilots of aircraft not equipped with landing lights should blink their navigation lights instead.

Aircraft on the Airport Between sunset and sunrise, a pilot wishing to attract the attention of the air traffic-control tower operator should turn on a landing light and taxi the aircraft in position so that light is visible to the tower operator. The landing light should remain on until appropriate signals are received from the tower.

Pilots should acknowledge light signals by moving the ailerons or rudder during the hours of daylight or by blinking the landing or navigation lights during the hours of darkness.

General Warning Signal A series of alternating red and green flashes from a directed traffic-control light are used as a general warning signal to advise a pilot to be on the alert for hazardous or unusual conditions.

Low Ceiling and Visibility Signal During the hours of daylight, the lighting of the rotating beacon means that ground visibility is less than 3 mi and/or that the ceiling is less than 1000 ft. During the hours of darkness, flashing lights outlining the traffic direction indicator (tetrahedron, wind tee, or other device) means that ground visibility is less than 3 mi and/or the ceiling is below 1000 ft. The lighting of either of these signals indicates that a clearance from Air Traffic Control is necessary for landing, takeoff, or flight in the traffic pattern if the airport is within a control zone.

13

Helicopters*

The development of helicopters into powerful, fast, and sophisticated aircraft has resulted primarily from the development efforts of U.S. military services. Although the need for aircraft which could take off and land vertically was recognized early in World War II, their role in that war was limited to liaison. In the Korean war, however, helicopters became relatively efficient, and many wounded soldiers owed their lives to the helicopter and its pilot.

In Vietnam the helicopter really assumed a top position among combat and support aircraft. Better gas-turbine engines and materials, and advanced rotor dynamics allowed the development of helicopters that gave true air mobility to the American fighting man under the most adverse conditions of combat, and permitted rescue of downed airmen under enemy fire and over adverse terrain.

"Cobra" attack helicopters could make gun runs at speeds over 160 knots. "Chinook" cargo helicopters had no difficulty in carrying nearly 20,000 lb. New research helicopters such as the Bell

*Revised by Major Robert S. Fairweather, Jr., U.S. Army.

Compound UH-1 Research Aircraft and Lockheed XH-51A are proving that speeds over 260 knots can be easily attained. Heavy-lift helicopters with fantastic cargo and precise positioning capabilities, like Boeing-Vertol's proposed tandem-rotor heavy-lift helicopter may soon be available.

Though commercial use lags behind military use, scheduled helicopter airlines flew nearly 25 million revenue passenger miles in 1968. The helicopter's importance is further indicated by an active civil fleet of more than 2500, more than 18,000 pilots, and by 1968, 1892 heliports and heli-stops in the United States, Canada, and Puerto Rico. The "chopper" serves also as an agricultural sprayer, construction crane, forest fire fighter, executive transport, and traffic control vehicle and ambulance. It has been very effective in oil exploration, survey, and ranching.

Rotary-Wing Aerodynamics

The aerodynamics of rotary-wing aircraft and airplanes are basically the same. Both use airfoils to produce lift; both are subjected to identical fundamental forces of lift, drag, thrust, and gravity. Because flight characteristics of the helicopter differ widely from those of the airplane, helicopter theory of flight requires separate discussion.

LIFT

The helicopter's airfoils are rotor blades which are turned at high speed. We have seen that for a given speed, an increased angle of attack increases lift until the stalling angle is reached; and for a given angle of attack, the greater the speed the greater the lift. The helicopter obtains high-speed airflow over the airfoils by high rotor rpm, rather than by high fuselage speed. In fact, it is normal for the tip speed of the rotor blades to be as much as 435 knots when the speed of the fuselage is zero. This explains why the helicopter does not require forward speed to produce lift, and why it can hover or fly backward, sideward, or forward.

AIRFLOW

During normal operation conditions, the direction of airflow is from the top down through the main rotor system. As the blades are rotated with a positive angle of attack, they, in effect, screw upward into the air; thus, a downwash of air (Figure 13.1) is established through the rotor system. Notice that the leading edge of each blade bites into air throughout the complete cycle of rotation, forcing the air downward.

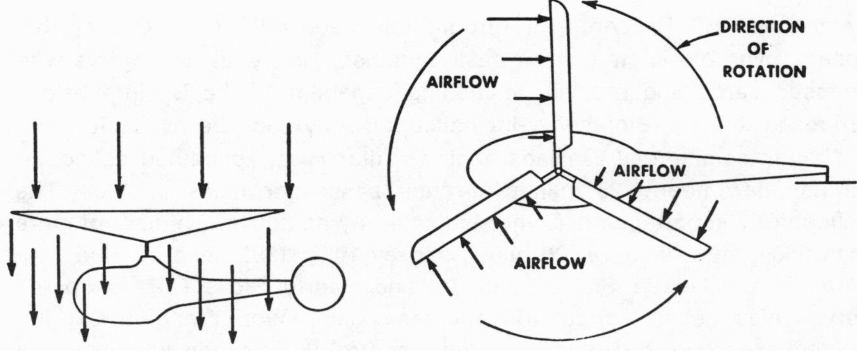

Figure 13.1 Downwash through the rotor system.

Figure 13.2 Airflow in the rotor system.

At the root of the blade, airflow is slightly more than zero; but the velocity progressively increases throughout the length of the blades and at the tip may be 435 knots or higher. It is the blade velocity that determines the resultant strength and direction of the relative wind at a positive angle of attack. The helicopter changes the angle of attack by varying the pitch of the main rotor blades. In a helicopter, the relative wind is developed throughout the complete cycle of 360° by rotation of the rotor system, and it usually varies considerably. This variation is dependent upon flight conditions.

ANGLE OF INCIDENCE

The angle of incidence is the angle formed by the chord of the airfoil and the longitudinal axis of the aircraft. The conventional airplane's angle of

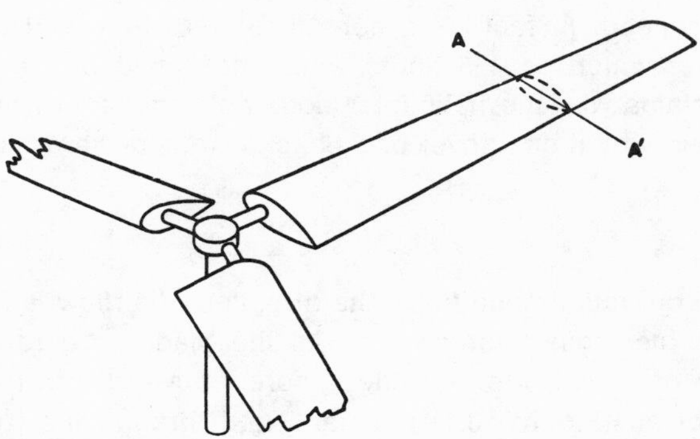

Figure 13.3 High-speed blade section.

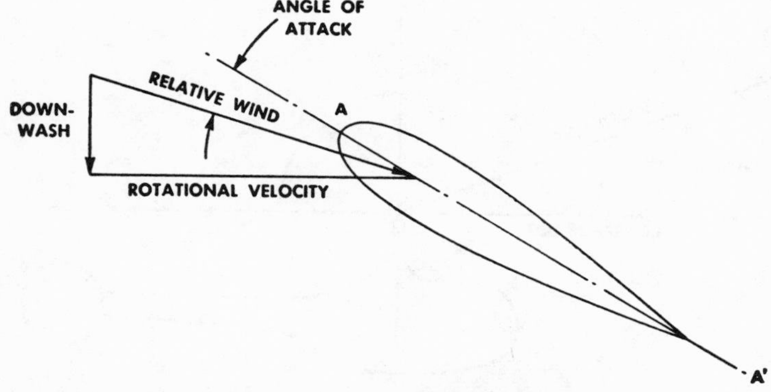

Figure 13.4 Relative wind components.

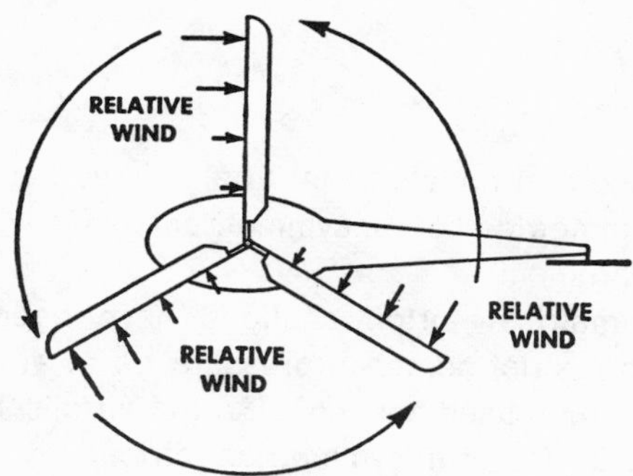

Figure 13.5 Direction of relative wind.

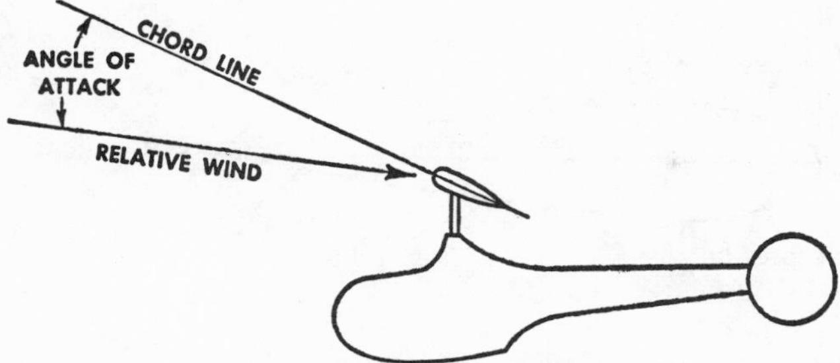

Figure 13.6 Rotor blade angle of attack.

incidence is built into the aircraft by the designer, and in most aircraft cannot be changed. The helicopter pilot, however, continually changes the angle of incidence during flight by increasing or decreasing the pitch of the main rotor blades.

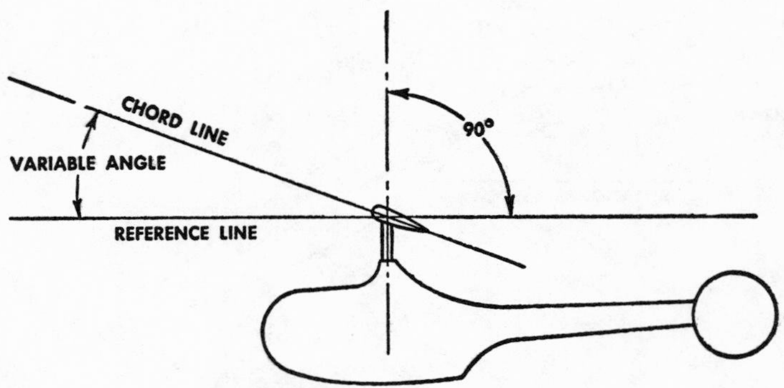

Figure 13.7 Rotor blade angle of incidence.

AIRFOIL SECTION

The type of wing used on conventional ariplanes varies considerably; the airfoils may be symmetrical or unsymmetrical, usually depending upon some specific requirement.

Historically, symmetrical airfoil sections have been used for rotor blades, primarily to restrict center-of-pressure travel and to permit easier blade construction. Increased testing of rotor airfoils by NASA and industry has resulted in use of unsymmetrical airfoils.

Newer aircraft, such as the Kaman UH-2K, the Bell Model 206A, and the Boeing-Vertol CH-46D and CH-47 use "droop-snoot" blades with cam-

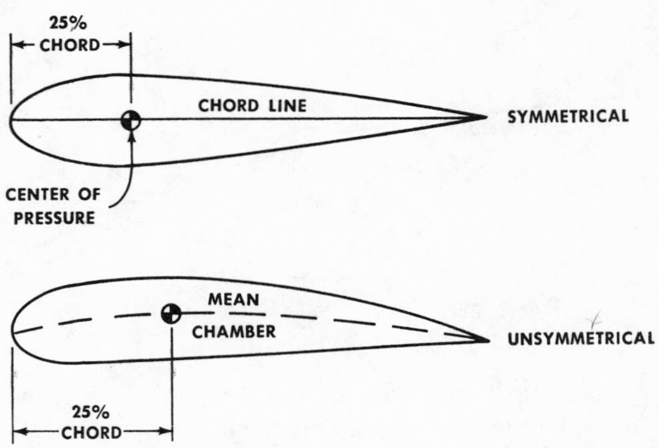

Figure 13.8 Airfoils.

bered leading edges and reflex curved trailing edges. These airfoils overcome center-of-pressure problems. They also give an increased stall angle of attack with generally improved stall characteristics, and improved hover and cruise efficiency. They postpone high-speed advancing blade drag, and result in negligible pitching moments. Both airfoils have a good lift-drag ratio throughout a wide range of velocities and spread lift forces over a wide area to equalize stresses. Usually a slight twist is built into the blade to help equalize these forces.

THRUST AND DRAG

As weight and lift are closely associated, so are thrust and drag. Thrust moves the helicopter in a designated direction and drag tends to hold it back.

The helicopter develops both lift and thrust in the main rotor system. In vertical ascent, thrust acts upward in a vertical direction; drag, the opposing force, acts vertically downward. Lift sustains the weight of the helicopter, and excess thrust is available to give translation or vertical acceleration. During vertical ascent, drag is considerably increased by the downwash of the main rotor system striking the fuselage. Thrust must be sufficient to overcome both drag and downwash. The force representing the total reaction of the airfoils with the air is divided into two components: one is lift, the other thrust. However, drag is a separate force from weight, as indicated in Figure 13.9.

At all times the lift forces of the rotor system are perpendicular to the tip-path plane. The tip-path plane is the imaginary plane described by the tips of the blades in making a cycle of rotation. The lift on the individual

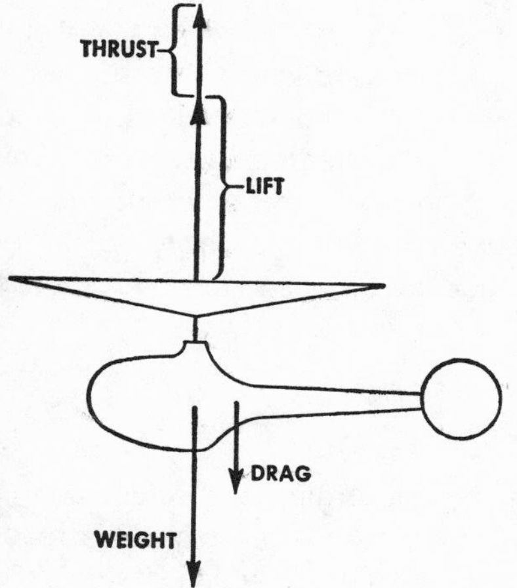

Figure 13.9 Forces in vertical ascent.

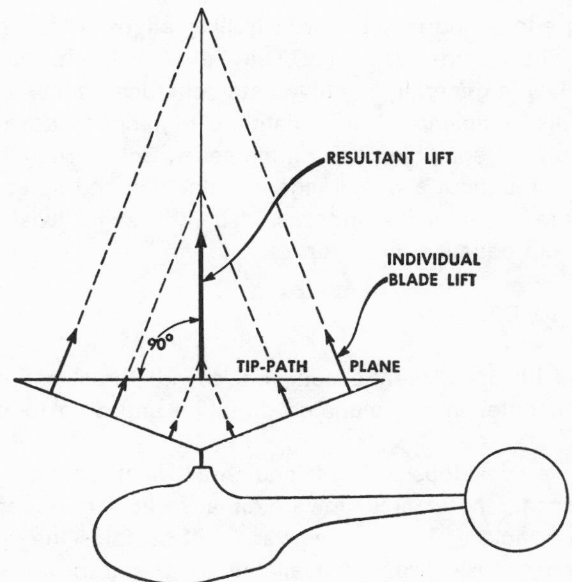

Figure 13.10 Direction of resultant lift.

blade is perpendicular to the airfoil, but the resultant lift developed by the several blades is perpendicular to the tip-path plane (Figure 13.10). Lift increases in magnitude from root to tip of blade because of increase in velocity.

In vertical flight the tip-path plane is horizontal; and in forward, backward, or sideward flight, the plane of rotation is tilted off the horizontal, thus inducing thrust in the direction of inclination. For example, to establish forward flight, resultant lift is inclined forward (Figure 13.11). Total force, being tilted off the vertical, acts both upward and forward; therefore it can be resolved into two components. One component is lift, and the other is thrust. Likewise, flight may be established sideward, or in any horizontal direction, by tilting the tip-path plane in the direction of desired flight. The rate of movement or speed depends upon the degree of tilt of the resultant lift force. Note the magnitude of thrust at the two speeds shown in Figure 13.12.

TORQUE

Torque effect is displayed in a helicopter by the turning of the fuselage in the opposite direction to the rotation of the main rotor system. This reaction is in accord with Newton's third law of motion, which states, "To every action there is an equal and opposite reaction." The engine is the

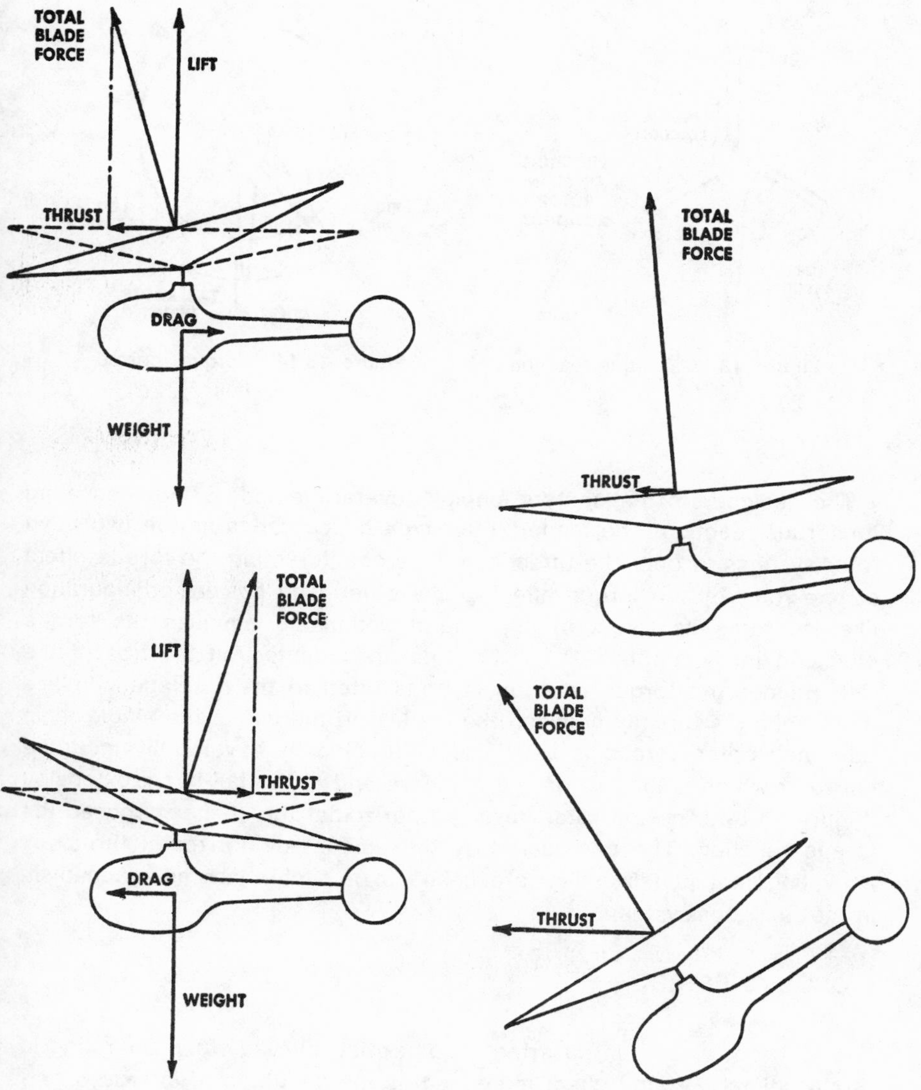

Figure 13.11 Forces in forward and rearward flight.

Figure 13.12 Effects of slow and high speed.

initiating force that drives the rotor system in a counterclockwise direction, and the reaction to this driving force would cause the fuselage of the helicopter to rotate with an equal force in a clockwise direction (Figure 13.13). Torque is of real concern to both the designer and the pilot. Adequate means must be provided not only to counteract torque, but also to exert positive control over its effect during flight.

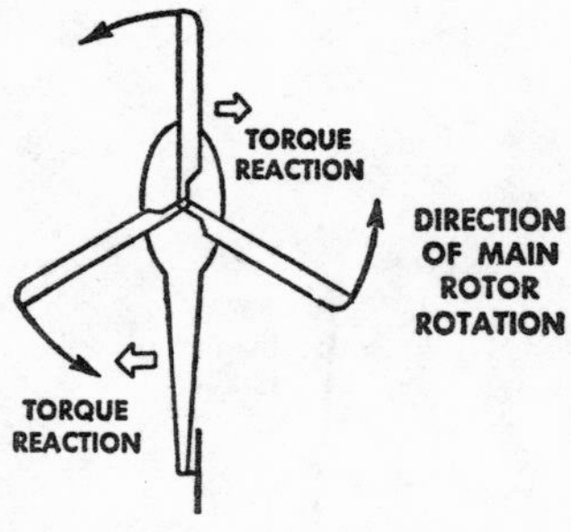

Figure 13.13 Torque reaction.

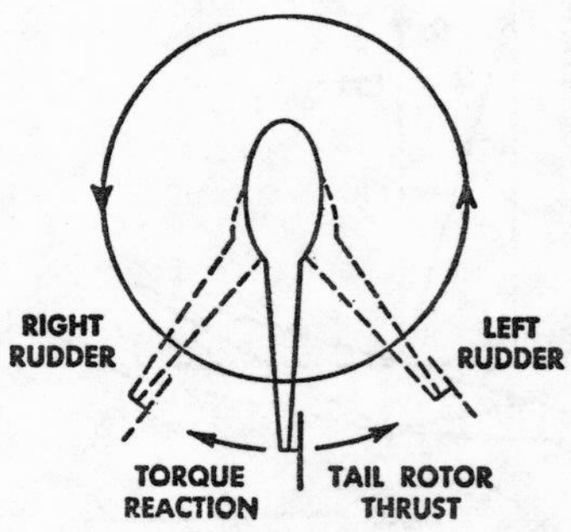

Figure 13.14 Torque correction.

The designers of helicopters employ several methods of compensating for torque reaction. The tandem-rotor type helicopter turns the two main rotor systems in opposite directions, thus counteracting the torque effect of one rotor by the torque effect of the other. The coaxial configuration likewise turns its rotors in opposite directions to equalize the torque effect. In jet helicopters, if the engines are mounted on the tips of the rotor blades, no torque reaction is transmitted to the fuselage because the reaction is directly between the blade and the air. In the single main rotor helicopter, torque is usually counteracted by a vertically mounted tail rotor which is located on the outboard end of the tail-boom extension (Figure 13.14). The tail rotor develops horizontal thrust that opposes the torque reaction. The pilot can vary the amount of horizontal thrust by activating foot pedals which are linked to a pitch-changing mechanism in the tail rotor system.

GROUND EFFECT

The high power cost in hovering is somewhat relieved when operating in ground effect. Ground effect is defined as the condition of improved performance encountered when hovering near the ground at a height no more than approximately one-half the rotor diameter. It is more pronounced the nearer the ground is approached. Improved lift and airfoil efficiency while operating in ground effect are due to two separate and distinct phenomena: (1) First and most important, the rotor tip vortex is reduced due to the downward and outward airflow pattern. (2) Downwash angle is reduced. This reduces induced drag, and permits lower angles of attack and decreased power requirements for the same lift (Figure 13.15).

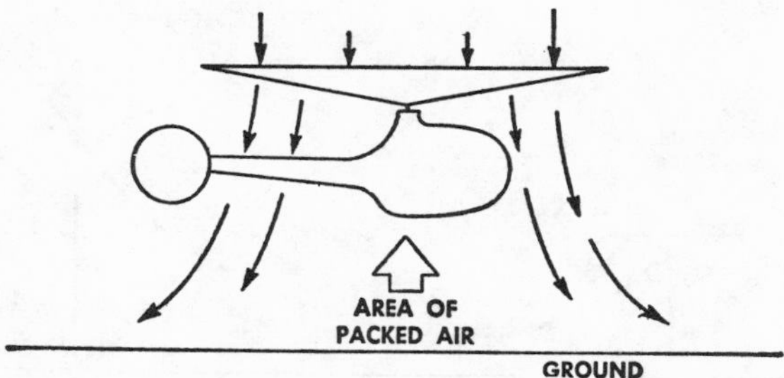

Figure 13.15 Ground cushion.

TRANSLATION LIFT

Translation lift is the additional lift developed by a helicopter in horizontal flight. This additional lift becomes noticeably effective at an airspeed of 10 to 20 knots, and it continues to increase in magnitude as speed is increased. As horizontal flight is progressively induced, a higher inflow of air is established through the rotor disc, and greater lift is produced because of increased rotor efficiency. However, when a speed of 45 to 50 knots is reached, translational lift is canceled out by fuselage drag. Figure 13.16 illustrates a typical power curve indicating percentage of power required compared to translation velocity.

When hovering 3 to 8 ft above the ground in a windless condition, the helicopter is aided by ground effect. But when the helicopter enters forward flight it leaves ground effect, in effect sliding off a cushion and

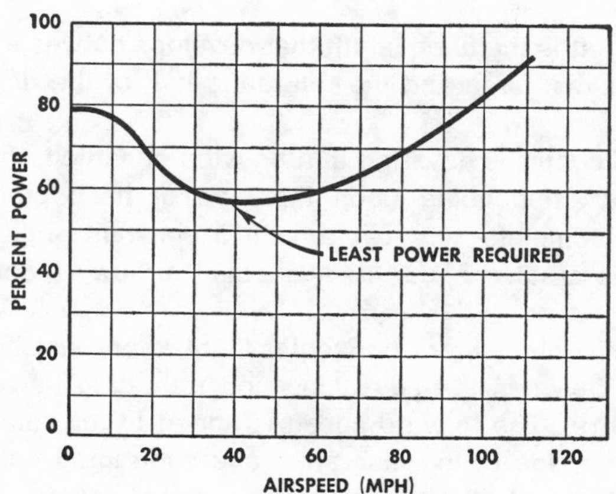

Figure 13.16 A typical power curve.

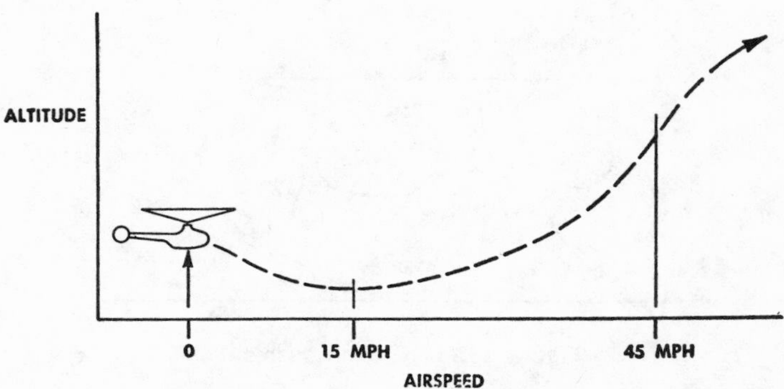

Figure 13.17 Translational lift.

entering into a critical transition period where reduced lift initially causes the helicopter to settle.

When a forward speed of about 15 knots is reached, translational lift becomes effective and the helicopter will gradually climb. As forward speed is increased, lift is increased and less power will be required to maintain straight and level flight (Figure 13.16).

Under actual flight conditions, during the transition from 0 to 15 knots, the pilot obtains additional lift to avoid settling during the critical transition period by increasing the pitch of the main rotor blades. When hovering in wind conditions of 10 knots or more, ground effect may not be present. The helicopter is in translational lift for all practical purposes and forward flight is established without the settling effect.

DISSYMMETRY OF LIFT

Dissymmetry of lift is the unequal lift that develops between the advancing half of the rotor disc area and the retreating half of the disc area during horizontal flight.

When the helicopter is hovering in a no-wind condition, the tip speed of about 435 knots, depending upon the type of helicopter, is constant throughout the complete 360° cycle, with a constant angle of attack on the blades. This creates equal lift and equal airflow velocity throughout the disc area.

When the helicopter enters horizontal flight, there will be a difference in tip airspeed between the advancing and retreating halves of the disc area (Figure 13.19). The forward speed is added to the rotational velocity on the advancing side of the disc area, and subtracted on the retreating side. Forward flight of 50 knots, therefore, would mean a differential of 100 knots between the advancing and retreating sides. This condition, if

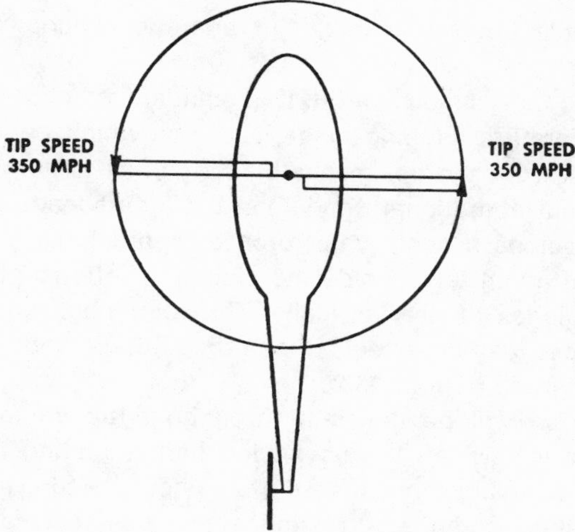

Figure 13.18 Hovering (zero airspeed).

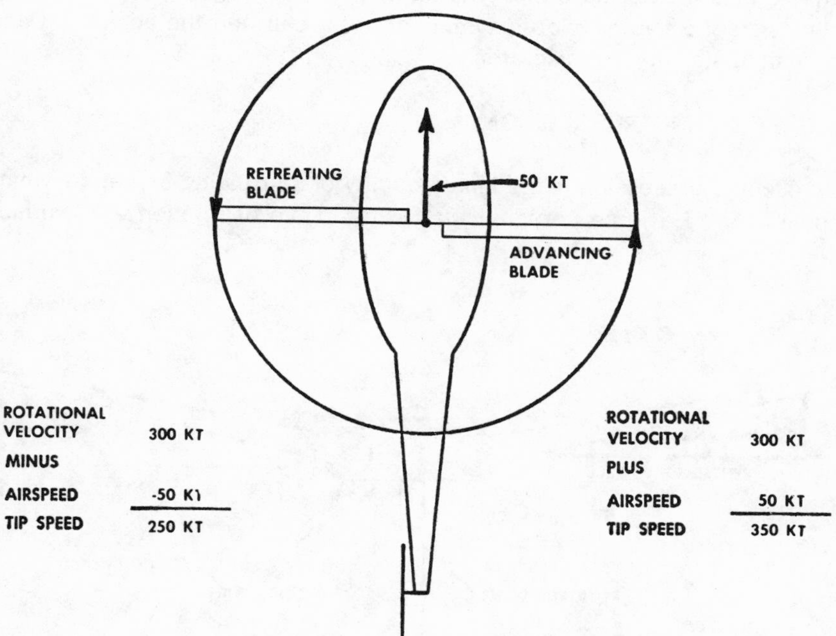

Figure 13.19 Differential tip speed in forward flight, 50 knots.

uncorrected, would develop unequal lift and the helicopter would turn over.

To counter this dissymmetry of lift, it is standard practice in rotor-head design to incorporate a flapping hinge, a device which permits the rotor blade to flap upward, or to design the blades to flex in the vertical direction. Under normal operational conditions the high-speed rotation of the rotor system develops a centrifugal force of approximately 20,000 lb on each blade. Centrifugal force holds the blades in a horizontal plane, and lift causes the blades to rise vertically. The rotor blades will take a resultant position between the effects of centrifugal force and lift and appear in a coned-up attitude (Figure 13.20).

Centrifugal force will be constant throughout the complete cycle of 360°. Lift will vary between the advancing and retreating portion of the disc area in forward flight because the advancing blade, having greater lift, will flap higher, and the retreating blade, having less lift, will flap lower. As each blade advances and flaps up in the direction of airflow, the effective span is lessened, thereby reducing the angle of attack and decreasing the effective lift area. As each blade retreats, less airspeed produces less lift, and the retreating blade assumes a more horizontal attitude which gives it more nearly its full span, greater area, and greater angle of attack, thus increasing the overall lift of the retreating blade. In this way, blades free to flap develop a symmetry of lift between the advancing and retreating sides of the disc area.

GYROSCOPIC PRECESSION

Gyroscopic precession is the innate quality of all rotating bodies by which application of a force perpendicular to the plane of rotation will produce

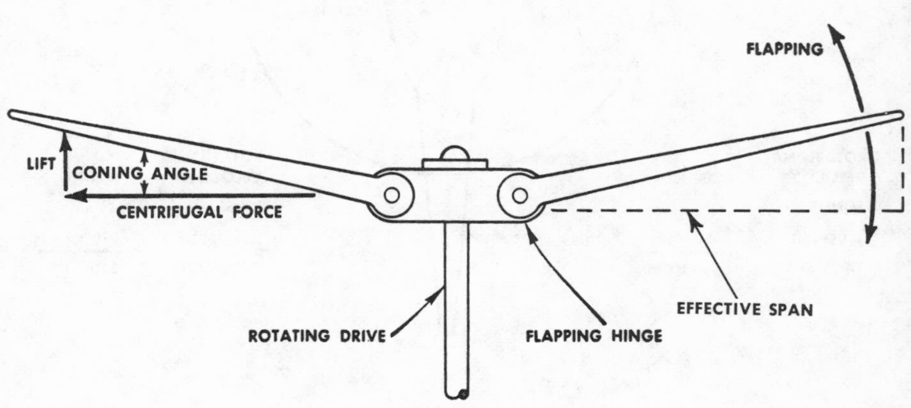

Figure 13.20 Flapping hinge device.

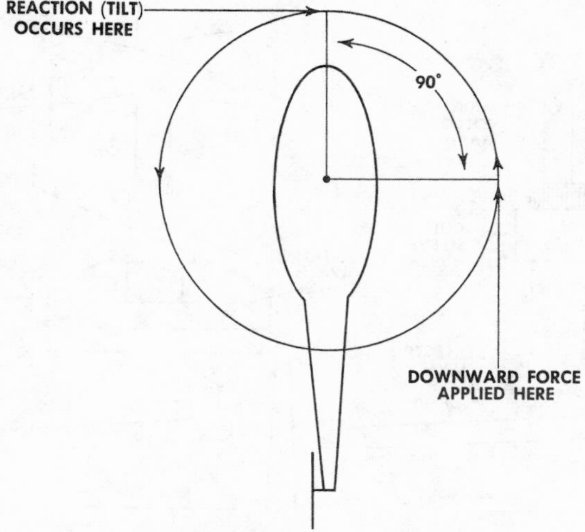

Figure 13.21 Gyroscopic precession.

a maximum displacement of the plane approximately 90° later in the cycle of rotation (Figure 13.21).

Thus if a downward force were applied to the right side of a rotating disc, gyroscopic precession would cause the plane of the disc to tilt to the front, providing the disc is turning from right to left. Maximum resulting displacement occurs about 90° further in the direction of turning, but speed of rotation, weight and diameter of the disc, and friction are factors which determine the actual displacement in a specific system. A main rotor follows these laws. If it is desired to tilt the plane of the rotor forward for forward flight, linkage must be provided to apply the force on the right side of the disc.

In helicopter design, this is usually handled by applying the force on the rim of a swash plate on which another rotating swash plate rides, applying the desired force to each sector of the rotor disc and thus the blade, as it passes.

AUTOROTATION

Autorotation is the process of producing lift with rotor blades that are kept rotating only by the developed aerodynamic forces resulting from the flow of air up through the rotor system. Under power-off conditions the helicopter will descend; the flow of air will be established upward through the blades. The rotor is automatically disengaged from the engine by a free-wheeling device, and the necessary power required to overcome parasite drag and induced drag of the rotor blades is obtained from the kinetic energy developed by the helicopter's weight in descent.

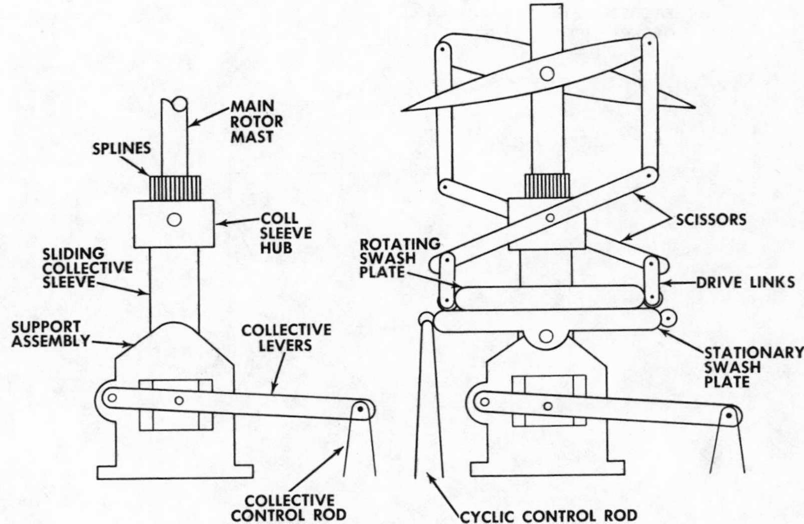

Figure 13.22 Cyclic and collective control head. Cyclic inputs tilt the swash plate, and as described in the text, the tip-path plane. Collective inputs act through the hub, with necessary flexibility provided by the drive links, to change the pitch of both blades equally, simultaneously, and in the same direction. This changes overall rotor lift.

During autorotation the pitch angle of the rotor blades must be reduced to minimum. The change in direction of airflow through the rotor causes a change in the direction of the relative wind which greatly increases the angle of attack at which the rotor blades are operating. If the pitch were

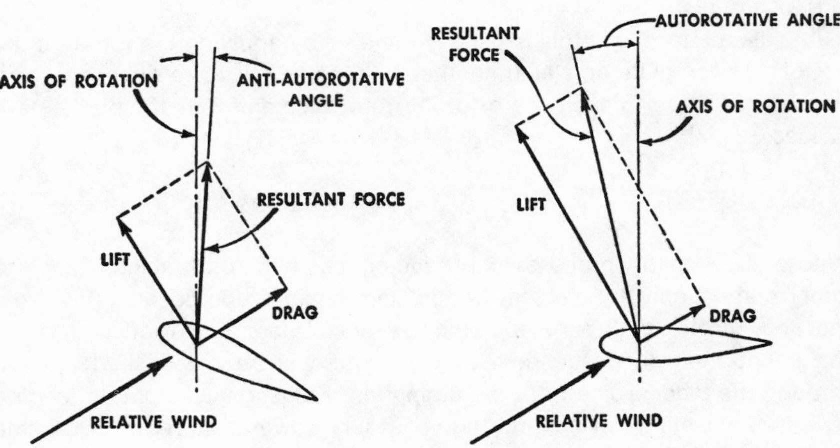

Figure 13.23 Low-pitch angle.

Figure 13.24 High-pitch angle.

not reduced, the blade would stall for much the same reason that an airplane's wing stalls when the nose of the airplane is pulled up too high. When the pitch angle of the blade is low and the angle of attack is large, the resultant lift force lies ahead of the axis of rotation of the blades, tending to keep the blades turning in their normal direction (Figures 13.23 and 13.24).

If, on the other hand, the pitch angle remains high, drag is increased and the resultant lift force lies behind the axis of rotation, tending to slow and stop the rotor. Autorotation is an emergency procedure that permits the pilot to land the helicopter safely in case of engine failure. It is necessary to maintain sufficient rotor rpm to provide both adequate airflow over the rotor blades and the required centrifugal force to hold the blades in an extended attitude; otherwise the blades would fold up and the helicopter would tumble out of control.

PENDULAR ACTION

The fuselage of the helicopter is suspended from the drive shaft that mounts the main rotor head. Because the fuselage is bulky and suspended from a single point of attachment, it is free to oscillate laterally and longitudinally much like a freely swinging pendulum. As the rotor system introduces horizontal translation, the fuselage is dragged in the direction of flight. During established forward flight, the fuselage will assume a nose-low attitude. In effect, as the tip-path plane is inclined forward, resultant lift is inclined from the vertical, introducing thrust. The main drive shaft of the helicopter will have a tendency to align itself with the inclined resultant lift force (Figure 13.25).

The pendular action of the fuselage swaying is exaggerated by overcontrolling; therefore, control stick movements should be moderate.

RESONANCE

Resonance is the energetic vibration of a body produced by application of a periodic force of nearly the same frequency as that of the free vibration of the affected body; also, it is the condition of two bodies adjusted to have the same frequency of vibration.

The helicopter is subject to two types of resonance: sympathetic resonance and ground resonance. *Sympathetic resonance* is a harmonic beat which develops when the natural vibration frequency of one mechanism is in phase with another vibration. In the case of the helicopter, the rotor system has its own or some other mechanism. Sympathetic resonance, however, has been successfully engineered out of most helicopters by controlling design features of gear boxes and other mechanisms.

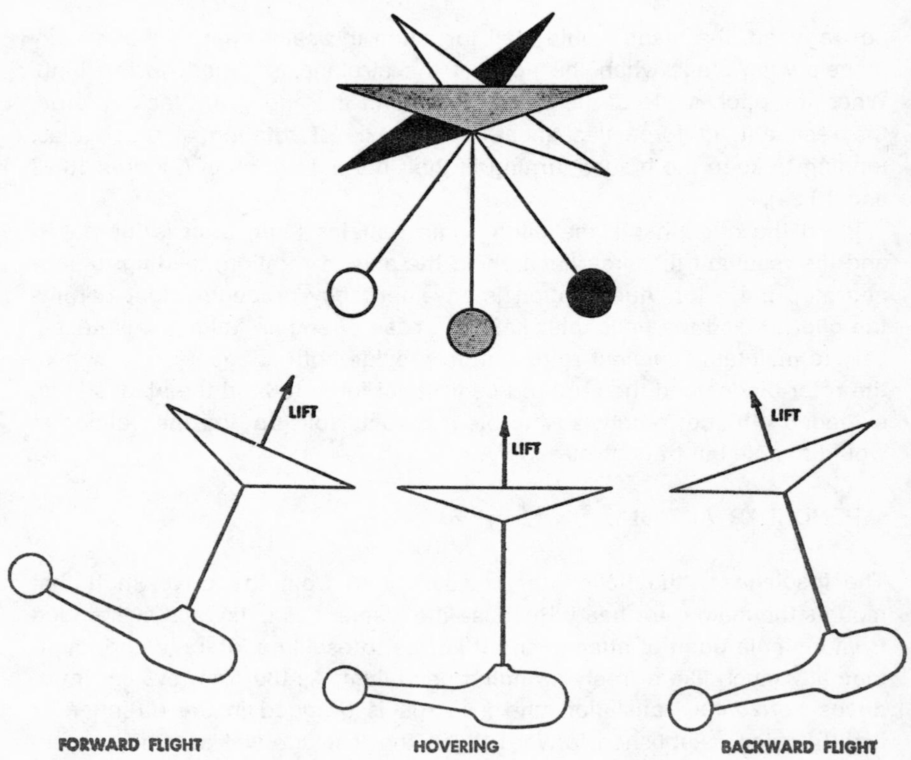

Figure 13.25 Pendular action.

Ground resonance, on the other hand, has persisted to plague helicopter designers, particularly during experimental stages. It is a self-excited vibration which develops when the landing gear repeatedly strikes the ground thus unseating the center of mass of the main rotor system. The pounding effect of the landing gear is prone to occur during takeoff and landing when the helicopter is 87% to 93% airborne. The aircraft, being light on the landing gear, bounces from one wheel to the other in rapid succession, setting up a pendular oscillation of the fuselage.

The succession of shocks is transmitted to the main rotor system, and the main rotor blades straddling the pounding wheel are forced to change their angular relationship. This condition unbalances the main rotor system, which in turn transmits the shock back to the landing gear (Figure 13.26). If this cycle of events continues, complete destruction is likely to occur. The fully articulated rotor system which employs a drag hinge for each rotor blade is more susceptible to ground resonance than the semirigid type of rotor. Present-day design employs various dampening devices

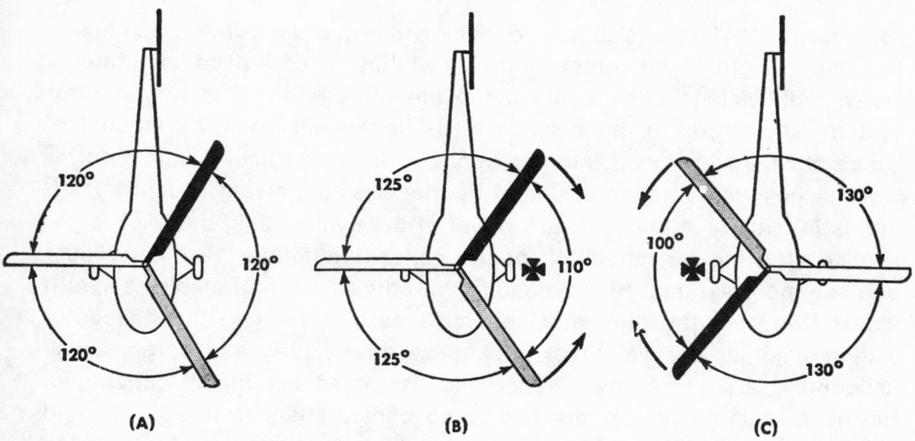

Figure 13.26 Ground resonance. (A) Normal; (B) and (C) successive shocks.

to control the unbalancing of the rotor system, and helicopter pilots are trained to avoid critical maneuvers conducive to agitating ground resonance. Tandem rotor and skid landing gear helicopters do not usually have ground resonance problems.

WEIGHT AND BALANCE

The loading of all single-rotor helicopters is critical because of their lack of inherent stability. All lift is applied to the fuselage at a single point, the

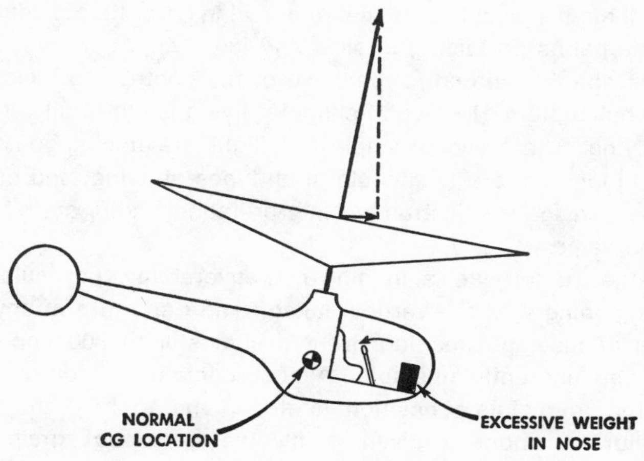

Figure 13.27 Excessive forward loading.

rotor mast; the fuselage is free to swing from this point like a pendulum. Loading forward of the center of gravity will introduce a nose-low attitude. When the fuselage tilts, it tilts the plane of rotation of the main rotor system. The degree of permissible tilt is dependent upon the amount of cyclic stick travel rigged into the controls of the particular helicopter.

If the nose-low attitude assumed by the fuselage, owing to faulty loading, is in excess of the rearward travel of the cyclic stick, the pilot is not able to stop the forward flight of the helicopter (Figure 13.27). It would be even more serious if faulty loading introduced uncontrollable rearward flight. Therefore the pilot must exercise care in loading the helicopter with respect to the weight of pilot, passengers, fuel, and cargo. Small helicopters are apt to be very critical as far as loading is concerned. However, in large helicopters the cargo compartment is usually located directly beneath the center of gravity, which facilitates loading. In the tandem rotor helicopters, loading normally is not as serious a problem because of the wide center-of-gravity range.

Helicopter Flying

The airplane pilot usually receives some surprises in learning to fly the helicopter. The controls are different in many ways from those of the airplane; and FAA check-out requires 25 hr of flight training. The airplane pilot is accustomed to changing from one type of airplane to another with a minimum of effort; but in a helicopter he must learn new and different control techniques peculiar to the rotary-wing aircraft. He must discard his valuable habits pertaining to slow and low flying.

He will probably overcontrol because of the control lag which is dominant in all helicopters. However, helicopter flying is not totally unrelated to airplane flying. The basic principles of flight are unchanged. Air experience and judgment are applicable in all types of flying, and understanding weather, navigation, instrument interpretation, radio, and related subjects is the same.

The marked difference is in high maneuverability, particularly at low speeds, beginning with the vertical takeoff and departure in any direction regardless of fuselage heading, from a standstill to 300 knots. But the helicopter is inherently unstable. Almost continuous control pressures are required to maintain position in flight, and to hold the aircraft in deft equilibrium about a given point, the center of gravity. Utmost dexterity is required, particularly while hovering. Many pilot trainees have compared hovering to balancing the aircraft on the point of a pencil.

Coordinated control is required at all times about the roll, pitch, and yaw axes, if the fuselage attitude is to be held constant.

Power System

While reciprocating aircraft engines were adapted to early helicopters, most helicopters now use turbine engines.

These turbines are designed generally on the "free-turbine" principle. That is, the engine consists of two separate rotors, usually mounted coaxially. One is the *gas generator,* and the other is the *power turbine.* The latter is connected by a transmission and shafts to the main and tail rotors. (Figure 13.28). The power turbine, whose speed is reflected in pilot's power instruments, operates at constant speed. Power changes are automatically or manually made by changing the fuel-air ratio for the gas generator and thus its output.

In this way changes in load on the power turbine are met by an increase or decrease in the velocity of high-speed gases from the gas generator through the blades of the power turbine. Because only the gas generator rotor mass must accelerate with throttle changes, the system is highly responsive to needed changes in power.

Flight Controls

The flight controls used in the single-rotor helicopter are the *cyclic stick,* the *collective-pitch stick* with its engine throttle handgrip, and the *foot pedals.*

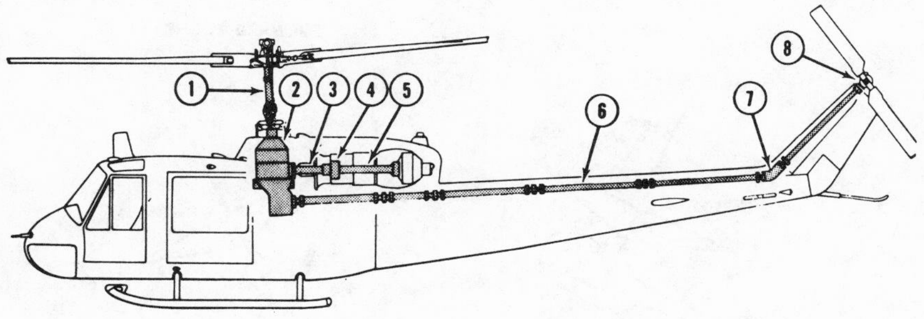

Figure 13.28 Power train system, Air Force TH-1F. 1. Main rotor mast. 2. Transmission. 3. Input drive shaft. 4. Shaft bearing block assembly. 5. Engine drive shaft. 6. Tail rotor drive shafts. 7. 42-degree gear box. 8. 90-degree gear box. (*Courtesy of U.S. Air Force.*)

THE CYCLIC STICK

The cyclic stick controls the horizontal direction of flight and the speed of the helicopter. It is connected by linkage to a control or "swash plate" (Figure 13.22), which in turn is connected to the main rotor blades. When the swash plate is level, pitch on the main rotor blades will be equal throughout the cycle of rotation; but if the swash plate is tilted, the pitch on the main rotor blades will vary throughout the cycle, proportional to the tilt of the swash plate.

Forward stick will cause the swash plate to tilt forward; the main rotor blade pitch will increase on the retreating blade and decrease the same number of degrees on the advancing blade. The equal but opposite change of pitch at points 180° apart will cause the tip-path plane to tilt forward.

Resultant lift is always perpendicular to the tip-path plane. When the tip-path plane is tilted forward, resultant lift is inclined forward, and thrust is developed in the direction of tip-path plane tilt. The rotor system will move rapidly in the direction of thrust and will drag the fuselage in that direction. The fuselage will pitch about the lateral axis, assuming a nose-

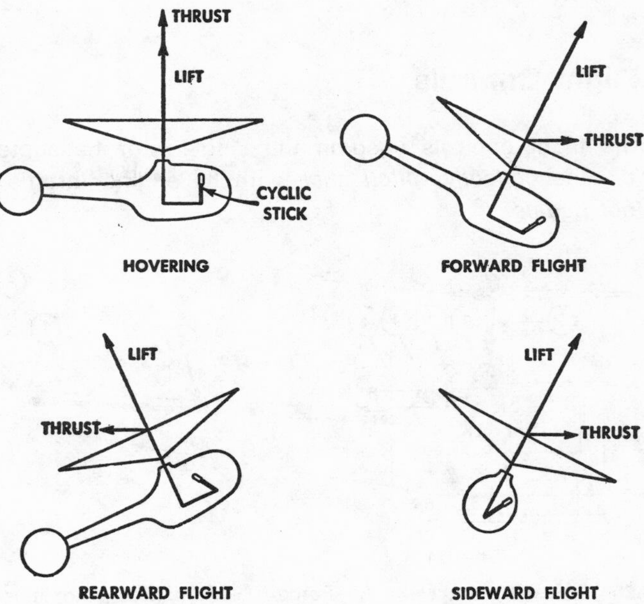

Figure 13.29 Directions of horizontal flight governed by cyclic stick.

low attitude. The swash plate is free to tilt in the direction of movement of the cyclic stick—forward, backward, and sideward, through all 360°. As the cyclic stick is moved in any direction, the swash plate will tilt in that direction, thus establishing tip-path plane inclination in the direction of cyclic stick movement. The directional speed of the helicopter is controlled by the degree of tilt of the swash plate. Figure 13.28 indicates the direction of flight in relation to cyclic stick movements.

THE COLLECTIVE-PITCH STICK

This control regulates the pitch setting of the main rotor blades by a collective sleeve which passes through the swash plate on the rotor head. As seen in Figure 13.22, collective imputs are made through the scissors linkage to change blade pitch equally, simultaneously, and in the same direction.

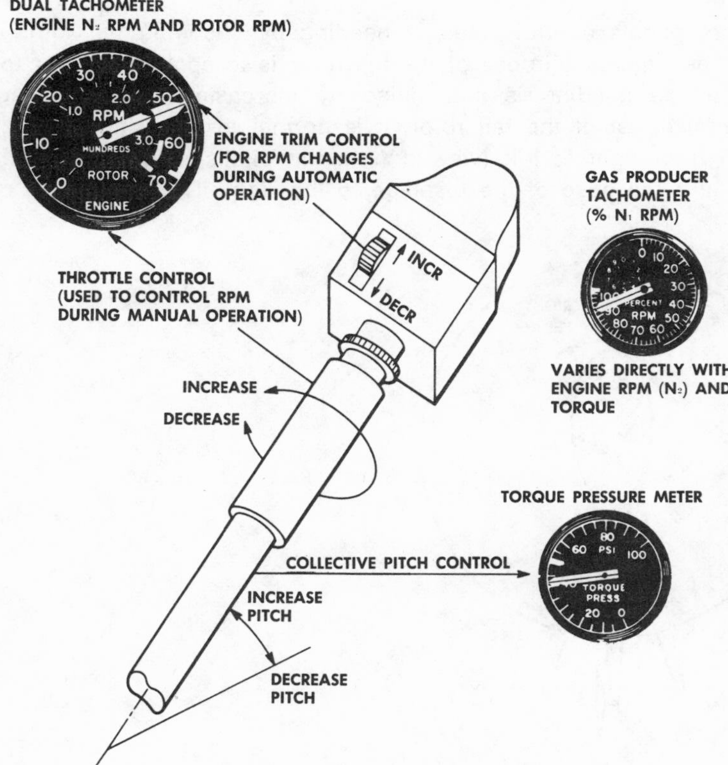

Figure 13.30 Rotor blade pitch and engine power coordination, collective stick.

The collective-pitch stick is a lever with up and down travel located to the pilot's left and manipulated by his left hand. In conjunction with the collective-pitch stick movement, there is a synchronizing mechanism which automatically changes engine power output proportionate to the change in pitch. As collective pitch is increased, the engine is required to develop more power in order to maintain constant main rotor rpm. Almost all helicopters have a throttle to override the synchronization mechanism during emergencies. The throttle, or an additional electrical trim control, is also used to make fine power adjustments.

In order to climb, main rotor blade pitch is increased; to descend, pitch is reduced. The rate of climb or descent is dependent upon the degree of movement of the collective-pitch stick. Acceleration and level-flight airspeed are also controlled by the collective-pitch setting.

THE FOOT PEDALS

The foot pedals control fuselage heading by changing tail rotor blade pitch. The primary purpose of the tail rotor is to compensate for torque, but fuselage heading is maintained by increasing or decreasing the horizontal thrust of the tail rotor. It is normal for the single main rotor to turn from right to left (viewed from the pilot's position), and torque would turn the nose of the fuselage to the right. The application of left

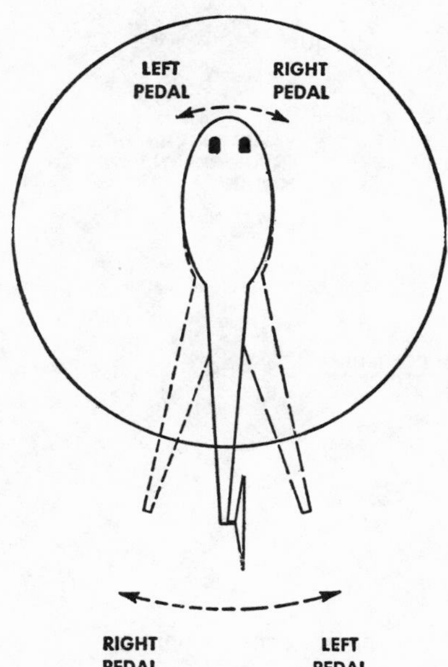

Figure 13.31 Fuselage heading control.

pedal increases the pitch on the tail rotor which increases its sideward thrust to the right, thus establishing fuselage heading (Figure 13.31).

Flight Maneuvers

Helicopter flight maneuvers such as hovering, normal takeoff, forward flight, climb, descent, and landings are basic. Advanced maneuvers include quick stops, backward and sideward flight, 360° hovering turns, maximum-performance takeoffs, running takeoffs, running landings, and steep approaches. The split-second coordination of controls required in the performance of the advanced maneuvers is gained by experience; therefore no attempt will be made to discuss the advanced techniques. Understanding the basic maneuvers makes plain the basic principles of helicopter flight.

HOVERING

Hovering implies zero airspeed with a constant attitude and heading. It is sustained motionless flight requiring a high degree of coordination and concentration. The right hand controls the cyclic stick, the left hand manipulates the collective-pitch stick and motorcycle-type throttle, and the feet use the foot pedals to compensate for torque. At the same time the pilot must observe engine rpm, be cognizant of height above ground, and also anticipate horizontal movement of the aircraft.

Hovering is normally performed between 3 and 10 ft above the ground. Since there is considerable lag in the controls of all helicopters, there is a strong tendency for the trainee to overcontrol. The airplane pilot usually requires 5 to 8 hr of flight training to achieve reasonable proficiency in the coordination of all controls essential for hovering.

The tip-path plane, controlled by the cyclic stick, must be horizontal in no-wind conditions; if wind is present, the tip-path plane must be inclined slightly into the wind to prevent drift. The pitch of the main rotor blade, controlled by the collective-pitch stick, must be accurately adjusted or the helicopter will not remain at a constant height above the ground. Engine rpm, controlled by the throttle, must be held constant. The turning effect of the fuselage introduced by torque reaction to engine power must be compensated for by proper pedal pressure. The coordination of cyclic stick, pitch and throttle, and foot pedals requires more than an average amount of concentration. Hovering is a basic maneuver because forward flight is started from the hover, and the approach to landing ends in the hover.

NORMAL TAKEOFF

The normal takeoff (Figure 13.31) employs a combination of two basic maneuvers: hovering, and climb with forward speed. Takeoffs should normally be made into the wind. To hold the desired heading, it helps to select a reference point in front of the helicopter; if the nose deviates from that line of vision, appropriate pedal pressure will correct the change in heading.

Once the hovering attitude is established, apply forward pressure to the cyclic stick. As the helicopter moves forward, it has a tendency to settle. This loss of altitude occurs because the vertical-lift vector is inclined forward, thus dividing total lift into two components: lift and thrust. To prevent settling, increase collective pitch, adding throttle to hold rpm, and apply additional left pedal to maintain heading. The coordination of cyclic stick, collective-pitch stick, throttle, and foot pedals is essential to establish safe forward flight from the hover.

When the helicopter reaches a forward speed of approximately 15 knots, translational lift becomes noticeably effective. This is an additional lift that is developed because the velocity of airflow through the rotor system is more effective. Translational lift continues to increase with forward speed, but it is nullified at approximately 50 knots by parasite drag.

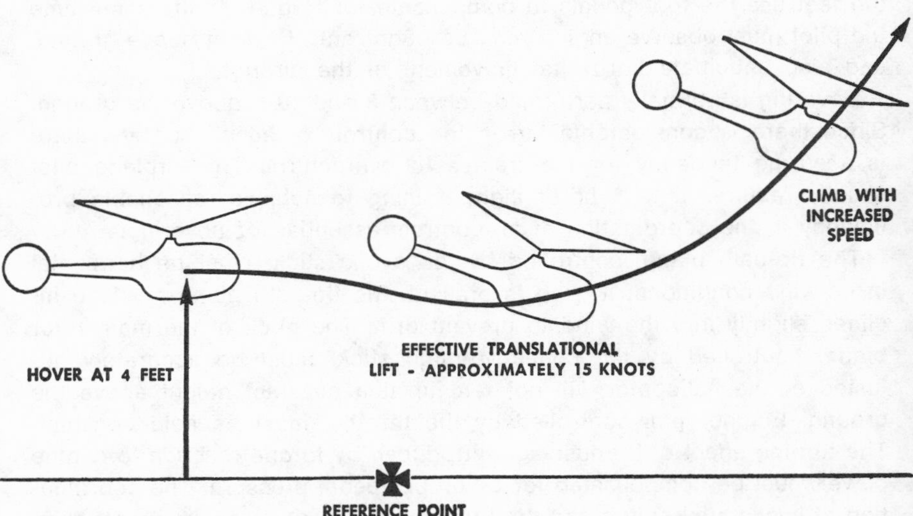

Figure 13.32 Normal takeoff.

CLIMBS AND DESCENTS

To climb, raise the collective-pitch stick. This increases the pitch simultaneously on all the main rotor blades. As blade pitch increases, add throttle to provide the additional power needed to maintain constant rotor rpm. The synchronizing unit is activated by collective-pitch stick movement. If more power is required to hold rotor speed, coordinate necessary additional throttle with pitch. While climbing it is necessary to increase left pedal pressure in order to compensate for torque; otherwise the fuselage would turn to the right.

To descend, use the reverse of the climb procedure. Control airspeed throughout all maneuvers by the cyclic stick. Pitch and throttle coordination, particularly during climbs and descents, is the most difficult technique to master. Also, any change in power requires a coordinated change in collective-pitch, throttle, and foot pedals.

STRAIGHT AND LEVEL FLIGHT

During straight and level flight, speed is determined by composite use of cyclic and collective stick. Altitude is controlled by the collective-pitch stick and throttle. The foot pedals correct yaw trim and compensate for power adjustments. Streamlining of the helicopter in forward flight decreases the pedal input needed to correct for torque. If a constant airspeed is established, increasing pitch with a coordinated adjustment of throttle will result in a climb; decreasing pitch will cause the helicopter to descend.

The cyclic control is sensitive, but response to cyclic stick movement will lag, thus delaying control corrections for attitude and speed. If the nose of the helicopter should rise, airspeed would fall off; a slight forward pressure on the cyclic stick will bring the nose down. However, if this correction is held too long, or if it is a large one, the nose of the helicopter will continue to drop beyond the desired attitude. Neutralize cyclic stick corrections before reaching the desired attitude or overcontrolling will result. The helicopter pilot must learn to anticipate the continued response to cyclic stick corrections even after neutralizing the control. If attitude is displaced by gust or turbulence, the helicopter may not return to straight and level flight as will an airplane. Therefore, maintain corrective control pressures at all times to maintain attitude.

NORMAL LANDING

The normal landing is performed by establishing an approach to the hovering attitude, followed by the vertical letdown to ground contact.

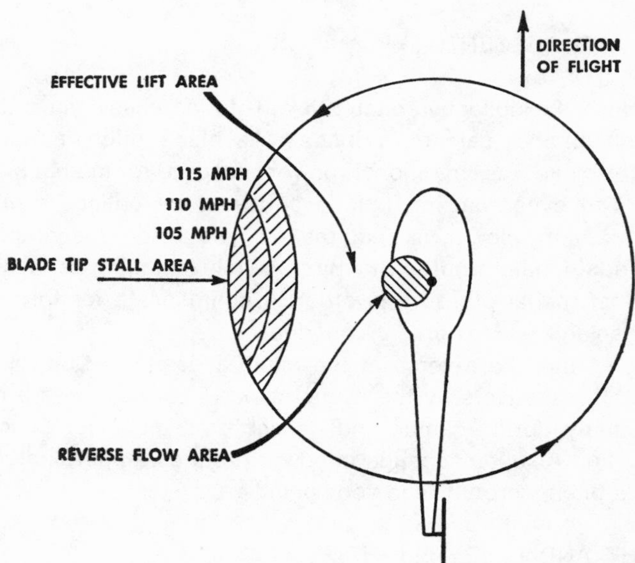

Figure 13.33 High-speed blade stall.

During the approach, maintain a constant ground speed and establish a constant glide angle. The cyclic control regulates speed, and the collective-pitch control regulates rate of descent. On entering the approach, apply slight backward pressure to the cyclic stick to slow the speed, and decrease collective pitch to set up rate of descent and glide angle. Just before establishing the hover, relax the back pressure on the cyclic control so that the helicopter will assume a level attitude. Increase collective pitch to prevent loss of altitude, use left pedal to maintain heading, and use more throttle to hold rpm. From the hover, make the vertical letdown by reducing collective pitch on the main rotor blades.

RECOURSE TO AUTOROTATION

Autorotation is an emergency procedure, used to make a landing in the event of loss of power, or any other emergency when use of the engine might endanger the landing. During autorotation no torque is developed, for the only reaction is that directly between the main rotor blades and air. Should a tail rotor fail, for example, continued engine torque would cause the fuselage to turn in the opposite direction to the rotation of the main rotor blades; by cutting power and using autorotation the helicopter pilot can prevent the turning of the fuselage and land in autorotation.

To establish autorotation, reduce the pitch angle of the rotor blades to minimum, for the reasons discussed on page 792. Place the collective-pitch stick in the minimum pitch position. Set up a flight path into the wind and establish a descending glide at best power-off glide speed (approximately 60 knots). Use right pedal as needed to neutralize tail-rotor horizontal thrust, since no torque is developed by the freely turning rotor system. Control attitude during the descent by manipulating the cyclic pitch control. Rotor rpm will be about the same as when the rotors are driven by the engine, or slightly higher. As the helicopter approaches the ground, slow the forward speed by the cyclic stick, and add sufficient collective pitch to slow the rate of descent. The simplest autorotative touchdown is the running-landing type, wherein the craft is permitted to contact the ground in a level attitude with a forward speed of about 15 knots. If the landing terrain is rough, use a flare-type autorotation, with minimum ground run.

RETREATING BLADE STALL

Upon entry into blade stall, the first effect is generally a noticeable vibration of the helicopter, followed by a pitch-up of the nose and a rolling tendency. The condition normally happens when operating at high speeds in conjunction with high blade loading, high-density altitude, low rotor rpm, steep turns, or turbulent air, and can best be corrected by reducing speed and bank, collective pitch, and increasing rotor rpm.

SETTLING WITH POWER

Three conditions are necessary to produce settling with power. They are (1) airspeed below translational lift airspeed, (2) a high rate of descent, and (3) power must be applied. To recover from this flight condition, increase directional airspeed, reduce power, and obtain translational lift.

EXTERNAL LOADS

One great advantage of rotary-wing aircraft is the capability to haul external loads. Two basic types of external-load suspension systems are used: single-point suspension, where the cargo hook is located near the center of gravity, free to swing fore and aft and laterally about a fixed point, and multipoint suspension through the use of load levelers which lift the load clear of the ground, dampen oscillations, and level the load.

Nylon or cable slings with clevises are used to attach the load to the cargo hook or attaching points. In some single-point systems, the hook is free to swivel, has spring centering devices to limit cargo swing, or is hoist-mounted.

Figure 13.34 Sikorsky CH-54 "Flying Crane" is designed for transport of large, bulky loads such as this pontoon bridge. A gross weight of 42,000 lb. permits useful load of 20,170 lb. Its speed is 90 knots, endurance 1.5 hr plus 30 min reserve and its Pratt & Whitney JFTD 12A-5A engines are rated at 4800 shp. Detachable cabin carries 33 fully equipped infantrymen. (*U.S. Army photograph.*)

The same pendular actions that applied between the fuselage and the main rotor are present between the load and the fuselage. In addition, the slings tend to act like springs and can cause vertical oscillations that will make the helicopter bounce. Therefore, move the controls smoothly and avoid excessive speeds and speed changes. External cargo generally requires less loading time than internal cargo, is independent of fuselage dimensions, and allows the pilot to jettison the load in emergencies. Present-day cargo helicopters are capable of hauling loads in excess of 20,000 lb.

OPERATIONAL LIMITATIONS

The performance limitations of a helicopter are determined primarily by the ratio of gross weight to available power. Many times the helicopter must operate at lower part loadings in order to perform a particular mission. For the helicopter to be a useful aircraft it must have both load-carrying ability and range. Like any other aircraft, payload must sometimes be sacrificed for range, and vice versa to reach a safe compromise.

Operational limitations are ultimately governed by atmospheric conditions, because helicopter performance is very sensitive to changes in air density. A decrease in atmospheric density brought about by an increase in altitude, decrease in barometric pressure, increase in temperature, or increase in humidity can prohibit hovering, as well as vertical takeoffs and landings.

Under such conditions the helicopter will have a certain minimum flying speed similar to the stalling speed of an airplane. A surface wind, sufficient to produce this minimum flying speed, will permit operation at zero ground speed. While increasing the minimum flying speed of the helicopter, this same decrease in atmospheric density will reduce the maximum safe flying speed thus narrowing the range of safe operating speeds. A knowledge of these effects is essential to a rescue helicopter pilot who must frequently hover at altitude.

At the opposite extreme in atmospheric conditions, the performance of the helicopter is greatly increased by increased air density. This is not altogether a good effect, however, because it may give a false impression of the helicopter's load-carrying potential. For example, a helicopter flying in very dense air might be able to hover, take off, and land vertically and have very good flight characteristics, while actually dangerously overloaded from a structural standpoint. The helicopter pilot must consider both operational and structural limitations, and the effects of the load and existing atmospheric conditions on each, in planning a particular mission.

Exemplary New Aircraft

While many current manufacturers are making a wide variety of significant contributions to improvements in rotary-wing aircraft, certain developments best illustrate new trends.

The Boeing-Vertol CH-47C (Figure 1.38) is a twin-turbine engine, tandem-rotor Army helicopter designed for transportation of cargo, troops, and weapons during day, night, visual, and instrument conditions. It has two Lycoming T55-L-11 shaft-turbine engines each rated at 3700 shp (maximum power). Its maximum load is 22,450 lb (20 nm radius mission), it has seating for 33 passengers, and has a range of 370 nm with 15,000 lb (4000 ft density altitude). It is fully equipped for flight in adverse weather with

ILS, VOR, ADF, and anti-icing equipment. A stability augmentation system automatically maintains stability about the pitch, roll, and yaw axes.

Its maximum gross weight is 46,000 lb; it is rated at 175 knots maximum airspeed. The CH-47C also has water flotation and taxi capabilities.

THE LOCKHEED RIGID-ROTOR HELICOPTER

Figure 13.20 illustrates the principle of the flapping-hinge rotor which was a brilliant breakthrough in Cierva's autogyro design. Though then essential, this hinge caused instability, limited forward speed, lagging control response, and severely limited allowable center of gravity movement.

The rigid-rotor concept uses the principle of gyroscopic precession 90° in the direction of rotation (Figure 13.20). A rigid rotor, with blades

Figure 13.35 Bell Helicopter Company's folding proprotor concept. The aircraft would utilize its rotors in helicopter fashion for vertical takeoff and landing; the rotors would then tilt forward to propel the aircraft at speeds up to 300 mph. For flight above this speed, they would be folded and locked in place to enter jet aircraft cruise speeds. (*Courtesy of Bell Helicopter.*)

cantilevered from the rotor hub with freedom to rotate only about each blade's feathering axis, is itself a gyro. Mounted on the same mast with the rotor is a gimbal-mounted control gyro consisting of spoke-like fly-weights, one for each rotor blade.

When, during rotation, the pilot through his control stick applies a force to the control rotor through the "swash plate" (Figure 13.22) the force is felt 90° in the direction of rotation. This force displaces the rotors from parallel planes, individually changing blade pitch through shafts from the control rotor blades to respective pitch horns on the main rotor blades. The resultant differential lift on the main rotor disk causes it to precess 90°, tilting in the direction of pitch or roll indicated by the original control force.

This compensating and corrective effect may be induced by force of the pilot's control stick, by gusts, or by the differing lift of the advancing

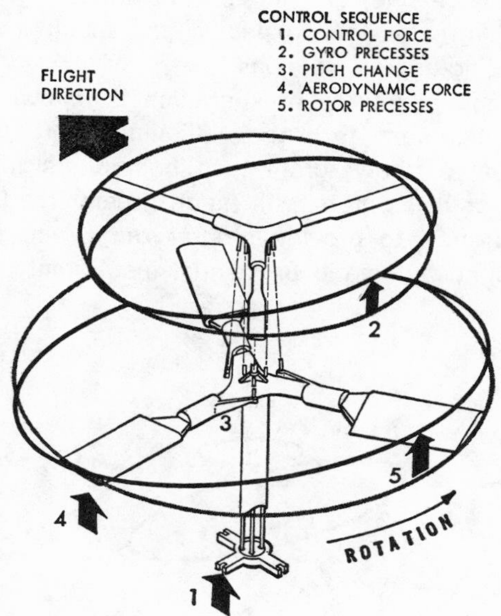

Figure 13.36 Lockheed rigid-rotor concept and cyclic blade response. All parts above the "swash plate" at 1 rotate. A control force applied at 1 acts at 2, 90° in the direction of rotation. (*Courtesy of Lockheed-California Co.*)

and retreating rotor blades. The result of this system is a substantial improvement in helicopter design possibilities, enhancing positive control response, stability, maximum speed, allowable c.g. variation, and low vibration levels.

CURRENT DEVELOPMENTS

Power-plant development is responsible for the major change taking place in rotary-wing aircraft. This development is almost solely in gas-turbine engines. The turbine engine apparently meets every requirement as the ideal power plant for the helicopter. Although fuel consumption of the gas turbine is greater than that of a comparable reciprocating engine, it is offset by consideration of engine weight, engine vibration, general maintenance, and performance at altitude.

In most cases, model conversion from reciprocating to turbine engines requires little design change, and flight tests have in general indicated greater speed, with greater load capacity, and much lower noise level than the reciprocating-engine versions.

Helicopter development at the present time is following these paths: turbine-powered helicopters for more efficient operation; multiengine helicopters for greater safety; crane-type helicopters for the lifting of massive loads; larger helicopters with much greater load-carrying capability; compound aircraft to provide greater range and speed; and the capability of sustained automatic or manual instrument flight in adverse weather.

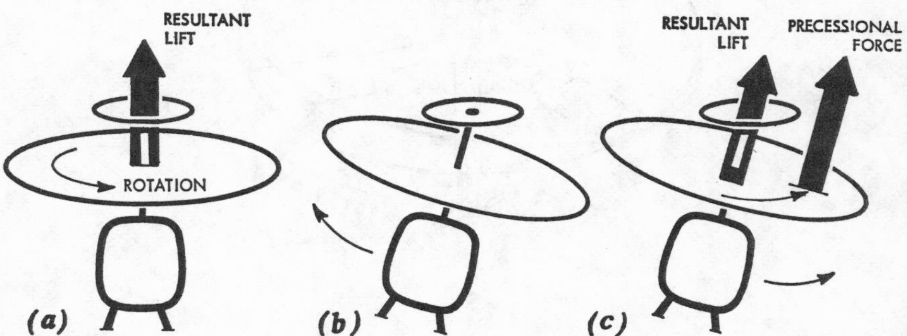

Figure 13.37 Gust reaction of rigid-rotor helicopter. (*a*) A strong gust may displace the fuselage and main rotor, but the control gyro remains in its plane of rotation. (*b*) The resultant angular variation of planes of the control gyro and main rotor changes blade pitch cyclically. (*c*) Resultant lift of the main rotor moves to a position forward of the rotor disk center, causing the rotor disk to precess or roll in a direction to restore the rotor disk and fuselage position. (*Courtesy of Lockheed-California Co.*)

FUTURE DEVELOPMENTS

Vertical takeoff and landing aircraft, using rotors for vertical takeoff and then transition to forward flight using the rotors as propellers in a fixed-wing configuration, have been successfully flown. An example of the tilt-wing principle is the Ling-Temco-Vought XC-142. Another method of accomplishing the transition is Bell Helicopter Company's folding proprotor concept (Figure 13.35).

Bell's proprotor aircraft takes advantage of the helicopter's takeoff and landing capability for operations from confined areas, then transitions by tilting the rotors forward to travel at speeds up to 270 kt. Higher speeds may be achieved by stopping the rotors and folding them back to minimize drag. Forward propulsion in this mode of operation would be supplied by the thrust of fan-jet engines.

Also under investigation for application to the tilt-rotor configuration is a method of varying the rotor's diameter. The largest diameter of the rotor system would be used to achieve maximum lift for takeoff and climb. Rotor diameter would be reduced after the rotor plane is tilted forward for use in high-speed flight.

14

Soaring*

The unavailability of lightweight engines led the early experimenters in heavier-than-air flying to concentrate their efforts on gliders. Among them were Sir George Cayley in the early 1800s in England, Lilienthal in Germany, and Montgomery and Chanute in the United States in the late 1800s. The Wright brothers first flew gliders at Kitty Hawk as a basis for their later powered flight. The success of the Wrights' first powered flights in 1903 caused interest in gliders to drop almost to the vanishing point until after World War I. The Wrights made some additional glider tests in 1911 at Kitty Hawk, where their best flight had a duration of 9¾ min. This record stood unchallenged for ten years.

The Treaty of Versailles, ending World War I, prohibited Germany from building or importing powered aircraft. In other countries all efforts were concentrated on the development of powered aircraft, while the Germans threw all their very considerable technical talent into powerless flight. Their pilots and machines were in the fore of every gliding and soaring development in the twenties and thirties.

*By Harner Selvidge, S. D., Sedona, Arizona.

WORLD WAR II

The Germans again led in the application of gliders for military purposes, but late in the war the Allies' gliders made notable contributions, particularly in the Normandy invasion. Unfortunately, the technology developed for the large man- and cargo-carrying gliders turned out to have little application for peacetime use. In fact, the major wartime contribution to peacetime gliding and soaring was the surplus of training gliders and sailplanes released for public sale. These aircraft, and a few of the thousands of glider pilots who trained in them, formed the backbone of the soaring movement in the United States in the late 1940s and the 1950s.

RECENT DEVELOPMENTS

After almost ten years of doldrums there was an almost explosive growth of soaring activities in the United States in the sixties. The Soaring Society of America experienced an increase in membership of 20 times from 1955 to 1970. American and foreign manufacturers now offer a wide variety of sailplanes for every need and purse. There are several hundred soaring clubs and dozens of commercial operators throughout the United States where instruction can be obtained, sailplanes rented and where tows are available.* Today, soaring in America is the equal of that anywhere in the world, and a large proportion of the world's soaring records are held by American pilots.

Modern Sailplanes

The modern sailplane of the 1970s is as much of an improvement on the gliders of the 1920s as the modern business jet is over the Jennies of the same era. Despite the smaller market for powerless aircraft, there have been groups of very talented and dedicated designers, both in the United States and abroad, who have made great progress in the last two decades in increasing the performance and utility of sailplanes.

SPECIAL FEATURES

There are numerous special features of modern sailplanes which, while not entirely unknown on powered aircraft, are generally found only in

*Details on this and other soaring information can be obtained from the Soaring Society of America, Box 66071, Los Angeles, California 90066.

Figure 14.1 Schweizer Model 1-26. Over 400 of these Schweizer Model 1-26 sailplanes have been made. It has all-metal wings, monocoque nose, and fabric-covered chrome-moly tubing fuselage. (*Courtesy of Schweizer Aircraft Corp.*)

sailplanes. The first is the provision for detachable wings and tail surfaces. The requirement for retrieving the sailplane in an auto-drawn trailer from remote landings makes it necessary to have wings and tail surfaces which can quickly and easily be removed by two or three persons and stowed for transit on the trailer. In the highest-performance ships the single-wheel landing gear is retractable (by hand) but in most cases, whether retractable or not, there is no shock-absorbing provision in the gear except for that furnished by the tire. The wheel is always

Figure 14.2 Schweizer Model 2-32. The Schweizer Model 2-32 is a high-performance all-metal two-seater with a 34 to 1 glide ratio. (*Courtesy of Schweizer Aircraft Corp.*)

provided with a hand-operated brake, but some ships also have a drogue chute deployed from the tail cone when landing.

Spoilers are almost universally used for glide path control, but some sailplanes also have flaps. The spoilers also can be used as speed-limiting dive brakes in many models so the nose can be pointed straight down without exceeding the red-line speed. Despite their sometimes cramped cockpits, most sailplanes have superb visibility through their large canopies.

One of the most outstanding features of modern sailplanes is their aerodynamic efficiency, which exceeds by far that of even the best performing military jet aircraft. They are also noted for their high structural strength, being designed for ultimate loads in the 8_g to 12_g range.

DESIGN TRENDS

In early sailplanes the main effort was to reduce weight to a minimum, since staying up was the main goal. Today, speed and distance are the principal objectives, and these call for the highest lift to drag ratio (L/D) at high speed ranges, combined with good circling performance at slow speeds. Weight is no longer so important. In fact, water ballast is sometimes added for contest and record flying. This added weight does not change either the lift or drag, so the ratio L/D is unchanged. This ratio is sometimes called the glide ratio or glide angle, since it gives the slope of the gliding flight path. For example, a sailplane with a maximum L/D of, say, 35, will be capable of gliding 35 miles from an altitude of one mile, in still air. The added ballast does not make the sailplane descend at a steeper angle, but merely makes it fly down the same slope at a faster speed. If lift conditions are strong, this more than counterbalances the slightly higher sink rate, which is a disadvantage when flying slowly. The water ballast can be dropped if lift conditions weaken.

Given a good airfoil and a smooth skin, the most important factor in obtaining a high L/D is the aspect ratio. Thus we see a trend toward very long narrow wings. Modern materials technology has permitted great strides to be made in this direction. The long wings reduce roll response greatly, and increase adverse yaw, but the advantages far outweigh the disadvantages. Drag reduction programs have also led to reductions in the cross-sectional area of the fuselages. The most important result of this is the necessity for the pilot to occupy a steeply reclining position in the cockpit. This reduces his visibility somewhat, and he can forget about elbow room, but the seats and controls can be arranged so that it is moderately comfortable.

Many of the best modern high-performance sailplanes have either a "T" or "V" tail. The reason is partly aerodynamic, but more important,

Figure 14.3 Libelle. The all-fiberglass LIBELLE, made by Glasflügel in Germany, is a high-performance sailplane widely used in the United States. (*Courtesy of Graham Thomson Ltd.*)

they are less likely to be damaged when landing in terrain covered with high vegetation.

As long as there have been sailplanes, pilots have dreamed of liberation from dependence on crews or outside mechanical help for launching into the air. The powered sailplane has been their goal, and many designs have been flown with power provided from every conceivable kind of small engine. Some featured fully retractable engines and propellers, while others merely featured the propeller when the launch was finished. None of these ever went into production bcause of high costs and lack of large market interest. However, there was a rebirth of interest in powered sailplanes in the late 1960s, particularly in Europe, and at least two manufacturers have such models in limited production.

MATERIALS

Like powered aircraft, the early gliders and sailplanes were constructed of wood, wires, and cloth. Even as late as the mid-1950s, some of the best sailplanes were made entirely of plywood. Some fuselages were made of conventional metal tube and fabric construction, but the trend was to all-metal structure and skin. Then in the 1960s plastic reinforced by fiberglass began to be widely used, particularly in European countries where labor costs were low. Fiberglass materials are strong, light, and can be formed easily into the necessary shapes with a very fine surface finish. Almost all of the high-performance sailplanes coming out of European factories are all fiberglass, while American-made ships are mostly all metal.

TABLE 14.1

Manufacturer	Model	Span (ft)	Aspect Ratio	Gross Wt. (lb)	Wing Load (lb/sq ft)	V_{stall} (mph)	V_{max} (mph)	$V_{L/D\,max}$ (mph)	L/D
Schweizer Aircraft Corp., U.S.A.	2-22E	43	9	900	4.8	35	90	47	17
Schweizer Aircraft Corp., U.S.A.	2-33	51	12	1040	4.7	35	98	47	22
Schweizer Aircraft Corp., U.S.A.	1-26D	40	10	700	4.4	30	114	49	23
Schleicher Aircraft, Germany	Ka-6CR	49	18	605	4.6	38	150	48	29
Schweizer Aircraft Corp., U.S.A.	2-32	57	18	1340	7.4	42	150	53	34
Glasflügel, Germany	Libelle	49	24	660	5.1	36	155	53	39
Bölkow, Germany	Phoebus C	56	21	825	5.4	36	124	56	42
Glasflügel, Germany	Kestrel	56	25	738	5.9	39	155	60	43
Schleicher Aircraft, Germany	ASW-15	60	26	860	6.2	40	150	62	48

TYPICAL CHARACTERISTICS

The following table gives some of the significant characteristics of some modern sailplanes now flying in the United States. Some are of American and some of foreign manufacture. The examples are chosen to be representative of the various classes, such as training, medium-performance, and high-performance types.

Launching Methods

A typical modern high-performance sailplane will weigh 660 lb fully loaded, and have a glide ratio (L/D) of 40. This means that it will take a pull (or thrust) of only 15 lb to keep it airborne in level flight. Unfortunately, getting it off the ground and flying is not so easy. The power required to accelerate the mass from a standing start, and to overcome the drag from the ground on the wheels, and to lift the aircraft to an altitude where sustained flight is possible, is many times that required merely to sustain flight.

Man's earliest flights in heavier-than-air machines were in "hang gliders," a set of wings resting on his shoulders from which he hung in flight. Launching was by running downhill into the wind. Inclined tracks, catapults, and rockets have also been used. The only widely used launching means of real historic importance is the bungee, or shock-cord method. It used the rubber rope made for landing-gear shock absorbers, and was developed in Germany and widely used in the early twenties. The glider is hooked to the point of a "V" of shock-cord, and each end of the shock-cord is pulled by half the launching crew who stretch it tight by running while the glider is held in place. Then it is released and shot into the air as from a giant slingshot, usually from the brow of a hill. Although widely used for years, it is never seen today, having been succeeded by better means.

WINCH LAUNCH

The use of a winch to launch sailplanes and gliders has been very common in Europe, although it has been less popular in the United States, where the ready availability of automobiles and light aircraft has made the winch less advantageous.

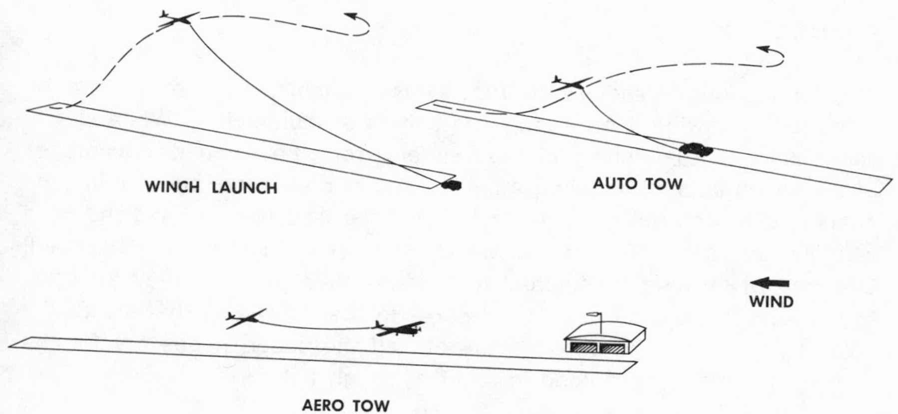

Figure 14.4 Launching methods.

In a winch launch, the aircraft is attached to the end of a long line which is rapidly wound up on a drum at the upwind end of the launching area. The aircraft climbs steeply at first, then levels off as it comes nearly overhead of the winch, where the pilot releases his end of the cable. The winch operator then continues to wind in the loose cable which is prevented from falling into a tangle by a parachute about 3 ft in diameter attached to the end of the cable. A guillotine is provided at the winch to cut the cable if the sailplane cannot release its end. An automobile engine with an automatic transmission is the customary power for the winch.

All kinds of ropes, wires and cables have been used for winch launches, with the best probably being the armored cable used by the military for towing aerial targets. It is strong, flexible, and will not kink. Since improper technique by the winch driver or carelessness on the part of the pilot can impart many *g*'s load to the aircraft, the FAA requires that a weak link be used in the launching cable at the aircraft end. It should break with a pull of about twice the weight of the aircraft.

The winch launch has the advantage of being cheap ($.50 per launch being a common charge in club operations), and it can be used for takeoffs from a very short field, since the ground roll is only a couple of hundred feet. The winch cable can be several thousand feet in length with the winch located in rough ground beyond the takeoff area. The big disadvantage is that the pilot is always released at the same spot, at a relatively low altitude, and has only a limited area and time in which to search for lift before he must land. The average altitude attained on a winch launch is about 40% of the length of the cable used.

AUTO TOW

If a long enough roadway or runway is available, a sailplane can be launched by towing it on a long line behind an automobile. While simple and cheap, this launching method suffers from the same disadvantages of the winch launch including a limited height of release, and a minimum chance to search out good areas of lift. If the field is small and the wind velocity low, a modification called an auto pulley launch can be used. One end of the line is attached to a stake, then over a pulley attached to the auto, thence back past the stake to the aircraft at the end of the field. This permits the car to move at half the speed necessary for the launch, a decided advantage in short or rough fields.

AEROPLANE TOW

When a sailplane is launched by aero tow it can choose any altitude for release, and can remain on tow until an area of lift is found before releasing. These advántages have made the aero tow the most widely used launching means by a wide margin, despite the somewhat higher cost. The requirements for the towplane are an FAA-approved tow-hook installation for attaching the towline, sufficient power to get a heavy sailplane out of a small field on a hot day, and the ability to climb at a slow speed (60 to 80 mph) indefinitely on a hot day without overheating the engine. A high horsepower-weight ratio is desirable; for example, a Super Cub with a 150-hp engine makes a good towplane and is widely used for this purpose.

The tow hook on the airplane is made so that the tow pilot can release his end of the towline in an emergency, as can the sailplane pilot. Towlines are generally ¼-in. diameter braided plastic and range in length from 25 to 200 ft, 150 ft being the length most commonly used in the United States. As in other types of launching a weak link is required if the towline's breaking strength is more than twice the weight of the sailplane being towed. After the sailplane has released, the towplane can land with the towline still attached, or it may be dropped in some safe designated area before landing.

Basic Airmanship in Sailplanes

In Chapter 8 material was presented relating to the handling of light powered aircraft. Except where the use of power was required, all these techniques are equally applicable and valid for sailplanes. The operation of controls in flight is identical. In fact, after a couple of familiarization flights in a sailplane, the power pilot all too often feels that flying sailplanes is nothing new and there is little for him to learn. This is a dangerous fallacy, and will surely lead to a serious accident.

It is true that the controls of a sailplane respond like those of a power plane, and the experienced pilot will soon handle them as effectively as those in any other aircraft. But in a powered aircraft he can buy time, altitude, and distance with his engine if he gets in a tight place because of carelessness or lack of experience. In the sailplane this crutch is not available. There are two things a pilot must learn before he can be considered a safe sailplane pilot: first, to plan ahead, particularly about his landing, to an extent far beyond that required of a power pilot; and second, he must learn the discipline which will always keep him within *easy and certain* gliding range of a landing spot suitable for (1) the conditions of the day, (2) his ability as a pilot, and (3) the capabilities of his aircraft. If he tries to cut his final glide to the airport landing pattern too fine, he will have no reserve if he encounters downdrafts en route, and he will be faced with an off-airport landing for which he may not be prepared. If he tries to land on the first 20 ft of the runway to show his great skill, a lurking area of sink can leave him with a cockpit full of fenceposts and barbed wire. The excellent safety record of soaring shows that the lack of an engine does not have to be a safety hazard, provided that the pilot plans ahead and observes proper soaring flight discipline.

The principal differences between soaring flight and powered flight are these:

TAKEOFF OR LAUNCHING

These are the regions where flight procedures differ the most from those of conventional powered aircraft.

Winch launch starts with the launching cable being hooked up to the sailplane. This should *never* be permitted unless the aircraft is occupied by a pilot, the canopy closed and locked, and everything ready for the takeoff. After the hook-up, a helper at one wing tip signals the winch operator who slowly takes up slack until the cable is tight along the ground. The pilot then signals his readiness to take off by "fanning" the rudder, and this signal is relayed to the winch operator. The cable is only then rapidly reeled in. The acceleration of the aircraft can be quite surprising, and it will usually be airborne within 100 ft or less.

The pilot holds the ship just off the ground until the airspeed builds up to about 1½ times stall speed, and then firmly and deliberately pulls the stick completely back against the stop. This is where the lady passengers scream, and the pilot passengers who have never experienced a winch launch gasp audibly. As the climb progresses, the downward pull of the launch cable puts a positive *g* load on the wings as the nose is pulled down by the cable, and the pilot resists this force by full up-elevator. Unlike normal pull-ups in free flight, the pilot does not feel this added *g* load in the seat of his pants. Nonetheless, it is there, and increases the stalling speed proportionally. However, in this unusual flight configuration, the elevator stalls out first, resulting in a pitching down of the nose and an increase in airspeed. This in turn unstalls the elevator which then forces the nose up again. This cycle rapidly repeats itself, and is called "porpoising." It is easily and instantly remedied by relaxing the stick pressure, thus shallowing the climb.

It is important to keep the airspeed well up during the climb so as not to be caught in this extremely nose-high attitude at slow speed in the event of a cable break. If the cable does break, move the stick smartly forward to maintain normal flying speed, and pull the release hook to drop the remains of the cable still attached to the ship. Land at whatever spot is appropriate for the altitude in hand.

As the launch progresses, the climb will flatten out until almost level flight is attained as the sailplane approaches a position almost above the winch. The winch operator will then cut the power. When the pilot feels this, he drops the nose slightly to take the tension off the cable and pulls the release. If he fails to release, or cannot, the winch driver will actuate a guillotine which cuts the cable at the winch.

Auto tows are quite similar to winch launches as far as winch is concerned. The main difference is that the winch is capable of accelerating the sailplane much faster in the initial part of the launch. Auto speed will need to be 50 to 60 mph in light winds; less in stronger winds.

There is a standard set of signals used in sailplane launching, and every soaring pilot should be familiar with them. For example, it is up to him to let the winch or car driver know if the speed is too fast or too slow. The pilot rocks his wings to request more speed, and fans his rudder to request a slower speed.

Aero tows are the most common means of launching sailplanes in the United States. They are somewhat like a combination of power-plane takeoffs combined with formation flying. Many soaring instructors find that learning to fly well on aero tow in turbulent air is the most difficult problem for their new students.

As in other types of launch, never hook up the cable until everything else is completely ready for takeoff. If it is the first flight of the day, hook up the towline and then release it while the helper is pulling on the towline. This confirms that the tow release mechanism will release under tension.

Reattach the towline and when the wing-tip runner signals by leveling the wings, the towplane taxis slowly forward and takes up the slack.

The sailplane pilot then signals his readiness to take off by "fanning" the rudder. The tow pilot applies full power and the takeoff roll starts. In the absence of strong winds, the sailplane pilot will need to make vigorous motions of the control stick to keep the wings level and the nose skid from rubbing on the ground in the early part of the takeoff run when the two aircraft are accelerating slowly. However, normal control is quickly achieved and the sailplane will shortly fly off the ground. Because the towplane will not yet be airborne, take great care to fly the sailplane only a few feet above the runway. Flying too high pulls the tail of the towplane up so far that its pilot never can get the tail down to a takeoff and climb attitude. Allowing the sailplane to balloon up too high suddenly could even dump the towplane up on its propeller. If the sailplane pilot holds his position properly, there will be very little drag on the towplane and it will quickly break off the ground.

There are two positions in aero tow: *high tow* and *low tow,* shown in Figure 14.5. The former is now used almost exclusively, but the FAA flight tests require that both be demonstrated. In high tow, the relative positions of towplane and sailplane on takeoff are maintained: The towed aircraft is directly behind and slightly above the towplane. This places it just above the wake turbulence caused by the wing-tip vortices of the towplane. In low tow position, it is just below the wake turbulence with the towplane well above it. The pilot can move directly from one position to the other by moving up or down through the wake. He will encounter moderate turbulence and a strong tendency to roll the sailplane, but this offers no problems to an alert pilot. The turbulence can be entirely avoided by going around it, by moving off to one side of the towplane (lots of rudder required), then moving down or up as the case may be, and then returning to the center position.

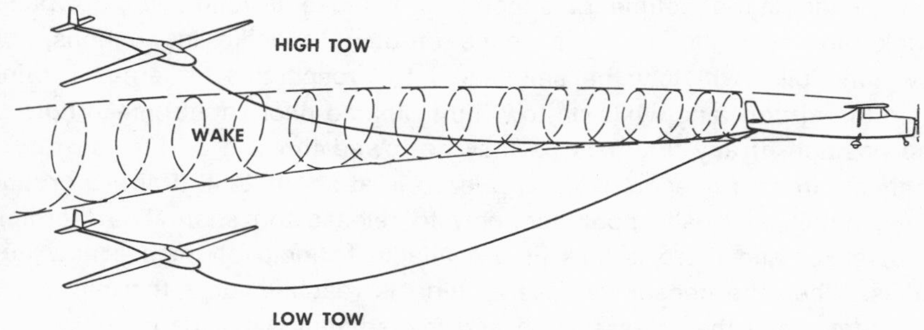

Figure 14.5 High and low tow positions.

If the air is smooth, flying an aero tow is very simple. The problems arise when it is turbulent, which is always the case when instability and strong thermals are present.

The sailplane pilot usually tries to keep the towplane at some fixed spot on his windshield canopy. If he can do this precisely, he will never have any trouble with slack in the towline no matter how rough the air. A capable towplane pilot will carefully fly at a constant attitude, but when he encounters a thermal the towplane will rise. The sailplane pilot should not wait to get to the updraft, but should immediately pull back on the stick to keep the towplane at the same position on the canopy. The reverse is true when the towplane sinks.

All this is easier said than done, and the common student fault of overcontrolling can create some difficult situations if he gets out of phase with the towplane movements. If the student gets too high, he can easily start to overtake the towplane when he makes his nose-down correction, since he is much cleaner than the towplane. This creates a lot of slack in the towline.

Any large amount of slack is dangerous for three reasons: first, in extreme cases it can loop back over the sailplane wing and yank it off when the slack is taken out. This has happened, and any time a large loop of slack starts coming back, pull the tow release at once and dive away from it. Second, although the towlines are plastic and have some spring in them, when slack is suddenly taken out there is a jerk which puts an unnecessary strain on the towline and the two aircraft. The towline may break at its weak link, perhaps leaving the sailplane on its own at a difficult time. Third, when the slack is suddenly taken out, unless the sailplane pilot is alert and holds his stick forward, the sudden pull of the towline will have a slingshot effect, ballooning the sailplane way up out of position again. When on tow in turbulent air is no time for the sailplane pilot to be looking at scenery. Constant alertness is required.

When the towplane banks for a turn, the sailplane does likewise, although lagging a couple of seconds will make it follow the towplane track more exactly. In the absence of other specific instructions, the towplane pilot will tow the sailplane into prospective lift areas upwind from the airport, and while on tow the sailplane pilot should make note of the position of any thermals he may be towed through so he can return to these areas if needed. Normal release is at about 2000 ft above ground level, but it is usually poor economy to release too soon. The thermals are weaker and there is less time available to look for them at low altitudes. When the chosen release altitude is reached, or a thermal is encountered, pull the release knob and immediately start the sailplane into a *right turn.* The towplane pilot will feel the release and start a diving *left turn* as soon as he visually confirms that the sailplane is free. The sailplane pilot *must* remember one signal: If the towplane pilot rocks his wings, it is a *mandatory* release signal. The tow pilot will release his end of the towline if the sailplane pilot does not.

FREE FLIGHT

The sailplane in free flight is handled just like a powered airplane, except that no power is available on demand for climbing. The elevators control the airspeed. The rate of roll is slower because of the large wingspan, and the effectiveness of the rudder is usually less. In soaring, a much greater proportion of the time is spent in slow flight regimes than in powered flying. When circling in a thermal to gain altitude it is common practice to fly only a few knots above stall speed. Thus the soaring pilot's experience with approaching stalls in turns is thousands of times that of the power pilot. Soaring pilots *must* be good at slow flight, using sound and feel as much as instruments.

Stall and spin recoveries are the same as for powered aircraft, but without power to help, the stick must be held forward longer. The spoiler or speed-limiting dive brakes help in holding down the excess speed which would otherwise be developed in the dive. While almost every aerobatic maneuver can be done after a fashion by sailplanes, they are very poorly designed for this purpose on account of the slow roll rate and small rudder. Thus the figures are sloppy, and except for the spin, inside loop, and chandelle, are generally hard to perform even poorly.

LANDING

Since the sailplane landing has to be right the first time, instructors give considerable attention to approach and landing practice. Actually, because of the excellent glide path control provided by the spoilers, it is very easy to land sailplanes on even a very small airport, provided the pilot has arrived in the traffic pattern with normal altitude. But the soaring pilot must be trained for the time when he may wish to land away from the airport in a small field, so landing drill is directed to precision spot landings. Power pilots and spectators are constantly amazed by the sight of good soaring pilots touching down time after time within a few feet of a given spot, and stopping with their nose a few *inches* from a target spot.

The *approach* is made in a normal rectangular pattern as with powered aircraft, and similarly the first key to a good landing is a good approach pattern. To be sure of reaching the field, the sailplane's pattern may be closer to the runway than the power plane's. This also keeps the two kinds of traffic separate in joint-use fields. *Pattern speed should never be less than 50% above stalling speed plus half the estimated wind velocity.* For example, if the sailplane stalls at 40 knots and the wind is estimated at 10 knots, the minimum pattern speed would be 65 knots. Hold this speed until flare-out, and you cannot have a stall-spin accident. If you are inexperienced, or the air is very turbulent and the wind gusty, it is well to add 5 or 10 knots to this minimum airspeed.

The *final approach* is also made as outlined in Chapter 8. Select the aiming point, or the flare-out point, about 50 yards short of the touchdown spot. Soaring schools used to teach the final approach by having a pilot visualize a line to the aiming point and then adjust the position of the sailplane along this line by the use of spoilers. A new approach has been in use in recent years which has been found to give students much greater accuracy in a much shorter time. It sounds about the same, but is basically different.

In this method the same aiming point is still used, but the student is told to aim the ship at the flare-out point with the elevaors as though he were strafing an enemy at that point. He is then told to use the spoilers for speed conrol to cancel out the effect of any change in pitch attitude caused by changes in aiming.

When the sailplane is almost at the chosen flare-out point and at an altitude of 5 to 20 ft depending on the angle of descent, the pilot smoothly rounds out the glide so that the flight path becomes parallel to the ground at an altitude of a foot or so. If the flare-out point is reached with the spoilers closed, the glide path will be quite flat, and there will be little attitude change required for the flare-out. On the other hand, full spoilers require a very steep glide angle to maintain airspeed, and the flare-out is much pronounced and should be started higher up. Slowly closing the spoilers simultaneously with the flare will make this maneuver less critical.

With the flare-out completed, you will be floating towards your chosen touchdown spot. Then imagine the spoiler control a throttle; if short, push it forward, closing the spoilers, extending the glide; if long, pull the control back, extending the spoilers to shorten the glide. When about 30 ft from the chosen touchdown spot, open the spoilers smoothly all the way and allow the glider to touch down in a normal attitude without the use of the elevators. Never make full stall landing intentionally in a sailplane because there is no shock capability in the landing gear except that in the sidewalls of the tire. Control the roll-out by the wheel brake, and for a faster stop, push the stick all the way forward, digging in the nose skid in front of the wheel. Remember the landing is not complete until the aircraft has come to a complete stop safely. Plan to stop well short of obstacles such as other aircraft.

Sailplane Instrumentation and Equipment

While the instrumentation of training sailplanes is frequently a bare minimum, the instrumentation of high-performance competition ships is quite complete. Conventional instruments are used for airspeed, altitude, acceleration, and turn and slip. The most important instrument for the soaring pilot is one which tells him whether he is going up or down. The regular rate-of-climb instrument used in power planes is much too slow and insensitive to be of much value in soaring, so a special instrument called a *variometer* is used for this purpose.

VARIOMETERS

When a soaring pilot encounters rising air he needs to know it immediately, so he can take the proper action to stay in the area of lift. The variometer utilizes the same principle of operation as the conventional rate-of-climb (i.e., measuring the airflow in or out of a small reservoir) but the soaring instrument has a very fast response of one second or less. Another feature widely used with this instrument is called "total energy compensation." If you push the stick forward, you will nose down and pick up speed. Your variometer will show a down reading. You have exchanged some of your potential energy (altitude) for kinetic energy (speed). The

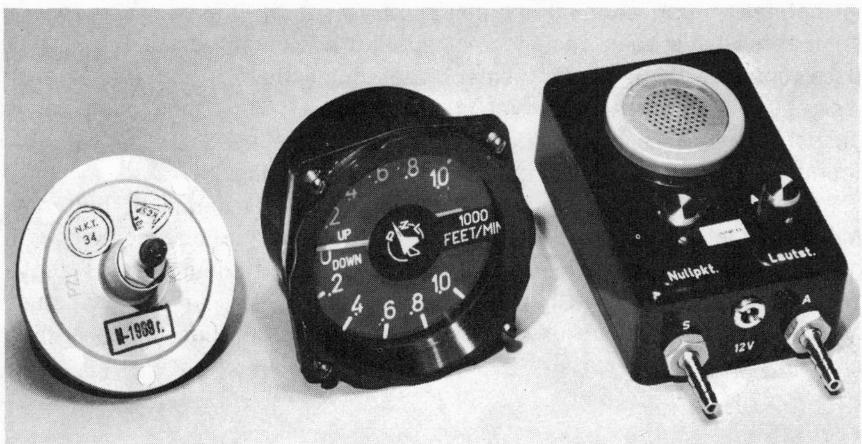

Figure 14.6 Soaring Instruments. Variometer instrument, center. Total energy compensation diaphragm, left; audio attachment, right. (*Courtesy of Rainco.*)

reverse would be true if you pulled the stick back. In the latter case you might think you had encountered rising air in a thermal, but it would only be what is called a "stick thermal."

What you want to know is whether you have really encountered rising air, or have just inadvertently mishandled the controls. The total energy compensator tells you this. It utilizes pitot pressure to measure airspeed and to operate a diaphragm which changes the volume of the variometer reservoir. When this is properly done, you can push the stick forward or pull it back without changing the variometer reading over a surprisingly large range of airspeeds. The total energy compensation must be individually adjusted for each model of sailplane, but it is well worth the effort.

It is a very common experience to be spiraling in the same thermal with several other sailplanes. Under such circumstances you cannot spend much time looking at your instruments, yet if you do not pay close attention to the variometer you may stray out of the best lift area. A solution to this problem is an audio attachment designed for use with any variometer. It generates an audio tone, whenever there is lift showing on the instrument. The pitch of the tone increases as the lift gets stronger. This permits you to spend more time looking out of the cockpit, and still constantly monitor the strength of the lift where you are flying.

COMPASSES

Since while soaring you are likely to spend a large part of the time circling in thermals, a conventional magnetic compass is of little use, and special compasses have been designed for soaring use, such as the Cook compass, made in England. Its element does not float in a liquid, is light in weight for a fast response, yet is well damped. The Cook compass is almost as good as a gyro compass, and can be used to roll out of a thermal, in or out of clouds, on a very precise heading.

Power sources for sailplanes are usually nickel cadmium batteries. Multi-channel VHF radios are commonly used for communication with ground crews and other sailplanes as well as FSS stations. Flights above 12,000 ft are common in the western United States, so many sailplanes carry elaborate pressure oxygen systems for long-duration flights at high altitudes.

Soaring Meteorology

To the power pilot, weather conditions are just one of the many considerations that are examined in planning and executing a flight. To the soaring pilot, favorable meteorological conditions are an absolute necessity for flight. If there is no lift, he cannot stay up. More than mechanical skill in flying his aircraft, the ability to understand the meteorological conditions which prevail during flight is the most important factor in making a top soaring pilot. In the broadest sense, the soaring pilot uses meteorological information in three ways: first, to permit forecasting the expected conditions perhaps a day in advance, so that he can plan flying activity to take advantage of them; second, to understand the existing conditions which prevail at the start of the flight; and third, to permit recognizing and properly interpreting the dynamic changes in the meteorological situation which may occur during the flight.

KINDS OF LIFT

There are five kinds of lift which the soaring pilot may use. On local and many cross-country flights only one of these will probably be used, but on some long flights each kind may be encountered and used if the pilot is alert and knowledgeable enough to recognize them.

Slope or ridge lift is found when the wind encounters an obstacle such as a slope or ridge, and is forced upward mechanically by the obstruction. It is the simplest kind of lift to recognize and understand, and was the only kind used by the pioneers in gliding and soaring. A wind of about 10 knots at right angles to the ridge is required to keep a sailplane aloft.

The source of the wind may be the pressure gradient flow after the passage of a cold front, for example, or it may be a sea breeze caused by the heating of the land. In a 20- or 25-knot wind it is possible to maintain an altitude one or two times the height of the ridge.

Convergence zones or *shear lines* are long line of lift found when airflows moving in different directions collide. When the air masses come together (and they do not have to be in exactly opposite directions), the air is forced up along their line of intersection, and while this band of lift is often very narrow, it is soarable even when the winds causing it are very light, say 10 knots or so.

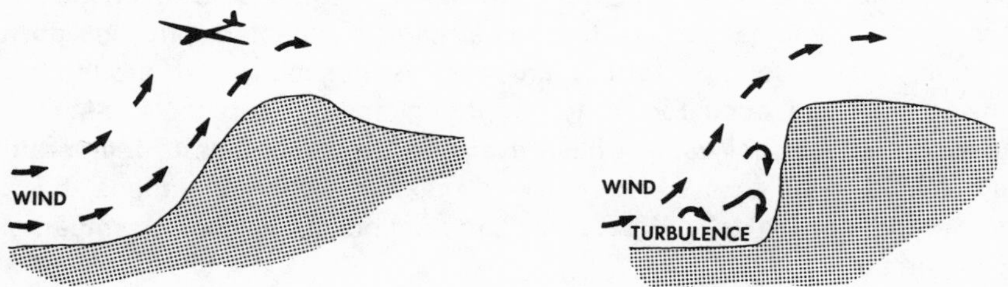

Figure 14.7 Wind flow at slopes or ridges.

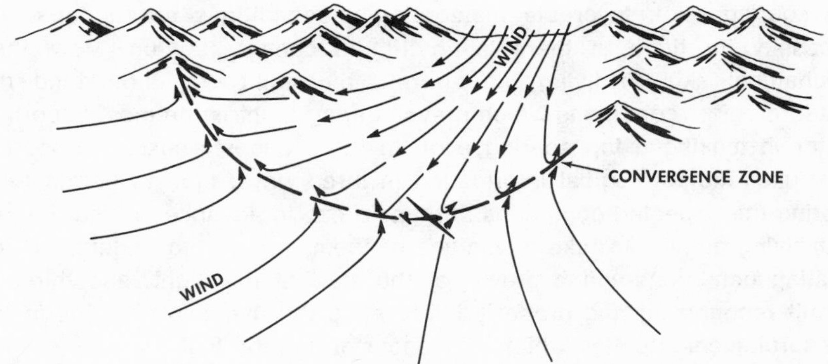

Figure 14.8 Lift at convergence zone.

The convergence of the winds may be caused by local mechanical effects such as hills or valleys dividing or channeling the flows, or it may be caused by major air-mass movements, such as cold fronts or their associated squall lines. One special case is the so-called "sea-breeze front" caused by stable air from the sea or a lake moving inland with the diurnal sea breeze and pushing against the less stable air over the land. This results in a miniature cold front roughly parallel to the coast, sometimes moving a good many miles inland, depending upon the strength of the wind. It is frequently marked by a line of small cumulus clouds.

Thermals are the most commonly used kind of lift in modern soaring, although it was not until about 1930 that soaring pilots understood and started using thermals on a regular basis for staying aloft. The term "thermal" is used to describe lift resulting from unstable air rising in columns or bubbles. If the air is moist enough, the thermal will be marked by a cumulus cloud, providing the lift reaches high enough to condense the moisture. Lift will be found right up through the cloud to the top of the visible moisture. Stability concepts are discussed in detail in Chapter 6.

The soaring pilot is interested in the time thermals will start, their strength, and the height of their tops. The weather bureau forecasters will usually know the cloud base and the top of the unstable layer, and can give a rough estimate of the thermal strengths expected, but they do not normally compute the starting time of the convection at ground level unless they are accustomed to preparing soaring forecasts. Since the soaring pilot will not usually have available the soundings of temperature and humidity which are necessary to make these computations, he will be forced to try to extract this information from some sympathetic weatherman.

Once the pilot has his forecast, he is on his own. He will need continually to update his information in the light of the actual conditions as he observes them through his instruments and visual observations. For example, if the thermals start earlier than forecast, they may also be stronger than expected. The ability to recognize changing meteorological conditions in the course of a flight is an attribute which sets the top pilots apart from their fellows. The soaring pilot who is seriously interested in improving his flying will study all the written material on soaring meteorology he can find.*

It is not necessary to have clouds to have thermals. Many long flights are made on days when there is not enough moisture to form clouds. The pilot then uses "dry thermals" which are just like those on moister days, but they are harder to locate since they have no clouds to mark their tops.

Another situation where the soaring pilot can get information from the clouds is when they line up in rows or "cloud streets." These are frequently parallel to the wind, so the happy soaring pilot finds himself dashing downwind under a line of clouds, sometimes going miles without needing to stop and circle to gain altitude. A less pleasant sight is a high cirrus overcast or stratus deck. This will cut off the solar heating of the ground and spell a quick end to thermals and the flight.

Mountain waves or *lee waves* described in Chapter 6 give the soaring pilot the chance to climb to remarkable heights. In the up-draft in *front* of the obstacle such as a ridge, a height of perhaps twice that of the ridge can be attained, but in the *lee* waves a height of ten times the obstacle height is not uncommon. Waves suitable for soaring can be expected when the wind at the top of the obstacle is about 25 knots or more, and the best conditions come with winds increasing with altitude. The occurrence of waves can usually be fairly well predicted by forecasters. Like slope or ridge soaring, the best conditions arise when the wind is blowing at right angles to the line of the ridge. Since wind direction and velocity are the primary criteria, the soaring pilot can do his own forecasting with winds-aloft data prepared for other aviation use.

Slope or Ridge Soaring

The very first gliding and soaring flights were made by launching the aircraft from the top of a hill or ridge into a wind blowing up the slope. This gives a kind of lift which is easily visualized and measured, and which provides the simplest kind of soaring. However, it is seldom possible to get very high by using slope lift, and unless the ridge is very long, flying an appreciable distance is also impossible. For this reason, slope soaring has lost most of its popularity except for training and duration flights.

*"Meteorology for Glider Pilots," by C. E. Walington, John Murray, London, 1961, 284 pages, is a must.

For good slope soaring it is necessary to have a wind component at a right angle to a hill or ridge with a strength of about 10 to 15 knots. A suitable nearby launching site is required as well as a suitable emergency landing site at the foot of the ridge in case the wind velocity should drop so that the ship could not re-land at the starting point.

LAUNCHING

Ridge lift is usually entered from a winch at the top of the ridge, or from an aero tow from any nearby point. When launched by a winch from a field at the top of the ridge, the pilot will probably find himself 500 ft above the ridge and can start one brief traverse along the edge of the ridge looking for strong enough lift to remain airborne. If he finds none, he returns at once while he has sufficient altitude.

FLIGHT PATH

Fy a path parallel to the top of the ridge, moving carefully upwind or downwind to find the exact path which gives the best lift. When reaching the end of the traverse (for example, where the ridge ends or changes direction) turn *into* the wind away from the slope and complete a teardrop turning pattern back to the original traverse path, but now flying in the opposite direction (Figure 14.9). At the other end, repeat the process, always turning into the wind away from the slope. If other sailplanes are also flying in the same area, do not fly directly below one in the other pilot's blind sector. When overtaking a ship going in the same direction, always pass on the *inside* next to the slope. This may violate the usual passing rule in other airspace, but it is necessary to avoid the possibility of the overtaken ship turning unexpectedly in front of the other. Since the name of the game is to stay up, in ridge soaring the pilot almost always flies at his minimum sinking speed, rather than the speed of best *L/D.*

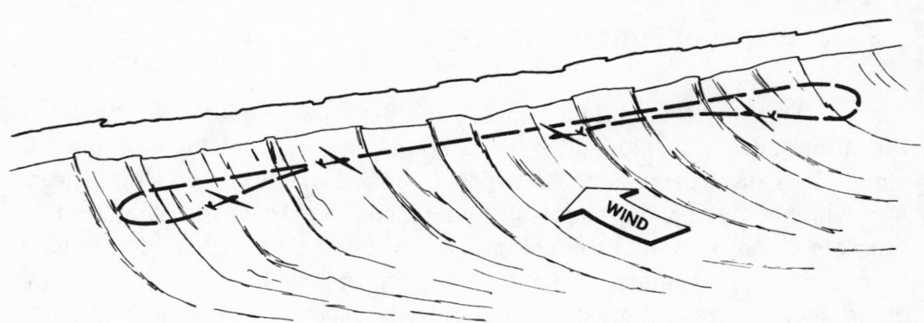

Figure 14.9 Flight paths in ridge soaring.

This means he is always on the edge of a stall and must be very alert at all times.

LANDING

If you wish to land back at the top of the ridge, never let yourself get too low to make that final turn in to land. Remember also that this landing will almost always be made downwind, and it is most important to maintain proper airspeed, no matter how fast the ground seems to be slipping by. If the wind weakens and you find yourself flying below the crest of the ridge, do not despair, but carefully fly in the best lift and wait in hopes that the wind will strengthen again, lifting you high enough to permit a landing on top.

Thermalling Techniques

Your ability to stay airborne and gain altitude above the launch point is the vital difference between soaring and gliding. You must be able to find the lift areas, and then stay in them until you have gained the maximum altitude they provide. Techniques for centering and staying in the lift areas can be taught, and most pilots become fairly proficient in this aspect of soaring. The thing which separates the good pilots from the ordinary ones is their ability to find the thermals in the first place. Yet this is one of the hardest things to teach. Some pilots seem to be born with a nose for thermals, and some apparently equally proficient ones seem never to acquire the knack.

CHARACTERISTICS OF THERMALS

Thermals are masses of air that are more buoyant than the surrounding air, usually because of an excess of temperature or moisture, or both. Some theoretical studies indicate that thermals are like a smoke-ring blown upwards, with the rising air in the center returning around the outside of the doughnut. This would mean that no lift would be found either above or below the ring. The experience of soaring pilots indicates that most of the time they can find lift directly under and above other soaring aircraft almost all the way to the ground. This supports the theory that thermals are usually *columns* of rising air. In diameter they can range from a few feet (notice the small circles soaring birds sometimes use) to many hundreds of feet. In height they usually start at the ground and rise to the altitude where the air in the column is at equilibrium with the surrounding air. This can be as high as 50,000 ft, the top of some large storms. But most soaring pilots leave the lift at cumulus cloud base, which will be 5000 to 10,000 ft above the ground in most circumstances of good soaring weather.

Thermals drift with the wind, and since wind velocity almost always increases with altitude, the thermal will lean with the wind. When winds get to 25 to 30 knots near the ground the thermals will be so badly blown apart that they are not usable for soaring. The air that goes up in a thermal must come down somewhere, and it does this in an area all around the rising air. However, since the descending air is spread over a much larger area than the rising air, the strength of the downdrafts is less than that of the updrafts. The soaring pilot soon learns that where there is strong lift, there is also strong sink nearby. This is important to remember in the final glide to a landing.

FINDING THERMALS

The variometer will tell you when you reach a thermal, but what direction should you take to have the best chance of finding one? Some of the common cues are listed below.

Cumulus clouds which are observed to be building, not decaying, are one of the most reliable indicators of lift. However, since the average life of a cumulus cloud is only about 20 min, they must constantly be observed to identify the growing ones. These are usually the ones with firm sharp edges. Top soaring pilots are always good cloud readers. On days when there is not enough moisture to make clouds, other indicators must be used.

Dust, scraps of paper, and other light particles can sometimes be seen carried up in strong thermals. The familiar dust devil, a common feature of the desert scene in summer, marks a very strong thermal lift area. But be wary of entering them at low altitudes as they are very turbulent, and can easily upset a sailplane.

Birds and other sailplanes which may be observed circling are good thermal indicators. Go over and join them. If you are below, be sure to take into account that the wind will be causing the lift area to slant with its direction. Many a sailplane pilot has been saved from an undesired landing by spotting a hawk or buzzard circling in a nearby thermal and joining him, and many times the birds will come over and join the sailplane.

Surface features which are more prone to generate thermals should be searched for. These are large black areas such as parking lots and plowed fields, and heat sources such as chimneys and fires. Avoid bodies of water and areas where rain has recently fallen, or which are irrigated.

Dry ground is best for thermals. Usually forested areas are poor for thermal production because of their excess moisture content. Thermals will rise earlier from high ground than from the nearby valleys, so an important rule is "stick to the higher ground."

THERMAL CENTERING TECHNIQUES

Using the aids in the above paragraphs, or perhaps by luck, you encounter thermal lift. How can you best find the strongest part, and stay in it? Normally the first indication of lift is shown by the reading of the variometer. This shows you are entering the area of lift which is usually roughly circular in shape, but you will have no idea if the center is directly ahead, or to one side. At this moment, notice that one wing or the other goes up. If this coincides with the increased reading of the variometer, it usually means that the lift is stronger on the side where the wing lifted. Count to perhaps four seconds, and if the lift is still increasing, start a steep turn into the direction of the lifted wing. If there is no wing indication, turn either way.

A simple and effective way of locating the center of the thermal is to fly a complete 360° circle, noting the variometer reading at the four 90° points. This will give a good idea of the strength and distribution of the lift in this area. Then for the second turn, move the center of the circle over in the direction which shows the strongest lift. Another way of accomplishing the same thing is to shallow the angle of bank when the lift is decreasing. This process is shown diagrammatically in Figure 14.10.

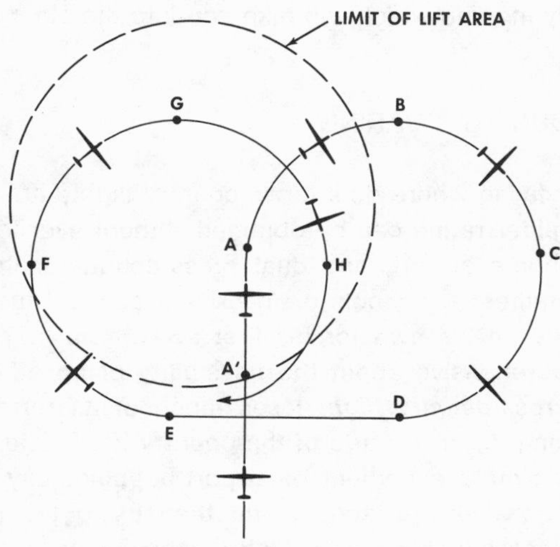

Figure 14.10 Thermal centering.

At point A′ the variometer starts showing lift at the edge of the thermal outlined by the dotted circle. After three or four seconds with the vario reading still increasing, you elect to turn right at A. As you turn to an easterly heading at B, the reading has dropped to about zero rate of climb, and you strongly suspect that you turned the wrong way or that the thermal is a very small one. However, continue the turn, perhaps steepening the bank somewhat. At C and D, the two other 90° points, the vario shows "down." You know then that the strong core of the thermal lies to to the west of the circle, so you roll out of the turn at D and fly straight for five or six seconds to point E where you roll back again into the right turn. The next circle will find small lift at F, strong lift at G, and small lift at H. Then shift the next circle northward so the entire circuit will be in the lift area.

When deciding which direction to turn in a thermal, remember the soaring rule-of-the-road: the first ship in a thermal sets the direction of circling. All others joining him later in the thermal (whether above or below) circle in the same direction. Further, anyone flying in a thermal should expect others to join him, so keep a sharp lookout.

Cloud flying is really thermal flying on instruments. It is difficult to fly in clouds legally in the United States, but it can sometimes be done. Since ice, hail, and turbulence may be encountered, there are two important cautions: first, choose a cumulus cloud that is in its early growing stage, so you will be in and out before it gets to thunderstorm size. Second, start to get out of the cloud when the icing or turbulence *begins* to get bad. It will always be more turbulent as you head for the side, and the ice will continue to build up during the exit time. Before entering the cloud get a heading firmly in mind which will take you into the clear air in the shortest time.

CROSS-COUNTRY SOARING

Unlike power flying where dual cross-country flights are a prerequisite for licensing, a glider rating can be obtained without ever leaving the familiar area of the home airport, and dual cross-country instruction is seldom offered in commercial schools or in private clubs. Thus the new soaring pilot is usually on his own for his first away from home landing, and is frequently apprehensive about the possibility of an off-airport landing.

The first cross-country flight loses much of its terror if preceded by careful planning. In most parts of the country long-distance flights can be made by the simple expedient of airport-hopping. Lay out your desired course in a downwind direction, and then using the glide ratio of the sailplane (with a suitable safety factor), and taking into account the expected wind direction and velocity, calculate the minimum altitude needed

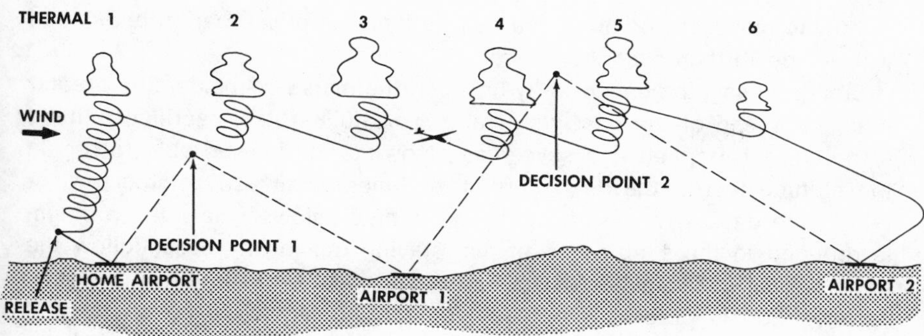

Figure 14.11 In planning flight to airport 2, the pilot has calculated the altitude of the two decision points shown. Staying above the dotted lines assures being able to land at any airport. Arriving above decision point 1, he continued. He was unable to get above decision point 2 in thermal 4, but saw the cloud marking thermal 5, so pressed on. Finding lift under cloud 5, no off-field landing between 1 and 2 was necessary.

in order either to glide back to the home airport or to go on to the next one. This altitude is marked on the chart, and you then know the alittude needed always to have an airport within easy gliding range if further lift fails to materialize. The same computation is made for the next leg, and so on. After a few such flights, you will have sufficient confidence and experience to face the possibility of an off-airport landing without undue concern.

Maximizing distance flown or minimizing elapsed time will soon become your major concern as a cross-country soaring pilot, since you will be endeavoring to surpass your own speed or distance records, or will be trying for one of the FAI soaring awards, or may be entered in a contest with other pilots. Saving time is one of the most important factors, even though the objective of the flight is merely to attain the greatest distance without regard to speed. The reason is this: The hours of the day in which lift will be found are strictly limited. Wasted minutes mean wasted miles. The maximum glide ratio of the sailplane is a widely quoted figure of merit, and you will always know its magnitude and the speed at which it is obtained. However, in cross-country flying you will not fly at this speed except perhaps while making the final glide of the day to a landing.

The best speed-to-fly to maximize the distance flown on a given day can be computed from the performance curves of the sailplane if an assumption is made about the strength of lift in the next thermal. This is usually possible to do with considerable success, since on a given day the thermals are usually found to be of about the same strength. Details of how to make this computation can be found in most soaring books and will not be further described here.

Suffice to say, the speed-to-fly between thermals is considerably *greater* than the speed of the best glide ratio. You deliberately sacrifice altitude to obtain extra speed and save time, knowing you will be able to regain the altitude lost in the next thermal. At times when you get too low, or late in the day when the lift weakens, fly much slower. Here the problem is reduced to the simple one of just staying up. In any case, follow the general plan of flying fast when in sink and slow when in lift.

Navigation is pure VFR pilotage for soaring flights, using charts and landmarks. Your concern for a prospective landing place will usually keep you well aware of the terrain beneath. However, it is easy to get disoriented after circling for some time in a thermal, and it is wise to check the course heading with the compass upon leaving the lift.

Choice of Landing Field In most cases, the cross-country soaring pilot faced with an off-airport landing will have a choice of several fields. There are numerous factors which should be considered in making the choice of which field to use. The first is the question of adequate size. This, in turn, will be influenced by the wind direction and velocity, possible obstructions at the approach end, and the condition of the surface. Ideally the surface should be smooth, dry, and uphill into the wind. Except in the case of a very strong wind, make landings uphill no matter what the wind direction. The long wingspan of modern sailplanes makes road landings hazardous because of roadside marker stakes which are invisible from the air. Landings in even medium-high crops such as wheat can be quite hazardous, because if one wing gets a little low at touchdown, the vegetation wil catch it and a violent ground loop will result. This seldom injures the pilot, but it frequently causes major damage to the sailplane. It is wise to avoid fields where livestock are seen. They may blunder into the landing path, or trample on the aircraft after landing when it may be left unattended. Lastly, if there is a choice, pick a field with easy access for the retrieve crew and trailer, but this should be the last in priority when choosing a site.

Wave Flying

When wind conditions are right, wave lift can be found behind very low ridges or obstacles, but for most pilots wave flying means going to 20,000, 30,000, or 40,000 ft in the lee of substantial mountain ranges. Wave flying means flying in strong winds and at high altitudes. Do not undertake it lightly.

FORECASTS

Conditions which produce good waves can usually be forecast with good accuracy. In general a wind at right angles to the ridge, and a velocity of 25 knots or more at the altitude of the ridge top is required. If the wind strongly increases with altitude, this is also advantageous, as is low-level and high-level instability with a stable layer in the middle altitudes. While lenticular clouds mark the wave when there is sufficient moisture present, dry and cloudless days can have just as good waves.

PREPARATION

Get ready for wave flying as carefully as if your life depended on it, which it does. Oxygen equipment suited to the task should be in first-class shape, and it should be a pressure demand system if the flight is expected to go above about 30,000 ft. Carry an emergency oxygen supply as a back-up. Frost from your breath will soon completely cover the inside of the canopy unless clear-vision panels are provided.

Have batteries fully charged and insulated agains the cold. Check the sealed recording barograph for operation in the cold. Dress warmly, particularly the legs and feet which will be in the shade with outside temperatures running −40° or lower.

LAUNCHING

While it is sometimes possible to get into wave lift from a lucky winch launch, almost all wave flights start from an aero tow which takes the sailplane right into the best lift area. This frequently means towing through, or under, the rotor zone which lies in the lee of the ridge, resulting in an exciting time for both towplane and sailplane pilots. Beginners should not try it.

The severest turbulence known in the atmosphere is found in the rotor zone. (Figure 6.30.) As in flying powered planes in turbulence, careful attitude flying is the key to survival, together with a willingness to release the towline if dangerous attitudes result, or if there is excessive slack in the towline. Upon exiting from the rotor zone on the upwind side, you will suddenly encounter the wave lift, and within a few seconds, after hanging on for dear life you will see the altimeter and rate of climb start winding up in air so smooth as to seem uncanny. Pull the release immediately and head into the wind for the climb. Mark the spot on the ground below, so you can come back if you lose the lift. Adjust your speed to stay over the same spot, occasionally moving forward or back to be sure you are in the area of maximum lift, and bear in mind that the wind is probably increasing greatly with altitude. The world's altitude record for a sailplane is 46,267 ft, made in a wave behind the Sierras.

WAVE CLOUDS

When there is sufficient moisture present, lenticular clouds will mark the tops of the waves, and if there are several moisture layers, the clouds will also be stacked in layers. There will also be a ragged-looking cumulus cloud marking the rotor zone if there is moisture at that level. The rotor zone is always centered at the same altitude as the top of the obstacle causing the wave system. These clouds are most useful in showing the areas of lift and turbulence. Another cloud sometimes associated with waves is the "Foehn" or cap cloud which comes pouring over the top of the obstacle, propelled by the high winds. (Figure 6.30). As the air flows down on the lee side of the obstacle, the cloud is warmed and evaporates. When the valley beyond is full of rotor clouds, or perhaps stratus, there will be a gap in the clouds where the air over the ridge is driven down and warmed. This is called the "Foehn gap" and sometimes provides a way to get on top, or back down, without going through the clouds. However, this can be hazardous, as the gap may suddenly fill with clouds, leaving you above a solid deck of clouds in mountainous terrain.

Soaring Safely

As a soaring pilot you start with many advantages which favor your safety. Unlike the power pilot you are not tempted into fog, rain, or snow storms, because there is no lift there. The sailplane flies and lands slowly, its structure is much stronger than that of power planes, and with its single wheel and nose skid it can land safely in terrain which would seriously damage aircraft with conventional gear. Its spoilers give it an unsurpassed glide angle control on approaches. The obvious disadvantage of the sailplane is the lack of power to extricate it from a critical situation, particularly on landing. But, trained in this problem from your very first flight, you can blame surprisingly few serious soaring accidents on a lack of power.

As with power planes there are too many stall-spin accidents close to the ground. The importance of maintaining adequate flying speed cannot be overemphasized. Many pilots who have just made the transition from power seem to feel that flying a sailplane is very simple, and start doing things, such as flying low and slowly, that they would probably never dream of doing in a power plane. All the admonitions given to power pilots apply to sailplanes: Keep up your flying speed; don't fly into clouds unless instrument-rated; don't try aerobatics unless qualified; keep a sharp lookout for other planes, etc.

All sailplanes are equipped with shoulder harness in addition to seat belts, and most pilots wear parachutes when engaged in competitive flying or cross-country flights over rough terrain.

To the familiar takeoff and landing check lists, you must add another: *the assembly check list.* Since the sailplane is frequently assembled on the field shortly before takeoff (having arrived disassembled on its trailer), use a check list to insure that all assembly operations have been properly carried out. Sailplanes have been known to take off and fly without controls hooked up, or without wing pins in place, but never well.

There are special sets of signals used in winch launching and aero tow. Learn these and use them. In addition, there are three important conventions or rules of the road which are unique to soaring. They have been mentioned in previous sections but are repeated here: (1) The first ship in a thermal sets the direction of turns in this thermal. All newcomers must turn in the same direction. (2) In slope soaring all turns are made into the wind, and all overtaking and passing is done on the downwind side. (3) After release from an aero tow, the sailplane turns to the right, and the towplane makes a diving turn to the left.

15

Northern Wilderness Flying*

The extensive lore associated with the art of wilderness flying developed over the past 40 years has been built largely about northern flying experience. The effects of cold on men and materials warrant placing more emphasis on the problems of flight in cold climates rather than on the peculiar techniques which are, of course, associated with wilderness flying over jungle and desert areas, to say nothing of the vast water wilderness of the world.

The transportation problems of the important subarctic are so similar to those of the arctic that the two are logically considered together. These problems also face the charter or sportsman pilot flying in the United States along the Canadian border, in mountainous areas, and in Southern Canada.

Northern Flying Developed by the Bush Pilots

HISTORY

In 1920 the four open-cockpit De Haviland biplanes of the Black Wolf Squad-

*By Terris Moore, Colby College; formerly President, University of Alaska.

ron flew from New York to Nome, Alaska, on the coast of the Bering Sea. This military flight, under the sponsorship of General "Billy" Mitchell, appears to stand as history's first important northern flying operation. That achievement becomes more remarkable when one recalls that Alaska had then no airfields, little radio communication, and no weather forecasting.

Then as now, however, this military flight contrasted sharply with civilian flying in the extent of the U.S. government resources which stood behind it. The "broken wings, smashed axles, busted tires and tail skids, broken oil-lines and leaking tanks" suffered by the four planes on the six weeks' flight to Alaska represented expenses beyond the financial risks which civilian operations would undertake in 1920. But military interests in northern flying relapsed and became dormant thereafter with Mitchell's passing and remained so until the outbreak of World War II. During the years between, Canadian and Alaskan civilian bush pilots developed the basic techniques of northern flying.

By the time World War II brought military flying back into the arctic again, the basic modern techniques of northern flying had been substantially developed. The airplane had become the automobile of the north, replacing also in its freighting capabilities bus, truck, and even railroad. There are still thousands of northern native people who, though entirely familiar with the airplanes which bring them their mail, food, and medical help, have never seen an automobile or a railroad. In all the five thousand miles of north country running from Newfoundland westerly to British Columbia and on to Bering Strait, Alaska, going north from this long line to the Pole, there are only four spindly north-running railroad lines and two meager road stems.

THE BUSH PILOT

Where the north begins, the bush pilot begins. His name incidentally derives from the Canadian word for the north woods, "the bush." Where the roads and railroads disappear as one goes north, the bush pilot takes over transportation. It is he whose self-reliant resourcefulness has developed the basic techniques of northern flying, which, with many minor variations and improvements, are the foundation of modern airmanship in the arctic, both military and civilian.

The term "bush flying" must be defined explicitly. It is the technique of airmanship involved in *wilderness* flying, where, the takeoffs and landings being away from airports, the pilot is confronted with the necessity of carrying them out in only modestly improved or even completely unprepared places; and where his ground handling and servicing must be frequently done without the usual airport, hangar, and shop facilities.

Originally all northern flying was bush flying. But as northern airports have come to be developed over the years, a growing part of northern flying has become simply conventional flying in the north, and not really bush flying. This is particularly true of military flying in the north. Military planes now, excepting only the liaison planes, do not lend themselves to the making of landings and takeoffs in unprepared or partially prepared places. They are airport-to-airport planes, designed for combat or transport at high altitudes and in ultracold atmospheres. And the techniques of using military planes for other than special rescue-type operation—even when the airports from which they must operate are in the arctic—have been standardized in Air Force Technical Orders. There is little need for the improvisation which to a considerable degree still characterizes northern bush flying. In fact, improvisation in northern military airport-to-airport flying, if it arises at all, is today correctly taken by the authorities to imply inadequate planning improper operation, or inadequate maintenance.

The Role of Bush Flying Today Very few special arctic *flight* problems are now encountered by military aircraft which they are not already designed to meet. This is because most of today's military aircraft, being designed for high-altitude flying where subzero temperatures are encountered in all parts of the world, come from the factory already equipped to cope with the problems of flight at arctic winter temperatures aloft. Thus for military aircraft today, special arctic techniques are limited as a practical matter to procedures for airport *ground* handling under extremely low temperatures, to search and rescue problems, and to liaison flying in support of isolated outposts or ground troops.

But in these aspects of military flying, and in the very considerable away-from-the-airport bush flying done by northern commercial and sportsman pilots, the resourcefulness, the ingenuity, and intelligent improvisation formerly demanded of all northern pilots should be familiar to every pilot flying in the north today.

What may perhaps be called the classic description of bush flying, *The Flying North,* sets forth vividly the trials and tribulations of the early Alaskan bush pilots. Though describing incidents of the 1920s, '30s, and '40s, it provides modern and practical descriptions of situations with which the present-day bush pilot may still have to cope. Many of the ways in which the early pilots solved their problems are still valid today in principle. The methods of those years are now out of date only in that (1) modern civilian bush planes have much higher horsepower for the same weight, and therefore have greatly improved takeoff and rate of climb performance; (2) in today's engine the danger of forced landing due to power failure has been reduced from an average of one per several hundred hours of flight time to one per 5000 or more hr of flight time; (3) modern bush planes have highly effective wheel brakes, often combined with tricycle landing gear: (4) the problem of flying between dry ground and deeply snow-covered landing strips has been solved by ski-wheel gear for even the smallest planes; and (5) excellent FAA facilities, and those of its equivalent, the Department of Transport in Canada, provide reliable and continuous in-flight radio communications and weather reporting not formerly available.

Winterizing

MODIFICATION OF AIRCRAFT FOR ARCTIC USE

Summer flying in the north does not require any special modification or adjustment of aircraft, but winter may; and "winterizing," in the sense of making adjustments, certainly will be required. Military aircraft coming off production lines in the middle 1950s and after have the necessary modifications for winter flying in the north in their design. Manufacturers of civil aircraft, particularly those like De Havilland of Canada and Cessna, whose aircraft are uniquely adaptable to northern flying, provide FAA-approved winterization kits.

These kits generally consist of easily installed baffles designed to increase engine temperatures approximately 50°F by partially covering the engine's cooling air inlets. This is considered a good compromise between effectiveness and FAA removal requirements for operation in the United States and the lower provinces of Canada. Kits also include oil-radiator shutters, intake system "lagging" (insulation), and carburetor-intake air baffles designed to improve mixture distribution in cold weather.

The more extensive modifications and revised operational procedures for true arctic operation are left to individual preference.

Extensive modifications of some aircraft are still definitely necessary. Winterizing of the aircraft in the fall and winter as cold weather approaches, or when the aircraft is flown into the northern winter from temperate regions, not only includes making what modifications of the aircraft may be necessary, but may include minor structural changes as well as simple adjustments, in order to cope with extremely low temperatures. Shops with mechanics able to do this well are found at such air centers as Fairbanks and Anchorage, Alaska; Edmonton and Winnipeg, Canada; and other American and Canadian cities along the border from Seattle through Bangor (Old Town), Maine, on east into the Maritime Provinces.

MODIFICATIONS

1. Cabin Heating A cabin heater which can maintain the temperature of instruments and cockpit accessories above 0°F and preferably above freezing, as well as warm pilot and passengers, is essential.

2. Defrosting The cabin heater outlets must be designed to provide a blast of warm air onto the windshield in front of the pilot's face. At subzero temperatures the inside of the windshield will frost up despite adequate cabin heat, and planning to wipe the frost away will not work.

3. Baffle Plates Baffles of proper size and shape will have to be placed to restrict the flow of engine-cooling air. This may be done by placing plates over the outlet at the rear of the cowling which stop the flow of air around the engine and minimize the cooling effect; however, in really cold weather, —30°F or lower, it is best to have plates on the forward side of the cowling and plates or "lagging" (asbestos sheathing) over the front oil sump of radial engines, over the front of the crankcase if exposed, and over the propeller governor. The external oil lines and oil-tank cooler may also have to be "lagged" with asbestos padding, and the oil-tank cooler vanes partly or entirely covered with shielding. All this is done in order to keep the engine oil temperature adequately high while the aircraft is in full flight through low subzero weather. Without this, it is quite possible for the engine oil to drop so low in temperature that partial congealing and inadequate lubrication develop, with the obvious danger of engine damage or even complete failure in flight.

4. Carburetor Air Intake In cold weather, fuel-air mixtures are inherently leaner due to increased air density. At − 40°F, the equivalent sea-level pressure altitude is − 5000 ft. This effect, coupled with improper fuel vaporization and distribution to cylinders, can cause engine roughness. In extreme cold, without heating the incoming air or restricting its flow, takeoff power will never be developed. The effects of these conditions are especially noticeable while operating on one magneto during ground checks, though opening the throttle above idling alone will cause the engine to quit.

For this reason an adequate carburetor heat system is absolutely essential. During warm-up and ground check, use of full carburetor heat will reduce the ram of air and thus enrich the mixture; it also improves fuel vaporization. Heat is also required for takeoff, climb, cruise, and descent into colder air near the surface, or for flight at reduced power.

Using carburetor heat requires close attention to engine temperatures; however, when operating in subzero cold, avoid using partial carburetor heat because this may raise the carburetor air temperature to the 32° to 80° range in which icing can be critical under certain atmospheric conditions. In addition to using heat, one can counter the effects of extreme cold by selecting relatively high manifold pressure and rpm settings, by avoiding excessive throttle movements both in flight and on the ground.

Some older light-aircraft air intakes simply cannot be redesigned for safe flight at extremely low temperatures, but most can. This should be discussed in detail with the A and E mechanic who does this part of the winterizing job. He must know the particular engine-cowling characteristics of the individual airplane in this regard, and if he does not, one should find a mechanic who does.

5. The Crankcase Drain The engine crankcase should be equipped with a quick-release drain of large enough diameter to allow cold or partially congealed oil to run through it, and an extension tube to pass through the cowling; and also, ideally, a little hole or hook upon which to hang a clean oil-drain canister into which to run the engine oil immediately upon landing, when staking out of doors for a northern winter night.

6. The Breather Tube If the engine breather tube extends more than ½ in. outside the engine wall, it should be cut off. Long breather tubes have a tendency to ice up and clog tight in flight in low subzero temperatures because of the condensation from the constant compression and expansion of air, and in the usual case where the oil tank has a tight-fittiing filter cap, pressure will build up and burst the tank or the oil cooler.

7. Oil Dilution In some airplanes an oil dilution system must be installed as a modification of the plane. This permits bleeding a standard amount of gasoline from the fuel line into the engine oil system as the very last step before shutting down the engine on nights when the temperature at starting time in the morning is expected to be in the 0 to +32°F range. This dilution system is not, however, much used on the smaller bush aircraft. In any case, the oil dilution system should not be relied upon at temperatures below 0°F, for at such temperatures full preheating becomes essential.

8. Emergency Equipment The winterizing procedure will include getting together and placing in semipermanent stowage in the plane the special winter forced-landing-in-the-bush emergency gear, which may save the lives of pilot and passengers. This equipment is analogous to lifeboats and lifesaving gear on an ocean-going vessel. The makeup of the list of equipment for this purpose is discussed in this chapter under the section Search and Rescue.

9. Auxiliary Equipment If there is any possibility of intentional landings and takeoffs being made in the bush away from airports, the following equipment should also be stowed in the plane as a part of the winterizing procedure: tie-down ropes, the firepot, engine tent, and any other accessories necessary for preheating the particular airplane; wing covers or a long-handled T-broom for brushing frost off the wings in the morning if wing covers are not used; a rope sufficiently long to scrape the frost off the tops of the wings by sawing it back and forth, in the event neither wing covers nor T-broom is at hand.

Ground Handling

Some ground handling requirements have been implied in the presentation of the list of winterizing procedures outlined above. To it the following points should be added.

SUMMER

In summer the only peculiar ground handling problem which seems to distinguish operations in the north from those in temperature regions is the appalling number of mosquitoes, blackflies, and tabanids (popularly known as "bulldogs" or "mooseflies") which for some strange reason are strongly attracted by open aircraft cabin windows if the plane is standing in the sun. The numbers which may collect inside the cabin may be even more than a nuisance because of the serious distraction they create if the pilot takes off without killing them. If they are killed, usually with an aerosol insecticide, the numbers of the bodies which collect over a period of time in crannies and cracks around the instrument pannel can become a menace to keeping the instruments clean. Keeping all cabin windows shut while on the ground seems to be the best solution. The northern

Figure 15.1 A typical subarctic bush pilot's airfield. Hood Lake, just outside Anchorage, Alaska, is a well-equipped bush ski landing strip (1947). (*Courtesy of Bradford Washburn, Boston Museum of Science.*)

sun is not usually so hot that this will create a serious overheating of the interior of the plane.

WINTER

The special procedures of winter ground handling, however, are not so easily carried out. For military aircraft, procedures for northern air bases have been worked out in detail in Technical Orders (Figure 15.1). But the following observations on the winter ground handling of civilian bush planes can also serve as a check list for military propeller planes, because general principles only are considered.

USE OF HEATED HANGARS

Heated hangars, if available, naturally solve most of the problems of winter ground handling of aircraft. But there is one danger with heated hangars which must be kept in mind. When a plane has been in a hangar all night at temperatures above freezing and then is brought outside in the morning into temperatures below freezing, any snow or freezing rain which is falling will at first melt on the wings, but subsequently will turn to ice. Crashes have occurred under such circumstances, where the pilot has started his takeoff run before the temperature of the wing surface has adjusted itself to the outside air; for by the time of beginning to be airborne, the wing surface had dropped below freezing and the resultant wing frost or frozen precipitation killed lift enough to prevent the plane from flying properly. Therefore, on bringing a plane out from a heated hangar, the pilot should, if there is any precipitation at all, delay his takeoff until the wing temperatures have become adequately adjusted.

Another important point in connection with heated hangars is the danger of condensation in fuel tanks when the plane is brought in. In the tank whose fuel selector valve is in the OFF position, water may collect which in summer would run off harmlessly into the carburetor water trap when the valve is turned to the ON position in flight. At extremely low temperatures in flight, this water, which would be harmless in summer, freezes at the valve and obstructs fuel flow. Forced landings from this cause are quite frequent in winter. The best protection is to refill the tanks immediately after flight before leaving the plane for the night, so that there are no airspaces in which condensation can occur. Also, after getting well aloft at the beginning of a flight, but after temperature adjustment has occurred, it is well to test the fuel flow from all tanks before getting too far from the takeoff field to return on the tank used for takeoff.

PARKING IN THE OPEN

The real problems of ground handling in winter develop when the airplane is staked down overnight outside the hangar or out in the bush. To present the handling of this operation chronologically, it should be said that by far the most important part of getting the airplane under way on a subzero morning is the work done on it the night before.

Landing Gear The first thing to do is to park the aircraft in such a way that the landing gear will not be frozen to the ground in the morning. Wheels are easily run onto a mat of insulating material of some sort (if indeed the wheels will be a problem at all). But skis require more thought, for when frozen down, not only are they harder to loosen, but the rough, freshly broken-out under-surfaces in the morning may set up a very heavy drag and create a takeoff problem. The usual bush pilot solution for this is to lay a short round log of firewood, or even spruce branches, in the snow at the place where the skis are to come to rest for the night, and simply taxi the ship onto this mat.

If ski friction on the snow is likely to create a heavily loaded takeoff problem in the morning, a quite effective and practical "ski wax" for airplane skis is arranged by getting a can of kerosene and a couple of burlap bags the night before. Before takeoff the bags may be soaked with kerosene and laid one in front of each of the skis so that the ski bottoms will get a good smearing of kerosene just at the start of the takeoff run.

The new plastic-undersurface Teflon skis reduce but do not eliminate freezedown of the skis. Ski-wheel gear (Figure 15.2), in which the skis can be retracted a few inches above the tire tread solves this problem: Merely retract the skis when the plane is parked.

Engine Oil The second problem springs from the fact that most engine oil congeals to the consistency of soft butter at temperatures slightly below 0°F, and to the consistency of laundry soap at temperatures far below zero. True, there are some engine oils now in existence which maintain the same free-flowing viscosity at these temperatures as at full operating temperatures. But unless the engine is lubricated with these engine oils, time-honored principles for handling congealed engine oils will have to be observed.

If the morning temperatures are going to be somewhere between 0° and 32°F, it may be possible to start the engine without preheating or draining the oil the night before—particularly if the engine is equipped for oil dilution. The smaller planes which can be started by hand do not have these oil-dilution systems, but aircraft with starters for the most part are now factory equipped with them. Remember that shutdown time

Figure 15.2 A typical ski-wheel landing gear design. Dr. Terris Moore examines the ski-wheel landing gear on his Supercub. Taken on Kahiltna Glacier, Mount McKinley, 1951. (*Courtesy of Bradford Washburn, Boston Museum of Science.*)

in the evening, not warm-up time in the morning is the time to use oil dilution. Engine manufacturers' recommendations for dilution must be carefully followed. A common error is to start dilution while the engine oil is so hot that the diluting gasoline is immediately vaporized; the beneficial result of diluting engine oil is then of course nil.

Engine Heating If the morning starting temperatures are going to be below 0°F, the pilot should definitely plan to preheat the engine before attempting to start it. If he should happen to have one of the smaller engines with new spark plugs, freshly ground valves, and snug-fitting rings, it may well be that the engine can actually be started somewhat below zero merely by pulling the propeller through by hand, without preheating the engine. But the pilot should not allow himself to be beguiled into doing this. For at temperatures below 0°F, starting the engine without preheating puts too much of a strain upon the close tolerances in various parts of the engine, under the extreme temperature differentials which will prevail immediately after the start, to warrant such cold starts by anyone who values his engine. Moreover, in the cabin, gyro instruments and the tachometer may be damaged by making subzero starts without preheating.

In preparation for preheating the engine, the usual process is to put the engine tent over the cowl the night before, wrapping it around beneath to serve also as an engine cover during the night. This will greatly reduce the formation of frost on the engine parts within the cowl. Moreover it will protect the engine spaces and cracks from filling with any blowing snow which may fly during the night—a potential source of water in the engine during preheating.

If the plane is staked out on a well-equipped airport, it may be possible to get the use of a motor-driven hot-air "Herman Nelson" type heater. If this is not available, a white gas, flameless heater is in wide use which is perfectly safe, and works on the same principle as a hand warmer. It has high capacity: Placed inside the cowl of a light aircraft cold-soaked at −40°F, and insulated by tarps and blankets, it heated the engine and oil supply overnight enough to permit a quick start in the morning. Lacking such a heater, a plumber's firepot or even a large blowtorch will do, placed under the engine tent. But the fire hazard is great. Standard practice, therefore, is to keep a fire extinguisher handy. The old-timer's further precautions— (a) tailing the aircraft into the wind so that in the event of fire under the engine the flames will blow away from the rest of the aircraft, and (b) cutting some long stakes and setting them up tepee-like to hold the engine cover away from the flames of the firepot—are still good practice. Another important precaution against fire when using open flames during preheating is to stop the engine at the time of engine shutdown the night before by completely turning off the fuel selector valve and letting the engine run the carburetor and lines dry, thus letting the engine die for want of fuel. If this is done, there is no gasoline left anywhere in the airplane forward of the firewall. This drying-up of the carburetor and fuel lines is something which cannot be contrived at starting time, and can be arranged only at the time of shutdown the night before.

If temperatures below −20°F are to be expected at starting time, it will probably be well to drain the engine oil immediately after shutdown, while it is still hot, into a canister kept for the purpose, and to take this oil into the pilot's night shelter. It is very easy to heat this oil to 150°F during the breakfast cooking operations the next morning. When poured back into the engine hot, this oil will aid a quicker preheating and more uniform distribution of heat throughout the engine. The pilot should not be misled into thinking that the oil is warm enough for use just because the outside of the canister is too hot to touch and the oil is bubbling as if it were boiling. If it has been heating rapidly over a hot flame, the oil in contact with the sides and bottom of the canister can be boiling hot while there is still a large lump of congealed oil in the center.

Engine heating is all-important for cold weather starting. To take short cuts at this time will result only in extensive delay because of engine damage, or because of the need to repeat the process until done properly.

Wing Frost or Ice At the time of tying down for the night, wing covers must be put on the wings to prevent frost or ice. This is a most surprising phenomenon to the uninitiated. A very thin film of frost on the upper surface of the wings will kill wing lift sufficiently to prevent any plane getting airborne properly from a normal takeoff run. Elevators, stabilizers, and ailerons must also be brushed completely clean on both sides and checked for ice obstruction to full deflection before takeoff.

The relative merits of using wing covers instead of brushing the wings in the morning with a long-handled T-broom is a question which only experience can answer satisfactorily for a particular aircraft and particular weather conditions. If the wing covers can be put on easily, then using them will always be the preferable course. For (a) they give more complete protection, (b) it takes less time to get the covers off in the morning than to do the necessary wing brushing, (c) actual ice may be almost impossible to brush off, whereas taking off the wing covers will usually break it up easily, and (d) if the type of wing covers which have built-in spoilers are used, the aircraft gets additional protection against being flown away by high winds during the night. Wing covers are bulky and heavy, and this is where nylon really comes into its own. Nylon covers are only a fraction of the weight of the canvas ones, not so bulky, and do not tear so easily. If carried in the fuselage on bush flights, the advantages of the smaller bulk and lighter weight of nylon wing covers will be especially appreciated.

Tying Down The fifth step in the process will be the tie-down arrangements. If the airplane is parked beside a hangar on an airport, the usual stakes and cables will serve; in fact they are usually much more dependably fast in the frozen ground of winter than in summer. On the other hand, if stakes must be driven, the frozen ground will present a real problem. The ordinary tie-down kit carried in the plane will be useless for a winter tie-down job in the bush. If the landing is on the ice of a lake or river, as is frequently the case in winter wilderness landings, the job is fairly simple; with an ax, or preferably a regular ice chisel (which will be easier) chop three "arches" in the ice, one under each wing and the tail. If these are cut so that the ice is at least 4 to 5 in. thick at its thinnest places, the strength of the arches will be easily able to hold a plane down even if the wind is lifting it up against the ropes.

If the landing is on a strip without tie-downs, or "in the rough" on a gravel bar or frozen tundra, the tie-down problem may still be solved if the air temperature is well below freezing. Tying down can be carried out by mixing water with snow into slush and cementing a branch or board or other object to the ground with the tie-down rope around it. A surprisingly strong tie-down can be constructed in this way. But if the air temperature happens to be above freezing, or only a little below, and the ground is still solid from the winter freeze, there will be a real problem.

The frequent attempts of pilots to make a secure tie-down by hanging weights under the wings of the plane are often based upon an illusion. Actually it will take a weight of many hundreds of pounds to give anything more than minor protection this way. It should be remembered that a weight hung under the wing does little more good than if it were simply placed in the cabin. How often has one seen airplanes weighted down in this way with 50 lb or so hung on each wing, creating a false sense of security, when actually the weights had less effect than would that of a pilot and passenger in the cabin! The use of wing spoilers, the best of which is the type built right into wing covers, will do at least as much good as a great deal of weight hung around the airplane. Quite effective wing spoilers can also be rather simply arranged by tying two-by-four lumber, or even tree branches, along the tops of the wings just above the leading edge.

Snow Runway Preparation The sixth step will be to think about the snow runway in the morning. Usually there will be nothing to do. But if the airplane is being staked out in the bush, the following point should be noted: If the pilot is going to have to snowshoe-tramp a runway for the morning takeoff on skis, it is much better to do it the night before, even if snow should fall during the night to the point where it has to be tramped again in the morning. The reason is that a snow runway tramped the night before (or taxied over by using the plane's power—an easier way of doing it than with the feet on snowshoes) will always be much firmer than one so made in the morning immediately before use. It is one of the curious phenomena of snow that even if the temperature is below freezing and the snow dry at the time of tramping the night before, the runway will be much "tighter" after standing overnight than if tramped just before use in the morning. And of course if the temperature is above freezing the evening before and below freezing in the morning, the evening is certainly the time to do the runway tramping.

Snow is most slippery at melting temperatures. Drag increases noticeably with subzero temperatures, and longer ski runways become necessary.

Batteries Before leaving the airplane the pilot must give thought to the storage battery. If the engine is small enough to be started easily by hand, and if the battery is fully charged and will only have to stand out for a few nights, there will be nothing to do beyond turning off the master switch. But the following facts about lead-sulfuric acid batteries are worth remembering, for such batteries are greatly weakened by cold.

A fully charged lead-sulfuric acid battery will produce 100% output at 80°F, 65% output at 32°F. 40% output at 0°F, and 10% output at −30°F. At 0°, the electrical load needed to crank an engine may be as much as 250% of the load at 80°F. The combined effect of these oppositely moving curves is something to ponder! It means that one must thoroughly preheat to get the engine load back to normal levels; and it also means that one must either take the battery indoors to keep it warm in subzero weather, or put it on charge for some hours prior to use, or "trickle-charge" (a slight charge of long duration) it overnight right in place in the plane's battery box. Charging warms it up chemically right at the point of need: in the plates and acid.

Another fact to remember about lead-sulfate lead-sulfuric acid batteries is that although a fully charged battery will not freeze until −95°F, a half-discharged battery will freeze at −40°F, and a battery fully discharged to a specific gravity of 1160 will freeze at 0°F. Conclusion: If the pilot is going to leave lead-sulfate batteries in an airplane parked outdoors, he should expect them to freeze and break unless they are not only left but kept in a fully charged condition. The pilot should also remember that lead-sulfate batteries slowly discharge themselves, so that even in a single month's time of standing they can become half or more discharged. And of course if the slightest electrical drain happens accidentally to be left on them, they could become fully discharged and freeze and break in a much shorter time.

Nickel-cadmium batteries are not subject to any of these failings, and moreover are lighter in weight. This is why they are increasingly coming into use in the North even though they are much more expensive than the lead-sulfate type.

Window Frost The last thing to do on leaving the plane is to open the windows very slightly, or open the cabin vents. Unless this is done, frost may form on the insides of the cabin windows because of the relatively warmer moist air left in the cabin. At very low temperatures this frost will not be easy to remove. Ordinary scrapers cannot be used because of the curved surfaces, and because some aircraft windshield materials scratch easily. If there may be blowing snow during the night, this ventilating of the cabin should of course be done in such a way as not to let blowing snow enter.

Refueling The pilot should definitely refuel the airplane before leaving it in summer or before placing it in a heated hangar in winter, in order to prevent condensation and collection of water in the tanks. But to insist on doing this at the end of staking an airplane out on a subzero day when all the preceding operations have been gone through would probably constitute a counsel of perfection! In the middle of the arctic or subarctic winter, when temperatures are virtually certain not to rise above freezing in the low sun of a short winter day, the danger of condensation in the partially empty gas tanks for a few nights and even days is small enough to ignore for a short time. But there may be a slight steady growth of frost crystals in the tanks if they are empty. Hence the refueling job should be done as soon as it can conveniently be arranged. Under these conditions refueling may be done the next morning when light has returned and the pilot can see what he is doing.

GETTING STARTED IN THE MORNING

Starts from a heated hangar have already been described. In the bush the process begins from what was done when the aircraft was staked down; and there probably being no power-driven heater available, the firepot will have to be used under the engine tent (Figure 15.3) unless possibly one of the modern catalytic heaters has been left under the engine overnight.

Since the firepot preheating process will have to be in operation anywhere from 20 to 60 min, this is the first thing to get started, so that while this heating is going on, other preparations can be made. If the temperature is low enough to endanger the operation of the instruments in the cabin, it will be essential also to have a separate firepot or blowtorch running in the cabin under the instrument panel, for in most airplanes the firewall prevents any appreciable amount of heat from under the engine getting to the instrument panel. (BEWARE OF AN EXPLOSION in the cabin if the cabin firepot goes out with the lower firepot still burning.)

Refueling Theoretically, refueling should not be done at all while the engine is being heated with an open-flame type of firepot, and this is an

Figure 15.3 "Firepotting" and firepotting equipment. The pilot, the Rt. Rev. William J. Gordon, Bishop of Alaska, is heating his Cessna 170 with a one-burner gasoline heater. He has placed a can containing engine oil, which he drained on landing, on top of the heater. The patches in the engine hood attest to the need for vigilance to avoid disaster by fire.

additional reason for doing it at night. The center tank should certainly not be filled just above where the engine is being firepotted with an open flame.

The most important thing to remember about refueling in the bush is *always* to strain the gas through a *chamois.* Canadian bush pilots seem to prefer felt to chamois; the writer always uses *both* a felt layer and a chamois in his gasoline funnel. Even the finest metal-mesh screens that will not pass water that may be in the fuel will, however, pass the very fine rust particles which (bush pilots soon learn) infest all gasoline that comes from drums. Only the filters and traps in use on the most active airports where gasoline is constantly being drawn through a pressure system can produce gasoline which may be safely run straight into the airplane's tanks. All other gasoline is dangerous unless run through a chamois. It is so because of the unavoidable condensation, with resultant rusting, of the drums or tanks in which gasoline is stored. A funnel with a good chamois is one of the most important pieces of equipment the bush pilot can carry with him.

While the firepotting is going on, the daily preflight check can be made. For airplanes which have been staked outdoors in the snow country, always include in this preflight check a very careful examination of the interior of the fuselage of the plane near the tail. Wind-driven snow goes through the cracks and control openings of the tail assembly and easily fills the tail of the aircraft with snow, making it dangerously tail-heavy but leaving nothing outside to attract attention to this condition. Be sure to look for it. The same danger exists with some aileron designs, and these too should be checked for internal wind-packed snow.

How long should firepotting go on? At least until the propeller can be moved freely by hand. And if the temperature is below zero, it should last long enough to be sure that some heat is distributed throughout the engine and that oil throughout the system has become warm enough not to congeal and stop the oil flow anywhere. With a standard plumber's firepot and a 150 hp engine at −20°F, this might take 30 min. If the temperature is down near −50°F, it will take at least a full hour with such equipment, and possibly more. But with the new viscosity-free-flowing oils, moving the propeller with the hand is no longer a valid test, and firepotting with such oils is done by time and by feeling of the engine, especially the magnetos, tachometer, and gyros, which might be injured with too cold a start.

Immediately upon starting the engine, the oil pressure should be watched closely, and if it does not come to normal within 20 sec or so and remain at normal, the engine should be stopped at once to preheat some more. Sometimes congealed oil in some parts of the engine will prevent the oil pressure from coming to normal on the oil pressure gage;

on the other hand, oil congealing in other parts of the system may cause the pressure to go far above normal—in fact right off the pressure-gage scale; and unless this is immediately stopped, the oil lines may burst at the fittings.

Ice-bridging of the spark-plug points is another phenomenon with which the northern pilot should be thoroughly familiar. It usually occurs when the engine has not been firepotted, or when heating has been inadequate, and the pilot is trying to start it cold at temperatures near zero. Under these conditions, if the engine fires a few times and possibly makes 6 to 10 revolutions, stops, and then cannot be started at all, the chances are good that the spark plugs have become ice-bridged. This happens when a few explosions warm the interior of the cylinders and cause condensation just above freezing. Then if there is no firing for some moments the spark-plug points cool below freezing and ice forms. If this takes place across the spark-plug points, the ice will probably short them out, and no amount of cranking thereafter will cause the engine to fire unless most of the other cylinders come on sufficiently to run the engine, in which case the repeated compression will melt the ice. But if most of the plugs in the engine have become ice-bridged, the engine cannot be started no matter how much it is cranked. The only thing to do in this case is to remove one plug from each cylinder and put the points in a stove or under a blowtorch. The practice of some pilots of laying a blowtorch right on the heads of the plugs while they are in place is simpler and quicker and will get rid of the ice, but it is rather rough treatment and may scorch the spark-plug harness.

Taking off with flat struts is of course very hard on the strut and on the aircraft, both at takeoff and at the following landing. Proper tightening of the oleo seals and constant watching of strut pressure will cure this trouble. A pilot flying from a warm airport to a cold one, or moving his aircraft from a warm hangar out into the cold, should expect trouble with oleo struts unless the struts have been properly winterized and unless air pressures have been increased to compensate for contraction of the air in extreme cold.

After taking off in slush or wet snow, landing gear should be left extended for a short time and then retracted and lowered two or three times to prevent thrown-up slush from freezing them immobile in the retracted position.

Condensation of water in oil tanks at very low temperatures means that oil sumps must be frequently drained. Therefore tank vents and crankcase breathers should be inspected frequently to make sure they are free from ice and snow. In some in-line engines the oil is carried in the crankcase. Thus it is left there during the night and heated by the firepot while heating the engine. But if the oil is not drained after each flight, condensation can cause water to accumulate. To prevent this it is well to give the quick-drain valve a brief turn after each flight to allow water in the drain pipe to escape while the oil is hot and the water in a fluid condition.

LOADING

No discussion of ground handling in northern flying would be complete without some mention of the overloading and the strange cargoes sometimes lashed to the outside of aircraft by bush pilots. The only valid comment which can be made is "Don't do it." The practice is dangerous, for the following reasons: (1) Overloading raises the stalling speed of the airplane. (2) Unless the overloading is done with the proper balance, the flight characteristics of the aircraft may be considerably altered. An airplane that is "forgiving" in its behavior with normal load can become vicious around the stalling point, snapping into a spin easily and coming out only with difficulty. This becomes particularly true if a rearward center of gravity has been created by the overload. (3) If an overloaded plane is flown through rough air, there may be some danger from structural failure which would otherwise be absent. The *g*-load safety factor built into the aircraft to handle turbulent air may be exceeded if the plane is flown through strong turbulence in an overloaded condition. In mountainous terrain this can of course be encountered in clear air.

It is a fact that canoes are quite frequently flown successfully, lashed to the struts of light seaplanes. The practice cannot be validly endorsed, other than by the comment that if this must be done, it should not be undertaken without careful briefing from a pilot with experience, because of the possible aerodynamic effects on the particular airplane.

In-Flight Problems

LIMITING LOW TEMPERATURES

One question that may arise is, How far down in temperature can one safely fly a plane? Metallurgists report that many metals lose their strength quite rapidly in temperatures of 40°, 50°, and 60° below zero. What is the danger of structural failure in flying a plane at these temperatures?

Bush pilots formerly made it a policy (and some still do) not to fly below 35° or 40° below zero. But there now seems to be an increasing amount of flying done at these temperatures, and few if any reports of structural failure due to extremely low temperatures seem to be resulting. There are at least two good reasons why this may be true. One is that at these very low temperatures the air is almost always dead calm, hence there is no strain from turbulence. Another is that pilots flying in these extreme temperatures usually fly in a thoroughly restrained manner. If an aircraft would normally stand 4.5 to 5 *g*'s in flight before failure, and a 60-below temperature reduced this strength by say 50% to 2.5 *g*, probably nothing would happen in flight with a 1.5-*g* load in very smooth air and the complete absence of any acrobatic flying.

An important but quite different argument against flying at temperatures below − 35 to 40°F, however, is that a forced landing in the wilderness at such temperatures is a very serious matter.

Temperatures below − 40°F, except in the Polar Basin itself, usually occur only under conditions of dead calm and in a very thin layer of air only a few hundred feet thick, close to the earth's surface. Thus the aircraft under these conditions makes most of its flight aloft where the air is warmer than at the surface. An example of this temperature inversion occurred when a thermometer at the base of the airport tower on old Weeks Field, Fairbanks, Alaska, read −30°F at the same time that the thermometer at the top of the tower read 0°F. A more normal inversion was one observed during the coldest flight the writer happens to have made. A standard thermometer in an official shelter at the base of the hill at College, Alaska, read − 64°F on the coldest day of the winter of 1952–53. At a house part way up the hill, 150 ft vertically above the base, the temperature was − 54°F. At the top of the hill, where the aircraft was tied down, approximately 225 ft higher than the base, the wing thermometer read − 52°F. Staked out and cold-soaked, the aircraft was firepotted and operating in about an hour and a quarter. Immediately after takeoff the wing thermometer showed a steady rise in temperature and at 1000 ft above the bottom of the hill the air temperature was −35°F; at 2000 ft it was − 24°F. This sort of temperature gradient may be considered normal for extremely low continental temperatures.

ICE FOG

This is undoubtedly one of the most serious problems of northern flying. There are quite different types of ice fog. The supercooled water-droplet variety can exist down to at least − 30°F in dead calm air. In fact laboratory experiments have shown that droplets can actually exist in liquid form down to −50°F. These droplets solidify instantly on contact with any object, and an aircraft moving in this kind of ice fog is immediately glazed with ice. The first problem for the pilot is that his windshield picks up an ice glaze from outside and rapidly becomes opaque. Flight may be possible for some time, however, because the coating is light and takes some time to build up enough thickness to appreciably alter the airfoil section of the wing. Since most ice fogs lie in comparatively thin layers only one of several hunded feet thick, close to the ground, the usual remedy is to climb out of it. Failing that, a "one eighty" or immediate landing is indicated.

The other type of ice fog (page 320) does not attach itself to aircraft, but seriously obscures horizontal visibility. Though airfleld buildings or lights may be dimly or sometimes quite clearly visible from above, the final approach through the shallow fog layer will be virtually blind. This is particularly true at dusk. At night, strong runway lights are valuable, but aircraft landing lights are worse than useless, for they give only a blinding glare.

WHITEOUT

Whiteout is another phenomenon peculiar to northern flying which can be exceedingly serious. It occurs most frequently in treeless regions when the ground is completely snow-covered and in addition the sky is overcast, perhaps with oncoming twilight. If the light conditions are such that downward, horizontally, and upward there is the same milkiness and no horizon is visible, the phenomenon of whiteout may occur. In this case the pilot suddenly and completely loses his orientation. He suddenly has no sense of horizon or up or down. He is quite as helpless as if he were flying in a dense fog, even though the visibility may actually be perfect. He is in instrument conditions. It is a terrifying experience.

Whiteout is much less detectable in advance and therefore more dangerous than ordinary fog, because the latter is easily seen at a distance and therefore avoided. Not so with whiteout. Though an experienced pilot will begin to get a warning from the onset of the symptoms just mentioned, it is not possible, as with fog, to see ahead just where the whiteout begins and ends. It is quite possible to get into it without realizing what is happening, until suddenly the pilot finds himself in instrument conditions—and possibly without the necessary equipment and training. Fortunately whiteout is not common except in the far north beyond the limit of trees, and in the Antarctic.

What to do about whiteout is easy to state but may be difficult to carry out. This is definitely and insistently to avoid whiteouts unless one is completely prepared for instrument flight.

If unexpectedly caught in a whiteout without blind-flying instruments, the situation is exceedingly serious, and not unlike the question of what to do if caught in fog or cloud of unknown depth and extent without blind-flying instruments: a neat little problem in the theory of escape.

The best advice probably is not to try to make a 180° turn without instruments, but instead to cut the power, pull on flaps, take hands off the stick, and hope somehow with the rudder to keep the plane out of a fatal spiral dive and let it settle to earth in a mushing glide at 10 knots above stall and, say, 100 fpm. The pilot should keep his eyes open for a glimpse of some land object which will restore his horizon and depth perception, and permit him to carry out a landing.

If the pilot has smoke bombs with him and is only a few hundred feet above the terrain, he may, by throwing out a bomb and reducing the speed to no more than a safe margin above stall, be able to glimpse the bomb behind him on the snow, regain his orientation and make a landing. Old-time bush pilots sometimes carried a sack of spruce boughs to throw out for this very purpose. The spruce boughs have an advantage over smoke bombs in remaining visible indefinitely rather than burning out in a few minutes. It seems a little excessive to counsel carrying a sack of spruce boughs in the plane. But this might be a good thing to take on an essential flight in which whiteout appears a possibility.

CARBURETOR ICING

It might be supposed that carburetor icing is especially serious in northern flying. Though serious enough, it is not more of a problem in the arctic than it is in winter, early spring, and later fall flying in the temperate zones. The standard discussions of carburetor icing as they apply to a particular aircraft are equally applicable to the same plane in northern flying.

Most carburetor icing occurs when the air has a high relative humidity and the temperature is between 45° and 60°F above zero, because under such conditions refrigeration effects inside the carburetor create condensation and also drop its internal temperature below freezing. Application of carburetor heat raises the temperature at the points where freezing occurs, and melts out the ice; better yet, if used in time, it prevents ice formation.

But with some carburetors there is a zone where in very low temperatures if carburetor heat is applied, this will *cause* icing. Under these conditions (usually 0° to −10°F) the carburetor will be operating at temperatures far below freezing. Now if the pilot pulls on the carburetor heat, he may raise the temperatures at critical points within the carburetor to just above freezing, and cause melting water to run to colder areas and freeze. Thus at low temperatures the pilot should be cautious about applying carburetor heat until he knows the exact peculiarities of his particular engine in this respect.

A very neat little problem can arise with some carburetor and engine cowling combinations. Some engines must in extreme subzero air have some carburetor heat on during throttle-back when descending, in order to prevent their dying in flight. How likely is this carburetor heat to cause icing within the carburetor, as just described? In most cases it will not, but there may be some of the older types of civilian plane in which it will. With them the only safe practical answer is to discuss the particular aircraft with an experienced northern A and E mechanic who knows that type of aircraft well with regard to these details.

ICING OF THE AIRCRAFT STRUCTURE IN FLIGHT.

The discussion of this subject in Chapter 6 will be equally applicable to northern flying. Two special conditions do, however, occur in the far north. One of these has already been mentioned: the supercooled water-droplet type of ice fog. The other is a rather rarer type of fine frost which occasionally occurs in very low subzero temperatures. In this case the frost collects not merely on the leading edges of the aircraft wings and structure, but rather evenly over the entire structure of the plane. Typically it builds up quite slowly so that the pilot can keep flying for some time; but eventually he has to land, perhaps on a frozen lake or river, and brush the frost off wings and tail assembly before taking to the air again.

NAVIGATION AND RADIO

These two factors become especially important in northern flying, and they are closely related. Because distances between towns ar so vast in the tremendous wilderness reaches of the north, navigation becomes a very serious matter. Getting lost, which may be regarded as a humorous situation in the States—involving landing on a farm to ask where one is or drawing up to a beach with a floatplane to ask the bathers—is never a joke in the far north, where habitations are exceedingly few and far between. No pilot should undertake a northern flight unless he is absolutely sure that his navigation is accurate and dependable.

The special navigational problems arising out of the fact that the magnetic compass becomes increasingly unreliable and finally useless as one draws within a few hundred miles of the North Magnetic Pole, are discussed in Chapter 11.

Many of the radio aids which make navigation so easy in the States do not yet exist in the far north. This subject becomes highly technical and complicated and is worth a chapter of its own. Suffice it to say here that in general the VHF and UHF radio systems so widely used in the States are only used to a limited degree in the far north, because these systems cannot give the long range which is obtainable from the older aircraft MF/HF sets developed durinng the 1930s and '40s. This long range is especially necessary for an aircraft down on the ground sending out signals. Moreover, the electrical static which is such a handicap to LF/MF radio in the States, particularly in summer, does not exist to nearly the same degree in the far north, because there are fewer thunderstorms within radio hearing range.

Discussion of in-flight problems of the north should not be closed without adding that most experienced northern pilots in general prefer northern flying to stateside operations, largely because the air in northern flying is so often "smooth as cream." With the sun rolling low around the horizon and never getting high in the sky, there is on the average very much less thermal turbulence in northern skies than in the States. The average precipitation also is considerably lower in the far north. Both of these factors tend to make for less cloudiness, smoother air, and therefore pleasanter flying.

Landings and Takeoffs "In the Rough"

The phrase "landing in the rough" is used by northern bush pilots to mean making a landing in an unprepared place, relying solely upon observations made from above in flight to carry it off. In the early days of northern flying, landings "in the rough" were quite frequent. And though the need for such landings is becoming less as airports and small airstrips have been placed throughout the north, nevertheless the northern pilot will not be fully acquainted with his subject if he does not know what is involved, nor fully accomplished in his profession if he has not had experience of this sort.

In general, the big problem with a landing "in the rough" is the great decision: whether to commit the airplane to the landing or not. By and large the successful bush pilots are the ones who in the past decided "No" at the right times and places. But it is not enough always to say "No" as a matter of principle. Any good airport pilot can make it an invariable rule to say "No" to the question of landing in the rough, but he will not then be a northern bush pilot. The fact of the matter is that landings in the rough can be made in remarkable locations and still keep the risk within reasonable limits. The competent bush pilot will be able to identify the occasions when the answer can be "Yes," and be willing and able to carry the operation out successfully.

ESTIMATING LANDING POSSIBILITIES

The method can be stated quite simply. A strip of ground, snow, or ice must be located, long enough and firm enough to get the plane down and to a stop and free of obstructions on the sides to clear the wings. And if it is an aircraft requiring more length of runway to take off than to land, the terrain must also be such as to allow the pilot to improve the strip after he is on the ground, sufficiently so that he can get into the air again. To appraise these possibilities from the air with any accuracy, the pilot must first of all know exactly what his airplane can and cannot do in the way of short landings and takeoffs, with different loads, at various altitudes and temperatures. Ordinary airport flying with civilian planes does not call for such precise knowledge on the part of the pilot. But the competent bush pilot, at the time of his first acquaintance with a new airplane, will make a point of carefully trying the plane out with just these questions in mind. This can be done easily at the local airfield by pacing off distances carefully to measure landing rolls and minimum takeoff runs necessary to get airborne with different load and air conditions.

A flap-equipped airplane lends itself well to placement landings. They are safely practiced by getting down about ten feet off the ground at least 100 yards away from the landing line. Then with flaps down, just enough power to keep the airspeed reasonably above the stalling point, and "hanging on the prop" in this condition, the pilot comes in, very gradually easing down his altitude to about 3 to 5 ft and possibly very slightly reducing power. As his wheels are approaching the line—experience will teach him just where for the particular airplane—he cuts the power; then as rapidly as he can move one hand (for the other will be busy holding the stick against air pressure) he drops the flap lever. This move, spilling the lift out of his flaps, will, if he is flying slowly enough at this point, drop him onto the ground right at the spot where he wishes to land. He then immediately applies brakes and keeps them on as hard as he can without nosing up the airplane, throughout the landing run to full stop.

On skis he practices this with different kinds of snow and ice landing surfaces. The takeoff, and particularly the landing runs on skis, with no brakes possible, differ widely with varying snow conditions.

Having learned from this practice how many airplane lengths he needs for landing and for takeoffs, he next practices these from the air in another part of the airport, with different markers and unknown distances, attempting to judge the distances from the air by measuring airplane lengths on the ground with his eye. In this way he will learn to estimate quite accurately from the air how much distance on the ground he will need for landing in an unfamiliar place.

In actual experience in the bush, the three principal uncertainties will be (1) just how rough the ground is (it will almost never be really smooth), (2) whether the ground is sloping, and (3) whether the surface is firm enough to keep the wheels from sinking in too deep to roll. "Dragging" the proposed landing place several times from about 10 to 20 ft high, with sufficient airspeed to keep flight safe, and studying the terrain carefully, constitute the best way to develop some answers to these questions.

During this appraisal operation, the pilot must remember that rocks and rough spots on the proposed landing area must be less high than the radius of the wheels; otherwise the wheels will catch and tear off the landing gear, instead of rolling over the obstacles. Also the pilot must remember that even a slight downhill grade will make it virtually essential to use the "spill the flaps" technique of placements landing; otherwise he probably will float an unpredictable distance down the hill beyond the point of intended touchdown. Also, even a slight downhill grade will very greatly increase the length of the landing roll once his wheels are on the ground. Because of these fundamental disadvantages in downhill landings, it is often considered preferable to land uphill, even at the cost of landing downwind. Whether the benefits of uphill will more than offset the disadvantages of downwind will be something for the pilot to judge in each particular case.

Also the matter of appraising the firmness of the ground by its appearance from 10 to 20 ft in the air is something for the pilot's judgment, for which descriptions in a book cannot begin to provide an adequate substitute for practical experience.

Replacing the stock wheels on the aircraft with large oversize wheels will help enable it to ride over rougher ground than is possible with stock-model wheels. This is because the longer radius of the oversize wheels enables them to roll over obstructions that would stop the shorter-radius wheels. Tandem wheel gear, if the wheels are of standard size only and not oversize, will do little, if indeed anything, toward overriding rough obstacles because the radius of the leading wheel—the critical consideration—remains unimproved. But tandem gear will help greatly in running on soft ground without sinking in because the ground pressure of the wheel tread has been halved. But tandem wheels render taxiing turns more difficult to make.

WILDERNESS LANDING PLACES

River Bars To pilots who have never flown in Alaska, accounts of the early fliers who used river bars (Figure 15.4) throughout the interior almost as if they were ready-made airports seem at times inexplicable, for river bars elsewhere are not usually firm enough, large enough, or smooth

Figure 15.4 Natural landing fields of the arctic. *Upper:* Braided streams, like the Yukon River in Alaska, with their broad expanses of gravel bar or snow-covered ice, or water in summer, provide a principal type of northern landing field. *Lower:* A gravel bar at Allakaket, Alaska, on the Koyukuk, a tributary of the Yukon. Such bars are frequently large enough and firm enough for safe operation of aircraft the size of the DC-3. (*Courtesy of The Rt. Rev. William J. Gordon.*)

enough for landing airplanes. For pilots who have not had practical experience with them, it should be said that river bars in the interior of Alaska, Yukon Territory, and parts of the Northwest Territories of Canada do possess certain qualities of firmness and smoothness not found in other rivers. The reason why becomes an interesting speculation in geology. This aspect of the subject does not seem to have been thoroughly investigated; but the writer notes that it seems to be a peculiar windblown loess-like material in these river gravels which gives them their firmness and smoothness; and also that these qualities seem to exist in those valleys which have glaciers at their headwaters. The rock flour getting into the river water from the glacial action above seems to add a binder to the river bar materials. Speculative theory aside, it is a fact that river bars in this region do not in general have the soft-as-sand consistency found elsewhere in river bars, but are usually firm enough to support the tires of light aircraft. The seriousness of snags or sticks and logs which may be lying about, and the depth of gullies cut out by the shifting water, will be the principal questions to answer when contemplating landings "in the rough" on these river bars.

Sea Beaches In the north, as elsewhere, sea beaches often offer opportunities for the pilot of a light aircraft to make successful landings "in the rough." Although in other places beach landings would probably be in violation of local law and of very little use since there would be other transportation facilities nearby, in the north sea-beach landings may occasionally be useful.

There are two main considerations in making sea-beach landings. The first is that on most beaches only the area between low-tide and high-tide lines will be firm enough to support the landing gear adequately. With no more knowledge than can be gained by looking down on it from above, the pilot must assume that the sand above high-tide mark will be so soft that ordinary wheel landing gear will sink in and the aircraft will nose over. Therefore if the pilot coming in to land finds the tide is at full high, the sound decision, if there is any appreciable amount of fuel left in the tanks, will almost certainly be "Don't land." He should remember that by throttling the engine back to the point where the aircraft is just kept airborne and then leaning out the engine mixture to the point of minimum gasoline ratio consistent with full power for this minimum throttle setting, the gasoline consumption per hour can be dropped to almost one third of what it is at normal cruise. Also the pilot should bear in mind that the interval between high and low tide is about 6 hr anywhere in the world. Thus if the pilot has only a 1-hr reserve left in his tanks as he comes in over the beach at high tide, he can stretch this hour to three, thus giving time to uncover half the area of the beach between high and low tide marks. Even a half-hour's supply can be stretched to 1½ hr, sufficient in many cases to uncover a strip of beach firm enough to set the wheels down.

If the pilot should, however, be confronted with the necessity of making an immediate landing at full high tide, the chances are he would be better off to avoid the soft sand above high-tide mark, and to land instead between the waves below high-tide mark. If he comes in low with flaps, "hanging on the propeller," 3 ft or so above where the waves are running on the beach, and "drop her in" by spilling the flaps just as a wave is running out, he will have a few seconds on firm sand between waves to bring the plane to a stop, or at least to swing it up into the loose sand above high-tide mark at considerably less than landing speed.

The other important point to remember in beach landings is that most sea beaches are sloping, and yet the landing must be made across and not up the slope. This means that the pilot will have to cope with the fact that aircraft rolling on sloping ground have an inherent tendency to turn into the uphill direction. This tendency is increased by the steepness of the hill and in practical terms is caused by the uphill wheel getting more drag as the aircraft rolls along. On both landing and takeoff, the pilot will have to apply opposite rudder away from the hill. At low speeds there may not be enough rudder control to hold the airplane straight. Only experience based on trials will give the pilot the necessary judgment to carry off landings on sea beaches with dependable success.

Tides in the Polar Basin are slight, amounting to but a foot on most beaches of the Arctic Ocean. In the subarctic, however, they may be considerable: Cook Inlet in Alaska has one of the world's higher tide ranges. Geophysicists tell us that in the Northern Hemisphere a narrow inlet on the west side of a north-south peninsula will produce very high tides. Examples are Cook Inlet, the Bay of Fundy in Nova Scotia, Inchon in west Korea, and presumably also Kamchatka.

Tidal Flats In the early years of bush flying, slippery tidal flats were sometimes used for landings and takeoffs with skis and with floats. The fully qualified bush pilot should be able to handle such situations if need arises.

Historically, the tidal flats have been used in two quite different ways. In Alaska, particularly near Valdez, they were used by bush pilot Bob Reeve, before the days of combination ski-wheel gear, to solve the problem of landing on mountain glaciers when takeoff had to be made from a snowless field or airport. The ingenious bush pilot's answer was "You land your wheel plane on a road beside a tidal flat, wheel it over to the tidal flat, put it on skis there, and then, because the mud is slippery, you just take off from the tidal flat on skis—mud flying in all directions behind you—and go on up to the glacier." And coming back the tidal flat is just as easy to land on as to take off from with skis.

In Portland, Maine, and no doubt in other places, the tidal flats between the airport and the city were in the past successfully used by floatplane pilots who did not have time to wait until the tide came in. Some floatplane float bottoms will slide almost as well as skis.

Roads In most states and territories landing on automobile roads is against the law. But in remote regions it is not against the law; and under emergency conditions such landings may of course become necessary. In general the problem is quite simple. To pilots who have not done it and

Figure 15.5 Sea-ice landing strip at Kotzebue, Alaska. Though there is a paved landing strip at Kotzebue, the sea ice is more convenient in winter because it is adjacent to the town and provides a variety of takeoff and landing directions. The picture was taken in November 1949.

may some day need to, it can be slated from experience that the narrowness of the road will be less of a problem than might be expected. But if there are any telephone or power lines along the road, at the usual standard distance from it, this usually makes the landing so dangerous that it should not be attempted at all.

Frozen Lakes These make excellent landing fields under certain conditions, especially for ski-planes (Figure 15.5). The ice must of course be thick enough to support the aircraft. A minimum of 4 to 5 in. will suffice for most light civilian planes, particularly if they are on skis, provided the thickness is uniform everywhere that the plane will be moving on the ice. A simple rule for clear uniform lake ice is to allow 6 in. for the first ton of weight and ½ in. extra for each subsequent ton. For sea ice these figures should be doubled.

The mere fact that a lake is snow-covered does not of itself indicate that the ice is sufficiently strong. Only a measurement of the ice by someone on the ground, or a reasonably sure indication of the ice thickness given by a knowledge of the number of freezing days preceding, is a safe basis for landing. Appearance of lake ice from the air can be quite misleading. Black-looking ice in the fall, following some days of severe cold with no wind or snow, can look very thin yet be sufficiently strong.

Glare ice can be more treacherous in a quite different and unexpected manner. A surprising number of aircraft are damaged each year in the early winter by inexperienced pilots landing with ski-planes on the glare ice of newly frozen lakes. To their surprise they are unable to stop the airplane, and it slides right on, crashing into the shore and woods. The landing slide of a ski-plane on glare ice (particularly if the pilot mistakenly believes that there is no wind and actually lands with a slight wind on his tail) can be an unexpectedly long one, especially if the skis are not equipped with "skegs."

A wheel landing on glare ice is subject to the same problem. Wheel brakes can be almost completely useless if the lake surface is glare ice; the plane will be almost as badly off in this respect as if it were on skis. A very smooth ice surface with a recent film of light rain on it will produce the ultimate in this type of difficulty. Far below zero the difficulty disappears, for then ice ceases to be slippery.

Another phenomenon of frozen lakes can be that of unseen "overflow water," under the snow but on top of the ice. This sometimes occurs at extremely low temperatures, when the inlet stream of the lake happens to freeze in such a way that the flowing water gets forced out and runs along on top of the ice and so out onto the top of the lake (often unseen beneath the snow cover and insulated from intense cold by it). Frequently this will flow along the shore line. Because the water is underneath the snow, it may not be seen until one is into it; and immediately that the plane's skis get into the water, rough ice forms on their under surfaces. About the only helpful comment is that overflow is most likely to occur somewhere near the mouth of an inlet stream and along the lake's shore line. Hence if the pilot does not know whether this overflow exists or not, it is best to land away from the inlet stream and well out from shore, and not to taxi near the shore until the pilot has got out and walked over to the shore to test for overflow water. Another way is to touch down but keep up a fast taxi and then take off without stopping. Any water coming up beneath the skis will get swept off by the snow before it freezes. Aloft again, from the air any water on top of the ice but beneath the snow, is very likely now to show up in the taxi tracks. If there is still any doubt, a second or even third "press-down" of this sort will make the true condition clear.

It should also be mentioned that many airplanes have been completely demolished because the pilot assumed that he could see the surface of the snow when trying to land under poor light conditions. This is difficult and many times impossible when landing in the middle of a lake during a northern winter, under an overcast sky in twilight. Under these conditions it may be utterly impossible to see the snow surface, and pilots have been known to fly right into the ice, thinking they had 200 to 300 ft of altitude. The remedy for this is to land parallel and close to a straight shore line where the brush or trees provide a contrasting reference line. There is another very good reason for not landing in the middle of a lake when the light is poor. Wind often piles up snowdrifts like ocean waves. These may freeze hard as concrete over a period of time. They are usually found in the center of the lake which is exposed to the wind. Thus the snow is smoother along the shore line and may be perfectly smooth on the side lee to the prevailing wind.

Frozen Rivers These are somtimes less suitable than frozen lakes for landings "in the rough," because of the effects produced by current. Currents are likely to create rough ice by breaking up the ice layers and running them up over each other; current also may produce variable ice, which in one place may be quite adequate to support a ski-plane, yet immediately nearby is treacherous ice which looks thick but is not. Also rivers even more than lakes produce overflow water which even in subzero weather may be running on top of the ice, but invisible under the snow. Once a plane is safely down, so that the pilot has a chance to walk around, frozen rivers usually offer good opportunities for airstrips so long as freezing temperatures prevail.

Winter Tundra The tundra in winter offers many excellent places to land light ski-planes, but the surface must of course be fairly well covered with snow. The small vegetation mounds which make some parts of the tundra rough in summer, are usually well filled in after a few snowfalls. In general, less snow is necessary on the tundra or barren grounds north of the limit of trees than on the patches of tundra farther south, because these mounds of vegetation are more prevalent farther south. On the other hand, the "polygonal ground" found in the far north may at times produce roughness, though in general it can be said that the summer appearance of these polygonal cracks from the air gives a greater impression of ground irregularity than is found when actually walking upon them.

Inviting though it may appear from the air to the inexperienced pilot, the summer tundra is no place to land a wheel plane "in the rough," relying solely upon observations made from the air. It is generally too soft and spongy to take the risk. Airstrips can sometimes be devised on the summer tundra by prior study and minor improvement on the ground, especially on the true barren grounds beyond the limit of trees. An example of this is the old airstrip beside the civilian community at Point Barrow.

Undoubtedly ski-planes can be successfully landed upon the unfrozen summer tundra. And possibly the modern very high-powered small planes which are still light in weight, might even be flown off the summer tundra with skis.

Mountains and Glaciers Occasionally airstrips can be worked out, with only minor improvement, on the rocks and ground of mountain ridge tops. But in general true landings "in the rough" can be made in the mountains only by float-planes on mountain ponds or lakes, or by ski-equipped planes on the surface of mountain glaciers.

The most serious problem in all mountain landings and takeoffs, whether "in the rough" or on slightly or even well-prepared airstrips, will be that of altitude; and if there is any appreciable wind, the problems of downdrafts and severe turbulence.

The effects of altitude are fairly simple and straightforward. They can be determined in advance by study of the engineering tables for the particular engine and aircraft to be used. The engine loses power as altitude increases, in general proportionately as the barometric pressure falls off. The aircraft landing speed increases with the decrease in the density of the air. But the pilot can obtain the true landing airspeed for a given altitude if he merely applies the navigator's correction which translates "indicated airspeed" for a given autitude, to actual ground speed. The usual rule of thumb is that to get the actual speed from the indicated airspeed, the pilot must add to the IAS 2% for each 1000 ft of altitude. This rule is good only for altitudes up to about 10,000 ft. The correction is actually slightly more than 2% per 1,000 ft for the lower altitudes, and slightly less than that in the higher-altitude layers and still less above 10,000 ft. The point is that the change goes not in a straight line but in a smooth curve, with a steadily decreasing rate of decrease in pressure with rise of altitude.

The operation can be simplified by stating that in landing an airplane even at high altitude, the pilot makes a landing normal in every way, including the fact that the stalling speed as it is *indicated* on his airspeed instrument will indicate the point of his actual stall, in exactly the same place on his instrument whether he is landing at sea level, at moderate altitude, or at very high altitudes.

Takeoffs are, as a practical matter, much more affected by high altitude than are landings. Not only will the airplane require greater actual speed to get airborne at its normal IAS, but for this very takeoff the power of the engine will have been considerably reduced by the altitude. The amount of this reduction in power can be accurately ascertained only from the engineering tables for the particular engine. In general it may be said that at 10,000 ft the power available (unless the engine has a supercharger, as few light civilian planes have) will be about one-third less than at sea level. But the snappiness of the takeoff and the rate of climb immediately available to clear obstacles will be reduced even more than one third. The reason is that these depend on the *excess* of power available above that required to overcome the ground friction in the takeoff and to maintain level flight after the plane is airborne. This *marginal* power will be reduced much more percentagewise than the engine's total power is reduced.

The adverse effects of high temperature, relatively unimportant with modern planes at low altitudes, can become a serious matter in takeoffs at high altitudes. The reason is that the margin of excess power necessary to get airborne and to develop a rate of climb is so greatly reduced that the introduction of another depressing factor—high temperature—may spell the difference between being able to take off or not. This point is well known to Rocky Mountain pilots who operate from high-altitude western airstrips. But high-altitude mountain takeoffs in the north, particularly when made from glacier surfaces, are not usually burdened with the additional handicap of a hot summer temperature, so frequent in Rocky Mountain summers.

The factors of downdrafts and severe air turbulence in mountain landings and takeoffs are so complicated, yet so important, that the best advice whioh can be given is the following: Do not undertake to make any landings and takeoffs in the mountains—either in the north or anywhere else, for that matter—at other than regularly approved airports until you have made a special study of and mastered this particular subject of downdrafts and turbulence. The only possible exception to this rule would be: If the day is clear and also the general air mass around the mountains is virtually dead calm and not moving, this particular danger factor is greatly reduced, and could be temporarily nonexistent.

Downdrafts and turbulence are caused by wind; usually not by local winds, but by the fundamental air-mass movement against the mountain range. If this air-mass movement gets up to 20 to 30 mph aloft, there will in general be moderate, smooth updrafts generated on the windward side of the range. On the leeward side of the range, but above the level of the crest, there will be standing waves of powerful updrafts running to increasingly high altitudes as one goes farther downwind. Very turbulent air and strong downdrafts will exist on the leeward side of the range below the level of the mountain crest.

If the air movement aloft rises to 40 to 50 mph or more, the turbulence and downdrafts on the leeward side of the mountains below the crest can get so wild as to make the aircraft practically unmanageable. Downdrafts (and updrafts) with speeds of up to several thousand feet per minute can be the rule on days with such air-mass movements. Do not believe the old saw that " a downdraft can't blow an airplane down into the ground because the air has no place to go down any more when it gets to the ground." The pilot who still harbors this idea should sometime go through the instructive experience of sitting on a cliff looking over the lee side of a mountain range down onto a lake on a windy day. Carefully noting what the gusts show on the water below, he will sometimes see vertical jets of air blowing straight down onto the water, as evidenced by wind-caused waves running outward in all directions from an area where a downdraft is striking the water. A light airplane flying into such a downward jet of air could obviously be plastered right down against the valley floor in full flight.

The existence of strong air-mass movements aloft in the mountains is not always easily recognized from on the ground in the valley below. Parts of some mountain valleys, even on such days, can be deceptively calm. The speed with which clouds around the mountain crest level are moving will more dependably tell the story. If there are no clouds to give this indication, snow blowing from ridges as seen with field glasses from below can sometimes give a reasonably reliable indication of the speed of the air-mass movement aloft.

Glaciers present many good landing opportunities for ski-planes in northern mountains (Figures 15.6 and 15.7). In general this is because snow fills crevasses and rough places in the upper parts of glaciers even during the summer. In winter the snowfall may develop not only the upper but also the middle and lower parts of glaciers into possible landing places. Fortunately the glacier crevasse systems, often so treacherous to persons down on the surface, are usually clearly revealed to the pilot

Figure 15.6 Noordyne Norseman on Muldrow Glacier. The Norseman has been an outstanding bush pilot's airplane since early in World War II. Here it is unloading a one-ton load of miscellaneous freight on Muldrow Glacier, Mount McKinley. Mount Brooks (11,940 ft) is in the background. Despite dramatic surroundings, there was an excellent 4000-ft landing strip—hard-packed snow over solid glacier ice with no crevasses. (*Courtesy of Bradford Washburn, Boston Museum of Science.*)

Figure 15.7 The author's Supercub-125 on Kahiltna Glacier. The photograph is taken at 10,100 ft. The camp was entirely stocked by air drops, and more than a dozen Supercub-125 landings were made here.

above, in somewhat the same way that a pilot from aloft can see things under water not visible to persons on the surface itself.

The two biggest problems in carrying out a glacier landing "in the rough" will be (1) which way the wind is blowing on the surface of the glacier (sometimes quite different from that a few hundred feet aloft), and (2) how steep the slope of the glacier is, and which way it is actually sloping.

Throwing out one of the small smoke bombs down onto the surface of the glacier is an excellent way of getting the wind direction. It is well worth keeping a few of these bombs, only about the size of a large sausage, in the airplane's emergency equipment but readily available to the pilot's hand for glacier flights. A satisfactory substitute can be to drop one of the standard aircraft message containers with a streamer attached. At the moment of impact the streamer will trail downwind and thus give its direction clearly.

As for slope, the experience of over 200 glacier landings and takeoffs at altitudes running up to 16,2000 ft, indicates that high-altitude landings should always be made going up the slope, and high-altitude takeoffs should be made going down the slope. It is recommended that for really high-altitude landings and takeoffs—say at 10,000 ft and above—no downhill landings or uphill takeoffs should ever be attempted, even into the wind. The increased landing speed caused by altitude, and the decreased engine power caused by altitude, completely rule them out.

For those reasons a dome-shaped, smoothly glaciated mountain summit represents the ideal-altitude landing surface, for all landings can be made uphill and all takeoffs downhill, yet all of them into the wind regardless of its direction. Second best is a saddle, and poorest is a simple slope.

The serious tendency of the older bush aircraft to ground-loop during downhill takeoffs has been considerably improved through (1) better-designed landing gear, more widely spaced, and (2) greater engine power and hence stronger prop wash, which gives more effective control to the rudder surfaces in keeping the nose straight during the takeoff run.

Arctic Ice Pack and Ice Islands The Arctic ice pack is usually so rough from the breaking of the edges of floes and the building up of pressure ridges, where the sea current and wind have driven the floes against one another, that the principal problem will be to find a large enough smooth area to land a plane on. For small, light ski-planes with low landing speeds, landing strips can be picked out quite generally all over the Arctic ice pack, and at times landings can be made even by wheel planes.

Another problem will be that of drifting. Except for those parts of the icepack that are frozen to the shore, any given landing place is likely to be "here today and gone tomorrow." Thus the pilot should choose places (except for emergency or purely momentary use) in those parts of the pack that are attached to the shore and not drifting.

The surface of the ice pack becomes very uneven and dangerously rotten in summer. What few areas there may be that are close to land in summer are likely to be quite unsatisfactory as landing places.

The problems of actual landings and takeoffs on the sea ice are completely overshadowed by the problems of survival on the Arctic ice pack. These latter problems, which are not really concerned with airmanship as such, require whole books for their treatment and are well set forth by Vilhjalmur Stefansson in *The Arctic Manual.*

The operations of the United States Air Force on the ice island known as T 3 are remarkable in that heavy, fast-landing military aircraft have been used. This has been possible because the ice which forms these floating islands is apparently of glacial origin and thus hundreds of feet thick instead of the 6 to 10-ft maximum thickness of the ordinary Arctic ice pack. Also the ice islands to which Air Force expeditions have been sent are so far out in the Arctic Basin as to constitute a mid-ocean type of operation. For some time to come the very techniques of conducting the operation will still be in process of development; pilot officers assigned to future expeditions of this type will undoubtedly be selected from the specially qualified.

Floatplaning Floatplane weather brings the time of year when "landings in the rough are made smooth." Almost everywhere in the north there are innumerable bodies of water, most of which are perfect landing and takeoff areas for floatplanes during the open-water season. This lasts anywhere from three to seven months, depending upon where in the arctic or subarctic one is. The specific stick and rudder techniques for handling floatplanes generally are available in the standard flight instruction manuals, and therefore will not be repeated here. *Seaplane Flying and Operations* by Fogg, Strohmeier and Brimm (Pitman, 1949), is a superior text on the basic techniques. The special northern aspects of floatplane flying, however, can be summarized in the following paragraphs.

Takeoffs and landings in northern wilderness lakes and rivers raise the inevitable question, How about hitting unknown submerged rocks and ripping out the bottoms of the floats? This is really not a serious problem for alert pilots, because (a) light floatplanes have a very shallow draught, as little as 8 to 10 in. in some Cub floatplanes; and (b) any rocks dangerously close to the surface are distinctly visible from the air in the clear water of northern lakes, or are plainly revealed, at least in rivers, by the current eddies and turbulence even where the water is muddy.

A special problem frequently encountered, however, is the matter of how to tie up a floatplane to a wilderness shore. If the pilot is fortunate enough to find a shelving sand beach, the plane is simply paddled in and then turned around and the heels of the floats drawn up on the beach. But in the much more frequent case of a rocky shore, what to do? Here it may be said from experience that a snug and secure tie-up can be contrived by simply laying a trimmed log—and it need not be a large one—along the rocks right at the water's edge. The floatplane is then drawn up onto this, facing outward with the heels of the floats resting upon the log. It should of course be tied with three lines run to the trunks of trees, or to rocks or bushes, one line straight from the tail and one diagonally out from each wing.

Essential floatplane equipment includes paddle, bilge pump for the floats, canvas bucket, and plenty of nylon rope. Without these no floatplane should leave home base for any northern wilderness flight. The canvas buckets can be quite useful in quickly flooding the forward float compartments in case it becomes necessary to ride out a gale.

There are two ways for floatplanes to ride out a high wind in the wilderness. One is to moor the plane out and partially flood the forward float compartments, until the total weight of the airplane empty is increased by 50%, with all of the weight well forward. This weight tends to hold the nose down and to prevent the aircraft from flying away, particularly since a moored floatplane normally rides at a very much lower angle of attack than that at which a land plane stands on the ground. In fact it is quite possible to set up a slight negative angle of attack for the wings, even with the floatplane swinging at her mooring. This position is fundamentally stable against a big blow because the airplane, being moored from the nose, tends constantly to weathercock into the gusts as they batter in from different directions. A further downward thrust from the mooring cable at a most effective place is obtained if the mooring cable is laid either in a bridle right on the mooring cleats at the tips of the floats, or from the propeller hub. If the wind is as strong as 60 to 80 knots, so that still further precautions must be taken, a very simple device is to hang floating logs or gas tins or drums, almost full of water, from the tiedown rings of the wings, so that the weights are just awash under the surface of the water. Because of their water buoyancy in this condition, they lay no serious weight directly on the wings; yet as the wings begin to fly and lift the aircraft upward in strong gusts, these logs or drums are immediately lifted up out of the water, lose their water buoyancy and exert their full weight in holding down the wings.

The principal weakness of mooring out in the manner described is that the mooring must be secured to an anchor that will not drag in the highest winds—something usually difficult to contrive on the spur of the moment on the shore of a wilderness lake. However, because the plane is streamlined and always weathercocking, the drag against the anchor will not be as great as might be supposed. This drag can be computed, for it is approximately equal to the horsepower thrust necessary to cruise the plane in flight at the same air speed at which the gale is blowing. This is of the order of 100 lb for a light aircraft of the Piper Cub type.

If it is impossible to set out an anchor which will not drag, then bedding the floatplane down on a beach will probably be the best way to ride out a big blow. If the plane can be tailed up onto a beach, it then becomes possible to flood all the float compartments completely with water. The pilot should also be careful first to set up a negative angle of attack on the wings by wedging up the heels of the floats if the natural slope of the beach is not steep enough. This negative angle of attack is necessary because even with all float compartments flooded, the plane will still weigh something on the order of only about 250% of its rated gross weight; and it should be remembered that lift varies as the square of the velocity. Therefore it does not require a wind of 250% of the normal takeoff speed to start blowing the plane away; a wind speed of somewhere near the square root of the increase only, that is, something less than 60% above the normal takeoff speed will be all that is necessary to bring the danger point. Hence this matter of the negative angle of attack should not be overlooked.

In the fall or spring of the year flying onto and off open water with air temperatures below freezing will of course splash the tail assembly of the plane with water, which may soon freeze into ice. There is much more danger of freezing up the control wires—especially the water-rudder wires and thereby the air-rudder control—than there is of freezing the hinges of the control surfaces themselves. This is because the manual control for the elevators and rudder exerts such powerful leverage from the control horns against the fulcrum in the control hinges that the ice is rather easily broken off the control joints themselves. But where the water-rudder cables run through their tiny cable guides, here is the spot where the water, draining backward immediately after getting airborne, is quick to freeze, locking the water-rudder cables tight and hence immobilizing the air rudder. Therefore, after getting airborne, the pilot should immediately seesaw the rudder controls back and forth until looking back he can actually see that all water has drained away from the cable guides or that ice has formed with the water-rudder cables running through it in a tunnel. The hand-pull cable which lowers and retracts the water rudder must also be pulled back and forth at the same time until all water has drained away from its cable guides or frozen into an open tunnel around the wire.

The northern bush pilot will probably find he needs to know how to operate floatplanes during freezing weather, onto and off a thinly ice-covered lake, and even onto and off snow-covered ground. Occasions for handling these unconventional situations are almost certain to arise sooner or later in northern flying.

For most pilots there is normally a period of some weeks during freeze-up when "you can't use floats on account of the ice, yet the ice isn't thick enough to be safe for skis." But sometimes during this freeze-up period the northern pilot will unexpectedly find that he simply must fly a floatplane onto breakable ice for some essential mission if it can possibly be done. For those who know the technique and are willing to give their floats some rough treatment, it is possible to operate some types of light planes onto all conditions of breakable ice, up to and including the point where the floats ride completely on the ice. Because it is not a commercial operation, the subject has not been sufficiently investigated to enable one to state that it can be successfully done with all types of floatplanes. But it has been successfully done with some light floatplanes in all conditions of breakable ice including fully supporting ice.

For a plane which has been through the operation before, the landing on breakable ice is in every way normal, except for the absolutely appalling noise of the breaking ice, which can best be likened to a landing on a greenhouse roof with masses of broken glass flying in all directions! The strong keels of the floats break the ice in such a way that typically the skin of the floats does not tear.

Turns while taxiing will create the biggest problem in a breakable ice operation. If the ice is thin, turns can be made slowly without damage or danger. But when the ice gets close to ¾ in. in thickness, taxiing turns with power cannot be made without imposing such stress from the ice edges on the sides of the rear of the floats that ripping of the floats becomes a possibility. If the pilot looks back and watches what is happening, this danger will become evident to him, and he can take the appropriate action. When the ice reaches this critical thickness it becomes necessary to make all turns by stopping the engine, getting out on the floats and breaking the ice around with a paddle or other tool, and then hand turning the seaplane with the paddle, to head straight in the direction of takeoff before applying power again.

The takeoff run will be very considerably lengthened, and as the ice becomes more than ½ in. thick, may become impossible, because of the greatly increased drag unless a taxiing run is first made to break up the ice in a lane for the takeoff. When this has been done, the broken-up ice does not create much drag, and the takeoff is easily and normally made. It should be added, however, that the use of a floatplane into and out of breakable ice cannot be really recommended and it is certainly not a commercial operation, because even when properly done there is a cumulative hammering effect on the float skins right on the edge of each bulkhead joint, which tends slowly to deform this area of the float skin.

As the thickness of the ice approaches 2 in., a lighter floatplane will land right on the ice without breaking through and simply slide along on the float keels like a ski-plane. WARNING: On glare ice there is so little resistance from these narrow-keel runners that the plane will slide an unexpectedly long distance and may crash into the shore unless the pilot makes his landing by heading out into the broad reaches of a large lake. Riding on the surface without breaking through, the pilot is now beginning to use his floatplane as a substitute for a ski-plane; and this, within certain limits, is reasonably feasible.

The big disadvantage of using floats as a substitute for skis is that unlike the ski landing gear, the float strut system has no shock absorber whatever. Any roughness in the ice or drifts in the snow will be transmitted with direct hammerlike blows right into the frame of the aircraft. Also, if any rough hummocky ice has developed—and pressure ridges do form quite soon on northern lakes in subzero temperatures—these rough spots will project up higher than the ridges of the keels, and the float skins will be struck and easily torn. A floatplane may seriously tear or crumple its floats on moderately rough ice which would cause a ski-plane no difficulty whatever.

The floats will also operate reasonably well as skis from deep, soft snow. But a floatplane will not be able to carry the load of a regular ski-plane without bogging down quite easily, for the V shape and the "step" in the float bottom dig into the snow and create a much greater drag. In any event even this would never be done during commercial operations because of the risk to the thin skin of the floats.

Search and Rescue and Emergency Gear

The dangers of running out of fuel or of getting lost or of having a forced landing and thus being down on the ground far out in the northern bush are very serious indeed, especially in winter. Absolutely no flights whatever should be made beyond gliding distance from a northern airport without having made a comprehensive plan to cover these contingencies. Most of what is needed can be built into or placed in the aircraft and can stay there for the particular season, and thus require no more than a brief check-over at the beginning of each flight. But the original list of equipment must be thought through slowly, with plenty of time to insure adequate coverage.

In planning the list of emergency equipment and procedures, the use of mathematical probabilities can be quite helpful. For example, modern aircraft engines will fail on the order of about once in 5000 hr of flight. Add to this the hazard that the pilot or navigator may get lost, or that because of some miscalculation the plane may run out of fuel, or that weather may close in both ahead and behind, demanding a forced landing, and the chances become something on the order of one in several hundred, for inexperienced pilots, that on any northern flight lasting several hours their airplane will have to make a forced landing in the northern wilderness far from any habitation. Such a forced landing is a seriously dangerous matter if it occurs in such a way that the airplane cannot get off again under its own power. If not found and rescued promptly in wintertime, the occupants, unless they are exceptionally experienced northern travelers, will not last long in the subzero temperatures which they may encounter. And even in the summertime it is highly possible that pilot and passengers may starve to death unless they are uninjured in the forced landing and are experienced in the ways of the northern wilderness. Adequate emergency survival equipment should be carried in the plane.

RADIO

If the plane is equipped with a powerful long-range two-way radio capable of reaching at least one radio range station throughout a long flight, the use of this radio will virtually insure the safety of the plane's occupants in the event of a forced landing, because the rescuers will know what has happened and exactly where to look. The chances of such a radio failing while in flight are small if equipment is properly maintained. But the chances of *both* radio failure and of engine failure also occurring in the same hour will be far less likely.

Some of the fundamentals for radio are discussed in this chapter under In-Flight Problems: Navigation and Radio. To those comments may be added the following as being especially pertinent to search and rescue operations. *The one great problem* in search and rescue work after an aircraft is lost and down in the bush, is to *find* the aircraft..

Today, the most important single rescue precaution one can take is to file a flight plan in advance with FAA (in Canada, DOT) and then stick to it or advise of a change.

After that has been done, the rest is usually relatively simple. For this reason, the critical moments in a forced landing, and those in which "something can be done about it," are those minutes, even seconds, while the plane is still in the air after the need for a forced landing has first impinged upon the pilot. Most light planes with engine off have a rate of sink of no more than 500 to 1000 fpm at most, and some as little as 350 to 400 fpm. On the very long-range flights usual in the north, the pilot will probably be flying at somewhere between 5000 and 10,000 ft for the greater visibility and ease in navigation this altitude affords, and also for the greater flight efficiency most planes develop at these altitudes. Hence the pilot is quite likely to have several minutes of time, even after engine failure, while the plane is still in the air, to inform the nearest monitoring radio range station that the plane is being forced down and exactly where on the map this is occurring. It cannot be overemphasized that these minutes or even seconds are vitally important, because the range of the aircraft's radio transmitter is potentially *many times* greater while the plane is still high in the air than after it is down on the ground.

This writer submits, from experience, that probably the most important single piece of emergency equipment that the pilot can put into his plane for northern flying is the best LF/MF radio transmitter that money can buy, plus an oversize reel-out type antenna with enough wire to go to the *second* point of resonance for the emergency frequency (2182 kHz and 8364 kHz), plus an intimate knowledge of how to tune up the transmitter in flight. An LF/MF set rather than VHF or UHF is desirable; for in northern flying the ability to reach out dependably over long range with the transmitter—at least several hundred miles—is essential. VHF and UHF will not do this, since they tend to be limited to line-of-sight ranges. Few of the LF/MF sets that can be put into a light aircraft will do the job of reaching out properly if they are equipped with a *fixed* antenna only. Of the HF "short-wave" sets which can be put into a light aircraft, only a set with a trailing antenna reeled out to at least the first point of resonance of a Hertzian antenna system, and preferably to its second point of resonance, will really do an adequate job. To operate such a trailing reel-out antenna, one must know how to tune the set up to it in flight and to pass the test for the special license required. Prior experience as a radio ham is invaluable for the purpose; but failing that, an intensive special course of a few weeks can do what is necessary for this purpose.

When reeled out to the second point of resonance, the aircraft Hertzian antenna becomes highly directional, in a cone about 15° off the direction of the length of the wire. The antenna then has to be "aimed," and this is not difficult to do. When all this is done, dependable clear two-way voice communication becomes possible over a range of 200 to 300 mi, even with the type of small 20-watt radio set appropriate for light aircraft. Often it works well two-way over a range up to 500 mi.

Obviously it is not feasible to reel out the trailing antenna and tune the transmitter to resonance *after* the plane has begun to come down in

(A)

(B)

Figure 15.8 Emergency locator transmitters are a priceless asset to survival. They transmit a coded beacon signal on 121.5 or 243 MHz, may be started by the force of deceleration on crashing, or manually, and permit rescue forces to locate downed aircraft quickly. (A) is a fixed or hand held transmitter. Omnidirectional antennas. Range, 100 m at 10,000 ft search altitude. Actuated by 6 *g* shock. Weight, 2.3 lb. (B) is similar but is a fixed, integral transmitter and antenna. Actuates on 10 *g* shock. (*Courtesy of Leigh Systems, Inc.*)

a forced landing. Therefore for safety's sake it is important that the antenna be reeled out and the transmitter tuned to resonance promptly after takeoff and the antenna left that way throughout the flight. An additional precaution is to leave the transmitter filament turned on hot so that in an emergency there will not be even a 20-sec delay for the transmitter to warm up. Flying along with the antenna trailing, the set in resonance, and the filament turned on and hot, all the pilot has to do in the event of an emergency is merely to press the microphone button and start telling the facts to the nearest 24-hr monitoring radio-range station, even though it may be a couple of hundred miles away. FAA and Canadian range stations monitor the 2182 kHz and 8364 kHz frequencies on continuous 24-hr guard.

500 kHz is an international short-range emergency frequency. Silence is maintained from 15 to 18, and from 45 to 48 min past each hour. During this period there is a much better chance of being heard.

Emergency Locator Beacons which are independently powered, electronic line-of-sight transmitters are a most valuable emergency asset, particularly when the possession of such a beacon is indicated on the flight plan.

They transmit on 121.5 MHz and 243 MHz and should have a power source capable of transmitting continuously for 24 to 48 hr. Most models are suitable for light aircraft.

The pilot will of course have filed a standard flight plan; but the pinpointing radio procedure described above will enormously improve the chances of being located promptly by the Search and Rescue organization, whose planes will not then be forced to comb over hundreds of miles conducting a needle-in-a-haystack search operation.

Provision must also be made against the contingency that for some reason a pilot will not have completed radio contact below making his forced landing, and hence will have to try to make contact after the aircraft is down on the ground. Although the range is very greatly reduced, nevertheless if the radio transmitter can be got to working on the ground, the chances of making radio contact with a nearby search plane in the air are good. For this emergency on the ground, the following pieces of radio equipment will be important:

1. A permanently installed variable loading coil in the antenna circuit of the transmitter, in order to tune up the set most effectively on the ground.

2. A small vial of sulfuric acid, or else battery tops which really are spillproof. In a large proportion of forced landings in the bush, the airplane will come to rest upside down, and the acid will promptly run out of the storage batteries. If the pilot carries a small quantity of sulfuric acid and the necessary instructions, he can reconstitute this into the

proper strength for replacement in the battery. Nickel-cadmium batteries are free of these difficulties.

3. A small portable and separate engine-driven generator. The capacity of most aircraft radio batteries to run the radio transmitter is limited to only a few minutes of transmission time. Hence if the plane gets down on the ground without having been able to get a radio message out, the pilot may need a separate engine-driven generator in order to send repeated signals until they are heard. The writer, for example, has a complete engine-generator set weighing no more than 18 lb which will charge the aircraft's 12-volt storage battery at 4 amps—quite sufficient to keep the transmitter on the air for at least 10 min out of each hour, since the transmitter draws no more than 24 amps. Such a portable generator can scarcely be listed as essential, but it does add to safety and may be worth taking when relative values of weight and space and the uncertainties of an unusually remote and difficult terrain indicate it.

SURVIVAL EQUIPMENT AND TECHNIQUES

There are almost as many different lists compiled for this purpose as there are outdoor experts. And this is in fact not so unreasonable as it might at first appear. The reason is that the ability to survive in the wilderness depends much more upon the personal skill of the individual than it does upon which particular items of equipment he has taken with him. In Alaska one can get no better advice than from the nearest Air Force Rescue detachment stationed there. In Canada, one should consult the RCMP or the RCAF.

Probably the most misleading aspect of this subject for the relatively inexperienced outdoorsman will be the selection of guns, ammunition, and fishing tackle—equipment for "living off the country." But this writer submits that these are the least important in the list, except possibly for a really experienced outdoorsman. An inexperienced person planning to live off the country in the far north, even with modern arms and fishing tackle, when he suddenly has to start doing it on a "root hog or die" basis, finds it about as difficult as would an Eskimo suddenly confronted with the necessity of making a living in one of our cities. With years of training, the Eskimo can learn to do this. And similarly a white man can learn to make a living in the north as well as the Eskimo. But it takes an immense amount of know-how. The arctic is "friendly" only to those with years of acquired knowledge; for others to be cast away in the northern wilderness will almost certainly mean starvation unless they bring their own food.

The emergency equipment list will differ with the seasons and also for different parts of the north. For example, mosquito repellents will be utterly useless in winter, essential in summer. A snow knife and a primus stove, both of which will be important for winter use north of the limit of trees, will be unnecessary further south where the snow is seldom sufficiently hard-packed to permit cutting snow blocks, and where wood and birchbark can be used to build shelters and to make fires. Here a good ax, of little use north of the limit of trees, will be essential.

Instead of offering a recommended list of equipment, or series of lists, the writer offers the following summary of needs which will have to be met. Specific lists are readily available from which to choose items to meet these needs, such as the list required by the RCAF controllers of the Northwest Staging Route (the Alaska Highway Route); the authorities at Thule, Greenland, issue their list for flights over the Greenland Ice Cap. FAA authorities at Anchorage have an excellent list appropriate to Alaska.

Any pilot contemplating a flight into the subarctic or arctic areas of Canada can and should obtain this information, as well as a wealth of other essential information relative to rescue, survival, and Canadian flight regulations, by writing to the nearest District Superintendent, Air Regulations, Department of Transport. These offices are located in Vancouver, B. C., Edmonton, Alta., Winnipeg, Man., Toronto, Ont., Montreal, Que., and Moncton, N. B.

The needs to be met are: repair tools, clothing, water, food, shelter, fire, sleeping gear, protection from insects (and in some cases from animals), signaling, and traveling. Comment will here be offered only on the less obvious but essential aspects of their selection and use.

Kit of Repair Tools This is placed at the head of the emergency equipment section because of the large number of cases in which a plane can be set down successfully in a forced landing, repaired by the pilot if he has tools, and then flown on to destination. The pilot should select the items for this tool kit in consultation with the A and E mechanic who does the work on the particular aircraft. The makeup of the tool kit will depend not only upon which tools will be most useful for the particular plane, but also on the pilot's ability to do repair work.

Clothing Books could of course be written on the subject of emergency clothing for northern use. The most important warning is *Don't go off on a flight during the cold months without parka, mittens, warm comfortable visored cap, felt shoes, mukluks, and the rest, adequate for* $-50°$ *and* $-60°F$ *cold.* Several layers are warmer than one heavy garment; also layers may be peeled off to adjust to the temperature. Lightweight, loosely woven material for the under layers is warmer than closely woven material. A light windproof parka should always be carried to wear over woolen clothing for protection against the wind. Even a very light oilskin raincoat is handy to throw on, when one has to land and refuel somewhere where there is a freezing wind blowing. Leather footwear will never do in subzero weather, and the ordinary civilian rubber "pacs" are not much better. Mukluks are good, but felt shoes are more convenient if there is much walking or snowshoeing to do at subzero temperatures. The shoes should be large enough so that for −50°F weather a pair of soft wool dress socks can be worn next the feet and also two pairs of woolen loggers' socks. A pair of felt insoles inside adds greatly to the warmth. Woolen underwear is essential. If the skin is irritated by wool, the fleece-lined sort can be worn, or a suit of very lightweight cotton long underwear next to the skin. Keeping the feet and the rest of body dry is vital to survival (Figure 15.9).

Water This is plentiful anywhere in the north in summer. But in winter north of the limit of trees an ax or ice chisel should be carried to chop through ice. Otherwise the only source of water may be to melt snow. The old argument still persists as to whether or not to eat snow to quench thirst. For what it may be worth, the writer of this chapter, over years of mountaineering and Arctic travel, has always eaten snow when he felt like it and never suffered any ill effects, except that in subzero temperatures there is a very unpleasant and possibly dangerous chilling of the mouth. On the other hand, the traveler can maintain a much better condition by melting snow in a pot from his cooking kit. The cooking kit therefore becomes a necessary item of emergency equipment, together with waterproofed matches and a small gasoline stove, when north of the trees or flying over glaciers.

Food At least 7 to 10 days' supply of food per person should be carried in the emergency kit of airplanes on northern wilderness flights. Expressed another way, the plane should carry about 20,000 calories per person. The best form in which to carry these 20,000 calories is of course the subject for endless debate. The best calorie-weight ratios are obtained through extensive use of oils and fats. An investigation has shown that the body can utilize a higher proportion of oils and fats in the diet in cold climate than in warm. Of course protein is also important to rebuild muscle tissue. Hence the pemmican of explorers, which is a mixture of lean meat (protein) and fat, is a frequently mentioned emergency food. This writer has lived on pemmican on expeditions, and from this experience believes that if weight and space permit, one should provide a food, for example, fat sausage, having nearly the same fat-protein and calorie-weight ratio as pemmican, with a taste more palatable to the inexperienced tongue. He would not unnecessarily impose the problem of adjusting to a strange and therefore unappetizing food like pemmican just at a time when other pressing and difficult adjustments have to be made.

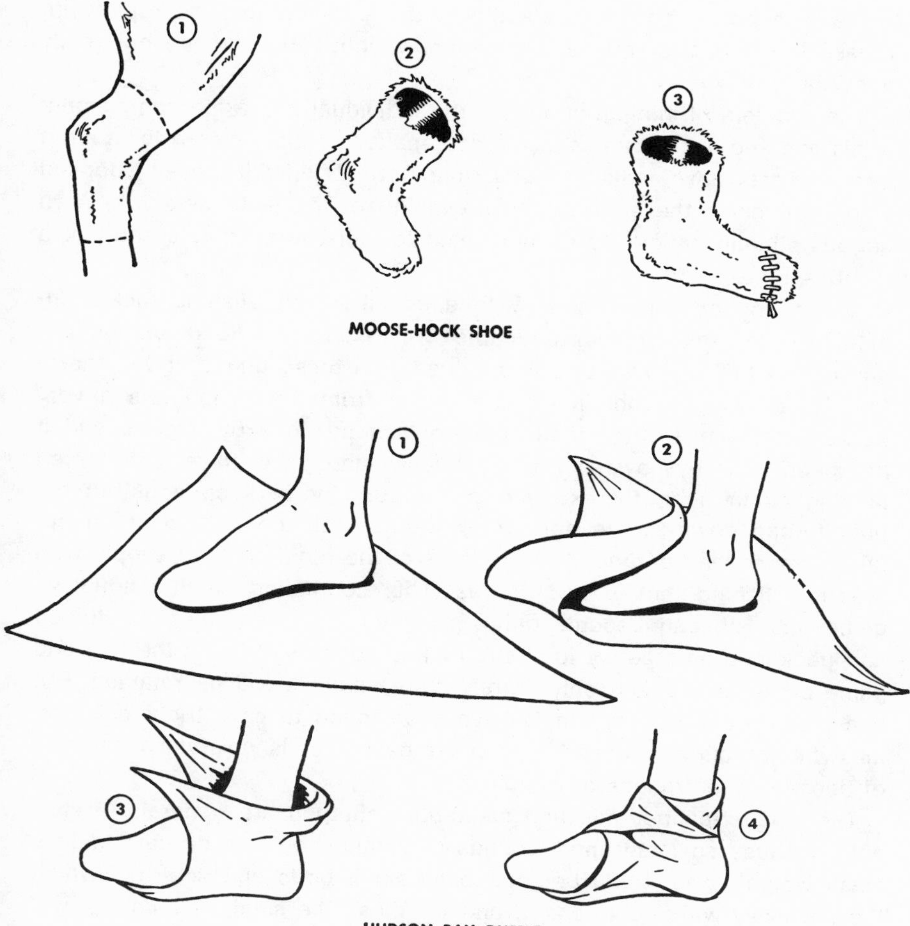

Figure 15.9 Emergency footwear. Care of the feet is vital to survival. The first principle is to keep them dry at all times. (*Courtesy of U.S. Air Force.*)

In another recent investigation of survival foods in the arctic, it was brought out that a diet composed exclusively of a certain type of candy bar kept the survivors in surprisingly good condition.

Consequently the writer concludes that the time-tested trinity of fats, proteins and carbohydrates has been reconfirmed; and that if chosen as described, with an approximately equal proportion in bulk of the three, it is a simple diet, easy to assemble, store, and keep in the plane as emergency food supply. Small amounts of dried fruits, salt, sugar, and cereal can be added for palatability; but these additions do rapidly increase the bulk and reduce the calories-weight ratio and are not really necessary.

The problem of vitamin supply, if the individual has a full complement in his body normally, can as a practical matter be disregarded for a short period. Tests have indicated that in a normal individual well supplied with vitamins in the body at the beginning of the test, diets with even serious vitamin deficiency do not begin to cause real trouble short of a month's time.

A combination rifle-shotgun with ammunition, and fishing tackle, including nylon gill-nets if practicable, will extend the food supply. But any notion that because one is supplied with these things, it will therefore be possible to obtain all one's food from the country, is a very treacherous one. Living off the country *can* be done by experts and it *has* been done by novices who were lucky enough to have their forced landing occur near, for example, a migrating herd of caribou. But the pilot forced down in the northern wilderness should not count on obtaining more than perhaps 10% to 30% of the required food supply with firearms, fishing tackle, and snares. This continuing small amount of game and fish can become quite important, however, after the tinned and packaged emergency food supply has been used up. If the fish and game are eaten cooked only "rare," more vitamins will be retained. But bears and arctic sea mammals have been found to have trichinosis and must be thoroughly cooked; and polar bear liver is *poisonous* because of dense concentrations of vitamin A.

The smaller-caliber rifle and small-bore shotgun are generally preferable because so many more rounds of ammunition can be carried in a small weight; also it will be principally small birds and squirrels which the castaway will find to shoot, and for these the small ammunition will be more appropriate. Gill nets, except for emergency use, such as in a genuine forced landing, are illegal in most regions. But their great advantage is that when set, they are working all the time, require no bait, and are very effective, particularly if made of nylon, for this seems to be invisible to fish. The book *Edible Plants of the Arctic* by A. E. Porsild could prove of some help in the summer if carried along.

Shelter A tent with sewn-in ground sheet and tie-up tunnel entrance will provide protection against blizzards in winter and swarms of insects in the arctic summer. Such tents can be obtained with both cloth and mosquito-netting entrance, the unused one being tied back. The center-pole type is usually the easiest to pitch and the cost comfortable to live in. An extra-thin nylon poncho thrown over the top is the most dependable way of making a tent rainproof. On flight north of the limit of trees one should add a collapsible or jointed aluminum pole and tent stakes.

Remember that a fully waterproof shelter will frost heavily inside in very cold weather. The results in wet clothing and bedding.

Snow itself is the best survival shelter because of its excellent wind resistance, structural strength, and efficient insulating capacity. In deep, wind-packed snow, a snow knife, saw, or long bread knife can be used to cut structural blocks.

The best one-man deep-snow shelter is a single trench, made by cutting out blocks, then using them to make an A-frame roof. For several, an excellent solution is to dig a cylindrical hole of 6 or 8 ft diameter, and cover it with tarps, parachutes, or other materials anchored with snow blocks. Then burrow spoke-like sleeping trenches into the sides.

Whenever possible in dug snow shelters, dig clear to the ground. Minimum ground temperature is about +18°F, and under shelter this heat will warm the sheltered air. With an outside temperature of −40°F, actual experiments have shown a temperature inside a snow shelter of +18°. This is warm enough to permit a downed airman to survive without a fire.

In light, fluffy snow, an adequate shelter strong enough to support the weight of several men can be made by piling up unpacked snow. With a 5-ft stick, describe a circle on the snow. Erect the stick at the center, and place another from the center to the circle edge as a guide to the center. Shovel snow into a cone, one foot higher than the center pole, with its base filling the circle. *Work slowly enough to avoid sweating.* Allow the snow to set for one hour. Using the guide stick, burrow into the center. Remove the center stick carefully, evacuate the inside until the walls are two feet thick. Then dig in the center to the ground surface to avail yourself of ground heat. A parachute pack, engine cowling, or piled snow make a suitable door. The shelter is completed by providing some insulation between body and ground.

Fire Matches in a waterproof container, or waterproofed by having the heads individually dipped in paraffin, a knife and an ax in timber country or a gasoline pressure stove will provide fire. Starting fires in the woods is a special art, thoroughly treated elsewhere; we may mention the fact that birch bark or a handful of small dry spruce twigs easily solves most fire-starting problems, even in the rain. A 2 to 3-in. length of miner's candle will save matches when starting a fire under difficult conditions.

Sleeping Gear A sleeping bag, rather than blankets, is essential for adequate protection against cold; a double bag filled with down or feathers will be necessary for subzero temperatures. The sleeping bag also provides emergency protection against insects in summer if a tent is not available.

In flights over glaciers or the Arctic ice pack it is essential to add a

Figure 15.10 A lean-to shelter in the subarctic. A lean-to covered with a parachute, tarpaulin, bark strips, or brush provides excellent shelter and considerable warmth with a fire, but in extreme cold the fire, without a reflecting surface behind it, will warm the shelter only slightly. Keeping the fire can become a full-time, energy draining chore.

light air mattress or some other insulating material, such as caribou hides or extra clothing. Sleep will be impossible without this, for even in a tent with a sewn-in floor, pitched on snow, ice, there must be an insulation layer to keep the sleeper in his bag off the icy floor. In the forested part of the subarctic, fir or spruce boughs can be cut and laid on the snow beneath the tent floor to do this job. A really comfortable bed may be had by building a spruce-bough mattress. Do this by cutting many small branches, not more than a foot long, avoiding thick, hard stems. Starting at the top, lay them like shingles with the stems toward the foot of the bed. The more layers, the better; if the mattress is thick enough, it will have a soft, springy action like a real mattress.

First-Aid Kit Standard first-aid kits are adequate for the north if dark glasses are added to protect against snow blindness. This can occur even on cloudy days on glaciers or snowfields, and is most painful and disabling. If dark glasses are not at hand, one might follow the example of the Eskimos, who make snowglasses by shaping a piece of driftwood to fit across the eyes and piercing a small hole in the slit center. This allows only a small amount of light to enter, but it is sufficient to see through. Almost any material can be used except metal. Never allow metal to come in contact with the skin in really cold weather; an incautious touch with lips or tongue can cause an instantaneous "freeze-on" with painful results.

Frostbite is insidious because one may not be aware of its onset. Propwash at −40°F can cause frostbite on the cheeks or nose in a few seconds. Crew members should watch each other's faces for white patches which indicate frostbite. Warming immediately with the hand will thaw out the flesh in light cases. In more severe cases warm the flesh with lukewarm water. *Do not apply snow to the place or rub the frostbitten parts with anything,* since this further damages the affected tissue. Frostbite affects the flesh in approximately the same way as a severe burn. Do not do anything to the affected part that you would not do to such a burned area. It is permissible to massage the area next to the frozen part, being careful not to touch the injured area. This will stimulate the blood circulation and expedite the thawing process. Really severe frostbite must be treated by a doctor as soon as possible.

Protection Against Insects Mosquitos and blackflies swarm in appalling numbers in many parts of the arctic and subarctic in early summer. Though not disease-bearing, their very numbers are a menace; they can kill horses. Headnets, gloves, trouser bottoms which tie around the tops of the boots, and clothing that mosquitoes cannot bite through, such as a light nylon parka, are essential. A fact seldom mentioned is that a very light nylon parka will give very convenient protection against mosquitoes if its wearer draws the hood up close to expose nothing but eyes, nose, and mouth. These and the backs of the hands are then easily protected by repellents. Chemical repellents are convenient, but headnets will of course outlast repellents and therefore provide a more basic protection. There will be no sleep unless protection is arranged. If there is no tent, getting inside the sleeping bag and stuffing the headnet from the inside outward into the breathing opening can do the trick.

Signaling The radio, already discussed, is of course the airplane's most important emergency signaling equipment. In addition a signaling mirror which can be aimed accurately through a hole or cross and double mirror on its back should also be carried, in order to be able to catch the eyes of scanners in searching aircraft.

If forced down, a floatplane should be moored well out in the water away from shore, to catch the attention of searchers. Overhanging trees and branches should be cut away from above any aircraft down among trees. Any fall of snow, even an overnight frost, should be brushed off the wings and fuselage to make the aircraft more visible to searchers from above. Choice of the airplane's color is also important for wilderness flying. The new high-visibility fluorescent paints can be very helpful not

NO	MEANING	SYMBOLS	NO	MEANING	SYMBOLS
1	Require doctor Serious injuries	I	9	Probably safe to land here	Δ
2	Require medical supplies	II	10	Require fuel and oil	L
3	Unable to proceed	X	11	All well All is well	LL
4	Require food and water	F	12	No (negative)	N
5	Require firearms and ammunition	≫	13	Yes (affirmative)	Y
6	Require map and compass	⊏	14	Not understood	JL
7	Indicate direction to proceed	K	15	Require engineer	W
8	Am proceeding in this direction	↑			

INSTRUCTIONS

1. Lay out these symbols using strips of fabric or parachutes, wood, stones, or other available materials.
2. Provide as much color contrast as possible.
3. If possible make symbols eight or more feet high.
4. Carefully lay out symbols exactly to avoid confusion.
5. Also make every effort to attract attention by means of radio, flags, smoke, etc.

AIRCRAFT ACKNOWLEDGMENTS–*Aircraft will indicate that ground signals–*

ARE SEEN AND UNDERSTOOD–*By rocking from side-to-side or By making green flashes with signal lamp.*

ARE NOT UNDERSTOOD–*By making a complete right-hand circuit or By making red flashes with signal lamp.*

Figure 15.11 International ground to air distress signals. (*Courtesy of U.S. Air Force.*)

only in the collision-prevention role for which they were primarily designed, but also in our problem of locating aircraft down in the wilderness.

One of the first things the pilot and occupants of the plane should do after a forced landing is immediately to assemble the materials for touching off a large smoky fire, so that this can be kindled without delay as soon as searching aircraft appear in the sky. A rising column of smoke, even a small one, is very noticeable from the air. If the plane is forced down in the snow, messages to search planes can be outlined with cut spruce branches, or tramped out in the snow (Figure 15.11). The aircraft should carry a flashlight with extra batteries to be able to flash an SOS (· · · – – – · · ·) should aircraft fly overhead during dusk or darkness.

Flares are usually listed as important emergency signaling equipment. Those of the small, railroad type seem to combine maximum lasting time with minimum bulk.

Remember this jingle:

"Use smoke by day and flame by night. Your signal can never be too big or bright."

Protection Against Animals The polar bear will stalk humans on the Arctic ice pack not from anger, but strictly from hunger. The large brown and grizzly bears of Alaska are treacherous and definitely dangerous; although they usually retreat upon encountering a human, the fact that they have killed and wounded many humans over the years in unprovoked as well as provoked attacks makes it safer to assume that if encountered they will charge. But a rifle heavy enough to kill these bears outright is a cumbersome thing to carry in a light airplane and must be of a heavier caliber than is best for shooting game for the pot. Hammering on a dishpan is the time-honored way of scaring off bears; they do not like that type of noise. One of the cooking pots struck repeatedly with a spoon is about as effective.

Traveling Snowshoes should always be carried in a ski-plane so that the pilot can tramp out a runway in fresh snow for takeoff. The snowshoes can also of course serve as a means of travel if necessary. However, it cannot be emphasized too strongly that the almost invariable rule in a forced landing in the bush is "Don't leave the aircraft." An individual roaming about in the wilderness is infinitely more difficult for rescuers to locate than is the downed aircraft itself; in fact, it is virtually impossible to locate a lone man. And in a real wilderness forced landing, the chances of walking out without getting hopelessly lost are slim indeed for any but genuine experts in the particular type of country encountered.

For the same reason there is an invariable rule in northern wilderness flying: DON'T BAIL OUT (except over a settlement) unless absolutely forced to do so by imminent and certain destruction of the aircraft in the air.

Index

The letter "i" following page numbers indicates illustration.